Index of Applications in Examples and Activities

Act: Activity; Ex: Example

Agriculture
Grape production: Ex 3.6
Strength of bark board: Ex 16.4
Tomato yield and planting density: Ex 15.12, Ex 15.13

Biology
Age and flexibility: Act 5.2
Age of a lobster: Ex 5.19
Bee mating behavior: Ex 3.12, Ex 3.13
Black bear habitat selection: Ex 5.9
Calling behavior of Amazonian frogs: Ex 5.22
Cannibalism in wolf spiders: Ex 5.20, Ex 5.21
Charitable behavior of chimpanzees: Ex 9.10, Ex 11.7
Chirp rate for crickets: Ex 10.15
Distance deer mice will travel for food: Ex 5.7, Ex 5.10
Dominant and nondominant hands: Act 3.2
Egg weights: Ex 7.31
Head circumference at birth: Ex 4.19
Loon chick survival factors: Ex 5.17
Predator inspection in guppies: Ex 6.18
Recognizing your roommate's scent: Ex 7.18
Reflexes with dominant and nondominant hands: Act 11.2
Repertoire size and body characteristics of nightingales: Ex 5.23
Scorpionfly courtship: Ex 8.4
Shark length and jaw width: Ex 13.11, Ex 13.12
Spider phobia: Ex 1.4

Business and Economics
Application processing times: Ex 7.8
Cable services: Ex 6.22
Car sales: Ex 7.1
Christmas Price Index: Ex 3.22
Cost of Big Macs: Ex 4.7, Ex 4.8, Ex 4.12
Cost of energy bars: Ex 14.11
Cost of residential air-conditioning: Ex 15.8, Ex 15.9
Credit cards paid in full: Ex 7.21
Daily wasted time at work: Ex 10.14
Education level and income: Ex 3.23
Express mail volume: Ex 7.35
Hybrid car sales: Ex 12.3
Licensing example attempts: Ex 7.9
Mortgage choices: Ex 6.16
Predicting house prices: Ex 14.5
Price of fish: Ex 14.13
Prices of industrial properties: Ex 14.17, Ex 14.19
Resume typos: Ex 3.3
Starting salaries of business school graduates: Ex 16.11, Ex 16.12

College Life
Academic success of college sophomores: Ex 14.1
Advantages of multiple SAT scores in college admissions: Act 8.1
Asking questions in seminar class: Ex 6.5
Back-to-college spending: Ex 3.7
College attendance: Ex 10.12
College choice do-over: Ex 1.5
Comparing job offers: Ex 4.18
Detecting plagiarism: Ex 10.9
Enrollments at public universities: Ex 3.15
Gender of college students: Ex 8.7
Graduation rates: Ex 1.10, Ex 13.5, Ex 13.10
Graduation rates and student-related expenditures: Ex 5.1
Graduation rates at small colleges: Ex 14.6, Ex 14.7, Ex 14.8, Ex 14.9
How safe are college campuses? Ex 1.6
Impact of internet and television use on college student reading habits: Ex 9.2
Importance of college education: Ex 9.4
Internet use by college students: Ex 9.1
Math SAT score distribution: Ex 3.14
Misreporting grade point average: Ex 3.17
Money spent on textbooks: Ex 8.1
Predicting graduation rates: Ex 5.13
Roommate satisfaction: Ex 15.7
Students with jumper cables: Ex 7.22
Study habits of college seniors: Ex 3.5
Time required to complete registration: Ex 7.29
Travel distance to college: Ex 3.1
Tuition at public universities: Ex 3.9
Verbal SAT scores: Ex 3.21
Visits to class web site: Ex 4.3, Ex 4.4

Demography and Population Characteristics
County population sizes: Ex 4.2
Head circumferences: Act 1.2
Heights and weights of American women: Ex 5.8
Heights of college athletes: Ex 1.1
Heights of mothers: Ex 4.17
Hitchhiker's thumb: Ex 6.17
Median ages in 2030: Ex 3.10
Newborn birth weights: Ex 7.27
Percentage of population with higher education degrees: Ex 4.9, Ex 4.10
Two-child families: Ex 6.14
Women's heights and number of siblings: Act 13.1

Education and Child Development

After-school activities: Ex 6.11
Chess lessons and memory improvement: Ex 11.6
Childcare for preschoolers: Ex 4.15
College plans of high school seniors: Ex 7.4
Combining exam scores: Ex 7.16
Helping hands: Ex 2.7, 2.9
IQ scores: Ex 4.16, Ex 7.28
Predictors of writing competence: Ex 14.4
School enrollment in Northern and Central Africa: Ex 3.11
Standardized test scores: Ex 4.14, Ex 10.16
Students' knowledge of geography: Act 3.1
Television viewing habits of children: Ex 3.16

Environmental Science

Cosmic radiation: Ex 9.7
Lead in tap water: Ex 10.7
Rainfall frequency distributions for Albuquerque: Ex 3.19
River water velocity and distance from shore: Ex 5.16
Soil and sediment characteristics: Ex 14.12, Ex 14.14, Ex 14.16
Water conservation: Ex 10.10
Water quality: Ex 1.2

Food Science

Calorie consumption at fast food restaurants: Ex 2.2
Fat content of hot dogs: Ex 8.6
Fish food: Ex 5.15
Pomegranate juice and tumor growth: Ex 5.5
Tannin concentration in wine: Ex 5.2, Ex 5.6

Leisure and Popular Culture

Car preferences: Ex 6.1
Do U Txt?: Ex 1.7
iPod shuffles: Ex 7.7
Life insurance for cartoon characters: Ex 2.3
Number of trials required to complete game: Ex 7.2
Probability a Hershey's Kiss will land on its base: Act 6.1
Selecting cards: Ex 6.20
Selection of contest winners: Ex 6.7
Tossing a coin: Ex 6.8
Twitter words: Act 1.1

Manufacturing and Industry

Bottled soda volumes: Ex 8.5
Comprehensive strength of concrete: Ex 7.14
Computer configurations: Ex 6.19
Computer sales: Ex 7.19
Corrosion of underground pipe coatings: Ex 15.14
Durable press rating of cotton fabric: Ex 14.18
DVD player warranties: Ex 6.24
Engineering stress test: Ex 7.3
Ergonomic characteristics of stool designs: Ex 15.10, Ex 15.11
Garbage truck processing times: Ex 7.30
GFI switches: Ex 6.12
Lifetime of compact florescent lightbulbs: Ex 10.2
On-time package delivery: Ex 10.18
Paint flaws: Ex 7.6
Testing for flaws: Ex 7.11, Ex 7.12

Marketing and Consumer Behavior

Car choices: Ex 6.10
Energy efficient refrigerators: Ex 7.5
High-pressure sales tactics: Ex 16.13
Impact of food labels: Ex 10.8
Online security: Ex 7.20
Satisfaction with cell phone service: Ex 4.6

Medical Science

Apgar scores: Ex 7.10, Ex 7.13
Affect of long work hours on sleep: Ex 11.10
Births and the lunar cycle: Ex 12.1, Ex 12.2
Blood platelet volume: Ex 8.2
Blood pressure and kidney disease: Ex 16.5
Blood test for ovarian cancer: Ex 10.6
Cardiovascular fitness of teens: Ex 10.11
Cerebral volume and ADHD: Ex 11.1
Chronic airflow obstruction: Ex 16.9
Contracting hepatitis from blood transfusion: Ex 8.8, Ex 8.9
Cooling treatment after oxygen deprivation in newborns: Ex 2.5
Diagnosing tuberculosis: Ex 6.15
Drive-through medicine: Ex 9.8
Effect of talking on blood pressure: Ex 11.4
Effects of ethanol on sleep time: Ex 15.6
Evaluating disease treatments: Ex 10.3
Facial expression and self-reported pain level: Ex 12.7
Growth hormone levels and diabetes: Ex 16.10
Hip-to-waist ratio and risk of heart attack: Ex 14.2
Hormones and body fat: Ex 15.4, Ex 15.5
Lead exposure and brain volume: Ex 5.12
Lyme disease: Ex 6.27
Markers for kidney disease: Ex 7.34
Maternal age and baby's birth weight: Ex 13.2
Medical errors: Ex 6.9
Parental smoking and infant health: Ex 16.2, Ex 16.3
Passive knee extension: Ex 4.1
Platelet volume and heart attack risk: Ex 15.1, Ex 15.2, Ex 15.3
Premature births: Ex 7.36
Sleep duration and blood leptin level: Ex 13.13
Slowing the growth rate of tumors: Ex 10.5
Stroke mortality and education: Ex 12.8
Surviving a heart attack: Ex 6.13
Time perception and nicotine withdrawal: Ex 10.13

Treating dyskinesia: Ex 16.8
Treatment for acute mountain sickness: Act 2.5
Ultrasound in treatment of soft-tissue injuries: Ex 11.5, Ex 11.8
Video games and pain management: Act 2.4
Vitamin B12 levels in human blood: Ex 16.7
Waiting time for cardiac procedures in Canada: Ex 9.9
Wart removal methods: Ex 11.9

Physical Sciences

Rainfall data: Ex 7.33
Snow cover and temperature: Ex 13.8
Wind chill factor: Ex 14.3

Politics and Public Policy

Fair hiring practices: Ex 6.29
Opinions on freedom of speech: Ex 11.11
Predicting election outcomes: Ex 13.3, Ex 13.6, Ex 13.7
Recall petition signatures: Act 9.3
Requests for building permits: Ex 6.31
School board politics: Ex 14.10
Support for affirmative action: Ex 9.1, Ex 9.4

Psychology, Sociology, and Social Issues

Benefits of acting out: Ex 1.3
Color and perceived taste: Act 12.2
Estimating sizes: Act 1.3
Extrasensory perception: Ex 6.33
Gender and salary: Ex 11.2
Golden rectangles: Ex 4.11
Hand-holding couples: Ex 6.30
Internet addiction: Ex 6.28
Motivation for revenge: Ex 2.4
One-boy family planning: Ex 6.32
Reading emotions: Ex 11.3
Stroop effect: Act 2.2
Subliminal messages: Ex 2.5
Weight regained proportions for three follow-up methods: Ex 12.6

Public Health and Safety

Careless or aggressive driving: Ex 9.5
Effect of cell phone distraction: Ex 2.8
Effects of McDonald's hamburger sales: Act 2.3
Nicotine content of cigarettes: Ex 10.17
Safety of bicycle helmets: Ex 5.3
Salmonella in restaurant eggs: Act 7.2
Teenage driver citations and traffic school: Ex 6.23

Sports

Age and marathon times: Ex 5.4, Ex 5.14
Calling a toss at a football game: Ex 6.6
Concussions in collegiate sports: Ex 12.4, Ex 12.5
Fairness of Euro coin-flipping in European sports: Act 6.2
Helium-filled footballs: Act 11.1
"Hot hand" in basketball: Act 6.3
Losing at golf: Ex 6.2, Ex 6.4
NBA player salaries: Ex 4.5, Ex 4.13
Olympic figure skating: Ex 3.20
Racing starts in competitive swimming: Ex 16.6
Soccer goalie action bias: Ex 6.26
Tennis ball diameters: Ex 10.1
Time to first goal in hockey: Ex 8.3
Treadmill time to exhaustion and ski time of biathletes: Ex 13.4, Ex 13.9
Wrestlers' weight loss by headstand: Ex 13.1

Surveys and Opinion Polls

Are cell phone users different?: Ex 2.1
Collecting and summarizing numerical data: Act 2.2
Designing a sampling plan: Facebook friending: Act 2.1
Selecting a random sample: Ex 2.2

Transportation

Accidents by bus drivers: Ex 3.18
Airborne times for San Francisco to Washington D.C. flight: Ex 9.3
Airline luggage weights: Ex 7.17
Airline passenger weights: Act 4.2
Automobile accidents by occupation: Ex 3.8
Comparing gasoline additives: Ex 2.10
Freeway traffic: Ex 7.15
Fuel efficiency of automobiles: Ex 16.1
Lost airline luggage: Ex 6.25
Motorcycle helmets: Ex 1.8, Ex 1.9
On-time airline flights: Ex 10.4
Predicting transit times: Ex 14.15
Turning directions on freeway off-ramp: Ex 6.3

EDITION 4

AP* Edition
Introduction to Statistics and Data Analysis

Roxy Peck
California Polytechnic State University, San Luis Obispo

Chris Olsen
Thomas Jefferson High School, Cedar Rapids, Iowa

Jay L. Devore
California Polytechnic State University, San Luis Obispo

BROOKS/COLE
CENGAGE Learning™

Australia • Brazil • Japan • Korea • Mexico • Singapore • Spain • United Kingdom • United States

BROOKS/COLE
CENGAGE Learning™

***Introduction to Statistics and Data Analysis,* Fourth Edition**
Roxy Peck, Chris Olsen, Jay L. Devore

Publisher: Richard Stratton
Senior Sponsoring Editor: Molly Taylor
Senior Developmental Editor: Jay Campbell
Associate Editor: Daniel Seibert
Senior Editorial Assistant: Shaylin Walsh
Associate Media Editor: Andrew Coppola
Marketing Manager: Ashley Pickering
Marketing Coordinator: Erica O'Connell
Marketing Communications Manager: Mary Anne Payumo
Content Project Manager: Susan Miscio
Art Director: Linda Helcher
Senior Print Buyer: Diane Gibbons
Rights Acquisition Specialist: Mandy Groszko
VP, Director, Advanced and Elective Program Products: Alison Zetterquist
Editorial Coordinator, Advanced and Elective Program Products: Jean Woy
Production Service/Compositor: Graphic World Inc.
Text designer: Rokusek Design
Cover designer: RHDG
Cover Image: UnderConsideration LLC

ISBN-13: 978-0-8400-6841-5

ISBN-10: 0-8400-6841-7

Brooks/Cole
20 Channel Center Street
Boston, MA 02210
USA

Cengage Learning is a leading provider of customized learning solutions with office locations around the globe, including Singapore, the United Kingdom, Australia, Mexico, Brazil and Japan. Locate your local office at **international.cengage.com/region.**

Cengage Learning products are represented in Canada by Nelson Education, Ltd.

For your course and learning solutions, visit **www.cengage.com.**

Purchase any of our products at your local college store or at our preferred online store **www.cengagebrain.com.**

Printed in the United States of America
1 2 3 4 5 6 7 14 13 12 11 10

To Beth Chance and Allan Rossman,
whose dedication to improving statistics education is inspirational

R. P.

To my wife, Sally, and my daughter, Anna

C. O.

To Carol, Allie, and Teri

J. D.

About the Cover

In 2007, designer Armin Vit noticed a relationship between the colors used in marketing materials for movies and the MPAA rating that the movie had received. To produce the image shown on the cover, movie posters from the five highest-grossing movies in each MPAA rating category (NC-17, R, PG-13, PG, and G) were analyzed to produce the horizontal bars in the cover image. Each bar represents the colors used in the poster for one of the movies. Arranging the bars by MPAA rating, Vit created this fascinating visual display that shows a progression from dark (NC-17) to light (G). The result is a data display that is both informative and artistically pleasing, making it a perfect image for the cover of a statistics text! To see the posters and to read more about how the image was constructed from the posters, see http://www.underconsideration.com/speakup/archives/003641.html

About the Authors

ROXY PECK is Emerita Associate Dean of the College of Science and Mathematics and Professor of Statistics Emerita at California Polytechnic State University, San Luis Obispo. A faculty member at Cal Poly from 1979 until 2009, Roxy served for 6 years as Chair of the Statistics Department before becoming Associate Dean, a position she held for 13 years. She received an M.S. in Mathematics and a Ph.D. in Applied Statistics from the University of California, Riverside. Roxy is nationally known in the area of statistics education, and she was presented with the Lifetime Achievement Award in Statistics Education at the U.S. Conference on Teaching Statistics in 2009. In 2003 she received the American Statistical Association's Founder's Award, recognizing her contributions to K–12 and undergraduate statistics education. She is a Fellow of the American Statistical Association and an elected member of the International Statistics Institute. Roxy served for 5 years as the Chief Reader for the Advanced Placement Statistics Exam and has chaired the American Statistical Association's Joint Committee with the National Council of Teachers of Mathematics on Curriculum in Statistics and Probability for Grades K–12 and the Section on Statistics Education. In addition to her texts in introductory statistics, Roxy is also co-editor of *Statistical Case Studies: A Collaboration Between Academe and Industry* and a member of the editorial board for *Statistics: A Guide to the Unknown,* 4th edition. Outside the classroom, Roxy likes to travel and spends her spare time reading mystery novels. She also collects Navajo rugs and heads to Arizona and New Mexico whenever she can find the time.

CHRIS OLSEN taught statistics in Cedar Rapids, Iowa, for over 25 years, and at Cornell College and Grinnell College. Chris is a past member (twice!) of the Advanced Placement Statistics Test Development Committee and has been a table leader and question leader at the AP Statistics reading for 11 years. As a long-time consultant to the College Board, Chris has led workshops and institutes for AP Statistics teachers in the United States and internationally. Chris was the Iowa recipient of the Presidential Award for Excellence in Science and Mathematics Teaching in 1986. He was a regional winner of the IBM Computer Teacher of the Year award in 1988 and received the Siemens Award for Advanced Placement in mathematics in 1999. Chris is a frequent contributor to the AP Statistics Electronic Discussion Group and has reviewed materials for *The Mathematics Teacher,* the AP Central web site, *The American Statistician,* and the *Journal of the American Statistical Association.* He also wrote a column for *Stats* magazine and was a member of the editorial board of the journal. Chris graduated from Iowa State University with a major in mathematics and, while acquiring graduate degrees at the University of Iowa, concentrated on statistics, computer programming, psychometrics, and test development. In his spare time he enjoys reading and hiking. He and his wife have a daughter, Anna, a Cal-Tech graduate in Civil Engineering, now working on a Post Doc at the University of Colorado, Boulder.

JAY L. DEVORE earned his undergraduate degree in Engineering Science from the University of California, Berkeley; spent a year at the University of Sheffield in England; and finished his Ph.D. in statistics at Stanford University. He previously taught at the University of Florida and at Oberlin College and has had visiting appointments at Stanford, Harvard, the University of Washington, New York University, and Columbia. From 1998 to 2006, Jay served as Chair of the Statistics Department at California Polytechnic State University, San Luis Obispo. The Statistics Department at Cal Poly has an international reputation for activities in statistics education. In addition to this book, Jay has written several widely used engineering statistics texts and a book in applied mathematical statistics. He is currently collaborating on a business statistics text, and he also serves as an Associate Editor for Reviews for several statistics journals. He is the recipient of a distinguished teaching award from Cal Poly and is a Fellow of the American Statistical Association. In his spare time, he enjoys reading, cooking and eating good food, playing tennis, and traveling to faraway places. He is especially proud of his wife, Carol, a retired elementary school teacher; his daughter Allison, the executive director of a nonprofit organization in New York City; and his daughter Teresa, an ESL teacher in New York City.

Brief Contents

CHAPTER 1 The Role of Statistics and the Data Analysis Process 1

CHAPTER 2 Collecting Data Sensibly 31

CHAPTER 3 Graphical Methods for Describing Data 95

CHAPTER 4 Numerical Methods for Describing Data 173

CHAPTER 5 Summarizing Bivariate Data 223

CHAPTER 6 Probability 319

CHAPTER 7 Random Variables and Probability Distributions 399

CHAPTER 8 Sampling Variability and Sampling Distributions 499

CHAPTER 9 Estimation Using a Single Sample 529

CHAPTER 10 Hypothesis Testing Using a Single Sample 577

CHAPTER 11 Comparing Two Populations or Treatments 637

CHAPTER 12 The Analysis of Categorical Data and Goodness-of-Fit Tests 699

CHAPTER 13 Simple Linear Regression and Correlation: Inferential Methods 741

CHAPTER 14 Multiple Regression Analysis 801

CHAPTER 15 Analysis of Variance 833

CHAPTER 16 **Nonparametric (Distribution-Free) Statistical Methods 16-1**

Appendix A: Statistical Tables 859

Appendix B: References 879

AP* Free Response Review Questions AP-1

Answers to Selected Odd-Numbered Exercises 883

Index 903

Sections and/or chapter numbers in color can be found at http://www.cengage.com/statistics/peck

AP* and Advanced Placement Program are registered trademarks of the College Entrance Examination Board, which is not involved in the production of, and does not endorse, this product.

Contents

Preface xv

AP* Statistics Curriculum Correlation Chart xxv
A Brief Note about the AP* Statistics Course and Exam xxviii
Preparing for the AP* Statistics Exam xxix
Taking the AP* Statistics Exam xxx

CHAPTER 1 **The Role of Statistics and the Data Analysis Process 1**

1.1 Why Study Statistics 2
1.2 The Nature and Role of Variability 3
1.3 Statistics and the Data Analysis Process 5
1.4 Types of Data and Some Simple Graphical Displays 10
Activity 1.1 Twitter Words 25
Activity 1.2 Head Sizes: Understanding Variability 26
Activity 1.3 Estimating Sizes 26
Activity 1.4 A Meaningful Paragraph 28

CHAPTER 2 **Collecting Data Sensibly 31**

2.1 Statistical Studies: Observation and Experimentation 32
2.2 Sampling 37
2.3 Simple Comparative Experiments 49
2.4 More on Experimental Design 65
2.5 More on Observational Studies: Designing Surveys (Optional) 70
2.6 Interpreting and Communicating the Results of Statistical Analyses 76
Activity 2.1 Facebook Friending 79
Activity 2.2 An Experiment to Test for the Stroop Effect 80
Activity 2.3 McDonald's and the Next 100 Billion Burgers 81
Activity 2.4 Video Games and Pain Management 81
Activity 2.5 Be Careful with Random Assignment! 82
Graphing Calculator Explorations 87
AP* Review Questions AP2-1

CHAPTER 3 **Graphical Methods for Describing Data 95**

3.1 Displaying Categorical Data: Comparative Bar Charts and Pie Charts 96
3.2 Displaying Numerical Data: Stem-and-Leaf Displays 107
3.3 Displaying Numerical Data: Frequency Distributions and Histograms 117
3.4 Displaying Bivariate Numerical Data 139
3.5 Interpreting and Communicating the Results of Statistical Analyses 148
Activity 3.1 Locating States 158
Activity 3.2 Bean Counters! 158
Graphing Calculator Explorations 165
Cumulative Review Exercises 168
AP* Review Questions AP3-1

CHAPTER 4 Numerical Methods for Describing Data 173

4.1 Describing the Center of a Data Set 174
4.2 Describing Variability in a Data Set 185
4.3 Summarizing a Data Set: Boxplots 194
4.4 Interpreting Center and Variability: Chebyshev's Rule, the Empirical Rule, and z Scores 200
4.5 Interpreting and Communicating the Results of Statistical Analyses 209
Activity 4.1 Collecting and Summarizing Numerical Data 214
Activity 4.2 Airline Passenger Weights 214
Activity 4.3 Boxplot Shapes 215
Graphing Calculator Explorations 219
AP* Review Questions AP4-1

CHAPTER 5 Summarizing Bivariate Data 223

5.1 Correlation 224
5.2 Linear Regression: Fitting a Line to Bivariate Data 235
5.3 Assessing the Fit of a Line 246
5.4 Nonlinear Relationships and Transformations 265
5.5 Logistic Regression (Optional) 286
5.6 Interpreting and Communicating the Results of Statistical Analyses 295
Activity 5.1 Exploring Correlation and Regression Technology Activity (Applets) 302
Activity 5.2 Age and Flexibility 302
Graphing Calculator Explorations 307
Cumulative Review Exercises 313
AP* Review Questions AP5-1

CHAPTER 6 Probability 319

6.1 Chance Experiments and Events 319
6.2 Definition of Probability 327
6.3 Basic Properties of Probability 334
6.4 Conditional Probability 342
6.5 Independence 353
6.6 Some General Probability Rules 363
6.7 Estimating Probabilities Empirically Using Simulation 377
Activity 6.1 Kisses 388
Activity 6.2 A Crisis for European Sports Fans? 388
Activity 6.3 The "Hot Hand" in Basketball 389
Graphing Calculator Explorations 394
AP* Review Questions AP6-1

CHAPTER 7 Random Variables and Probability Distributions 399

7.1 Random Variables 400
7.2 Probability Distributions for Discrete Random Variables 403
7.3 Probability Distributions for Continuous Random Variables 410
7.4 Mean and Standard Deviation of a Random Variable 415
7.5 Binomial and Geometric Distributions 430
7.6 Normal Distributions 442
7.7 Checking for Normality and Normalizing Transformations 460
7.8 Using the Normal Distribution to Approximate a Discrete Distribution 473
Activity 7.1 Is it Real? 478

Activity 7.2 Rotten Eggs? 478
Graphing Calculator Explorations 483
Cumulative Review Exercises 494
AP* Review Questions AP7-1

CHAPTER 8 **Sampling Variability and Sampling Distributions 499**

8.1 Statistics and Sampling Variability 500
8.2 The Sampling Distribution of a Sample Mean 504
8.3 The Sampling Distribution of a Sample Proportion 515
Activity 8.1 Do Students Who Take the SATs Multiple Times Have an Advantage in College Admissions? 521
Graphing Calculator Explorations 524
AP* Review Questions AP8-1

CHAPTER 9 **Estimation Using a Single Sample 529**

9.1 Point Estimation 530
9.2 Large-Sample Confidence Interval for a Population Proportion 536
9.3 Confidence Interval for a Population Mean 549
9.4 Interpreting and Communicating the Results of Statistical Analyses 563
Activity 9.1 Getting a Feel for Confidence Level 568
Activity 9.2 An Alternative Confidence Interval for a Population Proportion 570
Activity 9.3 Verifying Signatures on a Recall Petition 570
Activity 9.4 A Meaningful Paragraph 571
Graphing Calculator Explorations 574
AP* Review Questions AP9-1

CHAPTER 10 **Hypothesis Testing Using a Single Sample 577**

10.1 Hypotheses and Test Procedures 578
10.2 Errors in Hypothesis Testing 582
10.3 Large-Sample Hypothesis Tests for a Population Proportion 588
10.4 Hypothesis Tests for a Population Mean 602
10.5 Power and Probability of Type II Error 613
10.6 Interpreting and Communicating the Results of Statistical Analyses 622
Activity 10.1 Comparing the *t* and *z* Distributions 626
Activity 10.2 A Meaningful Paragraph 627
Graphing Calculator Explorations 630
Cumulative Review Exercises 632
AP* Review Questions AP10-1

CHAPTER 11 **Comparing Two Populations or Treatments 637**

11.1 Inferences Concerning the Difference Between Two Population or Treatment Means Using Independent Samples 638
11.2 Inferences Concerning the Difference Between Two Population or Treatment Means Using Paired Samples 658
11.3 Large-Sample Inferences Concerning the Difference Between Two Population or Treatment Proportions 671
11.4 Interpreting and Communicating the Results of Statistical Analyses 683
Activity 11.1 Helium-Filled Footballs? 687
Activity 11.2 Thinking About Data Collection 687
Activity 11.3 A Meaningful Paragraph 688
Graphing Calculator Explorations 695
AP* Review Questions AP11-1

CHAPTER 12 The Analysis of Categorical Data and Goodness-of-Fit Tests 699

12.1 Chi-Square Tests for Univariate Data 700
12.2 Tests for Homogeneity and Independence in a Two-way Table 711
12.3 Interpreting and Communicating the Results of Statistical Analyses 727
Activity 12.1 Pick a Number, Any Number ... 731
Activity 12.2 Color and Perceived Taste 732
Graphing Calculator Explorations 736
AP* Review Questions AP12-1

CHAPTER 13 Simple Linear Regression and Correlation: Inferential Methods 741

13.1 Simple Linear Regression Model 742
13.2 Inferences About the Slope of the Population Regression Line 755
13.3 Checking Model Adequacy 765
13.4 Inferences Based on the Estimated Regression Line (Optional) 776
13.5 Inferences About the Population Correlation Coefficient (Optional) 784
13.6 Interpreting and Communicating the Results of Statistical Analyses 788
Activity 13.1 Are Tall Women from "Big" Families? 790
Graphing Calculator Exploration 796
Cumulative Review Exercises 797
AP* Review Questions AP13-1

CHAPTER 14 Multiple Regression Analysis 801

14.1 Multiple Regression Models 802
14.2 Fitting a Model and Assessing Its Utility 815
14.3 Inferences Based on an Estimated Model 14-1
14.4 Other Issues in Multiple Regression 14-13
14.5 Interpreting and Communicating the Results of Statistical Analyses 14-25
Activity 14.1 Exploring the Relationship Between Number of Predictors and Sample Size 831

CHAPTER 15 Analysis of Variance 833

15.1 Single-Factor ANOVA and the *F* Test 834
15.2 Multiple Comparisons 847
15.3 The *F* Test for a Randomized Block Experiment 15-1
15.4 Two-Factor ANOVA 15-8
15.5 Interpreting and Communicating the Results of Statistical Analyses 15-19
Activity 15.1 Exploring Single-Factor ANOVA 855
Graphing Calculator Exploration 858

CHAPTER 16 Nonparametric (Distribution-Free) Statistical Methods 16-1

16.1 Distribution-Free Procedures for Inferences About a Difference Between Two Population or Treatment Means Using Independent Samples (Optional) 16-2
16.2 Distribution-Free Procedures for Inferences About a Difference Between Two Population or Treatment Means Using Paired Samples 16-10
16.3 Distribution-Free ANOVA 16-22

Appendix A: Statistical Tables 859
Appendix B: References 879
AP* Free-Response Questions AP-1
Answers to Selected Odd-Numbered Exercises 883
Index 903

Sections and/or chapter numbers in color can be found at http://www.cengage.com/statistics/peck

Letter from the Authors

We have designed this book with a particular eye toward the syllabus of the Advanced Placement Statistics course and the needs of high school teachers and students. Concerns expressed and questions asked in teacher workshops and on the AP Statistics Electronic Discussion Group have strongly influenced our coverage of certain topics, especially in the area of experimental design and probability.

Because the AP Statistics course places a great deal of emphasis on interpretation and communication, most chapters include separate sections titled "Interpreting and Communicating the Results of Statistical Analyses." These sections include advice on how to best communicate the results of a statistical analysis and also consider how to interpret statistical summary information found in journals and other published sources. New to this edition, the "Interpreting" sections now have end-of-chapter exercises associated with them. A subsection titled "A Word to the Wise" reminds readers of things that must be considered in order to ensure that statistical methods are employed in reasonable and appropriate ways.

The AP Edition also includes a page with advice to students on how they can be successful in the course and a mapping of the topics from the AP Statistics Course Description to the material in this text. Another new feature of the AP Edition is the addition of AP-style exercises in the book. Multiple-choice questions with five possible answer choices can be found at the ends of Chapters 2–13. In addition, a collection of free-response questions with a focus on clear communication, a hallmark of AP Statistics examination free-response items, can be found at the end of the book.

Teaching AP Statistics, especially for the first time, can be a challenge. Two of the resources for instructors are designed specifically to help AP Statistics teachers. The Annotated Instructor's Edition that accompanies this AP Edition now includes suggested assessments, activities, and helpful teaching tips from Kathy Fritz, an experienced AP Statistics teacher. The Instructor's Resource Binder, prepared by Chris Olsen, is full of wonderful resources for the AP Statistics teacher. These include:

- Additional examples from published sources (with references), classified by chapter in the text. These examples can be used to enrich your classroom discussions.
- "Model Responses"—examples of responses that can serve as a model for work that would be likely to receive a high mark on that AP exam.
- A collection of data explorations written by Chris Olsen that can be used throughout the year to help students prepare for the type of questions that they may encounter on the investigative task on the AP exam.
- Advice to AP Statistics teachers on preparing students for the AP exam, written by Brian Kotz.
- Activity worksheets prepared by Carol Marchetti that can be duplicated and used in class.
- A list of additional resources for activities, videos, and computer demonstrations, cross-referenced by chapter.
- A test bank that includes assessment items, quizzes, and chapter exams written by Chris Olsen, Josh Tabor, and Peter Flannigan-Hyde.

We hope that you will find that these supporting materials and this text provide you with the tools you need for an enjoyable and rewarding AP Statistics experience.

Preface

In a nutshell, statistics is about understanding the role that variability plays in drawing conclusions based on data. *Introduction to Statistics and Data Analysis,* Fourth Edition, develops this crucial understanding of variability through its focus on the data analysis process.

An Organization That Reflects the Data Analysis Process

Students are introduced early to the idea that data analysis is a process that begins with careful planning, followed by data collection, data description using graphical and numerical summaries, data analysis, and finally interpretation of results. This process is described in detail in Chapter 1, and the ordering of topics in the first ten chapters of the book mirrors this process: data collection, then data description, then statistical inference.

The logical order in the data analysis process can be pictured as shown in the following figure.

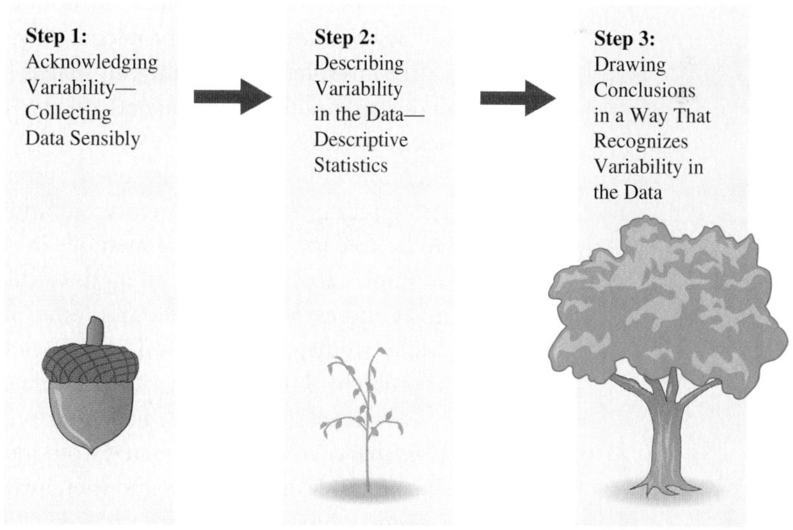

Unlike many introductory texts, *Introduction to Statistics and Data Analysis,* Fourth Edition, is organized in a manner consistent with the natural order of the data analysis process:

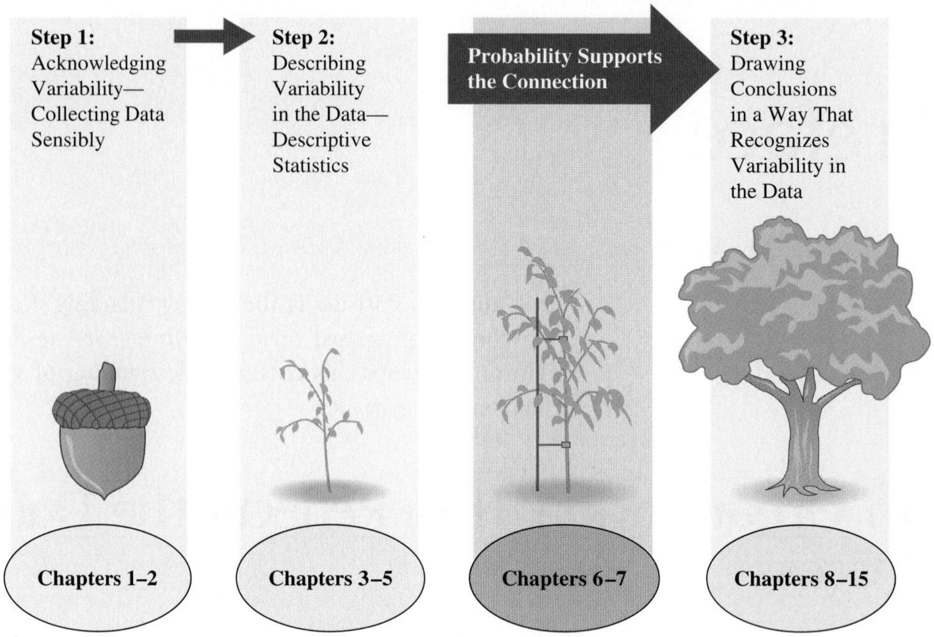

The Importance of Context and Real Data

Statistics is not about numbers; it is about data—numbers in context. It is the context that makes a problem meaningful and something worth considering. For example, exercises that ask students to compute the mean of 10 numbers or to construct a dotplot or boxplot of 20 numbers without context are arithmetic and graphing exercises. They become statistics problems only when a context gives them meaning and allows for interpretation. While this makes for a text that may appear "wordy" when compared to traditional mathematics texts, it is a critical and necessary component of a modern statistics text.

Examples and exercises with overly simple settings do not allow students to practice interpreting results in authentic situations or give students the experience necessary to be able to use statistical methods in real settings. We believe that the exercises and examples are a particular strength of this text, and we invite you to compare the examples and exercises with those in other introductory statistics texts.

Many students are skeptical of the relevance and importance of statistics. Contrived problem situations and artificial data often reinforce this skepticism. A strategy that we have employed successfully to motivate students is to present examples and exercises that involve data extracted from journal articles, newspapers, and other published sources. Most examples and exercises in the book are of this nature; they cover a very wide range of disciplines and subject areas. These include, but are not limited to, health and fitness, consumer research, psychology and aging, environmental research, law and criminal justice, and entertainment.

A Focus on Interpretation and Communication

Most chapters include a section titled "Interpreting and Communicating the Results of Statistical Analyses." These sections include advice on how to best communicate the results of a statistical analysis and also consider how to interpret statistical summaries found in journals and other published sources. A subsection titled "A Word to the Wise" reminds readers of things that must be considered in order to ensure that statistical methods are employed in reasonable and appropriate ways.

Consistent with Recommendations for the Introductory Statistics Course Endorsed by the American Statistical Association

In 2005, the American Statistical Association endorsed the report "College Guidelines in Assessment and Instruction for Statistics Education (GAISE Guidelines)," which included the following six recommendations for the introductory statistics course:

1. Emphasize statistical literacy and develop statistical thinking.
2. Use real data.
3. Stress conceptual understanding rather than mere knowledge of procedures.
4. Foster active learning in the classroom.
5. Use technology for developing conceptual understanding and analyzing data.
6. Use assessments to improve and evaluate student learning.

Introduction to Statistics and Data Analysis, Fourth Edition, is consistent with these recommendations and supports the GAISE guidelines in the following ways:

1. **Emphasize statistical literacy and develop statistical thinking.**
   Statistical literacy is promoted throughout the text in the many examples and exercises that are drawn from the popular press. In addition, a focus on the role of variability, consistent use of context, and an emphasis on interpreting and communicating results in context work together to help students develop skills in statistical thinking.
2. **Use real data.**
   The examples and exercises from Introduction to *Statistics and Data Analysis,* Fourth Edition, are context driven, and the reference sources include the popular press as well as journal articles.
3. **Stress conceptual understanding rather than mere knowledge of procedures.**
   Nearly all exercises in *Introduction to Statistics and Data Analysis,* Fourth Edition are multipart and ask students to go beyond just computation. They focus on interpretation and communication, not just in the chapter sections specifically devoted to this topic, but throughout the text. The examples and explanations are designed to promote conceptual understanding. Hands-on activities in each chapter are also constructed to strengthen conceptual understanding. Which brings us to . . .
4. **Foster active learning in the classroom.**
   While this recommendation speaks more to pedagogy and classroom practice, *Introduction to Statistics and Data Analysis,* Fourth Edition, provides more than 30 hands-on activities in the text and additional activities in the accompanying teacher resources that can be used in class or assigned to be completed outside of class.

5. **Use technology for developing conceptual understanding and analyzing data.**
The computer has brought incredible statistical power to the desktop of every investigator. The wide availability of statistical computer packages such as Minitab, S-Plus, JMP, and SPSS, and the graphical capabilities of the modern microcomputer have transformed both the teaching and learning of statistics. To highlight the role of the computer in contemporary statistics, we have included sample output throughout the book. In addition, numerous exercises contain data that can easily be analyzed by computer, though our exposition firmly avoids a presupposition that students have access to a particular statistical package. Technology manuals for specific packages, such as Minitab and SPSS, and for the graphing calculator are available in the online materials that accompany this text.
The appearance of handheld calculators with significant statistical and graphing capability has also changed statistics instruction in classrooms where access to computers is still limited. The computer revolution of a previous generation is now being writ small—or, possibly we should say, small*er*—for the youngest generation of investigators. There is not, as we write, anything approaching universal or even wide agreement about the proper role for the graphing calculator in college statistics classes, where access to a computer is more common. At the same time, for tens of thousands of students in Advanced Placement Statistics in our high schools, the graphing calculator is the only dependable access to statistical technology.
This text allows the teacher to balance the use of computers and calculators in a manner consistent with his or her philosophy and presents the power of the calculator in a series of Graphing Calculator Explorations. These are placed at the end of each chapter, unobtrusive to those teachers whose technology preference is the computer while still accessible to those teachers and students comfortable with graphing calculator technology. As with computer packages, our exposition avoids assuming the use of a particular calculator and presents the calculator capabilities in a generic format; specifically, we do not teach particular keystroke sequences, believing that the best source for such specific information is the calculator manual. For those using a TI graphing calculator, there is a technology manual available in the online materials that accompany this text. As much as possible, the calculator explorations are independent of each other, allowing teachers to pick and choose calculator topics that are most relevant to their particular courses.
6. **Use assessments to improve and evaluate student learning.**
Assessment materials in the form of a test bank, quizzes, and chapter exams are available in the teacher resources that accompany this text. The items in the test bank reflect the data-in-context philosophy of the text's exercises and examples.

Topic Coverage

Our book can be used in courses as short as one quarter or as long as one year in duration. Particularly in shorter courses, a teacher will need to be selective in deciding which topics to include and which to set aside. The book divides naturally into four major sections: collecting data and descriptive methods (Chapters 1–5), probability material (Chapters 6–8), the basic one- and two-sample inferential techniques (Chapters 9–12), and more advanced inferential methodology (Chapters 13–16). We include an early chapter (Chapter 5) on descriptive methods for bivariate numerical data. This early exposure raises questions and issues that should

CourseMate **CourseMate:** Interested in a simple way to complement your text and course content with study and practice materials? Cengage Learning's CourseMate brings course concepts to life with interactive learning, study, and exam preparation tools that support the printed textbook. Watch student comprehension soar as your class works with the printed textbook and the textbook-specific website. CourseMate goes beyond the book to deliver what you need!

This online component provides a rich array of interactive and supplementary material to accompany the text. Online quizzes, conceptual applets, videos, and a multimedia eBook give students dynamic tools for hands-on learning. An online Activities Manual allows students to take notes and record data with activities from the textbook as well as additional bonus activities for each chapter. Step-by-Step Technology Manuals for Microsoft Excel, Minitab, SPSS, JMP, and TI-84 calculators help students harness the problem-solving power of statistics technology with instruction on how to use these tools, with coverage correlated directly to Examples from the text. Downloadable data sets are also provided for every real-data problem marked in the book in the native file formats for each software type and calculator model covered by the Step-by-Step Manuals. The instructors-only area of CourseMate includes a number of additional classroom aids. Ask your sales representative about available discounts.

ENHANCED WebAssign **Enhanced WebAssign:** Exclusively from Cengage Learning, Enhanced WebAssign offers an extensive online program for statistics to encourage the practice that's so critical for concept mastery. The meticulously crafted pedagogy and exercises in our proven texts become even more effective in Enhanced WebAssign, supplemented by multimedia support and immediate feedback as students complete their assignments. Includes an Enhanced WebAssign Start Smart Guide for Students that helps students get up and running quickly with the program. Ask your sales representative about available discounts.

Key features include:

- As many as 1000 homework problems that match the text's end-of-section exercises
- New! Premium eBook with highlighting, note-taking, and search features as well as links to multimedia resources
- Practice Another Version feature on many problems (activated at the teacher's discretion), which allows students to attempt the same question with a new set of values until they feel ready to move on
- graphPad, which allows students to graph lines, segments, parabolas, and circles as they answer questions

Print

Fast Track to a 5: Preparing for the AP* Statistics Examination. This AP* test preparation guide includes an introduction to the student about the exam, a diagnostic test so that students can assess their level of preparedness, chapter-review sections with questions, and two complete practice tests in AP* format. It is keyed to this text and can be purchased with the text or separately. Prepared by Victoria Greenberg, Woodward Academy, College Park, Georgia; Viva Hathaway, Norview High School, Norfolk Public Schools, Norfolk, Virginia; and Ed Moulton, Norview High School, Norfolk Public Schools, Norfolk, Virginia.

Student Solutions Manual ***(ISBN: 978-0-8400-6840-8):*** Contains fully worked-out solutions to all of the odd-numbered exercises in the text, giving students a way to check their answers and ensure that they took the correct steps to arrive at an answer.

AP Notetaking Guide: This printed notebook helps you organize your notes and provides section-by-section summaries of key topics as well as other helpful study tools.

Teacher Resources

Print

Annotated Instructor's Edition ***(ISBN: 978-0-8400-6838-5):*** The Annotated Instructor's Edition contains answers for all exercises, including those not found in the answer section of the student edition. There also are suggested assignments and teaching tips for each section in the book written by Kathy Fritz, an experienced AP* Statistics teacher, along with an annotated table of contents with comments written by Roxy Peck.

Teacher's Resource Binder ***(ISBN: 978-1-111-57474-1):*** The Teacher's Resource Binder, prepared by Chris Olsen, is full of wonderful resources for both college professors and AP* Statistics teachers. These include:

- Additional examples from published sources (with references), classified by chapter in the text. These examples can be used to enrich your classroom discussions.
- Model responses—examples of responses that can serve as a model for work that would be likely to receive a high mark on the AP* exam.
- A collection of data explorations written by Chris Olsen that can be used throughout the year to help students prepare for the types of questions that they may encounter on the investigative task on the AP* Statistics Exam.
- Advice to AP* Statistics teachers on preparing students for the AP* Exam, written by Brian Kotz.
- Activity worksheets, prepared by Carol Marchetti, that can be duplicated and used in class.
- A list of additional resources for activities, videos, and computer demonstrations, cross-referenced by chapter.
- A test bank that includes assessment items, quizzes, and chapter exams written by Chris Olsen, Josh Tabor and Peter Flannigan-Hyde.

Available Online

- This online teacher database offers complete worked-out solutions to all exercises in the text, allowing you to create customized, secure solutions printouts (in PDF format) matched exactly to the problems you assign in class. Sign up for access at www.cengage.com/solutionbuilder.
- **ExamView®** ***(ISBN: 978-1-111-57423-9):*** ExamView testing software allows teachers to quickly create, deliver, and customize tests for class in print and online formats, and features automatic grading. Included is a test bank with hundreds of questions customized directly to the text, with all questions also provided in PDF and Microsoft® Word® formats for teachers who opt not to use the software component. ExamView is available within the PowerLecture CD.

- **PowerLecture *(ISBN: 978-1-57424-6):*** This CD-ROM provides the teacher with dynamic media tools for teaching. Create, deliver, and customize tests (both print and online) in minutes with ExamView® Computerized Testing. Easily build solution sets for homework or exams using Solution Builder's online solutions manual. Microsoft® PowerPoint® lecture slides, JoinIn® assessment material for classroom "clicker" systems, and figures from the book are also included on this CD-ROM.
- **E-book:** This new premium eBook has highlighting, note-taking, and search features as well as links to multimedia resources.
- **JoinIn™ on TurningPoint® (0-495-11881-8)**
  The easiest student classroom response system to use, JoinIn features instant classroom assessment and learning.

Acknowledgments

We are grateful for the thoughtful feedback from the following reviewers that has helped to shape this text over the last three editions:

Reviewers for the Fourth Edition

Debra Hall
Indiana University–Purdue University Indianapolis

Hazel Shedd
Hinds Community College, Rankin Campus

Austin Lampros
Colorado State University

Rick Gumina
Colorado State University

Cathleen M. Zucco-Teveloff
Rowan University

Donna Flint
South Dakota State University

Douglas A. Noe
Miami University

Steven T. Garren
James Madison University

Reviewers for the Third and Second Editions

Arun K. Agarwal, Jacob Amidon, Holly Ashton, Barb Barnet, Eddie Bevilacqua, Piotr Bialas, Kelly Black, Jim Bohan, Pat Buchanan, Gabriel Chandler, Andy Chang, Jerry Chen, Richard Chilcoat, Mary Christman, Marvin Creech, Ron Degged, Hemangini Deshmukh, Ann Evans, Guangxiong Fang, Sharon B. Finger, Steven Garren, Mark Glickman, Tyler Haynes, Sonja Hensler, Trish Hutchinson, John Imbrie, Bessie Kirkwood, Jeff Kollath, Christopher Lacke, Michael Leitner, Zia Mahmood, Art Mark, Pam Martin, David Mathiason, Bob Mattson, C. Mark Miller, Megan Mocko, Paul Myers, Kane Nashimoto, Helen Noble, Broderick Oluyede, Elaine Paris, Shelly Ray Parsons, Deanna Payton, Judy Pennington-Price, Michael Phelan, Alan Polansky, Michael Ratliff, David Rauth, Kevin J. Reeves, Lawrence D. Ries, Robb Sinn, Greg Sliwa, Angela Stabley, Jeffery D. Sykes, Yolanda Tra, Joe Ward, Nathan Wetzel, Mark Wilson, Yong Yu, and Toshiyuki Yuasa.

We would also like to express our thanks and gratitude to those whose support made this fourth edition possible:

- Molly Taylor, our editor, for her sage advice as she guided us along the way.
- Jay Campbell, our developmental editor, who amazed us with his ability to manage such a complicated process with kindness and humor, and who kept us on track and moving forward.
- Dan Seibert for leading the development of all of the supporting ancillaries.
- Mike Ederer, our production editor.
- Sandy Brown, our compositor.
- Chris Ufer and Rose Boul, who updated the art for this edition.
- Susan Miscio, our product content manager.
- Mary Jente for her careful manuscript review and copyediting.
- Michael Allwood for his heroic work in creating new student and instructor solutions manuals to accompany the text—a huge task he managed beautifully.
- Kathy Fritz for creating the new interactive PowerPoint presentations that accompany the text and also for sharing her insight in writing the Teaching Tips that accompany each chapter in the annotated instructor editions.
- Stephen Miller for a masterful job in checking the accuracy of examples and solutions.
- Brian Kotz for producing the video solutions.
- Josh Tabor and Peter-Flannagan Hyde for their contributions to the test bank that accompanies the book.
- Beth Chance and Francisco Garcia for producing the applet used in the confidence interval activities.
- Gary McClelland for producing the applets from *Seeing Statistics* used in the regression activities.
- Carolyn Crockett, our former editor at Cengage, for her support on the previous editions of this book.

And, as always, we thank our families, friends, and colleagues for their continued support.

Roxy Peck
Chris Olsen
Jay Devore

AP* Statistics Curriculum Correlation Chart

Below is a chart of the AP Statistics curriculum correlated to the appropriate sections of *Introduction to Statistics and Data Analysis, AP Edition.*

AP Statistics Topic	Corresponding Text Sections
I. Exploring data: Describing patterns and departures from patterns	
IA. Constructing and interpreting graphical displays of distributions of univariate data (dotplot, stemplot, histogram, cumulative frequency plot)	
IA1. Center and spread	1.4, 3.3
IA2. Clusters and gaps	1.4, 3.2, 3.3
IA3. Outliers and other unusual features	1.4, 3.2, 3.3
IA4. Shape	3.2, 3.3
IB. Summarizing distributions of univariate data	
IB1. Measuring center: median, mean	4.1
IB2. Measuring spread: range, interquartile range, standard deviation	4.2
IB3. Measuring position: quartiles, percentiles, standardized scores (*z*-scores)	4.2, 4.3, 4.4
IB4. Using Boxplots	4.3
IB5. The effect of changing units on summary measures	4.1, 4.2
1C. Comparing distributions of univariate data (dotplots, back-to-back stemplots, parallel boxplots)	
IC1. Comparing center and spread: within group, between group variation	1.4, 3.2, 3.3
IC2. Comparing clusters and gaps	1.4, 3.2, 3.3
IC3. Comparing outliers and other unusual features	1.4, 3.2, 3.3, 4.3
IC4. Comparing shapes	3.2, 3.3
1D. Exploring bivariate data	
ID1. Analyzing patterns in scatterplots	3.4
ID2. Correlation and linearity	5.1
ID3. Least-squares regression line	5.2
ID4. Residual plots, outliers, and influential points	5.3
ID5. Transformations to achieve linearity: logarithmic and power transformations	5.4
IE. Exploring categorical data	
IE1. Frequency tables and bar charts	1.4, 3.1
IE2. Marginal and joint frequencies for two-way tables	6.4
IE3. Conditional relative frequencies and associations	6.4
IE4. Comparing distributions using bar charts	3.1

AP Statistics Topic	Corresponding Text Sections
II. Sampling and experimentation: Planning and conducting a study	
IIA. Overview of methods of data collection	
IIA1. Census	2.1, 2.2
IIA2. Sample survey	2.1, 2.2, 2.5
IIA3. Experiment	2.1, 2.3, 2.4
IIA4. Observational study	2.1
IIB. Planning and conducting surveys	
IIB1. Characteristics of a well-designed and well-conducted survey	2.2, 2.5
IIB2. Populations, samples, and random selection	2.1, 2.2
IIB3. Sources of bias in sampling and surveys	2.2
IIB4. Sampling methods, including simple random sampling, stratified random sampling, and cluster sampling	2.2
IIC. Planning and conducting experiments	
IIC1. Characteristics of a well-designed and well-conducted experiment	2.1, 2.3, 2.4
IIC2. Treatments, control groups, experimental units, random assignments, and replication	2.3
IIC3. Sources of bias and confounding, including placebo effect and blinding	2.3, 2.4
IIC4. Completely randomized design	2.3, 2.4
IIC5. Randomized block design	2.3, 2.4
IID. Generalizability of results and types of conclusions that can be drawn from observational studies, experiments, and surveys	2.1
III. Anticipating patterns: Exploring random phenomena using probability and simulation	
IIIA. Probability	
IIIA1. Interpreting probability, including long-run relative frequency interpretation	6.1, 6.2, 6.3
IIIA2. "Law of Large Numbers" concept	6.2, 6.3
IIIA3. Addition rule, multiplication rule, conditional probability, and independence	6.5, 6.6
IIIA4. Discrete random variables and their probability distributions, including binomial and geometric	7.1, 7.2, 7.5
IIIA5. Simulation of random behavior and probability distributions	6.7
IIIA6. Mean (expected value) and standard deviation of a random variable, and linear transformation of a random variable	7.4
IIIB. Combining independent random variables	
IIIB1. Notion of independence versus dependence	6.5
IIIB2. Mean and standard deviation for sums and differences of independent random variables	7.4
IIIC. The normal distribution	
IIIC1. Properties of the normal distribution	7.6
IIIC2. Using tables of the normal distribution	7.6
IIIC3. The normal distribution as a model for measurements	7.6
IIID. Sampling distributions	
IIID1. Sampling distribution of a sample proportion	8.3
IIID2. Sampling distribution of a sample mean	8.2

AP Statistics Topic	Corresponding Text Sections
IIID3. Central Limit Theorem	8.2
IIID4. Sampling distribution of a difference between two independent sample proportions	11.3
IIID5. Sampling distribution of a difference between two independent sample means	11.1
IIID6. Simulation of sampling distributions	8.2, 8.3
IIID7. t-distribution	9.3
IIID8. Chi-square distribution	12.1
IV. Statistical inference: Estimating population parameters and testing hypotheses	
IVA. Estimation (point estimators and confidence intervals)	
IVA1. Estimating population parameters and margins of error	9.1
IVA2. Properties of point estimators, including unbiasedness and variability	9.1
IVA3. Logic of confidence intervals, meaning of confidence level and confidence intervals, and properties of confidence intervals	9.2
IVA4. Large sample confidence interval for a proportion	9.2
IVA5. Large sample confidence interval for a difference between two proportions	11.3
IVA6. Confidence interval for a mean	9.3
IVA7. Confidence interval for a difference between two means (unpaired and paired)	11.1, 11.2
IVA8. Confidence interval for the slope of a least-squares regression line	13.1, 13.2
IVB. Tests of significance	
IVB1. Logic of significance testing, null and alternative hypotheses; *p*-values; one and two-sided tests; concepts of Type I and Type II errors; concept of power	10.1, 10.2, 10.3, 10.5
IVB2. Large sample test for a proportion	10.3
IVB3. Large sample test for a difference between two proportions	11.3
IVB4. Test for a mean	10.4
IVB5. Test for a difference between two means (unpaired and paired)	11.1, 11.2
IVB6. Chi-square test for goodness of fit, homogeneity of proportions, and independence (one- and two-way tables)	12.1, 12.2, 12.3
IVB7. Test for the slope of a least-squares regression line	13.1, 13.2

A Brief Note About the AP* Statistics Course and Exam

Taking an Advanced Placement course can be one of your most rewarding and challenging high school experiences. AP Statistics will provide you with the opportunity to develop both concrete data analysis skills and a fundamental understanding of statistical concepts. The process of "thinking statistically" will be developed in this course, and it will serve you well, both in everyday life and in future college pursuits.

There is one important thing that you need to know if you are going to be successful in AP Statistics. Statistics is different from mathematics. Even though this class is most likely offered through the mathematics department at your school, AP Statistics is not like other math classes you have taken, and you need to be prepared for this. One primary purpose of this course is to provide you with the tools you need to collect data in reasonable ways and then learn something from the data. Being able to interpret statistical results in real contexts is an essential part of learning from data, and this is the main reason that communication is an important aspect of statistical problems. In statistics, meaning comes from context, and it is the interpretation of the analysis *in context* that is ultimately the desired outcome of analyzing data. So, don't be surprised if your teacher asks you to interpret, explain, justify, and draw conclusions! Communication in context is an important component of the scoring of the AP Statistics exam, and you need to practice this throughout the course in order to do well on the exam.

The AP Statistics exam consists of two sections, each designed to be completed in 90 minutes. A 40-question multiple-choice section is weighted equally with a 6-question free-response section. Each multiple-choice question has five possible answers, only one of which is correct. This section tests understanding of key statistical concepts and ideas. Although you will see many test prep guides that give tips on how to take multiple-choice exams, the best advice for scoring well on the multiple-choice part of the exam is this: Know the course material!

The free-response section of the exam consists of six questions, one of which is an investigative task. The investigative task (question 6 on the exam) is a longer question that will require you to apply what you have learned in your AP Statistics course. The investigative task will ask you to stretch your knowledge and integrate your statistical and communication skills while tackling a lengthy problem. The recommended time for the investigative task is 25 minutes, which means that you should plan to spend about 10 minutes on each of the other five questions in this section.

Your answers to the free-response questions will be evaluated on how you demonstrate general statistics knowledge and on the clarity and correctness of your interpretation and communication. To be successful on these questions, be sure to provide clear, organized, and complete explanations. This isn't easy, but it is a skill that can be developed through practice. This is something that you should keep in mind and work on throughout the entire year. It is not possible to achieve top scores on the free response section of the AP Statistics exam if communication is weak.

Most of all, the key to success in your AP Statistics course is to start with a positive attitude and resolve to invest a reasonable amount of time and effort in the course. It won't always be easy, but with the right attitude and commitment, we think that understanding, enjoyment, and a sense of accomplishment will follow.

Preparing for the AP* Statistics Exam

Advanced Placement Statistics is an exciting, practical course that is also very challenging academically. It is designed to help the student delve deeply into the methods and concepts used to make decisions based on data. Whether you are taking AP Statistics in a classroom or online, this year will prove to be both challenging and intellectually stimulating as you progress in your study of data collection, data analysis, and statistical inference.

The closer the school year gets to May, the more intimidating the looming Advanced Placement test may seem. Learning how to take all the information you have learned this year and apply it in a way that will demonstrate your expertise can be very overwhelming at times.

The best way to achieve success on any AP exam is to master it, rather than let it master you. In addition, if you think of these tests as a way to demonstrate how well you can think, you will have an advantage—attitude does help.

By February, long before the exam, you should make sure that you are registered to take it. Many schools take care of the paperwork and handle the fees for their AP students, but check with your teacher or the AP coordinator to be certain that you are on the list. This is especially important if you have a documented disability and need test accommodations. If you are studying AP independently, call AP Services at the College Board for the name of an AP coordinator at a local school who will help you through the registration process.

The evening before the exam is not a great time for partying—nor is it a great time for cramming. If you like, look over class notes or skim through your textbook, concentrating on the broad outlines rather than the small details of the course. This is a great time to get your things together for the next day. Sharpen a fistful of number 2 pencils with good erasers; be sure your calculator is in good working order with extra batteries in case you have a malfunction of some sort; check out your watch and make sure the alarm is off if it has one; package a healthy snack for the break like a piece of fruit, granola bar, and bottled water; make sure you have whatever identification is required as well as the admission ticket. Then relax, and get a good night's sleep.

On the day of the examination, it is wise to eat breakfast—studies show that students who eat a healthy breakfast before testing generally do better. Be careful not to drink a lot of liquids, thereby necessitating a trip to the bathroom during the test. Breakfast will give you the energy you need to power you through the test—and more. Remember, cell phones and other electronic devices, other than your approved calculator(s), are not allowed in the testing room. You will spend some time waiting while everyone is seated in the right room for the right test. That's before the test has even begun. With a short break between Section I and Section II, the statistics exam lasts well over 3 hours. Be prepared for a long test time. You don't want to be distracted by hunger pangs. Be sure to wear comfortable clothes; take along a sweater in case the heating or air-conditioning is erratic.

Taking the AP* Statistics Exam

The AP Statistics exam has two sections: Section I consists of 40 multiple-choice questions; Section II contains 6 free-response questions. You will have 90 minutes to complete the multiple-choice portion. The exam is then collected, and you will be given a short break. Then you then have 90 minutes for the free-response questions. You should answer all six questions. Some AP exams allow you to choose among the free-response questions, but statistics is *not* one of them. Keep an eye on your watch and devote about 10 minutes to each of questions 1–5 and about 25 minutes to question number 6. Since question number 6 carries more weight in determining your overall score, you want to be sure to at least try the first couple of parts of this question. Please note that watch alarms are *not* allowed.

Below is a chart to help you visualize the breakdown of the exam:

Section	Multiple-Choice Questions	Six Free-Response Questions	
Weight	50% of the exam	50% of the exam (weighted as follows)	
		Questions 1-5	Question 6
Number of Questions	40	37.5% of exam	12.5% of exam
Time Allowed	90 minutes	90 minutes	
Suggested Pace	2 minutes per question	10 minutes per question	25 minutes for this question

Strategies for the Multiple-Choice Section

Here are some rules of thumb to help you work your way through the multiple-choice questions:

Scoring of multiple-choice: There are five possible answers for each question. As of June 2010, there is no longer a penalty on the AP Statistics exam for wrong answers. You will simply not get credit for the wrong answer. Since there is no penalty for guessing, be sure to answer every question prior to the end of the 90 minutes allotted. This means you should bubble in a solution for each of the 40 questions.

Find questions you know first: Find questions you are confident of and work those first. (Generally the easier questions appear first on the exam.) Then return to the questions you skipped. If you skip a question to return to it later, be very careful to skip that line on the answer sheet.

Read each question carefully: Pressed for time, many students make the mistake of reading the questions too quickly or merely skimming them. By reading each question carefully, you may already have some idea about the correct answer. You can then look for that answer in the responses. Careful reading is especially important in EXCEPT questions (see the next section that describes the types of multiple-choice questions).

Eliminate any answer you know is wrong: You can write on the multiple-choice questions in the test book. As you read through the responses, draw a line through every answer you know is wrong. This will help you in choosing correct solutions on questions you aren't sure about.

Read each response, then choose the most best one: AP examinations are written to test your precise knowledge of a subject. Sometimes there are a few answers that seem correct, but one of them is a "best" choice and therefore the correct response.

Avoid absolute responses: These answers often include the words "always" or "never." For example, the statement "the data **are** normal" is an absolute answer. Instead, look for the phrase, "the data appear to be approximately normal."

Mark and skip tough questions: If you are hung up on a question, mark it in the margin of the question book. You can come back to it later if you have time. Make sure you skip that question on your answer sheet as well. In the end, be sure to answer ALL questions prior to the end of the 90 minutes.

Working backward: Some students find it beneficial to glance through the exam to get an idea of how to pace their per-question time allocation. Other students find it beneficial to work backward, as they may find that some of the more difficult questions help identify questions found at the beginning. If you decide to work backward, be sure to fill in the correct ovals. If you do decide to start from the beginning of the test, be careful not to spend too much time on the early questions, since questions toward the end of the exam become more difficult. Remember, your goal is to finish and answer the entire exam.

Types of Multiple-Choice Questions

There are various kinds of multiple-choice questions. Here are some suggestions for how to approach each one.

Classic/Best-Answer Questions

This is the most common type of multiple-choice question. It simply requires you to read the question and select the correct answer. For example:

1. A firm wants to determine if the proportion of workers who are satisfied with their job is higher than the 0.58 under the previous supervisors. Which of the following hypotheses should the firm test?

   (A) H_0: $\mu = 0.58$, H_a: $\mu > 0.58$
   (B) H_0: $p = 0.58$, H_a: $p > 0.58$
   (C) H_0: $\mu = 0.58$, H_a: $\mu < 0.58$
   (D) H_0: $p = 0.58$, H_a: $p < 0.58$
   (E) H_0: $p > 0.58$, H_a: $p < 0.58$

Answer: B. This is the only correct answer as the question is about proportions, the null is written as an $=$ statement, and the alternative is $>$ since they want to know if the proportion satisfied is higher since the change in supervisors.

EXCEPT Questions

In EXCEPT-style questions, you will notice all of the answer choices but one are correct. The best way to approach these questions is to treat them as true/false questions. Mark a T or an F in the margin next to each possible answer. There should be only one false answer, and that is the answer you should select. For example:

1. Researchers were interested in comparing students at private universities and students at public universities with respect to how much time they spent working in a typical week. They emailed a survey to 1000 students enrolled at a particular private university and to 2000 students enrolled at a particular public university. Data from the 400 private university students who responded to the survey and the 900 public university students who responded to the survey was used to determine that there was a significant difference in the mean number of hours worked in a typical week. Which of the following does NOT limit the researchers' ability to generalize to the two populations of interest?

   (A) The two sample sizes are not equal.
   (B) There may be bias introduced due to nonresponse.
   (C) The samples were not randomly selected.
   (D) All students in the private university sample attended the same university and all students in the public university sample attended the same university.
   (E) All of the above limit the researchers' ability to generalize to the populations of interest.

Answer: A. If the samples are chosen in a reasonable way, having samples of different sizes is not a problem. All of the other answer choices point to a problem with the way in which the sample was selected.

Analysis/Application Questions

These questions will require you to apply your knowledge of statistics to a given situation or problem. For example:

1. To estimate the proportion of students who plan to purchase tickets to an upcoming school fundraiser, a high school decides to sample 100 students as they register for the spring semester. There are 2000 students at the school. Which of the following sampling plans would result in a stratified random sample?

   (A) Number the students from 1 to 2000 and then use random numbers to select 100 students.
   (B) Survey the first 100 students to register.
   (C) Randomly select 100 students from a list of the 950 female students at the school.
   (D) Divide the students into early registrants (the first 1000 to register) and late registrants (the last 1000 to register). Use random numbers to identify 50 of the early registrants and 50 of the late registrants to survey.
   (E) Select one of the first 20 students to register using a random number table and then select every 20th student to register thereafter.

Answer: D. This is the only correct solution, since stratified sampling involves dividing the population into strata and then taking a random sample from each stratum.

Free-Response Questions

There are six free-response questions that should all be answered. These six questions account for 50% of the final score you receive on this exam and are weighted as follows. The first five free-response questions combine to make up 75% of your free-response score and the sixth question, the investigative task, will account for the remaining 25% of the grade. This means the first five make up 37.5% and the investigative task makes up 12.5% of the entire test. So it is important to answer all questions as completely as possible.

These questions can cover multiple content areas and connections between several topics. Each of the four key topics of the AP exam will be found in the free-response section. The following hints may help you prepare for this half of the exam.

You should plan to do a quick read of the six questions, since you won't know which question is on your strongest topic and questions are not placed in a particular topic order. As you are reading, you may want to make a quick note as to an idea you have on the subject of each question. Once you have done this, you should go to the easiest question you find in the first five questions. Answer it as completely as you can and then jump to question number six, the investigative task.

Now spend a little time, but no more than about 15–25 minutes, working on the investigative task. Since this carries $\frac{1}{4}$ of the weight for this portion of the test, it is very important that you take the time to make a serious attempt to answer this question. While this task is intended to stretch you beyond the course, typically it will begin with 1 or 2 parts that should be familiar to an AP statistics student. Many times, however, students don't get to this question and that means they throw away a question that weighs heavily on their grade.

At this point you should go back and answer the remaining four questions. If time permits, you should reread and note any key phrases or points that are made in a given question. Once you have answered the questions, be sure you read the prompt again to insure you have actually answered the question asked. Examination readers comment routinely that students don't actually answer the question that was asked. While the information you give may be correct, if it doesn't answer the question, you won't get credit.

Don't assume any question is asking for a "cookie cutter" type response. The AP readers who will review your answer will be reading for a correct answer in the context of the question, and not just a memorized process. In that light, also be sure to use statistical vocabulary correctly. If you are not sure about the correct vocabulary, it is permissible to use a short phrase in place of the word you are unsure about. Correct notation is also important. It won't hurt to define your notation for clarity, but be sure you are using the notation correctly. For example, students routinely lose credit for using notation for a statistic when they should be using parameter notation and vice-versa.

You will have 90 minutes for this section of the exam, so watch your time. As a recommendation from the College Board, you should allow about 10 minutes for each of the first 5 questions and 25 minutes for the investigative task. Then use any remaining time to read over your responses. However, earlier we recommended only about 15 minutes to begin with for the investigative task. This allows you to plan once you have begun answering the last question. In either case, it is important you take a watch and keep a close eye on your time. You want to be sure you have enough time to answer the questions that you are sure about and don't get bogged down giving more than is needed for any one question.

Key Points for Answering Free-Response Questions

In answering the free-response questions it is important to note the word choices used in the questions. Focus your writing for the AP Statistics Exam with these points in mind.

- **Read:** Carefully read the question and circle key phrases and comments you are to address. Watch for the specific wording and don't make assumptions about what you are being asked before completely reading the question.
- **Context:** Be sure to answer in the context of the problem. For a complete answer you are required to write the conclusions and interpretations in context.
- **Define:** You are expected to define all symbols you use. Be clear on parameter vs. statistic notation when answering. For example, when discussing a mean value, use the correct population and sample notation in your written responses. A sample mean notation $\bar{x}$ will be considered incorrect if you are supposed to use a population mean notation μ.
- **Vocabulary:** Use statistical vocabulary correctly. The AP readers don't need to hear fancy statistical lingo, especially if you use it incorrectly. This will weaken your response.
- **Check:** All assumptions need to be checked for **all** samples for hypothesis tests and confidence intervals.
- **Answer:** Did you actually answer the question? Reread to be sure you have answered what was asked.
- **Interpret:** Be ready to justify your work in a variety of statistical ways. Know how to read computer output, graphical displays, and tables. Provide correct analysis and comparisons as required.

Scoring Free-Response Questions

All six free-response questions will be scored using a four-point scale. However, as stated earlier, question six will be weighted more heavily than questions one through five. The four-point score is holistic in nature. This means the readers will consider your complete solution in addition to each of the parts. Therefore, it is important that you answer the question and not contradict yourself. You should NOT attempt more than one solution; the reader will read each solution and your score will be that of your weakest solution.

Keep in mind that both statistical knowledge as well as verbal communication is essential in the AP Statistics exam. To score a four, you must demonstrate that you are able to both correctly compute statistical values as well as properly interpret those values in the context of the question. Here are some general guidelines regarding the differences between zero and four on any free-response question. More specific guidelines can be found on the College Board website (http://www.collegeboard.com/student/testing/ap/sub_stats.html?stats) where you can download the PDF file of the course description.

Score	Statistical Knowledge (Be able to correctly use the statistical ideas and techniques.)	Communication (Demonstrate a clear and concise explanation of what work you performed and why.)
4	Demonstrates a complete understanding of the statistics and is able to perform correct statistical calculations. Even if you make minor arithmetic errors, the solution is plausible.	Your thoughts and explanations are correct, with all aspects of the explanation utilizing correct procedures, terminology, and appropriate conclusions, etc.
3	Able to demonstrate clear understanding of appropriate techniques but may have some minor gaps. Overall, this solution is substantially correct even if there are some errors.	Overall, the rationale in this solution is correct but there may be some missing assumptions, caveats, or even a bit unfinished in the final work. While there is a conclusion, it may be incomplete.
2	Has some parts correct but others have either incorrect or even possibly unreasonable answers. There is some understanding of the pieces yet little understanding of the relationship between them is demonstrated.	Vague or inappropriate explanations. May be missing components or diagrams needed for the explanation to be complete. Conclusions that are drawn are not complete.
1	Misuses the statistical components and develops unreasonable solutions. Very limited knowledge of statistics given.	Response is jumbled, messy, unclear or difficult to follow. Conclusions may not match the statistical work provided. Fails to provide a conclusion or answer the question posed. Incorrect diagrams or displays.
0	Very little, if any understanding of the statistical pieces needed for the problem	No strategy that will lead to a solution or no communication given at all.

Free-Response Sample Question

Here is an example of a hypothesis test question.

The average bubble content level for cans of a new soda must be near 100 "bubble units." If the amount is significantly less, the soda tastes flat. If it is significantly more, the soda tastes too bubbly. Each day, a quality control inspector takes a random sample of 25 cans to test if the population mean bubble content is consistent with the proper 100-unit setting. Any day that his results imply that the population mean bubble content might not be 100 bubble units, he has to contact the plant manager.

One day a sample's mean and standard deviation are 99.06 and 5.81 respectively. Do these data warrant a call to the plant manager? Give appropriate statistical evidence to support your conclusion.

Answer: This will require all four parts of a hypothesis test to be demonstrated in order to be scored a 4.

Part I—State the hypothesis.
The null hypothesis is that the population mean bubble content is 100 bubble units. The alternative hypothesis is that the population mean bubble content is not 100 bubble units.

H_0: μ = 100 bubble units, μ = average bubble content level
H_a: $\mu \neq$ 100 bubble units
$\alpha = .05$ Since no alpha given, we will use .05.

Part II—Identify the test procedure and any conditions or assumptions that must be met.
Given this alternative hypothesis and since the population standard deviation is unknown, I will conduct a two-sided, one-sample *t*-test for a population mean. To perform this test, I will assume that we are using a simple random sample, and I will assume that the distribution of bubble unit measurements is normally distributed.

Part III—Calculate the value of the test statistic and the P-value.
For a sample mean of 99.06, a sample standard deviation of 5.81, and a sample size of 25, I get a *t*-statistic of −0.809 on 24 degrees of freedom and a *P*-value of .4265 for this two-sided test.

$$t = \frac{99.06 - 100}{\frac{5.81}{\sqrt{25}}} = -0.809, \text{ with } df = 24$$

P-value=.4265

*Part IV—Give your conclusion **both** in context and linked to alpha.*
Since the *P*-value is quite large, much larger than .05 (.4265 > .05), I do not reject the claim that the population mean bubble content is 100 bubble units.

Therefore, these data do not warrant a call to the plant manager.

Here are some things to keep in mind as you answer the free response questions:

- Given an experimental design question, be sure to identify the treatment and clearly explain a method for random assignment. Think about whether you need to incorporate blocking, blinding, or a control group.
- For hypothesis testing questions, be sure to state the null and alternative hypotheses, identify the test procedure you have selected and check any assumptions required for use of the selected method, perform any necessary calculations, and give a conclusion in context.
- Finally, be careful **not** to include parallel solutions. If more than one solution is given, AP readers are instructed to score the weakest solution, so try not to lose points you have already scored because you doubt yourself. Be confident in your choice and cross out any dual answer that you don't want considered.

Peck, Olsen, Devore's

Introduction to Statistics and Data Analysis, Fourth Edition . . .

. . . Emphasizes Statistical Literacy and Statistical Thinking

Context Driven Applications ▶

Real data examples and exercises throughout the text are drawn from the popular press, as well as journal articles. Data sources are in a colored font for easy identification.

▼

EXERCISES 2.1 - 2.12

2.1 ✦ The article "Television's Value to Kids: It's All in How They Use It" (*Seattle Times*, July 6, 2005) described a study in which researchers analyzed standardized test results and television viewing habits of 1700 children. They found that children who averaged more than 2 hours of television viewing per day when they were younger than 3 tended to score lower on measures of reading ability and short-term memory.

a. Is the study described an observational study or an experiment?

b. Is it reasonable to conclude that watching two or more hours of television is the cause of lower reading scores? Explain.

2.2 The article "Acupuncture for Bad Backs: Even Sham Therapy Works" (*Time*, May 12, 2009) summarized a study conducted by researchers at the Group Health Center for Health Studies in Seattle. In this study, 638 adults with back pain were randomly assigned to one of four groups. People in group 1 received the usual care for back pain. People in group 2 received acupuncture at a set of points tailored specifically for each individual. People in group 3 received acupuncture at a standard set of points typically used in the treatment of back pain. Those in group 4 received fake acupuncture—they were poked with a toothpick at the same set of points used for the people in group 3! Two notable conclusions from the study were: (1) patients receiving real or fake acupuncture

Page 35

EXAMPLE 2.2 Think Before You Order That Burger!

The article "What People Buy from Fast-Food Restaurants: Caloric Content and Menu Item Selection" (*Obesity* [2009]: 1369–1374) reported that the average number of calories consumed at lunch in New York City fast food restaurants was 827. The researchers selected 267 fast food locations at random. The paper states that at each of these locations "adult customers were approached as they entered the restaurant and asked to provide their food receipt when exiting and to complete a brief survey." Approaching customers as they entered the restaurant and before they ordered may have influenced what they purchased. This introduces the potential for response bias. In addition, some people chose not to participate when approached. If those who chose not to participate differed from those who did participate, the researchers also need to be concerned about nonresponse bias. Both of these potential sources of bias limit the researchers' ability to generalize conclusions based on data from this study.

Page 40

Focus on Interpreting and Communicating

Chapter sections on interpreting and communicating results are designed to emphasize the importance of being able to interpret statistical output and communicate its meaning to non-statisticians. A subsection entitled "A Word to the Wise" reminds students of things that must be considered in order to ensure that statistical methods are used in reasonable and appropriate ways.

◀

3.5 Interpreting and Communicating the Results of Statistical Analyses

A graphical display, when used appropriately, can be a powerful tool for organizing and summarizing data. By sacrificing some of the detail of a complete listing of a data set, important features of the data distribution are more easily seen and more easily communicated to others.

Page 148

A Word to the Wise: Cautions and Limitations

When constructing and interpreting graphical displays, you need to keep in mind these things:

1. *Areas should be proportional to frequency, relative frequency, or magnitude of the number being represented.* The eye is naturally drawn to large areas in graphical displays, and it is natural for the observer to make informal comparisons based

Page 152

What to Look for in Published Data

Here are some questions you might ask yourself when attempting to extract information from a graphical data display:

- Is the chosen display appropriate for the type of data collected?
- For graphical displays of univariate numerical data, how would you describe the shape of the distribution, and what does this say about the variable being summarized?
- Are there any outliers (noticeably unusual values) in the data set? Is there any plausible explanation for why these values differ from the rest of the data? (The presence of outliers often leads to further avenues of investigation.)
- Where do most of the data values fall? What is a typical value for the data set? What does this say about the variable being summarized?
- Is there much variability in the data values? What does this say about the variable being summarized?

Page 151

Interpreting the Results of Statistical Analyses

When someone uses a web search engine, do they rely on the ranking of the search results returned or do they first scan the results looking for the most relevant? The authors of the paper "Learning User Interaction Models for Predicting Web Search Result Preferences" (*Proceedings of the 29th Annual ACM Conference on Research and Development in Information Retrieval*, 2006) attempted to answer this question by observing user behavior when they varied the position of the most relevant result in the list of resources returned in response to a web search. They concluded that people clicked more often on results near the top of the list, even when they were not relevant. They supported this conclusion with the comparative bar graph in Figure 3.37.

Page 149

Peck, Olsen, Devore's

Introduction to Statistics and Data Analysis, Fourth Edition . . .

. . . Encourages Conceptual Understanding and Active Learning

Hands-on Activities in Every Chapter

More than 30 hands-on activities in the text, and additional activities in the accompanying instructor resources, can be used to encourage active learning inside or outside the classroom.

ACTIVITY 2.1 Facebook Friending

Background: The article "Professors Prefer Face Time to Facebook" appeared in the student newspaper at Cal Poly, San Luis Obispo (*Mustang Daily*, August 27, 2009). The article examines how professors and students felt about using Facebook as a means of faculty-student communication. The student who wrote this article got mixed opinions when she interviewed students to ask whether they wanted to become Facebook friends with their professors. Two student comments included in the article were

> "I think the younger the professor is, the more you can relate to them and the less awkward it would be if you were to become friends on Facebook. The older the professor, you just would have to wonder, 'Why are they friending me?'"

and

> "I think becoming friends with professors on Facebook is really awkward. I don't want them being able to see into my personal life, and frankly, I am not really interested in what my professors do in their free time."

Even if the students interviewed had expressed a consistent opinion, it would still be unreasonable to think this represented general student opinion on this issue because only four students were interviewed and it is not clear from the article how these students were selected.

Page 79

EXPLORATION 2.3 Random Assignment to Treatments

The process of random assignment of subjects to treatments is critical in the proper design of an experiment. Random assignment can be accomplished using the graphing calculator's capability to generate integers from 1, 2 . . . *n*. We will illustrate how this can be done in some common experimental situations.

In the first experiment, we will assign subjects to treatments without trying to get the same number of subjects in each treatment group. This experiment investigates the effect of pizza on performance on a statistics exam. An instructor has decided to use three types of pizza (the treatments): sausage pizza, mushroom pizza, and cheese pizza. Twelve randomly selected students will take part in the experiment. The instructor's strategy for assigning treatments is very simple: Generate 12 random integers from the list {1, 2, 3}. *Before* any students are assigned, he arbitrarily assigns mushroom pizza = 1, cheese pizza = 2, and sausage pizza = 3.

We now randomly generate integers between 1 and 3 using

$$\text{int}(rand \times 3) + 1.$$

Our results were (remember that yours will surely be different)

3, 1, 1, 1, 1, 3, 1, 2, 1, 3, 1, 3

These numbers are used to assign each student to a treatment (pizza type) in the experiment, as shown. Entries in the table are student, treatment number, and (treatment).

1 3 (Sausage)	2 1 (Mushroom)	3 1 (Mushroom)	4 1 (Mushroom)
5 1 (Mushroom)	6 3 (Sausage)	7 1 (Mushroom)	8 2 (Cheese)
9 1 (Mushroom)	10 3 (Sausage)	11 1 (Mushroom)	12 3 (Sausage)

Page 89

Graphing Calculator Explorations

Found at the end of most chapters, these explorations allow students to actively experience technology and promote statistical thinking.

. . . Uses Technology to Develop Conceptual Understanding

Applets Allow Students to See the Concepts ▶

Within the Activities, applets are used to illustrate and promote a deeper understanding of the key statistical concepts.

Simulating Confidence Intervals

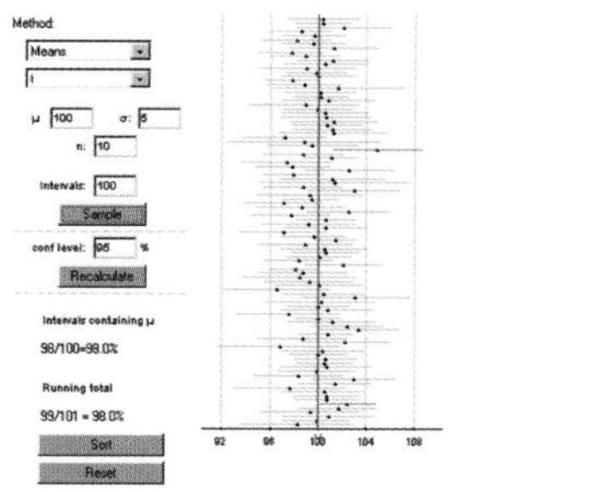

Continue generating intervals until you have seen at least 1000 intervals, and then answer the following question:

a. How does the proportion of intervals constructed that contain $\mu = 100$ compare to the stated confidence level

Page 569

. . . And Analyze Data

Real Data Sets

Real data sets promote statistical analysis, as well as technology use. They are formatted for Minitab, Excel, SPSS, SAS, JMP, TI-84, and ASCII and are indicated by the ● icon throughout the text.

▼

EXAMPLE 3.11 Progress for Children

● The report "Progress for Children" (UNICEF, April 2005) included the accompanying data on the percentage of primary-school-age children who were enrolled in school for 19 countries in Northern Africa and for 23 countries in Central Africa.

Northern Africa

54.6	34.3	48.9	77.8	59.6	88.5	97.4	92.5	83.9	96.9	88.9
98.8	91.6	97.8	96.1	92.2	94.9	98.6	86.6			

Central Africa

58.3	34.6	35.5	45.4	38.6	63.8	53.9	61.9	69.9	43.0	85.0
63.4	58.4	61.9	40.9	73.9	34.8	74.4	97.4	61.0	66.7	79.6
98.9										

We will construct a comparative stem-and-leaf display using the first digit of each observation as the stem and the remaining two digits as the leaf. To keep the display

Page 112

3.21 ● High school dropout rates (percentages) for 2008 for the 50 states were given in the 2008 Kids Count Data Book (www.aecf.org) and are shown in the following table:

State	Rate
Alabama	8%
Alaska	10%
Arizona	9%
Arkansas	9%
California	6%
Colorado	8%
Connecticut	5%
Delaware	7%
Florida	7%
Georgia	8%
Hawaii	8%
Idaho	6%

Page 116

Step-by-Step Technology Instructions

Complete online step-by-step instructions for Minitab, Excel, TI-84 Graphing Calculator, JMP, and SPSS are indicated by the icon throughout the text.

▼

EXAMPLE 3.16 TV Viewing Habits of Children

The article "Early Television Exposure and Subsequent Attention Problems in Children" (*Pediatrics*, April 2004) investigated the television viewing habits of children in the United States. Table 3.5 gives approximate relative frequencies (read from graphs that appeared in the article) for the number of hours spent watching TV per day for a sample of children at age 1 year and a sample of children at age 3 years. The data summarized in the article were obtained as part of a large scale national survey.

Page 124

Peck, Olsen, Devore's

Introduction to Statistics and Data Analysis, Fourth Edition . . .

. . . Evaluates Students' Understanding

Evaluate as You Teach Using Clickers

Using clicker content authored by Roxy Peck, evaluate your students' understanding immediately—in class—after teaching a concept. Whether it's a quick quiz, a poll to be used for in-class data, or just checking in to see if it is time to move on, our quality, tested content creates truly interactive classrooms with students' responses shaping the lecture as you teach.

The comparative bar chart shown illustrates how nonsmokers, previous smokers, and smokers differ with respect to their perceived risk of smoking. Which of the following is a correct conclusion based on this graph?

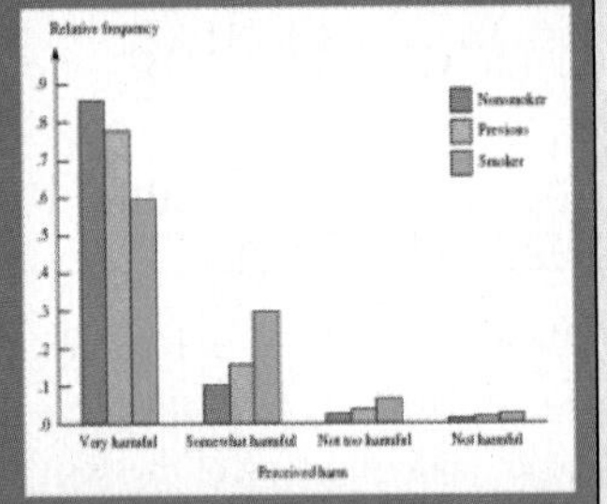

1. The proportion of smokers who perceive the risk of smoking to be very harmful is greater than the corresponding proportion of nonsmokers.
2. The biggest difference between smokers and previous smokers is in the not harmful category.
3. The proportion of smokers is higher than the proportion of nonsmokers and higher than the proportion of previous smokers in all but the very harmful category.
4. The proportion of nonsmokers is higher than the proportion of smokers in both the very harmful and somewhat harmful categories.

3.11 ✦ Poor fitness in adolescents and adults increases the risk of cardiovascular disease. In a study of 3110 adolescents and 2205 adults (*Journal of the American Medical Association*, December 21, 2005), researchers found 33.6% of adolescents and 13.9% of adults were unfit; the percentage was similar in adolescent males (32.9%) and females (34.4%), but was higher in adult females (16.2%) than in adult males (11.8%).

a. Summarize this information using a comparative bar graph that shows differences between males and females within the two different age groups.

b. Comment on the interesting features of your graphical display.

Page 106

Video Solutions Motivate Student Understanding

More than 90 exercises will have video solutions, presented by Brian Kotz of Montgomery College, which can be viewed online or downloaded for later viewing. These exercises will be designated by the ✦ in the text.

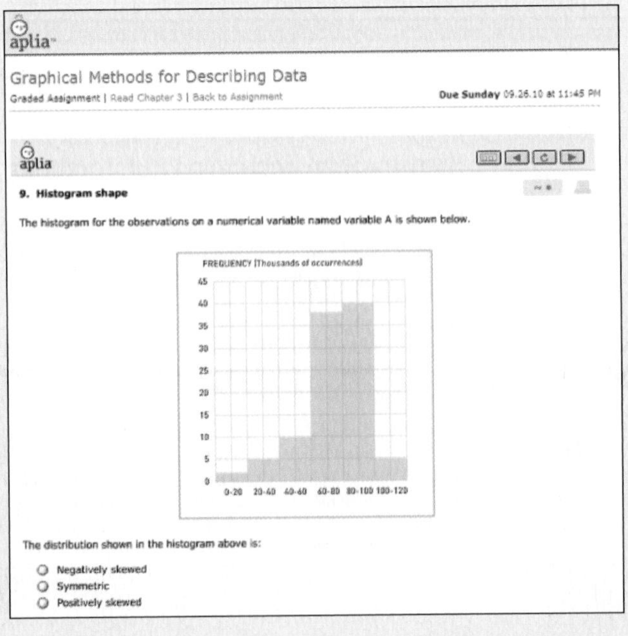

NEW Online Interactive Learning Solution

Aplia provides automatically graded assignments with detailed, immediate explanations for every question, along with innovative teaching materials.

CHAPTER 1

Andresr, 2010/Used under license from Shutterstock.com

The Role of Statistics and the Data Analysis Process

We encounter data and make conclusions based on data every day. **Statistics** is the scientific discipline that provides methods to help us make sense of data. Statistical methods, used intelligently, offer a set of powerful tools for gaining insight into the world around us. The widespread use of statistical analyses in diverse fields such as business, medicine, agriculture, social sciences, natural sciences, and engineering has led to increased recognition that statistical literacy—a familiarity with the goals and methods of statistics—should be a basic component of a well-rounded educational program.

The field of statistics teaches us how to make intelligent judgments and informed decisions in the presence of uncertainty and variation. In this chapter, we consider the nature and role of variability in statistical settings, introduce some basic terminology, and look at some simple graphical displays for summarizing data.

Make the most of your study time by accessing everything you need to succeed online with CourseMate.
Visit http://www.cengagebrain.com where you will find:

- An interactive eBook, which allows you to take notes, highlight, bookmark, search the text, and use in-context glossary definitions
- Step-by-step instructions for Minitab, Excel, TI-83/84, SPSS, and JMP
- Video solutions to selected exercises
- Data sets available for selected examples and exercises
- Online quizzes
- Flashcards
- Videos

1.1 Why Study Statistics?

There is an old saying that "without data, you are just another person with an opinion." While anecdotes and coincidences may make for interesting stories, you wouldn't want to make important decisions on the basis of anecdotes alone. For example, just because a friend of a friend ate 16 apricots and then experienced relief from joint pain doesn't mean that this is all you need to know to help one of your parents choose a treatment for arthritis! Before recommending the apricot treatment, you would definitely want to consider relevant data—that is, data that would allow you to investigate the effectiveness of this treatment.

It is difficult to function in today's world without a basic understanding of statistics. For example, here are a few headlines from articles that draw conclusions based on data that all appeared in a single issue of *USA Today* (June 29, 2009):

- "Infant Colic May Be Linked to Dads" is the headline of an article reporting on a study of the relationship between excessive crying and parents' depression. The study of more than 7600 babies and their parents concluded that excessive newborn crying is more likely to occur if the father reported symptoms of depression prior to the birth of the baby.
- The article "Many Adults Can't Name a Scientist" summarized the results of a survey of 1000 adults. Of those surveyed, 23% were unable to name a single famous scientist. Of those who did come up with a name, Albert Einstein was the scientist of choice, named by 47% of those surveyed.
- "Few See Themselves as 'Old' No Matter What Their Age" is the title of an article that described results from a large survey of 2969 adults. Those surveyed were asked at what age a person would be considered old. The resulting data revealed that there were notable differences in the answer to the question depending on the age of the responder. The average age identified as old by young adults (age 18–29) was 60, while the average was 69 for those who were age 30 to 49, 72 for those age 50 to 64, and 74 for those age 65 and older.
- The article "Poll Finds Generation Gap Biggest Since Vietnam War" summarized a study that explored opinions regarding social values and political views. Not surprisingly, large behavioral differences between young and old were noted in the use of the Internet, cell phones, and text messaging.
- The graph titled "If you were given $1000, what would you do?" reported on one aspect of a study of consumer purchasing and saving behavior. Something was definitely amiss in this report, however—the percentages for the response categories (save it, pay off credit card debt, use it for a vacation, etc.) added up to 107%!

To be an informed consumer of reports such as those described above, you must be able to do the following:

1. Extract information from tables, charts, and graphs.
2. Follow numerical arguments.
3. Understand the basics of how data should be gathered, summarized, and analyzed to draw statistical conclusions.

Your statistics course will help prepare you to perform these tasks.

Studying statistics will also enable you to collect data in a sensible way and then use the data to answer questions of interest. In addition, studying statistics will allow you to critically evaluate the work of others by providing you with the tools you need to make informed judgments. Throughout your personal and professional life, you will need to understand and use data to make decisions. To do this, you must be able to

1. Decide whether existing data is adequate or whether additional information is required.
2. If necessary, collect more information in a reasonable and thoughtful way.
3. Summarize the available data in a useful and informative manner.
4. Analyze the available data.
5. Draw conclusions, make decisions, and assess the risk of an incorrect decision.

People informally use these steps when making everyday decisions. Should you go out for a sport that involves the risk of injury? Will your college club do better by trying to raise funds with a benefit concert or with a direct appeal for donations? If you choose a particular major, what are your chances of finding a job when you graduate? How should you select a graduate program based on guidebook ratings that include information on percentage of applicants accepted, time to obtain a degree, and so on? The study of statistics formalizes the process of making decisions based on data and provides the tools for accomplishing the steps listed.

We hope that this textbook will help you to understand the logic behind statistical reasoning, prepare you to apply statistical methods appropriately, and enable you to recognize when statistical arguments are faulty.

1.2 The Nature and Role of Variability

Statistical methods allow us to collect, describe, analyze and draw conclusions from data. If we lived in a world where all measurements were identical for every individual, these tasks would be simple. Imagine a population consisting of all students at a particular university. Suppose that *every* student was enrolled in the same number of courses, spent exactly the same amount of money on textbooks this semester, and favored increasing student fees to support expanding library services. For this population, there is *no* variability in number of courses, amount spent on books, or student opinion on the fee increase. A researcher studying students from this population to draw conclusions about these three variables would have a particularly easy task. It would not matter how many students the researcher studied or how the students were selected. In fact, the researcher could collect information on number of courses, amount spent on books, and opinion on the fee increase by just stopping the next student who happened to walk by the library. Because there is no variability in the population, this one individual would provide complete and accurate information about the population, and the researcher could draw conclusions with no risk of error.

The situation just described is obviously unrealistic. Populations with no variability are exceedingly rare, and they are of little statistical interest because they present no challenge! In fact, variability is almost universal. It is variability that makes life (and the life of a statistician, in particular) interesting. We need to understand variability to be able to collect, describe, analyze, and draw conclusions from data in a sensible way.

Examples 1.1 and 1.2 illustrate how describing and understanding variability are the keys to learning from data.

EXAMPLE 1.1 If the Shoe Fits

The graphs in Figure 1.1 are examples of a type of graph called a histogram. (The construction and interpretation of such graphs is discussed in Chapter 3.) Figure 1.1(a) shows the distribution of the heights of female basketball players who played at a particular university between 2000 and 2008. The height of each bar in the graph indicates how many players' heights were in the corresponding interval. For example, 40 basketball players had heights between 72 inches and 74 inches, whereas only 2 players had heights between 66 inches and 68 inches Figure 1.1(b) shows the distribution of heights for members of the women's gymnastics team. Both histograms are based on the heights of 100 women.

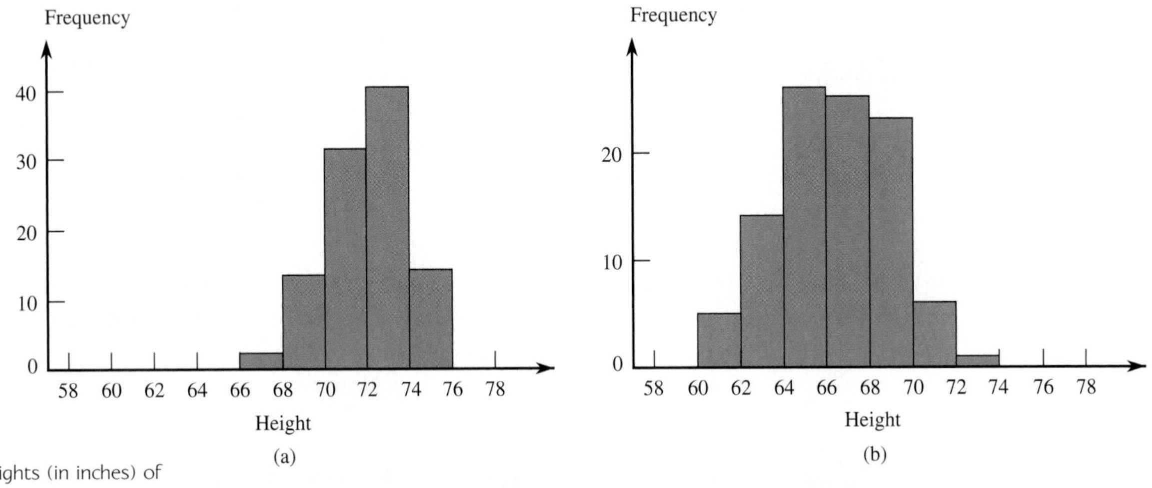

FIGURE 1.1
Histograms of heights (in inches) of female athletes: (a) basketball players; (b) gymnasts.

The first histogram shows that the heights of female basketball players varied, with most heights falling between 68 inches and 76 inches. In the second histogram we see that the heights of female gymnasts also varied, with most heights in the range of 60 inches to 72 inches It is also clear that there is more variation in the heights of the gymnasts than in the heights of the basketball players, because the gymnast histogram spreads out more about its center than does the basketball histogram.

Now suppose that a tall woman (5 feet 11 inches) tells you she is looking for her sister who is practicing with her team at the gym. Would you direct her to where the basketball team is practicing or to where the gymnastics team is practicing? What reasoning would you use to decide? If you found a pair of size 6 shoes left in the locker room, would you first try to return them by checking with members of the basketball team or the gymnastics team?

You probably answered that you would send the woman looking for her sister to the basketball practice and that you would try to return the shoes to a gymnastics team member. To reach these conclusions, you informally used statistical reasoning that combined your own knowledge of the relationship between heights of siblings and between shoe size and height with the information about the distributions of heights presented in Figure 1.1. You might have reasoned that heights of siblings tend to be similar and that a height as great as 5 feet 11 inches, although not impossible, would be unusual for a gymnast. On the other hand, a height as tall as 5 feet 11 inches would be a common occurrence for a basketball player. Similarly, you might have reasoned that tall people tend to have bigger feet and that short people tend to have smaller feet. The shoes found were a small size, so it is more likely that they belong to a gymnast than to a basketball player, because small heights and so small feet are usual for gymnasts and unusual for basketball players.

EXAMPLE 1.2 Monitoring Water Quality

As part of its regular water quality monitoring efforts, an environmental control board selects five water specimens from a particular well each day. The concentration of contaminants in parts per million (ppm) is measured for each of the five specimens, and then the average of the five measurements is calculated. The histogram in Figure 1.2 summarizes the average contamination values for 200 days.

Now suppose that a chemical spill has occurred at a manufacturing plant 1 mile from the well. It is not known whether a spill of this nature would contaminate groundwater in the area of the spill and, if so, whether a spill this distance from the well would affect the quality of well water.

One month after the spill, five water specimens are collected from the well, and the average contamination is 15.5 ppm. Considering the variation before the spill, would you interpret this as convincing evidence that the well water was affected by the spill? What if the calculated average was 17.4 ppm? 22.0 ppm? How is your reasoning related to the histogram in Figure 1.2?

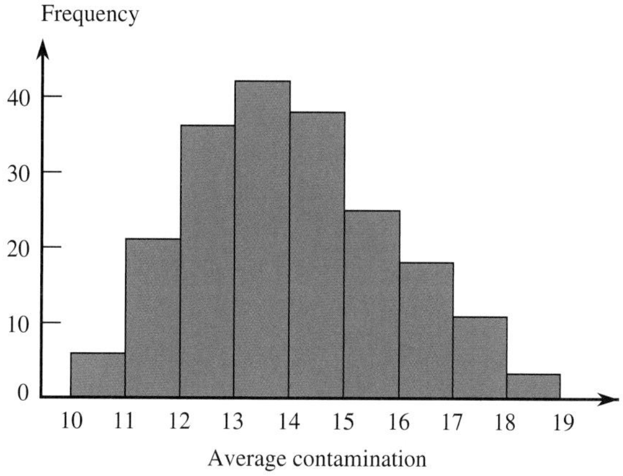

FIGURE 1.2
Frequency of average contamination concentration (in parts per million) in well water.

Before the spill, the average contaminant concentration varied from day to day. An average of 15.5 ppm would not have been an unusual value, so seeing an average of 15.5 ppm after the spill isn't necessarily an indication that contamination has increased. On the other hand, an average as large as 17.4 ppm is less common, and an average as large as 22.0 ppm is not at all typical of the pre-spill values. In this case, we would probably conclude that the well contamination level has increased.

In these two examples, reaching a conclusion required an understanding of variability. Understanding variability allows us to distinguish between usual and unusual values. The ability to recognize unusual values in the presence of variability is an important aspect of most statistical procedures and is also what enables us to quantify the chance of being incorrect when a conclusion is based on data. These concepts will be developed further in subsequent chapters.

1.3 Statistics and the Data Analysis Process

Statistics involves collecting, summarizing, and analyzing data. All three tasks are critical. Without summarization and analysis, raw data are of little value, and even sophisticated analyses can't produce meaningful information from data that were not collected in a sensible way.

Statistical studies are undertaken to answer questions about our world. Is a new flu vaccine effective in preventing illness? Is the use of bicycle helmets on the rise? Are injuries that result from bicycle accidents less severe for riders who wear helmets than for those who do not? How many credit cards do college students have? Do engineering students pay more for textbooks than do psychology students? Data collection and analysis allow researchers to answer such questions.

The data analysis process can be viewed as a sequence of steps that lead from planning to data collection to making informed conclusions based on the resulting data. The process can be organized into the following six steps:

1. **Understanding the nature of the problem.** Effective data analysis requires an understanding of the research problem. We must know the goal of the research and what questions we hope to answer. It is important to have a clear direction before gathering data to ensure that we will be able to answer the questions of interest using the data collected.
2. **Deciding what to measure and how to measure it.** The next step in the process is deciding what information is needed to answer the questions of interest. In some cases, the choice is obvious (for example, in a study of the relationship between the weight of a Division I football player and position played, you would need to collect data on player weight and position), but in other cases the choice of information is not as straightforward (for example, in a study of the relationship between preferred learning style and intelligence, how would you define learning style and measure it and what measure of intelligence would you use?). It is important to carefully define the variables to be studied and to develop appropriate methods for determining their values.
3. **Data collection.** The data collection step is crucial. The researcher must first decide whether an existing data source is adequate or whether new data must be collected. Even if a decision is made to use existing data, it is important to understand how the data were collected and for what purpose, so that any resulting limitations are also fully understood and judged to be acceptable. If new data are to be collected, a careful plan must be developed, because the type of analysis that is appropriate and the subsequent conclusions that can be drawn depend on how the data are collected.
4. **Data summarization and preliminary analysis.** After the data are collected, the next step usually involves a preliminary analysis that includes summarizing the data graphically and numerically. This initial analysis provides insight into important characteristics of the data and can provide guidance in selecting appropriate methods for further analysis.
5. **Formal data analysis.** The data analysis step requires the researcher to select and apply statistical methods. Much of this textbook is devoted to methods that can be used to carry out this step.
6. **Interpretation of results.** Several questions should be addressed in this final step. Some examples are: What can we learn from the data? What conclusions can be drawn from the analysis? and How can our results guide future research? The interpretation step often leads to the formulation of new research questions, which, in turn, leads back to the first step. In this way, good data analysis is often an iterative process.

For example, the admissions director at a large university might be interested in learning why some applicants who were accepted for the fall 2010 term failed to enroll at the university. The population of interest to the director consists of all accepted applicants who did not enroll in the fall 2010 term. Because this population is large and it may be difficult to contact all the individuals, the director might decide to collect data from only 300 selected students. These 300 students constitute a sample.

AP* EXAM TIP

The distinction between population and sample is very important in statistics.

DEFINITION

The entire collection of individuals or objects about which information is desired is called the **population** of interest. A **sample** is a subset of the population, selected for study.

Deciding how to select the 300 students and what data should be collected from each student are steps 2 and 3 in the data analysis process. The next step in the process involves organizing and summarizing data. Methods for organizing and summarizing data, such as the use of tables, graphs, or numerical summaries, make up the branch of statistics called **descriptive statistics**. The second major branch of statistics, **inferential statistics**, involves generalizing from a sample to the population from which it was selected. When we generalize in this way, we run the risk of an incorrect conclusion, because a conclusion about the population is based on incomplete information. An important aspect in the development of inferential techniques involves quantifying the chance of an incorrect conclusion.

DEFINITION

Descriptive statistics is the branch of statistics that includes methods for organizing and summarizing data. **Inferential statistics** is the branch of statistics that involves generalizing from a sample to the population from which the sample was selected and assessing the reliability of such generalizations.

Example 1.3 illustrates the steps in the data analysis process.

EXAMPLE 1.3 The Benefits of Acting Out

A number of studies have reached the conclusion that stimulating mental activities can lead to improved memory and psychological wellness in older adults. The article "A Short-Term Intervention to Enhance Cognitive and Affective Functioning in Older Adults" (*Journal of Aging and Health* [2004]: 562–585) describes a study to investigate whether training in acting has similar benefits. Acting requires a person to consider the goals of the characters in the story, to remember lines of dialogue, to move on stage as scripted, and to do all of this at the same time. The researchers conducting the study wanted to see if participation in this type of complex multitasking would show an improvement in the ability to function independently in daily life. Participants in the study were assigned to one of three groups. One group took part in an acting class for 4 weeks, one group spent a similar amount of time in a class on visual arts, and the third group was a comparison group (called the "no-treatment group") that did not take either class. A total of 124 adults age 60 to 86 participated in the study. At the beginning of the 4-week study period and again at the end of the 4-week study period, each participant took several tests designed to measure problem solving, memory span, self-esteem, and psychological well-being. After analyzing the data from this study, the researchers concluded that those in the acting group showed greater gains than both the visual arts group and the no-treatment group in both problem solving and psychological well-being. Several new areas of research were suggested in the discussion that followed the analysis. The researchers wondered whether the effect of studying writing or music would be similar to what was observed for acting and described plans to investigate this further. They also noted that the participants in this study were generally well educated and recommended study of a more diverse group before generalizing conclusions about the benefits of studying acting to the larger population of all older adults.

This study illustrates the nature of the data analysis process. A clearly defined research question and an appropriate choice of how to measure the variables of interest (the tests used to measure problem solving, memory span, self-esteem, and psychological well-being) preceded the data collection. Assuming that a reasonable method was used to collect the data (we will see how this can be evaluated in Chapter 2) and that appropriate methods of analysis were employed, the investigators reached the conclusion that the study of acting showed promise. However, they recognized the limitations of the study, which in turn led to plans for further research. As is often the case, the data analysis cycle led to new research questions, and the process began again.

Evaluating a Research Study The six data analysis steps can also be used as a guide for evaluating published research studies. The following questions should be addressed as part of a study evaluation:

- What were the researchers trying to learn? What questions motivated their research?
- Was relevant information collected? Were the right things measured?
- Were the data collected in a sensible way?
- Were the data summarized in an appropriate way?
- Was an appropriate method of analysis used, given the type of data and how the data were collected?
- Are the conclusions drawn by the researchers supported by the data analysis?

Example 1.4 illustrates how these questions can guide an evaluation of a research study.

EXAMPLE 1.4 Afraid of Spiders? You Are Not Alone!

Spider phobia is a common anxiety-producing disorder. In fact, the American Psychiatric Association estimates that between 7% and 15.1% of the population experiences spider phobia. An effective treatment for this condition involves participating in a therapist-led session in which the patient is exposed to live spiders. While this type of treatment has been shown to work for a large proportion of patients, it requires one-on-one time with a therapist trained in this technique. The article "Internet-Based Self-Help versus One-Session Exposure in the Treatment of Spider Phobia" (*Cognitive Behaviour Therapy* [2009]: 114–120), presented results from a study that compared the effectiveness of online self-help modules to in-person treatment. The article states

> A total of 30 patients were included following screening on the Internet and a structured clinical interview. The Internet treatment consisted of five weekly text modules, which were presented on a web page, a video in which exposure was modeled, and support provided via Internet. The live-exposure treatment was delivered in a 3-hour session following a brief orientation session. The main outcome measure was the behavioral approach test (BAT), and the authors used questionnaires measuring anxiety symptoms and depression as secondary measures. Results showed that the groups did not differ at post-treatment or follow-up, with the exception of the proportion showing clinically significant change on the BAT. At post-treatment, 46.2% of the Internet group and 85.7% of the live-exposure group achieved this change. At follow-up, the corresponding figures were 66.7% for the Internet group and 72.7% for the live treatment.

The researchers concluded that online treatment is a promising new approach for the treatment of spider phobia.

The researchers here had a well-defined research question—they wanted to know if online treatment is as effective as in-person exposure treatment. They were interested in this question because online treatment does not require individual time with a therapist, and so, if it works, it might be able to help a larger group of people at a much lower cost. The researchers noted which treatment was received and also recorded results of the BAT and several other measures of anxiety and depression. Participants in the study took these tests prior to beginning treatment, at the end of treatment, and 1 year after the end of treatment. This allowed the researchers to evaluate the immediate and long-term effects of the two treatments and to address the research question.

To assess whether the data were collected in a sensible way, it would be useful to know how the participants were selected and how it was determined which of the two treatments a particular participant received. The article indicates that participants were recruited through advertisements and articles in local newspapers and that most were female university students. We will see in Chapter 2 that this may limit our ability to generalize the results of this study. The participants were assigned to one of the two treatments at random, which is a good strategy for ensuring that one treatment does not tend to be favored over the other. The advantages of random assignment in a study of this type are also discussed in Chapter 2.

We will also have to delay discussion of the data analysis and the appropriateness of the conclusions because we do not yet have the necessary tools to evaluate these aspects of the study.

Many other interesting examples of statistical studies can be found in *Statistics: A Guide to the Unknown* and in *Forty Studies That Changed Psychology: Exploration into the History of Psychological Research* (the complete references for these two books can be found in the back of the book).

EXERCISES 1.1 - 1.11

1.1 Give a brief definition of the terms *descriptive statistics* and *inferential statistics.*

1.2 Give a brief definition of the terms *population* and *sample.*

1.3 Data from a poll conducted by Travelocity led to the following estimates: Approximately 40% of travelers check work e-mail while on vacation, about 33% take cell phones on vacation in order to stay connected with work, and about 25% bring laptop computers on vacation (*San Luis Obispo Tribune*, December 1, 2005). Are the given percentages population values or were they computed from a sample?

1.4 Based on a study of 2121 children between the ages of 1 and 4, researchers at the Medical College of Wisconsin concluded that there was an association between iron deficiency and the length of time that a child is bottle-fed (*Milwaukee Journal Sentinel*, November 26, 2005). Describe the sample and the population of interest for this study.

1.5 The student senate at a university with 15,000 students is interested in the proportion of students who favor a change in the grading system to allow for plus and minus grades (e.g., B+, B, B−, rather than just B). Two hundred students are interviewed to determine their attitude toward this proposed change. What is the population of interest? What group of students constitutes the sample in this problem?

1.6 The increasing popularity of online shopping has many consumers using Internet access at work to browse and shop online. In fact, the Monday after Thanksgiving has been nicknamed "Cyber Monday" because of the large increase in online purchases that occurs on that day. Data from a large-scale survey by a market research firm (*Detroit Free Press*, November 26, 2005) was used to compute estimates of the percent of men and women who shop online while at work. The resulting estimates probably won't make most employers happy—42% of the men and 32% of the women in the sample were shopping online at work! Are the estimates given computed using data from a sample or for the entire population?

1.7 The supervisors of a rural county are interested in the proportion of property owners who support the construction of a sewer system. Because it is too costly to contact all 7000 property owners, a survey of 500 owners (selected at random) is undertaken. Describe the population and sample for this problem.

1.8 A consumer group conducts crash tests of new model cars. To determine the severity of damage to 2010 Toyota Camrys resulting from a 10-mph crash into a concrete wall, the research group tests six cars of this type and assesses the amount of damage. Describe the population and sample for this problem.

1.9 A building contractor has a chance to buy an odd lot of 5000 used bricks at an auction. She is interested in determining the proportion of bricks in the lot that are cracked and therefore unusable for her current project, but she does not have enough time to inspect all 5000 bricks. Instead, she checks 100 bricks to determine whether each is cracked. Describe the population and sample for this problem.

1.10 The article "Brain Shunt Tested to Treat Alzheimer's" (*San Francisco Chronicle*, October 23, 2002) summarizes the findings of a study that appeared in the journal *Neurology*. Doctors at Stanford Medical Center were interested in determining whether a new surgical approach to treating Alzheimer's disease results in improved memory functioning. The surgical procedure involves implanting a thin tube, called a shunt, which is designed to drain toxins from the fluid-filled space that cushions the brain. Eleven patients had shunts implanted and were followed for a year, receiving quarterly tests of memory function. Another sample of Alzheimer's patients was used as a comparison group. Those in the comparison group received the standard care for Alzheimer's disease. After analyzing the data from this study, the investigators concluded that the "results suggested the treated patients essentially held their own in the cognitive tests while the patients in the control group steadily declined. However, the study was too small to produce conclusive statistical evidence."

a. What were the researchers trying to learn? What questions motivated their research?
b. Do you think that the study was conducted in a reasonable way? What additional information would you want in order to evaluate this study?

1.11 The newspaper article "Spray Away Flu" (*Omaha World-Herald*, June 8, 1998) reported on a study of the effectiveness of a new flu vaccine that is administered by nasal spray rather than by injection. The article states that the "researchers gave the spray to 1070 healthy children, 15 months to 6 years old, before the flu season two winters ago. One percent developed confirmed influenza, compared with 18% of the 532 children who received a placebo. And only one vaccinated child developed an ear infection after coming down with influenza. . . . Typically 30% to 40% of children with influenza later develop an ear infection." The researchers concluded that the nasal flu vaccine was effective in reducing the incidence of flu and also in reducing the number of children with flu who subsequently develop ear infections.

a. What were the researchers trying to learn? What questions motivated their research?
b. Do you think that the study was conducted in a reasonable way? What additional information would you want in order to evaluate this study?

Bold exercises answered in back ● Data set available online ✦ Video Solution available

1.4 Types of Data and Some Simple Graphical Displays

Every discipline has its own particular way of using common words, and statistics is no exception. You will recognize some of the terminology from previous math and science courses, but much of the language of statistics will be new to you. In this section, you will learn some of the terminology used to describe data.

Types of Data

The individuals or objects in any particular population typically possess many characteristics that might be studied. Consider a group of students currently enrolled in a statistics course. One characteristic of the students in the population is the brand of calculator owned (Casio, Hewlett-Packard, Sharp, Texas Instruments, and so on). Another characteristic is the number of textbooks purchased that semester, and yet another is the distance from the university to each student's permanent residence. A **variable** is any characteristic whose value may change from one individual or object to another. For example, *calculator brand* is a variable, and so are *number of textbooks purchased* and *distance to the university*. **Data** result from making observations either on a single variable or simultaneously on two or more variables.

A univariate data set consists of observations on a single variable made on individuals in a sample or population. There are two types of univariate data sets: categorical and numerical. In the previous example, *calculator brand* is a categorical variable, because each student's response to the query, "What brand of calculator do you own?" is a category. The collection of responses from all these students forms a categorical data set. The other two variables, *number of textbooks purchased* and *distance to the university*, are both numerical in nature. Determining the value of such a numerical variable (by counting or measuring) for each student results in a numerical data set.

AP* EXAM TIP

Being able to select an appropriate data analysis method depends on knowing whether the data are categorical or numerical, as well as how many variables are in the data set.

DEFINITION

A data set consisting of observations on a single characteristic is a **univariate data set.**

A univariate data set is **categorical** (or **qualitative**) if the individual observations are categorical responses.

A univariate data set is **numerical** (or **quantitative**) if each observation is a number.

EXAMPLE 1.5 College Choice Do-Over?

The Higher Education Research Institute at UCLA surveys over 20,000 college seniors each year. One question on the 2008 survey asked seniors the following question: If you could make your college choice over, would you still choose to enroll at your current college? Possible responses were definitely yes (DY), probably yes (PY), probably no (PN), and definitely no (DN). Responses for 20 students were:

DY	PN	DN	DY	PY	PY	PN	PY	PY	DY
DY	PY	DY	DY	PY	PY	DY	DY	PN	DY

(These data are just a small subset of the data from the survey. For a description of the full data set, see Exercise 1.18). Because the response to the question about college choice is categorical, this is a univariate categorical data set.

In Example 1.5, the data set consisted of observations on a single variable (college choice response), so this is univariate data. In some studies, attention focuses simultaneously on two different characteristics. For example, both height (in inches) and weight (in pounds) might be recorded for each individual in a group. The resulting data set consists of pairs of numbers, such as (68, 146). This is called a **bivariate data set. Multivariate data** result from obtaining a category or value for each of two or more attributes (so bivariate data are a special case of multivariate data). For example, multivariate data would result from determining height, weight, pulse rate, and systolic blood pressure for each individual in a group. Example 1.6 illustrates a bivariate data set.

EXAMPLE 1.6 How Safe Are College Campuses?

● Consider the accompanying data on violent crime on college campuses in Florida during 2005 (http://www.fbi.gov/ucr/05cius/data/table_09.html).

University/College	Student Enrollment	Number of Violent Crimes Reported in 2005
Florida A&M University	13,067	23
Florida Atlantic University	25,319	4
Florida Gulf Coast University	5,955	5
Florida International University	34,865	5
Florida State University	38,431	29
New College of Florida	692	1
Pensacola Junior College	10,879	2
Santa Fe Community College	13,888	3
Tallahassee Community College	12,775	0
University of Central Florida	42,465	19
University of Florida	47,993	17
University of North Florida	14,533	6
University of South Florida	42,238	19
University of West Florida	9,518	1

Here two variables—*student enrollment* and *number of violent crimes reported*—were recorded for each of the 14 schools. Because this data set consists of values of two variables for each school, it is a bivariate data set. Each of the two variables considered here is numerical (rather than categorical).

Two Types of Numerical Data

There are two different types of numerical data: *discrete* and *continuous.* Consider a number line (Figure 1.3) for locating values of the numerical variable being studied. Each possible number (2, 3.125, 8.12976, etc.) corresponds to exactly one point on the number line. Now suppose that the variable of interest is the number of courses in which a student is enrolled. If no student is enrolled in more than eight courses, the possible values are 1, 2, 3, 4, 5, 6, 7, and 8. These values are identified in Figure 1.4(a) by the dots at the points marked 1, 2, 3, 4, 5, 6, 7, and 8. These possible values are isolated from one another on the number line; around any possible value, we can place an interval that is small enough that no other possible value is included in the interval. On the other hand, the line segment in Figure 1.4(b) identifies a plausible set of possible values for the time (in seconds) it takes for the first kernel in a bag of microwave popcorn to pop. Here the possible values make up an entire interval on the number line, and no possible value is isolated from other possible values.

● Data set available online

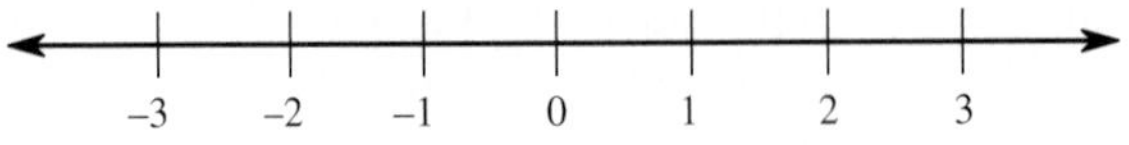

FIGURE 1.3
A number line.

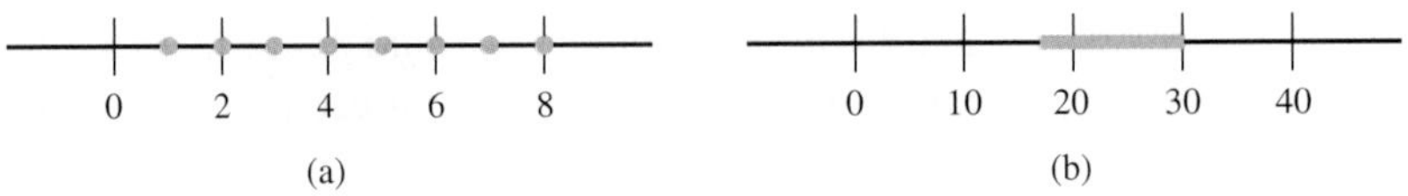

FIGURE 1.4
Possible values of a variable:
(a) number of cylinders;
(b) quarter-mile time.

DEFINITION

A numerical variable results in **discrete** data if the possible values of the variable correspond to isolated points on the number line.

A numerical variable results in **continuous** data if the set of possible values forms an entire interval on the number line.

Discrete data usually arise when observations are determined by counting (for example, the number of roommates a student has or the number of petals on a certain type of flower).

EXAMPLE 1.7 Do U Txt?

● The number of text messages sent on a particular day is recorded for each of 12 students. The resulting data set is

23	0	14	13	15	0	60	82	0	40	41	22

Possible values for the variable *number of text messages sent* are 0, 1, 2, 3. . . . These are isolated points on the number line, so this data set consists of discrete numerical data.

Suppose that instead of the number of text messages sent, the *time spent texting* had been recorded. Even though time spent may have been reported rounded to the nearest minute, the actual time spent could have been 6 minutes, 6.2 minutes, 6.28 minutes, or any other value in an entire interval. So, recording values of *time spent texting* would result in continuous data.

In general, data are continuous when observations involve making measurements, as opposed to counting. In practice, measuring instruments do not have infinite accuracy, so possible measured values, strictly speaking, do not form a continuum on the number line. However, any number in the continuum *could* be a value of the variable. The distinction between discrete and continuous data will be important in our discussion of probability models.

Frequency Distributions and Bar Charts for Categorical Data

An appropriate graphical or tabular display of data can be an effective way to summarize and communicate information. When the data set is categorical, a common way to present the data is in the form of a table, called a *frequency distribution.*

● Data set available online

A **frequency distribution for categorical data** is a table that displays the possible categories along with the associated frequencies and/or relative frequencies.

The **frequency** for a particular category is the number of times the category appears in the data set.

The **relative frequency** for a particular category is calculated as

$$\text{relative frequency} = \frac{\text{frequency}}{\text{number of obervations in the data set}}$$

The relative frequency for a particular category is the proporton of the observations that belong to that category. If the table includes relative frequencies, it is sometimes referred to as a **relative frequency distribution**.

EXAMPLE 1.8 Motorcycle Helmets—Can You See Those Ears?

The U.S. Department of Transportation established standards for motorcycle helmets. To ensure a certain degree of safety, helmets should reach the bottom of the motorcyclist's ears. The report "Motorcycle Helmet Use in 2005—Overall Results" (National Highway Traffic Safety Administration, August 2005) summarized data collected in June of 2005 by observing 1700 motorcyclists nationwide at selected roadway locations. Each time a motorcyclist passed by, the observer noted whether the rider was wearing no helmet, a noncompliant helmet, or a compliant helmet. Using the coding

NH = noncompliant helmet
CH = compliant helmet
N = no helmet

a few of the observations were

CH N CH NH N CH CH CH N N

There were also 1690 additional observations, which we didn't reproduce here! In total, there were 731 riders who wore no helmet, 153 who wore a noncompliant helmet, and 816 who wore a compliant helmet.

The corresponding frequency distribution is given in Table 1.1.

TABLE 1.1 Frequency Distribution for Helmet Use

Helmet Use Category	Frequency	Relative Frequency
No helmet	731	0.430 ← 731/1700
Noncompliant helmet	153	0.090 ← 153/1700
Compliant helmet	816	0.480
	1700 ↖ Total number of observations	1.000 ↖ Should total 1, but in some cases may be slightly off due to rounding

From the frequency distribution, we can see that a large number of riders (43%) were not wearing a helmet, but most of those who wore a helmet were wearing one that met the Department of Transportation safety standard.

A frequency distribution gives a tabular display of a data set. It is also common to display categorical data graphically. A bar chart is one of the most widely used types of graphical displays for categorical data.

Bar Charts

A **bar chart** is a graph of a frequency distribution of categorical data. Each category in the frequency distribution is represented by a bar or rectangle, and the picture is constructed in such a way that the *area* of each bar is proportional to the corresponding frequency or relative frequency.

Bar Charts

When to Use Categorical data.

How to Construct

1. Draw a horizontal axis, and write the category names or labels below the line at regularly spaced intervals.
2. Draw a vertical axis, and label the scale using either frequency or relative frequency.
3. Place a rectangular bar above each category label. The height is determined by the category's frequency or relative frequency, and all bars should have the same width. With the same width, both the height and the area of the bar are proportional to frequency and relative frequency.

What to Look For

- Frequently and infrequently occurring categories.

AP* EXAM TIP

Don't confuse bar charts with histograms (to be introduced in Chapter 3). These two types of graphs look very similar, but histograms are used with numerical data.

EXAMPLE 1.9 Revisiting Motorcycle Helmets

Example 1.8 used data on helmet use from a sample of 1700 motorcyclists to construct a frequency distribution (Table 1.1). Figure 1.5 shows the bar chart corresponding to this frequency distribution.

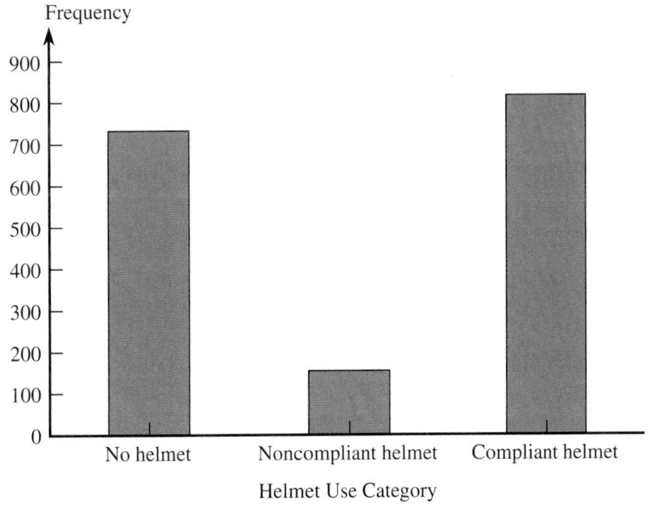

FIGURE 1.5
Bar chart of helmet use.

The bar chart provides a visual representation of the information in the frequency distribution. From the bar chart, it is easy to see that the compliant helmet use category occurred most often in the data set. The bar for compliant helmets is about five times as tall (and therefore has five times the area) as the bar for noncompliant helmets because approximately five times as many motorcyclists wore compliant helmets than wore noncompliant helmets.

Step-by-Step technology instructions available online

Dotplots for Numerical Data

A dotplot is a simple way to display numerical data when the data set is reasonably small. Each observation is represented by a dot above the location corresponding to its value on a horizontal measurement scale. When a value occurs more than once, there is a dot for each occurrence and these dots are stacked vertically.

Dotplots

When to Use Small numerical data sets.

How to Construct

1. Draw a horizontal line and mark it with an appropriate measurement scale.
2. Locate each value in the data set along the measurement scale, and represent it by a dot. If there are two or more observations with the same value, stack the dots vertically.

What to Look For Dotplots convey information about:

- A representative or typical value in the data set.
- The extent to which the data values spread out.
- The nature of the distribution of values along the number line.
- The presence of unusual values in the data set.

EXAMPLE 1.10 Making It to Graduation . . .

● The article "Keeping Score When It Counts: Graduation Rates and Academic Progress Rates for 2009 NCAA Men's Division I Basketball Tournament Teams" (The Institute for Diversity and Ethics in Sport, University of Central Florida, March 2009) compared graduation rates of basketball players to those of all student athletes for the universities and colleges that sent teams to the 2009 Division I playoffs. The graduation rates in the accompanying table represent the percentage of athletes who started college in 2002 who had graduated by the end of 2008. Also shown are the differences between the graduation rate for all student athletes and the graduation rate for basketball student athletes. (Note: Teams from 63 schools made it to the playoffs, but two of them—Cornell and North Dakota State—did not report graduation rates.)

Minitab, a computer software package for statistical analysis, was used to construct a dotplot of the 61 graduation rates for basketball players (see Figure 1.6). From this dotplot, we see that basketball graduation rates varied a great deal from school to school, ranging from a low of 8% to a high of 100%. We can also see that the graduation rates seem to cluster in several groups, denoted by the colored ovals that have been added to the dotplot. There are several schools with graduation rates of 100% (excellent!) and another group of 13 schools with graduation rates that are

● Data set available online

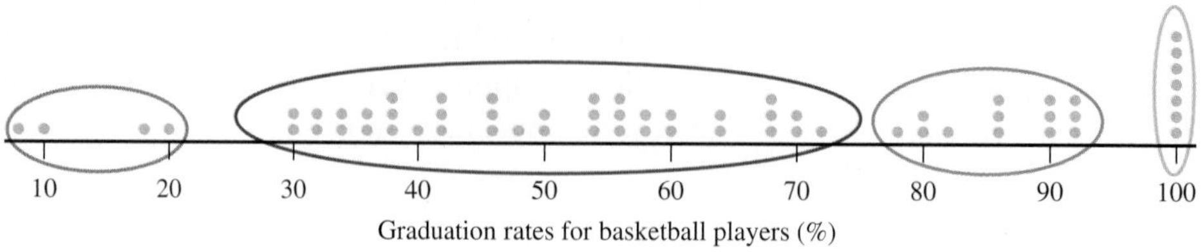

FIGURE 1.6
Minitab dotplot of graduation rates.

Graduation Rates (%)

Basketball	All Athletes	Difference (All - BB)	Basketball	All Athletes	Difference (All - BB)
63	75	12	57	70	13
56	57	1	45	57	12
31	86	55	86	85	−1
20	64	44	67	81	14
38	69	31	53	78	25
100	85	−15	55	69	14
70	96	26	92	75	−17
91	79	−12	69	84	15
92	89	−3	17	48	31
30	76	46	77	79	2
8	56	48	80	91	11
34	53	19	100	95	−5
29	82	53	86	94	8
71	83	12	37	69	32
33	81	48	42	63	21
89	96	7	50	83	33
89	97	8	57	71	14
60	67	7	38	78	40
100	80	−20	31	72	41
67	89	22	47	72	25
80	86	6	46	79	33
64	70	6	67	75	8
40	69	29	100	82	−18
42	75	33	89	95	6
100	94	−6	53	71	18
10	79	69	100	92	−8
55	72	17	50	83	33
46	83	37	41	68	27
60	79	19	100	80	−20
36	72	36	86	79	−7
53	78	25	82	92	10
36	71	35			

higher than most. The majority of schools are in the large cluster with graduation rates from about 30% to about 72%. And then there is that bottom group of four schools with embarrassingly low graduation rates for basketball players: Northridge (8%), Maryland (10%), Portland State (17%), and Arizona (20%).

Figure 1.7 shows two dotplots of graduation rates—one for basketball players and one for all student athletes. There are some striking differences that are easy to

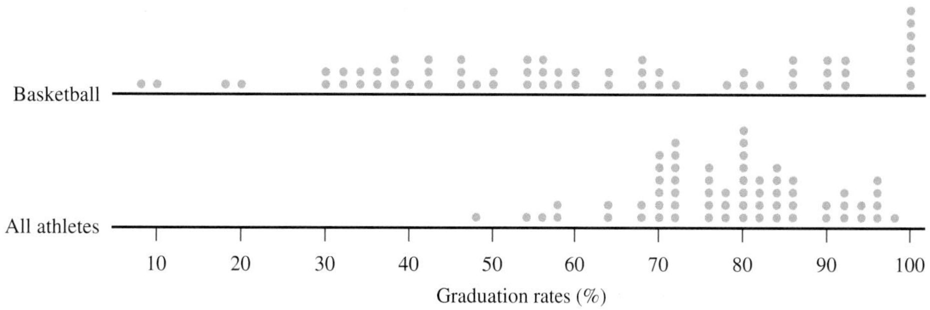

FIGURE 1.7
MINITAB dotplot of graduation rates for basketball players and for all athletes.

see when the data is displayed in this way. The graduation rates for all student athletes tend to be higher and to vary less from school to school than the graduation rates for basketball players.

The dotplots in Figure 1.7 are informative, but we can do even better. The data given here are an example of *paired data.* Each basketball graduation rate is paired with a graduation rate for all student athletes from the same school. When data are paired in this way, it is usually more informative to look at differences—in this case, the difference between the graduation rate for all student athletes and for basketball players for each school. These differences (all − basketball) are also shown in the data table. Figure 1.8 gives a dotplot of the 61 differences. Notice that one difference is equal to 0. This corresponded to a school for which the basketball graduation rate is equal to the graduation rate of all student athletes. There are 11 schools for which the difference is negative. Negative differences correspond to schools that have a graduation rate for basketball players that is higher than the graduation rate for all student athletes. The most interesting features of the difference dotplot are the very large number of positive differences and the wide spread. Positive differences correspond to schools that have a lower graduation rate for basketball players. There is a lot of variability in the graduation rate difference from school to school, and three schools have differences that are noticeably higher than the rest. (In case you were wondering, these schools were Clemson with a difference of 53%, American University with a difference of 55%, and Maryland with a difference of 69%.)

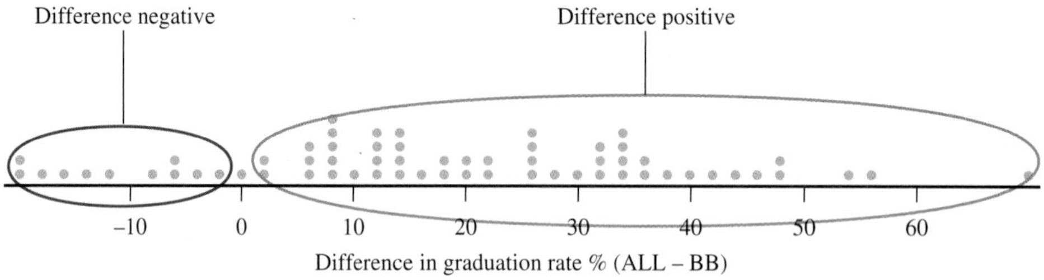

FIGURE 1.8
Dotplot of graduation rate differences (ALL − BB)

EXERCISES 1.12 - 1.31

1.12 Classify each of the following variables as either categorical or numerical. For those that are numerical, determine whether they are discrete or continuous.

a. Number of students in a class of 35 who turn in a term paper before the due date
b. Gender of the next baby born at a particular hospital
c. Amount of fluid (in ounces) dispensed by a machine used to fill bottles with soda pop
d. Thickness of the gelatin coating of a vitamin E capsule
e. Birth order classification (only child, firstborn, middle child, lastborn) of a math major

1.13 Classify each of the following variables as either categorical or numerical. For those that are numerical, determine whether they are discrete or continuous.

a. Brand of computer purchased by a customer
b. State of birth for someone born in the United States
c. Price of a textbook
d. Concentration of a contaminant (micrograms per cubic centimeter) in a water sample
e. Zip code (Think carefully about this one.)
f. Actual weight of coffee in a 1-pound can

1.14 For the following numerical variables, state whether each is discrete or continuous.

a. The number of insufficient-funds checks received by a grocery store during a given month
b. The amount by which a 1-pound package of ground beef decreases in weight (because of moisture loss) before purchase
c. The number of New York Yankees during a given year who will not play for the Yankees the next year
d. The number of students in a class of 35 who have purchased a used copy of the textbook

1.15 For the following numerical variables, state whether each is discrete or continuous.
a. The length of a 1-year-old rattlesnake
b. The altitude of a location in California selected randomly by throwing a dart at a map of the state
c. The distance from the left edge at which a 12-inch plastic ruler snaps when bent sufficiently to break
d. The price per gallon paid by the next customer to buy gas at a particular station

1.16 For each of the following situations, give a set of possible data values that might arise from making the observations described.
a. The manufacturer for each of the next 10 automobiles to pass through a given intersection is noted.
b. The grade point average for each of the 15 seniors in a statistics class is determined.
c. The number of gas pumps in use at each of 20 gas stations at a particular time is determined.
d. The actual net weight of each of 12 bags of fertilizer having a labeled weight of 50 pounds is determined.
e. Fifteen different radio stations are monitored during a 1-hour period, and the amount of time devoted to commercials is determined for each.

1.17 In a survey of 100 people who had recently purchased motorcycles, data on the following variables were recorded:

Gender of purchaser
Brand of motorcycle purchased
Number of previous motorcycles owned by purchaser
Telephone area code of purchaser
Weight of motorcycle as equipped at purchase

a. Which of these variables are categorical?
b. Which of these variables are discrete numerical?
c. Which type of graphical display would be an appropriate choice for summarizing the gender data, a bar chart or a dotplot?
d. Which type of graphical display would be an appropriate choice for summarizing the weight data, a bar chart or a dotplot?

1.18 The report "Findings from the 2008 Administration of the College Senior Survey" (Higher Education Research Institute, UCLA, June 2009) gave the following relative frequency distribution summarizing student responses to the question "If you could make your college choice over, would you still choose to enroll at your current college?"

Response	Relative Frequency
Definitely yes	.447
Probably yes	.373
Probably no	.134
Definitely no	.046

a. Use this information to construct a bar chart for the response data.
b. If you were going to use the response data and the bar chart from Part (a) as the basis for an article for your student paper, what would be a good headline for your article?

1.19 ● The article "Feasting on Protein" (*AARP Bulletin*, September 2009) gave the cost per gram of protein for 19 common food sources of protein.

Food	Cost (cents per gram of protein)
Chicken	1.8
Salmon	5.8
Turkey	1.5
Soybeans	3.1
Roast beef	2.7
Cottage cheese	3.1
Ground beef	2.3
Ham	2.1
Lentils	3.3
Beans	2.9
Yogurt	5.0
Milk	2.5
Peas	5.2
Tofu	6.9
Cheddar cheese	3.6
Nuts	5.2
Eggs	5.7
Peanut butter	1.8
Ice cream	5.3

a. Construct a dotplot of the cost-per-gram data.
b. Locate the cost per gram for meat and poultry items in your dotplot and highlight them in a different color. Based on the dotplot, do meat and poultry items appear to be a good value? That is, do they appear to be relatively low cost compared to other sources of protein?

1.20 ● Box Office Mojo (www.boxofficemojo.com) tracks movie ticket sales. Ticket sales (in millions of dollars) for each of the top 20 movies in 2007 and 2008 are shown in the accompanying table.

Movie (2007)	2007 Sales (millions of dollars)
Spider-Man 3	336.5
Shrek the Third	322.7
Transformers	319.2
Pirates of the Caribbean: At World's End	309.4
Harry Potter and the Order of the Phoenix	292.0
I Am Legend	256.4
The Bourne Ultimatum	227.5
National Treasure: Book of Secrets	220.0
Alvin and the Chipmunks	217.3
300	210.6
Ratatouille	206.4
The Simpsons Movie	183.1
Wild Hogs	168.3
Knocked Up	148.8
Juno	143.5
Rush Hour 3	140.1
Live Free or Die Hard	134.5
Fantastic Four: Rise of the Silver Surfer	131.9
American Gangster	130.2
Enchanted	127.8

Movie (2008)	2008 Sales (millions of dollars)
The Dark Knight	533.3
Iron Man	318.4
Indiana Jones and the Kingdom of the Crystal Skull	317.1
Hancock	227.9
WALL-E	223.8
Kung Fu Panda	215.4
Twilight	192.8
Madagascar: Escape 2 Africa	180.0
Quantum of Solace	168.4
Dr. Suess' Horton Hears a Who!	154.5
Sex and the City	152.6
Gran Torino	148.1
Mamma Mia!	144.1
Marley and Me	143.2
The Chronicles of Narnia: Prince Caspian	141.6
Slumdog Millionaire	141.3
The Incredible Hulk	134.8
Wanted	134.5
Get Smart	130.3
The Curious Case of Benjamin Button	127.5

(continued)

a. Construct a dotplot of the 2008 ticket sales data. Comment on any interesting features of the dotplot.

b. Construct a dotplot of the 2007 ticket sales data. Comment on any interesting features of the dotplot. In what ways are the distributions of the 2007 and 2008 ticket sales observations similar? In what ways are they different?

1.21 ● About 38,000 students attend Grant MacEwan College in Edmonton, Canada. In 2004, the college surveyed non-returning students to find out why they did not complete their degree (Grant MacEwan College Early Leaver Survey Report, 2004). Sixty-three students gave a personal (rather than an academic) reason for leaving. The accompanying frequency distribution summarizes primary reason for leaving for these 63 students.

Primary Reason for Leaving	Frequency
Financial	19
Health	12
Employment	8
Family issues	6
Wanted to take a break	4
Moving	2
Travel	2
Other personal reasons	10

Summarize the reason for leaving data using a bar chart and write a few sentences commenting on the most common reasons for leaving.

1.22 Figure EX-1.22 is a graph that appeared in *USA Today* (June 29, 2009). This graph is meant to be a bar graph of responses to the question shown in the graph.

a. Is response to the question a categorical or numerical variable?
b. Explain why a bar chart rather than a dotplot was used to display the response data.
c. There must have been an error made in constructing this graph. How can you tell that the graph is not a correct representation of the response data?

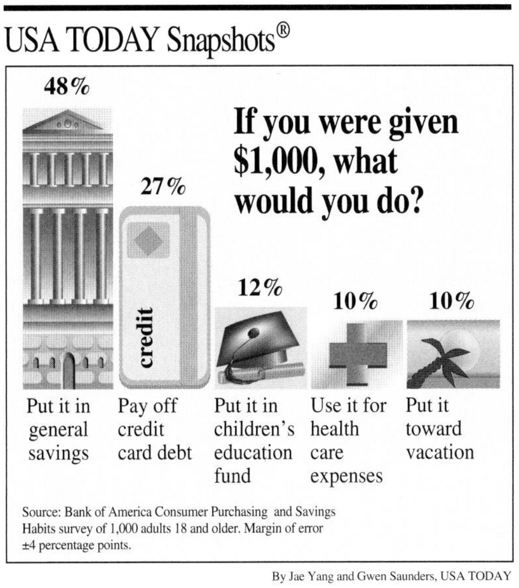

FIGURE EX-1.22

1.23 ● The online article "Social Networks: Facebook Takes Over Top Spot, Twitter Climbs" (Compete.com, February 9, 2009) included the accompanying data on number of unique visitors and total number of visits for January 2009 for the top 25 online social network sites. The data on total visits and unique visitors were used to compute the values in the final column of the data table, in which

$$\text{visits per unique visitor} = \frac{\text{total visits}}{\text{number of unique visitors}}$$

Site	Unique Visitors	Total Visits	Visits per Unique Visitor
facebook.com	68,557,534	1,191,373,339	17.3777
myspace.com	58,555,800	810,153,536	13.8356
twitter.com	5,979,052	54,218,731	9.0681
fixter.com	7,645,423	53,389,974	6.9833
linkedin.com	11,274,160	42,744,438	3.7914
tagged.com	4,448,915	39,630,927	8.9080
classmates.com	17,296,524	35,219,210	2.0362
myyearbook.com	3,312,898	33,121,821	9.9978
livejournal.com	4,720,720	25,221,354	5.3427
imeem.com	9,047,491	22,993,608	2.5414
reunion.com	13,704,990	20,278,100	1.4796
ning.com	5,673,549	19,511,682	3.4391
blackplanet.com	1,530,329	10,173,342	6.6478
bebo.com	2,997,929	9,849,137	3.2853
hi5.com	2,398,323	9,416,265	3.9262
yuku.com	1,317,551	9,358,966	7.1033
cafemom.com	1,647,336	8,586,261	5.2122
friendster.com	1,568,439	7,279,050	4.6410
xanga.com	1,831,376	7,009,577	3.8275
360.yahoo.com	1,499,057	5,199,702	3.4686
orkut.com	494,464	5,081,235	10.2762
urbanchat.com	329,041	2,961,250	8.9996
fubar.com	452,090	2,170,315	4.8006
asiantown.net	81,245	1,118,245	13.7639
tickle.com	96,155	109,492	1.1387

a. A dotplot of the total visits data is shown in Figure EX-1.23a. What are the most obvious features of the dotplot? What does it tell you about the online social networking sites?

b. A dotplot for the number of unique visitors is shown in Figure EX-1.23b. In what way is this dotplot different from the dotplot for total visits in Part (a)?

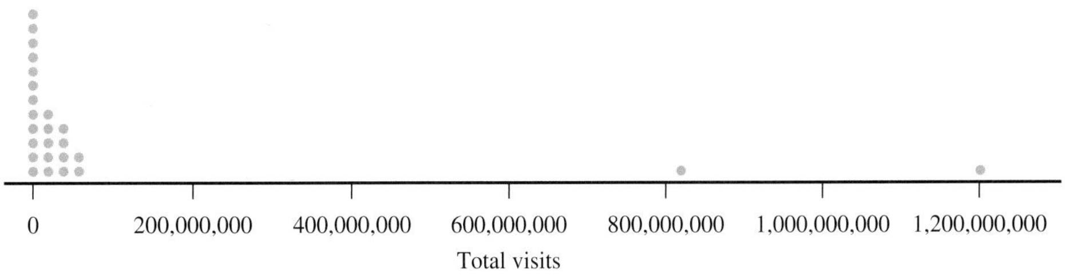

FIGURE EX-1.23a

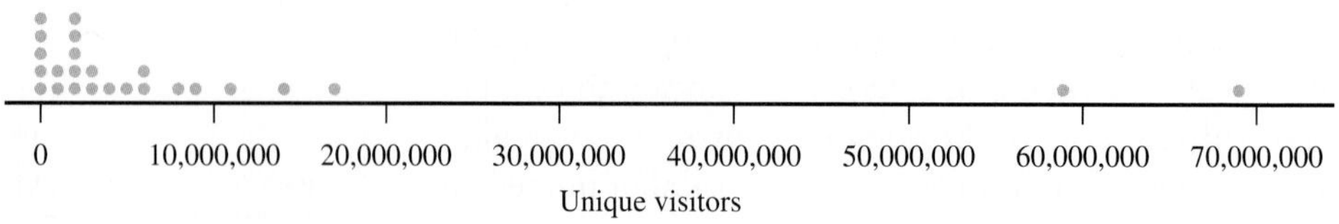

FIGURE EX-1.23b

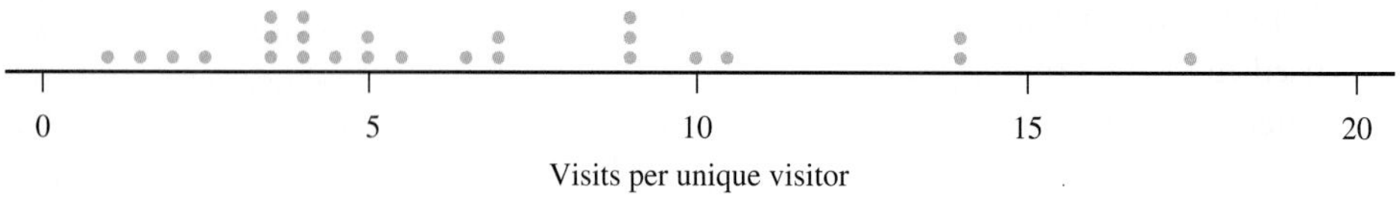

FIGURE EX-1.23c

What does this tell you about the online social networking sites?

c. A dotplot for the visits per unique visitor data is shown in Figure EX-1.23c. What new information about the online social networks is provided by this dotplot?

1.24 Heal the Bay is an environmental organization that releases an annual beach report card based on water quality (Heal the Bay Beach Report Card, May 2009). The 2009 ratings for 14 beaches in San Francisco County during wet weather were:

A+ C B A A+ A+ A A+ B D C D F F

a. Would it be appropriate to display the ratings data using a dotplot? Explain why or why not.
b. Summarize the wet weather ratings by constructing a relative frequency distribution and a bar chart.
c. The dry weather ratings for these same beaches were:

A B B A+ A F A A A A A A B A

Construct a bar graph for the dry weather ratings.

d. Do the bar graphs from parts (b) and (c) support the statement that beach water quality tends to be better in dry weather conditions? Explain.

1.25 ● The article "Going Wireless" (*AARP Bulletin*, June 2009) reported the estimated percentage of households with only wireless phone service (no landline) for the 50 states and the District of Columbia. In the accompanying data table, each state was also classified into one of three geographical regions—West (W), Middle states (M), and East (E).

Wireless %	Region	State
13.9	M	AL
11.7	W	AK
18.9	W	AZ
22.6	M	AR
9.0	W	CA
16.7	W	CO
5.6	E	CN
5.7	E	DE
20.0	E	DC
16.8	E	FL
16.5	E	GA
8.0	W	HI
22.1	W	ID
16.5	M	IL
13.8	M	IN
22.2	M	IA
16.8	M	KA
21.4	M	KY
15.0	M	LA
13.4	E	ME
10.8	E	MD
9.3	E	MA
16.3	M	MI
17.4	M	MN
19.1	M	MS
9.9	M	MO
9.2	W	MT
23.2	M	NE
10.8	W	NV
16.9	M	ND
11.6	E	NH
8.0	E	NJ
21.1	W	NM
11.4	E	NY
16.3	E	NC
14.0	E	OH
23.2	M	OK

(data continued on following page)

Wireless %	Region	State
17.7	W	OR
10.8	E	PA
7.9	E	RI
20.6	E	SC
6.4	M	SD
20.3	M	TN
20.9	M	TX
25.5	W	UT
10.8	E	VA
5.1	E	VT
16.3	W	WA
11.6	E	WV
15.2	M	WI
11.4	W	WY

a. Display the data graphically in a way that makes it possible to compare wireless percent for the three geographical regions.

b. Does the graphical display in Part (a) reveal any striking differences in wireless percent for the three geographical regions or are the distributions of wireless percent observations similar for the three regions?

1.26 ● Example 1.6 gave the accompanying data on violent crime on college campuses in Florida during 2005 (from the FBI web site):

University/College	Student Enrollment	Number of Violent Crimes Reported in 2005
Florida A&M University	13,067	23
Florida Atlantic University	25,319	4
Florida Gulf Coast University	5,955	5
Florida International University	34,865	5
Florida State University	38,431	29
New College of Florida	692	1
Pensacola Junior College	10,879	2
Santa Fe Community College	13,888	3
Tallahassee Community College	12,775	0
University of Central Florida	42,465	19
University of Florida	47,993	17
University of North Florida	14,533	6
University of South Florida	42,238	19
University of West Florida	9,518	1

a. Construct a dotplot using the 14 observations on number of violent crimes reported. Which schools stand out from the rest?

b. One of the Florida schools only has 692 students and a few of the schools are quite a bit larger than the rest. Because of this, it might make more sense to consider a crime rate by calculating the number of violent crimes reported per 1000 students. For example, for Florida A&M University the violent crime rate would be

$$\frac{23}{13067}(1000) = (.0018)(1000) = 1.8$$

Calculate the violent crime rate for the other 13 schools and then use those values to construct a dotplot. Do the same schools stand out as unusual in this dotplot?

c. Based on your answers from parts (a) and (b), write a couple of sentences commenting on violent crimes reported at Florida universities and colleges in 2005.

1.27 ● The article "Fliers Trapped on Tarmac Push for Rules on Release" (*USA Today*, July 28, 2009) gave the following data for 17 airlines on number of flights that were delayed on the tarmac for at least 3 hours for the period from October 2008 to May 2009:

Airline	Number of Delays	Rate per 10,000 Flights
ExpressJet	93	4.9
Continental	72	4.1
Delta	81	2.8
Comair	29	2.7
American Eagle	44	1.6
US Airways	46	1.6
JetBlue	18	1.4
American	48	1.3
Northwest	24	1.2
Mesa	17	1.1
United	29	1.1
Frontier	5	0.9
SkyWest	29	0.8
Pinnacle	13	0.7
Atlantic Southeast	11	0.6
AirTran	7	0.4
Southwest	11	0.1

Figure EX-1.27 shows two dotplots: one displays the number of delays data, and one displays the rate per 10,000 flights data.

a. If you were going to rank airlines based on flights delayed on the tarmac for at least three hours, would you use the *total number of flights* data or the *rate per 10,000 flights* data? Explain the reason for your choice.

b. Write a short paragraph that could be used as part of a newspaper article on flight delays that could accompany the dotplot of the *rate per 10,000 flights* data.

1.28 ● The article "Fraud, Identity Theft Afflict Consumers" (*San Luis Obispo Tribune*, February 2, 2005) included the accompanying breakdown of identity theft complaints by type.

Type of Complaint	Percent of All Complaints
Credit card fraud	28%
Phone or utilities fraud	19%
Bank fraud	18%
Employment fraud	13%
Other	22%

Construct a bar chart for these data and write a sentence or two commenting on the most common types of identity theft complaints.

1.29 ● A 2005 AP-IPSOS poll found that 21% of American adults surveyed said their child was heavier than doctors recommend. The reasons given as the most important contributing factor to the child's weight problem are summarized in the accompanying table.

Lack of exercise	38%
Easy access to junk food	23%
Genetics	12%
Eating unhealthy food	9%
Medical condition	8%
Overeating	7%

a. Construct a bar chart for the data on the most important contributing factor.

b. Do you think that it would be reasonable to combine some of these contributing factors into a single category? If so, which categories would you combine and why?

FIGURE EX-1.27

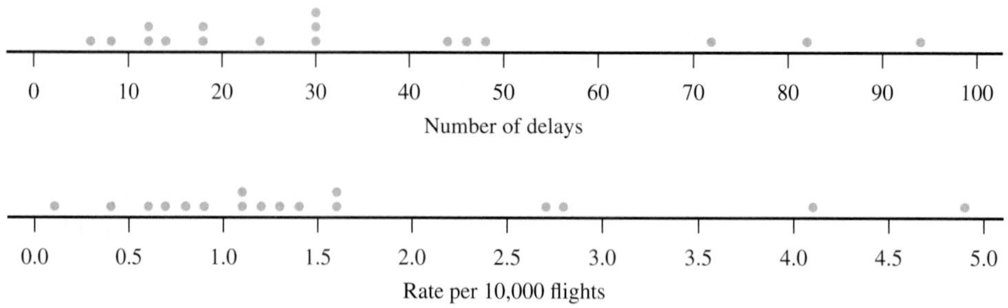

1.30 ✦ The article "Americans Drowsy on the Job and the Road" (Associated Press, March 28, 2001) summarized data from the 2001 Sleep in America poll. Each individual in a sample of 1004 adults was asked questions about his or her sleep habits. The article states that "40 percent of those surveyed say they get sleepy on the job and their work suffers at least a few days each month, while 22 percent said the problems occur a few days each week. And 7 percent say sleepiness on the job is a daily occurrence." Assuming that everyone else reported that sleepiness on the job was not a problem, summarize the given information by constructing a relative frequency bar chart.

1.31 "Ozzie and Harriet Don't Live Here Anymore" (*San Luis Obispo Tribune*, February 26, 2002) is the title of an article that looked at the changing makeup of America's suburbs. The article states that nonfamily households (for example, homes headed by a single professional or an elderly widow) now outnumber married couples with children in suburbs of the nation's largest metropolitan areas. The article goes on to state:

> In the nation's 102 largest metropolitan areas, "nonfamilies" comprised 29 percent of households in 2000, up from 27 percent in 1990. While the number of married-with-children homes grew too, the share did not keep pace. It declined from 28 percent to 27 percent. Married couples without children at home live in another 29 percent of suburban households. The remaining 15 percent are single-parent homes.

Use the given information on type of household in 2000 to construct a frequency distribution and a bar chart. (Be careful to extract the 2000 percentages from the given information).

ACTIVITY 1.1 Twitter Words

This activity requires Internet access.

TweetVolume is a web site that allows you to enter up to three words to produce a bar chart based on how often those words appear on Twitter.

1. Go to www.tweetvolume.com and spend a few minutes experimenting with different words to see how the site works. For example, in July 2010, the words statistics, sample and population resulted in the following bar chart.

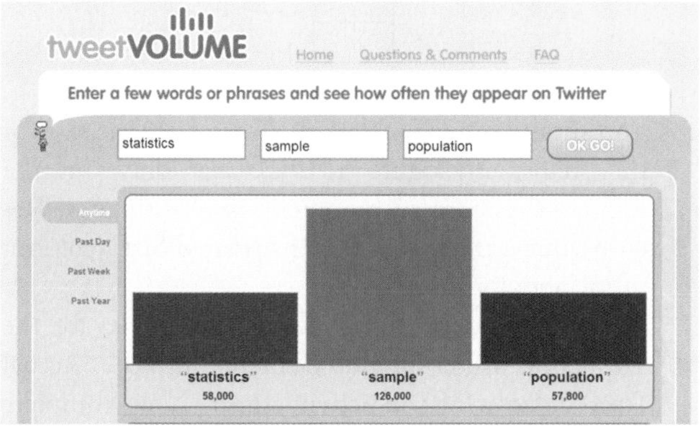

2. Find a set of three words that result in a bar chart in which all three bars are approximately the same height.
3. Find a set of three words that satisfy the following:
   i. One word begins with the letter *a*, one word begins with the letter *b*, and one word begins with the letter *c*.
   ii. The word that begins with the letter *a* is more common on Twitter (has the highest bar in the bar graph) than the other two words.
   iii. The word that begins with the letter *b* is more common on Twitter than the word that begins with the letter *c*.

ACTIVITY 1.2 Head Sizes: Understanding Variability

Materials needed: Each team will need a measuring tape.

For this activity, you will work in teams of 6 to 10 people.

1. Designate a team leader for your team by choosing the person on your team who celebrated his or her last birthday most recently.
2. The team leader should measure and record the head size (measured as the circumference at the widest part of the forehead) of each of the other members of his or her team.
3. Record the head sizes for the individuals on your team as measured by the team leader.
4. Next, each individual on the team should measure the head size of the team leader. Do not share your measurement with the other team members until all team members have measured the team leader's head size.
5. After all team members have measured the team leader's head, record the different team leader head size measurements obtained by the individuals on your team.
6. Using the data from Step 3, construct a dotplot of the team leader's measurements of team head sizes. Then, using the same scale, construct a separate dotplot of the different measurements of the team leader's head size (from Step 5).

Now use the available information to answer the following questions:

7. Do you think the team leader's head size changed in between measurements? If not, explain why the measurements of the team leader's head size are not all the same.
8. Which data set was more variable—head size measurements of the different individuals on your team or the different measurements of the team leader's head size? Explain the basis for your choice.
9. Consider the following scheme (you don't actually have to carry this out): Suppose that a group of 10 people measured head sizes by first assigning each person in the group a number between 1 and 10. Then person 1 measured person 2's head size, person 2 measured person 3's head size, and so on, with person 10 finally measuring person 1's head size. Do you think that the resulting head size measurements would be more variable, less variable, or show about the same amount of variability as a set of 10 measurements resulting from a single individual measuring the head size of all 10 people in the group? Explain.

ACTIVITY 1.3 Estimating Sizes

1. Construct an activity sheet that consists of a table that has 6 columns and 10 rows. Label the columns of the table with the following six headings: (1) Shape, (2) Estimated Size, (3) Actual Size, (4) Difference (Estimated − Actual), (5) Absolute Difference, and (6) Squared Difference. Enter the numbers from 1 to 10 in the "Shape" column.
2. Next you will be visually estimating the sizes of the shapes in Figure 1.9. Size will be described as the number of squares of this size

that would fit in the shape. For example, the shape

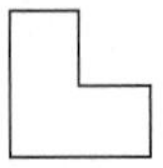

would be size 3, as illustrated by

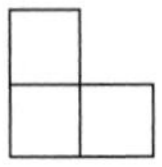

You should now quickly *visually* estimate the sizes of the shapes in Figure 1.9. *Do not* draw on the figure—these are to be quick visual estimates. Record your estimates in the "Estimated Size" column of the activity sheet.
3. Your instructor will provide the actual sizes for the 10 shapes, which should be entered into the "Actual Size" column of the activity sheet. Now complete the "Difference" column by subtracting the actual value from your estimate for each of the 10 shapes.
4. What would cause a difference to be negative? What would cause a difference to be positive?

FIGURE 1.9
Shapes for Activity 1.3.

5. Would the sum of the differences tell you if the estimates and actual values were in close agreement? Does a sum of 0 for the differences indicate that all the estimates were equal to the actual value? Explain.
6. Compare your estimates with those of another person in the class by comparing the sum of the absolute values of the differences between estimates and corresponding actual values. Who was better at estimating shape sizes? How can you tell?
7. Use the last column of the activity sheet to record the squared differences (for example, if the difference for shape 1 was -3, the squared difference would be $(-3)^2 = 9$. Explain why the sum of the squared differences can also be used to assess how accurate your shape estimates were.
8. For this step, work with three or four other students from your class. For each of the 10 shapes, form a new size estimate by computing the average of the size estimates for that shape made by the individuals in your group. Is this new set of estimates more accurate than your own individual estimates were? How can you tell?
9. Does your answer from Step 8 surprise you? Explain why or why not.

ACTIVITY 1.4 A Meaningful Paragraph

Write a meaningful paragraph that includes the following six terms: **sample, population, descriptive statistics, bar chart, numerical variable,** and **dotplot**.

A "meaningful paragraph" is a coherent piece of writing in an appropriate context that uses all of the listed words. The paragraph should show that you understand the meanings of the terms and their relationships to one another. A sequence of sentences that just define the terms is *not* a meaningful paragraph. When choosing a context, think carefully about the terms you need to use. Choosing a good context will make writing a meaningful paragraph easier.

Summary of Key Concepts and Formulas

TERM OR FORMULA	COMMENT
Population	The entire collection of individuals or measurements about which information is desired.
Sample	A part of the population selected for study.
Descriptive statistics	Numerical, graphical, and tabular methods for organizing and summarizing data.
Inferential statistics	Methods for generalizing from a sample to a population.
Categorical data	Individual observations are categorical responses (nonnumerical).
Numerical data	Individual observations are numerical (quantitative) in nature.
Discrete numerical data	Possible values are isolated points along the number line.
Continuous numerical data	Possible values form an entire interval along the number line.
Univariate, bivariate and multivariate data	Each observation consists of one (univariate), two (bivariate), or two or more (multivariate) responses or values.
Frequency distribution for categorical data	A table that displays frequencies, and sometimes relative frequencies, for each of the possible values of a categorical variable.
Bar chart	A graph of a frequency distribution for a categorical data set. Each category is represented by a bar, and the area of the bar is proportional to the corresponding frequency or relative frequency.
Dotplot	A graph of numerical data in which each observation is represented by a dot on or above a horizontal measurement scale.

Chapter Review Exercises 1.32 - 1.37

1.32 ● The report "Testing the Waters 2009" (www.nrdc.org) included information on the water quality at the 82 most popular swimming beaches in California. Thirty-eight of these beaches are in Los Angeles County. For each beach, water quality was tested weekly and the data below are the percent of the tests in 2008 that failed to meet water quality standards.

Los Angeles County

32	4	6	4	4	7	4	27	19	23
19	13	11	19	9	11	16	23	19	16
33	12	29	3	11	6	22	18	31	43
17	26	17	20	10	6	14	11		

Other Counties

0	0	0	2	3	7	5	11	5	7
15	8	1	5	0	5	4	1	0	1
1	0	2	7	0	2	2	3	5	3
0	8	8	8	0	0	17	4	3	7
10	40	3							

a. Construct a dotplot of the percent of tests failing to meet water quality standards for the Los Angeles County beaches. Write a few sentences describing any interesting features of the dotplot.
b. Construct a dotplot of the percent of tests failing to meet water quality standards for the beaches in other counties. Write a few sentences describing any interesting features of the dotplot.
c. Based on the two dotplots from Parts (a) and (b), describe how the percent of tests that fail to meet water quality standards for beaches in Los Angeles county differs from those of other counties.

1.33 The U.S. Department of Education reported that 14% of adults were classified as being below a basic literacy level, 29% were classified as being at a basic literacy level, 44% were classified as being at an intermediate literacy level, and 13% were classified as being at a proficient level (2003 *National Assessment of Adult Literacy*).

a. Is the variable *literacy level* categorical or numerical?
b. Would it be appropriate to display the given information using a dotplot? Explain why or why not.
c. Construct a bar chart to display the given data on literacy level.

1.34 ● ✦ The Computer Assisted Assessment Center at the University of Luton published a report titled "Technical Review of Plagiarism Detection Software." The authors of this report asked faculty at academic institutions about the extent to which they agreed with the statement "Plagiarism is a significant problem in academic institutions." The responses are summarized in the accompanying table. Construct a bar chart for these data.

Response	Frequency
Strongly disagree	5
Disagree	48
Not sure	90
Agree	140
Strongly agree	39

1.35 ● The article "Just How Safe Is That Jet?" (USA Today, March 13, 2000) gave the following relative frequency distribution that summarized data on the type of violation for fines imposed on airlines by the Federal Aviation Administration:

Type of Violation	Relative Frequency
Security	.43
Maintenance	.39
Flight operations	.06
Hazardous materials	.03
Other	.09

Use this information to construct a bar chart for type of violation, and then write a sentence or two commenting on the relative occurrence of the various types of violation.

1.36 ● Each year, *U.S. News and World Report* publishes a ranking of U.S. business schools. The following data give the acceptance rates (percentage of applicants admitted) for the best 25 programs in a recent survey:

16.3 12.0 25.1 20.3 31.9 20.7 30.1 19.5 36.2
46.9 25.8 36.7 33.8 24.2 21.5 35.1 37.6 23.9
17.0 38.4 31.2 43.8 28.9 31.4 48.9

Construct a dotplot, and comment on the interesting features of the plot.

1.37 ● Many adolescent boys aspire to be professional athletes. The paper "Why Adolescent Boys Dream of Becoming Professional Athletes" (*Psychological Reports* [1999]:1075–1085) examined some of the reasons. Each boy in a sample of teenage boys was asked the following question: "Previous studies have shown that more teenage boys say that they are considering becoming professional athletes than any other occupation. In your opinion, why do these boys want to become professional athletes?" The resulting data are shown in the following table:

Response	Frequency
Fame and celebrity	94
Money	56
Attract women	29
Like sports	27
Easy life	24
Don't need an education	19
Other	19

Construct a bar chart to display these data.

CHAPTER 2

Purestock/Kwame Zikomo/SuperStock

Collecting Data Sensibly

A primary goal of statistical studies is to collect data that can then be used to make informed decisions. It should come as no surprise that the ability to make good decisions depends on the quality of the information available. The data collection step is critical to obtaining reliable information; both the type of analysis that is appropriate and the conclusions that can be drawn depend on how the data are collected. In this chapter, we first consider two types of statistical studies and then focus on two widely used methods of data collection: sampling and experimentation.

Make the most of your study time by accessing everything you need to succeed online with CourseMate.
Visit http://www.cengagebrain.com where you will find:

- An interactive eBook, which allows you to take notes, highlight, bookmark, search the text, and use in-context glossary definitions
- Step-by-step instructions for Minitab, Excel, TI-83/84, SPSS, and JMP
- Video solutions to selected exercises
- Data sets available for selected examples and exercises
- Online quizzes
- Flashcards
- Videos

2.1 Statistical Studies: Observation and Experimentation

On September 25, 2009, results from a study of the relationship between spanking and IQ were reported by a number of different news media. Some of the headlines that appeared that day were:

"Spanking lowers a child's IQ" (*Los Angeles Times*)
"Do you spank? Studies indicate it could lower your kid's IQ" (*SciGuy, Houston Chronicle*)
"Spanking can lower IQ" (NBC4i, Columbus, Ohio)
"Smacking hits kids' IQ" (*newscientist.com*)

In the study that these headlines refer to, the investigators followed 806 kids age 2 to 4 and 704 kids age 5 to 9 for 4 years. IQ was measured at the beginning of the study and again 4 years later. The researchers found that at the end of the study, the average IQ of kids who were not spanked was 5 points higher than that of kids who were spanked among the kids who were 2 to 4 years old when the study began, and 2.8 points higher among the kids who were 5 to 9 years old when the study began.

These headlines all imply that spanking was the cause of the observed difference in IQ. Is this conclusion reasonable? The answer depends in a critical way on the study design. We'll return to these headlines and decide if they are on target after first considering some important aspects of study design.

Observation and Experimentation

Data collection is an important step in the data analysis process. When we set out to collect information, it is important to keep in mind the questions we hope to answer on the basis of the resulting data. Sometimes we are interested in answering questions about characteristics of a single existing population or in comparing two or more well-defined populations. To accomplish this, we select a sample from each population under consideration and use the sample information to gain insight into characteristics of those populations.

For example, an ecologist might be interested in estimating the average shell thickness of bald eagle eggs. A social scientist studying a rural community may want to determine whether gender and attitude toward abortion are related. These are examples of studies that are *observational* in nature. In these studies, we want to observe characteristics of members of an existing population or of several populations, and then use the resulting information to draw conclusions. In an observational study, it is important to obtain a sample that is representative of the corresponding population.

Sometimes the questions we are trying to answer deal with the effect of certain explanatory variables on some response and cannot be answered using data from an observational study. Such questions are often of the form, "What happens when ... ?" or, "What is the effect of ... ?" For example, an educator may wonder what would happen to test scores if the required lab time for a chemistry course were increased from 3 hours to 6 hours per week. To answer such questions, the researcher conducts an experiment to collect relevant data. The value of some response variable (test score in the chemistry example) is recorded under different experimental conditions (3-hour lab and 6-hour lab). In an experiment, the researcher manipulates one or more explanatory variables, also sometimes called **factors**, to create the experimental conditions.

AP* EXAM TIP

These definitions are important when deciding what conclusions can be drawn from a statistical study. If asked "What conclusions can be made from this study?", the very first consideration should be whether the study is observational or experimental.

DEFINITION

A study is an **observational study** if the investigator observes characteristics of a sample selected from one or more existing populations. The goal of an observational study is usually to draw conclusions about the corresponding population or about differences between two or more populations. In a well-designed observational study, the sample is selected in a way that is designed to produce a sample that is respresentative of the population.

A study is an **experiment** if the investigator observes how a response variable behaves when one or more explanatory variables, also called factors, are manipulated. The usual goal of an experiment is to determine the effect of the manipulated explanatory variables (factors) on the response variable. In a well-designed experiment, the composition of the groups that will be exposed to different experimental conditions is determined by random assignment.

The type of conclusion that can be drawn from a statistical study depends on the study design. Both observational studies and experiments can be used to compare groups, but in an experiment the researcher controls who is in which group, whereas this is not the case in an observational study. This seemingly small difference is critical when it comes to drawing conclusions based on data from the study.

A well-designed experiment can result in data that provide evidence for a cause-and-effect relationship. This is an important difference between an observational study and an experiment. In an observational study, it is impossible to draw clear cause-and-effect conclusions because we cannot rule out the possibility that the observed effect is due to some variable other than the explanatory variable being studied. Such variables are called confounding variables.

AP* EXAM TIP

Confounding is a very important concept. You should be able to recognize confounding variables given the description of a study. You should also be able to speculate intelligently about possible confounding variables when designing studies (especially experiments).

DEFINITION

A **confounding variable** is one that is related to both group membership and the response variable of interest in a research study.

Consider the role of confounding variables in the following three studies:

- The article "Panel Can't Determine the Value of Daily Vitamins" (*San Luis Obispo Tribune*, July 1, 2003) summarized the conclusions of a government advisory panel that investigated the benefits of vitamin use. The panel looked at a large number of studies on vitamin use and concluded that the results were "inadequate or conflicting." A major concern was that many of the studies were observational in nature and the panel worried that people who take vitamins might be healthier just because they tend to take better care of themselves in general. This potential confounding variable prevented the panel from concluding that taking vitamins is the cause of observed better health among those who take vitamins.
- Studies have shown that people over age 65 who get a flu shot are less likely than those who do not get a flu shot to die from a flu-related illness during the following year. However, recent research has shown that people over age 65 who get a flu shot are also less likely than those who don't to die from *any* cause during the following year (*International Journal of Epidemiology*, December 21, 2005).

This has lead to the speculation that those over age 65 who get flu shots are healthier as a group than those who do not get flu shots. If this is the case, observational studies that compare two groups—those who get flu shots and those who do not—may overestimate the effectiveness of the flu vaccine because general health differs in the two groups. General health is a possible confounding variable in such studies.

- The article "Heartfelt Thanks to Fido" (*San Luis Obispo Tribune*, July 5, 2003) summarized a study that appeared in the *American Journal of Cardiology* (March 15, 2003). In this study researchers measured heart rate variability (a measure of the heart's ability to handle stress) in patients who had recovered from a heart attack. They found that heart rate variability was higher (which is good and means the heart can handle stress better) for those who owned a dog than for those who did not. Should someone who suffers a heart attack immediately go out and get a dog? Well, maybe not yet. The American Heart Association recommends additional studies to determine if the improved heart rate variability is attributable to dog ownership or due to the fact that dog owners get more exercise. If in fact dog owners do tend to get more exercise than nonowners, level of exercise is a confounding variable that would prevent us from concluding that owning a dog is the cause of improved heart rate variability.

Each of the three studies described above illustrates why potential confounding variables make it unreasonable to draw a cause-and-effect conclusion from an observational study.

Let's return to the study on spanking and IQ described at the beginning of this section. Is this study an observational study or an experiment? Two groups were compared (children who were spanked and children who were not spanked), but the researchers did not randomly assign children to the spanking or no-spanking groups. The study is observational, and so cause-and-effect conclusions such as "spanking lowers IQ" are not justified based on the observed data. What we can say is that there is evidence that, as a group, children who are spanked tend to have a lower IQ than children who are not spanked. What we cannot say is that spanking is the cause of the lower IQ. It is possible that other variables—such as home or school environment, socio-economic status, or parents' education—are related to both IQ and whether or not a child was spanked. These are examples of possible confounding variables.

Fortunately, not everyone made the same mistake as the writers of the headlines given earlier in this section. Some examples of headlines that got it right are:

"Lower IQ's measured in spanked children" (*world-science.net*)
"Children who get spanked have lower IQs" (*livescience.com*)
"Research suggests an association between spanking and lower IQ in children" (*CBSnews.com*)

Drawing Conclusions from Statistical Studies

In this section, two different types of conclusions have been described. One type involves generalizing from what we have seen in a sample to some larger population, and the other involves reaching a cause-and-effect conclusion about the effect of an explanatory variable on a response. When is it reasonable to draw such conclusions? The answer depends on the way that the data were collected. Table 2.1 summarizes the types of conclusions that can be made with different study designs.

As you can see from Table 2.1, it is important to think carefully about the objectives of a statistical study before planning how the data will be collected. Both

TABLE 2.1 Drawing Conclusions from Statistical Studies

Study Description	Reasonable to Generalize Conclusions about Group Characteristics to the Population?	Reasonable to Draw Cause-and-Effect Conclusion?
Observational study with sample selected at random from population of interest	Yes	No
Observational study based on convenience or voluntary response sample (poorly designed sampling plan)	No	No
Experiment with groups formed by random assignment of individuals or objects to experimental conditions		
Individuals or objects used in study are volunteers or not randomly selected from some population of interest	No	Yes
Individuals or objects used in study are randomly selected from some population of interest	Yes	Yes
Experiment with groups not formed by random assignment to experimental conditions (poorly designed experiment)	No	No

observational studies and experiments must be carefully designed if the resulting data are to be useful. The common sampling procedures used in observational studies are considered in Section 2.2. In Sections 2.3 and 2.4, we consider experimentation and explore what constitutes good practice in the design of simple experiments.

EXERCISES 2.1 - 2.12

2.1 ✦ The article "Television's Value to Kids: It's All in How They Use It" (*Seattle Times*, July 6, 2005) described a study in which researchers analyzed standardized test results and television viewing habits of 1700 children. They found that children who averaged more than 2 hours of television viewing per day when they were younger than 3 tended to score lower on measures of reading ability and short-term memory.

a. Is the study described an observational study or an experiment?

b. Is it reasonable to conclude that watching two or more hours of television is the cause of lower reading scores? Explain.

2.2 The article "Acupuncture for Bad Backs: Even Sham Therapy Works" (*Time*, May 12, 2009) summarized a study conducted by researchers at the Group Health Center for Health Studies in Seattle. In this study, 638 adults with back pain were randomly assigned to one of four groups. People in group 1 received the usual care for back pain. People in group 2 received acupuncture at a set of points tailored specifically for each individual. People in group 3 received acupuncture at a standard set of points typically used in the treatment of back pain. Those in group 4 received fake acupuncture—they were poked with a toothpick at the same set of points used for the people in group 3! Two notable conclusions from the study were: (1) patients receiving real or fake acupuncture experienced a greater reduction in pain than those receiving usual care; and (2) there was no significant difference in pain reduction for those who received acupuncture (at individualized or the standard set of points) and those who received fake acupuncture toothpick pokes.

a. Is this study an observational study or an experiment? Explain.
b. Is it reasonable to conclude that receiving either real or fake acupuncture was the cause of the observed reduction in pain in those groups compared to the usual care group? What aspect of this study supports your answer?

2.3 The article "Display of Health Risk Behaviors on MySpace by Adolescents" (*Archives of Pediatrics and Adolescent Medicine* [2009]:27–34) described a study in which researchers looked at a random sample of 500 publicly accessible MySpace web profiles posted by 18-year-olds. The content of each profile was analyzed. One of the conclusions reported was that displaying sport or hobby involvement was associated with decreased references to risky behavior (sexual references or references to substance abuse or violence).

a. Is the study described an observational study or an experiment?
b. Is it reasonable to generalize the stated conclusion to all 18-year-olds with a publicly accessible MySpace web profile? What aspect of the study supports your answer?
c. Not all MySpace users have a publicly accessible profile. Is it reasonable to generalize the stated conclusion to all 18-year-old MySpace users? Explain.
d. Is it reasonable to generalize the stated conclusion to all MySpace users with a publicly accessible profile? Explain.

2.4 Can choosing the right music make wine taste better? This question was investigated by a researcher at a university in Edinburgh (*www.decanter.com/news*). Each of 250 volunteers was assigned at random to one of five rooms where they were asked to taste and rate a glass of wine. In one of the rooms, no music was playing and a different style of music was playing in each of the other four rooms. The researchers concluded that cabernet sauvignon is perceived as being richer and more robust when bold music is played than when no music is heard.

a. Is the study described an observational study or an experiment?
b. Can a case be made for the researcher's conclusion that the music played was the cause for the higher rating? Explain.

2.5 Consider the following graphical display that appeared in the *New York Times:*

From the Most Selective Colleges, More Graduates

Students are less likely to graduate from less selective public colleges than more selective ones, even after controlling for the qualifications of the students. Below are the graduation rates for different groups of students, at different types of colleges.

GRADUATION RATES
6-year graduation rates, for students who entered college in 1999.

STUDENT GROUPINGS	**MOST** SELECTIVE	**2ND MOST** SELECTIVE	**3RD MOST** SELECTIVE	**LEAST** SELECTIVE
3.5 high school G.P.A. or higher, 1,200 SAT or higher	89%	82%	71%	59%
3.5 or higher and 1,000 to 1,190, or 3 to 3.5 and 1,200 or higher	83%	75%	63%	62%
3 to 3.5 and 1,000 to 1,190	75%	67%	56%	50%
Less than 3 or less than 1,000 or both	71%	60%	52%	48%

Note: Selectivity of colleges is based on average SAT scores of student body. Colleges in the most selective group have an average SAT score of more than 1,200; those in the least selective group have an average score of less than 1,000.

Sources: William G. Bowen, Matthew M. Chingos, Michael S. McPherson THE NEW YORK TIMES

Based on the data summarized in the graph, we can see that students who have a high school GPA or 3.5 or higher and a combined SAT score of over 1200 have an 89% graduation rate when they attend a "most selective" college, but only a 59% graduation rate when they attend a "least selective" college. Give an example of a potential confounding variable that might explain why the following statement is not reasonable: If all the students that have a GPA of 3.5 or higher and a combined SAT score of 1200 or higher and that were admitted to a "least selective" college were moved to a "most selective" college, the graduation rate for these students would be approximately 89%.

2.6 "Fruit Juice May Be Fueling Pudgy Preschoolers, Study Says" is the title of an article that appeared in the *San Luis Obispo Tribune* (February 27, 2005). This article describes a study that found that for 3- and 4-year-olds, drinking something sweet once or twice a day doubled the risk of being seriously overweight one year later. The authors of the study state

> Total energy may be a confounder if consumption of sweet drinks is a marker for other dietary factors associated with overweight (*Pediatrics*, November 2005).

Give an example of a dietary factor that might be one of the potentially confounding variables the study authors are worried about.

2.7 The article "Americans are 'Getting the Wrong Idea' on Alcohol and Health" (Associated Press, April 19, 2005) reported that observational studies in recent years that have concluded that moderate drinking is associated with a reduction in the risk of heart disease may be misleading. The article refers to a study conducted by the Centers for Disease Control and Prevention that showed that moderate drinkers, as a group, tended to be better educated, wealthier, and more active than nondrinkers. Explain why the existence of these potentially confounding variables prevents drawing the conclusion that moderate drinking is the cause of reduced risk of heart disease.

2.8 An article titled "Guard Your Kids Against Allergies: Get Them a Pet" (*San Luis Obispo Tribune*, August 28, 2002) described a study that led researchers to conclude that "babies raised with two or more animals were about half as likely to have allergies by the time they turned six."

a. Do you think this study was an observational study or an experiment? Explain.
b. Describe a potential confounding variable that illustrates why it is unreasonable to conclude that being raised with two or more animals is the cause of the observed lower allergy rate.

2.9 Researchers at the Hospital for Sick Children in Toronto compared babies born to mothers with diabetes to babies born to mothers without diabetes ("Conditioning and Hyperanalgesia in Newborns Exposed to Repeated Heel Lances," *Journal of the American Medical Association* [2002]: 857–861). Babies born to mothers with diabetes have their heels pricked numerous times during the first 36 hours of life in order to obtain blood samples to monitor blood sugar level. The researchers noted that the babies born to diabetic mothers were more likely to grimace or cry when having blood drawn than the babies born to mothers without diabetes. This led the researchers to conclude that babies who experience pain early in life become highly sensitive to pain. Comment on the appropriateness of this conclusion.

2.10 Based on a survey conducted on the DietSmart.com web site, investigators concluded that women who regularly watched *Oprah* were only one-seventh as likely to crave fattening foods as those who watched other daytime talk shows (*San Luis Obispo Tribune*, October 14, 2000).

a. Is it reasonable to conclude that watching *Oprah* causes a decrease in cravings for fattening foods? Explain.
b. Is it reasonable to generalize the results of this survey to all women in the United States? To all women who watch daytime talk shows? Explain why or why not.

2.11 ✦ A survey of affluent Americans (those with incomes of $75,000 or more) indicated that 57% would rather have more time than more money (*USA Today*, January 29, 2003).

a. What condition on how the data were collected would make the generalization from the sample to the population of affluent Americans reasonable?
b. Would it be reasonable to generalize from the sample to say that 57% of all Americans would rather have more time than more money? Explain.

2.12 Does living in the South cause high blood pressure? Data from a group of 6278 whites and blacks questioned in the Third National Health and Nutritional Examination Survey between 1988 and 1994 (see CNN.com web site article of January 6, 2000, titled "High Blood Pressure Greater Risk in U.S. South, Study Says") indicates that a greater percentage of Southerners have high blood pressure than do people in any other region of the United States. This difference in rate of high blood pressure was found in every ethnic group, gender, and age category studied. List at least two possible reasons we cannot conclude that living in the South causes high blood pressure.

Bold exercises answered in back ● Data set available online ✦ Video Solution available

2.2 Sampling

Many studies are conducted in order to generalize from a sample to the corresponding population. As a result, it is important that the sample be representative of the population. To be reasonably sure of this, we must carefully consider the way in which the sample is selected. It is sometimes tempting to take the easy way out and gather data in a haphazard way; but if a sample is chosen on the basis of convenience alone, it becomes impossible to interpret the resulting data with confidence. For example, it might be easy to use the students in your statistics class as a sample of students at your university. However, not all majors include a statistics course in their curriculum, and most students take statistics in their sophomore or junior year. The difficulty is that it is not clear whether or how these factors (and others that we might not be aware of) affect any conclusions based on information from such a sample.

There is no way to tell just by looking at a sample whether it is representative of the population from which it was drawn. Our only assurance comes from the method used to select the sample.

There are many reasons for selecting a sample rather than obtaining information from an entire population (a **census**). Sometimes the process of measuring the characteristics of interest is destructive, as with measuring the lifetime of flashlight batteries or the sugar content of oranges, and it would be foolish to study the entire population. But the most common reason for selecting a sample is limited resources. Restrictions on available time or money usually prohibit observation of an entire population.

Bias in Sampling

Bias in sampling is the tendency for samples to differ from the corresponding population in some systematic way. Bias can result from the way in which the sample is selected or from the way in which information is obtained once the sample has been chosen. The most common types of bias encountered in sampling situations are selection bias, measurement or response bias, and nonresponse bias.

Selection bias (sometimes also called undercoverage) is introduced when the way the sample is selected systematically excludes some part of the population of interest. For example, a researcher may wish to generalize from the results of a study to the population consisting of all residents of a particular city, but the method of selecting individuals may exclude the homeless or those without telephones. If those who are excluded from the sampling process differ in some systematic way from those who are included, the sample is virtually guaranteed to be unrepresentative of the population. If this difference between the included and the excluded occurs on a variable that is important to the study, conclusions based on the sample data may not be valid for the population of interest. Selection bias also occurs if only volunteers or self-selected individuals are used in a study, because those who choose to participate (for example, in a call-in telephone poll) may well differ from those who choose not to participate.

Measurement or response bias occurs when the method of observation tends to produce values that systematically differ from the true value in some way. This might happen if an improperly calibrated scale is used to weigh items or if questions on a survey are worded in a way that tends to influence the response. For example, a Gallup survey sponsored by the American Paper Institute (*Wall Street Journal*, May 17, 1994) included the following question: "It is estimated that disposable diapers account for less than 2 percent of the trash in today's landfills. In contrast, beverage containers, third-class mail and yard waste are estimated to account for about 21 percent of trash in landfills. Given this, in your opinion, would it be fair to tax or ban disposable diapers?" It is likely that the wording of this question prompted people to respond in a particular way.

Other things that might contribute to response bias are the appearance or behavior of the person asking the question, the group or organization conducting the study, and the tendency for people not to be completely honest when asked about illegal behavior or unpopular beliefs.

Although the terms *measurement bias* and *response bias* are often used interchangeably, the term *measurement bias* is usually used to describe systematic deviation from the true value as a result of a faulty measurement instrument (as with the improperly calibrated scale).

Nonresponse bias occurs when responses are not obtained from all individuals selected for inclusion in the sample. As with selection bias, nonresponse bias can distort results if those who respond differ in important ways from those who do not respond. Although some level of nonresponse is unavoidable in most surveys, the biasing effect on the resulting sample is lowest when the response rate is high. To minimize nonresponse bias, it is critical that a serious effort be made to follow up with individuals who do not respond to an initial request for information.

The nonresponse rate for surveys or opinion polls varies dramatically, depending on how the data are collected. Surveys are commonly conducted by mail, by phone, and by personal interview. Mail surveys are inexpensive but often have high nonresponse rates. Telephone surveys can also be inexpensive and can be implemented quickly, but they work well only for short surveys and they can also have high nonresponse rates. Personal interviews are generally expensive but tend to have better response rates. Some of the many challenges of conducting surveys are discussed in Section 2.5.

Types of Bias

Selection Bias

Tendency for samples to differ from the corresponding population as a result of systematic exclusion of some part of the population.

Measurement or Response Bias

Tendency for samples to differ from the corresponding population because the method of observation tends to produce values that differ from the true value.

Nonresponse Bias

Tendency for samples to differ from the corresponding population because data are not obtained from all individuals selected for inclusion in the sample.

AP* EXAM TIP

These types of bias are easily confused. When answering questions about bias, be sure to provide an explanation that shows your understanding of the bias problem in a particular situation.

It is important to note that bias is introduced by the way in which a sample is selected or by the way in which the data are collected from the sample. Increasing the size of the sample, although possibly desirable for other reasons, does nothing to reduce bias if the method of selecting the sample is flawed or if the nonresponse rate remains high. A good discussion of types of bias appears in the sampling book by Lohr listed in the references in the back of the book.

Potential sources of bias are illustrated in the following examples.

EXAMPLE 2.1 Are Cell Phone Users Different?

Many surveys are conducted by telephone and participants are often selected from phone books that include only landline telephones. For many years, it was thought that this was not a serious problem because most cell phone users also had a landline phone and so they still had a chance of being included in the survey. But the number of people with only cell phones is growing, and this trend is a concern for survey organizations. The article "Omitting Cell Phone Users May Affect Polls" (*Associated Press*, September 25, 2008) described a study that examined whether people who only have a cell phone are different that those who have landline phones. One finding from the study was that for people under the age of 30 with only a cell phone, 28% were Republicans compared to 36% of landline users. This suggests that researchers who use telephone surveys need to worry about how selection bias might influence the ability to generalize the results of a survey if only landlines are used.

EXAMPLE 2.2 Think Before You Order That Burger!

The article "What People Buy from Fast-Food Restaurants: Caloric Content and Menu Item Selection" (*Obesity* [2009]: 1369–1374) reported that the average number of calories consumed at lunch in New York City fast food restaurants was 827. The researchers selected 267 fast food locations at random. The paper states that at each of these locations "adult customers were approached as they entered the restaurant and asked to provide their food receipt when exiting and to complete a brief survey." Approaching customers as they entered the restaurant and before they ordered may have influenced what they purchased. This introduces the potential for response bias. In addition, some people chose not to participate when approached. If those who chose not to participate differed from those who did participate, the researchers also need to be concerned about nonresponse bias. Both of these potential sources of bias limit the researchers' ability to generalize conclusions based on data from this study.

Random Sampling

Most of the inferential methods introduced in this text are based on the idea of random selection. The most straightforward sampling method is called simple random sampling. A **simple random sample** is a sample chosen using a method that ensures that each different possible sample of the desired size has an equal chance of being the one chosen. For example, suppose that we want a simple random sample of 10 employees chosen from all those who work at a large design firm. For the sample to be a simple random sample, each of the many different subsets of 10 employees must be equally likely to be the one selected. A sample taken from only full-time employees would not be a simple random sample of *all* employees, because someone who works part-time has no chance of being selected. Although a simple random sample may, by chance, include only full-time employees, it must be selected in such a way that each possible sample, and therefore *every* employee, has the same chance of inclusion in the sample. *It is the selection process, not the final sample, which determines whether the sample is a simple random sample.*

The letter n is used to denote sample size; it is the number of individuals or objects in the sample. For the design firm scenario of the previous paragraph, $n = 10$.

DEFINITION

A **simple random sample of size *n*** is a sample that is selected from a population in a way that ensures that every different possible sample of the desired size has the same chance of being selected.

The definition of a simple random sample implies that every individual member of the population has an equal chance of being selected. *However, the fact that every individual has an equal chance of selection, by itself, is not enough to guarantee that the sample is a simple random sample.* For example, suppose that a class is made up of 100 students, 60 of whom are female. A researcher decides to select 6 of the female students by writing all 60 names on slips of paper, mixing the slips, and then picking 6. She then selects 4 male students from the class using a similar procedure. Even though every student in the class has an equal chance of being included in the sample (6 of 60 females are selected and 4 of 40 males are chosen), the resulting sample is *not* a simple random sample because not all different possible samples of 10 students from the class have the same chance of selection. Many possible samples of 10 students—for example, a sample of 7 females and 3 males or a sample of all females—have no chance of being selected. The sample selection method described here is not necessarily a bad choice (in fact, it is an example of stratified sampling, to be discussed in more detail shortly), but it does not produce a simple random sample, and this must be considered when a method is chosen for analyzing data resulting from such a sampling method.

Selecting a Simple Random Sample A number of different methods can be used to select a simple random sample. One way is to put the name or number of each member of the population on different but identical slips of paper. The process of thoroughly mixing the slips and then selecting n slips one by one yields a random sample of size n. This method is easy to understand, but it has obvious drawbacks. The mixing must be adequate, and producing the necessary slips of paper can be extremely tedious, even for relatively small populations.

A commonly used method for selecting a random sample is to first create a list, called a **sampling frame**, of the objects or individuals in the population. Each item on the list can then be identified by a number, and a table of random digits or a random number generator can be used to select the sample. A random number generator is a procedure that produces a sequence of numbers that satisfies properties associated with the notion of randomness. Most statistics software packages include a random number generator, as do many calculators. A small table of random digits can be found in Appendix A, Table 1.

For example, suppose a list containing the names of the 427 customers who purchased a new car during 2009 at a large dealership is available. The owner of the dealership wants to interview a sample of these customers to learn about customer satisfaction. She plans to select a simple random sample of 20 customers. Because it would be tedious to write all 427 names on slips of paper, random numbers can be used to select the sample. To do this, we can use three-digit numbers, starting with 001 and ending with 427, to represent the individuals on the list.

The random digits from rows 6 and 7 of Appendix A, Table 1 are shown here:

$\underline{0\,9\,3}\;\underline{8\,7\,6}\;\underline{7\,9\,9}\;\underline{5\,6\,2}\;\underline{5\,6\,5}\;\underline{8\,4\,2}\;6\,4$
$\underline{4\,1\,0}\;\underline{1\,0\,2}\;\underline{2\,0\,4}\;\underline{7\,5\,1}\;\underline{1\,9\,4}\;\underline{7\,9\,7}\;5\,1$

We can use blocks of three digits from this list (underlined in the lists above) to identify the individuals who should be included in the sample. The first block of three digits is 093, so the 93rd person on the list will be included in the sample. The next five blocks of three digits (876, 799, 562, 565, and 842) do not correspond to anyone on the list, so we ignore them. The next block that corresponds to a person on the list is 410, so that person is included in the sample. This process would continue until 20 people have been selected for the sample. We would ignore any three-digit repeats since any particular person should only be selected once for the sample.

Another way to select the sample would be to use computer software or a graphing calculator to generate 20 random numbers. For example, Minitab produced the following when 20 random numbers between 1 and 427 were requested.

289	67	29	26	205	214	422	31	233	98
10	203	346	186	232	410	43	293	25	371

These numbers could be used to determine which 20 customers to include in the sample.

When selecting a random sample, researchers can choose to do the sampling with or without replacement. **Sampling with replacement** means that after each successive item is selected for the sample, the item is "replaced" back into the population and may therefore be selected again at a later stage. In practice, sampling with replacement is rarely used. Instead, the more common method is to not allow the same item to be included in the sample more than once. After being included in the sample, an individual or object would not be considered for further selection. Sampling in this manner is called **sampling without replacement.**

DEFINITION

Sampling without replacement: Once an individual from the population is selected for inclusion in the sample, it may not be selected again in the sampling process. A sample selected without replacement includes *n* distinct individuals from the population.

Sampling with replacement: After an individual from the population is selected for inclusion in the sample and the corresponding data are recorded, the individual is placed back in the population and can be selected again in the sampling process. A sample selected with replacement might include any particular individual from the population more than once.

Although these two forms of sampling are different, when the sample size n is small relative to the population size, as is often the case, there is little practical difference between them. In practice, the two can be viewed as equivalent if the sample size is at most 10% of the population size.

EXAMPLE 2.3 Selecting a Random Sample of Glass Soda Bottles

Breaking strength is an important characteristic of glass soda bottles. Suppose that we want to measure the breaking strength of each bottle in a random sample of size $n = 3$ selected from four crates containing a total of 100 bottles (the population). Each crate contains five rows of five bottles each. We can identify each bottle with a number from 1 to 100 by numbering across the rows in each crate, starting with the top row of crate 1, as pictured:

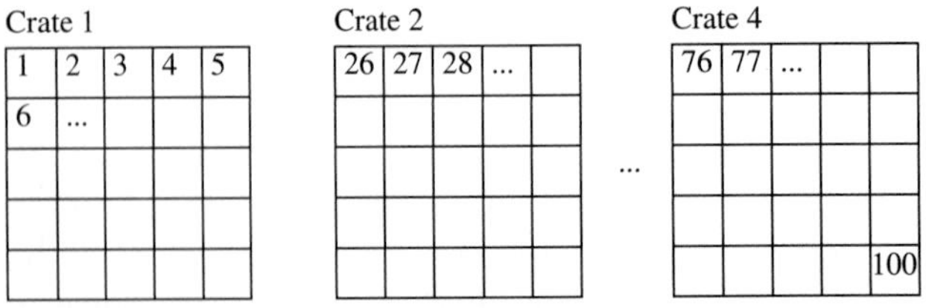

© BananaStock/Alamy Images

Using a random number generator from a calculator or statistical software package, we could generate three random numbers between 1 and 100 to determine which bottles would be included in our sample. This might result in bottles 15 (row 3 column 5 of crate 1), 89 (row 3 column 4 of crate 4), and 60 (row 2 column 5 of crate 3) being selected.

Step-by-Step technology instructions available online

The goal of random sampling is to produce a sample that is likely to be representative of the population. Although random sampling does not *guarantee* that the sample will be representative, it does allow us to assess the risk of an unrepresentative sample. It is the ability to quantify this risk that will enable us to generalize with confidence from a random sample to the corresponding population.

An Important Note Concerning Sample Size

It is a common misconception that if the size of a sample is relatively small compared to the population size, the sample cannot possibly accurately reflect the population. Critics of polls often make statements such as, "There are 14.6 million registered voters in California. How can a sample of 1000 registered voters possibly reflect public opinion when only about 1 in every 14,000 people is included in the sample?" These critics do not understand the power of random selection!

Consider a population consisting of 5000 applicants to a state university, and suppose that we are interested in math SAT scores for this population. A dotplot of the values in this population is shown in Figure 2.1(a). Figure 2.1(b) shows dotplots of the math SAT scores for individuals in five different random samples from the population, ranging in sample size from $n = 50$ to $n = 1000$. Notice that the samples tend to reflect the distribution of scores in the population. If we were interested in using the

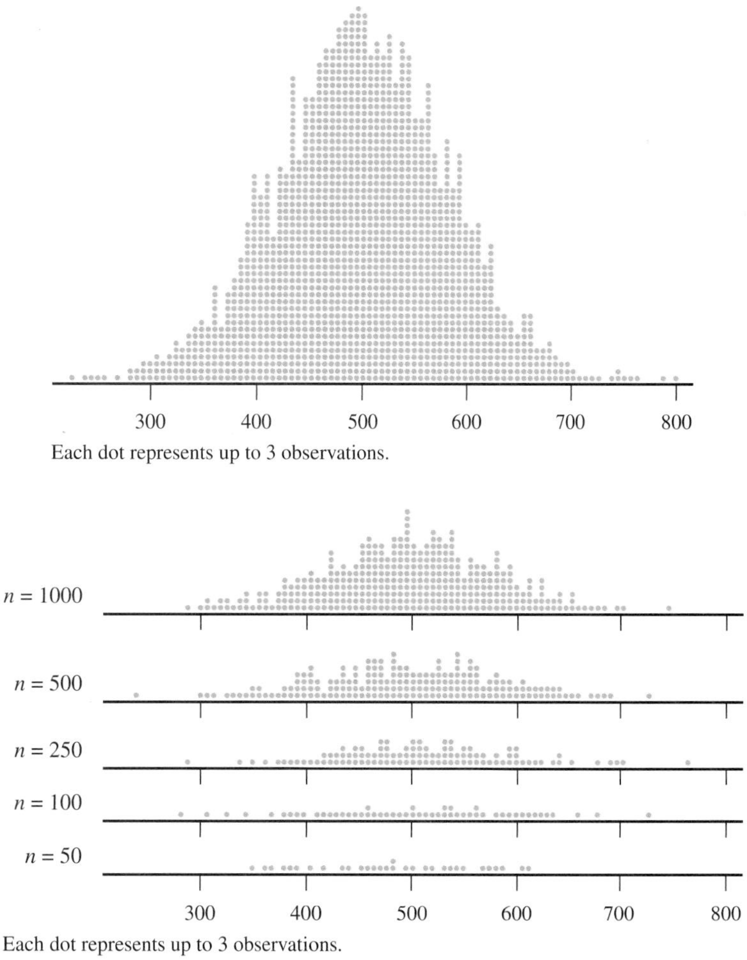

FIGURE 2.1
(a) Dotplot of math SAT scores for the entire population. (b) Dotplots of math SAT scores for random samples of sizes 50, 100, 250, 500, and 1000.

sample to estimate the population average or to say something about the variability in SAT scores, even the smallest of the samples ($n = 50$) pictured would provide reliable information. Although it is possible to obtain a simple random sample that does not do a reasonable job of representing the population, this is likely only when the sample size is very small, and unless the population itself is small, this risk does not depend on what fraction of the population is sampled. The random selection process allows us to be confident that the resulting sample adequately reflects the population, even when the sample consists of only a small fraction of the population.

Other Sampling Methods

Simple random sampling provides researchers with a sampling method that is objective and free of selection bias. In some settings, however, alternative sampling methods may be less costly, easier to implement, and sometimes even more accurate.

Stratified Random Sampling When the entire population can be divided into a set of nonoverlapping subgroups, a method known as **stratified sampling** often proves easier to implement and more cost-effective than simple random sampling. In stratified random sampling, separate simple random samples are independently selected from each subgroup. For example, to estimate the average cost of malpractice insurance, a researcher might find it convenient to view the population of all doctors practicing in a particular metropolitan area as being made up of four subpopulations: (1) surgeons, (2) internists and family practitioners, (3) obstetricians, and (4) a group that includes all other areas of specialization. Rather than taking a random simple sample from the population of all doctors, the researcher could take four separate simple random samples—one from the group of surgeons, another from the internists and family practitioners, and so on. These four samples would provide information about the four subgroups as well as information about the overall population of doctors.

When the population is divided in this way, the subgroups are called **strata** and each individual subgroup is called a stratum (the singular of strata). Stratified sampling entails selecting a separate simple random sample from each stratum. Stratified sampling can be used instead of simple random sampling if it is important to obtain information about characteristics of the individual strata as well as of the entire population, although a stratified sample is not required to do this—subgroup estimates can also be obtained by using an appropriate subset of data from a simple random sample.

The real advantage of stratified sampling is that it often allows us to make more accurate inferences about a population than does simple random sampling. In general, it is much easier to produce relatively accurate estimates of characteristics of a homogeneous group than of a heterogeneous group. For example, even with a small sample, it is possible to obtain an accurate estimate of the average grade point average (GPA) of students graduating with high honors from a university. The individual GPAs of these students are all quite similar (a homogeneous group), and even a sample of three or four individuals from this subpopulation should be representative. On the other hand, producing a reasonably accurate estimate of the average GPA of *all* seniors at the university, a much more diverse group of GPAs, is a more difficult task. Thus, if a varied population can be divided into strata, with each stratum being much more homogeneous than the population with respect to the characteristic of interest, then a stratified random sample can produce more accurate estimates of population characteristics than a simple random sample of the same size.

Cluster Sampling Sometimes it is easier to select groups of individuals from a population than it is to select individuals themselves. **Cluster sampling** involves dividing the population of interest into nonoverlapping subgroups, called **clusters**. Clusters are then selected at random, and then *all* individuals in the selected clusters are included in the sample. For example, suppose that a large urban high school has 600 senior students, all of whom are enrolled in a first period homeroom. There are 24 senior homerooms, each with approximately 25 students. If school administrators wanted to select a sample of roughly 75 seniors to participate in an evaluation of the college and career placement advising available to students, they might find it much easier to select three of the senior homerooms at random and then include all the students in the selected homerooms in the sample. In this way, an evaluation survey could be administered to all students in the selected homerooms at the same time—certainly easier logistically than randomly selecting 75 students and then administering the survey to those individual seniors.

Because whole clusters are selected, the ideal situation for cluster sampling is when each cluster mirrors the characteristics of the population. When this is the case, a small number of clusters results in a sample that is representative of the population. If it is not reasonable to think that the variability present in the population is reflected in each cluster, as is often the case when the cluster sizes are small, then it becomes important to ensure that a large number of clusters are included in the sample.

Be careful not to confuse clustering and stratification. Even though both of these sampling strategies involve dividing the population into subgroups, both the way in which the subgroups are sampled and the optimal strategy for creating the subgroups are different. In stratified sampling, we sample from every stratum, whereas in cluster sampling, we include only selected whole clusters in the sample. Because of this difference, to increase the chance of obtaining a sample that is representative of the population, we want to create homogeneous groups for strata and heterogeneous (reflecting the variability in the population) groups for clusters.

AP* EXAM TIP

When describing a sampling plan, be sure to convey your understanding of the sampling procedure and give a complete description of how the sample will be selected.

Systematic Sampling **Systematic sampling** is a procedure that can be used when it is possible to view the population of interest as consisting of a list or some other sequential arrangement. A value k is specified (for example, $k = 50$ or $k = 200$). Then one of the first k individuals is selected at random, after which every kth individual in the sequence is included in the sample. A sample selected in this way is called a **1 in k systematic sample**.

For example, a sample of faculty members at a university might be selected from the faculty phone directory. One of the first $k = 20$ faculty members listed could be selected at random, and then every 20th faculty member after that on the list would also be included in the sample. This would result in a 1 in 20 systematic sample.

The value of k for a 1 in k systematic sample is generally chosen to achieve a desired sample size. For example, in the faculty directory scenario just described, if there were 900 faculty members at the university, the 1 in 20 systematic sample described would result in a sample size of 45. If a sample size of 100 was desired, a 1 in 9 systematic sample could be used (because $900/100 = 9$).

As long as there are no repeating patterns in the population list, systematic sampling works reasonably well. However, if there are such patterns, systematic sampling can result in an unrepresentative sample. For example, suppose that workers at the entry station of a state park have recorded the number of visitors to the park each day for the past 10 years. In a 1 in 70 systematic sample of days from this list, we would pick one of the first 70 days at random and then every 70th day after that. But if the first day selected happened to be a Wednesday, *every* day selected in the entire sample would also be a Wednesday (because there are 7 days a week and 70 is a multiple of 7). It is unlikely that such a sample would be representative of the entire collection of days. The number of visitors is likely to be higher on weekend days, and no Saturdays or Sundays would be included in the sample.

Convenience Sampling: Don't Go There! It is often tempting to resort to "convenience" sampling—that is, using an easily available or convenient group to form a sample. This is a recipe for disaster! Results from such samples are rarely informative, and it is a mistake to try to generalize from a convenience sample to any larger population.

One common form of convenience sampling is sometimes called **voluntary response sampling.** Such samples rely entirely on individuals who volunteer to be a part of the sample, often by responding to an advertisement, calling a publicized telephone number to register an opinion, or logging on to an Internet site to complete a survey. It is extremely unlikely that individuals participating in such voluntary response surveys are representative of any larger population of interest.

EXERCISES 2.13 - 2.32

2.13 As part of a curriculum review, the psychology department would like to select a simple random sample of 20 of last year's 140 graduates to obtain information on how graduates perceived the value of the curriculum. Describe two different methods that might be used to select the sample.

2.14 A petition with 500 signatures is submitted to a university's student council. The council president would like to determine the proportion of those who signed the petition who are actually registered students at the university. There is not enough time to check all 500 names with the registrar, so the council president decides to select a simple random sample of 30 signatures. Describe how this might be done.

2.15 During the previous calendar year, a county's small claims court processed 870 cases. Describe how a simple random sample of size $n = 50$ might be selected from the case files to obtain information regarding the average award in such cases.

2.16 The financial aid advisor of a university plans to use a stratified random sample to estimate the average amount of money that students spend on textbooks each term. For each of the following proposed stratification schemes, discuss whether it would be worthwhile to stratify the university students in this manner.

a. Strata corresponding to class standing (freshman, sophomore, junior, senior, graduate student)
b. Strata corresponding to field of study, using the following categories: engineering, architecture, business, other
c. Strata corresponding to the first letter of the last name: A–E, F–K, etc.

2.17 Suppose that a group of 1000 orange trees is laid out in 40 rows of 25 trees each. To determine the sugar content of fruit from a sample of 30 trees, researcher A suggests randomly selecting five rows and then randomly selecting six trees from each sampled row. Researcher B suggests numbering each tree on a map of the trees from 1 to 1000 and using random numbers to select 30 of the trees. Which selection method is preferred? Explain.

2.18 ✦ For each of the situations described, state whether the sampling procedure is simple random sampling, stratified random sampling, cluster sampling, systematic sampling, or convenience sampling.

a. All first-year students at a university are enrolled in 1 of 30 sections of a seminar course. To select a sample of freshmen at this university, a researcher selects four sections of the seminar course at random from the 30 sections and all students in the four selected sections are included in the sample.
b. To obtain a sample of students, faculty, and staff at a university, a researcher randomly selects 50 faculty members from a list of faculty, 100 students from a list of students, and 30 staff members from a list of staff.
c. A university researcher obtains a sample of students at his university by using the 85 students enrolled in his Psychology 101 class.
d. To obtain a sample of the seniors at a particular high school, a researcher writes the name of each senior on a slip of paper, places the slips in a box and mixes them, and then selects 10 slips. The students whose names are on the selected slips of paper are included in the sample.
e. To obtain a sample of those attending a basketball game, a researcher selects the 24th person through the door. Then, every 50th person after that is also included in the sample.

2.19 Of the 6500 students enrolled at a community college, 3000 are part time and the other 3500 are full time. The college can provide a list of students that is sorted so that all full-time students are listed first, followed by the part-time students.

a. Describe a procedure for selecting a stratified random sample that uses full-time and part-time students as the two strata and that includes 10 students from each stratum.

b. Does every student at this community college have the same chance of being selected for inclusion in the sample? Explain.

2.20 Briefly explain why it is advisable to avoid the use of convenience samples.

2.21 A sample of pages from this book is to be obtained, and the number of words on each selected page will be determined. For the purposes of this exercise, equations are not counted as words and a number is counted as a word only if it is spelled out—that is, *ten* is counted as a word, but *10* is not.

a. Describe a sampling procedure that would result in a simple random sample of pages from this book.

b. Describe a sampling procedure that would result in a stratified random sample. Explain why you chose the specific strata used in your sampling plan.

c. Describe a sampling procedure that would result in a systematic sample.

d. Describe a sampling procedure that would result in a cluster sample.

e. Using the process you gave in Part (a), select a simple random sample of at least 20 pages, and record the number of words on each of the selected pages. Construct a dotplot of the resulting sample values, and write a sentence or two commenting on what it reveals about the number of words on a page.

f. Using the process you gave in Part (b), select a stratified random sample that includes a total of at least 20 selected pages, and record the number of words on each of the selected pages. Construct a dotplot of the resulting sample values, and write a sentence or two commenting on what it reveals about the number of words on a page.

2.22 In 2000, the chairman of a California ballot initiative campaign to add "none of the above" to the list of ballot options in all candidate races was quite critical of a Field poll that showed his measure trailing by 10 percentage points. The poll was based on a random sample of 1000 registered voters in California. He is quoted by the Associated Press (January 30, 2000) as saying, "Field's sample in that poll equates to one out of 17,505 voters," and he added that this was so dishonest that Field should get out of the polling business! If you worked on the Field poll, how would you respond to this criticism?

2.23 The authors of the paper "Digital Inequality: Differences in Young Adults' Use of the Internet" (*Communication Research* [2008]: 602–621) were interested in determining if people with higher levels of education use the Internet in different ways than those who do not have as much formal education. To answer this question, they used data from a national telephone survey. Approximately 1300 households were selected for the survey, and 270 of them completed the interview. What type of bias should the researchers be concerned about and why?

2.24 The authors of the paper "Illicit Use of Psychostimulants among College Students" (*Psychology, Health & Medicine* [2002]: 283–287) surveyed college students about their use of legal and illegal stimulants. The sample of students surveyed consisted of students enrolled in a psychology class at a small, competitive college in the United States.

a. Was this sample a simple random sample, a stratified sample, a systematic sample, or a convenience sample? Explain.

b. Give two reasons why the estimate of the proportion of students who reported using illegal stimulants based on data from this survey should not be generalized to all U.S. college students.

2.25 The paper "Deception and Design: The Impact of Communication Technology on Lying Behavior" (*Computer-Human Interaction* [2009]: 130–136) describes an investigation into whether lying is less common in face-to-face communication than in other forms of communication such as phone conversations or e-mail. Participants in this study were 30 students in an upper-division communications course at Cornell University who received course credit for participation. Participants were asked to record all of their social interactions for a week, making note of any lies told. Based on data from these records, the authors of the paper concluded that students lie more often in phone conversations than in face-to-face conversations and more often in face-to-face conversations than in e-mail. Discuss the limitations of this study, commenting on the way the sample was selected and potential sources of bias.

2.26 The authors of the paper "Popular Video Games: Quantifying the Presentation of Violence and its Context" (*Journal of Broadcasting & Electronic Media* [2003]: 58–76) investigated the relationship between video game rating—suitable for everyone (E), suitable for 13 years of age and older (T), and suitable for 17 years of age and older (M)—and the number of violent interactions per minute of play. The sample of games examined consisted of 60 video games—the 20 most popular (by sales) for each of three game systems. The researchers concluded that video games rated for older children had significantly more violent interactions per minute than did those games rated for more general audiences.

a. Do you think that the sample of 60 games was selected in a way that makes it reasonable to think it is representative of the population of all video games?
b. Is it reasonable to generalize the researchers' conclusion to all video games? Explain why or why not.

2.27 Participants in a study of honesty in online dating profiles were recruited through print and online advertisements in the *Village Voice,* one of New York City's most prominent weekly newspapers, and on Craigslist New York City ("The Truth About Lying in Online Dating Profiles," *Computer-Human Interaction* [2007]: 1–4). The actual height, weight, and age of the participants were compared to what appeared in their online dating profiles. The resulting data was then used to draw conclusions about how common deception was in online dating profiles. What concerns do you have about generalizing conclusions based on data from this study to the population of all people who have an online dating profile? Be sure to address at least two concerns and give the reason for your concern.

2.28 The report "Undergraduate Students and Credit Cards in 2004: An Analysis of Usage Rates and Trends" (Nellie Mae, May 2005) estimated that 21% of undergraduates with credit cards pay them off each month and that the average outstanding balance on undergraduates' credit cards is $2169. These estimates were based on an online survey that was sent to 1260 students. Responses were received from 132 of these students. Is it reasonable to generalize the reported estimates to the population of all undergraduate students? Address at least two possible sources of bias in your answer.

2.29 Suppose that you were asked to help design a survey of adult city residents in order to estimate the proportion that would support a sales tax increase. The plan is to use a stratified random sample, and three stratification schemes have been proposed.

Scheme 1: Stratify adult residents into four strata based on the first letter of their last name (A–G, H–N, O–T, U–Z).

Scheme 2: Stratify adult residents into three strata: college students, nonstudents who work full time, nonstudents who do not work full time.

Scheme 3: Stratify adult residents into five strata by randomly assigning residents into one of the five strata.

Which of the three stratification schemes would be best in this situation? Explain.

2.30 The article "High Levels of Mercury Are Found in Californians" (*Los Angeles Times*, February 9, 2006) describes a study in which hair samples were tested for mercury. The hair samples were obtained from more than 6000 people who voluntarily sent hair samples to researchers at Greenpeace and The Sierra Club. The researchers found that nearly one-third of those tested had mercury levels that exceeded the concentration thought to be safe. Is it reasonable to generalize this result to the larger population of U.S. adults? Explain why or why not.

2.31 ✦ Whether or not to continue a Mardi Gras Parade through downtown San Luis Obispo, CA, is a hotly debated topic. The parade is popular with students and many residents, but some celebrations have led to complaints and a call to eliminate the parade. The local newspaper conducted online and telephone surveys of its readers and was surprised by the results. The survey web site received more than 400 responses, with more than 60% favoring continuing the parade, while the telephone response line received more than 120 calls, with more than 90% favoring banning the parade (*San Luis Obispo Tribune*, March 3, 2004). What factors may have contributed to these very different results?

2.32 The article "Gene's Role in Cancer May Be Overstated" (*San Luis Obispo Tribune*, August 21, 2002) states that "early studies that evaluated breast cancer risk among gene mutation carriers selected women in families where sisters, mothers, and grandmothers all had breast cancer. This created a statistical bias that skewed risk estimates for women in the general population." Is the bias described here selection bias, measurement bias, or nonresponse bias? Explain.

2.3 Simple Comparative Experiments

Sometimes the questions we are trying to answer deal with the effect of certain explanatory variables on some response. Such questions are often of the form, "What happens when . . . ?" or "What is the effect of . . . ?" For example, an industrial engineer may be considering two different workstation designs and might want to know whether the choice of design affects work performance. A medical researcher may want to determine how a proposed treatment for a disease compares to a standard treatment. Experiments provide a way to collect data to answer these types of questions.

DEFINITION

An **experiment** is a study in which one or more explanatory variables are manipulated in order to observe the effect on a response variable.

The **explanatory variables** are those variables that have values that are controlled by the experimenter. Explanatory variables are also called **factors.**

The **response variable** is a variable that is not controlled by the experimenter and that is measured as part of the experiment.

An **experimental condition** is any particular combination of values for the explanatory variables. Experimental conditions are also called **treatments.**

Suppose we are interested in determining the effect of room temperature on performance on a first-year calculus exam. In this case, the explanatory variable is room temperature (it can be manipulated by the experimenter). The response variable is exam performance (the variable that is not controlled by the experimenter and that will be measured).

In general, we can identify the explanatory variables and the response variable easily if we can describe the purpose of the experiment in the following terms:

The purpose is to assess the effect of _______________ on _______________.
explanatory variable   response variable

Let's return to the example of an experiment to assess the effect of room temperature on exam performance. We might decide to use two room temperature settings, 65° and 75°. This would result in an experiment with two experimental conditions (or equivalently, two treatments) corresponding to the two temperature settings.

Suppose that there are 10 sections of first-semester calculus that have agreed to participate in our study. We might design an experiment in this way: Set the room temperature (in degrees Fahrenheit) to 65° in five of the rooms and to 75° in the other five rooms on test day, and then compare the exam scores for the 65° group and the 75° group. Suppose that the average exam score for the students in the 65° group was noticeably higher than the average for the 75° group. Could we conclude that the increased temperature resulted in a lower average score? Based on the information given, the answer is no because many other factors might be related to exam score. Were the sections at different times of the day? Did they have the same instructor? Different textbooks? Did the sections differ with respect to the abilities of the students? Any of these other factors could provide a plausible explanation (having nothing to do with room temperature) for why the average test score was different for the two groups. It is not possible to separate the effect of temperature from the effects of these other factors. As a consequence, simply setting the room temperatures as described makes for a poorly designed experiment.

A well-designed experiment requires more than just manipulating the explanatory variables; the design must also eliminate other possible explanations or the experimental results will not be conclusive.

The goal is to design an experiment that will allow us to determine the effects of the explanatory variables on the chosen response variable. To do this, we must take into consideration any extraneous variables that, although not of interest in the current study, might also affect the response variable.

DEFINITION

An **extraneous variable** is one that is not one of the explanatory variables in the study but is thought to affect the response variable.

A well-designed experiment copes with the potential effects of extraneous variables by using random assignment to experimental conditions and sometimes also by incorporating direct control and/or blocking into the design of the experiment. Each of these strategies—random assignment, direct control, and blocking—is described in the paragraphs that follow.

A researcher can **directly control** some extraneous variables. In the calculus test example, the textbook used is an extraneous variable because part of the differences in test results might be attributed to this variable. We could control this variable directly, by requiring that all sections use the same textbook. Then any observed differences between temperature groups could not be explained by the use of different textbooks. The extraneous variable *time of day* might also be directly controlled in this way by having all sections meet at the same time.

The effects of some extraneous variables can be filtered out by a process known as **blocking**. Extraneous variables that are addressed through blocking are called *blocking variables*. Blocking creates groups (called blocks) that are similar with respect to blocking variables; then all treatments are tried in each block. In our example, we might use *instructor* as a blocking variable. If five instructors are each teaching two sections of calculus, we would make sure that for each instructor, one section was part of the 65° group and the other section was part of the 75° group. With this design, if we see a difference in exam scores for the two temperature groups, the extraneous variable *instructor* can be ruled out as a possible explanation, because all five instructors' students were present in each temperature group. (Had we controlled the instructor variable by choosing to have only one instructor, that would be an example of direct control. Of course we can't directly control both time of day and instructor.) If one instructor taught all the 65° sections and another taught all the 75° sections, we would be unable to distinguish the effect of temperature from the effect of the instructor. In this situation, the two variables (temperature and instructor) are said to be **confounded.**

Two variables are **confounded** if their effects on the response variable cannot be distinguished from one another.

If an extraneous variable is confounded with the explanatory variables (which define the treatments), it is not possible to draw an unambiguous conclusion about the effect of the treatment on the response. Both direct control and blocking are effective in ensuring that the controlled variables and blocking variables are not confounded with the variables that define the treatments.

We can directly control some extraneous variables by holding them constant, and we can use blocking to create groups that are similar to essentially filter out the effect of others. But what about variables, such as student ability in our calculus test example, which cannot be controlled by the experimenter and which would be difficult to use as blocking variables? These extraneous variables are handled by the use of **random assignment** to experimental groups. Random assignment ensures that our experiment does not systematically favor one experimental condition over any other and attempts to create experimental groups that are as much alike as possible. For example, if the students requesting calculus could be assigned to one of the ten available sections using a random mechanism, we would expect the resulting groups to be similar with respect to student ability as well as with respect to other extraneous variables that are not directly controlled or used as a basis for blocking. Note that random assignment in an experiment is different from random selection of subjects. The ideal situation would be to have both random selection of subjects and random assignment of subjects to experimental conditions, as this would allow conclusions from the experiment to be generalized to a larger population. *For many experiments the random selection of subjects is not possible. As long as subjects are assigned at random to experimental conditions, it is still possible to assess treatment effects.*

To get a sense of how random assignment tends to create similar groups, suppose that 50 college freshmen are available to participate as subjects in an experiment to investigate whether completing an online review of course material before an exam improves exam performance. The 50 subjects vary quite a bit with respect to achievement, which is reflected in their math and verbal SAT scores, as shown in Figure 2.2.

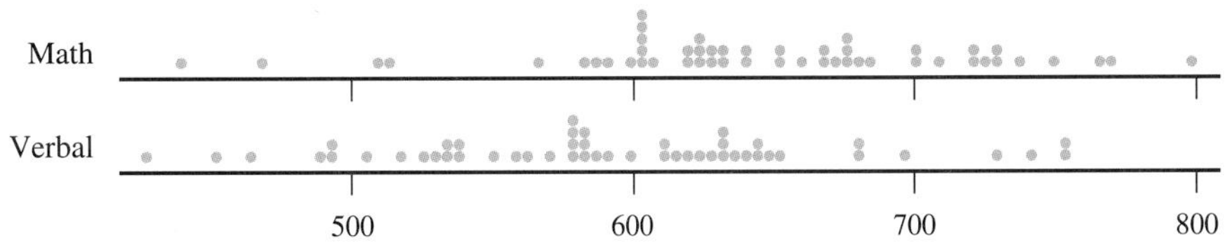

FIGURE 2.2
Dotplots of math and verbal SAT scores for 50 freshmen.

If these 50 students are to be assigned to the two experimental groups (one that will complete the online review and one that will not), we want to make sure that the assignment of students to groups does not favor one group over the other by tending to assign the higher achieving students to one group and the lower achieving students to the other.

Creating groups of students with similar achievement levels in a way that considers both verbal and math SAT scores simultaneously would be difficult, so we rely on random assignment. Figure 2.3(a) shows the math SAT scores of the students assigned to each of the two experimental groups (one shown in orange and one shown in blue) for each of three different random assignments of students to groups. Figure 2.3(b) shows the verbal SAT scores for the two experimental groups for each of the same three random assignments. Notice that each of the three random assignments produced groups that are similar with respect to *both* verbal and math SAT scores. So, if any of these three assignments were used and the two groups differed on exam performance, we could rule out differences in math or verbal SAT scores as possible competing explanations for the difference.

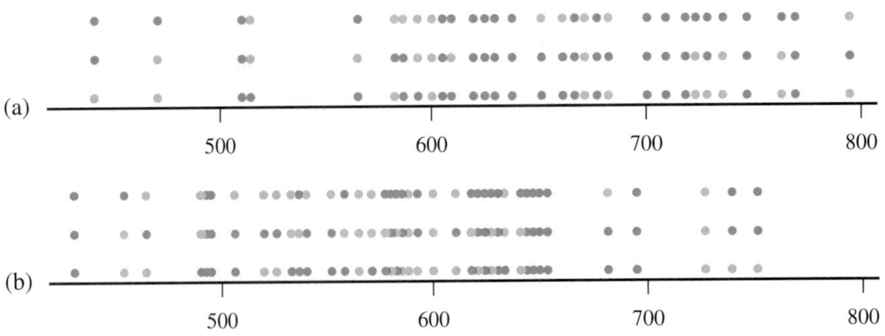

FIGURE 2.3
Dotplots for three different random assignments to two groups, one shown in orange and one shown in blue: (a) math SAT score; (b) verbal SAT score.

Not only will random assignment tend to create groups that are similar with respect to verbal and math SAT scores, but it will also tend to even out the groups with respect to other extraneous variables. *As long as the number of subjects is not too small, we can rely on the random assignment to produce comparable experimental groups. This is the reason that random assignment is a part of all well-designed experiments.*

Not all experiments require the use of human subjects. For example, a researcher interested in comparing three different gasoline additives with respect to gasoline mileage might conduct an experiment using a single car with an empty tank. One gallon of gas with one of the additives will be put in the tank, and the car will be driven along a standard route at a constant speed until it runs out of gas. The total distance traveled on the gallon of gas could then be recorded. This could be repeated a number of times—10, for example—with each additive.

The experiment just described can be viewed as consisting of a sequence of trials. Because a number of extraneous variables (such as variations in environmental conditions like wind speed or humidity and small variations in the condition of the car) might have an effect on gas mileage, it would not be a good idea to use additive 1 for the first 10 trials, additive 2 for the next 10 trials, and so on. A better approach would be to randomly assign additive 1 to 10 of the 30 planned trials, and then randomly assign additive 2 to 10 of the remaining 20 trials. The resulting plan for carrying out the experiment might look as follows:

Trial	1	2	3	4	5	6	7	. . .	30
Additive	2	2	3	3	2	1	2	. . .	1

When an experiment can be viewed as a sequence of trials, random assignment involves the random assignment of treatments to trials. *Remember that random assignment—either of subjects to treatments or of treatments to trials—is a critical component of a good experiment.*

Random assignment can be effective only if the number of subjects or observations in each experimental condition (treatment) is large enough for each experimental group to reliably reflect variability in the population. For example, if there were only 20 students requesting calculus, it is unlikely that we would get equivalent groups for comparison, even with random assignment to the ten sections. **Replication** is the design strategy of making multiple observations for each experimental condition. Together, replication and random assignment allow the researcher to be reasonably confident of comparable experimental groups.

To illustrate the design of a simple experiment, consider the dilemma of Anna, a waitress in a local restaurant. She would like to increase the amount of her tips, and her strategy is simple: She will write "Thank you" on the back of some of the checks before giving them to the patrons and on others she will write nothing. She plans to calculate the percentage of the tip as her measure of success (for example, a 15% tip is common). She will compare the average percentage of the tips calculated from

Key Concepts in Experimental Design

Random Assignment

Random assignment (of subjects to treatments or of treatments to trials) to ensure that the experiment does not systematically favor one experimental condition (treatment) over another.

Blocking

Using extraneous variables to create groups (blocks) that are similar. All experimental conditions (treatments) are then tried in each block.

Direct Control

Holding extraneous variables constant so that their effects are not confounded with those of the experimental conditions (treatments).

Replication

Ensuring that there is an adequate number of observations for each experimental condition.

checks with and without the handwritten "Thank you." If writing "Thank you" does not produce higher tips, she may try a different strategy.

Anna is untrained in the art of planning experiments, but already she has taken some common sense steps in the right direction to answer her question—Will writing "Thank you" produce the desired outcome of higher tips? Anna has defined a manageable problem, and collecting the appropriate data is feasible. It should be easy to gather data as a normal part of her work. Anna wonders whether writing "Thank you" on the customers' bills will have an effect on the amount of her tip. In the language of experimentation, we would refer to the writing of "Thank you" and the not writing of "Thank you" as **treatments** (the two experimental conditions to be compared in the experiment). The two treatments together are the possible values of the **explanatory variable**. The tipping percentage is the **response variable**. The idea behind this terminology is that the tipping percentage is a *response* to the treatments *writing "Thank you"* or *not writing "Thank you."* Anna's experiment may be thought of as an attempt to explain the variability in the response variable in terms of its presumed cause, the variability in the explanatory variable. That is, as she manipulates the explanatory variable, she expects the response by her customers to vary. Anna has a good start, but now she must consider the four fundamental design principles.

Replication. Anna cannot run a successful experiment by gathering tipping information on only one person for each treatment. There is no reason to believe that any single tipping incident is representative of what would happen in other incidents, and therefore it would be impossible to evaluate the two treatments with only two subjects. To interpret the effects of a particular treatment, she must **replicate** each treatment in the experiment.

Blocking. Suppose that Anna works on both Thursdays and Fridays. Because day of the week might affect tipping behavior, Anna should block on day of the week and make sure that observations for both treatments are made on each of the two days.

Direct Control and Random Assignment. There are a number of extraneous variables that might have an effect on the size of tip. Some restaurant patrons will be seated near the window with a nice view; some will have to wait for a table, whereas others may be seated immediately; and some may be on a fixed income and cannot afford a large tip. Some of these variables can be directly controlled. For example, Anna may choose to use only window tables in her experiment, thus eliminating table location as a potential confounding variable. Other variables, such as length of wait and customer income, cannot be easily controlled. As a result, it is important that Anna use random assignment to decide which of the window tables will be in the "Thank you" group and which will be in the "No thank you" group. She might do this by flipping a coin as she prepares the check for each window table. If the coin lands with the head side up, she could write "Thank you" on the bill, omitting the "Thank you" when a tail is observed.

The accompanying box summarizes how experimental designs deal with extraneous variables.

Taking Extraneous Variables into Account

Extraneous variables are variables other than the explanatory variables in an experiment that may also have an effect on the response variable. There are several strategies for dealing with extraneous variables in order to avoid confounding.

Extraneous variables that we know about and choose to incorporate into the experimental design:

Strategies

Direct control—holds extraneous variables fixed so that they can't affect the response variable

Blocking—allows for valid comparisons because each treatment is tried in each block

Extraneous variables that we don't know about or choose not to incorporate into the experimental design through direct control or blocking:

Strategy

Random assignment

Extraneous variables that are not incorporated into the design of the experiment are sometimes called **lurking variables.***

*For more on lurking variables, see "Lurking Variables: Some Examples" (*The American Statistician* [1981]: 227–233).

A Note on Random Assignment

There are several strategies that can be used to perform random assignment of subjects to treatments or treatments to trials. Two common strategies are:

- Write the name of each subject or a unique number that corresponds to a subject on a slip of paper. Place all of the slips in a container and mix well. Then draw out the desired number of slips to determine those that will be assigned to the first treatment group. This process of drawing slips of paper then continues until all treatment groups have been determined.

- Assign each subject a unique number from 1 to *n,* where *n* represents the total number of subjects. Use a random number generator or table of random numbers to obtain numbers that will identify which subjects will be assigned to the first treatment group. This process would be repeated, ignoring any random numbers generated that correspond to subjects that have already been assigned to a treatment group, until all treatment groups have been formed.

The two strategies above work well and can be used for experiments in which the desired number of subjects in each treatment group has been predetermined.

Another strategy that is sometimes employed is to use a random mechanism (such as tossing a coin or rolling a die) to determine which treatment will be assigned to a particular subject. For example, in an experiment with two treatments, you might toss a coin to determine if the first subject is assigned to treatment 1 or treatment 2. This could continue for each subject—if the coin lands H, the subject is assigned to treatment 1, and if the coin lands T, the subject is assigned to treatment 2. This strategy is fine, but may result in treatment groups of unequal size. For example, in an experiment with 100 subjects, 53 might be assigned to treatment 1 and 47 to treatment 2. If this is acceptable, the coin flip strategy is a reasonable way to assign subjects to treatments.

But, suppose you want to ensure that there is an equal number of subjects in each treatment group. Is it acceptable to use the coin flip strategy until one treatment group is complete and then just assign all of the remaining subjects to groups that are not yet full? The answer to this question is that it is probably not acceptable. For example, suppose a list of 20 subjects is in order by age from youngest to oldest and that we want to form two treatment groups each consisting of 10 subjects. Tossing a coin to make the assignments might result in the following (based on using the first row of random digits in Appendix A, Table 1, with an even number representing H and an odd number representing T):

Subject	Random Number	Coin Toss Equivalent	Treatment Group
1	4	H	1
2	5	T	2
3	1	T	2
4	8	H	1
5	5	T	2
6	0	H	1
7	3	T	2
8	3	T	2
9	7	T	2
10	1	T	2
11	2	H	1
12	8	H	1
13	4	H	1
14	5	T	2
15	1	T	2
16			1
17	Treatment group 2 filled. Assign all others to treatment group 1.		1
18			1
19			1
20			1

If the list of subjects was ordered by age, treatment group 1 would end up with a disproportionate number of older people. This strategy usually results in one treatment group drawing disproportionately from the end of the list. So, the only time the strategy of assigning at random until groups fill up and then assigning the remaining subjects to the group that is not full is reasonable is if you can be sure that the list is in random order with respect to all variables that might be related to the response variable. Because of this, it is best to avoid this strategy. Activity 2.5 investigates potential difficulties with this type of strategy.

On the other hand, if the number of subjects is large, it may not be important that every treatment group has exactly the same number of subjects. If this is the case, it is reasonable to use a coin flip strategy (or other strategies of this type) that does not involve stopping assignment of subjects to a group that becomes full.

Evaluating an Experimental Design

The key concepts of experimental design provide a framework for evaluating an experimental design, as illustrated in the following examples.

EXAMPLE 2.4 Revenge Is Sweet

The article "The Neural Basis of Altruistic Punishment" (*Science*, August 27, 2004) described a study that examined motivation for revenge. Subjects in the study were all healthy, right-handed men. Subjects played a game with another player in which they could both earn money by trusting each other or one player could double-cross the other player and keep all of the money. In some cases the double cross was required by the rules of the game in certain circumstances, while in other cases the double cross was the result of a deliberate choice. The victim of a double cross was then given the opportunity to retaliate by imposing a fine, but sometimes the victim had to spend some of his own money in order to impose the fine. This study was an experiment with four experimental conditions or treatments:

1. double cross not deliberate (double cross dictated by the rules of the game) and no cost to the victim to retaliate
2. double cross deliberate and no cost to the victim to retaliate
3. double cross not deliberate and a cost to the victim to retaliate
4. double cross deliberate and a cost to the victim to retaliate

All subjects chose revenge (imposed a fine on the double-crosser) when the double cross was deliberate and retaliation was free, and 86% of the subjects chose revenge when the double cross was deliberate, even if it cost them money. Only 21% imposed a fine if the double cross was dictated by the rules of the game and was not deliberate.

Assuming that the researchers randomly assigned the subjects to the four experimental conditions, this study is an experiment that incorporated random assignment, direct control (controlled sex, health, and handedness by using only healthy, right-handed males as subjects), and replication (many subjects assigned to each experimental condition).

EXAMPLE 2.5 Subliminal Messages

The article "The Most Powerful Manipulative Messages Are Hiding in Plain Sight" (*Chronicle of Higher Education*, January 29, 1999) reported the results of an interesting experiment on priming—the effect of subliminal messages on how we behave. In the experiment, subjects completed a language test in which they were asked to construct a sentence using each word in a list of words. One group of subjects received a list of words related to politeness, and a second group was given a list of words related to rudeness. Subjects were told to complete the language test and then come into the hall and find the researcher so that he could explain the next part of the test. When each subject came into the hall, he or she found the researcher engaged in conversation. The researcher wanted to see whether the subject would interrupt the conversation. The researcher found that 63% of those primed with words related to rudeness interrupted the conversation, whereas only 17% of those primed with words related to politeness interrupted.

If we assume that the researcher randomly assigned the subjects to the two groups, then this study is an experiment that compares two treatments (primed with words related to rudeness and primed with words related to politeness). The response variable, *politeness*, has the values *interrupted conversation* and *did not interrupt conversation*. The experiment uses replication (many subjects in each treatment group) and random assignment to control for extraneous variables that might affect the response.

Many experiments compare a group that receives a particular treatment to a **control group** that receives no treatment.

EXAMPLE 2.6 Chilling Newborns? Then You Need a Control Group...

Researchers for the National Institute of Child Health and Human Development studied 208 infants whose brains were temporarily deprived of oxygen as a result of complications at birth (*The New England Journal of Medicine*, October 13, 2005). These babies were subjects in an experiment to determine if reducing body temperature for three days after birth improved their chances of surviving without brain damage. The experiment was summarized in a paper that stated "infants were randomly assigned to usual care (control group) or whole-body cooling." Including a control group in the experiment provided a basis for comparison of death and disability rates for the proposed cooling treatment and those for usual care. Some extraneous variables that might also affect death and disability rates, such as the duration of oxygen deprivation, could not be directly controlled, so to ensure that the experiment did not unintentionally favor one experimental condition over the other, random assignment of the infants to the two groups was critical. Because this was a well-designed experiment, the researchers were able to use the resulting data and statistical methods that you will see in Chapter 11 to conclude that cooling did reduce the risk of death and disability for infants deprived of oxygen at birth.

Visualizing the Underlying Structure of Some Common Experimental Designs

Simple diagrams are sometimes used to highlight important features of some common experimental designs. The structure of an experiment that is based on random assignment of experimental units (the units to which treatments are assigned, usually subjects or trials) to one of two treatments is displayed in Figure 2.4. The diagram can be easily adapted for an experiment with more than two treatments. In any particular setting, we would also want to customize the diagram by indicating what the treatments are and what response will be measured. This is illustrated in Example 2.7.

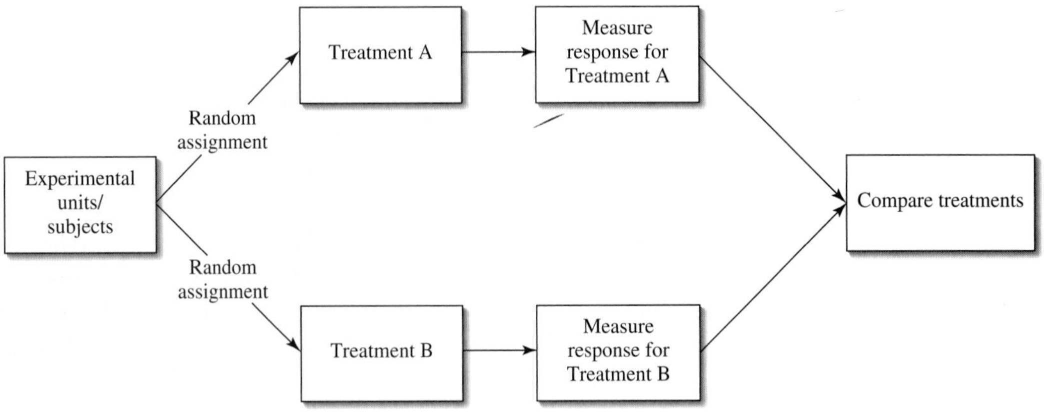

FIGURE 2.4
Diagram of an experiment with random assignment of experimental units to two treatments.

EXAMPLE 2.7 A Helping Hand

Can moving their hands help children learn math? This is the question investigated by the authors of the paper "Gesturing Gives Children New Ideas about Math" (*Psychological Science* [2009]: 267–272). An experiment was conducted to compare two different methods for teaching children how to solve math problems of the form $3 + 2 + 8 = \_\_\_\_ + 8$. One method involved having students point to the $3 + 2$ on the left side of the equal sign with one hand and then point to the blank on the right side of the equal sign before filling in the blank to complete the equation. The other method did not involve using these hand gestures. The paper states that the study used children ages 9 and 10 who were given a pretest containing six problems of the type described above. Only children who answered all six questions incorrectly became subjects in the experiment. There were a total of 128 subjects.

To compare the two methods, the 128 children were assigned at random to the two experimental conditions. Children assigned to one experimental condition were taught a method that used hand gestures and children assigned to the other experimental condition were taught a similar strategy that did not involve using hand gestures. Each child then took a test with six problems and the number correct was determined for each child. The researchers used the resulting data to reach the conclusion that the average number correct for children who used the method that incorporated hand gestures was significantly higher than the average number correct for children who were taught the method that did not use hand gestures.

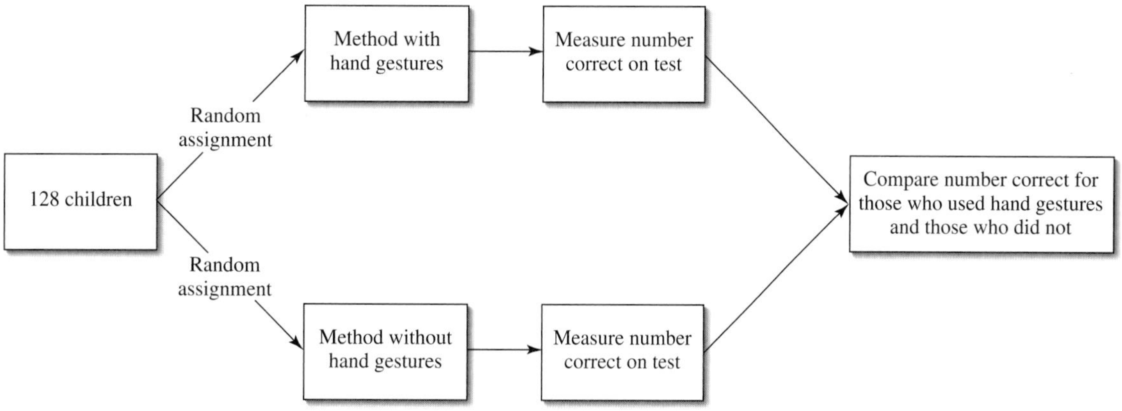

FIGURE 2.5
Diagram for the experiment of Example 2.7.

The basic structure of this experiment can be diagramed as shown in Figure 2.5. This type of diagram provides a nice summary of the experiment, but notice that several important characteristics of the experiment are not captured in the diagram. For example, the diagram does not show that some extraneous variables were considered by the researchers and directly controlled. In this example, both age and prior math knowledge were directly controlled by using only children who were 9 and 10 years old and who were not able to solve any of the questions on the pretest correctly. *So, be aware that while a diagram of an experiment may be a useful tool, it usually cannot stand alone in describing an experimental design.*

Some experiments consist of a sequence of trials, and treatments are assigned at random to the trials. The diagram in Figure 2.6 illustrates the underlying structure of such an experiment. Example 2.8 shows how this diagram can be customized to describe a particular experiment.

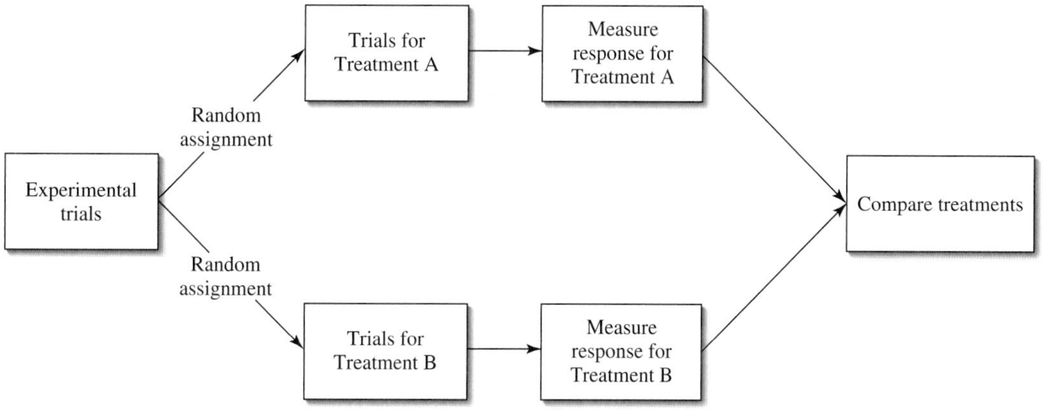

FIGURE 2.6
Diagram of an experiment with random assignment of treatments to trials.

EXAMPLE 2.8 Distracted? Watch Out for Those Cars!

The paper "Effect of Cell Phone Distraction on Pediatric Pedestrian Injury Risk" (*Pediatrics* [2009]: e179–e185) describes an experiment to investigate whether pedestrians who are talking on a cell phone are at greater risk of an accident when crossing the street than when not talking on a cell phone. No children were harmed in this experiment—a virtual interactive pedestrian environment was used! One possible way of conducting such an experiment would be to have a person cross 20 streets in this virtual environment. The person would talk on a cell phone for some crossings and would not use the cell phone for others. It would be important to randomly assign the two treatments (talking on the phone, not talking on the phone) to the 20 trials (the 20 simulated street crossings). This would result in a design that did not favor one treatment over the other because the pedestrian became more careful with experience or more tired and, therefore, easily distracted over time. The basic structure of this experiment is diagramed in Figure 2.7.

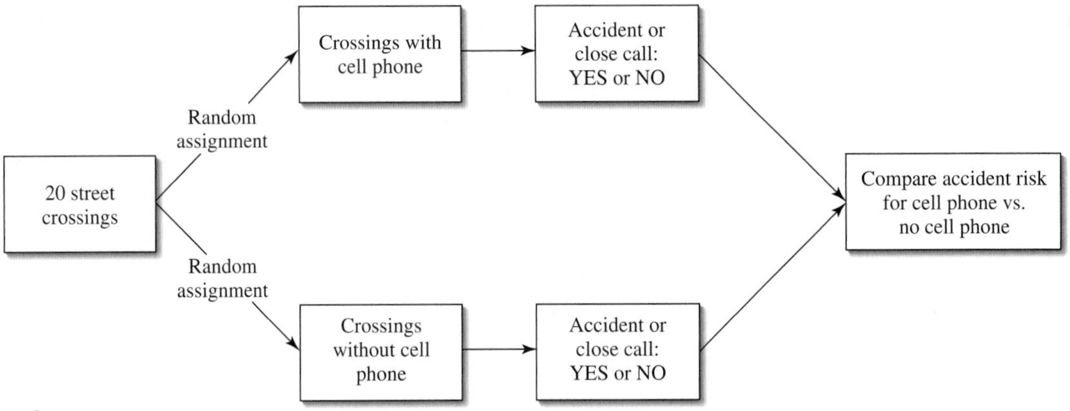

FIGURE 2.7
Diagram for the experiment of Example 2.8 with random assignment to trials.

The actual experiment conducted by the authors of the paper was a bit more sophisticated than the one just described. In this experiment, 77 children age 10 and 11 each performed simulated crossings with and without a cell phone. Random assignment was used to decide which children would cross first with the cell phone followed by no cell phone and which children could cross first with no cell phone. The structure of this experiment is diagramed in Figure 2.8.

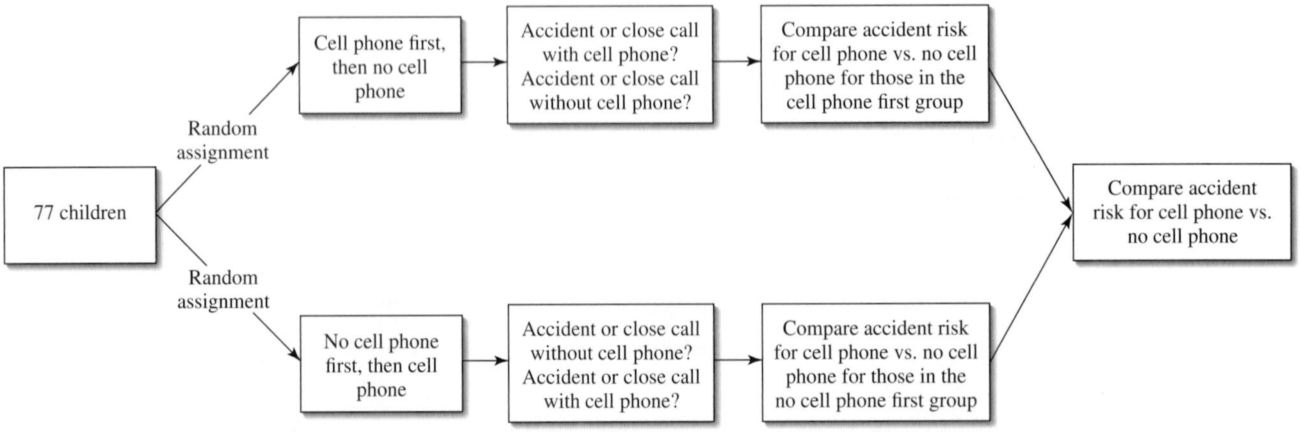

FIGURE 2.8
Diagram for the Experiment of Example 2.8 with 77 children.

As was the case in Example 2.7, note that while the diagram is informative, by itself, it does not capture all of the important aspects of the design. In particular, it does not capture the direct control of age (only children age 10 and 11 were used as subjects in the experiment).

Experimental designs in which experimental units are assigned at random to treatments or in which treatments are assigned at random to trials (like those of the experiments in Examples 2.7 and 2.8) are called **completely randomized designs**.

Diagrams are also useful for highlighting the structure of experiments that use blocking. This is illustrated in Example 2.9.

EXAMPLE 2.9 A Helping Hand Revisited

Let's return to the experiment described in Example 2.7. Take a minute to go back and re-read that example. The experiment described in Example 2.7, a completely randomized design with 128 subjects, was used to compare two different methods for teaching kids how to solve a particular type of math problem. Age and prior math knowledge were extraneous variables that the researchers thought might be related to performance on the math test given at the end of the lesson, so the researchers chose to directly control these variables. The 128 children were assigned at random to the two experimental conditions (treatments). The researchers relied on random assignment to create treatment groups that would be roughly equivalent with respect to other extraneous variables.

But suppose that we were worried that gender might also be related to performance on the math test. One possibility would be to use direct control of gender—that is, we might use only boys or only girls as subjects in the experiment. Then if we saw a difference in test performance for the two teaching methods, it could not be due to one experimental group containing more boys and fewer girls than the other group. The downside to this strategy is that if we use only boys in the experiment, there is no basis for also generalizing any conclusions from the experiment to girls.

Another strategy for dealing with extraneous variables is to incorporate blocking into the design. In the case of gender, we could create two blocks, one consisting of girls and one consisting of boys. Then, once the blocks are formed, we would randomly assign the girls to the two treatments and randomly assign the boys to the two treatments. In the actual study, the group of 128 children included 81 girls and 47 boys. A diagram that shows the structure of an experiment that includes blocking using gender is shown in Figure 2.9.

FIGURE 2.9 Diagram for the experiment of Example 2.9 using gender to form blocks.

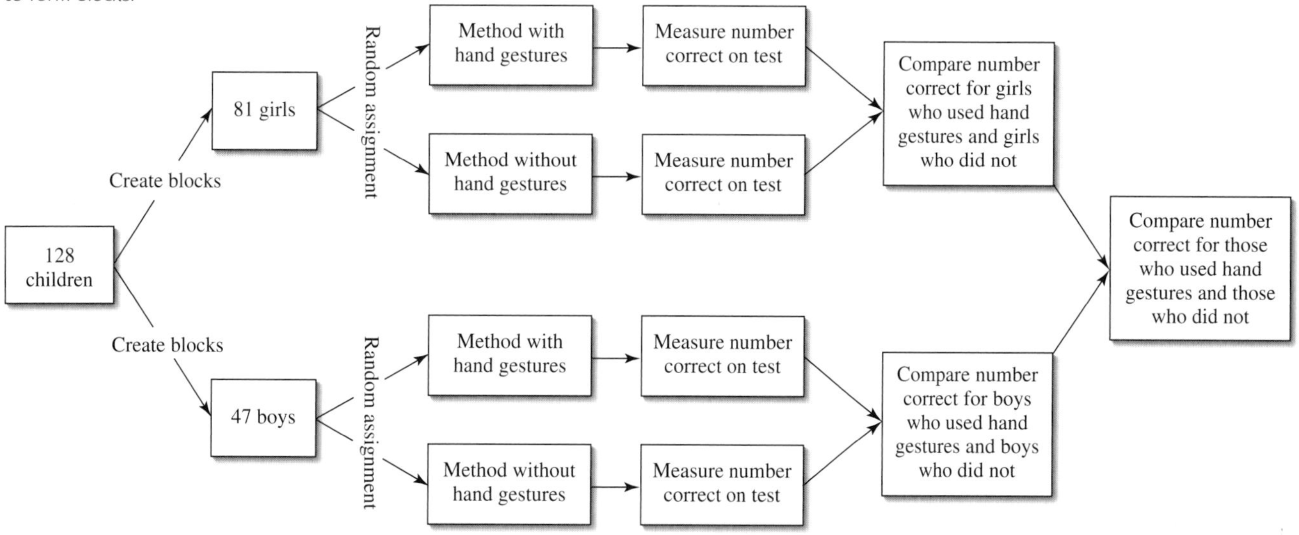

When blocking is used, the design is called a **randomized block design**. Note that one difference between the diagram that describes the experiment in which blocking is used (Figure 2.9) and the diagram of the original experiment (Figure 2.5) is at what point the random assignment occurs. *When blocking is incorporated in an experiment, the random assignment to treatments occurs after the blocks have been formed and is done separately for each block.*

Before proceeding with an experiment, you should be able to give a satisfactory answer to each of the following 10 questions.

1. What is the research question that data from the experiment will be used to answer?
2. What is the response variable?
3. How will the values of the response variable be determined?
4. What are the explanatory variables for the experiment?
5. For each explanatory variable, how many different values are there, and what are these values?
6. What are the treatments for the experiment?
7. What extraneous variables might influence the response?
8. How does the design incorporate random assignment of subjects to treatments (or treatments to subjects) or random assignment of treatments to trials?
9. For each extraneous variable listed in Question 7, how does the design protect against its potential influence on the response through blocking, direct control, or random assignment?
10. Will you be able to answer the research question using the data collected in this experiment?

EXERCISES 2.33 - 2.47

2.33 The head of the quality control department at a printing company would like to carry out an experiment to determine which of three different glues results in the greatest binding strength. Although they are not of interest in the current investigation, other factors thought to affect binding strength are the number of pages in the book and whether the book is being bound as a paperback or a hardback.

a. What is the response variable in this experiment?

b. What explanatory variable will determine the experimental conditions?

c. What two extraneous variables are mentioned in the problem description? Are there other extraneous variables that should be considered?

2.34 A study of college students showed a temporary gain of up to 9 IQ points after listening to a Mozart piano sonata. This conclusion, dubbed the Mozart effect, has since been criticized by a number of researchers who have been unable to confirm the result in similar studies. Suppose that you wanted to see whether there is a Mozart effect for students at your school.

a. Describe how you might design an experiment for this purpose.

b. Does your experimental design include direct control of any extraneous variables? Explain.

c. Does your experimental design use blocking? Explain why you did or did not include blocking in your design.

d. What role does random assignment play in your design?

2.35 The following is from an article titled "After the Workout, Got Chocolate Milk?" that appeared in the *Chicago Tribune* (January 18, 2005):

> Researchers at Indiana University at Bloomington have found that chocolate milk effectively helps athletes recover from an intense workout. They had nine cyclists bike, rest four hours, then bike again, three separate times. After each workout, the cyclists downed chocolate milk or energy drinks Gatorade or Endurox (two to three glasses per hour); then, in the second workout of each set, they cycled to exhaustion. When they drank chocolate milk, the amount of time they could cycle until they were exhausted was similar to when they drank Gatorade and longer than when they drank Endurox.

The article is not explicit about this, but in order for this to have been a well-designed experiment, it must have incorporated random assignment. Briefly explain where the researcher would have needed to use random assign in order for the conclusion of the experiment to be valid.

2.36 The report "Comparative Study of Two Computer Mouse Designs" (Cornell Human Factors Laboratory Technical Report RP7992) included the following description of the subjects used in an experiment:

> Twenty-four Cornell University students and staff (12 males and 12 females) volunteered to participate in the study. Three groups of 4 men and 4 women were selected by their stature to represent the 5th percentile (female 152.1 ± 0.3 cm, male 164.1 ± 0.4 cm), 50th percentile (female 162.4 ± 0.1 cm, male 174.1 ± 0.7 cm), and 95th percentile (female 171.9 ± 0.2 cm, male 185.7 ± 0.6 cm) ranges . . . All subjects reported using their right hand to operate a computer mouse.

This experimental design incorporated direct control and blocking.

a. Are the potential effects of the extraneous variable stature (height) addressed by blocking or direct control?
b. Whether the right or left hand is used to operate the mouse was considered to be an extraneous variable. Are the potential effects of this variable addressed by blocking or direct control?

2.37 The Institute of Psychiatry at Kings College London found that dealing with "infomania" has a temporary, but significant derogatory effect on IQ (*Discover*, November 2005). In this experiment, researchers divided volunteers into two groups. Each subject took an IQ test. One group had to check e-mail and respond to instant messages while taking the test, and the second group took the test without any distraction. The distracted group had an average score that was 10 points lower than the average for the control group. Explain why it is important that the researchers created the two experimental groups in this study by using random assignment.

2.38 In an experiment to compare two different surgical procedures for hernia repair ("A Single-Blinded, Randomized Comparison of Laparoscopic Versus Open Hernia Repair in Children," *Pediatrics* [2009]: 332–336), 89 children were assigned at random to one of the two surgical methods. The researchers relied on the random assignment of subjects to treatments to create comparable groups with respect to extraneous variables that they did not control. One such extraneous variable was age. After random assignment to treatments, the researchers looked at the age distribution of the children in each of the two experimental groups (laparoscopic repair (LR) and open repair (OR)). The accompanying figure is from the paper.

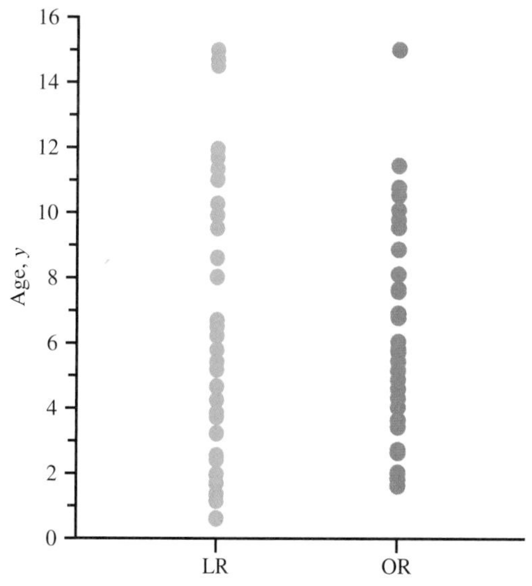

Based on this figure, has the random assignment of subjects to experimental groups been successful in creating groups that are similar with respect to the ages of the children in the groups? Explain.

2.39 In many digital environments, users are allowed to choose how they are represented visually online. Does how people are represented online affect online behavior? This question was examined by the authors of the paper "The Proteus Effect: The Effect of Transformed Self-Representation on Behavior" (*Human Communication Research* [2007]: 271–290). Participants were randomly assigned either an attractive avatar (a graphical image that represents a person) to represent them or an unattractive avatar.

a. The researchers concluded that when interacting with a person of the opposite gender in an online virtual environment, those assigned an attractive avatar moved significantly closer to the other person than those who had been assigned an unattractive avatar. This difference was attributed to the attractiveness of the avatar. Explain why the researchers would not have been able to reach this conclusion if participants had been allowed to choose one of the two avatars (attractive, unattractive) to represent them online.

b. Construct a diagram to represent the underlying structure of this experiment.

2.40 To examine the effect of exercise on body composition, healthy women age 35 to 50 were classified as either active (9 hours or more of physical activity per week) or sedentary ("Effects of Habitual Physical Activity on the Resting Metabolic Rates and Body Composition of Women aged 35 to 50 Years," *Journal of the American Dietetic Association* [2001]: 1181–1191). Percent body fat was measured and the researchers found that percent body fat was significantly lower for women who were active than for sedentary women.

a. Is the study described an experiment? If so, what are the explanatory variable and the response variable? If not, explain why it is not an experiment.

b. From this study alone, is it reasonable to conclude that physical activity is the cause of the observed difference in body fat percentage? Justify your answer.

2.41 Does playing action video games provide more than just entertainment? The authors of the paper "Action-Video-Game Experience Alters the Spatial Resolution of Vision" (*Psychological Science* [2007]: 88–94) concluded that spatial resolution, an important aspect of vision, is improved by playing action video games. They based this conclusion on data from an experiment in which 32 volunteers who had not played action video games were "equally and randomly divided between the experimental and control groups." Subjects in each group played a video game for 30 hours over a period of 6 weeks. Those in the experimental group played Unreal Tournament 2004, an action video game. Those in the control group played the game Tetris, a game that does not require the user to process multiple objects at once. Explain why the random assignment to the two groups is an important aspect of this experiment.

2.42 Construct a diagram to represent the subliminal messages experiment of Example 2.5.

2.43 Construct a diagram to represent the gasoline additive experiment described on page 52.

2.44 An advertisement for a sweatshirt that appeared in *SkyMall Magazine* (a catalog distributed by some airlines) stated the following: "This is not your ordinary hoody! Why? Fact: Research shows that written words on containers of water can influence the water's structure for better or worse depending on the nature and intent of the word. Fact: The human body is 70% water. What if positive words were printed on the inside of your clothing?" For only $79, you could purchase a hooded sweatshirt that had over 200 positive words (such as hope, gratitude, courage and love) in 15 different languages printed on the inside of the sweatshirt so that you could benefit from being surrounded by these positive words. The reference to the "fact" that written words on containers of water can influence the water's structure appears to be based on the work of Dr. Masaru Emoto who typed words on paper, pasted the words on bottles of water, and observed how the water reacted to the words by seeing what kind of crystals were formed in the water. He describes several of his experiments in his self-published book, *The Message from Water*. If you were going to interview Dr. Emoto, what questions would you want to ask him about his experiment?

2.45 An experiment was carried out to assess the effect of Sweet Talk, a text messaging support system for patients with diabetes ("A Randomized Controlled Trial of Sweet Talk," *Diabetic Medicine* [2006]: 1332–1338). Participants in the experiment were 92 patients, age 8 to 18, with type I diabetes who had been on conventional insulin treatment for at least one year. Participants were assigned at random to one of three experimental groups:

Group 1: continued conventional insulin therapy
Group 2: continued conventional insulin therapy with Sweet Talk support
Group 3: followed a new intensive insulin therapy with Sweet Talk support

One response variable was a measure of glucose concentration in the blood. There was no significant difference in glucose concentration between groups 1 and 2, but group 3 showed a significant improvement in this measure compared to groups 1 and 2.

a. Explain why it is not reasonable to attribute the observed improvement in group 3 compared to group 1 to the use of Sweet Talk, even though subjects were randomly assigned to the three experimental groups.

b. How would you modify this experiment so that you could tell if improvement in glucose concentration was attributable to the intensive insulin therapy, the use of Sweet Talk, or a combination of the two?

c. Draw a diagram showing the structure of the modified experiment from Part (b).

2.46 The Pew Research Center conducted a study of gender bias. The report "Men or Women: Who is the Better Leader? A Paradox in Public Attitudes" (www.pewsocialtrends.org, August 28, 2008) describes how the study was conducted:

> In the experiment, two separate random samples of more than 1000 registered voters were asked to read a profile sent to them online of a hypothetical candidate for U.S. Congress in their district. One random sample of 1161 respondents read a profile of Ann Clark, described as a lawyer, a churchgoer, a member of the local Chamber of Commerce, an environmentalist and a member of the same party as the survey respondent. They were then asked what they liked and didn't like about her, whether they considered her qualified and whether they were inclined to vote for her. There was no indication that this was a survey about gender or gender bias. A second random sample of 1139 registered voters was asked to read a profile of Andrew Clark, who—except for his gender—was identical in every way to Ann Clark. These respondents were then asked the same questions.

a. What are the two treatments in this experiment?

b. What are the response variables in this experiment?

c. Explain why "taking two separate random samples" has the same benefits as random assignment to the two treatments in this experiment.

2.47 Red wine contains flavonol, an antioxidant thought to have beneficial health effects. But to have an effect, the antioxidant must be absorbed into the blood. The article "Red Wine is a Poor Source of Bioavailable Flavonols in Men" (*The Journal of Nutrition* [2001]: 745–748) describes a study to investigate three sources of dietary flavonol—red wine, yellow onions, and black tea—to determine the effect of source on absorption. The article included the following statement:

> We recruited subjects via posters and local newspapers. To ensure that subjects could tolerate the alcohol in the wine, we only allowed men with a consumption of at least seven drinks per week to participate ... Throughout the study, the subjects consumed a diet that was low in flavonols.

a. What are the three treatments in this experiment?

b. What is the response variable?

c. What are three extraneous variables that the researchers chose to control in the experiment?

2.4 More on Experimental Design

The previous section covered basic principles for designing simple comparative experiments—control, blocking, random assignment, and replication. The goal of an experimental design is to provide a method of data collection that (1) minimizes extraneous sources of variability in the response so that any differences in response for various experimental conditions can be more easily assessed and (2) creates experimental groups that are similar with respect to extraneous variables that cannot be controlled either directly or through blocking.

In this section, we look at some additional considerations that you may need to think about when planning an experiment.

Use of a Control Group

If the purpose of an experiment is to determine whether some treatment has an effect, it is important to include an experimental group that does not receive the treatment. Such a group is called a **control group**. The use of a control group allows the experimenter to assess how the response variable behaves when the treatment is not used. This provides a baseline against which the treatment groups can be compared to determine whether the treatment had an effect.

EXAMPLE 2.10 Comparing Gasoline Additives

Stockbyte/Getty Images

Suppose that an engineer wants to know whether a gasoline additive increases fuel efficiency (miles per gallon). Such an experiment might use a single car (to eliminate car-to-car variability) and a sequence of trials in which 1 gallon of gas is put in an empty tank, the car is driven around a racetrack at a constant speed, and the distance traveled on the gallon of gas is recorded.

To determine whether the additive increases gas mileage, it would be necessary to include a control group of trials in which distance traveled was measured when gasoline without the additive was used. The trials would be assigned *at random* to one of the two experimental conditions (additive or no additive).

Even though this experiment consists of a sequence of trials all with the same car, random assignment of trials to experimental conditions is still important because there will always be uncontrolled variability. For example, temperature or other environmental conditions might change over the sequence of trials, the physical condition of the car might change slightly from one trial to another, and so on. Random assignment of experimental conditions to trials will tend to even out the effects of these uncontrollable factors.

AP* EXAM TIP

The experimental design terminology introduced in this section (such as *control group, placebo,* and *blinding*) is very important in describing experimental designs. You should be able to both read and write with understanding using these terms.

Although we usually think of a control group as one that receives no treatment, in experiments designed to compare a new treatment to an existing standard treatment, the term control group is sometimes also used to describe the group that receives the current standard treatment.

Not all experiments require the use of a control group. For example, many experiments are designed to compare two or more conditions—an experiment to compare density for three different formulations of bar soap or an experiment to determine how oven temperature affects the cooking time of a particular type of cake. However, sometimes a control group is included even when the ultimate goal is to compare two or more different treatments. An experiment with two treatments and no control group might allow us to determine whether there is a difference between the two treatments and even to assess the magnitude of the difference if one exists, but it would not allow us to assess the individual effect of either treatment. For example, without a control group, we might be able to say that there is no difference in the increase in mileage for two different gasoline additives, but we would not be able to tell if this was because both additives increased gas mileage by a similar amount or because neither additive had any effect on gas mileage.

Use of a Placebo

In experiments that use human subjects, use of a control group may not be enough to determine whether a treatment really does have an effect. People sometimes respond merely to the power of suggestion! For example, suppose a study designed to determine whether a particular herbal supplement is effective in promoting weight loss uses an experimental group that takes the herbal supplement and a control group that takes nothing. It is possible that those who take the herbal supplement and believe that they are taking something that will help them to lose weight may be more motivated and may unconsciously change their eating behavior or activity level, resulting in weight loss.

Although there is debate about the degree to which people respond, many studies have shown that people sometimes respond to treatments with no active ingredients and that they often report that such "treatments" relieve pain or reduce symptoms. So, if an experiment is to enable researchers to determine whether a treatment really has an effect, comparing a treatment group to a control group may not be enough. To address the problem, many experiments use what is called a placebo.

DEFINITION

A **placebo** is something that is identical (in appearance, taste, feel, etc.) to the treatment received by the treatment group, except that it contains no active ingredients.

For example, in the herbal supplement experiment, rather than using a control group that received *no* treatment, the researchers might want to include a placebo group. Individuals in the placebo group would take a pill that looked just like the herbal supplement but did not contain the herb or any other active ingredient. As long as the subjects did not know whether they were taking the herb or the placebo, the placebo group would provide a better basis for comparison and would allow the researchers to determine whether the herbal supplement had any real effect over and above the "placebo effect."

Single-Blind and Double-Blind Experiments

Because people often have their own personal beliefs about the effectiveness of various treatments, it is desirable to conduct experiments in such a way that subjects do not know what treatment they are receiving. For example, in an experiment comparing four different doses of a medication for relief of headache pain, someone who knows that he is receiving the medication at its highest dose may be subconsciously influenced to report a greater degree of headache pain reduction. By ensuring that subjects are not aware of which treatment they receive, we can prevent the subjects' personal perceptions from influencing the response.

An experiment in which subjects do not know what treatment they have received is described as *single-blind.* Of course, not all experiments can be made single-blind. For example, in an experiment to compare the effect of two different types of exercise on blood pressure, it is not possible for participants to be unaware of whether they are in the swimming group or the jogging group! However, when it is possible, "blinding" the subjects in an experiment is generally a good strategy.

In some experiments, someone other than the subject is responsible for measuring the response. To ensure that the person measuring the response does not let personal beliefs influence the way in which the response is recorded, the researchers should make sure that the measurer does not know which treatment was given to any particular individual. For example, in a medical experiment to determine whether a new vaccine reduces the risk of getting the flu, doctors must decide whether a particular individual who is not feeling well actually has the flu or some other unrelated illness. If the doctor knew that a participant with flu-like symptoms had received the new flu vaccine, she might be less likely to determine that the participant had the flu and more likely to interpret the symptoms as being the result of some other illness.

There are two ways in which blinding might occur in an experiment. One involves blinding the subjects, and the other involves blinding the individuals who measure the response. If subjects do not know which treatment was received *and* those measuring the response do not know which treatment was given to which subject, the experiment is described as **double-blind.** If only one of the two types of blinding is present, the experiment is single-blind.

DEFINITION

A **double-blind** experiment is one in which neither the subjects nor the individuals who measure the response know which treatment was received.

A **single-blind** experiment is one in which the subjects do not know which treatment was received but the individuals measuring the response do know which treatment was received, or one in which the subjects do know which treatment was received but the individuals measuring the response do not know which treatment was received.

Experimental Units and Replication

An **experimental unit** is the smallest unit to which a treatment is applied. In the language of experimental design, treatments are assigned at random to experimental units, and replication means that each treatment is applied to more than one experimental unit.

Replication is necessary for random assignment to be an effective way to create similar experimental groups and to get a sense of the variability in the values of the response for individuals who receive the same treatment. As we will see in Chapters 9–15, this enables us to use statistical methods to decide whether differences in the responses in different treatment groups can be attributed to the treatment received or whether they can be explained by chance variation (the natural variability seen in the responses to a single treatment).

Be careful when designing an experiment to ensure that there is replication. For example, suppose that children in two third-grade classes are available to participate in an experiment to compare two different methods for teaching arithmetic. It might at first seem reasonable to select one class at random to use one method and then assign the other method to the remaining class. But what are the experimental units here? If treatments are randomly assigned to classes, classes are the experimental units. Because only one class is assigned to each treatment, this is an experiment with no replication, even though there are many children in each class. We would *not* be able to determine whether there was a difference between the two methods based on data from this experiment, because we would have only one observation per treatment.

One last note on replication: Do not confuse replication in an experimental design with replicating an experiment. Replicating an experiment means conducting a new experiment using the same experimental design as a previous experiment; it is a way of confirming conclusions based on a previous experiment, but it does not eliminate the need for replication in each of the individual experiments themselves.

Using Volunteers as Subjects in an Experiment

Although the use of volunteers in a study that involves collecting data through sampling is never a good idea, it is a common practice to use volunteers as subjects in an experiment. Even though the use of volunteers limits the researcher's ability to generalize to a larger population, random assignment of the volunteers to treatments should result in comparable groups, and so treatment effects can still be assessed.

EXERCISES 2.48 - 2.59

2.48 Explain why some studies include both a control group and a placebo treatment. What additional comparisons are possible if both a control group and a placebo group are included?

2.49 Explain why blinding is a reasonable strategy in many experiments.

2.50 Give an example of an experiment for each of the following:

a. Single-blind experiment with the subjects blinded
b. Single-blind experiment with the individuals measuring the response blinded
c. Double-blind experiment
d. An experiment for which it is not possible to blind the subjects

2.51 ✦ Swedish researchers concluded that viewing and discussing art soothes the soul and helps relieve medical conditions such as high blood pressure and constipation (AFP International News Agency, October 14, 2005). This conclusion was based on a study in which 20 elderly women gathered once a week to discuss different works of art. The study also included a control group of 20 elderly women who met once a week to discuss their hobbies and interests. At the end of 4 months, the art discussion group was found to have a more positive attitude, to have lower blood pressure, and to use fewer laxatives than the control group.

a. Why would it be important to determine if the researchers assigned the women participating in the study at random to one of the two groups?
b. Explain why you think that the researchers included a control group in this study.

2.52 In an experiment to compare two different surgical procedures for hernia repair ("A Single-Blinded, Randomized Comparison of Laparoscopic Versus Open Hernia Repair in Children," *Pediatrics* [2009]: 332–336), 89 children were assigned at random to one of the two surgical methods. The methods studied were laparoscopic repair and open repair. In laparoscopic repair, three small incisions are made and the surgeon works through these incisions with the aid of a small camera that is inserted through one of the incisions. In the open repair, a larger incision is used to open the abdomen. One of the response variables in this study was the amount of medication that was given after the surgery for the control of pain and nausea. The paper states "For postoperative pain, rescue fentanyl (1 μg/kg) and for nausea, ondansetron (0.1 mg/kg) were given as judged necessary by the attending nurse blinded to the operative approach."

a. Why do you think it was important that the nurse who administered the medications did not know which type of surgery was performed?
b. Explain why it was not possible for this experiment to be double-blind.

2.53 The article "Placebos Are Getting More Effective. Drug Makers Are Desperate to Know Why." (*Wired Magazine*, August 8, 2009) states that "according to research, the color of a tablet can boost the effectiveness even of genuine meds—or help convince a patient that a placebo is a potent remedy." Describe how you would design an experiment to investigate if adding color to Tylenol tablets would result in greater perceived pain relief. Be sure to address how you would select subjects, how you would measure pain relief, what colors you would use, and whether or not you would include a control group in your experiment.

2.54 A novel alternative medical treatment for heart attacks seeds the damaged heart muscle with cells from the patient's thigh muscle ("Doctors Mend Damaged Hearts with Cells from Muscles," *San Luis Obispo Tribune*, November 18, 2002). Doctor Dib from the Arizona Heart Institute evaluated the approach on 16 patients with severe heart failure. The article states that "ordinarily, the heart pushes out more than half its blood with each beat. Dib's patients had such severe heart failure that their hearts pumped just 23 percent. After bypass surgery and cell injections, this improved to 36 percent, although it was impossible to say how much, if any, of the new strength resulted from the extra cells."

a. Explain why it is not reasonable to generalize to the population of all heart attack victims based on the data from these 16 patients.
b. Explain why it is not possible to say whether any of the observed improvement was due to the cell injections, based on the results of this study.
c. Describe a design for an experiment that would allow researchers to determine whether bypass surgery plus cell injections was more effective than bypass surgery alone.

2.55 ✦ The article "Doctor Dogs Diagnose Cancer by Sniffing It Out" (*Knight Ridder Newspapers*, January 9, 2006) reports the results of an experiment described in the journal *Integrative Cancer Therapies*. In this experiment, dogs were trained to distinguish between people with breast and lung cancer and people without cancer by sniffing exhaled breath. Dogs were trained to lay down if they detected cancer in a breath sample. After training, dogs' ability to detect cancer was tested using breath samples from people whose breath had not been used in training the dogs. The paper states "The researchers blinded both the dog handlers and the experimental observers to the identity of the breath samples." Explain why this blinding is an important aspect of the design of this experiment.

2.56 An experiment to evaluate whether vitamins can help prevent recurrence of blocked arteries in patients who have had surgery to clear blocked arteries was described in the article "Vitamins Found to Help Prevent Blocked Arteries" (Associated Press, September 1, 2002). The study involved 205 patients who were given either a treatment consisting of a combination of folic acid, vitamin B12, and vitamin B6 or a placebo for 6 months.

a. Explain why a placebo group was used in this experiment.
b. Explain why it would be important for the researchers to have assigned the 205 subjects to the two groups (vitamin and placebo) at random.
c. Do you think it is appropriate to generalize the results of this experiment to the population of all patients who have undergone surgery to clear blocked arteries? Explain.

2.57 Pismo Beach, California, has an annual clam festival that includes a clam chowder contest. Judges rate clam chowders from local restaurants, and the judging is done in such a way that the judges are not aware of which chowder is from which restaurant. One year, much to the dismay of the seafood restaurants on the waterfront, Denny's chowder was declared the winner! (When asked what the ingredients were, the cook at Denny's said he wasn't sure—he just had to add the right amount of nondairy creamer to the soup stock that he got from Denny's distribution center!)

a. Do you think that Denny's chowder would have won the contest if the judging had not been "blind?" Explain.
b. Although this was not an experiment, your answer to Part (a) helps to explain why those measuring the response in an experiment are often blinded. Using your answer in Part (a), explain why experiments are often blinded in this way.

2.58 The *San Luis Obispo Tribune* (May 7, 2002) reported that "a new analysis has found that in the majority of trials conducted by drug companies in recent decades, sugar pills have done as well as—or better than—antidepressants." What effect is being described here? What does this imply about the design of experiments with a goal of evaluating the effectiveness of a new medication?

2.59 The article "A Debate in the Dentist's Chair" (*San Luis Obispo Tribune*, January 28, 2000) described an ongoing debate over whether newer resin fillings are a better alternative to the more traditional silver amalgam fillings. Because amalgam fillings contain mercury, there is concern that they could be mildly toxic and prove to be a health risk to those with some types of immune and kidney disorders. One experiment described in the article used sheep as subjects and reported that sheep treated with amalgam fillings had impaired kidney function.

a. In the experiment, a control group of sheep that received no fillings was used but there was no placebo group. Explain why it is not necessary to have a placebo group in this experiment.
b. The experiment compared only an amalgam filling treatment group to a control group. What would be the benefit of also including a resin filling treatment group in the experiment?
c. Why do you think the experimenters used sheep rather than human subjects?

2.5 More on Observational Studies: Designing Surveys (Optional)

Designing an observational study to compare two populations on the basis of some easily measured characteristic is relatively straightforward, with attention focusing on choosing a reasonable method of sample selection. However, many observational studies attempt to measure personal opinion or attitudes using responses to a survey. In such studies, both the sampling method and the design of the survey itself are critical to obtaining reliable information.

At first glance it might seem that a survey is a simple method for acquiring information. However, it turns out that designing and administering a survey is not an easy task. Great care must be taken in order to obtain good information from a survey.

Survey Basics

A **survey** is a voluntary encounter between strangers in which an interviewer seeks information from a respondent by engaging in a special type of conversation. This conversation might take place in person, over the telephone, or even in the form of a written questionnaire, and it is quite different from usual social conversations. Both the interviewer and the respondent have certain roles and responsibilities. The interviewer gets to decide what is relevant to the conversation and may ask questions—possibly personal or even embarrassing questions. The respondent, in turn, may refuse to participate in the conversation and may refuse to answer any particular question. But having agreed to participate in the survey, the respondent is responsible for answering the questions truthfully. Let's consider the situation of the respondent.

The Respondent's Tasks

Understanding of the survey process has been improved in the past two decades by contributions from the field of psychology, but there is still much uncertainty about how people respond to survey questions. Survey researchers and psychologists generally agree that the respondent is confronted with a sequence of tasks when asked a question: comprehension of the question, retrieval of information from memory, and reporting the response.

Task 1: Comprehension Comprehension is the single most important task facing the respondent, and fortunately it is the characteristic of a survey question that is most easily controlled by the question writer. Understandable directions and questions are characterized by (1) a vocabulary appropriate to the population of interest, (2) simple sentence structure, and (3) little or no ambiguity. Vocabulary is often a problem. As a rule, it is best to use the simplest possible word that can be used without sacrificing clear meaning.

Simple sentence structure also makes it easier for the respondent to understand the question. A famous example of difficult syntax occurred in 1993 when the Roper organization created a survey related to the Holocaust. One question in this survey was

> "Does it seem possible or does it seem impossible to you that the Nazi extermination of the Jews never happened?"

The question has a complicated structure and a double negative—"impossible . . . never happened"—that could lead respondents to give an answer opposite to what they actually believed. The question was rewritten and given a year later in an otherwise unchanged survey:

> "Does it seem possible to you that the Nazi extermination of the Jews never happened, or do you feel certain that it happened?"

This question wording is much clearer, and in fact the respondents' answers were quite different, as shown in the following table (the "unsure" and "no opinion" percentages have been omitted):

Original Roper Poll		Revised Roper Poll	
Impossible	65%	Certain it happened	91%
Possible	12%	Possible it never happened	1%

It is also important to filter out ambiguity in questions. Even the most innocent and seemingly clear questions can have a number of possible interpretations. For example, suppose that you are asked, "When did you move to Cedar Rapids?" This would seem to be an unambiguous question, but some possible answers might be (1) "In 1971," (2) "When I was 23," and (3) "In the summer." The respondent must decide which of these three answers, if any, is the appropriate response. It may be possible to lessen the ambiguity with more precise questions:

1. In what year did you move to Cedar Rapids?
2. How old were you when you moved to Cedar Rapids?
3. In what season of the year did you move to Cedar Rapids?

One way to find out whether or not a question is ambiguous is to field-test the question and to ask the respondents if they were unsure how to answer a question.

Ambiguity can also arise from the placement of questions as well as from their phrasing. Here is an example of ambiguity uncovered when the order of two questions differed in two versions of a survey on happiness. The questions were

1. Taken altogether, how would you say things are these days: Would you say that you are very happy, pretty happy, or not too happy?
2. Taking things altogether, how would you describe your marriage: Would you say that your marriage is very happy, pretty happy, or not too happy?

The proportions of responses to the general happiness question differed for the different question orders, as follows:

Response to General Happiness Question

	General Asked First	General Asked Second
Very happy	52.4%	38.1%
Pretty happy	44.2%	52.8%
Not too happy	3.4%	9.1%

If the goal in this survey was to estimate the proportion of the population that is generally happy, these numbers are quite troubling—they cannot both be right! What seems to have happened is that Question 1 was interpreted differently depending on whether it was asked first or second. When the general happiness question was asked after the marital happiness question, the respondents apparently interpreted it to be asking about their happiness in all aspects of their lives *except* their marriage. This was a reasonable interpretation, given that they had just been asked about their marital happiness, but it is a different interpretation than when the general happiness question was asked first. The troubling lesson here is that even carefully worded questions can have different interpretations in the context of the rest of the survey.

Task 2: Retrieval from Memory Retrieving relevant information from memory to answer the question is not always an easy task, and it is not a problem limited to questions of fact. For example, consider this seemingly elementary "factual" question:

How many times in the past 5 years did you visit your dentist's office?

a. 0 times
b. 1–5 times
c. 6–10 times
d. 11–15 times
e. more than 15 times

It is unlikely that many people will remember with clarity every single visit to the dentist in the past 5 years. But generally, people will respond to such a question with answers consistent with the memories and facts they are able to reconstruct given the time they have to respond to the question. An individual may, for example, have a sense that he usually makes about two trips a year to the dentist's office, so he may extrapolate the typical year and get 10 times in 5 years. Then there may be three particularly memorable visits, say, for a root canal in the middle of winter. Thus, the best recollection is now 13, and the respondent will choose Answer (d), 11–15 times. Perhaps not exactly correct, but the best that can be reported under the circumstances.

What are the implications of this relatively fuzzy memory for those who construct surveys about facts? First, the investigator should understand that most factual answers are going to be approximations of the truth. Second, events closer to the time of a survey are easier to recall.

Attitude and opinion questions can also be affected in significant ways by the respondent's memory of recently asked questions. For example, one study contained a survey question asking respondents their opinion about how much they followed politics. When that question was preceded by a factual question asking whether they knew the name of the congressional representative from their district, the percentage who reported they follow politics "now and then" or "hardly ever" jumped from 21% to 39%! Respondents apparently concluded that, because they didn't know the answer to the previous knowledge question, they must not follow politics as much as they might have thought otherwise. In a survey that asks for an opinion about the degree to which the respondent believes drilling for oil should be permitted in national parks, the response might be different if the question is preceded by questions about the high price of gasoline than if the question is preceded by questions about the environment.

Task 3: Reporting the Response The task of formulating and reporting a response can be influenced by the social aspects of the survey conversation. In general, if a respondent agrees to take a survey, he or she will be motivated to answer truthfully. Therefore, if the questions are not too difficult (taxing the respondent's knowledge or memory) and if there are not too many questions (taxing the respondent's patience), the answers to questions will be reasonably accurate. However, it is also true that the respondents often wish to present themselves in a favorable light. This desire leads to what is known as a social desirability bias. Sometimes this bias is a response to the particular wording in a question. In 1941, the following questions were analyzed in two different forms of a survey (emphasis added):

1. Do you think the United States should *forbid* public speeches against democracy?
2. Do you think the United States should *allow* public speeches against democracy?

It would seem logical that these questions are opposites and that the proportion who would not allow public speeches against democracy should be equal to the proportion who would forbid public speeches against democracy. But only 45% of those respondents offering an opinion on Question 1 thought the United States should "forbid," whereas 75% of the respondents offering an opinion on Question 2 thought the United States should "not allow" public speeches against democracy. Most likely, respondents reacted negatively to the word *forbid,* as forbidding something sounds much harsher than not allowing it.

Some survey questions may be sensitive or threatening, such as questions about sex, drugs, or potentially illegal behavior. In this situation, a respondent not only will want to present a positive image but also will certainly think twice about admitting illegal behavior! In such cases, the respondent may shade the actual truth or may even lie about particular activities and behaviors. In addition, the tendency toward positive presentation is not limited to obviously sensitive questions. For example, consider the question about general happiness previously described. Several investigators have reported higher happiness scores in face-to-face interviews than in responses to a mailed questionnaire. Presumably, a happy face presents a more positive image of the respondent to the interviewer. On the other hand, if the interviewer was a clearly unhappy person, a respondent might shade answers to the less happy side of the scale, perhaps thinking that it is inappropriate to report happiness in such a situation.

It is clear that constructing surveys and writing survey questions can be a daunting task. Keep in mind the following three things:

1. Questions should be understandable by the individuals in the population being surveyed. Vocabulary should be at an appropriate level, and sentence structure should be simple.
2. Questions should, as much as possible, recognize that human memory is fickle. Questions that are specific will aid the respondent by providing better memory cues. The limitations of memory should be kept in mind when interpreting the respondent's answers.
3. As much as possible, questions should not create opportunities for the respondent to feel threatened or embarrassed. In such cases respondents may introduce a social desirability bias, the degree of which is unknown to the interviewer. This can compromise conclusions drawn from the survey data.

Constructing good surveys is a difficult task, and we have given only a brief introduction to this topic. For a more comprehensive treatment, we recommend the book by Sudman and Bradburn listed in the references in the back of the book.

EXERCISES 2.60 - 2.65

2.60 A tropical forest survey conducted by Conservation International included the following statements in the material that accompanied the survey:

> "A massive change is burning its way through the earth's environment."
>
> "The band of tropical forests that encircle the earth is being cut and burned to the ground at an alarming rate."
>
> "Never in history has mankind inflicted such sweeping changes on our planet as the clearing of rain forest taking place right now!"

The survey that followed included the questions given in Parts (a)–(d) below. For each of these questions, identify a word or phrase that might affect the response and possibly bias the results of any analysis of the responses.

a. "Did you know that the world's tropical forests are being destroyed at the rate of 80 acres per minute?"
b. "Considering what you know about vanishing tropical forests, how would you rate the problem?"
c. "Do you think we have an obligation to prevent the man-made extinction of animal and plant species?"
d. "Based on what you know now, do you think there is a link between the destruction of tropical forests and changes in the earth's atmosphere?"

2.61 Fast-paced lifestyles, in which students balance the requirements of school, after-school activities, and jobs, are thought by some to lead to reduced sleep. Suppose that you are assigned the task of designing a survey that will provide answers to the accompanying questions. Write a set of survey questions that might be used. In some cases, you may need to write more than one question to adequately address a particular issue. For example, responses might be different for weekends and school nights. You may also have to define some terms to make the questions understandable to the target audience, which is adolescents.

Topics to be addressed:
How much sleep do the respondents get? Is this enough sleep?
Does sleepiness interfere with schoolwork?
If they could change the starting and ending times of the school day, what would they suggest?
(Sorry, they cannot reduce the total time spent in school during the day!)

2.62 Asthma is a chronic lung condition characterized by difficulty in breathing. Some studies have suggested that asthma may be related to childhood exposure to some animals, especially dogs and cats, during the first year of life ("Exposure to Dogs and Cats in the First Year of Life and Risk of Allergic Sensitization at 6 to 7 Years of Age," *Journal of the American Medical Association* [2002]: 963–972). Some environmental factors that trigger an asthmatic response are (1) cold air, (2) dust, (3) strong fumes, and (4) inhaled irritants.

a. Write a set of questions that could be used in a survey to be given to parents of young children suffering from asthma. The survey should include questions about the presence of pets in the first year of the child's life as well as questions about the presence of pets today. Also, the survey should include questions that address the four mentioned household environmental factors.
b. It is generally thought that low-income persons, who tend to be less well educated, have homes in environments where the four environmental factors are present. Mindful of the importance of comprehension, can you improve the questions in Part (a) by making your vocabulary simpler or by changing the wording of the questions?
c. One problem with the pet-related questions is the reliance on memory. That is, parents may not actually remember when they got their pets. How might you check the parents' memories about these pets?

2.63 In national surveys, parents consistently point to school safety as an important concern. One source of violence in junior high schools is fighting ("Self-Reported Characterization of Seventh-Grade Student Fights," *Journal of Adolescent Health* [1998]: 103–109). To construct a knowledge base about student fights, a school administrator wants to give two surveys to students after fights are broken up. One of the surveys is to be given to the participants, and the other is to be given to students who witnessed the fight. The type of information desired includes (1) the cause of the fight, (2) whether or not the fight was a continuation of a previous fight, (3) whether drugs or alcohol was a factor, (4) whether or not the fight was gang related, and (5) the role of bystanders.

a. Write a set of questions that could be used in the two surveys. Each question should include a set of possible responses. For each question, indicate whether it would be used on both surveys or just on one of the two.
b. How might the tendency toward positive self-presentation affect the responses of the fighter to the survey questions you wrote for Part (a)?
c. How might the tendency toward positive self-presentation affect the responses of a bystander to the survey questions you wrote for Part (a)?

2.64 Doctors have expressed concern about young women drinking large amounts of soda and about their decreased consumption of milk ("Teenaged Girls, Carbonated Beverage Consumption, and Bone Fractures," *Archives of Pediatric and Adolescent Medicine* [2000]: 610–613). In parts (a)–(d), construct two questions that might be included in a survey of teenage girls. Each question should include possible responses from which the respondent can select. (Note: The questions as written are vague. Your task is to clarify the questions for use in a survey, not just to change the syntax!)

a. How much "cola" beverage does the respondent consume?
b. How much milk (and milk products) is consumed by the respondent?
c. How physically active is the respondent?
d. What is the respondent's history of bone fractures?

2.65 A survey described in the paper "The Adolescent Health Review: A Brief Multidimensional Screening Instrument" (*Journal of Adolescent Health* [2001]:131–139) attempted to address psychosocial factors thought to be of importance in preventive health care for adolescents. For each risk area in the following list, construct a question that would be comprehensible to students in grades 9–12 and that would provide information about the risk factor. Make your questions multiple-choice, and provide possible responses.

a. Lack of exercise
b. Poor nutrition
c. Emotional distress
d. Sexual activity
e. Cigarette smoking
f. Alcohol use

2.6 Interpreting and Communicating the Results of Statistical Analyses

Statistical studies are conducted to allow investigators to answer questions about characteristics of some population of interest or about the effect of some treatment. Such questions are answered on the basis of data, and how the data are obtained determines the quality of information available and the type of conclusions that can be drawn. As a consequence, when describing a study you have conducted (or when evaluating a published study), you must consider how the data were collected.

The description of the data collection process should make it clear whether the study is an observational study or an experiment. For observational studies, some of the issues that should be addressed are:

1. What is the population of interest? What is the sampled population? Are these two populations the same? If the sampled population is only a subset of the population of interest, **undercoverage** limits our ability to generalize to the population of interest. For example, if the population of interest is all students at a particular university, but the sample is selected from only those students who choose to list their phone number in the campus directory, undercoverage may be a problem. We would need to think carefully about whether it is reasonable to consider the sample as representative of the population of all students at the university. **Overcoverage** results when the sampled population is actually larger than the population of interest. This would be the case if we were interested in the population of all high schools that offer Advanced Placement (AP) Statistics but sampled from a list of all schools that offered an AP class in any subject. Both undercoverage and overcoverage can be problematic.
2. How were the individuals or objects in the sample actually selected? A description of the sampling method helps the reader to make judgments about whether the sample can reasonably be viewed as representative of the population of interest.
3. What are potential sources of bias, and is it likely that any of these will have a substantial effect on the observed results? When describing an observational study, you should acknowledge that you are aware of potential sources of bias and explain any steps that were taken to minimize their effect. For example, in a mail survey, nonresponse can be a problem, but the sampling plan may seek to minimize its effect by offering incentives for participation and by following up one or more times with those who do not respond to the first request. A common misperception is that increasing the sample size is a way to reduce bias in observational studies, but this is not the case. For example, if measurement bias is

present, as in the case of a scale that is not correctly calibrated and tends to weigh too high, taking 1000 measurements rather than 100 measurements cannot correct for the fact that the measured weights will be too large. Similarly, a larger sample size cannot compensate for response bias introduced by a poorly worded question.

For experiments, some of the issues that should be addressed are:

1. What is the role of random assignment? All good experiments use random assignment as a means of coping with the effects of potentially confounding variables that cannot easily be directly controlled. When describing an experimental design, you should be clear about how random assignment (subjects to treatments, treatments to subjects, or treatments to trials) was incorporated into the design.
2. Were any extraneous variables directly controlled by holding them at fixed values throughout the experiment? If so, which ones and at which values?
3. Was blocking used? If so, how were the blocks created? If an experiment uses blocking to create groups of homogeneous experimental units, you should describe the criteria used to create the blocks and their rationale. For example, you might say something like "Subjects were divided into two blocks—those who exercise regularly and those who do not exercise regularly—because it was believed that exercise status might affect the responses to the diets."

Because each treatment appears at least once in each block, the block size must be at least as large as the number of treatments. Ideally, the block sizes should be equal to the number of treatments, because this presumably would allow the experimenter to create small groups of extremely homogeneous experimental units. For example, in an experiment to compare two methods for teaching calculus to first-year college students, we may want to block on previous mathematics knowledge by using math SAT scores. If 100 students are available as subjects for this experiment, rather than creating two large groups (above-average math SAT score and below-average math SAT score), we might want to create 50 blocks of two students each, the first consisting of the two students with the highest math SAT scores, the second containing the two students with the next highest scores, and so on. We would then select one student in each block at random and assign that student to teaching method 1. The other student in the block would be assigned to teaching method 2.

A Word to the Wise: Cautions and Limitations

It is a big mistake to begin collecting data before thinking carefully about research objectives and developing a plan. A poorly designed plan for data collection may result in data that do not enable the researcher to answer key questions of interest or to generalize conclusions based on the data to the desired populations of interest.

Clearly defining the objectives at the outset enables the investigator to determine whether an experiment or an observational study is the best way to proceed. Watch out for the following *inappropriate* actions:

1. Drawing a cause-and-effect conclusion from an observational study. Don't do this, and don't believe it when others do it!
2. Generalizing results of an experiment that uses volunteers as subjects to a larger population. This is not sensible without a convincing argument that the group of volunteers can reasonably be considered a representative sample from the population.
3. Generalizing conclusions based on data from a sample to some population of interest. This is sometimes a sensible thing to do, but on other occasions it is not

reasonable. Generalizing from a sample to a population is justified only when there is reason to believe that the sample is likely to be representative of the population. This would be the case if the sample was a random sample from the population and there were no major potential sources of bias. If the sample was not selected at random or if potential sources of bias were present, these issues would have to be addressed before a judgment could be made regarding the appropriateness of generalizing the study results.

For example, the Associated Press (January 25, 2003) reported on the high cost of housing in California. The median home price was given for each of the 10 counties in California with the highest home prices. Although these 10 counties are a sample of the counties in California, they were not randomly selected and (because they are the 10 counties with the highest home prices) it would not be reasonable to generalize to all California counties based on data from this sample.

4. Generalizing conclusions based on an observational study that used voluntary response or convenience sampling to a larger population. This is almost never reasonable.

EXERCISES 2.66 - 2.69

2.66 The following paragraph appeared in *USA Today* (August 6, 2009):

> **Cement doesn't hold up to scrutiny**
>
> A common treatment that uses medical cement to fix cracks in the spinal bones of elderly people worked no better than a sham treatment, the first rigorous studies of a popular procedure reveal. Pain and disability were virtually the same up to six months later, whether patients had a real treatment or a fake one, shows the research in today's *New England Journal of Medicine.* Tens of thousands of Americans each year are treated with bone cement, especially older women with osteoporosis. The researchers said it is yet another example of a procedure coming into wide use before proven safe and effective. Medicare pays $1,500 to $2,100 for the outpatient procedure.

The paper referenced in this paragraph is "A Randomized Trial of Vertebroplasty for Painful Osteoporotic Vertebral Fractures" (*New England Journal of Medicine* [2009]: 557–568). Obtain a copy of this paper through your university library or your instructor. Read the following sections of the paper: the abstract on page 557; the study design section on page 558; the participants section on pages 558–559; the outcome assessment section on pages 559–560; and the discussion section that begins on page 564.

The summary of this study that appeared in *USA Today* consisted of just one paragraph. If the newspaper had allowed four paragraphs, other important aspects of the study could have been included. Write a four-paragraph summary that the paper could have used. Remember—you are writing for the *USA Today* audience, not for the readers of the *New England Journal of Medicine*!

2.67 The article "Effects of Too Much TV Can Be Undone" (*USA Today*, October 1, 2007) included the following paragraph:

> Researchers at Johns Hopkins Bloomberg School of Public Health report that it's not only how many hours children spend in front of the TV, but at what age they watch that matters. They analyzed data from a national survey in which parents of 2707 children were interviewed first when the children were 30–33 months old and again when they were $5\frac{1}{2}$, about their TV viewing and their behavior.

a. Is the study described an observational study or an experiment?

b. The article says that data from a sample of 2707 parents were used in the study. What other information about the sample would you want in order to evaluate the study?

c. The actual paper referred to by the *USA Today* article was "Children's Television Exposure and Behavioral and Social Outcomes at 5.5 years: Does Timing of Exposure Matter?" (*Pediatrics* [2007]: 762–769). The paper describes the sample as follows:

> The study sample included 2707 children whose mothers completed telephone interviews at both 30 to 33 months and 5.5 years and reported television exposure at both time points. Of those completing both interviewers, 41 children (1%) were excluded because of missing data on television exposure at one or both time points. Compared with those enrolled in the HS clinical trial, parents in the study sample were disproportionately older, white, more educate, and married.

The "HS clinical trial" referred to in the excerpt from the paper was a nationally representative sample used in the Healthy Steps for Young Children national evaluation. Based on the above description of the study sample, do you think that it is reasonable to regard the sample as representative of parents of all children at age 5.5 years? Explain.

d. The *USA Today* article also includes the following summary paragraph:

> The study did not examine what the children watched and can't show TV was the cause of later problems, but it does "tell parents that even if kids are watching TV early in life, and they stop, it could reduce the risk for behavioral and social problems later," Mistry says.

What potentially confounding variable is identified in this passage?

e. The passage in Part (d) says that the study cannot show that TV was the cause of later problems. Is the quote from Kamila Mistry (one of the study authors) in the passage consistent with the statement about cause? Explain.

2.68 The short article "Developing Science-Based Food and Nutrition Information" (*Journal of the American Dietetic Association* [2001]: 1144–1145) includes some guidelines for evaluating a research paper. Obtain a copy of this paper through your university library or your instructor. Read this article and make a list of questions that can be used to evaluate a research study.

2.69 An article titled "I Said, Not While You Study: Science Suggests Kids Can't Study and Groove at the Same Time" appeared in the *Washington Post* (September 5, 2006). This provides an example of a reporter summarizing the result of a scientific study in a way that is designed to make it accessible to the newspaper's readers. You can find the newspaper article online by searching on the title or by going to http://www.washingtonpost.com/wp-dyn/content/article/2006/09/03/AR2006090300592.html. The study referenced in the newspaper article was published in the *Proceedings of the National Academies of Science* and can be found at http://www.pnas.org/content/103/31/11778.full.

Read the newspaper article and then take a look at the published paper. Comment on whether you think that the author was successful in communicating the findings of the study to the intended audience.

ACTIVITY 2.1 Facebook Friending

Background: The article "Professors Prefer Face Time to Facebook" appeared in the student newspaper at Cal Poly, San Luis Obispo (*Mustang Daily*, August 27, 2009). The article examines how professors and students felt about using Facebook as a means of faculty-student communication. The student who wrote this article got mixed opinions when she interviewed students to ask whether they wanted to become Facebook friends with their professors. Two student comments included in the article were

> "I think the younger the professor is, the more you can relate to them and the less awkward it would be if you were to become friends on Facebook. The older the professor, you just would have to wonder, 'Why are they friending me?'"

and

> "I think becoming friends with professors on Facebook is really awkward. I don't want them being able to see into my personal life, and frankly, I am not really interested in what my professors do in their free time."

Even if the students interviewed had expressed a consistent opinion, it would still be unreasonable to think this represented general student opinion on this issue because only four students were interviewed and it is not clear from the article how these students were selected.

In this activity, you will work with a partner to develop a plan to assess student opinion about being Facebook friends with professors at your school.

1. Suppose you will select a sample of 50 students at your school to participate in a survey. Write one or more questions that you would ask each student in the sample.
2. Discuss with your partner whether you think it would be easy or difficult to obtain a simple random sample of 50 students at your school and to obtain the desired information from all the students selected for the sample. Write a summary of your discussion.
3. With your partner, decide how you might go about selecting a sample of 50 students from your school that reasonably could be considered representative of the population of interest even if it may not be a simple random sample. Write a brief description of your sampling plan, and point out the aspects of your plan that you think make it reasonable to argue that it will be representative.
4. Explain your plan to another pair of students. Ask them to critique your plan. Write a brief summary of the comments you received. Now reverse roles, and provide a critique of the plan devised by the other pair.
5. Based on the feedback you received in Step 4, would you modify your original sampling plan? If not, explain why this is not necessary. If so, describe how the plan would be modified.

ACTIVITY 2.2 An Experiment to Test for the Stroop Effect

Background: In 1935, John Stroop published the results of his research into how people respond when presented with conflicting signals. Stroop noted that most people are able to read words quickly and that they cannot easily ignore them and focus on other attributes of a printed word, such as text color. For example, consider the following list of words:

green blue red blue yellow red

It is easy to quickly read this list of words. It is also easy to read the words even if the words are printed in color, and even if the text color is different from the color of the word. For example, people can read the words in the list

green blue red blue yellow red

as quickly as they can read the list that isn't printed in color.

However, Stroop found that if people are asked to name the text colors of the words in the list (red, yellow, blue, green, red, green), it takes them longer. Psychologists believe that this is because the reader has to inhibit a natural response (reading the word) and produce a different response (naming the color of the text).

If Stroop is correct, people should be able to name colors more quickly if they do not have to inhibit the word response, as would be the case if they were shown the following:

1. Design an experiment to compare times to identify colors when they appear as text to times to identify colors when there is no need to inhibit a word response. Indicate how random assignment is incorporated into your design. What is your response variable? How will you measure it? How many subjects will you use in your experiment, and how will they be chosen?
2. When you are satisfied with your experimental design, carry out the experiment. You will need to construct your list of colored words and a corresponding list of colored bars to use in the experiment. You will also need to think about how you will implement the random assignment scheme.
3. Summarize the resulting data in a brief report that explains whether your findings are consistent with the Stroop effect.

ACTIVITY 2.3 McDonald's and the Next 100 Billion Burgers

Background: The article "Potential Effects of the Next 100 Billion Hamburgers Sold by McDonald's" (*American Journal of Preventative Medicine* [2005]: 379–381) estimated that 992.25 million pounds of saturated fat would be consumed as McDonald's sells its next 100 billion hamburgers. This estimate was based on the assumption that the average weight of a burger sold would be 2.4 oz. This is the average of the weight of a regular hamburger (1.6 oz.) and a Big Mac (3.2 oz.). The authors took this approach because

> McDonald's does not publish sales and profits of individual items. Thus, it is not possible to estimate how many of McDonald's first 100 billion beef burgers sold were 1.6 oz hamburgers, 3.2 oz. Big Macs (introduced in 1968), 4.0 oz. Quarter Pounders (introduced in 1973), or other sandwiches.

This activity can be completed as an individual or as a team. Your instructor will specify which approach (individual or team) you should use.

1. The authors of the article believe that the use of 2.4 oz. as the average size of a burger sold at McDonald's is "conservative," which would result in the estimate of 992.25 million pounds of saturated fat being lower than the actual amount that would be consumed. Explain why the authors' belief might be justified.
2. Do you think it would be possible to collect data that could lead to an estimate of the average burger size that would be better than 2.4 oz.? If so, explain how you would recommend collecting such data. If not, explain why you think it is not possible.

ACTIVITY 2.4 Video Games and Pain Management

Background: Video games have been used for pain management by doctors and therapists who believe that the attention required to play a video game can distract the player and thereby decrease the sensation of pain. The paper "Video Games and Health" (*British Medical Journal* [2005]:122–123) states

> However, there has been no long term follow-up and no robust randomized controlled trials of such interventions. Whether patients eventually tire of such games is also unclear. Furthermore, it is not known whether any distracting effect depends simply on concentrating on an interactive task or whether the content of games is also an important factor as there have been no controlled trials comparing video games with other distracters. Further research should examine factors within games such as novelty, users' preferences, and relative levels of challenge and should compare video games with other potentially distracting activities.

1. Working with a partner, select one of the areas of potential research suggested in the passage from the paper and formulate a specific question that could be addressed by performing an experiment.
2. Propose an experiment that would provide data to address the question from Step 1. Be specific about how subjects might be selected, what the experimental conditions (treatments) would be, and what response would be measured.
3. At the end of Section 2.3 there are 10 questions that can be used to evaluate an experimental design. Answer these 10 questions for the design proposed in Step 2.
4. After evaluating your proposed design, are there any changes you would like to make to your design? Explain.

ACTIVITY 2.5 Be Careful with Random Assignment!

When individuals climb to high altitudes, a condition known as acute mountain sickness (AMS) may occur. AMS is brought about by a combination of reduced air pressure and lower oxygen concentration that occurs at high altitudes. Two standard treatments for AMS are a medication, acetazolamide (which stimulates breathing and reduces mild symptoms) and the use of portable hyperbaric chambers.

With increasing numbers of younger inexperienced mountaineers, it is important to re-evaluate these treatments for the 12 to 14 year age group. An experimental plan under consideration is to study the first 18 youngsters diagnosed with AMS at a high altitude park ranger station whose parents consent to participation in the experiment. Equal numbers of each treatment are desired and the researchers are considering the following strategy for random assignment of treatments: Assign the treatments using a coin flip until one treatment has been assigned nine times; then assign the other treatment to the remaining subjects.

The table below presents data on the first 18 young climbers whose parents consented to participation in the experiment.

Order	Gender	Age (yr)
1	male	12.90
2	female	13.34
3	male	12.39
4	male	13.95
5	male	13.63
6	male	13.62
7	female	12.55
8	female	13.54
9	male	12.34
10	female	13.74
11	female	13.78
12	male	14.05
13	female	14.22
14	female	13.91
15	male	14.39
16	female	13.54
17	female	13.85
18	male	14.11

1. Describe how you would implement a strategy equivalent to the one proposed by the researchers. Your plan should assign the treatments M (medicine) and H (hyperbaric chamber) to these climbers as they appear at the ranger station.
2. Implement your strategy in Step (1), assigning treatments to climbers 1–18.
3. Looking at which climbers were assigned to each of the two groups, do you feel that this method worked well? Why or why not?
4. Compute the proportion of females in the medicine group. How does this proportion compare to the proportion of females in the entire group of 18 subjects?
5. Construct two dotplots—one of the ages of those assigned to the medicine treatment and one of the ages of those assigned to the hyperbaric chamber treatment. Are the age distributions for the two groups similar?
6. Compute the average age of those assigned to the medicine group. How does it compare to the average age for the other treatment group?
7. Record the proportion of females in the medicine group, the average age of those assigned to the medicine group, and the average age of those assigned to the hyperbaric chamber group obtained by each student on your class.
8. Using the values from Step (6), construct a dotplot of each of the following: the proportion of females in the medicine group, the average age of those assigned to the medicine group, and the average age of those assigned to the hyperbaric chamber group.
9. Using the results of the previous steps, evaluate the success of this random assignment strategy. Write a short paragraph explaining to the researchers whether or not they should use the proposed strategy for random assignment and why.

Summary of Key Concepts and Formulas

TERM OR FORMULA	COMMENT
Observational study	A study that observes characteristics of an existing population.
Simple random sample	A sample selected in a way that gives every different sample of size n an equal chance of being selected.
Stratified sampling	Dividing a population into subgroups (strata) and then taking a separate random sample from each stratum.
Cluster sampling	Dividing a population into subgroups (clusters) and forming a sample by randomly selecting clusters and including all individuals or objects in the selected clusters in the sample.
1 in k systematic sampling	A sample selected from an ordered arrangement of a population by choosing a starting point at random from the first k individuals on the list and then selecting every kth individual thereafter.
Confounding variable	A variable that is related both to group membership and to the response variable.
Measurement or response bias	The tendency for samples to differ from the population because the method of observation tends to produce values that differ from the true value.
Selection bias	The tendency for samples to differ from the population because of systematic exclusion of some part of the population.
Nonresponse bias	The tendency for samples to differ from the population because measurements are not obtained from all individuals selected for inclusion in the sample.
Experiment	A procedure for investigating the effect of *experimental conditions* (treatments) on a *response variable.*
Treatments	The experimental conditions imposed by the experimenter.
Extraneous variable	A variable that is not an explanatory variable in the study but is thought to affect the response variable.
Direct control	Holding extraneous variables constant so that their effects are not confounded with those of the experimental conditions.
Blocking	Using extraneous variables to create groups that are similar with respect to those variables and then assigning treatments at random within each block, thereby filtering out the effect of the blocking variables.

TERM OR FORMULA	COMMENT
Random assignment	Assigning experimental units to treatments or treatments to trials at random.
Replication	A strategy for ensuring that there is an adequate number of observations on each experimental treatment.
Placebo treatment	A treatment that resembles the other treatments in an experiment in all apparent ways but that has no active ingredients.
Control group	A group that receives no treatment.
Single-blind experiment	An experiment in which the subjects do not know which treatment they received but the individuals measuring the response do know which treatment was received, or an experiment in which the subjects do know which treatment they received but the individuals measuring the response do not know which treatment was received.
Double-blind experiment	An experiment in which neither the subjects nor the individuals who measure the response know which treatment was received.

Chapter Review Exercises 2.70 - 2.85

2.70 A pollster for the Public Policy Institute of California explains how the Institute selects a sample of California adults ("It's About Quality, Not Quantity," *San Luis Obispo Tribune*, January 21, 2000):

> That is done by using computer-generated random residential telephone numbers with all California prefixes, and when there are no answers, calling back repeatedly to the original numbers selected to avoid a bias against hard-to-reach people. Once a call is completed, a second random selection is made by asking for the adult in the household who had the most recent birthday. It is as important to randomize who you speak to in the household as it is to randomize the household you select. If you didn't, you'd primarily get women and older people.

Comment on this approach to selecting a sample. How does the sampling procedure attempt to minimize certain types of bias? Are there sources of bias that may still be a concern?

2.71 Based on a survey of 4113 U.S. adults, researchers at Stanford University concluded that Internet use leads to increased social isolation. The survey was conducted by an Internet-based polling company that selected its samples from a pool of 35,000 potential respondents, all of whom had been given free Internet access and WebTV hardware in exchange for agreeing to regularly participate in surveys conducted by the polling company. Two criticisms of this study were expressed in an article that appeared in the *San Luis Obispo Tribune* (February 28, 2000). The first criticism was that increased social isolation was measured by asking respondents if they were talking less to family and friends on the phone. The second criticism was that the sample was selected only from a group that was induced to participate by the offer of free Internet service, yet the results were generalized to all U.S. adults. For each criticism, indicate what type of bias is being described and why it might make you question the conclusion drawn by the researchers.

2.72 The article "I'd Like to Buy a Vowel, Drivers Say" (*USA Today*, August 7, 2001) speculates that young people prefer automobile names that consist of just numbers and/or letters that do not form a word (such as Hyundai's XG300, Mazda's 626, and BMW's 325i). The article goes on to state that Hyundai had planned to identify the car that was eventually marketed as the XG300 with the name Concerto, until they determined that consumers hated it and that they thought XG300 sounded more "technical" and deserving of a higher price. Do the students at your school feel the same way? Describe how you would go about selecting a sample to answer this question.

2.73 A study in Florida is examining whether health literacy classes and using simple medical instructions that include pictures and avoid big words and technical terms can keep Medicaid patients healthier (*San Luis Obispo Tribune*, October 16, 2002). Twenty-seven community health centers are participating in the study. For 2 years, half of the centers will administer standard care. The other centers will have patients attend classes and will provide special health materials that are easy to understand. Explain why it is important for the researchers to assign the 27 centers to the two groups (standard care and classes with simple health literature) at random.

2.74 Is status related to a student's understanding of science? The article "From Here to Equity: The Influence of Status on Student Access to and Understanding of Science" (*Culture and Comparative Studies* [1999]: 577–602) described a study on the effect of group discussions on learning biology concepts. An analysis of the relationship between status and "rate of talk" (the number of on-task speech acts per minute) during group work included gender as a blocking variable. Do you think that gender is a useful blocking variable? Explain.

2.75 The article "Tots' TV-Watching May Spur Attention Problems" (*San Luis Obispo Tribune*, April 5, 2004) describes a study that appeared in the journal *Pediatrics*. In this study, researchers looked at records of 2500 children who were participating in a long-term health study. They found that 10% of these children had attention disorders at age 7 and that hours of television watched at age 1 and age 3 was associated with an increased risk of having an attention disorder at age 7.

a. Is the study described an observational study or an experiment?

b. Give an example of a potentially confounding variable that would make it unwise to draw the conclusion that hours of television watched at a young age is the cause of the increased risk of attention disorder.

2.76 A study of more than 50,000 U.S. nurses found that those who drank just one soda or fruit punch a day tended to gain much more weight and had an 80% increased risk in developing diabetes compared to those who drank less than one a month. (*The Washington Post*, August 25, 2004). "The message is clear. . . . Anyone who cares about their health or the health of their family would not consume these beverages," said Walter Willett of the Harvard School of Public Health, who helped conduct the study. The sugar and beverage industries said that the study was fundamentally flawed. "These allegations are inflammatory. Women who drink a lot of soda may simply have generally unhealthy lifestyles," said Richard Adamson of the American Beverage Association.

a. Do you think that the study described was an observational study or an experiment?

b. Is it reasonable to conclude that drinking soda or fruit punch causes the observed increased risk of diabetes? Why or why not?

2.77 "Crime Finds the Never Married" is the conclusion drawn in an article from *USA Today* (June 29, 2001). This conclusion is based on data from the Justice Department's National Crime Victimization Survey, which estimated the number of violent crimes per 1000 people, 12 years of age or older, to be 51 for the never married, 42 for the divorced or separated, 13 for married individuals, and 8 for the widowed. Does being single cause an increased risk of violent crime? Describe a potential confounding variable that illustrates why it is unreasonable to conclude that a change in marital status causes a change in crime risk.

2.78 The article "Workers Grow More Dissatisfied" in the *San Luis Obispo Tribune* (August 22, 2002) states that "a survey of 5000 people found that while most Americans continue to find their jobs interesting, and are even satisfied with their commutes, a bare majority like their jobs." This statement was based on the fact that only 51 percent of those responding to a mail survey indicated that they were satisfied with their jobs. Describe any potential sources of bias that might limit the researcher's ability to draw conclusions about working Americans based on the data collected in this survey.

2.79 According to the article "Effect of Preparation Methods on Total Fat Content, Moisture Content, and Sensory Characteristics of Breaded Chicken Nuggets and Beef Steak Fingers" (*Family and Consumer Sciences Research Journal* [1999]: 18–27), sensory tests were conducted using 40 college student volunteers at Texas Women's University. Give three reasons, apart from the relatively small sample size, why this sample may not be ideal as the basis for generalizing to the population of all college students.

2.80 Do ethnic group and gender influence the type of care that a heart patient receives? The following passage is from the article "Heart Care Reflects Race and Sex, Not Symptoms" (*USA Today*, February 25, 1999, reprinted with permission):

> Previous research suggested blacks and women were less likely than whites and men to get cardiac catheterization or coronary bypass surgery for chest pain or a heart attack. Scientists blamed differences in illness severity, insurance coverage, patient preference, and health care access. The researchers eliminated those differences by videotaping actors—two black men, two black women, two white men, and two white women—describing chest pain from identical scripts. They wore identical gowns, used identical gestures, and were taped from the same position. Researchers asked 720 primary care doctors at meetings of the American College of Physicians or the American Academy of Family Physicians to watch a tape and recommend care. The doctors thought the study focused on clinical decision making.

Evaluate this experimental design. Do you think this is a good design or a poor design, and why? If you were designing such a study, what, if anything, would you propose to do differently?

2.81 An article in the *San Luis Obispo Tribune* (September 7, 1999) described an experiment designed to investigate the effect of creatine supplements on the development of muscle fibers. The article states that the researchers "looked at 19 men, all about 25 years of age and similar in weight, lean body mass, and capacity to lift weights. Ten were given creatine—25 grams a day for the first week, followed by 5 grams a day for the rest of the study. The rest were given a fake preparation. No one was told what he was getting. All the men worked out under the guidance of the same trainer. The response variable measured was gain in fat-free mass (in percent)."

a. What extraneous variables are identified in the given statement, and what strategy did the researchers use to deal with them?

b. Do you think it was important that the men participating in the experiment were not told whether they were receiving creatine or the placebo? Explain.

c. This experiment was not conducted in a double-blind manner. Do you think it would have been a good idea to make this a double-blind experiment? Explain.

2.82 Researchers at the University of Houston decided to test the hypothesis that restaurant servers who squat to the level of their customers would receive a larger tip ("Effect of Server Posture on Restaurant Tipping," *Journal of Applied Social Psychology* [1993]: 678–685). In the experiment, the waiter would flip a coin to determine whether he would stand or squat next to the table. The waiter would record the amount of the bill and of the tip and whether he stood or squatted.

a. Describe the treatments and the response variable.

b. Discuss possible extraneous variables and how they could be controlled.

c. Discuss whether blocking would be necessary.

d. Identify possible confounding variables.

e. Discuss the role of random assignment in this experiment.

2.83 You have been asked to determine on what types of grasslands two species of birds, northern harriers and short-eared owls, build nests. The types of grasslands to be used include undisturbed native grasses, managed native grasses, undisturbed nonnative grasses, and managed nonnative grasses. You are allowed a plot of land 500 meters square to study. Explain how you would determine where to plant the four types of grasses. What role would random assignment play in this determination? Identify any confounding variables. Would this study be considered an observational study or an experiment? (Based on the article "Response of Northern Harriers and Short-Eared Owls to Grassland Management in Illinois," *Journal of Wildlife Management* [1999]: 517–523.)

2.84 A manufacturer of clay roofing tiles would like to investigate the effect of clay type on the proportion of tiles that crack in the kiln during firing. Two different types of clay are to be considered. One hundred tiles can be placed in the kiln at any one time. Firing temperature varies slightly at different locations in the kiln, and firing temperature may also affect cracking. Discuss the design of an experiment to collect information that could be used to decide between the two clay types. How does your proposed design deal with the extraneous variable *temperature*?

2.85 A mortgage lender routinely places advertisements in a local newspaper. The advertisements are of three different types: one focusing on low interest rates, one featuring low fees for first-time buyers, and one appealing to people who may want to refinance their homes. The lender would like to determine which advertisement format is most successful in attracting customers to call for more information. Describe an experiment that would provide the information needed to make this determination. Be sure to consider extraneous variables, such as the day of the week that the advertisement appears in the paper, the section of the paper in which the advertisement appears, or daily fluctuations in the interest rate. What role does random assignment play in your design?

Graphing Calculator Explorations

EXPLORATION 2.1 Calculators and the Study of Statistics

You must be able to use your calculator in order to be able to analyze data. In previous math classes you may have used your calculator for graphing functions, finding solutions to equations, and arithmetic calculations. In statistics you will use your calculator differently and will also use new calculator keys and menu items. Graphing Calculator Explorations are intended to help you get maximum utility from your calculator. These explorations highlight some important features of your calculator. In order to speak to the widest possible audience, the explorations will be generic in nature, rather than showcasing a particular calculator.

Calculators vary in statistical capability and in the applications that can be downloaded from the web. The characteristics of a graphing calculator that are important for the study of statistics are:

- Capability to perform elementary statistical calculations (computing means, standard deviations, correlation coefficients, and regression equations)
- Capability to generate statistical graphs (boxplots, histograms, and scatterplots)
- Row-and-column data entry format

EXPLORATION 2.2 Generating Random Integers

Procedures for generating random numbers have been around for a long time. The earliest techniques for generating random numbers were throwing dice, dealing cards, and selecting well-mixed numbered balls from a container. Today, computers and calculators use algorithms to generate "random" numbers. These algorithms generate what are called "pseudo-random" numbers. For most purposes, the "random" numbers generated by today's computers and calculators are perfectly fine, and we will refer to these numbers as random.

Generating random numbers is a built-in function of graphing calculators. To learn the appropriate keystrokes for your calculator you will need to consult your calculator manual; look for "rand," or possibly "random" in the index. On some calculators the precision can be adjusted and in our discussions we will generally use four digit accuracy. On most calculators, a single keystroke or a short sequence of keystrokes will produce a random number between 0 and 1. Locate that function and then generate five random numbers using the procedures presented in your manual. Some calculators will repeat the process each time you press "enter" or "execute." Try pressing the enter/execute button four times after you get the first random number. If a random number appears each time, smile—this will save many keystrokes! The numbers we obtained (yours will be different) are 0.5147, 0.4058, 0.7338, 0.0440, and 0.3394. Random number generators typically produce a random number, r, such that $0 \leq r < 1$. Your calculator may have additional random number functions, such as randInt() to generate integers. To see if you calculator has this built-in capability, look in the manual's index for something like "random integer." In the discussions that follow, we will *not* assume you have a random integer capability, but if you do, please use it!

If you do not have a built-in capability to generate random integers, the method in the box below will be helpful.

Converting Random Numbers to Integers, 1, 2, 3, . . . , *n*

To convert a calculator-generated decimal random number r, $0 \leq r < 1$, into a random integer in the range 1, 2, 3, . . . , n, multiply r by n, add 1, and ignore the digits to the right of the decimal.

This will involve a sequence of keystrokes something like the following, where we use "*rand*" to mean the keystrokes needed to generate r:

rand $\times$ n + 1.

Most scientific calculators have an "int" or "floor" function, which will truncate the decimal by "rounding down." If your calculator has this capability, you can accomplish the integer random number generation in one sequence of keystrokes:

int(*rand* $\times$ n) + 1.

Example: Generating Random Numbers Generate five random integers between 1 and 100 for purposes of sampling from a population with 100 individuals. The keystrokes to generate a random integer between 1 and 100 are:

int(*rand* $\times$ 100) + 1.

(Remember, *rand* stands for the sequence of keystrokes needed to get the random number between 0 and 1 and *int* stands for the keystrokes necessary to truncate a decimal to an integer.)

The numbers we obtained (though of course your numbers will differ) are

11 55 29 38 37

We would then include the individuals identified by these numbers in the sample. (Note that in this example we are sampling from a population. If we were sampling without replacement and the random number generated by the calculator resulted in two or more random integers that were the same, we would have ignored the duplicates and generated additional random integers as needed.)

Adding 1 in the formula above is not some sort of magic. Because the *rand* keystrokes return random numbers in the range $0 \leq r < 1$, it is possible for *rand* to deliver a 0. If you are not bothered by random integers starting at 0, you need not waste keystrokes by adding 1 each time. Also note that the arithmetic random number generators in calculators are shipped from the factory with a number called a "seed," needed to start the random number generation process. If two calculators in your class are "right out of the box" you may notice that the random numbers generated by these calculators are the same. This will not be a problem for very long; calculator users will typically press the *rand* sequence different numbers of times, and sequences will soon differ in actual classroom use.

EXPLORATION 2.3 Random Assignment to Treatments

The process of random assignment of subjects to treatments is critical in the proper design of an experiment. Random assignment can be accomplished using the graphing calculator's capability to generate integers from 1, 2 . . . *n*. We will illustrate how this can be done in some common experimental situations.

In the first experiment, we will assign subjects to treatments without trying to get the same number of subjects in each treatment group. This experiment investigates the effect of pizza on performance on a statistics exam. An instructor has decided to use three types of pizza (the treatments): sausage pizza, mushroom pizza, and cheese pizza. Twelve randomly selected students will take part in the experiment. The instructor's strategy for assigning treatments is very simple: Generate 12 random integers from the list {1, 2, 3}. *Before* any students are assigned, he arbitrarily assigns mushroom pizza = 1, cheese pizza = 2, and sausage pizza = 3.

We now randomly generate integers between 1 and 3 using

$\text{int}(rand \times 3) + 1$.

Our results were (remember that yours will surely be different)

3, 1, 1, 1, 1, 3, 1, 2, 1, 3, 1, 3

These numbers are used to assign each student to a treatment (pizza type) in the experiment, as shown. Entries in the table are student, treatment number, and (treatment).

1	3 (Sausage)	2	1 (Mushroom)	3	1 (Mushroom)	4	1 (Mushroom)
5	1 (Mushroom)	6	3 (Sausage)	7	1 (Mushroom)	8	2 (Cheese)
9	1 (Mushroom)	10	3 (Sausage)	11	1 (Mushroom)	12	3 (Sausage)

We can quickly see some problems using this method of assignment: More than 50% of the subjects were assigned to mushroom pizza, and there is no replication of the cheese pizza treatment! What if we want to have equal-sized treatment groups? We might try to achieve equal treatment group sizes by adding a rule to our procedure: "Once any treatment group has four subjects assigned, do not assign any more subjects to that treatment." Unfortunately, this approach can cause problems (see the discussion on random assignment in Section 2.3). Fortunately, we have another strategy.

First, we number the subjects from 1–12. Then we generate 12 random numbers between 0 and 1, ignoring any repeats. The first four random numbers generated are associated with treatment 1, the next four with treatment 2, and finally the last four random numbers are associated with treatment 3. One possible result of this process is shown below.

1	1	1	1	2	2	2	2	3	3	3	3
.5441	.6379	.9295	.6742	.7980	.5522	.3377	.2187	.6217	.8811	.1243	.4500

Finally, subject 1 is associated with the smallest of the 12 random numbers; subject 2 is associated with the second smallest random number, and so on. This would result in the following assignment of subjects to treatments.

1	1	1	1	2	2	2	2	3	3	3	3
.5441	.6379	.9295	.6742	.7980	.5522	.3377	.2187	.6217	.8811	.1243	.4500
5	8	12	9	10	6	3	2	7	11	1	4

In this random assignment of subjects to treatments, subjects 5, 8, 12, and 9 get mushroom pizza; subjects 10, 6, 3, and 2 get cheese pizza; and the rest get sausage pizza.

Random Assignment to Treatments—with Blocking Random assignment in a situation in which the experimenter is using blocking to control an extraneous variable could also be implemented using random integers. Suppose the instructor in the previous example has some seats near the window and some seats that are not by the window. It is possible that students near the window might be distracted and that this might affect exam performance. Because of this, it would be reasonable to block by position in the room. Suppose that six students will participate in the experiment. We need to consider the blocking strategy as we assign treatments.

Our random assignment is restricted a bit compared to what we did earlier because now we need to have each treatment represented in each block. Suppose that the six students are seated for the exam in the arrangement shown in the table below.

Near Window	Not Near Window

We now want to assign treatments at random to the students within each block. A sequence of random integers between 1 and 3 can be used for this purpose. One possible sequence is:

3 3 2 1 1 3 1 2 1 1 3 2

The treatments are assigned as shown in the table below, starting with the "Near Window" block and then, once the assignment for the "Near Window" block is completed, moving to the "Not Near Window" block. Remember that mushroom pizza = 1, cheese pizza = 2, and sausage pizza = 3.

Random Integer	Decision
3	Assign student in row one of near window block to sausage pizza treatment
3	Ignore, as there is already a student assigned to sausage pizza in the near window block
2	Assign student in row two of near window block to cheese pizza treatment
—	Assign student in row three of near window block to mushroom pizza treatment (since that is the only treatment that has not already been assigned in this block)
1	Assign student in row one of not near window block to mushroom pizza treatment
1	Ignore, as there is already a student assigned to mushroom pizza in the near window block
3	Assign student in row two of not near window block to sausage pizza treatment
—	Assign student in row three of near window block to cheese pizza treatment (since that is the only treatment that has not already been assigned in this block)

The final assignment of treatments to subjects within each block is shown in the table below. Note that each treatment appears once in each block.

Near Window	Not Near Window
Sausage	Mushroom
Cheese	Sausage
Mushroom	Cheese

Now it's your turn to try it.

Acupuncture is a popular alternative treatment for chronic back pain. Does the treatment work, or is it psychological? To try to find out, an experiment is planned at a local clinic. As the statistical expert of the day, you have been asked to assign the treatments (real or simulated acupuncture). Use the method discussed in this exploration to assign 12 subjects to the two treatments.

EXPLORATION 2.4 Generating Random Real Numbers

In previous Explorations, we used the *rand* function to generate random numbers between 0 and 1 and then converted them to integers. In this Exploration, we will use the *rand* function for generating random *real* numbers in some interval (a, b).

The need for random real numbers sometimes arises in sampling situations in which it is not possible to make a list of the elements of the population. For example, suppose we want to study chemical residue from the use of pesticides on farms in Iowa. A map of Iowa is overlaid with a grid of 1-mile by 1-mile squares. Picking squares at random in order to measure chemical residue would be a good start, but within any randomly selected square the chemical residue measurement must be taken at some actual location in the square. To determine this location, imagine a coordinate system with the origin in the southwest corner of a square of land. Since each square is 1 mile by 1 mile, generating a random point in a square of land is easy using the *rand* function: generate two random real numbers between 0 and 1, and use them as x- and y-coordinates for the square. Suppose the *rand* function generated 0.45059 and 0.98906. We would convert this to (0.45059, 0.98906), which would then determine the location where the measurement should be made.

Suppose now that we want to select random locations from a map of the wilds of Saskatchewan, Canada, in order to estimate the amount of a particular mineral in the soil. Here we can use the "natural" coordinates provided by the latitude and longitude of the map to determine location. Saskatchewan's latitudes range from 49 to 60N, and longitudes from 102 to 110W. For generating random points in Saskatchewan, we can use the *rand* function and a little algebra.

We approach this problem in stages. First, consider the problem of generating a random number between 0 and b. One solution is to generate a random number between 0 and 1, and multiply it by the positive real number, b. Algebraically we see that if *rand* represents the random number generated,

$$0 \le rand < 1$$
$$b \times (0) \le b \times (rand) < b \times (1)$$
$$0 \le b \times (rand) < b$$

Our ability to generate random real numbers is not limited to intervals that begin at 0. To generate a random real number between any two real numbers, a and b, we can do a bit more algebra:

$$0 \le rand < 1$$
$$(b - a) \times (0) \le (b - a) \times (rand) < (b - a) \times (1)$$
$$0 \le (b - a) \times (rand) < (b - a)$$
$$0 + a \le (b - a) \times (rand) + a < (b - a) + a$$
$$a \le (b - a) \times (rand) + a < b$$

Saskatchewan is located between the latitudes 49 and 60N and longitudes 102 and 110W. So,

$$102 \le (110 - 102) \times (rand) + 102 < 110$$

generates a random longitude in Saskatchewan and

$$49 \le (60 - 49) \times (rand) + 49 < 60$$

generates a random latitude in Saskatchewan.

For example, using *rand,* we might get: 0.6217 and 0.8811. Substituting these values into the formulas above results in this random location:

$$(110 - 102) \times (0.6217) + 102 = 106.97^\circ W$$
$$(60 - 49) \times (0.8811) + 49 = 58.69^\circ N$$

This random location is somewhere close to Fond du Lac, on Lake Athabasca, just down the road from Uranium City!

Now it's your turn to try it.

To provide some quick practice with generating random numbers using your calculator and also to learn about an interesting use of random numbers, we will find an area using what are known as "Monte Carlo" methods. We will learn something of the mathematics and statistics behind why this works in later chapters, but you can watch it unfold now.

Our story begins with a simple 1-inch by 1-inch square, and a diagonal line segment as shown below. We will use random numbers to approximate the area inside the square and below the line. Of course, as we remember from geometry, the area will be 0.5 square inches. The really neat thing is that we can use this method when the line turns into any mathematical function.

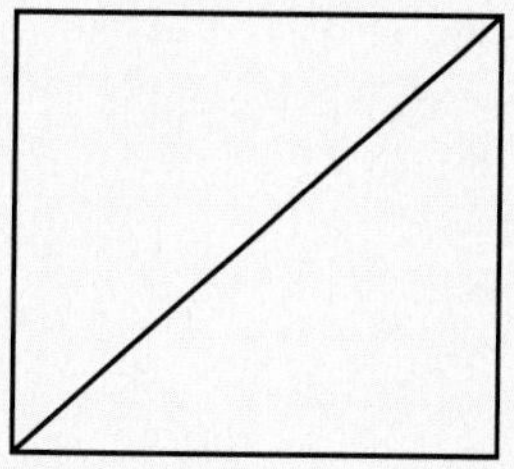

If we imagine a coordinate system with the origin at the lower left corner of the square, the line is: $y = x$. The Monte Carlo method of calculating an area hinges on this fact: If we generate random points inside the square, the proportion of the points "below the line" will reflect the area under the line. (We made the area of the square equal one for easy calculation.) The more points we generate, the closer the proportion of points below the line will be to—in this case—0.5.

To see this unfold, generate 20 random numbers and fill in the table below. (It doesn't matter whether you go across or down as you fill the table.)

x										
y										

Now consider the ordered pairs (x, y) from the columns of the table. If x is less than y, the point will be above the line. If x is greater than y, the point will be below the line. Approximately 5 of these points should be below the line! If you think your results are just lucky random numbers, try another 10 points—how many of the 20 points are below the line? If you are really suspicious, try another 20. If you still don't believe, keep adding points. Keep track of the proportion of points below the line after each additional 5 points—the proportion gets closer and closer to 0.5 as the number of points generated gets larger.

AP* Review Questions for Chapters 1 and 2

1. College students who reported being Internet users were surveyed, and data on the following attributes were recorded:

   I. number of times they accessed the Internet in the previous 24 hours
   II. length of the most recent Internet session
   III. purpose of the last Internet session (e-mail, shopping, downloading music, etc.)
   IV. approximate number of e-mails sent per day

   Which of these variables is/are numerical?

   (A) II only
   (B) III only
   (C) I and IV only
   (D) I, II, and IV only
   (E) I, III, and IV only

2. Which of the following numerical variable(s) are discrete?

   I. number of books in a student's backpack
   II. weight of a student's backpack
   III. number of students in a class who carry a backpack
   IV. thickness of the fabric used in making a student's backpack

   (A) I only
   (B) II only
   (C) I and III only
   (D) I and IV only
   (E) I, II, III, and IV are all discrete

3. The term used to describe the bias that occurs if some segment of a population is systematically excluded from a sample is

   (A) selection bias.
   (B) measurement bias.
   (C) response bias.
   (D) exclusion bias.
   (E) visibility bias.

4. Two variables are confounded if

   (A) their effects on the treatments cannot be ascertained.
   (B) their effects on the sampling design cannot be observed.
   (C) their effects on the response variable cannot be distinguished.
   (D) their effects on the experimental design cannot be justified.
   (E) their effects on the blocking factor cannot be measured.

5. In utilizing direct control, which of the following are held constant?

   (A) values of an extraneous variable
   (B) values of a blocking variable
   (C) values of a response variable
   (D) values of an explanatory variable
   (E) values of a lurking variable

6. Fifty college students were asked what type of movie they had seen most recently. The responses are summarized in the frequency distribution shown.

Type of Movie	Frequency
Comedy	23
Drama	9
Action	7
Western	4
Animated	4
Other	3
Total	50

   What is the relative frequency for the comedy category?

   (A) 23
   (B) 23/27
   (C) 0.23
   (D) 0.46
   (E) 46

7. In a study to determine if the color of the label might affect whether potential customers would buy a particular brand of bottled tea, 100 volunteer subjects were recruited. They were shown two different label designs and asked which design they would be most likely to purchase. One label was blue with a photograph of a woman drinking the tea. The other label was green and did not include the photo. The 100 volunteers were divided at random into two groups. One group was shown the blue label first, followed by the green label. The other group was shown the green

label first followed by the blue label. Which of the following is confounded with the treatments?

(A) color of cover (blue or green)
(B) cover composition (photo or no photo)
(C) preferred label (which label the person was most likely to purchase)
(D) group membership (blue first or green first)
(E) There are no confounding variables.

8. In order to estimate the proportion of students at a college who spend more than 2 hours per day on Facebook, a random sample of students at the college is selected and each student is interviewed about his or her use of Facebook. The students conducting the survey are worried that people who spend a lot of time on Facebook might be embarrassed to admit it and that their responses to the survey might not be honest. What type of bias are the students conducting the survey worried about?

(A) selection bias
(B) nonresponse bias
(C) measurement or response bias
(D) bias due to confounding
(E) They shouldn't worry—there is no obvious source of bias.

9. To estimate the proportion of students who plan to purchase tickets to an upcoming school fundraiser, a high school decides to sample 100 students as they register for the spring semester. There are 2000 students at the school. Which of the following sampling plans would result in a stratified random sample?

(A) Number the students from 1 to 2000 and then use random numbers to select 100 students.
(B) Survey the first 100 students to register.
(C) Randomly select 100 students from a list of the 950 female students at the school.
(D) Divide the students into early registrants (the first 1000 to register) and late registrants (the last 1000 to register). Use random numbers to identify 50 of the early registrants and 50 of the late registrants to survey.
(E) Select one of the first 20 students to register using a random number table and then select every 20th student to register thereafter.

10. Which of the following describes a situation in which it is reasonable to reach a cause-and-effect conclusion based on data from a statistical study?

(A) The study is based on a random sample from a population of interest.
(B) The study is observational, and the sample used is not a convenience sample.
(C) The study is an experiment that uses random assignment to assign volunteers to experimental conditions (treatments).
(D) The study is observational, and the two samples used are not convenience samples.
(E) It is always reasonable to reach a cause-and-effect conclusion based on data from a statistical study.

11. A reporter for a local newspaper wants to survey county residents about their opinions on a proposal to raise property taxes to benefit the county library. He decides to ask 30 county residents whether they support this tax increase. He will select his sample by asking every third person entering the library starting at noon on a Friday. He will continue until he has asked a total of 30 county residents. Which type of bias is likely to be introduced by the way the sample will be selected?

(A) nonresponse bias
(B) response bias
(C) selection bias
(D) measurement bias
(E) No bias is introduced.

12. A random sample of 100 students at a particular college is to be selected, and each person selected will be asked how many times they went to a movie in a theater during the last year. The sample mean will then be used as an estimate of the mean number of times students at this college went to a movie in the last year. Which of the following is a reason to consider increasing the sample size for this study from 100 to 200?

(A) A larger sample size will reduce nonresponse bias.
(B) A larger sample size will reduce the response bias due to people not being able to accurately remember how many times they went to a movie in the last year.
(C) A larger sample size will reduce sampling variability—the differences in the sample mean that occur from sample to sample due to chance.
(D) It is less likely that one of the high values in the population (corresponding to a person who goes to a very large number of movies) will be included in a larger sample.
(E) All of the above are valid reasons to increase the sample size.

13. Researchers were interested in comparing students at private universities and students at public universities with respect to how much time they spent working in a typical week. They e-mailed a survey to 1000 students enrolled at a particular private university and to 2000 students enrolled at a particular public university. Data from the 400 private university students who responded to the survey and the 900 public university students who responded to the survey were used to determine that there was a significant difference in the mean number of hours worked in a typical week. Which of the following does *not* limit the researchers' ability to generalize to the two populations of interest?

(A) The two sample sizes are not equal.
(B) There may be bias introduced due to nonresponse.
(C) The samples were not randomly selected.
(D) All students in the private university sample attended the same university, and all students in the public university sample attended the same university.
(E) All of the above limit the researchers' ability to generalize to the populations of interest.

Use the following to answer questions 14–15.

One hundred volunteer subjects participated in a study to determine if room temperature affects people's ability to concentrate. Female volunteers were given 10 minutes to try to memorize the words on a list of 50 nonsense words. The room temperature was controlled at 65 degrees (a cold room) while they completed the task. Male volunteers were also given 10 minutes to try to memorize the same list of words, but for the males, room temperature was controlled at 85 degrees (a hot room). At the end of the 10 minutes, each subject was asked to list as many of the words as he or she could remember, and the number correct was recorded. The resulting data were then used to determine if the mean number of words differed for the cold room and hot room conditions.

14. Which of the following is a confounding variable—that is, which of the following is confounded with the treatments?

(A) room temperature (cold or hot)
(B) gender (male or female)
(C) number of nonsense words recalled
(D) length of time given to memorize the words
(E) can't tell because volunteers were used

15. The poor design of this experiment results in a variable that is confounded with the treatments. Which of the following changes to the design would be effective in eliminating this confounding?

(A) Use only one room temperature.
(B) Use only male subjects in the study and assign the males to one of the two room-temperature conditions at random.
(C) Assign the volunteers at random to one of the two room-temperature conditions.
(D) Create two blocks by putting all of the females in one block and all of the males in the other block. Then, within each block, assign subjects at random to one of the room-temperature conditions.
(E) B, C, and D are all strategies that would be effective.

CHAPTER 3

Florin Tirlea/iStockphoto

Graphical Methods for Describing Data

Most college students (and their parents) are concerned about the cost of a college education. *The Chronicle of Higher Education* (August 2008) reported the average tuition and fees for 4-year public institutions in each of the 50 U.S. states for the 2006-2007 academic year. Average tuition and fees (in dollars) are given for each state:

4712	4422	4669	4937	4452	4634	7151	7417	3050	3851
3930	4155	8038	6284	6019	4966	5821	3778	6557	7106
7629	7504	7392	4457	6320	5378	5181	2844	9003	9333
3943	5022	4038	5471	9010	4176	5598	9092	6698	7914
5077	5009	5114	3757	9783	6447	5636	4063	6048	2951

Make the most of your study time by accessing everything you need to succeed online with CourseMate.
Visit http://www.cengagebrain.com where you will find:

- An interactive eBook, which allows you to take notes, highlight, bookmark, search the text, and use in-context glossary definitions
- Step-by-step instructions for Minitab, Excel, TI-83/84, SPSS, and JMP
- Video solutions to selected exercises
- Data sets available for selected examples and exercises
- Online quizzes
- Flashcards
- Videos

Several questions could be posed about these data. What is a typical value of average tuition and fees for the 50 states? Are observations concentrated near the typical value, or does average tuition and fees differ quite a bit from state to state? Are there any states whose average tuition and fees are somehow unusual compared to the rest? What proportion of the states have average tuition and fees exceeding $6000? Exceeding $8000?

Questions such as these are most easily answered if the data can be organized in a sensible manner. In this chapter, we introduce some techniques for organizing and describing data using tables and graphs.

3.1 Displaying Categorical Data: Comparative Bar Charts and Pie Charts

AP* EXAM TIP

To decide which graphical display to use, ask basic questions first: Is the data categorical or numerical? How many data sets are there? How many variables are there?

Comparative Bar Charts

In Chapter 1 we saw that categorical data could be summarized in a frequency distribution and displayed graphically using a bar chart. Bar charts can also be used to give a visual comparison of two or more groups. This is accomplished by constructing two or more bar charts that use the same set of horizontal and vertical axes, as illustrated in Example 3.1.

EXAMPLE 3.1 How Far Is Far Enough

Each year The Princeton Review conducts a survey of high school students who are applying to college and parents of college applicants. The report "2009 College Hopes & Worries Survey Findings" (www.princetonreview.com/uploadedFiles/Test_Preparation/Hopes_and_Worries/colleg_hopes_worries_details.pdf) included a summary of how 12,715 high school students responded to the question "Ideally how far from home would you like the college you attend to be?" Also included was a summary of how 3007 parents of students applying to college responded to the question "How far from home would you like the college your child attends to be?" The accompanying relative frequency table summarized the student and parent responses.

	FREQUENCY		RELATIVE FREQUENCY	
Ideal Distance	Students	Parents	Students	Parents
Less than 250 miles	4450	1594	.35	.53
250 to 500 miles	3942	902	.31	.30
500 to 1000 miles	2416	331	.19	.11
More than 1000 miles	1907	180	.15	.06

When constructing a comparative bar chart we use the relative frequency rather than the frequency to construct the scale on the vertical axis so that we can make meaningful comparisons even if the sample sizes are not the same. The comparative bar chart for these data is shown in Figure 3.1. It is easy to see the differences between students and parents. A higher proportion of parents prefer a college close to home, and a higher

Step-by-Step technology instructions available online

proportion of students than parents believe that the ideal distance from home would be more than 500 miles.

To see why it is important to use relative frequencies rather than frequencies to compare groups of different sizes, consider the *incorrect* bar chart constructed using the frequencies rather than the relative frequencies (Figure 3.2). The incorrect bar chart conveys a very different and misleading impression of the differences between students and parents.

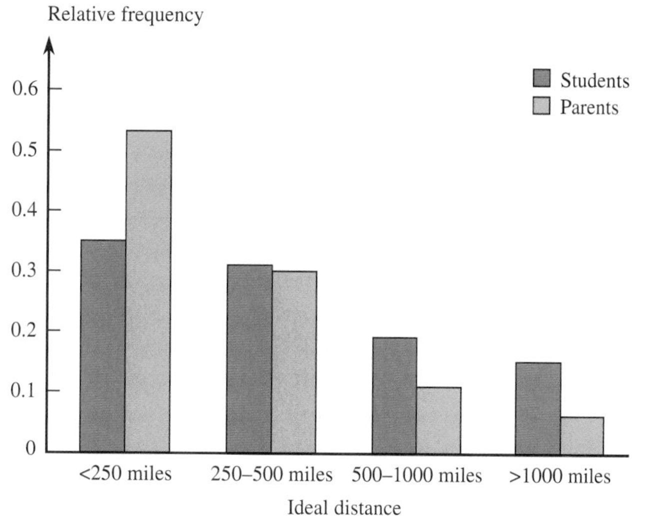

FIGURE 3.1
Comparative bar chart of ideal distance from home.

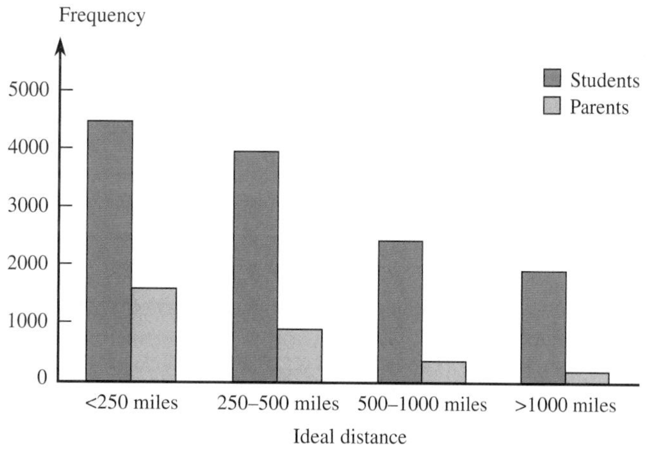

FIGURE 3.2
An *incorrect* comparative bar chart for the data of Example 3.1.

Pie Charts

A categorical data set can also be summarized using a pie chart. In a pie chart, a circle is used to represent the whole data set, with "slices" of the pie representing the possible categories. The size of the slice for a particular category is proportional to the corresponding frequency or relative frequency. Pie charts are most effective for summarizing data sets when there are not too many different categories.

EXAMPLE 3.2 Life Insurance for Cartoon Characters??

The article "Fred Flintstone, Check Your Policy" (*The Washington Post,* October 2, 2005) summarized the results of a survey of 1014 adults conducted by the Life and Health Insurance Foundation for Education. Each person surveyed was asked to select which of five fictional characters, Spider-Man, Batman, Fred Flintstone, Harry Potter, and Marge Simpson, he or she thought had the greatest need for life insurance. The resulting data are summarized in the pie chart of Figure 3.3.

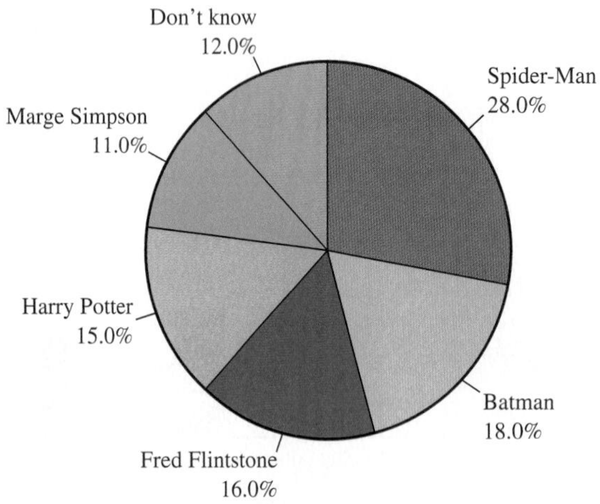

FIGURE 3.3
Pie chart of data on which fictional character most needs life insurance.

The survey results were quite different from an insurance expert's assessment. His opinion was that Fred Flintstone, a married father with a young child, was by far the one with the greatest need for life insurance. Spider-Man, unmarried with an elderly aunt, would need life insurance only if his aunt relied on him to supplement her income. Batman, a wealthy bachelor with no dependents, doesn't need life insurance in spite of his dangerous job!

Pie Chart for Categorical Data

When to Use Categorical data with a relatively small number of possible categories. Pie charts are most useful for illustrating proportions of the whole data set for various categories.

How to Construct

1. Draw a circle to represent the entire data set.
2. For each category, calculate the "slice" size. Because there are 360 degrees in a circle

   $$\text{slice size} = 360 \cdot (\text{category relative frequency})$$

3. Draw a slice of appropriate size for each category. This can be tricky, so most pie charts are generated using a graphing calculator or a statistical software package.

What to Look For

- Categories that form large and small proportions of the data set.

EXAMPLE 3.3 Watch Those Typos

Typos on a résumé do not make a very good impression when applying for a job. Senior executives were asked how many typos in a résumé would make them not consider a job candidate ("Job Seekers Need a Keen Eye," *USA Today*, August 3, 2009). The resulting data are summarized in the accompanying relative frequency distribution.

Number of Typos	Frequency	Relative Frequency
1	60	.40
2	54	.36
3	21	.14
4 or more	10	.07
Don't know	5	.03

To draw a pie chart by hand, we would first compute the slice size for each category. For the one typo category, the slice size would be

$$\text{slice size} = (.40)(360) = 144 \text{ degrees}$$

144 degrees, to represent first attempt category

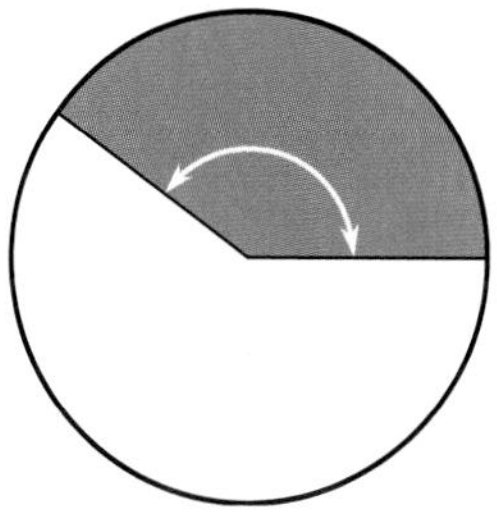

We would then draw a circle and use a protractor to mark off a slice corresponding to about 144°, as illustrated here in the figure shown in the margin. Continuing to add slices in this way leads to a completed pie chart.

It is much easier to use a statistical software package to create pie charts than to construct them by hand. A pie chart for the typo data, created with the statistical software package Minitab, is shown in Figure 3.4.

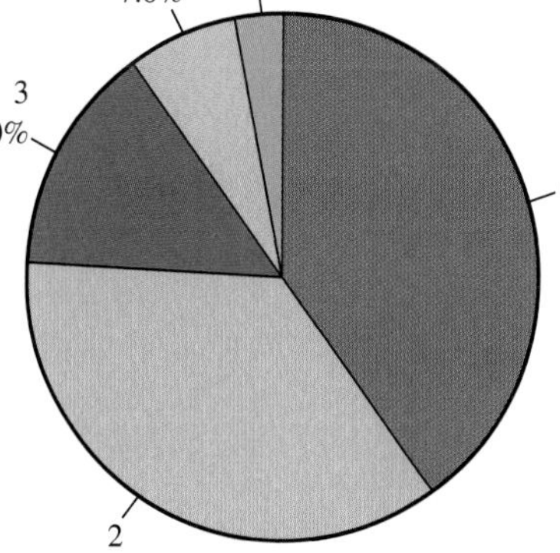

FIGURE 3.4
Pie chart for the typo data of Example 3.3.

Pie charts can be used effectively to summarize a single categorical data set if there are not too many different categories. However, pie charts are not usually the best tool if the goal is to compare groups on the basis of a categorical variable. This is illustrated in Example 3.4.

Step-by-Step technology instructions available online

EXAMPLE 3.4 Scientists and Nonscientists Do Not See Eye-to-Eye

Scientists and nonscientists were asked to indicate if they agreed or disagreed with the following statement: "When something is run by the government, it is usually inefficient and wasteful." The resulting data (from "Scientists, Public Differ in Outlooks," *USA Today*, July 10, 2009) were used to create the two pie charts in Figure 3.5.

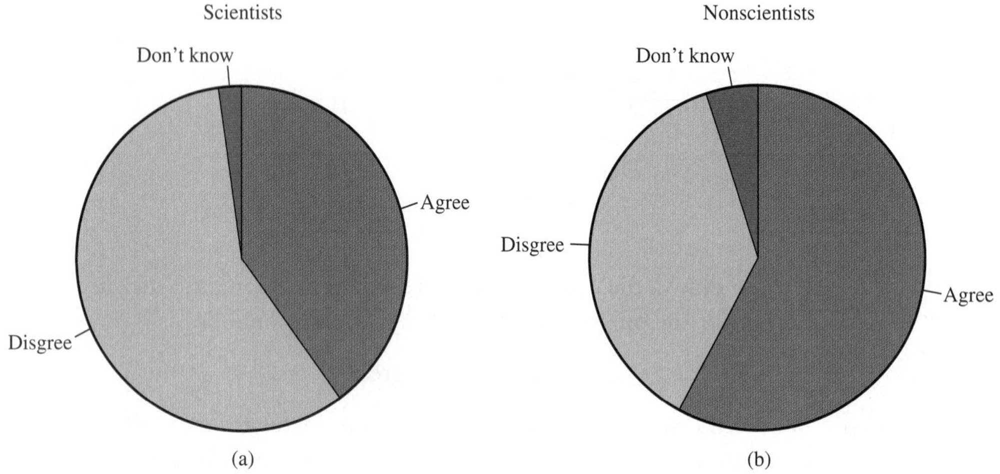

FIGURE 3.5
Pie charts for Example 3.4: (a) scientist data; (b) nonscientist data.

Although differences between scientists and nonscientists can be seen by comparing the pie charts of Figure 3.5, it can be difficult to compare category proportions using pie charts. A comparative bar chart (Figure 3.6) makes this type of comparison easier.

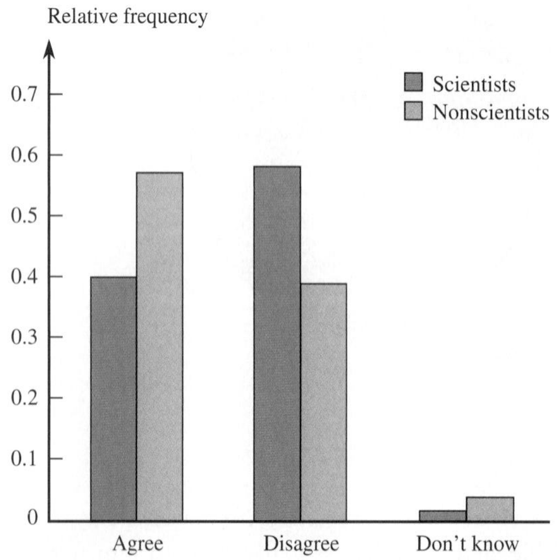

FIGURE 3.6
Comparative bar chart for the scientist and nonscientist data.

A Different Type of "Pie" Chart: Segmented Bar Graphs

A pie chart can be difficult to construct by hand, and the circular shape sometimes makes it difficult to compare areas for different categories, particularly when the relative frequencies for categories are similar. The **segmented bar graph** (also sometimes called a stacked bar graph) avoids these difficulties by using a rectangular bar rather than a circle to represent the entire data set. The bar is divided into segments, with different segments representing different categories. As with pie charts, the area of the segment for a particular category is proportional to the relative frequency for that category. Example 3.5 illustrates the construction of a segmented bar graph.

EXAMPLE 3.5 How College Seniors Spend Their Time

Each year, the Higher Education Research Institute conducts a survey of college seniors. In 2008, approximately 23,000 seniors participated in the survey ("Findings from the 2008 Administration of the College Senior Survey," Higher Education Research Institute, June 2009). The accompanying relative frequency table summarizes student response to the question: "During the past year, how much time did you spend studying and doing homework in a typical week?"

STUDYING/HOMEWORK

Amount of Time	Relative Frequency
2 hours or less	.074
3 to 5 hours	.227
6 to 10 hours	.285
11 to 15 hours	.181
16 to 20 hours	.122
Over 20 hours	.111

To construct a segmented bar graph for these data, first draw a bar of any fixed width and length, and then add a scale that ranges from 0 to 1, as shown.

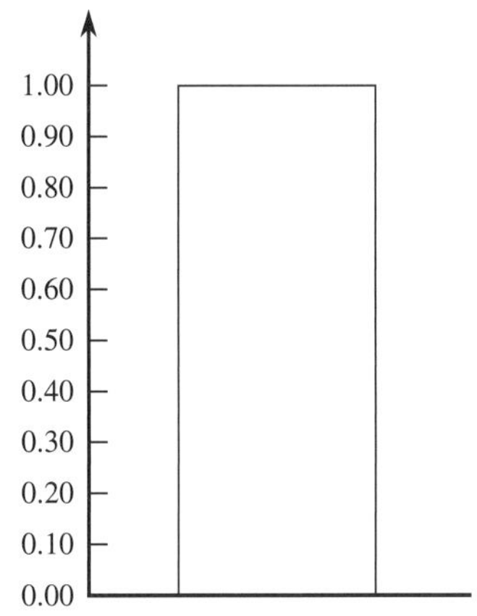

Then divide the bar into six segments, corresponding to the six possible time categories in this example. The first segment, corresponding to the 2 hours or less category, ranges from 0 to .074. The second segment, corresponding to 3 to 5 hours, ranges from .074 to .301 (for a length of .227, the relative frequency for this category), and so on. The segmented bar graph is shown in Figure 3.7.

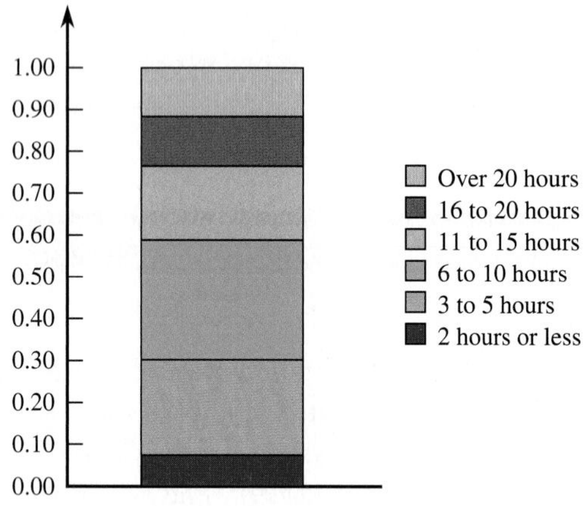

FIGURE 3.7
Segmented bar graph for the study time data of Example 3.5.

The same report also gave data on amount of time spent on exercise or sports in a typical week. Figure 3.8 shows horizontal segmented bar graphs (segmented bar graphs can be displayed either vertically or horizontally) for both time spent studying and time spent exercising. Viewing these graphs side by side makes it easy to see how students differ with respect to time spent on these two types of activities.

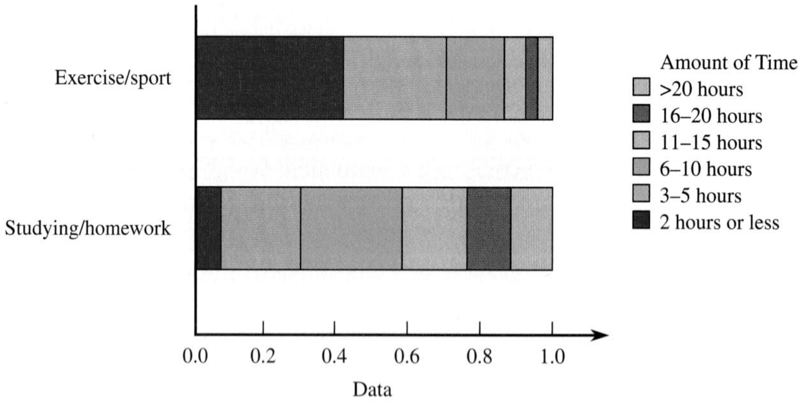

FIGURE 3.8
Segmented bar graphs for time spent studying and time spent exercising.

Other Uses of Bar Charts and Pie Charts

As we have seen in previous examples, bar charts and pie charts can be used to summarize categorical data sets. However, they are occasionally used for other purposes, as illustrated in Examples 3.6 and 3.7.

EXAMPLE 3.6 Grape Production

● The 2008 Grape Crush Report for California gave the following information on grape production for each of four different types of grapes (California Department of Food and Agriculture, March 10, 2009):

Type of Grape	Tons Produced
Red Wine Grapes	1,715,000
White Wine Grapes	1,346,000
Raisin Grapes	494,000
Table Grapes	117,000
Total	**3,672,000**

Although this table is not a frequency distribution, it is common to represent information of this type graphically using a pie chart, as shown in Figure 3.9. The pie represents the total grape production, and the slices show the proportion of the total production for each of the four types of grapes.

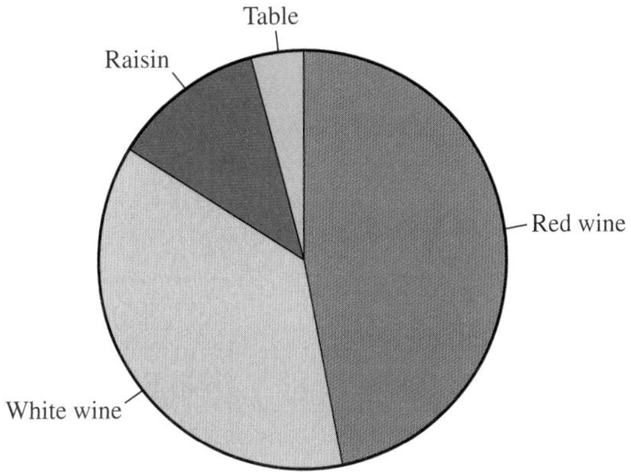

FIGURE 3.9
Pie chart for grape production data.

EXAMPLE 3.7 Back-to-College Spending

The National Retail Federation's 2008 Back to College Consumer Intentions and Actions Survey (www.nrf.com) asked each person in a sample of college students how much they planned to spend in various categories during the upcoming academic year. The average amounts of money (in dollars) that men and women planned to spend for five different types of purchases are shown in the accompanying table.

Type of Purchase	Average for Men	Average for Women
Clothing and Accessories	$207.46	$198.15
Shoes	$107.22	$88.65
School Supplies	$86.85	$81.56
Electronics and Computers	$533.17	$344.90
Dorm or Apartment Furnishings	$266.69	$266.98

● Data set available online

Even though this table is not a frequency distribution, this type of information is often represented graphically in the form of a bar chart, as illustrated in Figure 3.10. From the bar chart, we can see that the average amount of money that men and women plan to spend is similar for all of the types of purchases except for electronics and computers, in which the average for men is quite a bit higher than the average for women.

AP* EXAM TIP

When making graphical displays using categorical data, be careful to use labels that clearly convey the different categories.

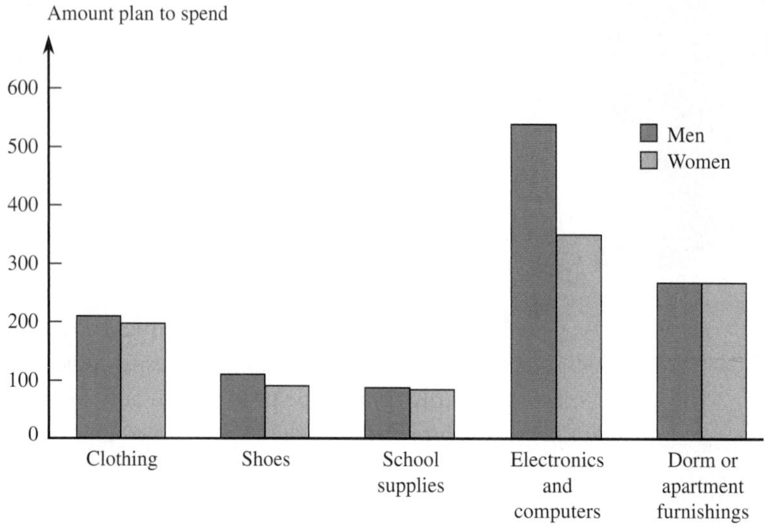

FIGURE 3.10
Comparative bar chart for the back-to-college spending data of men and women.

EXERCISES 3.1 - 3.14

3.1 Each person in a nationally representative sample of 1252 young adults age 23 to 28 years old was asked how they viewed their "financial physique" ("2009 Young Adults & Money Survey Findings," Charles Schwab, 2009). "Toned and fit" was chosen by 18% of the respondents, while 55% responded "a little bit flabby," and 27% responded "seriously out of shape." Summarize this information in a pie chart.

3.2 The accompanying graphical display appeared in *USA Today* (October 22, 2009). It summarizes survey responses to a question about whether visiting social networking sites is allowed at work. Which of the graph types introduced in this section is used to display the responses? (*USA Today* frequently adds artwork and text to their graphs to try to make them look more interesting.)

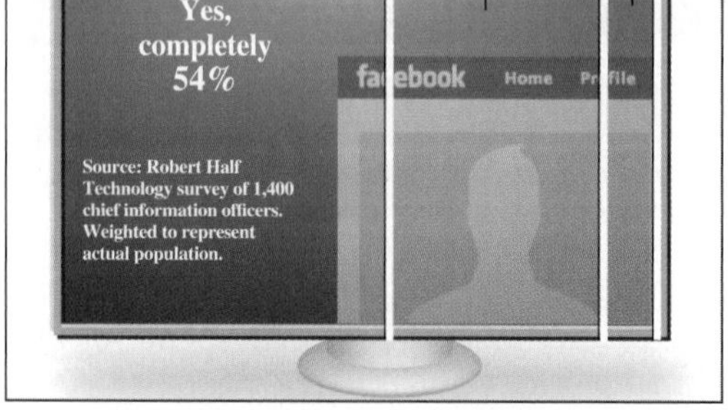

By Jae Yang and Julie Snider, USA TODAY

3.3 The survey referenced in the previous exercise was conducted by Robert Half Technology. This company issued a press release ("Whistle—But Don't Tweet—While You Work," www.roberthalftechnology.com, October 6, 2009) that provided more detail than in the *USA Today* snapshot graph. The actual question asked was "Which of the following most closely describes your company's policy on visiting social networking sites, such as Facebook, MySpace and Twitter, while at work?" The responses are summarized in the following table:

Response Category	Relative Frequency (expressed as percent)
Prohibited completely	54%
Permitted for business purposes only	19%
Permitted for limited personal use	16%
Permitted for any type of personal use	10%
Don't know/no answer	1%

a. Explain how the survey response categories and corresponding relative frequencies were used or modified to produce the graphical display in Exercise 3.2.
b. Using the original data in the table, construct a segmented bar graph.
c. What are two other types of graphical displays that would be appropriate for summarizing these data?

3.4 The National Confectioners Association asked 1006 adults the following question: "Do you set aside a personal stash of Halloween candy?" Fifty-five percent of those surveyed responded no, 41% responded yes, and 4% either did not answer the question or said they did not know (*USA Today*, October 22, 2009). Use the given information to construct a pie chart.

3.5 The report "Communicating to Teens (Aged 12–17)" (U.S. Department of Health and Human Services, www.cdc.gov) suggests that teens can be classified into five groups based on attitude, behavior, and conformity. The report also includes estimates of the percentage of teens who fall into each of these groups. The groups are described in the accompanying table.

Group and Description	Percentage of Teens in This Group
Explorer: creative, independent, and differs from the norm.	10%
Visible: well known and popular because of looks, personality or athletic ability	30%
Status Quo: display traditional values of moderation and achievement, seek mainstream acceptance	38%
Non-Teen: behave more like adults or young children because of lack of social skills or indifference to teen culture and style	14%
Isolator: psychologically isolated from both peers and adults	8%

Construct an appropriate graph to summarize the information in the table. Explain why you chose this particular type of graph.

3.6 The Center for Science in the Public Interest evaluated school cafeterias in 20 school districts across the United States. Each district was assigned a numerical score on the basis of rigor of food codes, frequency of food safety inspections, access to inspection information, and the results of cafeteria inspections. Based on the score assigned, each district was also assigned one of four grades. The scores and grades are summarized in the accompanying table, which appears in the report "Making the Grade: An Analysis of Food Safety in School Cafeterias" (cspi.us/new/pdf/makingthegrade.pdf, 2007).

Top of the Class | Passing | Barely Passing | Failing

Jurisdiction	Overall Score (out of 100)
City of Fort Worth, TX	80
King County, WA	79
City of Houston, TX	78
Maricopa County, AZ	77
City and County of Denver, CO	75
Dekalb County, GA	73
Farmington Valley Health District, CT	72
State of Virginia	72
Fulton County, GA	68
City of Dallas, TX	67
City of Philadelphia, PA	67
City of Chicago, IL	65
City and County of San Francisco, CA	64
Montgomery County, MD	63
Hillsborough County, FL	60
City of Minneapolis, MN	60
Dade County, FL	59
State of Rhode Island	54
District of Columbia	46
City of Hartford, CT	37

a. Two variables are summarized in the figure, grade and overall score. Is overall score a numerical or categorical variable? Is grade (indicated by the different colors in the figure) a numerical or categorical variable?
b. Explain how the figure is equivalent to a segmented bar graph of the grade data.
c. Construct a dotplot of the overall score data. Based on the dotplot, suggest an alternate assignment of grades (top of class, passing, etc.) to the 20 school districts. Explain the reasoning you used to make your assignment.

3.7 The article "Housework around the World" (*USA Today*, September 15, 2009) included the percentage of women who say their spouses never help with household chores for five different countries.

Country	Percentage
Japan	74%
France	44%
United Kingdom	40%
United States	34%
Canada	31%

a. Display the information in the accompanying table in a bar chart.
b. The article did not state how the author arrived at the given percentages. What are two questions that you would want to ask the author about how the data used to compute the percentages were collected?
c. Assuming that the data that were used to compute these percentages were collected in a reasonable way, write a few sentences describing how the five countries differ in terms of spouses helping their wives with housework.

3.8 The report "Findings from the 2008 Administration of the College Senior Survey" (Higher Education Research Institute, 2009) asked a large number of college seniors how they would rate themselves compared to the average person of their age with respect to physical health. The accompanying relative frequency table summarizes the responses for men and women.

Rating of Physical Health	Relative Frequency	
	Men	Women
Highest 10%	.220	.101
Above average	.399	.359
Average	.309	.449
Below average	.066	.086
Lowest 10%	.005	.005

a. Construct a comparative bar graph of the responses that allows you to compare the responses of men and women.
b. There were 8110 men and 15,260 women who responded to the survey. Explain why it is important that the comparative bar graph be constructed using the relative frequencies rather than the actual numbers of people (the frequencies) responding in each category.
c. Write a few sentences commenting on how college seniors perceive themselves with respect to physical health and how men and women differ in their perceptions.

3.9 The article "Rinse Out Your Mouth" (Associated Press, March 29, 2006) summarized results from a survey of 1001 adults on the use of profanity. When asked "How many times do you use swear words in conversations?" 46% responded a few or more times per week, 32% responded a few times a month or less, and 21% responded never. Use the given information to construct a segmented bar chart.

3.10 The article "The Need to Be Plugged In" (Associated Press, December 22, 2005) described the results of a survey of 1006 adults who were asked about various technologies, including personal computers, cell phones, and DVD players. The accompanying table summarizes the responses to questions about how essential these technologies were.

Response	Relative Frequency		
	Personal Computer	Cell Phone	DVD Player
Cannot imagine living without	.46	.41	.19
Would miss but could do without	.28	.25	.35
Could definitely live without	.26	.34	.46

Construct a comparative bar chart that shows the distribution of responses for the three different technologies.

3.11 ✦ Poor fitness in adolescents and adults increases the risk of cardiovascular disease. In a study of 3110 adolescents and 2205 adults (*Journal of the American Medical Association*, December 21, 2005), researchers found 33.6% of adolescents and 13.9% of adults were unfit; the percentage was similar in adolescent males (32.9%) and females (34.4%), but was higher in adult females (16.2%) than in adult males (11.8%).
a. Summarize this information using a comparative bar graph that shows differences between males and females within the two different age groups.
b. Comment on the interesting features of your graphical display.

3.12 A survey of 1001 adults taken by Associated Press–Ipsos asked "How accurate are the weather forecasts in your area?" (*San Luis Obispo Tribune*, June 15, 2005). The responses are summarized in the table below.

Extremely	4%
Very	27%
Somewhat	53%
Not too	11%
Not at all	4%
Not sure	1%

a. Construct a pie chart to summarize these data.
b. Construct a bar chart to summarize these data.
c. Which of these charts—a pie chart or a bar chart—best summarizes the important information? Explain.

3.13 In a discussion of accidental deaths involving roadside hazards, the web site highwaysafety.com included a pie chart like the one shown:

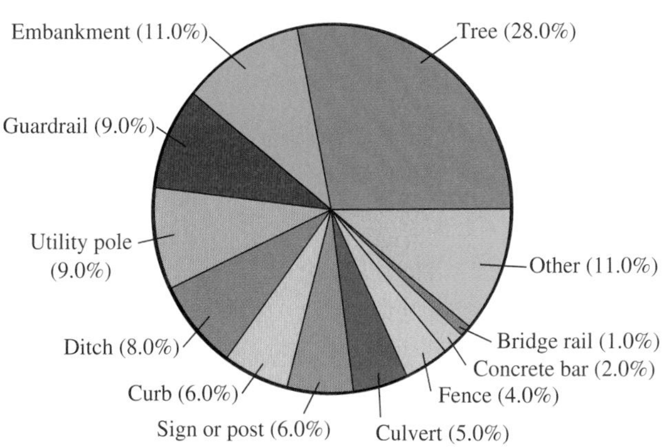

a. Do you think this is an effective use of a pie chart? Why or why not?
b. Construct a bar chart to show the distribution of deaths by object struck. Is this display more effective than the pie chart in summarizing this data set? Explain.

3.14 The article "Death in Roadwork Zones at Record High" (*San Luis Obispo Tribune*, July 25, 2001) included a bar chart similar to this one:

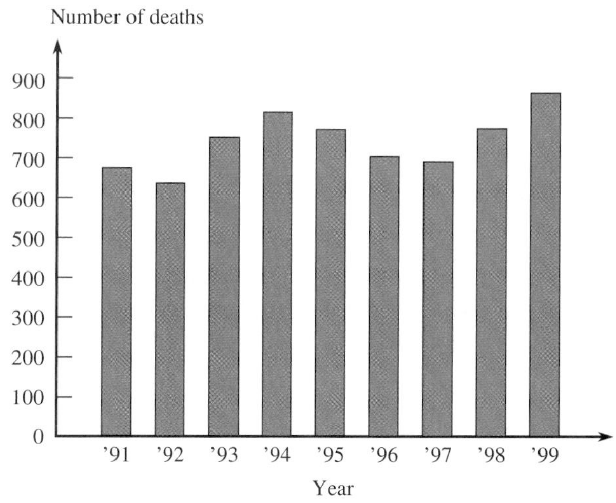

a. Comment on the trend over time in the number of people killed in highway work zones.
b. Would a pie chart have also been an effective way to summarize these data? Explain why or why not.

3.2 Displaying Numerical Data: Stem-and-Leaf Displays

A stem-and-leaf display is an effective and compact way to summarize univariate numerical data. Each number in the data set is broken into two pieces, a stem and a leaf. The **stem** is the first part of the number and consists of the beginning digit(s). The **leaf** is the last part of the number and consists of the final digit(s). For example, the number 213 might be split into a stem of 2 and a leaf of 13 or a stem of 21 and a leaf of 3. The resulting stems and leaves are then used to construct the display.

EXAMPLE 3.8 Should Doctors Get Auto Insurance Discounts?

● Many auto insurance companies give job-related discounts of between 5 and 15%. The article "Auto-Rate Discounts Seem to Defy Data" (*San Luis Obispo Tribune*, June 19, 2004) included the accompanying data on the number of automobile accidents per year for every 1000 people in 40 occupations.

Occupation	Accidents per 1000	Occupation	Accidents per 1000
Student	152	Banking-finance	89
Physician	109	Customer service	88
Lawyer	106	Manager	88
Architect	105	Medical support	87
Real estate broker	102	Computer-related	87
Enlisted military	199	Dentist	86
Social worker	198	Pharmacist	85
Manual laborer	196	Proprietor	84
Analyst	195	Teacher, professor	84
Engineer	194	Accountant	84
Consultant	194	Law enforcement	79
Sales	193	Physical therapist	78
Military officer	191	Veterinarian	78
Nurse	190	Clerical, secretary	77
School administrator	190	Clergy	76
Skilled labor	190	Homemaker	76
Librarian	190	Politician	76
Creative arts	190	Pilot	75
Executive	189	Firefighter	67
Insurance agent	189	Farmer	43

4	3
5	
6	7
7	56667889
8	44567788999
9	000013445689
10	2569
11	
12	
13	
14	
15	2

Stem: Tens
Leaf: Ones

FIGURE 3.11
Stem-and-leaf display for accident rate per 1000 for forty occupations

Figure 3.11 shows a stem-and-leaf display for the accident rate data.

The numbers in the vertical column on the left of the display are the **stems**. Each number to the right of the vertical line is a **leaf** corresponding to one of the observations in the data set. The legend

Stem: Tens
Leaf: Ones

tells us that the observation that had a stem of 4 and a leaf of 3 corresponds to an occupation with an accident rate of 43 per 1000 (as opposed to 4.3 or 0.43). Similarly, the observation with the stem of 10 and leaf of 2 corresponds to 102 accidents per 1000 (the leaf of 2 is the ones digit) and the observation with the stem of 15 and leaf of 2 corresponds to 152 accidents per 1000.

The display in Figure 3.11 suggests that a typical or representative value is in the stem 8 or 9 row, perhaps around 90. The observations are mostly concentrated in the 75 to 109 range, but there are a couple of values that stand out on the low end (43 and 67) and one observation (152) that is far removed from the rest of the data on the high end.

Step-by-step technology instructions available online

● Data set available online

From the point of view of an auto insurance company it might make sense to offer discounts to occupations with low accident rates—maybe farmers (43 auto accidents per 1000 farmers) or firefighters (67 accidents per 1000 firefighters) or even some of the occupations with accident rates in the 70s. The "discounts seem to defy data" in the title of the article refers to the fact that some insurers provide discounts to doctors and engineers, but not to homemakers, politicians, and other occupations with lower accident rates. Two possible explanations were offered for this apparent discrepancy. One is that it is possible that while some occupations have higher accident rates, they also have lower average cost per claim. Accident rates alone may not reflect the actual cost to the insurance company. Another possible explanation is that the insurance companies may offer the discounted auto insurance in order to attract people who would then also purchase other types of insurance such as malpractice or liability insurance.

The leaves on each line of the display in Figure 3.11 have been arranged in order from smallest to largest. Most statistical software packages order the leaves this way, but it is not necessary to do so to get an informative display that still shows many of the important characteristics of the data set, such as shape and spread.

Stem-and-leaf displays can be useful to get a sense of a typical value for the data set, as well as a sense of how spread out the values in the data set are. It is also easy to spot data values that are unusually far from the rest of the values in the data set. Such values are called outliers. The stem-and-leaf display of the accident rate data (Figure 3.11) shows an outlier on the low end (43) and an outlier on the high end (152).

DEFINITION

An **outlier** is an unusually small or large data value. A precise rule for deciding when an observation is an outlier is given in Chapter 4.

Stem-and-Leaf Displays

When to Use Numerical data sets with a small to moderate number of observations (does not work well for very large data sets)

How to Construct

1. Select one or more leading digits for the stem values. The trailing digits (or sometimes just the first one of the trailing digits) become the leaves.
2. List possible stem values in a vertical column.
3. Record the leaf for every observation beside the corresponding stem value.
4. Indicate the units for stems and leaves someplace in the display.

What to Look For The display conveys information about

- a representative or typical value in the data set
- the extent of spread about a typical value
- the presence of any gaps in the data
- the extent of symmetry in the distribution of values
- the number and location of peaks

EXAMPLE 3.9 Tuition at Public Universities

● The introduction to this chapter gave data on average tuition and fees at public institutions in the year 2007 for the 50 U.S. states. The observations ranged from a low value of 2844 to a high value of 9783. The data are reproduced here:

4712	4422	4669	4937	4452	4634	7151	7417	3050	3851
3930	4155	8038	6284	6019	4966	5821	3778	6557	7106
7629	7504	7392	4457	6320	5378	5181	2844	9003	9333
3943	5022	4038	5471	9010	4176	5598	9092	6698	7914
5077	5009	5114	3757	9783	6447	5636	4063	6048	2951

A natural choice for the stem is the leading (thousands) digit. This would result in a display with 7 stems (2, 3, 4, 5, 6, 7, 8, and 9). Using the first two digits of a number as the stem would result in 69 stems (28, 29, . . . , 97). A stem-and-leaf display with 56 stems would not be an effective summary of the data. *In general, stem-and-leaf displays that use between 5 and 20 stems tend to work well.*

If we choose the thousands digit as the stem, the remaining three digits (the hundreds, tens, and ones) would form the leaf. For example, for the first few values in the first column of data, we would have

4712 → stem = 4, leaf = 712
3930 → stem = 3, leaf = 930
7629 → stem = 7, leaf = 629

The leaves have been entered in the display of Figure 3.12 in the order they are encountered in the data set. Commas are used to separate the leaves only when each leaf has two or more digits. Figure 3.12 shows that most states had average tuition and fees in the $4000 to $7000 range and that the typical average tuition and fees is around $6000. A few states have average tuition and fees at public four-year institutions that are quite a bit higher than most other states (the five states with the highest values were Vermont, New Jersey, Pennsylvania, Ohio, and New Hampshire).

● Data set available online

```
2 | 844, 951
3 | 050, 851, 930, 778, 943, 757
4 | 712, 422, 669, 937, 452, 634, 155, 966, 457, 038, 176, 063
5 | 821, 378, 181, 022, 471, 598, 077, 009, 114, 636
6 | 284, 019, 557, 320, 698, 447, 048
7 | 151, 417, 106, 629, 504, 392, 914
8 | 038                                      Stem: Thousands
9 | 003, 333, 010, 092, 783                  Leaf: Ones
```

FIGURE 3.12
Stem-and-leaf display of average tuition and fees.

An alternative display (Figure 3.13) results from dropping all but the first digit of the leaf. This is what most statistical computer packages do when generating a display; little information about typical value, spread, or shape is lost in this truncation and the display is simpler and more compact.

```
2 | 89
3 | 089797
4 | 746946194010
5 | 8310450016
6 | 2053640
7 | 1416539
8 | 0                       Stem: Thousands
9 | 03007                   Leaf: Hundreds
```

FIGURE 3.13
Stem-and-leaf display of the average tuition and fees data using truncated stems.

Repeated Stems to Stretch a Display

Sometimes a natural choice of stems gives a display in which too many observations are concentrated on just a few stems. A more informative picture can be obtained by dividing the leaves at any given stem into two groups: those that begin with 0, 1, 2, 3, or 4 (the "low" leaves) and those that begin with 5, 6, 7, 8, or 9 (the "high" leaves). Then each stem value is listed twice when constructing the display, once for the low leaves and once again for the high leaves. It is also possible to repeat a stem more than twice. For example, each stem might be repeated five times, once for each of the leaf groupings {0, 1}, {2, 3}, {4, 5}, {6, 7}, and {8, 9}.

EXAMPLE 3.10 Median Ages in 2030

● The accompanying data on the Census Bureau's projected median age in 2030 for the 50 U.S. states and Washington D.C. appeared in the article "2030 Forecast: Mostly Gray" (*USA Today*, April 21, 2005). The median age for a state is the age that divides the state's residents so that half are younger than the median age and half are older than the median age.

Projected Median Age

41.0	32.9	39.3	29.3	37.4	35.6	41.1	43.6	33.7	45.4	35.6	38.7
39.2	37.8	37.7	42.0	39.1	40.0	38.8	46.9	37.5	40.2	40.2	39.0
41.1	39.6	46.0	38.4	39.4	42.1	40.8	44.8	39.9	36.8	43.2	40.2
37.9	39.1	42.1	40.7	41.3	41.5	38.3	34.6	30.4	43.9	37.8	38.5
46.7	41.6	46.4									

The ages in the data set range from 29.3 to 46.9. Using the first two digits of each data value for the stem results in a large number of stems, while using only the first digit results in a stem-and-leaf display with only three stems.

The stem-and-leaf display using single digit stems and leaves truncated to a single digit is shown in Figure 3.14. A stem-and-leaf display that uses repeated stems is shown in Figure 3.15. Here each stem is listed twice, once for the low leaves (those beginning with 0, 1, 2, 3, 4) and once for the high leaves (those beginning with 5, 6, 7, 8, 9). This display is more informative than the one in Figure 3.14, but is much more compact than a display based on two-digit stems.

2	9
3	02345567777778888899999999
4	00000011111122233345666

Stem: Tens
Leaf: Ones

FIGURE 3.14
Stem-and-leaf display for the projected median age data.

2H	9
3L	0234
3H	5567777778888899999999
4L	0000001111112223334
4H	56666

Stem: Tens
Leaf: Ones

FIGURE 3.15
Stem-and-leaf display for the projected median age data using repeated stems.

● Data set available online

Comparative Stem-and-Leaf Displays

Frequently an analyst wishes to see whether two groups of data differ in some fundamental way. A comparative stem-and-leaf display, in which the leaves for one group are listed to the right of the stem values and the leaves for the second group are listed to the left, can provide preliminary visual impressions and insights.

EXAMPLE 3.11 Progress for Children

● The report "Progress for Children" (UNICEF, April 2005) included the accompanying data on the percentage of primary-school-age children who were enrolled in school for 19 countries in Northern Africa and for 23 countries in Central Africa.

Northern Africa

54.6	34.3	48.9	77.8	59.6	88.5	97.4	92.5	83.9	96.9	88.9
98.8	91.6	97.8	96.1	92.2	94.9	98.6	86.6			

Central Africa

58.3	34.6	35.5	45.4	38.6	63.8	53.9	61.9	69.9	43.0	85.0
63.4	58.4	61.9	40.9	73.9	34.8	74.4	97.4	61.0	66.7	79.6
98.9										

We will construct a comparative stem-and-leaf display using the first digit of each observation as the stem and the remaining two digits as the leaf. To keep the display simple the leaves will be truncated to one digit. For example, the observation 54.6 would be processed as

$$54.6 \rightarrow \text{stem} = 5, \text{leaf} = 4 \text{ (truncated from 4.6)}$$

and the observation 34.3 would be processed as

$$34.3 \rightarrow \text{stem} = 3, \text{leaf} = 4 \text{ (truncated from 4.3)}$$

The resulting comparative stem-and-leaf display is shown in Figure 3.16.

Central Africa		Northern Africa
4854	3	4
035	4	8
838	5	49
6113913	6	
943	7	76
5	8	8386
87	9	7268176248

Stem: Tens
Leaf: Ones

FIGURE 3.16
Comparative stem-and-leaf display for percentage of children enrolled in primary school.

From the comparative stem-and-leaf display you can see that there is quite a bit of variability in the percentage enrolled in school for both Northern and Central African countries and that the shapes of the two data distributions are quite different. The percentage enrolled in school tends to be higher in Northern African countries than in Central African countries, although the smallest value in each of the two data sets is about the same. For Northern African countries the distribution of values has a single peak in the 90s with the number of observations declining as we move toward the stems corresponding to lower percentages enrolled in school. For Central African countries the distribution is more symmetric, with a typical value in the mid 60s.

● Data set available online

EXERCISES 3.15 - 3.21

3.15 ● The U.S. Department of Health and Human Services provided the data in the accompanying table in the report "Births: Preliminary Data for 2007" (*National Vital Statistics Reports*, March 18, 2009). Entries in the table are the birth rates (births per 1,000 of population) for the year 2007.

State	Births per 1,000 of Population
Alabama	14.0
Alaska	16.2
Arizona	16.2
Arkansas	14.6
California	15.5
Colorado	14.6
Connecticut	11.9
Delaware	14.1
District of Columbia	15.1
Florida	13.1
Georgia	15.9
Hawaii	14.9
Idaho	16.7
Illinois	14.1
Indiana	14.2
Iowa	13.7
Kansas	15.1
Kentucky	14.0
Louisiana	15.4
Maine	10.7
Maryland	13.9
Massachusetts	12.1
Michigan	12.4
Minnesota	14.2
Mississippi	15.9
Missouri	13.9
Montana	13.0
Nebraska	15.2
Nevada	16.1
New Hampshire	10.8
New Jersey	13.4
New Mexico	15.5
New York	13.1
North Carolina	14.5
North Dakota	13.8
Ohio	13.2
Oklahoma	15.2
Oregon	13.2
Pennsylvania	12.1
Rhode Island	11.7
South Carolina	14.3
South Dakota	15.4
Tennessee	14.1
Texas	17.1
Utah	20.8
Vermont	10.5
Virginia	14.1
Washington	13.8
West Virginia	12.1
Wisconsin	13.0
Wyoming	15.1

Construct a stem-and-leaf display using stems 10, 11 . . . 20. Comment on the interesting features of the display.

3.16 ● ✦ The National Survey on Drug Use and Health, conducted in 2006 and 2007 by the Office of Applied Studies, led to the following state estimates of the total number of people ages 12 and older who had used a tobacco product within the last month.

State	Number of People (in thousands)
Alabama	1,307
Alaska	161
Arizona	1,452
Arkansas	819
California	6,751
Colorado	1,171
Connecticut	766
Delaware	200
District of Columbia	141
Florida	4,392
Georgia	2,341
Hawaii	239
Idaho	305
Illinois	3,149
Indiana	1,740
Iowa	755
Kansas	726
Kentucky	1,294
Louisiana	1,138
Maine	347
Maryland	1,206
Massachusetts	1,427
Michigan	2,561
Minnesota	1,324

(continued)

State	Number of People (in thousands)
Mississippi	763
Missouri	1,627
Montana	246
Nebraska	429
Nevada	612
New Hampshire	301
New Jersey	1,870
New Mexico	452
New York	4,107
North Carolina	2,263
North Dakota	162
Ohio	3,256
Oklahoma	1,057
Oregon	857
Pennsylvania	3,170
Rhode Island	268
South Carolina	1,201
South Dakota	202
Tennessee	1,795
Texas	5,533
Utah	402
Vermont	158
Virginia	1,771
Washington	1,436
West Virginia	582
Wisconsin	1,504
Wyoming	157

a. Construct a stem-and-leaf display using thousands (of thousands) as the stems and truncating the leaves to the tens (of thousands) digit.

b. Write a few sentences describing the shape of the distribution and any unusual observations.

c. The four largest values were for California, Texas, Florida, and New York. Does this indicate that tobacco use is more of a problem in these states than elsewhere? Explain.

d. If you wanted to compare states on the basis of the extent of tobacco use, would you use the data in the given table? If yes, explain why this would be reasonable. If no, what would you use instead as the basis for the comparison?

3.17 ● The article "Going Wireless" (*AARP Bulletin*, June 2009) reported the estimated percentage of households with only wireless phone service (no land line) for the 50 U.S. states and the District of Columbia. In the accompanying data table, each state was also classified into one of three geographical regions—West (W), Middle states (M), and East (E).

Wireless %	Region	State
13.9	M	AL
11.7	W	AK
18.9	W	AZ
22.6	M	AR
9.0	W	CA
16.7	W	CO
5.6	E	CN
5.7	E	DE
20.0	E	DC
16.8	E	FL
16.5	E	GA
8.0	W	HI
22.1	W	ID
16.5	M	IL
13.8	M	IN
22.2	M	IA
16.8	M	KA
21.4	M	KY
15.0	M	LA
13.4	E	ME
10.8	E	MD
9.3	E	MA
16.3	M	MI
17.4	M	MN
19.1	M	MS
9.9	M	MO
9.2	W	MT
23.2	M	NE
10.8	W	NV
16.9	M	ND
11.6	E	NH
8.0	E	NJ
21.1	W	NM
11.4	E	NY
16.3	E	NC
14.0	E	OH
23.2	M	OK
17.7	W	OR
10.8	E	PA
7.9	E	RI
20.6	E	SC
6.4	M	SD
20.3	M	TN
20.9	M	TX
25.5	W	UT
10.8	E	VA
5.1	E	VT
16.3	W	WA
11.6	E	WV
15.2	M	WI
11.4	W	WY

a. Construct a stem-and-leaf display for the wireless percentage using the data from all 50 states and the District of Columbia. What is a typical value for this data set?

b. Construct a back-to-back stem-and-leaf display for the wireless percentage of the states in the West and the states in the East. How do the distributions of wireless percentages compare for states in the East and states in the West?

3.18 The article "Economy Low, Generosity High" (*USA Today*, July 28, 2009) noted that despite a weak economy in 2008, more Americans volunteered in their communities than in previous years. Based on census data (www.volunteeringinamerica.gov), the top and bottom five states in terms of percentage of the population who volunteered in 2008 were identified. The top five states were Utah (43.5%), Nebraska (38.9%), Minnesota (38.4%), Alaska (38.0%), and Iowa (37.1%). The bottom five states were New York (18.5%), Nevada (18.8%), Florida (19.6%), Louisiana (20.1%), and Mississippi (20.9%).

a. For the data set that includes the percentage who volunteered in 2008 for each of the 50 states, what is the largest value? What is the smallest value?

b. If you were going to construct a stem-and-leaf display for the data set consisting of the percentage who volunteered in 2008 for the 50 states, what stems would you use to construct the display? Explain your choice.

3.19 ● The article "Frost Belt Feels Labor Drain" (*USA Today*, May 1, 2008) points out that even though total population is increasing, the pool of young workers is shrinking in many states. This observation was prompted by the data in the accompanying table. Entries in the table are the percent change in the population of 25- to 44-year-olds over the period from 2000 to 2007. A negative percent change corresponds to a state that had fewer 25- to 44-year-olds in 2007 than in 2000 (a decrease in the pool of young workers).

State	% Change
Alabama	−4.1
Alaska	−2.5
Arizona	17.8
Arkansas	0.9
California	−0.4
Colorado	4.1
Connecticut	−9.9
Delaware	−2.2
District of Columbia	1.8
Florida	5.8
Georgia	7.2
Hawaii	−1.3
Idaho	11.1
Illinois	−4.6
Indiana	−3.1
Iowa	−6.5
Kansas	−5.3
Kentucky	−1.7
Louisiana	−11.9
Maine	−8.7
Maryland	−5.7
Massachusetts	−9.6
Michigan	−9.1
Minnesota	−4.5
Mississippi	−5.2
Missouri	−2.9
Montana	−3.7
Nebraska	−5.6
Nevada	22.0
New Hampshire	−7.5
New Jersey	−7.8
New Mexico	0.6
New York	−8.0
North Carolina	2.4
North Dakota	−10.9
Ohio	−8.2
Oklahoma	−1.6
Oregon	4.4
Pennsylvania	−9.1
Rhode Island	−8.8
South Carolina	0.1
South Dakota	−4.1
Tennessee	0.6
Texas	7.3
Utah	19.6
Vermont	−10.4
Virginia	−1.1
Washington	1.6
West Virginia	−5.4
Wisconsin	−5.0
Wyoming	−2.3

a. The smallest value in the data set is −11.9 and the largest value is 22.0. One possible choice of stems for a stem-and-leaf display would be to use the tens digit, resulting in stems of −1, −0, 0, 1, and 2. Notice that because there are both negative and positive values in the data set, we would want to use two 0 stems—one where we can enter leaves for the negative percent changes that are between 0 and −9.9, and one where we could enter leaves for the positive percent changes that are between 0 and 9.9. Construct a stem-and-leaf plot using these five stems. (Hint: Think of each data value as having two digits before the decimal place, so 4.1 would be regarded as 04.1.)

b. Using two-digit stems would result in more than 30 stems, which is more than we would usually want for a stem-and-leaf display. Describe a strategy for using repeated stems that would result in a stem-and-leaf display with about 10 stems.

c. The article described "the frost belt" as the cold part of the country—the Northeast and Midwest—noting that states in the frost belt generally showed a decline in the number of people in the 25- to 44-year-old age group. How would you describe the group of states that saw a marked increase in the number of 25- to 44-year-olds?

3.20 ● ✦ A report from Texas Transportation Institute (Texas A&M University System, 2005) titled "Congestion Reduction Strategies" included the accompanying data on extra travel time for peak travel time in hours per year per traveler for different sized urban areas.

Very Large Urban Areas	Extra Hours per Year per Traveler
Los Angeles, CA	93
San Francisco, CA	72
Washington DC, VA, MD	69
Atlanta, GA	67
Houston, TX	63
Dallas, Fort Worth, TX	60
Chicago, IL-IN	58
Detroit, MI	57
Miami, FL	51
Boston, MA, NH, RI	51
New York, NY-NJ-CT	49
Phoenix, AZ	49
Philadelphia, PA-NJ-DE-MD	38

Large Urban Areas	Extra Hours per Year per Traveler
Riverside, CA	55
Orlando, FL	55
San Jose, CA	53
San Diego, CA	52
Denver, CO	51
Baltimore, MD	50
Seattle, WA	46
Tampa, FL	46
Minneapolis, St Paul, MN	43
Sacramento, CA	40
Portland, OR, WA	39
Indianapolis, IN	38
St Louis, MO-IL	35
San Antonio, TX	33
Providence, RI, MA	33
Las Vegas, NV	30
Cincinnati, OH-KY-IN	30
Columbus, OH	29
Virginia Beach, VA	26
Milwaukee, WI	23
New Orleans, LA	18
Kansas City, MO-KS	17
Pittsburgh, PA	14
Buffalo, NY	13
Oklahoma City, OK	12
Cleveland, OH	10

a. Construct a comparative stem-and-leaf plot for annual delay per traveler for each of the two different sizes of urban areas.

b. Is the following statement consistent with the display constructed in Part (a)? Explain.

The larger the urban area, the greater the extra travel time during peak period travel.

3.21 ● High school dropout rates (percentages) for 2008 for the 50 states were given in the 2008 Kids Count Data Book (www.aecf.org) and are shown in the following table:

State	Rate
Alabama	8%
Alaska	10%
Arizona	9%
Arkansas	9%
California	6%
Colorado	8%
Connecticut	5%
Delaware	7%
Florida	7%
Georgia	8%
Hawaii	8%
Idaho	6%

(continued)

State	Rate
Illinois	6%
Indiana	8%
Iowa	3%
Kansas	5%
Kentucky	7%
Louisiana	10%
Maine	6%
Maryland	6%
Massachusetts	4%
Michigan	6%
Minnesota	3%
Mississippi	7%
Missouri	7%
Montana	9%
Nebraska	4%
Nevada	10%
New Hampshire	3%
New Jersey	4%
New Mexico	10%
New York	5%
North Carolina	8%
North Dakota	7%
Ohio	5%
Oklahoma	8%
Oregon	6%
Pennsylvania	5%
Rhode Island	6%
South Carolina	7%
South Dakota	6%

(continued)

State	Rate
Tennessee	7%
Texas	7%
Utah	7%
Vermont	4%
Virginia	4%
Washington	7%
West Virginia	8%
Wisconsin	4%
Wyoming	6%

Note that dropout rates range from a low of 3% to a high of 10%. In constructing a stem-and-leaf display for these data, if we regard each dropout rate as a two-digit number and use the first digit for the stem, then there are only two possible stems, 0 and 1. One solution is to use repeated stems. Consider a scheme that divides the leaf range into five parts: 0 and 1, 2 and 3, 4 and 5, 6 and 7, and 8 and 9. Then, for example, stem 0 could be repeated as

0 with leaves 0 and 1
0t with leaves 2 and 3
0f with leaves 4 and 5
0s with leaves 6 and 7
0* with leaves 8 and 9

Construct a stem-and-leaf display for this data set that uses stems 0t, 0f, 0s, 0*, and 1. Comment on the important features of the display.

3.3 Displaying Numerical Data: Frequency Distributions and Histograms

A stem-and-leaf display is not always an effective way to summarize data; it is unwieldy when the data set contains a large number of observations. Frequency distributions and histograms are displays that work well for large data sets.

Frequency Distributions and Histograms for Discrete Numerical Data

Discrete numerical data almost always result from counting. In such cases, each observation is a whole number. As in the case of categorical data, a frequency distribution for discrete numerical data lists each possible value (either individually or grouped into intervals), the associated frequency, and sometimes the corresponding relative frequency. Recall that relative frequency is calculated by dividing the frequency by the total number of observations in the data set.

EXAMPLE 3.12 Promiscuous Queen Bees

● Queen honey bees mate shortly after they become adults. During a mating flight, the queen usually takes multiple partners, collecting sperm that she will store and use throughout the rest of her life. The authors of the paper "The Curious Promiscuity of Queen Honey Bees" (*Annals of Zoology* [2001]: 255–265) studied the behavior of 30 queen honey bees to learn about the length of mating flights and the number of partners a queen takes during a mating flight. The accompanying data on number of partners were generated to be consistent with summary values and graphs given in the paper.

Number of Partners

12	2	4	6	6	7	8	7	8	11
8	3	5	6	7	10	1	9	7	6
9	7	5	4	7	4	6	7	8	10

The corresponding relative frequency distribution is given in Table 3.1. The smallest value in the data set is 1 and the largest is 12, so the possible values from 1 to 12 are listed in the table, along with the corresponding frequency and relative frequency.

TABLE 3.1 Relative Frequency Distribution for Number of Partners

Number of Partners	Frequency	Relative Frequency
1	1	.033
2	1	.033
3	1	.033
4	3	.100
5	2	.067
6	5	.167
7	7	.233
8	4	.133
9	2	.067
10	2	.067
11	1	.033
12	1	.033
Total	30	.999

$\frac{1}{30} = .033$

Differs from 1 due to rounding

From the relative frequency distribution, we can see that five of the queen bees had six partners during their mating flight. The corresponding relative frequency, $\frac{5}{30} = .167$, tells us that the proportion of queens with six partners is .167, or equivalently 16.7% of the queens had six partners. Adding the relative frequencies for the values 10, 11, and 12 gives

$$.067 + .033 + .033 = .133$$

indicating that 13.3% of the queens had 10 or more partners.

● Data set available online

It is possible to create a more compact frequency distribution by grouping some of the possible values into intervals. For example, we might group together 1, 2, and 3 partners to form an interval of 1–3, with a corresponding frequency of 3. The grouping of other values in a similar way results in the relative frequency distribution shown in Table 3.2.

TABLE 3.2 Relative Frequency Distribution of Number of Partners Using Intervals

Number of Partners	Frequency	Relative Frequency
1–3	3	.100
4–6	10	.333
7–9	13	.433
10–12	4	.133

A histogram for discrete numerical data is a graph of the frequency or relative frequency distribution, and it is similar to the bar chart for categorical data. Each frequency or relative frequency is represented by a rectangle centered over the corresponding value (or range of values) and the area of the rectangle is proportional to the corresponding frequency or relative frequency.

Histogram for Discrete Numerical Data

When to Use Discrete numerical data. Works well, even for large data sets.

How to Construct

1. Draw a horizontal scale, and mark the possible values of the variable.
2. Draw a vertical scale, and mark it with either frequency or relative frequency.
3. Above each possible value, draw a rectangle centered at that value (so that the rectangle for 1 is centered at 1, the rectangle for 5 is centered at 5, and so on). The height of each rectangle is determined by the corresponding frequency or relative frequency. Often possible values are consecutive whole numbers, in which case the base width for each rectangle is 1.

What to Look For

- Center or typical value
- Extent of spread or variability
- General shape
- Location and number of peaks
- Presence of gaps and outliers

AP* EXAM TIP

When constructing graphical displays with numerical data, take extra care to make sure the spacing of intervals on the horizontal axis accurately reflects the corresponding interval widths.

EXAMPLE 3.13 Revisiting Promiscuous Queen Bees

The queen bee data of Example 3.12 were summarized in a frequency distribution. The corresponding histogram is shown in Figure 3.17. Note that each rectangle in the histogram is centered over the corresponding value. When relative frequency instead of frequency is used for the vertical scale, the scale on the vertical axis is different but all essential characteristics of the graph (shape, location, spread) are unchanged.

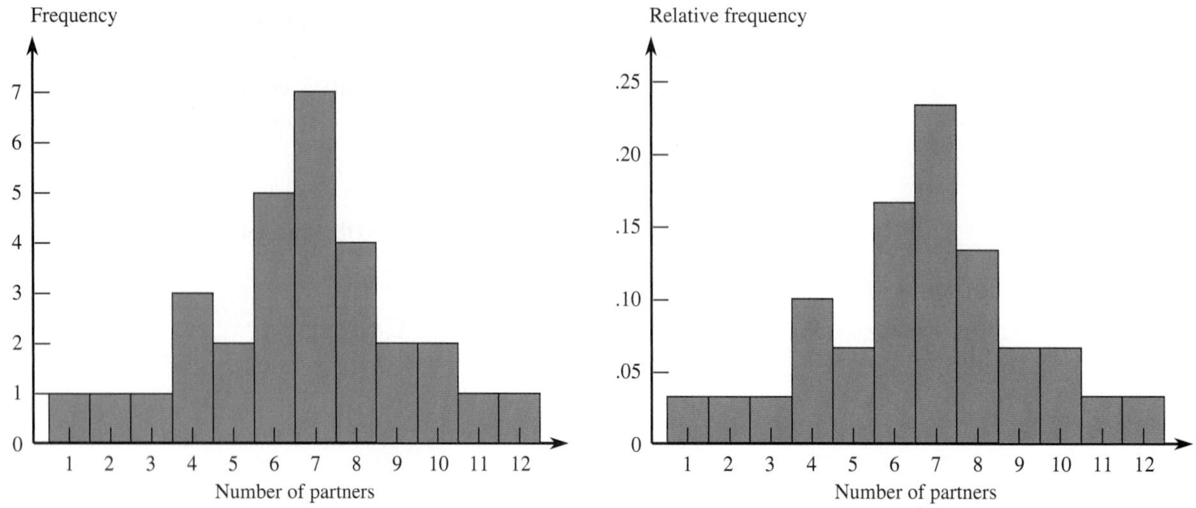

FIGURE 3.17
Histogram and relative frequency histogram of queen bee data.

A histogram based on the grouped frequency distribution of Table 3.2 can be constructed in a similar fashion, and is shown in Figure 3.18. A rectangle represents the frequency or relative frequency for each interval. For the interval 1–3, the rectangle extends from .5 to 3.5 so that there are no gaps between the rectangles of the histogram.

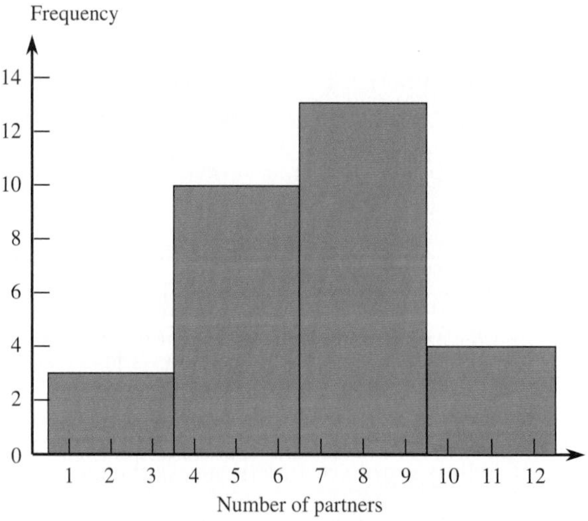

FIGURE 3.18
Histogram of queen bee data using intervals.

Sometimes a discrete numerical data set contains a large number of possible values and perhaps also has a few large or small values that are far away from most of the data. In this case, rather than forming a frequency distribution with a very long list of possible values, it is common to group the observed values into intervals or ranges. This is illustrated in Example 3.14.

EXAMPLE 3.14 Math SAT Score Distribution

Each of the 1,530,128 students who took the math portion of the SAT exam in 2009 received a score between 200 and 800. The score distribution was summarized in a frequency distribution table that appeared in the College Board report titled "2009 College Bound Seniors." A relative frequency distribution is given in Table 3.3 and

TABLE 3.3 Relative Frequency Distribution of Math SAT Score

Math SAT Score	Frequency	Relative Frequency
200–299	97,296	0.064
300–399	295,693	0.193
400–499	449,238	0.294
500–599	454,497	0.297
600–699	197,741	0.129
700–800	35,663	0.023

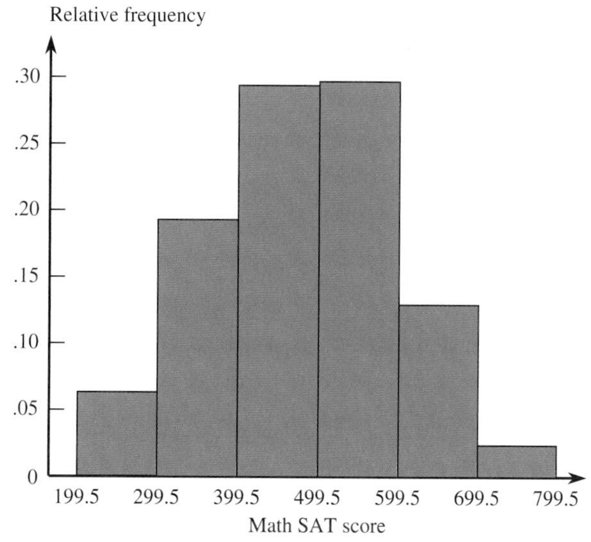

FIGURE 3.19
Relative frequency histogram for the math SAT data.

the corresponding relative frequency histogram is shown in Figure 3.19. Notice that rather than list each possible individual score value between 200 and 800, the scores are grouped into intervals (200 to 299, 300 to 399, etc.). This results in a much more compact table that still communicates the important features of the data set. Also, notice that because the data set is so large, the frequencies are also large numbers. Because of these large frequencies, it is easier to focus on the relative frequencies in our interpretation. From the relative frequency distribution and histogram, we can see that while there is a lot of variability in individual math SAT scores, the majority were in the 400 to 600 range and a typical value for math SAT looks to be something in the low 500s.

Before leaving this example, take a second look at the relative frequency histogram of Figure 3.19. Notice that there is one rectangle for each score interval in the relative frequency distribution. For simplicity we have chosen to treat the very last interval, 700 to 800, as if it were 700 to 799 so that all of the score ranges in the frequency distribution are the same width. Also note that the rectangle representing the score range 400 to 499 actually extends from 399.5 to 499.5 on the score scale. This is similar to what happens in histograms for discrete numerical data where there is no grouping. For example, in Figure 3.17 the rectangle representing 2 is centered at 2 but extends from 1.5 to 2.5 on the number of partners scale.

Frequency Distributions and Histograms for Continuous Numerical Data

The difficulty in constructing tabular or graphical displays with continuous data, such as observations on reaction time (in seconds) or weight of airline passenger carry-on luggage (in pounds), is that there are no natural categories. The way out of this dilemma is to define our own categories. For carry-on luggage weight, we might expect weights up to about 30 pounds. One way to group the weights into 5-pound intervals is shown in Figure 3.20. Then each observed data value could be classified into one of these intervals. The intervals used are sometimes called **class intervals**. The class intervals play the same role that the categories or individual values played in frequency distributions for categorical or discrete numerical data.

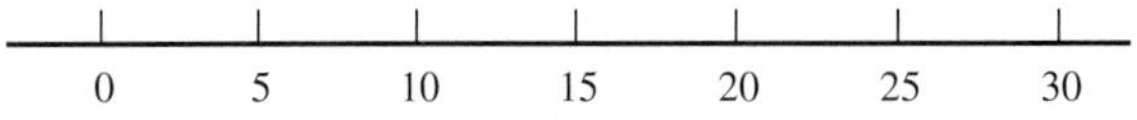

FIGURE 3.20
Suitable class intervals for carry-on luggage weight data.

There is one further difficulty we need to address. Where should we place an observation such as 20, which falls on a boundary between classes? Our convention is to define intervals so that such an observation is placed in the upper rather than the lower class interval. Thus, in a frequency distribution, one class might be 15 to <20, where the symbol < is a substitute for the phrase *less than.* This class will contain all observations that are greater than or equal to 15 and less than 20. The observation 20 would then fall in the class 20 to <25.

EXAMPLE 3.15 Enrollments at Public Universities

● States differ widely in the percentage of college students who are enrolled in public institutions. The National Center for Education Statistics provided the accompanying data on this percentage for the 50 U.S. states for fall 2007.

Percentage of College Students Enrolled in Public Institutions

96	86	81	84	77	90	73	53	90	96	73
93	76	86	78	76	88	86	87	64	60	58
89	86	80	66	70	90	89	82	73	81	73
72	56	55	75	77	82	83	79	75	59	59
43	50	64	80	82	75					

The smallest observation is 46 (Massachusetts) and the largest is 96 (Alaska and Wyoming). It is reasonable to start the first class interval at 40 and let each interval have a width of 10. This gives class intervals of 40 to <50, 50 to <60, 60 to <70, 70 to <80, 80 to <90, and 90 to <100.

Table 3.4 displays the resulting frequency distribution, along with the relative frequencies.

● Data set available online

TABLE 3.4 Frequency Distribution for Percentage of College Students Enrolled in Public Institutions

Class Interval	Frequency	Relative Frequency
40 to <50	1	.02
50 to <60	7	.14
60 to <70	4	.08
70 to <80	15	.30
80 to <90	17	.34
90 to <100	6	.12
	50	1.00

Various relative frequencies can be combined to yield other interesting information. For example,

$$\begin{pmatrix}\text{proportion of states}\\ \text{with percent in public}\\ \text{institutions less than 60}\end{pmatrix} = \begin{pmatrix}\text{proportion in 40}\\ \text{to <50 class}\end{pmatrix} + \begin{pmatrix}\text{proportion in 50}\\ \text{to <60 class}\end{pmatrix}$$

$$= .02 + .14 = .16 \quad (16\%)$$

and

$$\begin{pmatrix}\text{proportion of states}\\ \text{with percent in}\\ \text{public institutions}\\ \text{between 60 and 90}\end{pmatrix} = \begin{pmatrix}\text{proportion}\\ \text{in 60 to}\\ \text{<70 class}\end{pmatrix} + \begin{pmatrix}\text{proportion}\\ \text{in 70 to}\\ \text{<80 class}\end{pmatrix} + \begin{pmatrix}\text{proportion}\\ \text{in 80 to}\\ \text{<90 class}\end{pmatrix}$$

$$= .08 + .30 + .34 = .72 \quad (72\%)$$

There are no set rules for selecting either the number of class intervals or the length of the intervals. Using a few relatively wide intervals will bunch the data, whereas using a great many relatively narrow intervals may spread the data over too many intervals, so that no interval contains more than a few observations. Neither type of distribution will give an informative picture of how values are distributed over the range of measurement, and interesting features of the data set may be missed. In general, with a small amount of data, relatively few intervals, perhaps between 5 and 10, should be used. With a large amount of data, a distribution based on 15 to 20 (or even more) intervals is often recommended. The quantity

$$\sqrt{\text{number of observations}}$$

is often used as an estimate of an appropriate number of intervals: 5 intervals for 25 observations, 10 intervals when the number of observations is 100, and so on.

Two people making reasonable and similar choices for the number of intervals, their width, and the starting point of the first interval will usually obtain similar histograms of the data.

Histograms for Continuous Numerical Data

When the class intervals in a frequency distribution are all of equal width, it is easy to construct a histogram using the information in a frequency distribution.

Histogram for Continuous Numerical Data When the Class Interval Widths are Equal

When to Use Continuous numerical data. Works well, even for large data sets.

How to Construct

1. Mark the boundaries of the class intervals on a horizontal axis.
2. Use either frequency or relative frequency on the vertical axis.
3. Draw a rectangle for each class directly above the corresponding interval (so that the edges are at the class interval boundaries). The height of each rectangle is the frequency or relative frequency of the corresponding class interval.

What to Look For

- Center or typical value
- Extent of spread, variability
- General shape
- Location and number of peaks
- Presence of gaps and outliers

EXAMPLE 3.16 TV Viewing Habits of Children

The article "Early Television Exposure and Subsequent Attention Problems in Children" (*Pediatrics*, April 2004) investigated the television viewing habits of children in the United States. Table 3.5 gives approximate relative frequencies (read from graphs that appeared in the article) for the number of hours spent watching TV per day for a sample of children at age 1 year and a sample of children at age 3 years. The data summarized in the article were obtained as part of a large scale national survey.

TABLE 3.5 Relative Frequency Distribution for Number of Hours Spent Watching TV per Day

TV Hours per Day	Age 1 Year Relative Frequency	Age 3 Years Relative Frequency
0 to <2	.270	.630
2 to <4	.390	.195
4 to <6	.190	.100
6 to <8	.085	.025
8 to <10	.030	.020
10 to <12	.020	.015
12 to <14	.010	.010
14 to <16	.005	.005

Figure 3.21(a) is the relative frequency histogram for the 1-year-old children and Figure 3.21(b) is the relative frequency histogram for 3-year-old children. Notice that both histograms have a single peak with the majority of children in both age groups concentrated in the smaller TV hours intervals. Both histograms are quite stretched out at the upper end, indicating some young children watch a lot of TV.

The big difference between the two histograms is at the low end, with a much higher proportion of 3-year-old children falling in the 0 to 2 TV hours interval than is the case for 1-year-old children. A typical number of TV hours per day for 1-year-old children would be somewhere between 2 and 4 hours, whereas a typical number of TV hours for 3-year-old children is in the 0 to 2 hours interval.

Step-by-step technology instructions available online

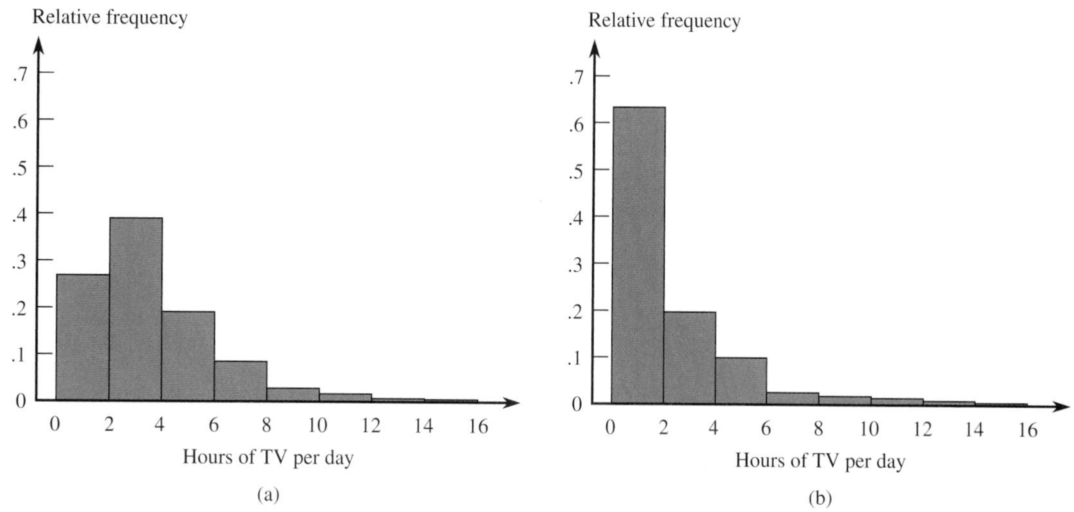

FIGURE 3.21
Histogram of TV hours per day: (a) 1-year-old children; (b) 3-year-old children.

Class Intervals of Unequal Widths Figure 3.22 shows a data set in which a great many observations are concentrated at the center of the data set, with only a few unusual, or stray, values both below and above the main body of data. If a frequency distribution is based on short intervals of equal width, a great many intervals will be required to capture all observations, and many of them will contain no observations, as shown in Figure 3.22(a). On the other hand, only a few wide intervals will capture all values, but then most of the observations will be grouped into a few intervals, as shown in Figure 3.22(b). In such situations, it is best to use a combination of wide class intervals where there are few data points and shorter intervals where there are many data points, as shown in Figure 3.22(c).

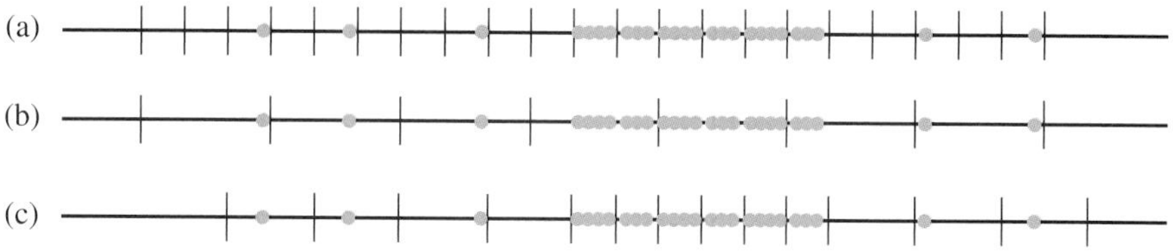

FIGURE 3.22
Three choices of class intervals for a data set with outliers: (a) many short intervals of equal width; (b) a few wide intervals of equal width; (c) intervals of unequal width.

Constructing a Histogram for Continuous Data When Class Interval Widths are Unequal

When class intervals are not of equal width, frequencies or relative frequencies should not be used on the vertical axis. Instead, the height of each rectangle, called the **density** for the class interval, is given by

$$\text{density} = \text{rectangle height} = \frac{\text{relative frequency of class interval}}{\text{class interval width}}$$

The vertical axis is called the **density scale.**

The use of the density scale to construct the histogram ensures that the area of each rectangle in the histogram will be proportional to the corresponding relative frequency. The formula for density can also be used when class widths are equal. However, when the intervals are of equal width, the extra arithmetic required to obtain the densities is unnecessary.

EXAMPLE 3.17 Misreporting Grade Point Average

When people are asked for the values of characteristics such as age or weight, they sometimes shade the truth in their responses. The article "Self-Reports of Academic Performance" (*Social Methods and Research* [November 1981]: 165–185) focused on such characteristics as SAT scores and grade point average (GPA). For each student in a sample, the difference in GPA (reported – actual) was determined. Positive differences resulted from individuals reporting GPAs larger than the correct values. Most differences were close to 0, but there were some rather large errors. Because of this, the frequency distribution based on unequal class widths shown in Table 3.6 gives an informative yet concise summary.

TABLE 3.6 Frequency Distribution for Errors in Reported GPA

Class Interval	Relative Frequency	Width	Density
−2.0 to <−0.4	.023	1.6	0.014
−0.4 to <−0.2	.055	.2	0.275
−0.2 to <−0.1	.097	.1	0.970
−0.1 to <0	.210	.1	2.100
0 to <0.1	.189	.1	1.890
0.1 to <0.2	.139	.1	1.390
0.2 to <0.4	.116	.2	0.580
0.4 to <2.0	.171	1.6	0.107

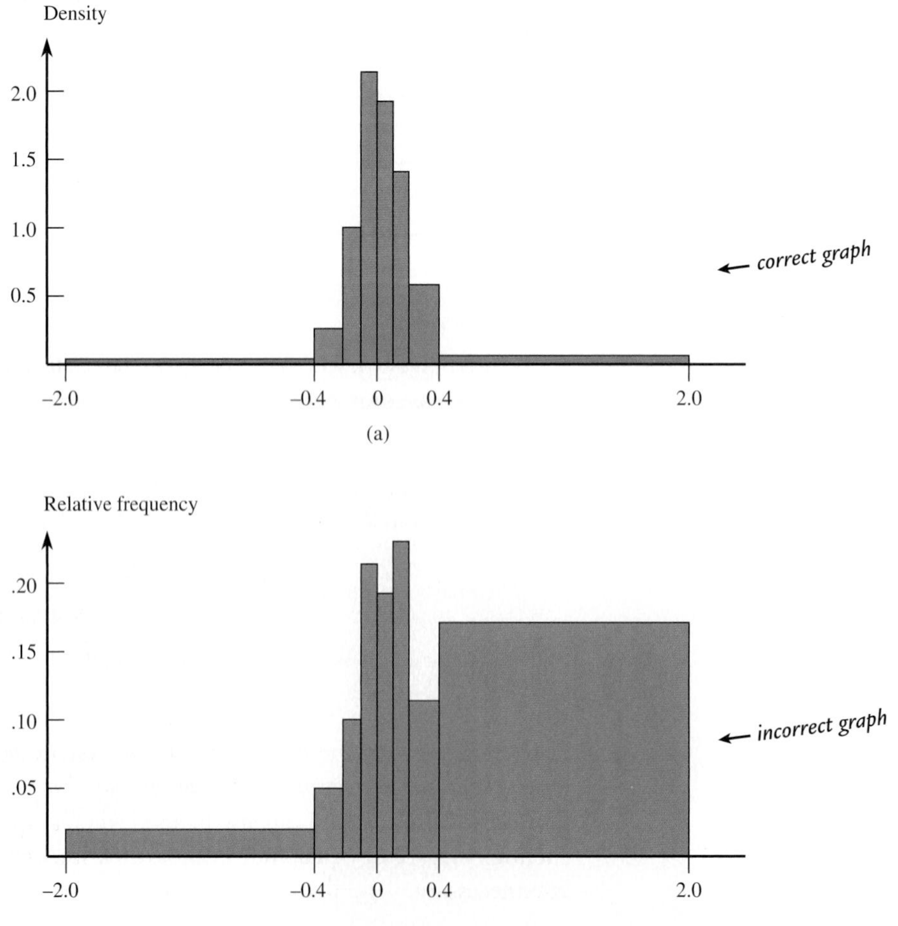

FIGURE 3.23
Histograms for errors in reporting GPA: (a) a correct histogram (height = density); (b) an incorrect histogram (height = relative frequency).

Figure 3.23 displays two histograms based on this frequency distribution. The histogram in Figure 3.23(a) is correctly drawn, with density used to determine the height of each bar. The histogram in Figure 3.23(b) has height equal to relative frequency and is therefore not correct. In particular, this second histogram considerably exaggerates the incidence of grossly overreported and underreported values—the areas of the two most extreme rectangles are much too large. The eye is naturally drawn to large areas, so it is important that the areas correctly represent the relative frequencies.

AP* EXAM TIP

The shape of a univariate data distribution is an important characteristic. Be sure to learn the terminology used to describe distribution shape.

Histogram Shapes

General shape is an important characteristic of a histogram. In describing various shapes it is convenient to approximate the histogram itself with a smooth curve (called a *smoothed histogram*). This is illustrated in Figure 3.24.

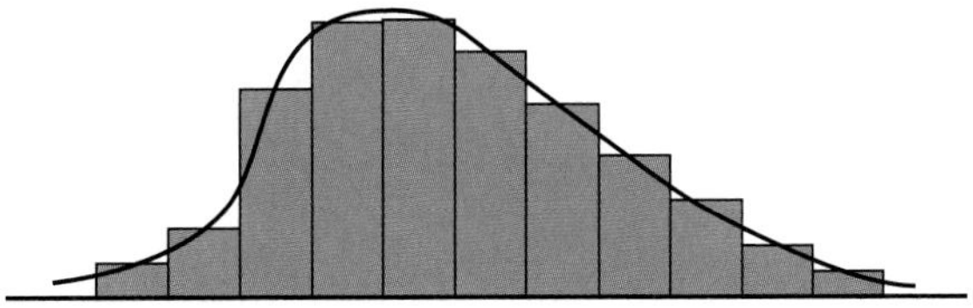

FIGURE 3.24
Approximating a histogram with a smooth curve.

One description of general shape relates to the number of peaks, or **modes**.

DEFINITION

A histogram is said to be **unimodal** if it has a single peak, **bimodal** if it has two peaks, and **multimodal** if it has more than two peaks.

These shapes are illustrated in Figure 3.25.

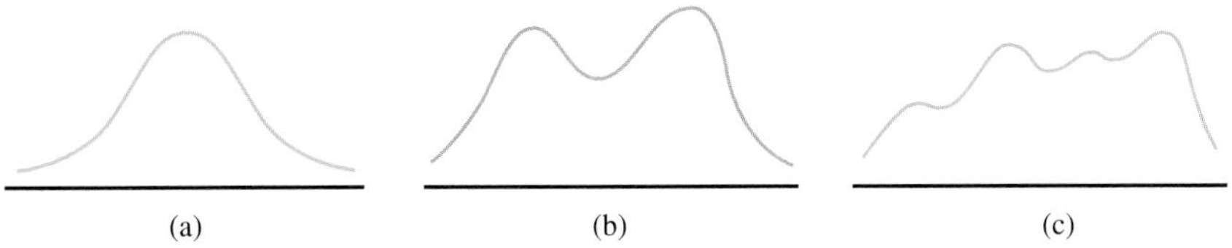

FIGURE 3.25
Smoothed histograms with various numbers of modes: (a) unimodal; (b) bimodal; (c) multimodal.

Bimodality sometimes occurs when the data set consists of observations on two quite different kinds of individuals or objects. For example, consider a large data set consisting of driving times for automobiles traveling between San Luis Obispo, California, and Monterey, California. This histogram would show two peaks, one for those cars that took the inland route (roughly 2.5 hours) and another for those cars traveling up the coast highway (3.5–4 hours). However, bimodality does not automatically follow in such situations. Bimodality will occur in the histogram of the combined groups only if the centers of the two separate histograms are far apart relative to the variability in the two data sets. Thus, a large data set consisting of heights of college students would probably not produce a bimodal histogram because the typical height for males (about 69 in.) and the typical height for females (about 66 in.) are not very far apart. Many histograms encountered in practice are unimodal, and multimodality is not as common.

Unimodal histograms come in a variety of shapes. A unimodal histogram is **symmetric** if there is a vertical line of symmetry such that the part of the histogram to the left of the line is a mirror image of the part to the right. (Bimodal and multimodal

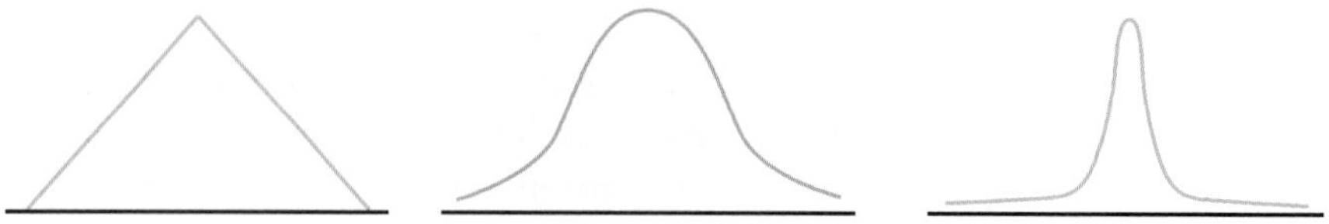

FIGURE 3.26
Several symmetric unimodal smoothed histograms.

histograms can also be symmetric in this way.) Several different symmetric smoothed histograms are shown in Figure 3.26.

Proceeding to the right from the peak of a unimodal histogram, we move into what is called the **upper tail** of the histogram. Going in the opposite direction moves us into the **lower tail**.

DEFINITION

A unimodal histogram that is not symmetric is said to be **skewed**. If the upper tail of the histogram stretches out much farther than the lower tail, then the distribution of values is **positively skewed** or **right skewed**. If, on the other hand, the lower tail is much longer than the upper tail, the histogram is **negatively skewed** or **left skewed**.

These two types of skewness are illustrated in Figure 3.27. Positive skewness is much more frequently encountered than is negative skewness. An example of positive skewness occurs in the distribution of single-family home prices in Los Angeles County; most homes are moderately priced (at least for California), whereas the relatively few homes in Beverly Hills and Malibu have much higher price tags.

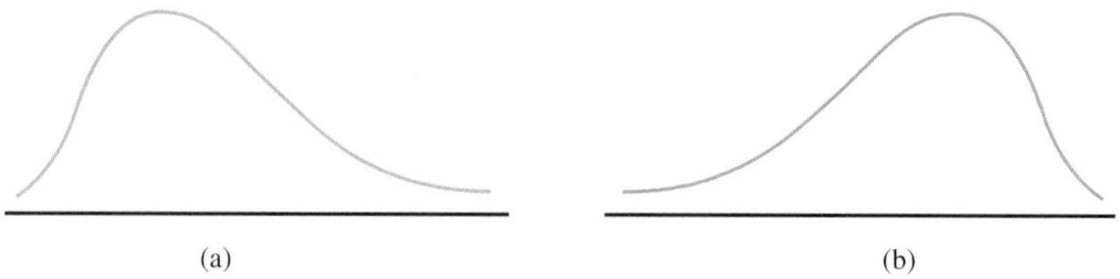

FIGURE 3.27
Two examples of skewed smoothed histograms: (a) positive skew; (b) negative skew.

One rather specific shape, a **normal curve**, arises more frequently than any other in statistical applications. Many histograms can be well approximated by a normal curve (for example, characteristics such as arm span and the weight of an apple). Here we briefly mention several of the most important qualitative properties of normal curves, postponing a more detailed discussion until Chapter 7. A normal curve is both symmetric and bell-shaped; it looks like the curve in Figure 3.28(a). However, not all bell-shaped curves are normal. In a normal curve, starting from the top of the bell the height of the curve decreases at a well-defined rate when moving toward either tail. (This rate of decrease is specified by a certain mathematical function.)

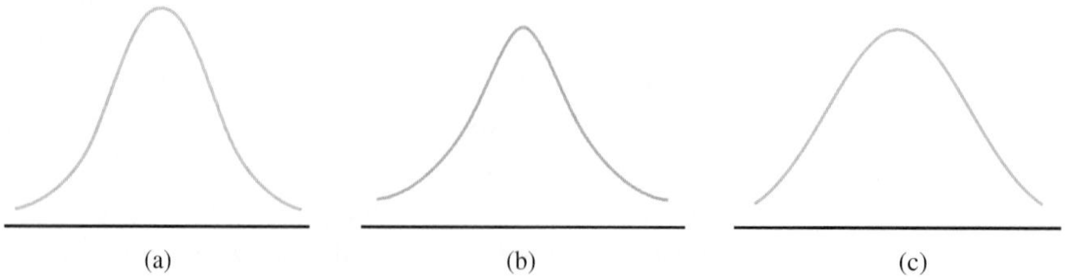

FIGURE 3.28
Three examples of bell-shaped histograms: (a) normal; (b) heavy-tailed; (c) light-tailed.

A curve with tails that do not decline as rapidly as the tails of a normal curve is called **heavy-tailed** (compared to the normal curve). Similarly, a curve with tails that decrease more rapidly than the normal tails is called **light-tailed**. Figures 3.28(b) and 3.28(c) illustrate these possibilities. The reason that we are concerned about the tails in a distribution is that many inferential procedures that work well (i.e., they result in accurate conclusions) when the population distribution is approximately normal perform poorly when the population distribution is heavy-tailed.

Do Sample Histograms Resemble Population Histograms?

Sample data are usually collected to make inferences about a population. The resulting conclusions may be in error if the sample is unrepresentative of the population. So how similar might a histogram of sample data be to the histogram of all population values? Will the two histograms be centered at roughly the same place and spread out to about the same extent? Will they have the same number of peaks, and will the peaks occur at approximately the same places?

A related issue concerns the extent to which histograms based on different samples from the same population resemble one another. If two different sample histograms can be expected to differ from one another in obvious ways, then at least one of them might differ substantially from the population histogram. If the sample differs substantially from the population, conclusions about the population based on the sample are likely to be incorrect. **Sampling variability**—the extent to which samples differ from one another and from the population—is a central idea in statistics. Example 3.18 illustrates sampling variability in histogram shapes.

EXAMPLE 3.18 What You Should Know About Bus Drivers . . .

● A sample of 708 bus drivers employed by public corporations was selected, and the number of traffic accidents in which each bus driver was involved during a 4-year period was determined ("Application of Discrete Distribution Theory to the Study of Noncommunicable Events in Medical Epidemiology," in *Random Counts in Biomedical and Social Sciences*, G. P. Patil, ed. [University Park, PA: Pennsylvania State University Press, 1970]). A listing of the 708 sample observations might look like this:

3 0 6 0 0 2 1 4 1 . . . 6 0 2

The frequency distribution (Table 3.7) shows that 117 of the 708 drivers had no accidents, a relative frequency of 117/708 = .165 (or 16.5%). Similarly, the proportion

TABLE 3.7 Frequency Distribution for Number of Accidents by Bus Drivers

Number of Accidents	Frequency	Relative Frequency
0	117	.165
1	157	.222
2	158	.223
3	115	.162
4	78	.110
5	44	.062
6	21	.030
7	7	.010
8	6	.008
9	1	.001
10	3	.004
11	1	.001
	708	.998

● Data set available online

of sampled drivers who had 1 accident is .222 (or 22.2%). The largest sample observation was 11.

Although the 708 observations actually constituted a sample from the population of all bus drivers, we will regard the 708 observations as constituting the entire population. The first histogram in Figure 3.29, then, represents the population histogram. The other four histograms in Figure 3.29 are based on four different samples of 50 observations each selected at random from this population. The five histograms

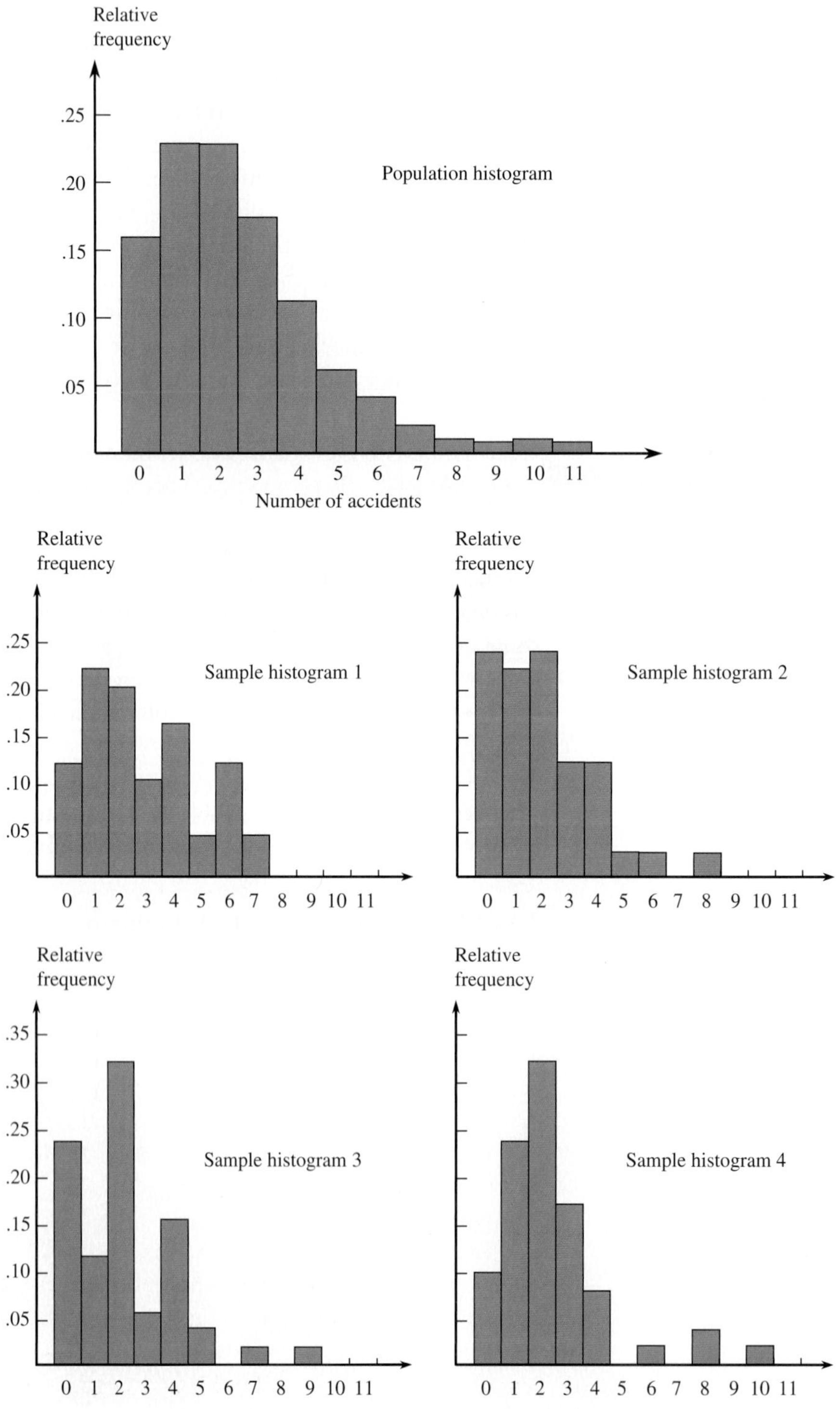

FIGURE 3.29
Comparison of population and sample histograms for number of accidents.

certainly resemble one another in a general way, but some dissimilarities are also obvious. The population histogram rises to a peak and then declines smoothly, whereas the sample histograms tend to have more peaks, valleys, and gaps. Although the population data set contained an observation of 11, none of the four samples did. In fact, in the first two samples, the largest observations were 7 and 8, respectively. In Chapters 8–15 we will see how sampling variability can be described and taken into account when we use sample data to draw conclusions about a population.

Cumulative Relative Frequencies and Cumulative Relative Frequency Plots

Rather than wanting to know what proportion of the data fall in a particular class, we often wish to determine the proportion falling below a specified value. This is easily done when the value is a class boundary.

Consider the following intervals and relative frequencies for carry-on luggage weight for passengers on flights between Phoenix and New York City during October 2009:

Class	0 to 5	5 to <10	10 to <15	15 to <20	. . .
Relative frequency	.05	.10	.18	.25	. . .

Then

proportion of passengers with carry-on luggage weight less than
15 lbs. = proportion in one of the first three classes
= .05 + .10 + .18
= .33

Similarly,

proportion of passengers with carry-on luggage weight less than
20 lbs. = .05 + .10 + .18 + .25 = .33 + .25 = .58

Each such sum of relative frequencies is called a **cumulative relative frequency**. Notice that the cumulative relative frequency .58 is the sum of the previous cumulative relative frequency .33 and the "current" relative frequency .25. The use of cumulative relative frequencies is illustrated in Example 3.19.

EXAMPLE 3.19 Albuquerque Rainfall

The National Climatic Data Center has been collecting weather data for many years. Annual rainfall totals for Albuquerque, New Mexico, from 1950 to 2008 (www.ncdc.noaa.gov/oa/climate/research/cag3/city.html) were used to construct the relative frequency distribution shown in Table 3.8. The table also contains a column of cumulative relative frequencies.

The proportion of years with annual rainfall less than 10 inches is .585, the cumulative relative frequency for the 9 to <10 interval. What about the proportion of years with annual rainfall less than 8.5 inches? Because 8.5 is not the endpoint of one of the intervals in the frequency distribution, we can only estimate this from the information given. The value 8.5 is halfway between the endpoints of the 8 to 9 inter-

TABLE 3.8 Relative Frequency distribution for Albuquerque Rainfall Data with Cumulative Relative Frequencies

Annual Rainfall (inches)	Frequency	Relative Frequency	Cumulative Relative Frequency
4 to <5	3	0.052	0.052
5 to <6	6	0.103	0.155 = .052 + .103
6 to <7	5	0.086	0.241 = .052 + .103 + .086 or .155 + .086
7 to <8	6	0.103	0.344
8 to <9	10	0.172	0.516
9 to <10	4	0.069	0.585
10 to <11	12	0.207	0.792
11 to <12	6	0.103	0.895
12 to <13	3	0.052	0.947
13 to <14	3	0.052	0.999

val, so it is reasonable to estimate that half of the relative frequency of .172 for this interval belongs in the 8 to 8.5 range. Then

$$\begin{pmatrix}\text{estimate of proportion of}\\ \text{years with rainfall less}\\ \text{than 8.5 inches}\end{pmatrix} = .052 + .103 + .086 + .103 + \frac{1}{2}(.172) = .430$$

This proportion could also have been computed using the cumulative relative frequencies as

$$\begin{pmatrix}\text{estimate of proportion of}\\ \text{years with rainfall less}\\ \text{than 8.5 inches}\end{pmatrix} = .344 + \frac{1}{2}(.172) = .430$$

Similarly, since 11.25 is one-fourth of the way between 11 and 12,

$$\begin{pmatrix}\text{estimate of proportion of}\\ \text{years with rainfall less}\\ \text{than 11.25 inches}\end{pmatrix} = .792 + \frac{1}{4}(.103) = .818$$

A **cumulative relative frequency** plot is just a graph of the cumulative relative frequencies against the upper endpoint of the corresponding interval. The pairs

(upper endpoint of interval, cumulative relative frequency)

are plotted as points on a rectangular coordinate system, and successive points in the plot are connected by a line segment. For the rainfall data of Example 3.19, the plotted points would be

(5, .052)	(6, .155)	(7, .241)	(8, .344)	(9, .516)
(10, .585)	(11, .792)	(12, .895)	(13, .947)	(14, .999)

One additional point, the pair (lower endpoint of first interval, 0), is also included in the plot (for the rainfall data, this would be the point (4 0)), and then points are connected by line segments. Figure 3.30 shows the cumulative relative frequency plot for the rainfall data. The cumulative relative frequency plot can be used to obtain approximate answers to questions such as

What proportion of the observations is smaller than a particular value?

and

What value separates the smallest *p* percent from the larger values?

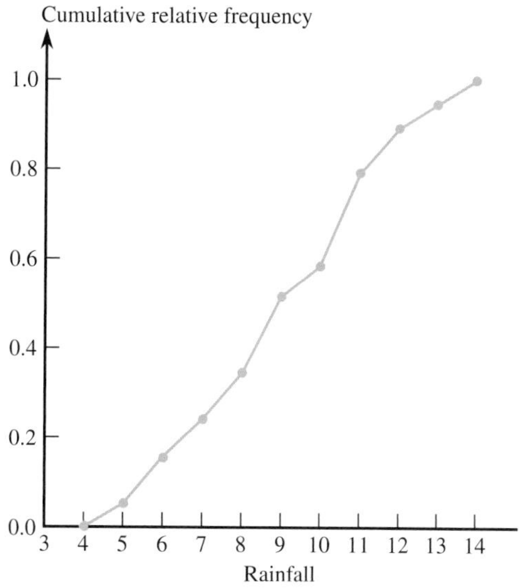

FIGURE 3.30
Cumulative relative frequency plot for the rainfall data of Example 3.19.

For example, to determine the approximate proportion of years with annual rainfall less than 9.5 inches, we would follow a vertical line up from 9.5 on the *x*-axis and then read across to the *y*-axis to obtain the corresponding relative frequency, as illustrated in Figure 3.31(a). Approximately .55, or 55%, of the years had annual rainfall less than 9.5 inches.

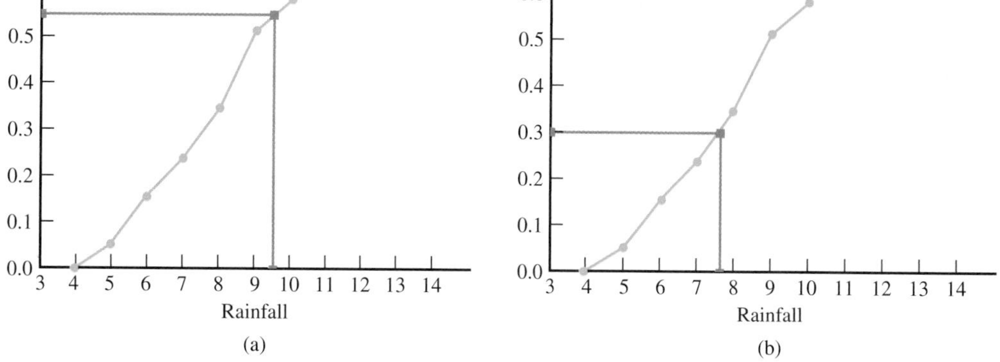

FIGURE 3.31
Using the cumulative relative frequency plot.
(a) Determining the approximate proportion of years with annual rainfall less than 9.5 inches.
(b) Finding the amount of rainfall that separates the 30% of years with the lowest rainfall from the 70% with higher rainfall.

Similarly, to find the amount of rainfall that separates the 30% of years with the smallest annual rainfall from years with higher rainfall, start at .30 on the cumulative relative frequency axis and move across and then down to find the corresponding rainfall amount, as shown in Figure 3.31(b). Approximately 30% of the years had annual rainfall of less than 7.6 inches.

EXERCISES 3.22 - 3.37

3.22 ● The article "Americans on the Move" (*USA Today*, November 30, 2007) included the data in the accompanying table. Entries in the table are the percentage of state residents who had moved during 2006.

State	Percentage of Residents Who Moved During 2006
Alabama	16.1
Alaska	21.2
Arizona	20.2
Arkansas	18.9
California	15.9
Colorado	19.6
Connecticut	13.1
Delaware	14.0
District of Columbia	18.8
Florida	17.4
Georgia	18.8
Hawaii	14.5
Idaho	21.0
Illinois	15.0
Indiana	16.8
Iowa	17.0
Kansas	18.7
Kentucky	16.8
Louisiana	18.9
Maine	14.4
Maryland	14.5
Massachusetts	13.6
Michigan	14.2
Minnesota	14.2
Mississippi	17.2
Missouri	17.5
Montana	17.5
Nebraska	18.0
Nevada	22.0
New Hampshire	13.7
New Jersey	11.1
New Mexico	16.8
New York	11.5
North Carolina	17.5
North Dakota	17.2
Ohio	15.7
Oklahoma	19.2
Oregon	20.2
Pennsylvania	12.7
Rhode Island	13.4
South Carolina	16.6
South Dakota	16.7
Tennessee	16.6
Texas	19.1
Utah	20.7
Vermont	14.5
Virginia	16.3
Washington	19.5
West Virginia	12.7
Wisconsin	15.3
Wyoming	18.8

(continued)

Construct a histogram of these data using class intervals of 10 to <12, 12 to <14, 14 to <16, and so on. Write a few sentences to describe the shape, center, and spread of the distribution.

3.23 ● The accompanying data on annual maximum wind speed (in meters per second) in Hong Kong for each year in a 45-year period were given in an article that appeared in the journal *Renewable Energy* (March, 2007). Use the annual maximum wind speed data to construct a histogram. Is the histogram approximately symmetric, positively skewed, or negatively skewed? Would you describe the histogram as unimodal, bimodal, or multimodal?

30.3	39.0	33.9	38.6	44.6	31.4	26.7	51.9	31.9
27.2	52.9	45.8	63.3	36.0	64.0	31.4	42.2	41.1
37.0	34.4	35.5	62.2	30.3	40.0	36.0	39.4	34.4
28.3	39.1	55.0	35.0	28.8	25.7	62.7	32.4	31.9
37.5	31.5	32.0	35.5	37.5	41.0	37.5	48.6	28.1

3.24 ● The accompanying relative frequency table is based on data from the 2007 College Bound Seniors Report for California (College Board, 2008).

Score on SAT Reasoning Exam	Relative Frequency for Males	Relative Frequency for Females
200 to <250	.0404	.0183
250 to < 300	.0546	.0299
300 to <350	.1076	.0700
350 to < 400	.1213	.0896
400 to < 450	.1465	.1286
450 to < 500	.1556	.1540
500 to < 550	.1400	.1667
550 to <600	.1126	.1550
600 to < 650	.0689	.1050
650 to < 700	.0331	.0529
700 to < 750	.0122	.0194
750 to <800	.0072	.0105

a. Construct a relative frequency histogram for SAT reasoning score for males.
b. Construct a relative frequency histogram for SAT reasoning score for females.
c. Based on the histograms from Parts (a) and (b), write a few sentences commenting on the similarities and differences in the distribution of SAT reasoning scores for males and females.

3.25 ● The data in the accompanying table represents the percentage of workers who are members of a union for each U.S. state and the District of Columbia (*AARP Bulletin*, September 2009).

State	% of Workers who Belong to a Union
Alabama	9.8
Alaska	23.5
Arizona	8.8
Arkansas	5.9
California	18.4
Colorado	8.0
Connecticut	16.9
Delaware	12.2
District of Columbia	13.4
Florida	6.4
Georgia	3.7
Hawaii	24.3
Idaho	7.1
Illinois	16.6
Indiana	12.4

(continued)

State	% of Workers who Belong to a Union
Iowa	10.6
Kansas	7.0
Kentucky	8.6
Louisiana	4.6
Maine	12.3
Maryland	15.7
Massachusetts	12.6
Michigan	18.8
Minnesota	16.1
Mississippi	5.3
Missouri	11.2
Montana	12.2
Nebraska	8.3
Nevada	16.7
New Hampshire	3.5
New Jersey	6.1
New Mexico	10.6
New York	18.3
North Carolina	7.2
North Dakota	24.9
Ohio	14.2
Oklahoma	6.6
Oregon	16.6
Pennsylvania	15.4
Rhode Island	16.5
South Carolina	3.9
South Dakota	5.0
Tennessee	5.5
Texas	4.5
Utah	5.8
Vermont	4.1
Virginia	10.4
Washington	19.8
West Virginia	13.8
Wisconsin	15.0
Wyoming	7.7

a. Construct a histogram of these data using class intervals of 0 to <5, 5 to <10, 10 to <15, 15 to <20, and 20 to <25.
b. Construct a dotplot of these data. Comment on the interesting features of the plot.
c. For this data set, which is a more informative graphical display—the dotplot from Part (b) or the histogram constructed in Part (a)? Explain.
d. Construct a histogram using about twice as many class intervals as the histogram in Part (a). Use 2.5 to <5 as the first class interval. Write a few sentences that explain why this histogram does a better job of displaying this data set than does the histogram in Part (a).

3.26 ● Medicare's new medical plans offer a wide range of variations and choices for seniors when picking a drug plan (*San Luis Obispo Tribune*, November 25, 2005). The monthly cost for a stand-alone drug plan varies from plan to plan and from state to state. The accompanying table gives the premium for the plan with the lowest cost for each state.

State	Cost per Month (dollars)
Alabama	14.08
Alaska	20.05
Arizona	6.14
Arkansas	10.31
California	5.41
Colorado	8.62
Connecticut	7.32
Delaware	6.44
District of Columbia	6.44
Florida	10.35
Georgia	17.91
Hawaii	17.18
Idaho	6.33
Illinois	13.32
Indiana	12.30
Iowa	1.87
Kansas	9.48
Kentucky	12.30
Louisiana	17.06
Maine	19.60
Maryland	6.44
Massachusetts	7.32
Michigan	13.75
Minnesota	1.87
Mississippi	11.60
Missouri	10.29
Montana	1.87
Nebraska	1.87
Nevada	6.42
New Hampshire	19.60
New Jersey	4.43
New Mexico	10.65
New York	4.10
North Carolina	13.27
North Dakota	1.87
Ohio	14.43
Oklahoma	10.07
Oregon	6.93
Pennsylvania	10.14
Rhode Island	7.32
South Carolina	16.57
South Dakota	1.87
Tennessee	14.08
Texas	10.31
Utah	6.33
Vermont	7.32
Virginia	8.81
Washington	6.93
West Virginia	10.14
Wisconsin	11.42
Wyoming	1.87

a. Use class intervals of \$0 to <\$3, \$3 to <\$6, \$6 to <\$9, etc., to create a relative frequency distribution for these data.
b. Construct a histogram and comment on its shape.
c. Using the relative frequency distribution or the histogram, estimate the proportion of the states that have a minimum monthly plan of less than \$13.00 a month.

3.27 ● The following two relative frequency distributions were constructed using data that appeared in the report "Undergraduate Students and Credit Cards in 2004" (Nellie Mae, May 2005). One relative frequency distribution is based on credit bureau data for a random sample of 1413 college students, while the other is based on the result of a survey completed by 132 of the 1260 college students who received the survey.

Credit Card Balance (dollars)— Credit Bureau Data	Relative Frequency
0 to <100	.18
100 to <500	.19
500 to <1000	.14
1000 to <2000	.16
2000 to <3000	.10
3000 to <7000	.16
7000 or more	.07

Credit Card Balance (dollars)— Survey Data	Relative Frequency
0 to <100	.18
100 to <500	.22
500 to <1000	.17
1000 to <2000	.22
2000 to <3000	.07
3000 to <7000	.14
7000 or more	.00

a. Construct a histogram for the credit bureau data. For purposes of constructing the histogram, assume that none of the students in the sample had a balance higher than $15,000 and that the last interval can be regarded as 7000 to <15,000. Be sure to use the density scale when constructing the histogram.

b. Construct a histogram for the survey data. Use the same scale that you used for the histogram in Part (a) so that it will be easy to compare the two histograms.

c. Comment on the similarities and differences in the histograms from Parts (a) and (b).

d. Do you think the high nonresponse rate for the survey may have contributed to the observed differences in the two histograms? Explain.

3.28 ● U.S. Census data for San Luis Obispo County, California, were used to construct the following frequency distribution for commute time (in minutes) of working adults (the given frequencies were read from a graph that appeared in the *San Luis Obispo Tribune* [September 1, 2002] and so are only approximate):

Commute Time	Frequency
0 to <5	5,200
5 to <10	18,200
10 to <15	19,600
15 to <20	15,400
20 to <25	13,800
25 to <30	5,700
30 to <35	10,200
35 to <40	2,000
40 to <45	2,000
45 to <60	4,000
60 to <90	2,100
90 to <120	2,200

a. Notice that not all intervals in the frequency distribution are equal in width. Why do you think that unequal width intervals were used?

b. Construct a table that adds a relative frequency and a density column to the given frequency distribution (see Example 3.17).

c. Use the densities computed in Part (b) to construct a histogram for this data set. (Note: The newspaper displayed an incorrectly drawn histogram based on frequencies rather than densities!) Write a few sentences commenting on the important features of the histogram.

d. Compute the cumulative relative frequencies, and construct a cumulative relative frequency plot.

e. Use the cumulative relative frequency plot constructed in Part (d) to answer the following questions.

i. Approximately what proportion of commute times were less than 50 minutes?

ii. Approximately what proportion of commute times were greater than 22 minutes?

iii. What is the approximate commute time value that separates the shortest 50% of commute times from the longest 50%?

3.29 Student loans can add up, especially for those attending professional schools to study in such areas as medicine, law, or dentistry. Researchers at the University of Washington studied medical students and gave the following information on the educational debt of medical students on completion of their residencies (*Annals of Internal Medicine* [March 2002]: 384–398):

Educational Debt (dollars)	Relative Frequency
0 to <5000	.427
5000 to <20,000	.046
20,000 to <50,000	.109
50,000 to <100,000	.232
100,000 or more	.186

a. What are two reasons that you could not use the given information to construct a histogram with the educational debt intervals on the horizontal axis and relative frequency on the y-axis?

b. Suppose that no student had an educational debt of $150,000 or more upon completion of his or her residency, so that the last class in the relative frequency distribution would be 100,000 to <150,000. Summarize this distribution graphically by constructing a histogram of the educational debt data. (Don't forget to use the density scale for the heights of the bars in the histogram, because the interval widths aren't all the same.)

c. Based on the histogram of Part (b), write a few sentences describing the educational debt of medical students completing their residencies.

3.30 An exam is given to students in an introductory statistics course. What is likely to be true of the shape of the histogram of scores if:

a. the exam is quite easy?

b. the exam is quite difficult?

c. half the students in the class have had calculus, the other half have had no prior college math courses, and the exam emphasizes mathematical manipulation?

Explain your reasoning in each case.

3.31 The accompanying frequency distribution summarizes data on the number of times smokers who had successfully quit smoking attempted to quit before their final successful attempt ("Demographic Variables, Smoking Variables, and Outcome Across Five Studies," *Health Psychology* [2007]: 278–287).

Number of Attempts	Frequency
0	778
1	306
2	274
3–4	221
5 or more	238

Assume that no one had made more than 10 unsuccessful attempts, so that the last entry in the frequency distribution can be regarded as 5–10 attempts. Summarize this data set using a histogram. Be careful—the class intervals are not all the same width, so you will need to use a density scale for the histogram. Also remember that for a discrete variable, the bar for 1 will extend from 0.5 to 1.5. Think about what this will mean for the bars for the 3–4 group and the 5–10 group.

3.32 ● Example 3.19 used annual rainfall data for Albuquerque, New Mexico, to construct a relative frequency distribution and cumulative relative frequency plot. The National Climate Data Center also gave the accompanying annual rainfall (in inches) for Medford, Oregon, from 1950 to 2008.

28.84	20.15	18.88	25.72	16.42	20.18	28.96	20.72	23.58	10.62
20.85	19.86	23.34	19.08	29.23	18.32	21.27	18.93	15.47	20.68
23.43	19.55	20.82	19.04	18.77	19.63	12.39	22.39	15.95	20.46
16.05	22.08	19.44	30.38	18.79	10.89	17.25	14.95	13.86	15.30
13.71	14.68	15.16	16.77	12.33	21.93	31.57	18.13	28.87	16.69
18.81	15.15	18.16	19.99	19.00	23.97	21.99	17.25	14.07	

a. Construct a relative frequency distribution for the Medford rainfall data.
b. Use the relative frequency distribution of Part (a) to construct a histogram. Describe the shape of the histogram.
c. Construct a cumulative relative frequency plot for the Medford rainfall data.
d. Use the cumulative relative frequency plot of Part (c) to answer the following questions:
   i. Approximately what proportion of years had annual rainfall less than 15.5 inches?
   ii. Approximately what proportion of years had annual rainfall less than 25 inches?
   iii. Approximately what proportion of years had annual rainfall between 17.5 and 25 inches?

3.33 The National Climate Data Center referenced in the previous exercise and Example 3.19 also gives rainfall data for a number of other U.S. cities. Go to the web site www.ncdc.noaa.gov/oa/climate/research/cag3/city.html and select one of the other cities. Use the data from 1950 to the most recent year for which data is available for the city you have selected to construct a relative frequency distribution and histogram. Write a few sentences comparing the distribution of annual rainfall values for the city you selected to the rainfall distribution for Medford, Oregon. (Use the histogram for Medford constructed in Exercise 3.32.)

3.34 The authors of the paper "Myeloma in Patients Younger than Age 50 Years Presents with More Favorable Features and Shows Better Survival" (*Blood* [2008]: 4039–4047) studied patients who had been diagnosed with stage 2 multiple myeloma prior to the age of 50. For each patient who received high dose chemotherapy, the number of years that the patient lived after the therapy (survival time) was recorded. The cumulative relative frequencies in the accompanying table were approximated from survival graphs that appeared in the paper.

Years Survived	Cumulative Relative Frequency
0 to <2	.10
2 to <4	.52
4 to <6	.54
6 to <8	.64
8 to <10	.68
10 to <12	.70
12 to <14	.72
14 to <16	1.00

a. Use the given information to construct a cumulative relative frequency plot.
b. Use the cumulative relative frequency plot from Part (a) to answer the following questions:
   i. What is the approximate proportion of patients who lived fewer than 5 years after treatment?
   ii. What is the approximate proportion of patients who lived fewer than 7.5 years after treatment?
   iii. What is the approximate proportion of patients who lived more than 10 years after treatment?

3.35

a. Use the cumulative relative frequencies given in the previous exercise to compute the relative frequencies for each class interval and construct a relative frequency distribution.

b. Summarize the survival time data with a histogram.

c. Based on the histogram, write a few sentences describing survival time of the stage 2 myeloma patients in this study.

d. What additional information would you need in order to decide if it is reasonable to generalize conclusions about survival time from the group of patients in the study to all patients younger than 50 years old who are diagnosed with multiple myeloma and who receive high dose chemotherapy?

3.36 Construct a histogram corresponding to each of the five frequency distributions, I–V, given in the following table, and state whether each histogram is symmetric, bimodal, positively skewed, or negatively skewed:

	Frequency				
Class Interval	I	II	III	IV	V
0 to <10	5	40	30	15	6
10 to <20	10	25	10	25	5
20 to <30	20	10	8	8	6
30 to <40	30	8	7	7	9
40 to <50	20	7	7	20	9
50 to <60	10	5	8	25	23
60 to <70	5	5	30	10	42

3.37 Using the five class intervals 100 to 120, 120 to 140, . . . , 180 to 200, devise a frequency distribution based on 70 observations whose histogram could be described as follows:

a. symmetric
b. bimodal
c. positively skewed
d. negatively skewed

3.4 Displaying Bivariate Numerical Data

A bivariate data set consists of measurements or observations on two variables, x and y. For example, x might be the distance from a highway and y the lead content of soil at that distance. When both x and y are numerical variables, each observation consists of a pair of numbers, such as (14, 5.2) or (27.63, 18.9). The first number in a pair is the value of x, and the second number is the value of y.

An unorganized list of bivariate data provides little information about the distribution of either the x values or the y values separately and even less information about how the two variables are related to one another. Just as graphical displays can be used to summarize univariate data, they can also help with bivariate data. The most important graph based on bivariate numerical data is a **scatterplot.**

In a scatterplot each observation (pair of numbers) is represented by a point on a rectangular coordinate system, as shown in Figure 3.32(a). The horizontal axis is identified with values of x and is scaled so that any x value can be easily located. Similarly, the vertical or y-axis is marked for easy location of y values. The point corresponding to any particular (x, y) pair is placed where a vertical line from the value on

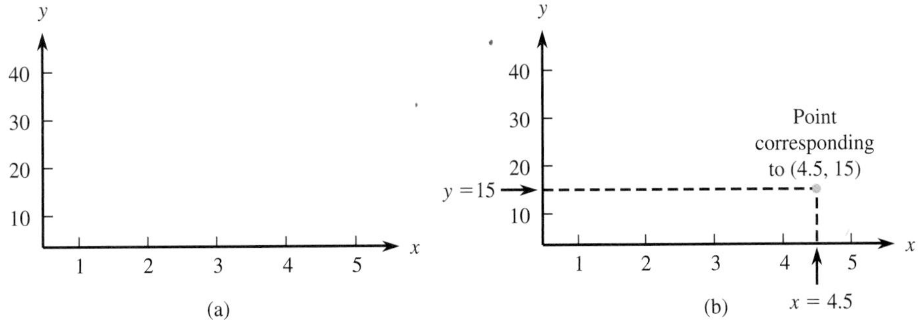

FIGURE 3.32
Constructing a scatterplot:
(a) rectangular coordinate system;
(b) point corresponding to (4.5, 15).

the x-axis meets a horizontal line from the value on the y-axis. Figure 3.32(b) shows the point representing the observation (4.5, 15); it is above 4.5 on the horizontal axis and to the right of 15 on the vertical axis.

EXAMPLE 3.20 Olympic Figure Skating

● Do tall skaters have an advantage when it comes to earning high artistic scores in figure skating competitions? Data on x = height (in cm) and y = artistic score in the free skate for both male and female singles skaters at the 2006 Winter Olympics are shown in the accompanying table. (Data set courtesy of John Walker.)

Name	Gender	Height	Artistic
PLUSHENKO Yevgeny	M	178	41.2100
BUTTLE Jeffrey	M	173	39.2500
LYSACEK Evan	M	177	37.1700
LAMBIEL Stephane	M	176	38.1400
SAVOIE Matt	M	175	35.8600
WEIR Johnny	M	172	37.6800
JOUBERT Brian	M	179	36.7900
VAN DER PERREN Kevin	M	177	33.0100
TAKAHASHI Daisuke	M	165	36.6500
KLIMKIN Ilia	M	170	32.6100
ZHANG Min	M	176	31.8600
SAWYER Shawn	M	163	34.2500
LI Chengjiang	M	170	28.4700
SANDHU Emanuel	M	183	35.1100
VERNER Tomas	M	180	28.6100
DAVYDOV Sergei	M	159	30.4700
CHIPER Gheorghe	M	176	32.1500
DINEV Ivan	M	174	29.2500
DAMBIER Frederic	M	163	31.2500
LINDEMANN Stefan	M	163	31.0000
KOVALEVSKI Anton	M	171	28.7500
BERNTSSON Kristoffer	M	175	28.0400
PFEIFER Viktor	M	180	28.7200
TOTH Zoltan	M	185	25.1000
ARAKAWA Shizuka	F	166	39.3750
COHEN Sasha	F	157	39.0063
SLUTSKAYA Irina	F	160	38.6688
SUGURI Fumie	F	157	37.0313
ROCHETTE Joannie	F	157	35.0813
MEISSNER Kimmie	F	160	33.4625
HUGHES Emily	F	165	31.8563
MEIER Sarah	F	164	32.0313
KOSTNER Carolina	F	168	34.9313
SOKOLOVA Yelena	F	162	31.4250
YAN Liu	F	164	28.1625
LEUNG Mira	F	168	26.7000
GEDEVANISHVILI Elene	F	159	31.2250
KORPI Kiira	F	166	27.2000
POYKIO Susanna	F	159	31.2125

● Data set available online

Name	Gender	Height	Artistic
ANDO Miki	F	162	31.5688
EFREMENKO Galina	F	163	26.5125
LIASHENKO Elena	F	160	28.5750
HEGEL Idora	F	166	25.5375
SEBESTYEN Julia	F	164	28.6375
KARADEMIR Tugba	F	165	23.0000
FONTANA Silvia	F	158	26.3938
PAVUK Viktoria	F	168	23.6688
MAXWELL Fleur	F	160	24.5438

Figure 3.33(a) gives a scatterplot of the data. Looking at the data and the scatterplot, we can see that

1. Several observations have identical x values but different y values (for example, x = 176 cm for both Stephane Lambiel and Min Zhang, but Lambiel's artistic score was 38.1400 and Zhang's artistic score was 31.8600). Thus, the value of y is *not* determined *solely* by the value of x but by various other factors as well.

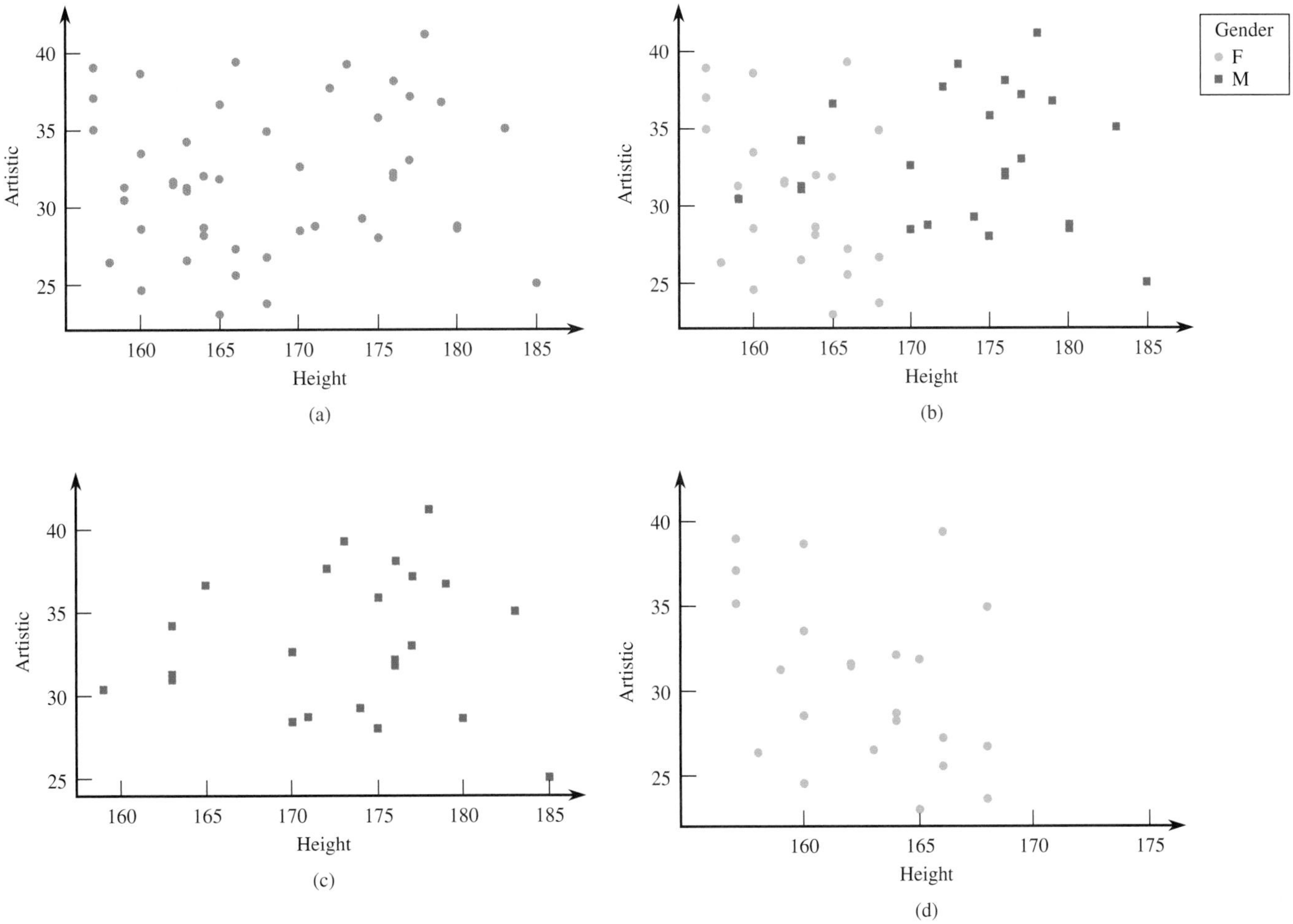

FIGURE 3.33
Scatterplots for the data of Example 3.20: (a) scatterplot of data; (b) scatterplot of data with observations for males and females distinguished by color; (c) scatterplot for male skaters; (d) scatterplot for female skaters.

2. At any given height there is quite a bit of variability in artistic score. For example, for those skaters with height 160 cm, artistic scores ranged from a low of about 24.5 to a high of about 39.
3. There is no noticeable tendency for artistic score to increase as height increases. There does not appear to be a strong relationship between height and artistic score.

The data set used to construct the scatter plot included data for both male and female skaters. Figure 3.33(b) shows a scatterplot of the (height, artistic score) pairs with observations for male skaters shown in blue and observations for female skaters shown in orange. Not surprisingly, the female skaters tend to be shorter than the male skaters (the observations for females tend to be concentrated toward the left side of the scatterplot). Careful examination of this plot shows that while there was no apparent pattern in the combined (male and female) data set, there may be a relationship between height and artistic score for female skaters.

Figures 3.33(c) and 3.33(d) show separate scatterplots for the male and female skaters, respectively. It is interesting to note that it appears that for female skaters, higher artistic scores seem to be associated with smaller height values, but for men there does not appear to be a relationship between height and artistic score. The relationship between height and artistic score for women is not evident in the scatterplot of the combined data.

The horizontal and vertical axes in the scatterplots of Figure 3.33 do not intersect at the point (0, 0). In many data sets, the values of x or of y or of both variables differ considerably from 0 relative to the ranges of the values in the data set. For example, a study of how air conditioner efficiency is related to maximum daily outdoor temperature might involve observations at temperatures of 80°, 82°, . . . , 98°, 100°. In such cases, the plot will be more informative if the axes intersect at some point other than (0, 0) and are marked accordingly. This is illustrated in Example 3.21.

EXAMPLE 3.21 Taking Those "Hard" Classes Pays Off

● The report titled "2007 College Bound Seniors" (College Board, 2007) included the accompanying table showing the average score on the writing and math sections of the SAT for groups of high school seniors completing different numbers of years of study in six core academic subjects (arts and music, English, foreign languages, mathematics, natural sciences, and social sciences and history). Figure 3.34(a) and (b) show two scatterplots of x = total number of years of study and y = average writing SAT score. The scatterplots were produced by the statistical computer package Minitab. In Figure 3.34(a), we let Minitab select the scale for both axes. Figure 3.34(b) was obtained by specifying that the axes would intersect at the point (0, 0). The second plot does not make effective use of space. It is more crowded than the first plot, and such crowding can make it more difficult to see the general nature of any relationship. For example, it can be more difficult to spot curvature in a crowded plot.

!! Step-by-step technology instructions available online

● Data set available online

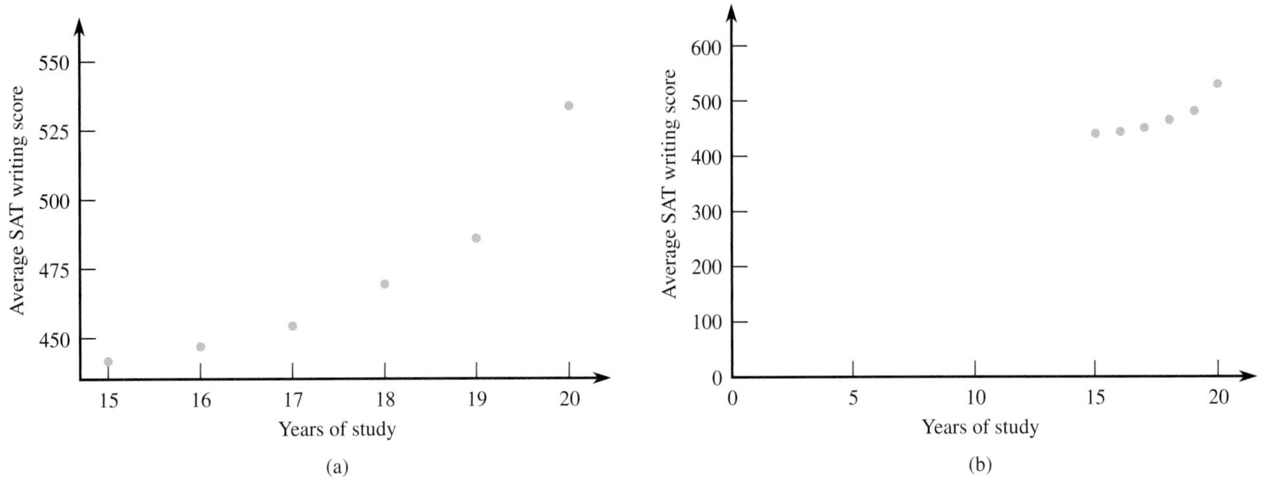

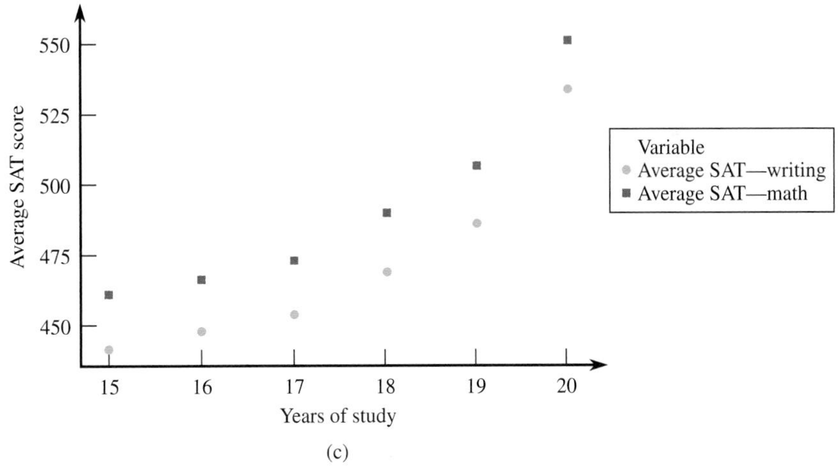

FIGURE 3.34
Minitab scatterplots of data in Example 3.21:
(a) scale for both axes selected by Minitab;
(b) axes intersect at the point (0, 0);
(c) math and writing on same plot.

Years of Study	Average Writing Score	Average Math Score
15	442	461
16	447	466
17	454	473
18	469	490
19	486	507
20	534	551

The scatterplot for average writing SAT score exhibits a fairly strong curved pattern, indicating that there is a strong relationship between average writing SAT score and the total number of years of study in the six core academic subjects. Although the pattern in the plot is curved rather than linear, it is still easy to see that the average writing SAT score increases as the number of years of study increases. Figure 3.34(c) shows a scatterplot with the average writing SAT scores represented by blue squares and the average math SAT scores represented by orange dots. From this plot we can see that while the average math SAT scores tend to be higher than the average writing scores at all of the values of total number of years of study, the general curved form of the relationship is similar.

In Chapter 5, methods for summarizing bivariate data when the scatterplot reveals a pattern are introduced. Linear patterns are relatively easy to work with. A curved pattern, such as the one in Example 3.21, is a bit more complicated to analyze, and methods for summarizing such nonlinear relationships are developed in Section 5.4.

Time Series Plots

Data sets often consist of measurements collected over time at regular intervals so that we can learn about change over time. For example, stock prices, sales figures, and other socio-economic indicators might be recorded on a weekly or monthly basis. A **time-series plot** (sometimes also called a time plot) is a simple graph of data collected over time that can be invaluable in identifying trends or patterns that might be of interest.

A time-series plot can be constructed by thinking of the data set as a bivariate data set, where y is the variable observed and x is the time at which the observation was made. These (x, y) pairs are plotted as in a scatterplot. Consecutive observations are then connected by a line segment; this aids in spotting trends over time.

EXAMPLE 3.22 The Cost of Christmas

The Christmas Price Index is computed each year by PNC Advisors, and it is a humorous look at the cost of the giving all of the gifts described in the popular Christmas song "The Twelve Days of Christmas." The year 2008 was the most costly year since the index began in 1984, with the "cost of Christmas" at $21,080. A plot of the Christmas Price Index over time appears on the PNC web site (www.pncchristmaspriceindex.com) and the data given there were used to construct the time-series plot of Figure 3.35. The plot shows an upward trend in the index from

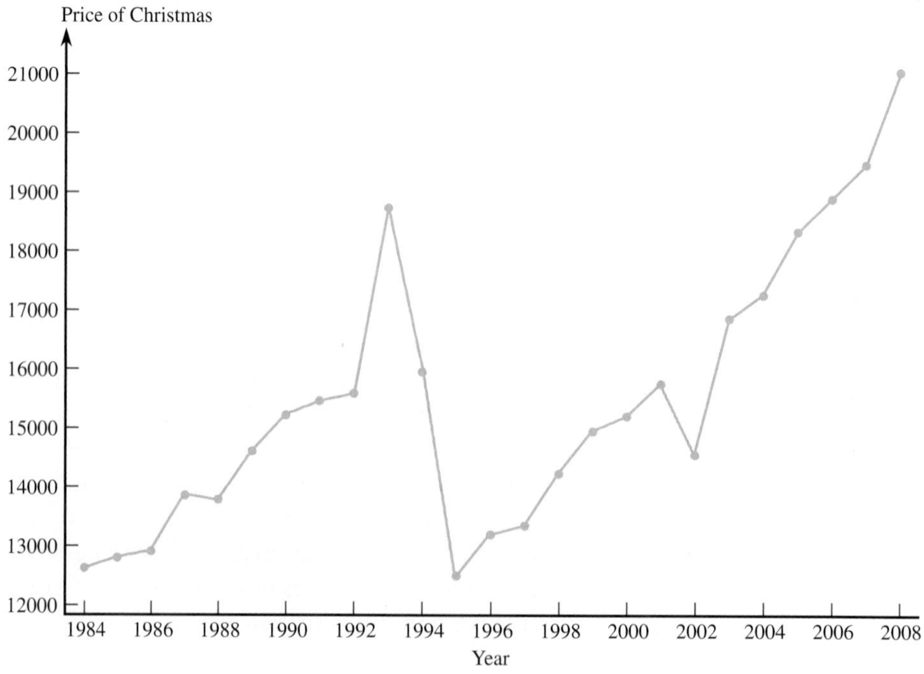

FIGURE 3.35
Time-series plot for the Christmas Price Index data of Example 3.22.

1984 until 1993. A dramatic drop in the cost occurred between 1993 and 1995, but there has been a clear upward trend in the index since then. You can visit the web site to see individual time-series plots for each of the twelve gifts that are used to determine the Christmas Price Index (a partridge in a pear tree, two turtle doves, etc.). See if you can figure out what caused the dramatic decline in 1995.

EXAMPLE 3.23 Education Level and Income—Stay in School!

The time-series plot shown in Figure 3.36 appears on the U.S. Census Bureau web site. It shows the average earnings of workers by educational level as a proportion of the average earnings of a high school graduate over time. For example, we can see from this plot that in 1993 the average earnings for people with bachelor's degrees was about 1.5 times the average for high school graduates. In that same year, the average earnings for those who were not high school graduates was only about 75% (a proportion of .75) of the average for high school graduates. The time-series plot also shows that the gap between the average earnings for high school graduates and those with a bachelor's degree or an advanced degree widened during the 1990s.

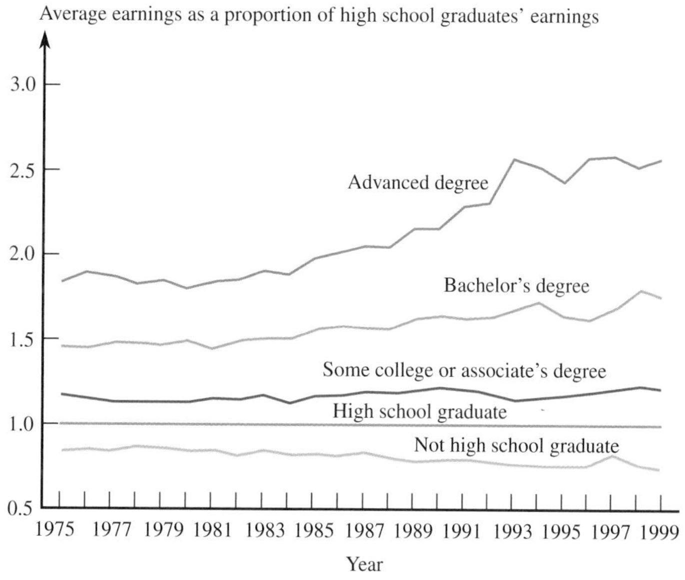

FIGURE 3.36
Time-series plot for average earnings as a proportion of the average earnings of high school graduates.

EXERCISES 3.38 - 3.45

3.38 ● *Consumer Reports Health* (www.consumerreports.org) gave the accompanying data on saturated fat (in grams), sodium (in mg), and calories for 36 fast-food items.

Fat	Sodium	Calories
2	1042	268
5	921	303
3	250	260
2	770	660
1	635	180
6	440	290
4.5	490	290
5	1160	360
3.5	970	300
1	1120	315
2	350	160
3	450	200
6	800	320
3	1190	420
2	1090	120
5	570	290
3.5	1215	285
2.5	1160	390
0	520	140
2.5	1120	330
1	240	120
3	650	180
1	1620	340
4	660	380
3	840	300
1.5	1050	490
3	1440	380
9	750	560
1	500	230
1.5	1200	370
2.5	1200	330
3	1250	330
0	1040	220
0	760	260
2.5	780	220
3	500	230

a. Construct a scatterplot using y = calories and x = fat. Does it look like there is a relationship between fat and calories? Is the relationship what you expected? Explain.

b. Construct a scatterplot using y = calories and x = sodium. Write a few sentences commenting on the difference between the relationship of calories to fat and calories to sodium.

c. Construct a scatterplot using y = sodium and x = fat. Does there appear to be a relationship between fat and sodium?

d. Add a vertical line at $x = 3$ and a horizontal line at $y = 900$ to the scatterplot in Part (c). This divides the scatterplot into four regions, with some of the points in the scatterplot falling into each of the four regions. Which of the four regions corresponds to healthier fast-food choices? Explain.

3.39 The report "Wireless Substitution: Early Release of Estimates from the National Health Interview Survey" (Center for Disease Control, 2009) gave the following estimates of the percentage of homes in the United States that had only wireless phone service at 6-month intervals from June 2005 to December 2008.

Date	Percent with Only Wireless Phone Service
June 2005	7.3
December 2005	8.4
June 2006	10.5
December 2006	12.8
June 2007	13.6
December 2007	15.8
June 2008	17.5
December 2008	20.2

Construct a time-series plot for these data and describe the trend in the percent of homes with only wireless phone service over time. Has the percent increased at a fairly steady rate?

3.40 ● The accompanying table gives the cost and an overall quality rating for 15 different brands of bike helmets (www.consumerreports.org).

Cost	Rating
35	65
20	61
30	60
40	55
50	54
23	47
30	47
18	43
40	42
28	41
20	40

(continued)

Cost	Rating
25	32
30	63
30	63
40	53

a. Construct a scatterplot using y = quality rating and x = cost.
b. Based on the scatterplot from Part (a), does there appear to be a relationship between cost and quality rating? Does the scatterplot support the statement that the more expensive bike helmets tended to receive higher quality ratings?

3.41 ● The accompanying table gives the cost and an overall quality rating for 10 different brands of men's athletic shoes and nine different brands of women's athletic shoes (www.consumerreports.org).

Cost	Rating	Type
65	71	Men's
45	70	Men's
45	62	Men's
80	59	Men's
110	58	Men's
110	57	Men's
30	56	Men's
80	52	Men's
110	51	Men's
70	51	Men's
65	71	Women's
70	70	Women's
85	66	Women's
80	66	Women's
45	65	Women's
70	62	Women's
55	61	Women's
110	60	Women's
70	59	Women's

a. Using the data for all 19 shoes, construct a scatterplot using y = quality rating and x = cost. Write a sentence describing the relationship between quality rating and cost.
b. Construct a scatterplot of the 19 data points that uses different colors or different symbols to distinguish the points that correspond to men's shoes from those that correspond to women's shoes. How do men's and women's athletic shoes differ with respect to cost and quality rating? Are the relationships between cost and quality rating the same for men and women? If not, how do the relationships differ?

3.42 ● The article "Medicine Cabinet is a Big Killer" (*The Salt Lake Tribune*, August 1, 2007) looked at the number of prescription-drug-overdose deaths in Utah over the period from 1991 to 2006. Construct a time-series plot for these data and describe the trend over time. Has the number of overdose deaths increased at a fairly steady rate?

Year	Number of Overdose Deaths
1991	32
1992	52
1993	73
1994	61
1995	68
1996	64
1997	85
1998	89
1999	88
2000	109
2001	153
2002	201
2003	237
2004	232
2005	308
2006	307

3.43 ● The article "Cities Trying to Rejuvenate Recycling Efforts" (*USA Today*, October 27, 2006) states that the amount of waste collected for recycling has grown slowly in recent years. This statement was supported by the data in the accompanying table. Use these data to construct a time-series plot. Explain how the plot is or is not consistent with the given statement.

Year	Recycled Waste (in millions of tons)
1990	29.7
1991	32.9
1992	36.0
1993	37.9
1994	43.5
1995	46.1
1996	46.4
1997	47.3
1998	48.0
1999	50.1
2000	52.7
2001	52.8
2002	53.7
2003	55.8
2004	57.2
2005	58.4

3.44 ● Some days of the week are more dangerous than others, according to Traffic Safety Facts produced by the National Highway Traffic Safety Administration. The average number of fatalities per day for each day of the week are shown in the accompanying table.

Average Fatalities per Day
(day of the week)

	Mon	Tue	Wed	Thurs	Fri	Sat	Sun
1978–1982	103	101	107	116	156	201	159
1983–1987	98	96	99	108	140	174	140
1988–1992	97	94	97	106	139	168	135
1993–1997	97	93	96	102	129	148	127
1998–2002	99	96	98	104	129	149	130
Total	99	96	100	107	138	168	138

a. Using the midpoint of each year range (e.g., 1980 for the 1978–1982 range), construct a time-series plot that shows the average fatalities over time for each day of the week. Be sure to label each line clearly as to which day of the week it represents.
b. Write a sentence or two commenting on the difference in average number of fatalities for the days of the week. What is one possible reason for the differences?
c. Write a sentence or two commenting on the change in average number of fatalities over time. What is one possible reason for the change?

3.45 The accompanying time-series plot of movie box office totals (in millions of dollars) over 18 weeks of summer for both 2001 and 2002 appeared in *USA Today* (September 3, 2002):

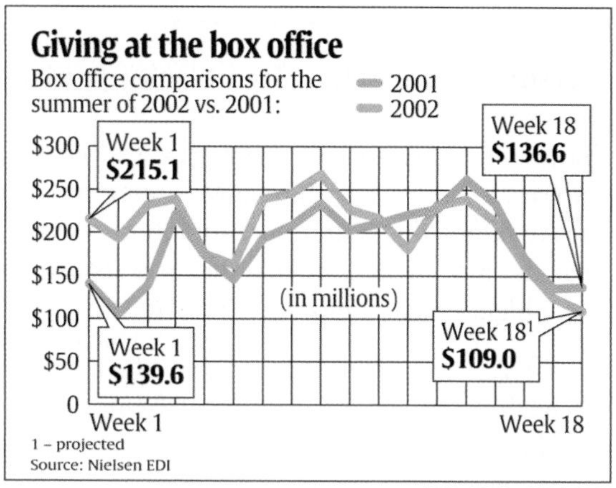

By Karl Gelles, USA TODAY

Patterns that tend to repeat on a regular basis over time are called seasonal patterns. Describe any seasonal patterns that you see in the summer box office data. Hint: Look for patterns that seem to be consistent from year to year.

3.5 Interpreting and Communicating the Results of Statistical Analyses

A graphical display, when used appropriately, can be a powerful tool for organizing and summarizing data. By sacrificing some of the detail of a complete listing of a data set, important features of the data distribution are more easily seen and more easily communicated to others.

Communicating the Results of Statistical Analyses

When reporting the results of a data analysis, a good place to start is with a graphical display of the data. A well-constructed graphical display is often the best way to highlight the essential characteristics of the data distribution, such as shape and spread for numerical data sets or the nature of the relationship between the two variables in a bivariate numerical data set.

For effective communication with graphical displays, some things to remember are

- Be sure to select a display that is appropriate for the given type of data.
- Be sure to include scales and labels on the axes of graphical displays.
- In comparative plots, be sure to include labels or a legend so that it is clear which parts of the display correspond to which samples or groups in the data set.

- Although it is sometimes a good idea to have axes that do not cross at (0, 0) in a scatterplot, the vertical axis in a bar chart or a histogram should always start at 0 (see the cautions and limitations later in this section for more about this).
- Keep your graphs simple. A simple graphical display is much more effective than one that has a lot of extra "junk." Most people will not spend a great deal of time studying a graphical display, so its message should be clear and straightforward.
- Keep your graphical displays honest. People tend to look quickly at graphical displays, so it is important that a graph's first impression is an accurate and honest portrayal of the data distribution. In addition to the graphical display itself, data analysis reports usually include a brief discussion of the features of the data distribution based on the graphical display.
- For categorical data, this discussion might be a few sentences on the relative proportion for each category, possibly pointing out categories that were either common or rare compared to other categories.
- For numerical data sets, the discussion of the graphical display usually summarizes the information that the display provides on three characteristics of the data distribution: center or location, spread, and shape.
- For bivariate numerical data, the discussion of the scatterplot would typically focus on the nature of the relationship between the two variables used to construct the plot.
- For data collected over time, any trends or patterns in the time-series plot would be described.

Interpreting the Results of Statistical Analyses

When someone uses a web search engine, do they rely on the ranking of the search results returned or do they first scan the results looking for the most relevant? The authors of the paper "Learning User Interaction Models for Predicting Web Search Result Preferences" (*Proceedings of the 29th Annual ACM Conference on Research and Development in Information Retrieval*, 2006) attempted to answer this question by observing user behavior when they varied the position of the most relevant result in the list of resources returned in response to a web search. They concluded that people clicked more often on results near the top of the list, even when they were not relevant. They supported this conclusion with the comparative bar graph in Figure 3.37.

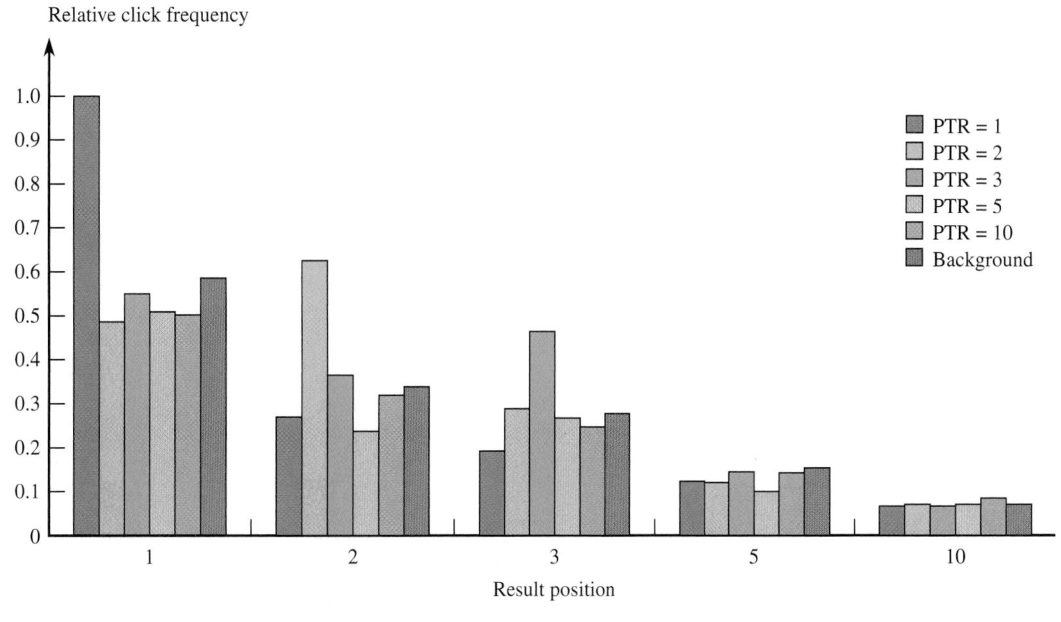

FIGURE 3.37 Comparative bar graph for click frequency data.

Although this comparative bar chart is a bit complicated, we can learn a great deal from this graphical display. Let's start by looking at the first group of bars. The different bars correspond to where in the list of search results the result that was considered to be most relevant was located. For example, in the legend PTR = 1 means that the most relevant result was in position 1 in the list returned. PTR = 2 means that the most relevant result was in the second position in the list returned, and so on. PTR = Background means that the most relevant result was not in the first 10 results returned. The first group of bars shows the proportion of times users clicked on the first result returned. Notice that all users clicked on the first result when it was the most relevant, but nearly half clicked on the first result when the most relevant result was in the second position and more than half clicked on the first result when the most relevant result was even farther down the list.

The second group of bars represents the proportion of users who clicked on the second result. Notice that the proportion who clicked on the second result was highest when the most relevant result was in that position. Stepping back to look at the entire graphical display, we see that users tended to click on the most relevant result if it was in one of the first three positions, but if it appeared after that, very few selected it. Also, if the most relevant result was in the third or a later position, users were more likely to click on the first result returned, and the likelihood of a click on the most relevant result decreased the farther down the list it appeared. To fully understand why the researchers' conclusions are justified, we need to be able to extract this kind of information from graphical displays.

The use of graphical data displays is quite common in newspapers, magazines, and journals, so it is important to be able to extract information from such displays. For example, data on test scores for a standardized math test given to eighth graders in 37 states, 2 territories (Guam and the Virgin Islands), and the District of Columbia were used to construct the stem-and-leaf display and histogram shown in Figure 3.38. Careful examination of these displays reveals the following:

1. Most of the participating states had average eighth-grade math scores between 240 and 280. We would describe the shape of this display as negatively skewed, because of the longer tail on the low end of the distribution.
2. Three of the average scores differed substantially from the others. These turn out to be 218 (Virgin Islands), 229 (District of Columbia), and 230 (Guam). These

21H	8
22L	
22H	9
23L	0
23H	
24L	
24H	79
25L	014
25H	6667779999
26L	0003344
26H	55778
27L	12233
27H	667
28L	01

Stem: Tens
Leaf: Ones

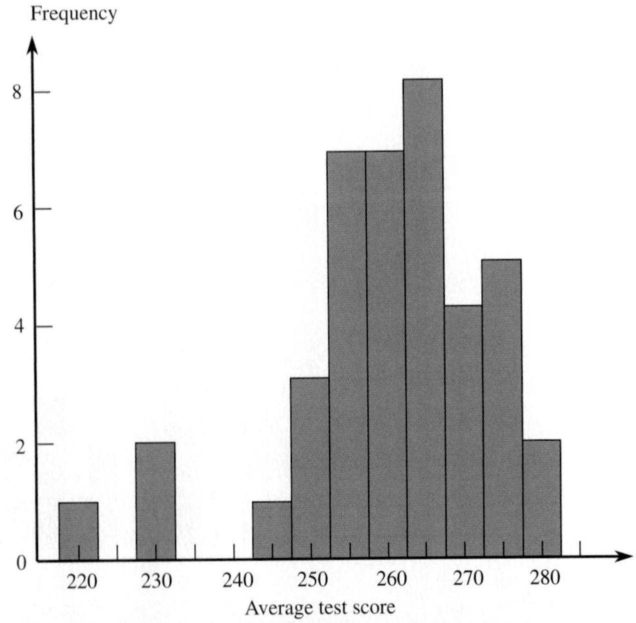

FIGURE 3.38
Stem-and-leaf display and histogram for math test scores.

three scores could be described as outliers. It is interesting to note that the three unusual values are from the areas that are not states.

3. There do not appear to be any outliers on the high side.
4. A "typical" average math score for the 37 states would be somewhere around 260.
5. There is quite a bit of variability in average score from state to state.

How would the displays have been different if the two territories and the District of Columbia had not participated in the testing? The resulting histogram is shown in Figure 3.39. Note that the display is now more symmetric, with no noticeable outliers. The display still reveals quite a bit of state-to-state variability in average score, and 260 still looks reasonable as a "typical" average score. Now suppose that the two highest values among the 37 states (Montana and North Dakota) had been even higher. The stem-and-leaf display might then look like the one given in Figure 3.40. In this stem-and-leaf display, two values stand out from the main part of the display. This would catch our attention and might cause us to look carefully at these two states to determine what factors may be related to high math scores.

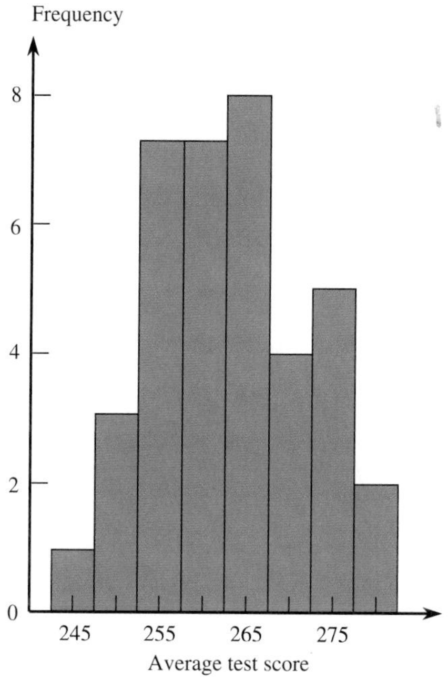

FIGURE 3.39
Histogram frequency for the modified math score data.

24H	79
25L	014
25H	6667779999
26L	0003344
26H	55778
27L	12233
27H	667
28L	
28H	
29L	
29H	68

Stem: Tens
Leaf: Ones

FIGURE 3.40
Stem-and-leaf display for modified math score data.

What to Look for in Published Data

Here are some questions you might ask yourself when attempting to extract information from a graphical data display:

- Is the chosen display appropriate for the type of data collected?
- For graphical displays of univariate numerical data, how would you describe the shape of the distribution, and what does this say about the variable being summarized?
- Are there any outliers (noticeably unusual values) in the data set? Is there any plausible explanation for why these values differ from the rest of the data? (The presence of outliers often leads to further avenues of investigation.)
- Where do most of the data values fall? What is a typical value for the data set? What does this say about the variable being summarized?
- Is there much variability in the data values? What does this say about the variable being summarized?

Of course, you should always think carefully about how the data were collected. If the data were not gathered in a reasonable manner (based on sound sampling methods or experimental design principles), you should be cautious in formulating any conclusions based on the data.

Consider the histogram in Figure 3.41, which is based on data published by the National Center for Health Statistics. The data set summarized by this histogram consisted of infant mortality rates (deaths per 1000 live births) for the 50 states in the United States. A histogram is an appropriate way of summarizing these data (although with only 50 observations, a stem-and-leaf display would also have been reasonable). The histogram itself is slightly positively skewed, with most mortality rates between 7.5 and 12. There is quite a bit of variability in infant mortality rate from state to state—perhaps more than we might have expected. This variability might be explained by differences in economic conditions or in access to health care. We may want to look further into these issues. Although there are no obvious outliers, the upper tail is a little longer than the lower tail. The three largest values in the data set are 12.1 (Alabama), 12.3 (Georgia), and 12.8 (South Carolina)—all Southern states. Again, this may suggest some interesting questions that deserve further investigation. A typical infant mortality rate would be about 9.5 deaths per 1000 live births. This represents an improvement, because researchers at the National Center for Health Statistics stated that the overall rate for 1988 was 10 deaths per 1000 live births. However, they also point out that the United States still ranked 22 out of 24 industrialized nations surveyed, with only New Zealand and Israel having higher infant mortality rates.

A Word to the Wise: Cautions and Limitations

When constructing and interpreting graphical displays, you need to keep in mind these things:

1. *Areas should be proportional to frequency, relative frequency, or magnitude of the number being represented.* The eye is naturally drawn to large areas in graphical displays, and it is natural for the observer to make informal comparisons based

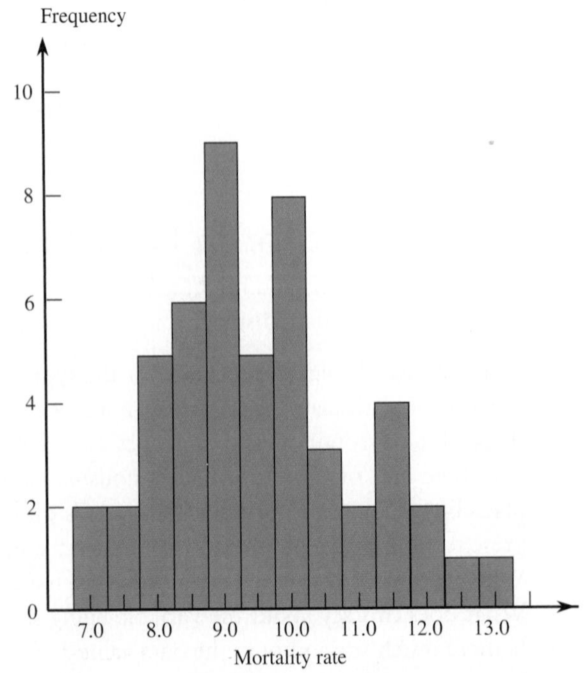

FIGURE 3.41
Histogram of infant mortality rates.

on area. Correctly constructed graphical displays, such as pie charts, bar charts, and histograms, are designed so that the areas of the pie slices or the bars are proportional to frequency or relative frequency. Sometimes, in an effort to make graphical displays more interesting, designers lose sight of this important principle, and the resulting graphs are misleading. For example, consider the following graph (*USA Today*, October 3, 2002):

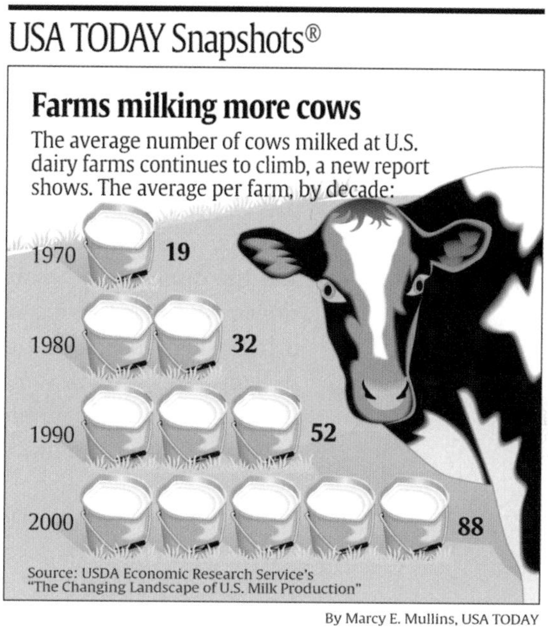

USA TODAY. October 03, 2002. Reprinted with permission.

In trying to make the graph more visually interesting by replacing the bars of a bar chart with milk buckets, areas are distorted. For example, the two buckets for 1980 represent 32 cows, whereas the one bucket for 1970 represents 19 cows. This is misleading because 32 is not twice as big as 19. Other areas are distorted as well.

Another common distortion occurs when a third dimension is added to bar charts or pie charts. For example, the pie chart at the bottom left of the page appeared in *USA Today* (September 17, 2009).

Adding the third dimension distorts the areas and makes it much more difficult to interpret correctly. A correctly drawn pie chart is shown below.

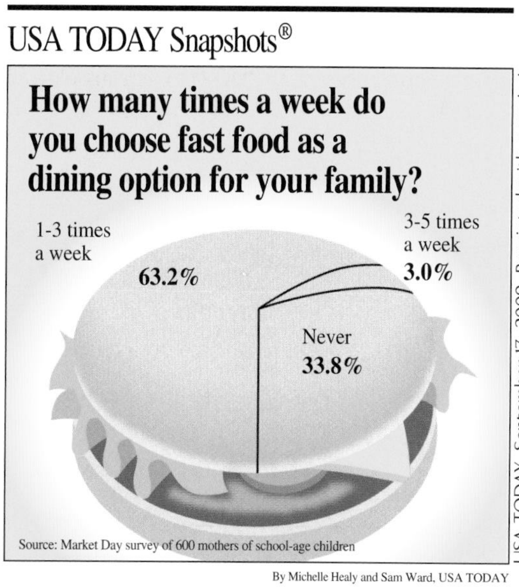

USA TODAY. September 17, 2009. Reprinted with permission.

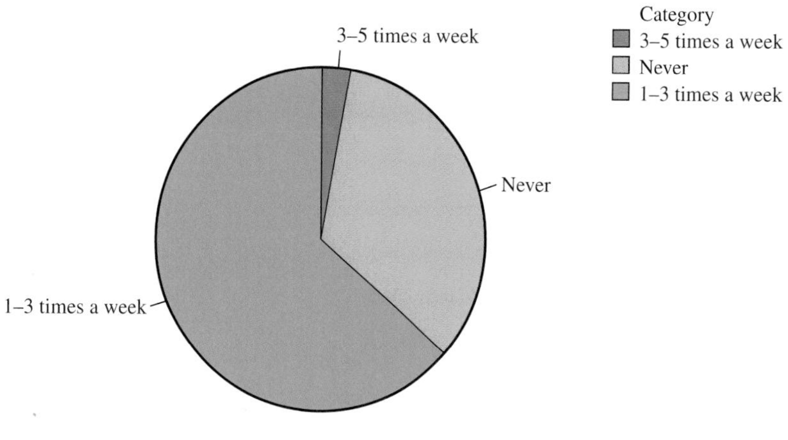

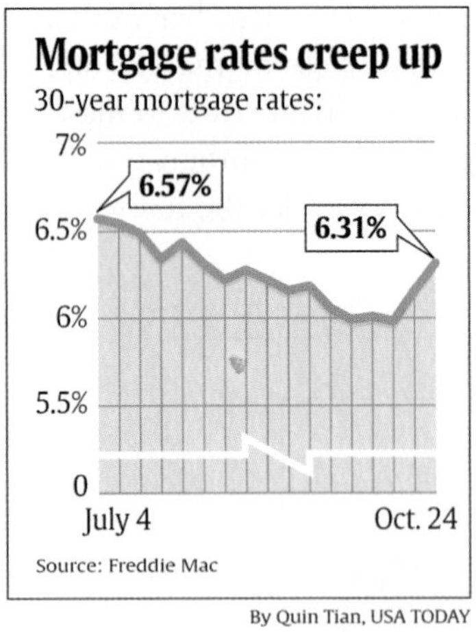

2. *Be cautious of graphs with broken axes.* Although it is common to see scatterplots with broken axes, be extremely cautious of time-series plots, bar charts, or histograms with broken axes. The use of broken axes in a scatterplot does not distort information about the nature of the relationship in the bivariate data set used to construct the display. On the other hand, in time-series plots, broken axes can sometimes exaggerate the magnitude of change over time. Although it is not always inadvisable to break the vertical axis in a time-series plot, it is something you should watch for, and if you see a time-series plot with a broken axis, as in the accompanying time-series plot of mortgage rates (*USA Today*, October 25, 2002), you should pay particular attention to the scale on the vertical axis and take extra care in interpreting the graph.

   In bar charts and histograms, the vertical axis (which represents frequency, relative frequency, or density) should *never* be broken. If the vertical axis is broken in this type of graph, the resulting display will violate the "proportional area" principle and the display will be misleading. For example, the accompanying bar chart is similar to one appearing in an advertisement for a software product designed to help teachers raise student test scores. By starting the vertical axis at 50, the gain for students using the software is exaggerated. Areas of the bars are not proportional to the magnitude of the numbers represented—the area for the rectangle representing 68 is more than three times the area of the rectangle representing 55!

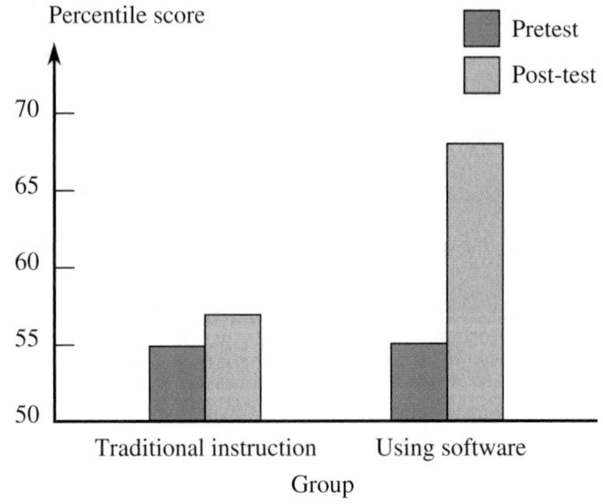

3. *Watch out for unequal time spacing in time-series plots.* If observations over time are not made at regular time intervals, special care must be taken in constructing the time-series plot. Consider the accompanying time-series plot, which is similar to one appearing in the *San Luis Obispo Tribune* (September 22, 2002) in an article on online banking:

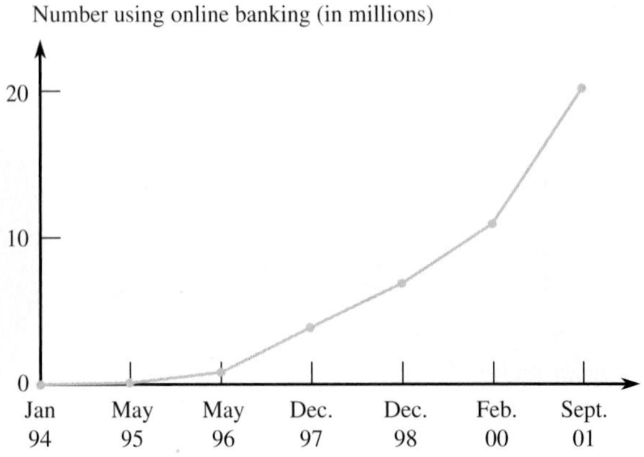

Notice that the intervals between observations are irregular, yet the points in the plot are equally spaced along the time axis. This makes it difficult to make a coherent assessment of the rate of change over time. This could have been remedied by spacing the observations differently along the time axis, as shown in the following plot:

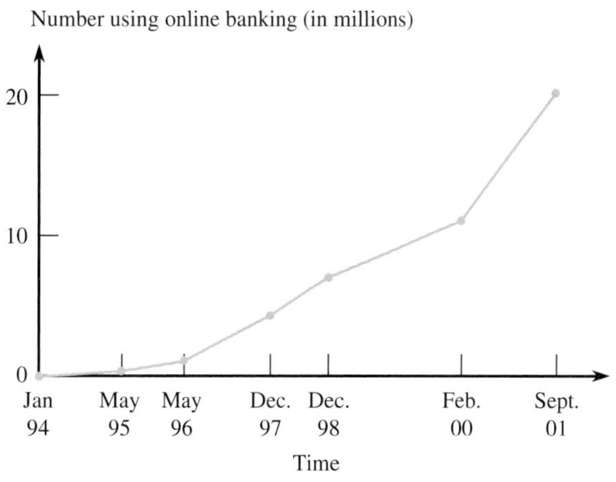

4. *Be careful how you interpret patterns in scatterplots.* A strong pattern in a scatterplot means that the two variables tend to vary together in a predictable way, but it does not mean that there is a cause-and-effect relationship between the two variables. We will consider this point further in Chapter 5, but in the meantime, when describing patterns in scatterplots, be careful not to use wording that implies that changes in one variable *cause* changes in the other.
5. *Make sure that a graphical display creates the right first impression.* For example, consider the graph below from *USA Today* (June 25, 2002). Although this graph does not violate the proportional area principle, the way the "bar" for the "none" category is displayed makes this graph difficult to read, and a quick glance at this graph would leave the reader with an incorrect impression.

EXERCISES 3.46 - 3.51

3.46 The accompanying comparative bar chart is from the report "More and More Teens on Cell Phones" (Pew Research Center, www.pewresearch.org, August 19, 2009).

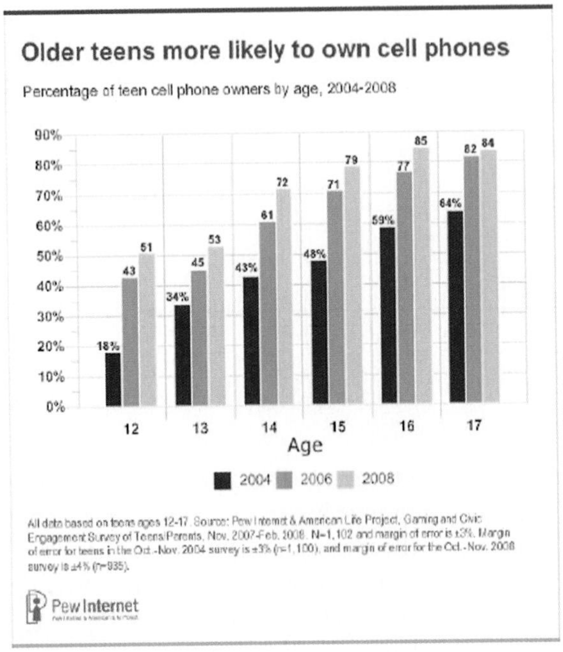

Suppose that you plan to include this graph in an article that you are writing for your school newspaper. Write a few paragraphs that could accompany the graph. Be sure to address what the graph reveals about how teen cell phone ownership is related to age and how it has changed over time.

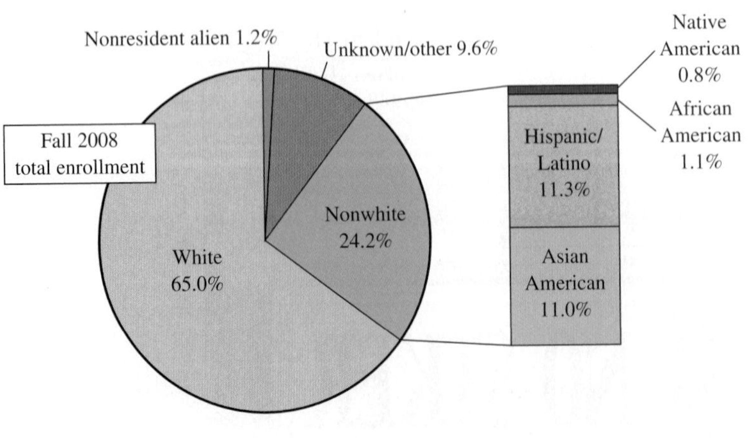

FIGURE EX-3.47

3.47 Figure EX-3.47 is from the Fall 2008 Census Enrollment Report at Cal Poly, San Luis Obispo. It uses both a pie chart and a segmented bar graph to summarize data on ethnicity for students enrolled at the university in Fall 2008.

a. Use the information in the graphical display to construct a single segmented bar graph for the ethnicity data.
b. Do you think that the original graphical display or the one you created in Part (a) is more informative? Explain your choice.
c. Why do you think that the original graphical display format (combination of pie chart and segmented bar graph) was chosen over a single pie chart with 7 slices?

3.48 The accompanying graph appeared in *USA Today* (August 5, 2008). This graph is a modified comparative bar graph. Most likely, the modifications (incorporating hands and the earth) were made to try to make a display that readers would find more interesting.

a. Use the information in the *USA Today* graph to construct a traditional comparative bar graph.
b. Explain why the modifications made in the *USA Today* graph may make interpretation more difficult than with the traditional comparative bar graph.

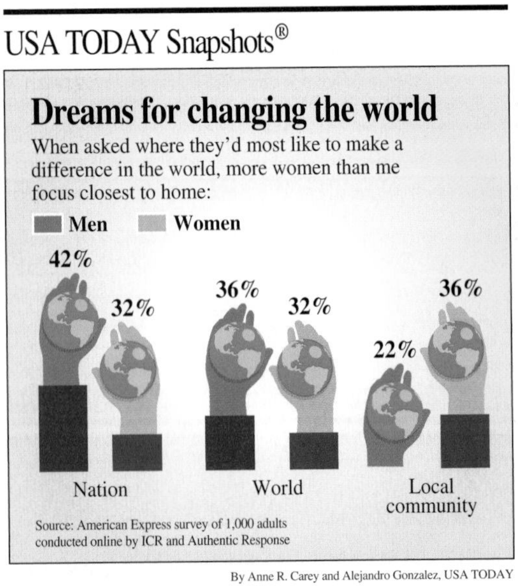

By Anne R. Carey and Alejandro Gonzalez, USA TODAY

3.49 The two graphical displays below appeared in *USA Today* (June 8, 2009 and July 28, 2009). One is an appropriate representation and the other is not. For each of the two, explain why it is or is not drawn appropriately.

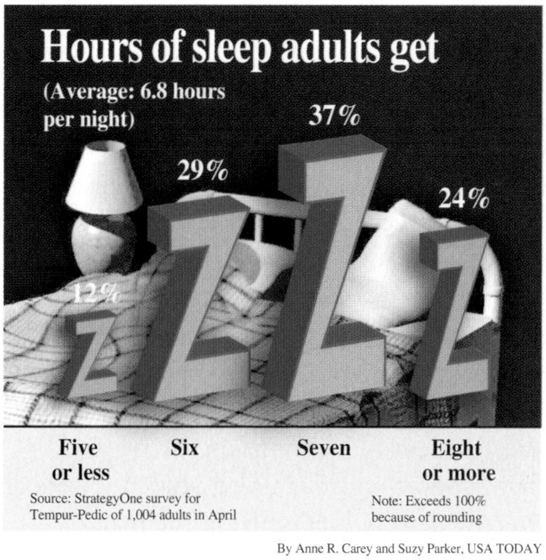

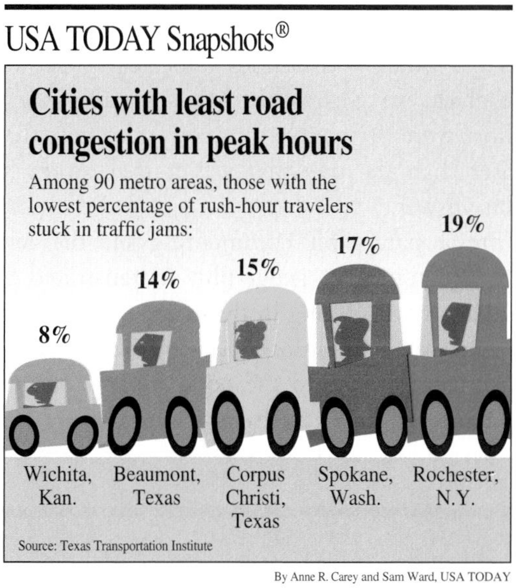

3.50 The following graphical display is meant to be a comparative bar graph (*USA Today*, August 3, 2009). Do you think that this graphical display is an effective summary of the data? If so, explain why. If not, explain why not and construct a display that makes it easier to compare the ice cream preferences of men and women.

3.51 Explain why the following graphical display (*USA Today*, September 17, 2009) is misleading.

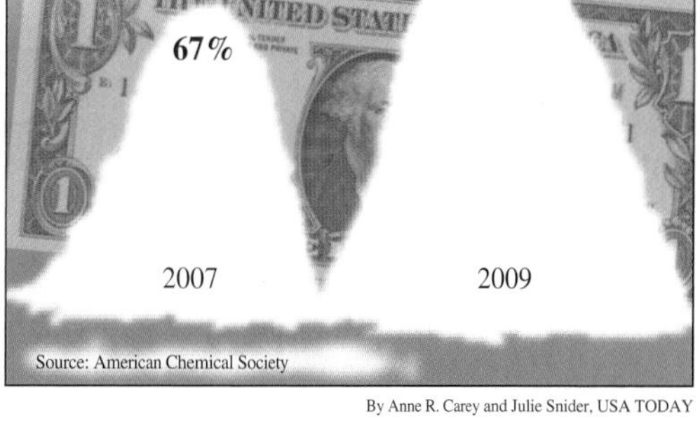

ACTIVITY 3.1 Locating States

Background: A newspaper article bemoaning the state of students' knowledge of geography claimed that more students could identify the island where the 2002 season of the TV show *Survivor* was filmed than could locate Vermont on a map of the United States. In this activity, you will collect data that will allow you to estimate the proportion of students who can correctly locate the states of Vermont and Nebraska.

1. Working as a class, decide how you will select a sample that you think will be representative of the students from your school.
2. Use the sampling method from Step 1 to obtain the subjects for this study. Subjects should be shown the accompanying map of the United States and asked to point out the state of Vermont. After the subject has given his or her answer, ask the subject to point out the state of Nebraska. For each subject, record whether or not Vermont was correctly identified and whether or not Nebraska was correctly identified.

3. When the data collection process is complete, summarize the resulting data in a table like the one shown here:

Response	Frequency
Correctly identified both states	
Correctly identified Vermont but not Nebraska	
Correctly identified Nebraska but not Vermont	
Did not correctly identify either state	

4. Construct a pie chart that summarizes the data in the table from Step 3.
5. What proportion of sampled students were able to correctly identify Vermont on the map?
6. What proportion of sampled students were able to correctly identify Nebraska on the map?
7. Construct a comparative bar chart that shows the proportion correct and the proportion incorrect for each of the two states considered.
8. Which state, Vermont or Nebraska, is closer to the state in which your school is located? Based on the pie chart, do you think that the students at your school were better able to identify the state that was closer than the one that was farther away? Justify your answer.
9. Write a paragraph commenting on the level of knowledge of U.S. geography demonstrated by the students participating in this study.
10. Would you be comfortable generalizing your conclusions in Step 8 to the population of students at your school? Explain why or why not.

ACTIVITY 3.2 Bean Counters!

Materials needed: A large bowl of dried beans (or marbles, plastic beads, or any other small, fairly regular objects) and a coin.

In this activity, you will investigate whether people can hold more in the right hand or in the left hand.

1. Flip a coin to determine which hand you will measure first. If the coin lands heads side up, start with the right hand. If the coin lands tails side up, start with the left hand. With the designated hand, reach into the bowl and grab as many beans as possible. Raise the hand over the bowl and count to 4. If no beans drop during the count to 4, drop the beans onto a piece of paper and record the number of beans grabbed. If any beans drop during the count, restart the count. That is, you must hold the beans for a count of 4 without any beans falling before you can determine the number grabbed. Repeat the process with the other hand, and then record the following information: (1) right-hand number, (2) left-hand number, and (3) dominant hand (left or right, depending on whether you are left- or right-handed).

2. Create a class data set by recording the values of the three variables listed in Step 1 for each student in your class.
3. Using the class data set, construct a comparative stem-and-leaf display with the right-hand counts displayed on the right and the left-hand counts displayed on the left of the stem-and-leaf display. Comment on the interesting features of the display and include a comparison of the right-hand count and left-hand count distributions.
4. Now construct a comparative stem-and-leaf display that allows you to compare dominant-hand count to nondominant-hand count. Does the display support the theory that dominant-hand count tends to be higher than nondominant-hand count?
5. For each observation in the data set, compute the difference

   dominant-hand count − nondominant-hand count

   Construct a stem-and-leaf display of the differences. Comment on the interesting features of this display.
6. Explain why looking at the distribution of the differences (Step 5) provides more information than the comparative stem-and-leaf display (Step 4). What information is lost in the comparative display that is retained in the display of the differences?

Summary of Key Concepts and Formulas

TERM OR FORMULA	COMMENT
Frequency distribution	A table that displays frequencies, and sometimes relative and cumulative relative frequencies, for categories (categorical data), possible values (discrete numerical data), or class intervals (continuous data).
Comparative bar chart	Two or more bar charts that use the same set of horizontal and vertical axes.
Pie chart	A graph of a frequency distribution for a categorical data set. Each category is represented by a slice of the pie, and the area of the slice is proportional to the corresponding frequency or relative frequency.
Segmented bar graph	A graph of a frequency distribution for a categorical data set. Each category is represented by a segment of the bar, and the area of the segment is proportional to the corresponding frequency or relative frequency.
Stem-and-leaf display	A method of organizing numerical data in which the stem values (leading digit(s) of the observations) are listed in a column, and the leaf (trailing digit(s)) for each observation is then listed beside the corresponding stem. Sometimes stems are repeated to stretch the display.
Histogram	A picture of the information in a frequency distribution for a numerical data set. A rectangle is drawn above each possible value (discrete data) or class interval. The rectangle's area is proportional to the corresponding frequency or relative frequency.
Histogram shapes	A (smoothed) histogram may be unimodal (a single peak), bimodal (two peaks), or multimodal. A unimodal histogram may be symmetric, positively skewed (a long right or upper tail), or negatively skewed. A frequently occurring shape is one that is approximately normal.
Cumulative relative frequency plot	A graph of a cumulative relative frequency distribution.
Scatterplot	A picture of bivariate numerical data in which each observation (x, y) is represented as a point with respect to a horizontal x-axis and a vertical y-axis.
Time-series plot	A graphical display of numerical data collected over time.

Chapter Review Exercises 3.52 - 3.71

3.52 The article "Most Smokers Wish They Could Quit" (*Gallup Poll Analyses*, November 21, 2002) noted that smokers and nonsmokers perceive the risks of smoking differently. The accompanying relative frequency table summarizes responses regarding the perceived harm of smoking for each of three groups: a sample of 241 smokers, a sample of 261 former smokers, and a sample of 502 nonsmokers. Construct a comparative bar chart for these data. Do not forget to use relative frequencies in constructing the bar chart because the three sample sizes are different. Comment on how smokers, former smokers, and nonsmokers differ with respect to perceived risk of smoking.

	Frequency		
Perceived Risk of Smoking	Smokers	Former Smokers	Nonsmokers
Very harmful	145	204	432
Somewhat harmful	72	42	50
Not too harmful	17	10	15
Not at all harmful	7	5	5

3.53 Each year the College Board publishes a profile of students taking the SAT. In the report "2005 College Bound Seniors: Total Group Profile Report," the average SAT scores were reported for three groups defined by first language learned. Use the data in the accompanying table to construct a bar chart of the average verbal SAT score for the three groups.

First Language Learned	Average Verbal SAT
English	519
English and another language	486
A language other than English	462

3.54 The report referenced in Exercise 3.53 also gave average math SAT scores for the three language groups, as shown in the following table.

First Language Learned	Average Math SAT
English	521
English and another language	513
A language other than English	521

Construct a comparative bar chart for the average verbal and math scores for the three language groups. Write a few sentences describing the differences and similarities between the three language groups as shown in the bar chart.

3.55 ● The Connecticut Agricultural Experiment Station conducted a study of the calorie content of different types of beer. The calorie content (calories per 100 ml) for 26 brands of light beer are (from the web site brewery.org):

29 28 33 31 30 33 30 28 27 41 39 31 29
23 32 31 32 19 40 22 34 31 42 35 29 43

Construct a stem-and-leaf display using stems 1, 2, 3, and 4. Write a sentence or two describing the calorie content of light beers.

3.56 The stem-and-leaf display of Exercise 3.16 uses only four stems. Construct a stem-and-leaf display for these data using repeated stems 1H, 2L, 2H, . . . , 4L. For example, the first observation, 29, would have a stem of 2 and a leaf of 9. It would be entered into the display for the stem 2H, because it is a "high" 2—that is, it has a leaf that is on the high end (5, 6, 7, 8, 9).

3.57 ● The article "A Nation Ablaze with Change" (*USA Today*, July 3, 2001) gave the accompanying data on percentage increase in population between 1990 and 2000 for the 50 U.S. states. Also provided in the table is a column that indicates for each state whether the state is in the eastern or western part of the United States (the states are listed in order of population size):

State	Percentage Change	East/West
California	13.8	W
Texas	22.8	W
New York	5.5	E
Florida	23.5	E
Illinois	8.6	E
Pennsylvania	3.4	E
Ohio	4.7	E
Michigan	6.9	E
New Jersey	8.9	E
Georgia	26.4	E
North Carolina	21.4	E

(continued)

State	Percentage Change	East/West
Virginia	14.4	E
Massachusetts	5.5	E
Indiana	9.7	E
Washington	21.1	W
Tennessee	16.7	E
Missouri	9.3	E
Wisconsin	9.6	E
Maryland	10.8	E
Arizona	40.0	W
Minnesota	12.4	E
Louisiana	5.9	E
Alabama	10.1	E
Colorado	30.6	W
Kentucky	9.7	E
South Carolina	15.1	E
Oklahoma	9.7	W
Oregon	20.4	W
Connecticut	3.6	E
Iowa	5.4	E
Mississippi	10.5	E
Kansas	8.5	W
Arkansas	13.7	E
Utah	29.6	W
Nevada	66.3	W
New Mexico	20.1	W
West Virginia	0.8	E
Nebraska	8.4	W
Idaho	28.5	W
Maine	3.9	E
New Hampshire	11.4	E
Hawaii	9.3	W
Rhode Island	4.5	E
Montana	12.9	W
Delaware	17.6	E
South Dakota	8.5	W
North Dakota	0.5	W
Alaska	14.0	W
Vermont	8.2	E
Wyoming	8.9	W

a. Construct a stem-and-leaf display for percentage growth for the data set consisting of all 50 states. Hints: Regard the observations as having two digits to the left of the decimal place. That is, think of an observation such as 8.5 as 08.5. It will also be easier to truncate leaves to a single digit; for example, a leaf of 8.5 could be truncated to 8 for purposes of constructing the display.

b. Comment on any interesting features of the data set. Do any of the observations appear to be outliers?

c. Now construct a comparative stem-and-leaf display for the eastern and western states. Write a few sentences comparing the percentage growth distributions for eastern and western states.

3.58 ● People suffering from Alzheimer's disease often have difficulty performing basic activities of daily living (ADLs). In one study ("Functional Status and Clinical Findings in Patients with Alzheimer's Disease," *Journal of Gerontology* [1992]: 177–182), investigators focused on six such activities: dressing, bathing, transferring, toileting, walking, and eating. Here are data on the number of ADL impairments for each of 240 patients:

Number of impairments	0	1	2	3	4	5	6
Frequency	100	43	36	17	24	9	11

a. Determine the relative frequencies that correspond to the given frequencies.
b. What proportion of these patients had at most two impairments?
c. Use the result of Part (b) to determine what proportion of patients had more than two impairments.
d. What proportion of the patients had at least four impairments?

3.59 Does the size of a transplanted organ matter? A study that attempted to answer this question ("Minimum Graft Size for Successful Living Donor Liver Transplantation," *Transplantation* [1999]:1112–1116) presented a scatterplot much like the following ("graft weight ratio" is the weight of the transplanted liver relative to the ideal size liver for the recipient):

a. Discuss interesting features of this scatterplot.
b. Why do you think the overall relationship is negative?

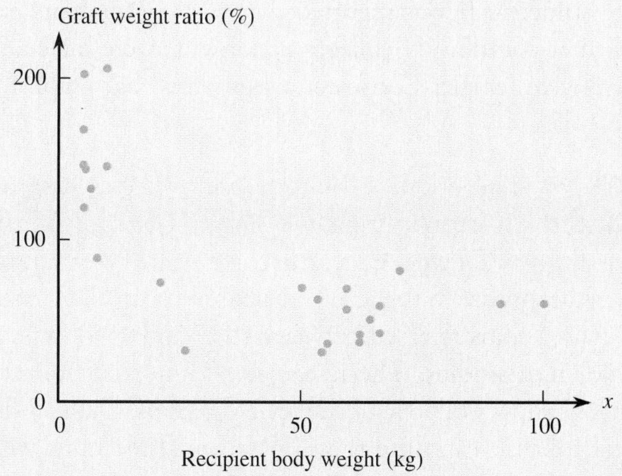

3.60 ● The National Telecommunications and Information Administration published a report titled "Falling Through the Net: Toward Digital Inclusion" (U.S. Department of Commerce, October 2000) that included the following information on access to computers in the home:

Year	Percentage of Households with a Computer
1985	8.2
1990	15.0
1994	22.8
1995	24.1
1998	36.6
1999	42.1
2000	51.0

a. Construct a time-series plot for these data. Be careful—the observations are not equally spaced in time. The points in the plot should not be equally spaced along the x-axis.

b. Comment on any trend over time.

3.61 According to the National Association of Home Builders, the average size of a home in 1950 was 983 ft^2. The average size increased to 1500 ft^2 in 1970, 2080 ft^2 in 1990; and 2330 ft^2 in 2003 (*San Luis Obispo Tribune*, October 16, 2005).

a. Construct a time-series plot that shows how the average size of a home has changed over time.

b. If the trend of the time-series plot were to continue, what would you predict the average home size to be in 2010?

3.62 The paper "Community Colleges Start to Ask, Where Are the Men?" (*Chronicle of Higher Education*, June 28, 2002) gave data on gender for community college students. It was reported that 42% of students enrolled at community colleges nationwide were male and 58% were female. Construct a segmented bar graph for these data.

3.63 ● The article "Tobacco and Alcohol Use in G-Rated Children's Animated Films" (*Journal of the American Medical Association* [1999]: 1131–1136) reported exposure to tobacco and alcohol use in all G-rated animated films released between 1937 and 1997 by five major film studios. The researchers found that tobacco use was shown in 56% of the reviewed films. Data on the total tobacco exposure time (in seconds) for films with tobacco use produced by Walt Disney, Inc., were as follows:

223 176 548 37 158 51 299 37 11 165
74 92 6 23 206 9

Data for 11 G-rated animated films showing tobacco use that were produced by MGM/United Artists, Warner Brothers, Universal, and Twentieth Century Fox were also given. The tobacco exposure times (in seconds) for these films was as follows:

205 162 6 1 117 5 91 155 24 55 17

Construct a comparative stem-and-leaf display for these data. Comment on the interesting features of this display.

3.64 ● The accompanying data on household expenditures on transportation for the United Kingdom appeared in "Transport Statistics for Great Britain: 2002 Edition" (in *Family Spending: A Report on the Family Expenditure Survey* [The Stationary Office, 2002]). Expenditures (in pounds per week) included costs of purchasing and maintaining any vehicles owned by members of the household and any costs associated with public transportation and leisure travel.

Year	Average Transportation	Percentage of Household Expenditures for Transportation
1990	247.20	16.2
1991	259.00	15.3
1992	271.80	15.8
1993	276.70	15.6
1994	283.60	15.1
1995	289.90	14.9
1996	309.10	15.7
1997	328.80	16.7
1998	352.20	17.0
1999	359.40	17.2
2000	385.70	16.7

a. Construct time-series plots of the transportation expense data and the percent of household expense data.

b. Do the time-series plots of Part (a) support the statement that follows? Explain why or why not. Statement: Although actual expenditures have been increasing, the percentage of the total household expenditures that go toward transportation has remained relatively stable.

3.65 The article "The Healthy Kids Survey: A Look at the Findings" (*San Luis Obispo Tribune,* October 25, 2002) gave the accompanying information for a sample of fifth graders in San Luis Obispo County. Responses are to the question:

"After school, are you home alone without adult supervision?"

Response	Percentage
Never	8
Some of the time	15
Most of the time	16
All of the time	61

a. Summarize these data using a pie chart.
b. Construct a segmented bar graph for these data.
c. Which graphing method—the pie chart or the segmented bar graph—do you think does a better job of conveying information about response? Explain.

3.66 "If you were taking a new job and had your choice of a boss, would you prefer to work for a man or a woman?" That was the question posed to individuals in a sample of 576 employed adults (*Gallup at a Glance,* October 16, 2002). Responses are summarized in the following table:

Response	Frequency
Prefer to work for a man	190
Prefer to work for a woman	92
No difference	282
No opinion	12

a. Construct a pie chart to summarize this data set, and write a sentence or two summarizing how people responded to this question.
b. Summarize the given data using a segmented bar graph.

3.67 ● 2005 was a record year for hurricane devastation in the United States (*San Luis Obispo Tribune,* November 30, 2005). Of the 26 tropical storms and hurricanes in the season, four hurricanes hit the mainland: Dennis, Katrina, Rita, and Wilma. The United States insured catastrophic losses since 1989 (approximate values read from a graph that appeared in the *San Luis Obispo Tribune,* November 30, 2005) are as follows:

Year	Cost (in billions of dollars)
1989	7.5
1990	2.5
1991	4.0
1992	22.5
1993	5.0
1994	18.0
1995	9.0
1996	8.0
1997	2.6
1998	10.0
1999	9.0
2000	3.0
2001	27.0
2002	5.0
2003	12.0
2004	28.5
2005	56.8

Construct a time-series plot that shows the insured catastrophic loss over time. What do you think causes the peaks in the graph?

3.68 An article in the *San Luis Obispo Tribune* (November 20, 2002) stated that 39% of those with critical housing needs (those who pay more than half their income for housing) lived in urban areas, 42% lived in suburban areas, and the rest lived in rural areas. Construct a pie chart that shows the distribution of type of residential area (urban, suburban, or rural) for those with critical housing needs.

3.69 ● Living-donor kidney transplants are becoming more common. Often a living donor has chosen to donate a kidney to a relative with kidney disease. The following data appeared in a *USA Today* article on organ transplants ("Kindness Motivates Newest Kidney Donors," June 19, 2002):

	Number of Kidney Transplants	
Year	Living-Donor to Relative	Living-Donor to Unrelated Person
1994	2390	202
1995	2906	400
1996	2916	526
1997	3144	607
1998	3324	814
1999	3359	930
2000	3679	1325
2001	3879	1399

a. Construct a time-series plot for the number of living-donor kidney transplants where the donor is a relative of the recipient. Describe the trend in this plot.

b. Use the data from 1994 and 2001 to construct a comparative bar chart for the type of donation (relative or unrelated). Write a few sentences commenting on your display.

3.70 ● Many nutritional experts have expressed concern about the high levels of sodium in prepared foods. The following data on sodium content (in milligrams) per frozen meal appeared in the article "Comparison of 'Light' Frozen Meals" (Boston Globe, April 24, 1991):

720	530	800	690	880	1050	340	810	760
300	400	680	780	390	950	520	500	630
480	940	450	990	910	420	850	390	600

Two histograms for these data are shown:

a. Do the two histograms give different impressions about the distribution of values?

b. Use each histogram to determine approximately the proportion of observations that are less than 800, and compare to the actual proportion.

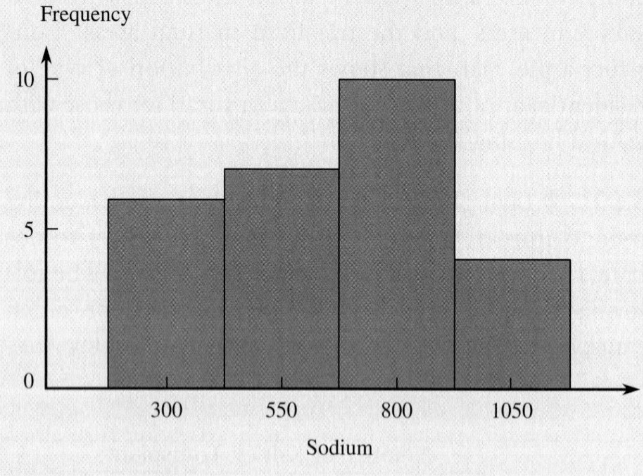

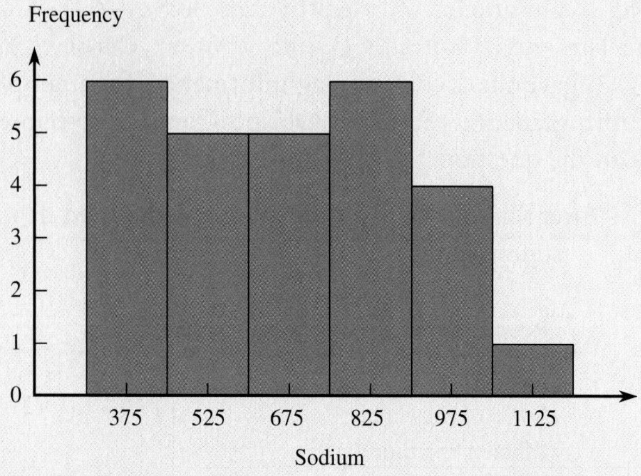

3.71 ● Americium 241 (^{241}Am) is a radioactive material used in the manufacture of smoke detectors. The article "Retention and Dosimetry of Injected ^{241}Am in Beagles" (*Radiation Research* [1984]: 564–575) described a study in which 55 beagles were injected with a dose of ^{241}Am (proportional to each animal's weight). Skeletal retention of ^{241}Am (in microcuries per kilogram) was recorded for each beagle, resulting in the following data:

0.196	0.451	0.498	0.411	0.324	0.190	0.489
0.300	0.346	0.448	0.188	0.399	0.305	0.304
0.287	0.243	0.334	0.299	0.292	0.419	0.236
0.315	0.447	0.585	0.291	0.186	0.393	0.419
0.335	0.332	0.292	0.375	0.349	0.324	0.301
0.333	0.408	0.399	0.303	0.318	0.468	0.441
0.306	0.367	0.345	0.428	0.345	0.412	0.337
0.353	0.357	0.320	0.354	0.361	0.329	

a. Construct a frequency distribution for these data, and draw the corresponding histogram.

b. Write a short description of the important features of the shape of the histogram.

Graphing Calculator Explorations

EXPLORATION 3.1 Using Lists on Your Calculator

Calculators and computers work their magic by storing numbers in "memory locations." To perform an addition, the computer looks in its "memory" for the two numbers, retrieves them, and adds them. In the early days of calculators there were very few of these expensive memory cells and calculations were performed one at a time while the user entered numbers. The modern scientific calculator allows a very useful extension of a single memory cell: a *group* of memory cells known as a "list." Using a list, a whole set of data, complete with a "name," can be stored in the calculator and analyzed as a whole. This list capability makes the calculator a very powerful tool for analyzing data. Since all the numbers are in the calculator at the same time, graphic representations of data such as those presented in this chapter are possible.

The actual capabilities of lists and the keystrokes to use these capabilities vary from calculator to calculator, so we will not be overly specific about particular calculator keystrokes. *Your best source for learning about your calculator is the manual that came with it!* You need the manual to fully understand and realize the potential of your calculator. Your calculator may implement some of its capabilities with special keys or menus, and the menus may include functions that require additional information that must be entered in a particular order. You don't need to memorize all these details. That's why you have the manual!

To use your calculator for statistical analysis you must be able to manipulate lists effectively. The accompanying table describes some of the list-based calculator features that will be important to you in performing statistical analysis. In future Explorations, we will assume that you are familiar with these list features.

Capability	Why It Is Important
Create a list	Some lists are provided automatically for your use, already labeled "List 1 or L1," or "List 2 or L2," etc. You will want to save data in lists with more informative names than these, such as "height" or "time."
Enter data into a list	This knowledge is, of course, fundamental to all analyses you will be performing.
Delete a list from the calculator	As powerful as your calculator is, there is a limit to its memory—there will come a time when you will need to delete the old data to prepare for the new.
Insert a number in a certain location in the list Or Delete a particular number in the list	If you are like everyone else, you will eventually add an extra number you did not intend or leave out a number from where it should be. Correcting these errors is a lot faster than deleting a whole list and starting over.
Copy data from one list to another	This will give you one of those things so precious to everyone who works with a finicky calculator (or finicky fingers?): a backup copy of the data!
Perform arithmetic operations with lists	Rather than perform the same arithmetic sequence separately on a set of numbers, you can do the calculations one list at a time. For example, to change units from inches to centimeters, you can multiply *all* the numbers on the list by 2.54. Usually, this is done with a statement something like 2.54 × ListName1 → ListName2. (The equal sign, =, is sometimes used in place of the arrow symbol.)

You need to be familiar with list manipulation to do effective statistical work with your calculator. As we proceed we will be more specific—and more detailed—

about how you can utilize your calculator's list capabilities. The calculator manual may have a chapter called "Using Lists." We strongly encourage you to read it!

EXPLORATION 3.2 Setting the Statistics Window

As we move into graphical descriptions of data, we need to consider how to use your calculator to produce graphs and plots of data. If you have used your calculator to graph functions, some of what follows will be a review. If you are new to the world of graphing calculators you will need a basic understanding of how to set up your calculator's "viewing window" for displaying graphs.

The metaphor of viewing the "world" through a "window" is a good one for thinking about the calculator window. If you think of the Cartesian *x-y* axes as the calculator's "world view" and your calculator view window as a portal through which to view this Cartesian world, you will be in the right frame of mind.

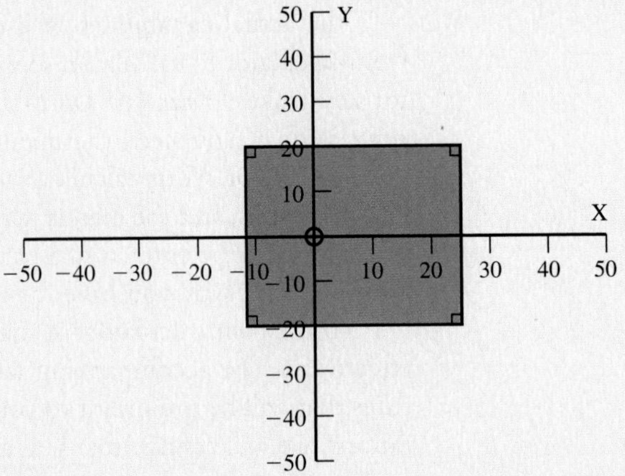

As you set up your calculator for graphing, your first problem will be, "Where in the *world* do I put my view *window?*" The quick and easy answer: You put your view window where your data is! We will illustrate how to do this by constructing a histogram, using the data from Exercise 3.17, "Going wireless." To illustrate how to set the view window, we will begin with a slightly bad graph of a histogram and then gradually improve it. First, we want you to do something a bit strange, but trust us. Enter the function $y = 100/x$ into your calculator. Now enter the data from "Going wireless" into your calculator in List 1. After entering the data, navigate your calculator's menu system to the histogram option. Actual keystrokes will vary among calculators, but the terms "Stat Graph" and "Stat Plot" are commonly used in calculators.

```
WINDOW
 Xmin=0
 Xmax=30
 Xscl=1
 Ymin=-5
 Ymax=16
 Yscl=1
 Xres=1
```

FIGURE 3.42

The properties of the view window are based on settings that you will manually enter into the calculator. (Your calculator may have the capability of automatically placing the view window over the appropriate position in its Cartesian system. Pretend for the moment that you are unaware of this.) To set up the view window you must navigate to your calculator's menu system, or possibly just press a "window" key. When you find the graph setup screen, it will look something like Figure 3.42. (There may be different or additional information on your screen but the numbers here will be our focus for this Exploration. Your numbers may have different values from these; for ease in following the discussion you may wish to change the values on your calculator to match those in the figure.)

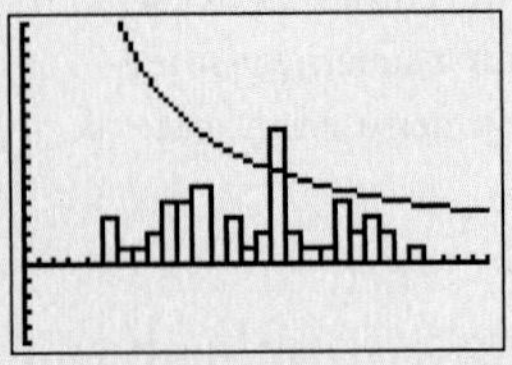

FIGURE 3.43

The numbers on this screen determine where the viewing window is placed over the calculator's "world" coordinate system. Exit from the setup window and plot a histogram, by using a "graph" key or a menu, depending on your calculator. You should have something like what is shown in Figure 3.43. (Your graph will get better as we go.)

Notice that there actually is a histogram there, but there is a pesky function overlaying the histogram. Suspiciously, it looks something like $y = 100/x$! What's the problem here? First, remember that the calculator's world is the *x*-*y* coordinate system. If you have been using the calculator to plot mathematical functions and they are still "in" the calculator, both your last function and the histogram will be drawn. Oddly, this happens by design. Since a calculator user most likely will not graph a mathematical function and a histogram at the same time, the calculator graphing space is shared to save calculator memory. The solution to the histogram-and-function problem is easy: Don't graph the function. You can now delete the function and redraw the histogram.

We will need to manually reposition the viewing window in the calculator world for a better look at the data. Return to the view window setup screen and make the following changes: set Xmin to 4 and Xmax to 28 and redraw the histogram. The histogram in the view window will now be positioned something like Figure 3.44.

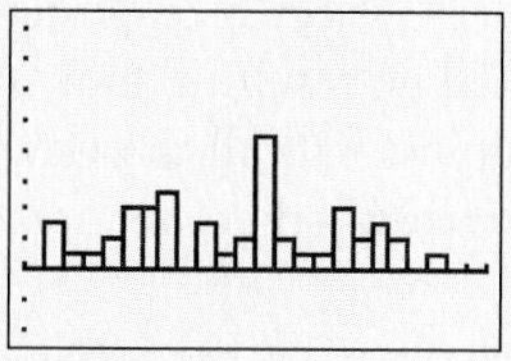

FIGURE 3.44

This is certainly an improvement but the histogram is still rather small compared to the screen, sacrificing some detail. To correct this problem we will adjust the top of the view window. Return to the graph setup screen and locate the lines for YMin and YMax. Change the YMin to -1 and the YMax to 16. Now regraph the histogram. You should see a very well-spaced histogram similar to Figure 3.45.

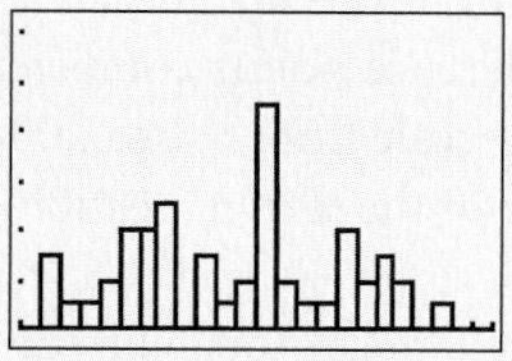

FIGURE 3.45

You will find that adjusting the view window is a frequent task in creating effective statistical graphs. While each of the statistical plots has its own individuality, your construction of them will always involve positioning the view window over the Cartesian world view of your calculator. Even if the calculator has an automatic function to position statistical graphs, you will find it necessary sometimes to "improve" on the calculator's automatic choice. When you manually change your graph, keep in mind the idea of positioning a view window over a Cartesian coordinate system. This will help you organize your thoughts about how to change the view window and make the task less frustrating.

EXPLORATION 3.3 Scaling the Histogram

When we constructed a histogram in the previous Exploration there were some numbers that we temporarily ignored in the view screen. We would like to return to those numbers now because they can seriously affect the look of a histogram. When we left the histogram the numbers in our view window were set as shown in Figure 3.46. These settings place the view window over the calculator's Cartesian system for effective viewing of the histogram from the "Going wireless" data.

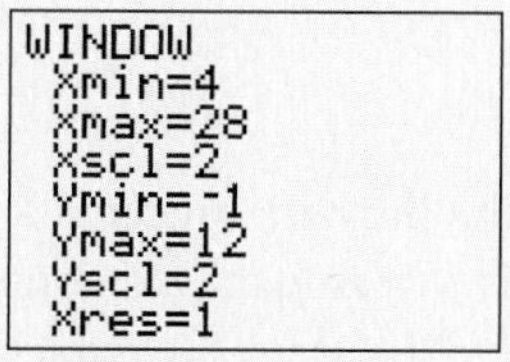

FIGURE 3.46

We would now like to experiment a bit with the "Xscale." In the statistical graphs produced by the calculator the Xscale and Yscale choices will control the placement of the little "tick" marks on the *x*- and *y*-axis. In Exploration 3.2, the Xscale and Yscale were set at 1. Change the Xscale and Yscale values to 2 and redraw the histogram. You should see a graph similar to Figure 3.47. The *x*- and *y*-axis tick marks now appear at multiples of 2.

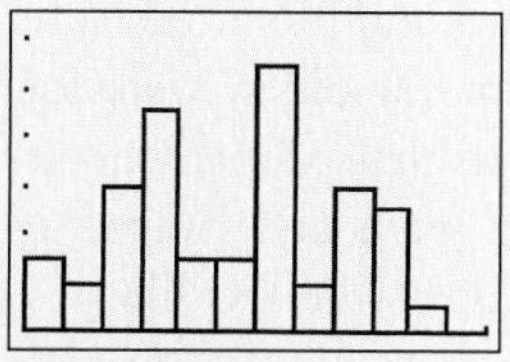

FIGURE 3.47

Note that changing the Xscale has altered not only the tick marks but also the class intervals for the histogram. The choice of class intervals can significantly change the look and feel of the histogram. The choice of Xscale can affect judgments about the shape of the histogram. Because of this possibility it is wise to look at a histogram with varying choices of the Xscale value. If the shape appears very similar for different choices of Xscale, you can interpret and describe the shape with more confidence. However, if different Xscale choices alter the look of the histogram you should probably be more tentative.

EXPLORATION 3.4 The Scatterplot

In this Exploration, we consider graphing a scatterplot of bivariate data. Here are the steps for creating a scatterplot:

1. Navigate your calculator's menu system to select the type of graph you want.
2. Select an appropriate viewing window.
3. Select data from two lists rather than one.
4. Indicate which list will correspond to the horizontal axis and which will correspond to the vertical axis.

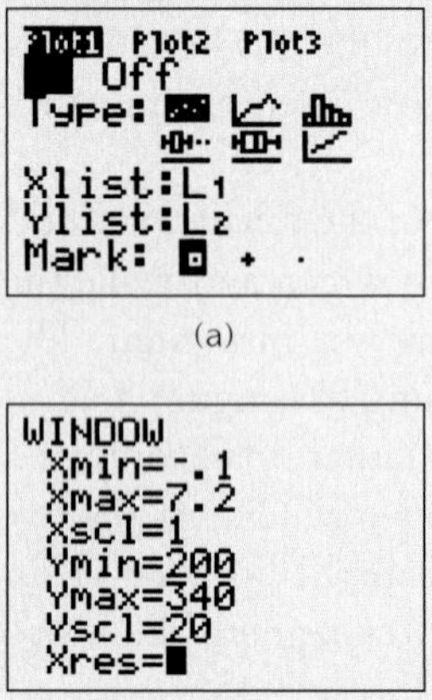

(a) (b)

FIGURE 3.48

Figure 3.48(a) shows the selection for a scatterplot. We have selected graphing parameters and scale information as indicated Figure 3.48(b). The resulting plot is shown in Figure 3.49. The *x* and *y* scales are set so that the points will fill the view screen. Notice also that the plot is set to be made up of small squares—they are more easily seen than small dots.

One problem that frequently arises with scatterplots on calculators is the "disappearing" axis (in this case, the horizontal axis) and the lack of a discernible scale on either axis. The calculator has been hardwired to plot the *x*-axis and *y*-axis, but these will not be displayed if the view screen is not set up for both positive and negative values for the axes. Unfortunately the demands for axes as reference points compete with the desire for detail in a scatter plot. Although selecting a *y* scale from −1 to 200 would show each axis, the points would cluster close to the top of the screen, possibly hiding some detail or pattern from the data analyst.

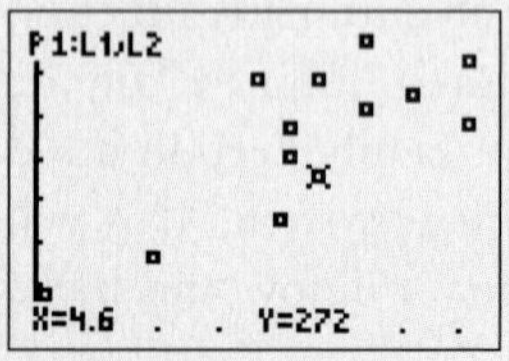

FIGURE 3.49

There are no easy solutions to this problem, but use of the "trace" capability on your calculator can help a little. Pressing the trace button causes the calculator to display the coordinates of the location of a little crosshair icon. You can move this icon about the screen by pressing special "arrow" keys on your calculator. If you are displaying data rather than a function, pressing the trace button and then arrow keys may move the crosshair icon from point to point, displaying the coordinates of the points of your scatter plot. The scatter plot in Figure 3.49 shows the crosshair icon on a point (4.6, 272).

In your classroom your instructor may want you to sketch a scatter plot on a particular assignment, and most likely will want some sort of axes and scales. The scaling information is easily found in the viewing window and translated to the sketch of the plot on your paper.

Cumulative Review Exercises CR3.1 - CR3.16

CR3.1 Does eating broccoli reduce the risk of prostate cancer? According to an observational study from the Fred Hutchinson Cancer Research Center (see the CNN.com web site article titled "Broccoli, Not Pizza Sauce, Cuts Cancer Risk, Study Finds," January 5, 2000), men who ate more cruciferous vegetables (broccoli, cauliflower, brussels sprouts, and cabbage) had a lower risk of prostate cancer. This study made separate comparisons for men who ate different levels of vegetables. According to one of the investigators, "at any given level of total vegetable consumption, as the percent of cruciferous vegetables increased, the prostate cancer risk decreased." Based on this study, is it reasonable to conclude that eating cruciferous vegetables causes a reduction in prostate cancer risk? Explain.

CR3.2 An article that appeared in *USA Today* (August 11, 1998) described a study on prayer and blood pressure. In this study, 2391 people 65 years or older, were followed for 6 years. The article stated that people who attended a religious service once a week and prayed or studied the Bible at least once a day were less likely to have high blood pressure. The researcher then concluded that "attending religious services lowers blood pressure". The headline for this article was "Prayer Can Lower Blood Pressure." Write a few sentences commenting on the appropriateness of the researcher's conclusion and on the article headline.

CR3.3 Sometimes samples are composed entirely of volunteer responders. Give a brief description of the dangers of using voluntary response samples.

CR3.4 A newspaper headline stated that at a recent budget workshop, nearly three dozen people supported a sales tax increase to help deal with the city's financial deficit (*San Luis Obispo Tribune*, January 22, 2005). This conclusion was based on data from a survey acknowledged to be unscientific, in which 34 out of the 43 people who chose to attend the budget workshop recommended raising the sales tax. Briefly discuss why the survey was described as "unscientific" and how this might limit the conclusions that can be drawn from the survey data.

CR3.5 "More than half of California's doctors say they are so frustrated with managed care they will quit, retire early, or leave the state within three years." This conclusion from an article titled "Doctors Feeling Pessimistic, Study Finds" (*San Luis Obispo Tribune*, July 15, 2001) was based on a mail survey conducted by the California Medical Association. Surveys were mailed to 19,000 California doctors, and 2000 completed surveys were returned. Describe any concerns you have regarding the conclusion drawn.

CR3.6 Based on observing more than 400 drivers in the Atlanta area, two investigators at Georgia State University concluded that people exiting parking spaces did so more slowly when a driver in another car was waiting for the space than when no one was waiting ("Territorial Defense in Parking Lots: Retaliation Against Waiting Drivers," *Journal of Applied Social Psychology* [1997]: 821–834). Describe how you might design an experiment to determine whether this phenomenon is true for your city. What is the response variable? What are some extraneous variables and how does your design control for them?

CR3.7 An article from the Associated Press (May 14, 2002) led with the headline "Academic Success Lowers Pregnancy Risk." The article described an evaluation of a program that involved about 350 students at 18 Seattle schools in high crime areas. Some students took part in a program beginning in elementary school in which teachers showed children how to control their impulses, recognize the feelings of others, and get what they want without aggressive behavior. Others did not participate in the program. The study concluded that the program was effective because by the time young women in the program reached age 21, the pregnancy rate among them was 38%, compared to 56% for the women in the experiment who did not take part in the program. Explain why this conclusion is valid only if the women in the experiment were randomly assigned to one of the two experimental groups.

CR3.8 Researchers at the University of Pennsylvania suggest that a nasal spray derived from pheromones (chemicals emitted by animals when they are trying to attract a mate) may be beneficial in relieving symptoms of premenstrual syndrome (PMS) (*Los Angeles Times*, January 17, 2003).

a. Describe how you might design an experiment using 100 female volunteers who suffer from PMS to determine whether the nasal spray reduces PMS symptoms.

b. Does your design from Part (a) include a placebo treatment? Why or why not?

c. Does your design from Part (a) involve blinding? Is it single-blind or double-blind? Explain.

CR3.9 Students in California are required to pass an exit exam in order to graduate from high school. The pass rate for San Luis Obispo High School has been rising, as have the rates for San Luis Obispo County and the state of California (*San Luis Obispo Tribune*, August 17, 2004). The percentage of students who passed the test was as follows:

Year	District	Pass Rate
2002	San Luis Obispo High School	66%
2003		72%
2004		93%
2002	San Luis Obispo County	62%
2003		57%
2004		85%
2002	State of California	32%
2003		43%
2004		74%

a. Construct a comparative bar chart that allows the change in the pass rate for each group to be compared.

b. Is the change the same for each group? Comment on any difference observed.

CR3.10 A poll conducted by the Associated Press–Ipsos on public attitudes found that most Americans are convinced that political corruption is a major problem (*San Luis Obispo Tribune*, December 9, 2005). In the poll, 1002 adults were surveyed. Two of the questions and the summarized responses to these questions follow:

How widespread do you think corruption is in public service in America?

Hardly anyone	1%
A small number	20%
A moderate number	39%
A lot of people	28%
Almost everyone	10%
Not sure	2%

In general, which elected officials would you say are more ethical?

Democrats	36%
Republicans	33%
Both equally	10%
Neither	15%
Not sure	6%

a. For each question, construct a pie chart summarizing the data.
b. For each question, construct a segmented bar chart displaying the data.
c. Which type of graph (pie chart or segmented bar graph) does a better job of presenting the data? Explain.

CR3.11 ● The article "Determination of Most Representative Subdivision" (*Journal of Energy Engineering* [1993]: 43–55) gave data on various characteristics of subdivisions that could be used in deciding whether to provide electrical power using overhead lines or underground lines. Data on the variable x = total length of streets within a subdivision are as follows:

1280	5320	4390	2100	1240	3060	4770	1050
360	3330	3380	340	1000	960	1320	530
3350	540	3870	1250	2400	960	1120	2120
450	2250	2320	2400	3150	5700	5220	500
1850	2460	5850	2700	2730	1670	100	5770
3150	1890	510	240	396	1419	2109	

a. Construct a stem-and-leaf display for these data using the thousands digit as the stem. Comment on the various features of the display.
b. Construct a histogram using class boundaries of 0 to <1000, 1000 to <2000, and so on. How would you describe the shape of the histogram?
c. What proportion of subdivisions has total length less than 2000? between 2000 and 4000?

CR3.12 ● The paper "Lessons from Pacemaker Implantations" (*Journal of the American Medical Association* [1965]: 231–232) gave the results of a study that followed 89 heart patients who had received electronic pacemakers. The time (in months) to the first electrical malfunction of the pacemaker was recorded:

24	20	16	32	14	22	2	12	24	6	10	20
8	16	12	24	14	20	18	14	16	18	20	22
24	26	28	18	14	10	12	24	6	12	18	16
34	18	20	22	24	26	18	2	18	12	12	8
24	10	14	16	22	24	22	20	24	28	20	22
26	20	6	14	16	18	24	18	16	6	16	10
14	18	24	22	28	24	30	34	26	24	22	28
30	22	24	22	32							

a. Summarize these data in the form of a frequency distribution, using class intervals of 0 to <6, 6 to <12, and so on.
b. Compute the relative frequencies and cumulative relative frequencies for each class interval of the frequency distribution of Part (a).
c. Show how the relative frequency for the class interval 12 to <18 could be obtained from the cumulative relative frequencies.
d. Use the cumulative relative frequencies to give approximate answers to the following:
   i. What proportion of those who participated in the study had pacemakers that did not malfunction within the first year?
   ii. If the pacemaker must be replaced as soon as the first electrical malfunction occurs, approximately what proportion required replacement between 1 and 2 years after implantation?
e. Construct a cumulative relative frequency plot, and use it to answer the following questions.
   i. What is the approximate time at which about 50% of the pacemakers had failed?
   ii. What is the approximate time at which only about 10% of the pacemakers initially implanted were still functioning?

CR3.13 How does the speed of a runner vary over the course of a marathon (a distance of 42.195 km)? Consider determining both the time (in seconds) to run the first 5 km and the time (in seconds) to run between the 35 km and 40 km points, and then subtracting the 5-km time from the 35–40-km time. A positive value of this difference corresponds to a runner slowing down toward the end of the race. The histogram below is based on times of runners who participated in several different Japanese marathons ("Factors Affecting Runners' Marathon Performance," *Chance* [Fall 1993]: 24–30). What are some interesting features of this histogram? What is a typical difference value? Roughly what proportion of the runners ran the late distance more quickly than the early distance?

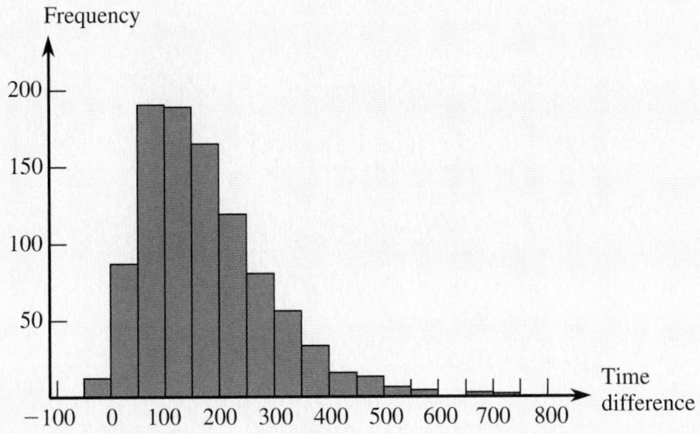

CR3.14 Data on x = poverty rate (%) and y = high school dropout rate (%) for the 50 U.S. states and the District of Columbia were used to construct the following scatterplot (*Chronicle of Higher Education*, August 31, 2001):

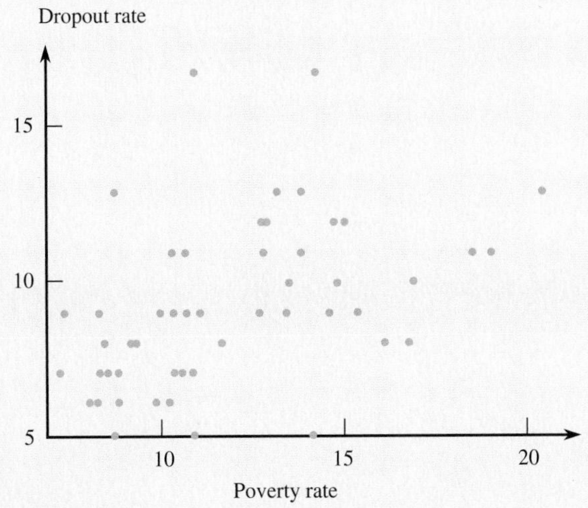

Write a few sentences commenting on this scatterplot. Would you describe the relationship between poverty rate and dropout rate as positive (y tends to increase as x increases), negative (y tends to decrease as x increases), or as having no discernible relationship between x and y?

CR3.15 ✦ One factor in the development of tennis elbow, a malady that strikes fear into the hearts of all serious players of that sport, is the impact-induced vibration of the racket-and-arm system at ball contact. It is well known that the likelihood of getting tennis elbow depends on various properties of the racket used. Consider the accompanying scatterplot of x = racket resonance frequency (in hertz) and y = sum of peak-to-peak accelerations (a characteristic of arm vibration, in meters per second per second) for n = 23 different rackets ("Transfer of Tennis Racket Vibrations into the Human Forearm," *Medicine and Science in Sports and Exercise* [1992]: 1134–1140). Discuss interesting features of the data and of the scatterplot.

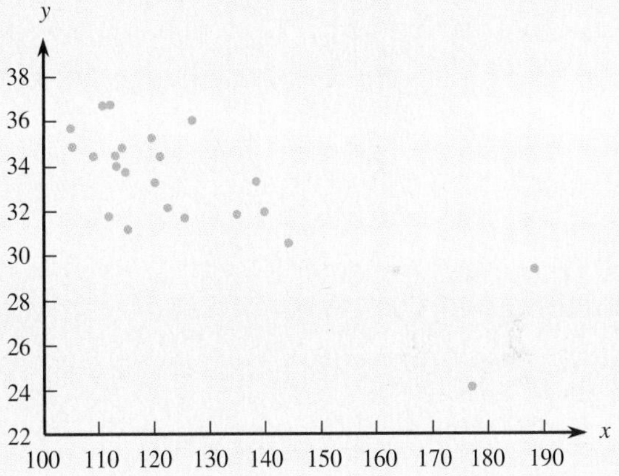

CR3.16 An article that appeared in *USA Today* (**September 3, 2003**) included a graph similar to the one shown here summarizing responses from polls conducted in 1978, 1991, and 2003 in which a sample of American adults were asked whether or not it was a good time or a bad time to buy a house.

a. Construct a time-series plot that shows how the percentage that thought it was a good time to buy a house has changed over time.
b. Add a new line to the plot from Part (a) showing the percentage that thought it was a bad time to buy a house over time. Be sure to label the lines clearly.
c. Which graph, the given bar chart or the time-series plot, best shows the trend over time?

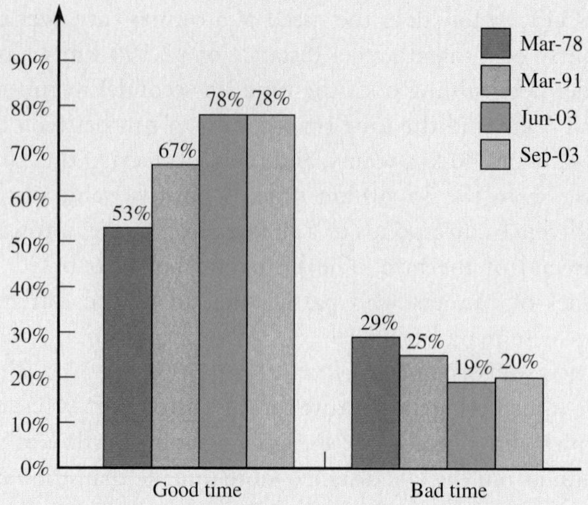

AP* Review Questions for Chapter 3

1. The comparative bar chart shown here is potentially misleading because

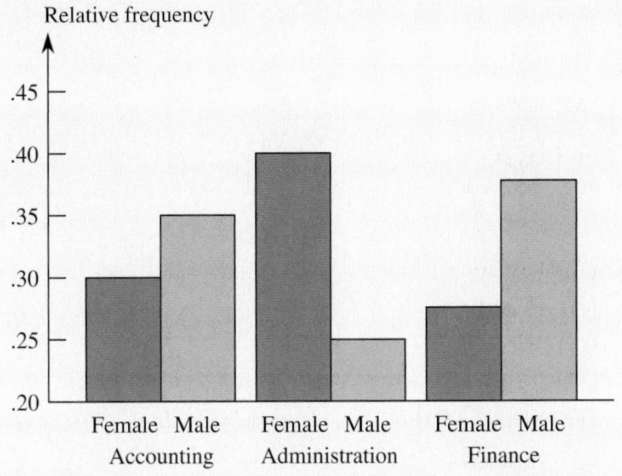

(A) Frequency, not relative frequency, should have been used for the vertical axis.
(B) The vertical axis does not start at zero.
(C) The three female bars should appear next to each other, and the three male bars should appear next to each other.
(D) The vertical axis has increments of 0.05 instead of 0.10.
(E) Two separate bar charts should have been used.

2. *Time* magazine carried out a national online poll of 501 13-year-olds. One question asked 13-year-olds at what age they thought it was appropriate for them to begin dating, and another question asked at what age their parents thought it was appropriate for them to begin dating. The results are shown in the comparative bar chart below. Based on this graph, which of the following statements is correct?

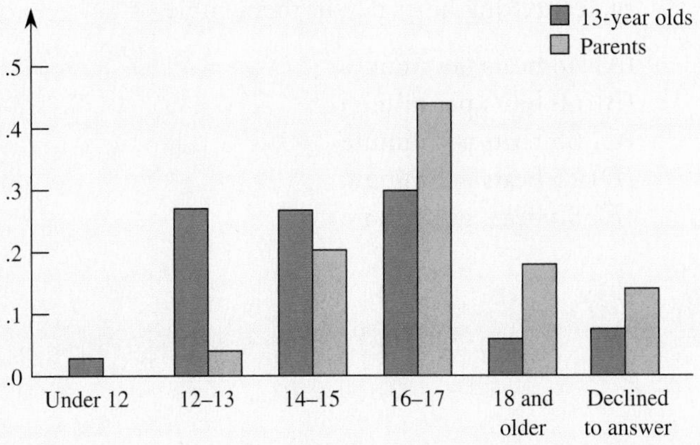

(A) The proportion of parents is higher in the 16–17, 18 and older, and the declined-to-answer categories than the proportion of 13-year-olds.
(B) The proportion of parents who believe it is appropriate for their child to start dating at age 12–13 is higher than the proportion of 13-year-olds who believe this.
(C) A smaller proportion of 13-year-olds than their parents believe it is appropriate for them to start dating when they are under 12 years of age.
(D) The same proportion of 13-year-olds and their parents believe it is appropriate for them to start dating when they are 16–17 years of age.
(E) Parents and children generally agree on when it is appropriate to begin dating.

3. The stem-and-leaf display below shows the service times (in seconds) for a sample of 25 customers at Frank's Hotdogs.

Leaf Unit = 1.0

8	0113467789
9	1233
10	245
11	34
12	05
13	23
14	
15	9
16	
17	
18	
19	
20	0

The smallest value in the data set corresponds to what value?

(A) 80 seconds
(B) 8 seconds
(C) 0 seconds
(D) 0.8 seconds
(E) 0.08 seconds

*AP and the Advanced Placement Program are registered trademarks of the College Entrance Examination Board, which was not involved in the production of, and does not endorse, this product.

4. The lengths (in feet) of 142 roller coasters are summarized in the following histogram.

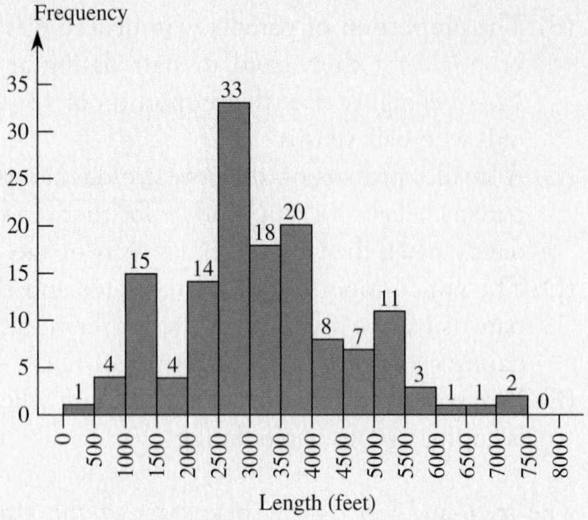

What is the proportion of roller coasters with a length less than 2500 feet?

(A) .500
(B) .38
(C) .268
(D) .232
(E) .099

5. Which of the following stem-and-leaf plots corresponds to the data distribution that is negatively (left) skewed?

I.

Leaf Unit = 0.10

1	467789
2	23557
3	2256
4	0238
5	08
6	011
7	7

II.

Leaf Unit = 0.10

4	8
5	3569
6	01789
7	1222778
8	02567
9	16
10	1

III.

Leaf Unit = 0.10

3	3
4	8
5	35
6	1789
7	22778
8	0567
9	16678
10	1234669

(A) I only
(B) II only
(C) III only
(D) I and III only
(E) None of these stem-and-leaf plots is negatively skewed.

6. The resting heart rates (in beats per minute) of 228 adults are summarized in the histogram below.

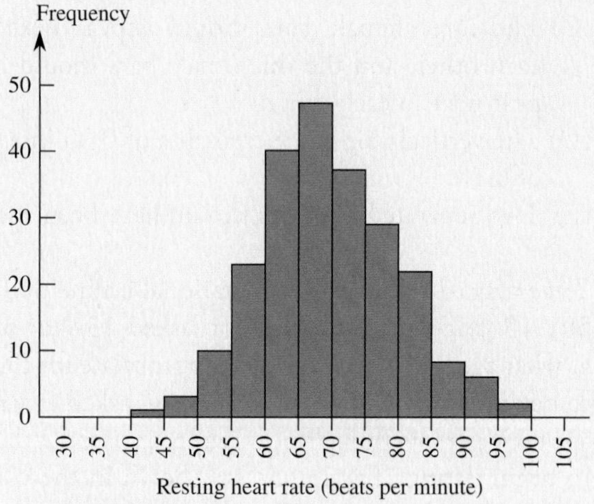

Which of the following values best describes the typical resting heart rate in this sample?

(A) 48 beats per minute
(B) 60 beats per minute
(C) 65 beats per minute
(D) 75 beats per minute
(E) 80 beats per minute

7. If a frequency distribution is based on intervals of unequal widths, the vertical axis used to construct the corresponding histogram must use which of the following?

(A) a frequency scale
(B) a relative frequency scale
(C) a density scale
(D) Either a frequency or a relative frequency scale can be used.
(E) A frequency, a relative frequency, or a density scale may be used.

8. The frequency distribution shown summarizes data on the percentage of college students enrolled in public institutions for the 50 U.S. states.

Percentage Enrolled	Frequency
40 to <50	1
50 to <60	5
60 to <70	2
70 to <80	11
80 to <90	25
90 to <100	6

What is the relative frequency for the 50 to <60 interval?

(A) .05
(B) .10
(C) 5
(D) 10
(E) 50

9. The frequency distribution shown summarizes data on the percentage of college students enrolled in public institutions for the 50 U.S. states.

Percentage Enrolled	Frequency
40 to <50	1
50 to <60	5
60 to <70	2
70 to <80	11
80 to <90	25
90 to <100	6

What is the *cumulative* relative frequency for the 50 to <60 interval?

(A) .05
(B) .06
(C) .12
(D) 5
(E) 6

10. The cumulative relative frequency plot shown was constructed using data on the percentage of college students enrolled in public institutions for the 50 U.S. states. Which of the following is closest to the approximate *proportion* of states that have fewer than 60 percent of college students enrolled in public institutions?

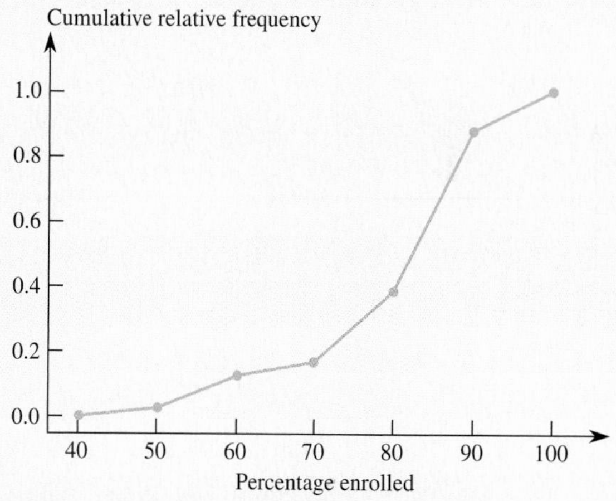

(A) 0
(B) .20
(C) .40
(D) .60
(E) .80

11. Which of the three scatterplots below suggests that there is not a relationship between the two variables used to construct the plot?

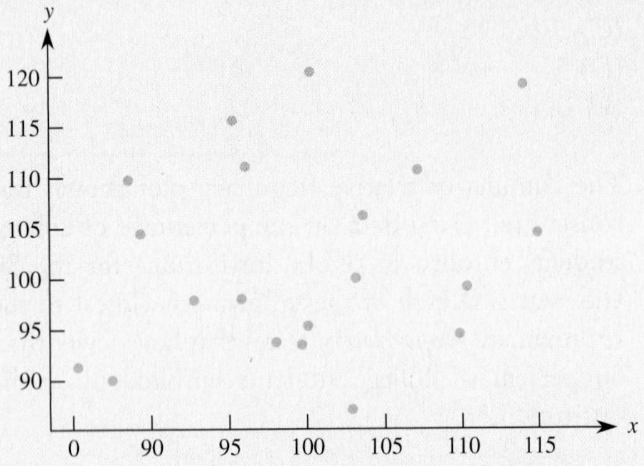

(I)

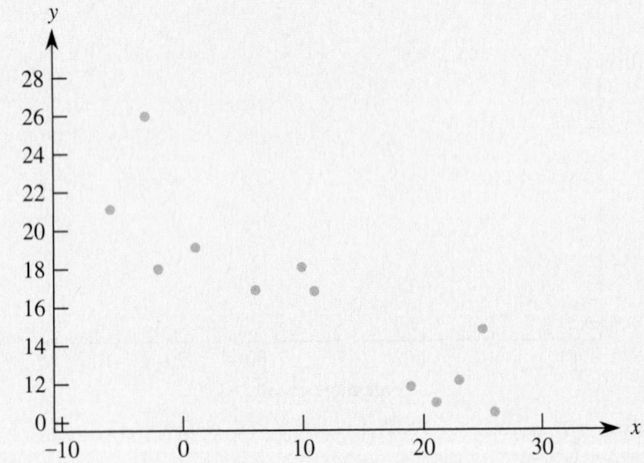

(II)

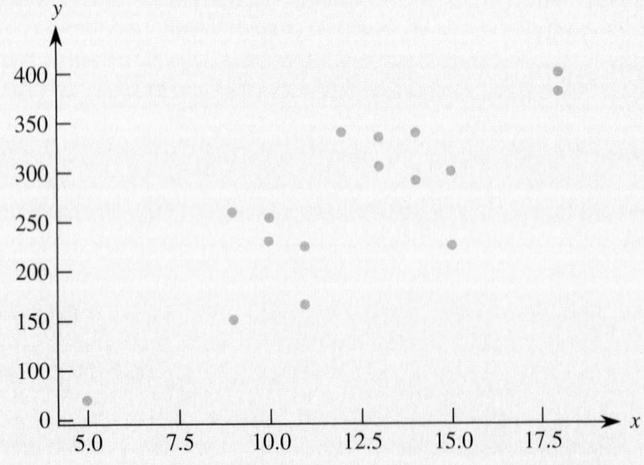

(III)

(A) I only
(B) II only
(C) III only
(D) I and II only
(E) II and III only

12. Which of the following best describes the time series plot below?

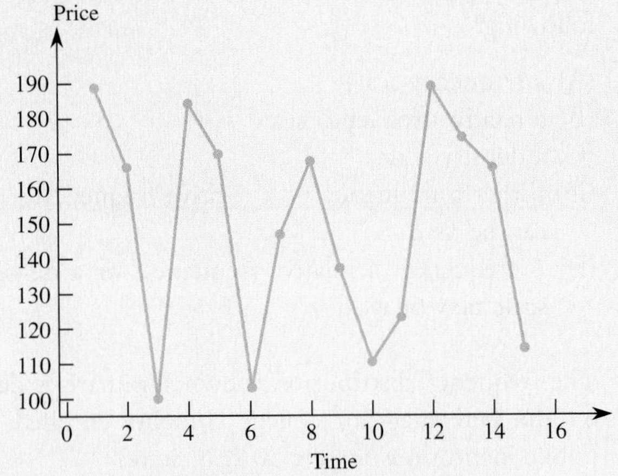

(A) There is a positive linear relationship.
(B) There is a negative linear relationship.
(C) There is an upward trend over time.
(D) There is a downward trend over time.
(E) There is no apparent long-term trend.

13. In a study of the birds in a national park, three species (labeled A, B, and C) were observed. Each bird in a sample of size 36 was classified by species. The species data were then used to construct the pie chart below. Approximately how many birds in the sample were species C?

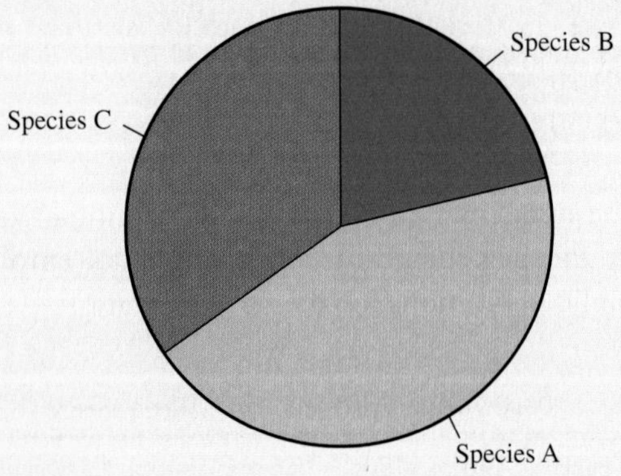

(A) 8
(B) 12
(C) 20
(D) 24
(E) 30

14. For which of the following variables would it be appropriate to construct a histogram?

(A) color of hair
(B) brand of stereo
(C) species of trees
(D) gender of an individual
(E) length of a phone call

15. Which of the following variables would have a distribution that is negatively (left) skewed?

(A) number of textbooks in students' backpacks
(B) weights of strawberries
(C) scores on an easy test
(D) scores on a hard test
(E) None of the above variables would have a distribution that is negatively skewed.

CHAPTER 4

Hideji Watanabe/Sebun Photo/
amana images/Getty Images

Numerical Methods for Describing Data

In 2006, Medicare introduced a new prescription drug program. The article "Those Most in Need May Miss Drug Benefit Sign-Up" (*USA Today*, May 9, 2006) notes that only 24% of those eligible for low-income subsidies under this program had signed up just 2 weeks before the enrollment deadline. The article also gave the percentage of those eligible who had signed up in each of 49 states and the District of Columbia (information was not available for Vermont):

24	27	12	38	21	26	23	33	19	19	26	28
16	21	28	20	21	41	22	16	29	26	22	16
27	22	19	22	22	22	30	20	21	34	26	20
25	19	17	21	27	19	27	34	20	30	20	21
14	18										

Make the most of your study time by accessing everything you need to succeed online with CourseMate.
Visit http://www.cengagebrain.com where you will find:

- An interactive eBook, which allows you to take notes, highlight, bookmark, search the text, and use in-context glossary definitions
- Step-by-step instructions for Minitab, Excel, TI-83/84, SPSS, and JMP
- Video solutions to selected exercises
- Data sets available for selected examples and exercises
- Online quizzes
- Flashcards
- Videos

What is a typical value for this data set? Is the nationwide figure of 24% representative of the individual state percentages? The enrollment percentages differ widely from state to state, ranging from a low of 12% (Arizona) to a high of 41% (Kentucky). How might we summarize this variability numerically? In this chapter, we show how to calculate numerical summary measures that describe more precisely both the center and the extent of spread in a data set. In Section 4.1, we introduce the mean and the median, the two most widely used measures of the center of a distribution. The variance and the standard deviation are presented in Section 4.2 as measures of variability. In later sections, we will see some additional ways that measures of center and spread can be used to describe data distributions.

4.1 Describing the Center of a Data Set

When describing numerical data, it is common to report a value that is representative of the observations. Such a number describes roughly where the data are located or "centered" along the number line, and is called a measure of center. The two most widely used measures of center are the *mean* and the *median.*

The Mean

The mean of a numerical data set is just the familiar arithmetic average: the sum of the observations divided by the number of observations. It is helpful to have concise notation for the variable on which observations were made, for the number of observations in the data set, and for the individual observations:

x = the variable for which we have sample data
n = the number of observations in the data set (the sample size)
x_1 = the first observation in the data set
x_2 = the second observation in the data set
⋮
x_n = the nth (last) observation in the data set

For example, we might have a sample consisting of $n = 4$ observations on x = battery lifetime (in hours):

$$x_1 = 5.9 \qquad x_2 = 7.3 \qquad x_3 = 6.6 \qquad x_4 = 5.7$$

Notice that the value of the subscript on x has no relationship to the magnitude of the observation. In this example, x_1 is just the first observation in the data set and not necessarily the smallest observation, and x_n is the last observation but not necessarily the largest.

The sum of $x_1, x_2, \ldots, x_n$ can be denoted by $x_1 + x_2 + \cdots + x_n$, but this is cumbersome. The Greek letter Σ is traditionally used in mathematics to denote summation. In particular, Σx denotes the sum of all the x values in the data set under consideration.*

DEFINITION

The **sample mean** of a sample consisting of numerical observations $x_1, x_2, \ldots, x_n$, denoted by $\bar{x}$, is

$$\bar{x} = \frac{\text{sum of all observations in the sample}}{\text{number of observations in the sample}} = \frac{x_1 + x_2 + \cdots + x_n}{n} = \frac{\Sigma x}{n}$$

*It is also common to see Σx written as Σx_i or even as $\sum_{i=1}^{n} x_i$, but for simplicity we will usually omit the summation indices.

EXAMPLE 4.1 Improving Knee Extension

● Increasing joint extension is one goal of athletic trainers. In a study to investigate the effect of a therapy that uses ultrasound and stretching (Trae Tashiro, Masters Thesis, University of Virginia, 2004) passive knee extension was measured after treatment. Passive knee extension (in degrees) is given for each of 10 participants in the study:

$$x_1 = 59 \quad x_2 = 46 \quad x_3 = 64 \quad x_4 = 49 \quad x_5 = 56$$
$$x_6 = 70 \quad x_7 = 45 \quad x_8 = 52 \quad x_9 = 63 \quad x_{10} = 52$$

The sum of these sample values is $59 + 46 + 64 + \cdots + 52 = 556$, and the sample mean passive knee extension is

$$\bar{x} = \frac{\Sigma x}{n} = \frac{556}{10} = 55.6$$

We would report 55.6 degrees as a representative value of passive knee extension for this sample (even though there is no person in the sample that actually had a passive knee extension of 55.6 degrees).

The data values in Example 4.1 were all integers, yet the mean was given as 55.6. It is common to use more digits of decimal accuracy for the mean. This allows the value of the mean to fall between possible observable values (for example, the average number of children per family could be 1.8, whereas no single family will have 1.8 children).

The sample mean $\bar{x}$ is computed from sample observations, so it is a characteristic of the particular sample in hand. It is customary to use Roman letters to denote sample characteristics, as we have done with $\bar{x}$. Characteristics of the population are usually denoted by Greek letters. One of the most important of such characteristics is the population mean.

DEFINITION

The **population mean**, denoted by μ, is the average of all x values in the entire population.

For example, the average fuel efficiency for *all* 600,000 cars of a certain type under specified conditions might be $\mu = 27.5$ mpg. A sample of $n = 5$ cars might yield efficiencies of 27.3, 26.2, 28.4, 27.9, 26.5, from which we obtain $\bar{x} = 27.26$ for this particular sample (somewhat smaller than μ). However, a second sample might give $\bar{x} = 28.52$, a third $\bar{x} = 26.85$, and so on. The value of $\bar{x}$ varies from sample to sample, whereas there is just one value for μ. In later chapters, we will see how the value of $\bar{x}$ from a particular sample can be used to draw various conclusions about the value of μ. Example 4.2 illustrates how the value of $\bar{x}$ from a particular sample can differ from the value of μ and how the value of $\bar{x}$ differs from sample to sample.

● Data set available online

EXAMPLE 4.2 County Population Sizes

The 50 states plus the District of Columbia contain 3137 counties. Let x denote the number of residents of a county. Then there are 3137 values of the variable x in the population. The sum of these 3137 values is 293,655,404 (2004 Census Bureau estimate), so the population average value of x is

$$\mu = \frac{293{,}655{,}404}{3137} = 93{,}610.27 \text{ residents per county}$$

We used the Census Bureau web site to select three different samples at random from this population of counties, with each sample consisting of five counties. The results appear in Table 4.1, along with the sample mean for each sample. Not only are the three $\bar{x}$ values different from one another—because they are based on three different samples and the value of $\bar{x}$ depends on the x values in the sample—but also none of the three values comes close to the value of the population mean, μ. If we did not know the value of μ but had only Sample 1 available, we might use $\bar{x}$ as an *estimate* of μ, but our estimate would be far off the mark.

TABLE 4.1 Three Samples from the Population of All U.S. Counties (x = number of residents)

SAMPLE 1		SAMPLE 2		SAMPLE 3	
County	x Value	County	x Value	County	x Value
Fayette, TX	22,513	Stoddard, MO	29,773	Chattahoochee, GA	13,506
Monroe, IN	121,013	Johnston, OK	10,440	Petroleum, MT	492
Greene, NC	20,219	Sumter, AL	14,141	Armstrong, PA	71,395
Shoshone, ID	12,827	Milwaukee, WI	928,018	Smith, MI	14,306
Jasper, IN	31,624	Albany, WY	31,473	Benton, MO	18,519
	$\sum x = 208{,}196$		$\sum x = 1{,}013{,}845$		$\sum x = 118{,}218$
	$\bar{x} = 41{,}639.2$		$\bar{x} = 202{,}769.0$		$\bar{x} = 23{,}643.6$

Alternatively, we could combine the three samples into a single sample with $n = 15$ observations:

$$x_1 = 22{,}513, \ldots, x_5 = 31{,}624, \ldots, x_{15} = 18{,}519$$

$$\sum x = 1{,}340{,}259$$

$$\bar{x} = \frac{1{,}340{,}259}{15} = 89{,}350.6$$

This value is closer to the value of μ but is still somewhat unsatisfactory as an estimate. The problem here is that the population of x values exhibits a lot of variability (the largest value is $x = 9{,}937{,}739$ for Los Angeles County, California, and the smallest value is $x = 52$ for Loving County, Texas, which evidently few people love). Therefore, it is difficult for a sample of 15 observations, let alone just 5, to be reasonably representative of the population. In Chapter 9, you will see how to take variability into account when deciding on a sample size.

One potential drawback to the mean as a measure of center for a data set is that its value can be greatly affected by the presence of even a single *outlier* (an unusually large or small observation) in the data set.

EXAMPLE 4.3 Number of Visits to a Class Web Site

● Forty students were enrolled in a section of a general education course in statistical reasoning during one fall quarter at Cal Poly, San Luis Obispo. The instructor made course materials, grades, and lecture notes available to students on a class web site, and course management software kept track of how often each student accessed any of the web pages on the class site. One month after the course began, the instructor requested a report that indicated how many times each student had accessed a web page on the class site. The 40 observations were:

20	37	4	20	0	84	14	36	5	331	19	0
0	22	3	13	14	36	4	0	18	8	0	26
4	0	5	23	19	7	12	8	13	16	21	7
13	12	8	42								

The sample mean for this data set is $\bar{x} = 23.10$. Figure 4.1 is a Minitab dotplot of the data. Many would argue that 23.10 is not a very representative value for this sample, because 23.10 is larger than most of the observations in the data set—only 7 of 40 observations, or 17.5%, are larger than 23.10. The two outlying values of 84 and 331 (no, that was *not* a typo!) have a substantial impact on the value of $\bar{x}$.

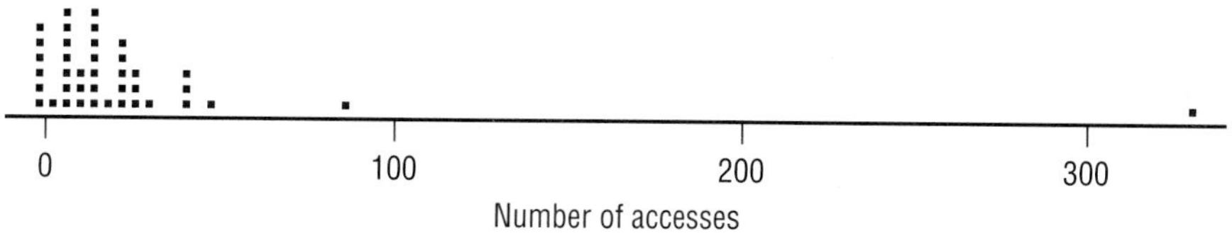

FIGURE 4.1
A Minitab dotplot of the data in Example 4.3.

We now turn our attention to a measure of center that is not as sensitive to outliers—the median.

The Median

The median strip of a highway divides the highway in half, and the median of a numerical data set does the same thing for a data set. Once the data values have been listed in order from smallest to largest, the **median** is the middle value in the list, and it divides the list into two equal parts. Depending on whether the sample size n is even or odd, the process of determining the median is slightly different. When n is an odd number (say, 5), the sample median is the single middle value. But when n is even (say, 6), there are two middle values in the ordered list, and we average these two middle values to obtain the sample median.

!! Step-by-Step technology instructions available online

● Data set available online

DEFINITION

The **sample median** is obtained by first ordering the n observations from smallest to largest (with any repeated values included, so that every sample observation appears in the ordered list). Then

$$\text{sample median} = \begin{cases} \text{the single middle value if } n \text{ is odd} \\ \text{the average of the middle two values if } n \text{ is even} \end{cases}$$

EXAMPLE 4.4 Web Site Data Revised

The sample size for the web site access data of Example 4.3 was $n = 40$, an even number. The median is the average of the 20th and 21st values (the middle two) in the ordered list of the data. Arranging the data in order from smallest to largest produces the following ordered list (with the two middle values highlighted):

0	0	0	0	0	0	3	4	4	4	5	5
7	7	8	8	8	12	12	13	13	13	14	14
16	18	19	19	20	20	21	22	23	26	36	36
37	42	84	331								

The median can now be determined:

$$median = \frac{13 + 13}{2} = 13$$

Looking at the dotplot (Figure 4.1), we see that this value appears to be a more typical value for the data set than the sample mean $\bar{x} = 23.10$ is.

The sample mean can be sensitive to even a single value that lies far above or below the rest of the data. The value of the mean is pulled out toward such an outlying value or values. The median, on the other hand, is quite *in*sensitive to outliers. For example, the largest sample observation (331) in Example 4.4 can be increased by any amount without changing the value of the median. Similarly, an increase in the second or third largest observations does not affect the median, nor would a decrease in several of the smallest observations.

This stability of the median is what sometimes justifies its use as a measure of center in some situations. For example, the article "Educating Undergraduates on Using Credit Cards" (Nellie Mae, 2005) reported that the mean credit card debt for undergraduate students in 2001 was $2327, whereas the median credit card debt was only $1770. In this case, the small percentage of students with unusually high credit card debt may be resulting in a mean that is not representative of a typical student's credit card debt.

Comparing the Mean and the Median

Figure 4.2 shows several smoothed histograms that might represent either a distribution of sample values or a population distribution. Pictorially, the median is the value on the measurement axis that separates the smoothed histogram into two parts, with .5 (50%) of the area under each part of the curve. The mean is a bit harder to visualize. If the histogram were balanced on a triangle (a fulcrum), it would tilt unless the triangle was positioned at the mean. The mean is the balance point for the distribution.

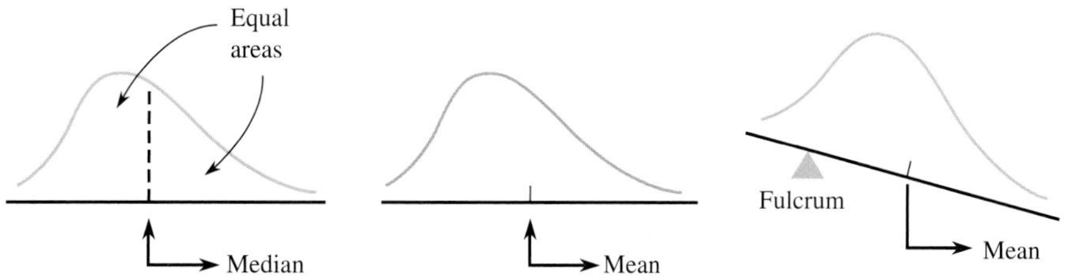

FIGURE 4.2
The mean and the median.

When the histogram is symmetric, the point of symmetry is both the dividing point for equal areas and the balance point, and the mean and the median are equal. However, when the histogram is unimodal (single-peaked) with a longer upper tail (positively skewed), the outlying values in the upper tail pull the mean up, so it generally lies above the median. For example, an unusually high exam score raises the mean but does not affect the median. Similarly, when a unimodal histogram is negatively skewed, the mean is generally smaller than the median (see Figure 4.3).

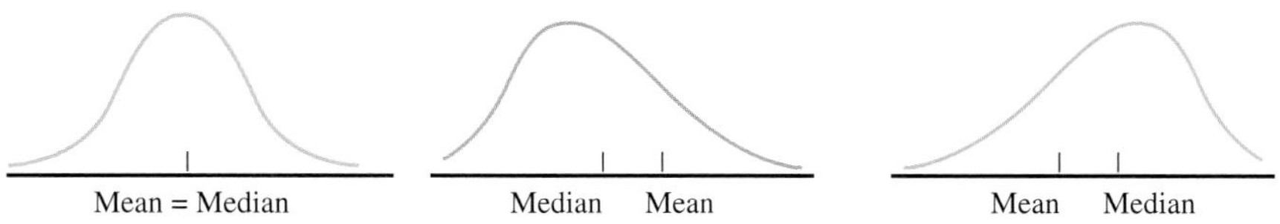

FIGURE 4.3
Relationship between the mean and the median.

Trimmed Means

The extreme sensitivity of the mean to even a single outlier and the extreme insensitivity of the median to a substantial proportion of outliers can sometimes make both of them suspect as a measure of center. A *trimmed mean* is a compromise between these two extremes.

DEFINITION

A **trimmed mean** is computed by first ordering the data values from smallest to largest, deleting a selected number of values from each end of the ordered list, and finally averaging the remaining values.

The **trimming percentage** is the percentage of values deleted from *each* end of the ordered list.

Sometimes the number of observations to be deleted from each end of the data set is specified. Then the corresponding trimming percentage is calculated as

$$\text{trimming percentage} = \left(\frac{\text{number deleted from each end}}{n}\right) \cdot 100$$

In other cases, the trimming percentage is specified and then used to determine how many observations to delete from each end, with

$$\text{number deleted from each end} = \left(\frac{\text{trimming percentage}}{100}\right) \cdot n$$

If the number of observations to be deleted from each end resulting from this calculation is not an integer, it can be rounded to the nearest integer (which changes the trimming percentage a bit).

EXAMPLE 4.5 NBA Salaries

● The web site HoopsHype (hoopshype.com/salaries) publishes salaries of NBA players. Salaries for the players of the Chicago Bulls in 2009 were

Player	2009 Salary
Brad Miller	\$12,250,000
Luol Deng	\$10,370,425
Kirk Hinrich	\$9,500,000
Jerome James	\$6,600,000
Tim Thomas	\$6,466,600
John Salmons	\$5,456,000
Derrick Rose	\$5,184,480
Tyrus Thomas	\$4,743,598
Joakim Noah	\$2,455,680
Jannero Pargo	\$2,000,000
James Johnson	\$1,594,080
Lindsey Hunter	\$1,306,455
Taj Gibson	\$1,039,800
Aaron Gray	\$1,000,497

A Minitab dotplot of these data is shown in Figure 4.4(a). Because the data distribution is not symmetric and there are outliers, a trimmed mean is a reasonable choice for describing the center of this data set.

There are 14 observations in this data set. Deleting the two largest and the two smallest observations from the data set and then averaging the remaining values would result in a $\left(\frac{2}{14}\right)(100) = 14\%$ trimmed mean. Based on the Bulls' salary data, the two largest salaries are \$12,250,000 and \$10,370,425, and the two smallest are \$1,039,800 and \$1,000,497. The average of the remaining 10 observations is

$$14\% \text{ trimmed mean} = \frac{9{,}500{,}000 + \cdots + 1{,}306{,}445}{10} = \frac{45{,}306{,}893}{10} = 4{,}530{,}689$$

The mean (\$4,997,687) is larger than the trimmed mean because of the few unusually large values in the data set.

For the L.A. Lakers, the difference between the mean (\$7,035,947) and the 14% trimmed mean (\$5,552,607) is even more dramatic because in 2009 one

● Data set available online

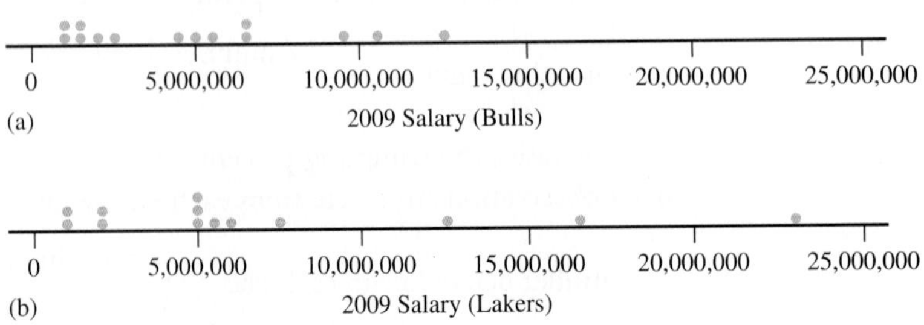

FIGURE 4.4
Minitab dotplots for NBA salary data (a) Bulls (b) Lakers.

player on the Lakers earned over \$23 million and two players earned well over \$10 million (see Figure 4.4(b)).

Categorical Data

The natural numerical summary quantities for a categorical data set are the relative frequencies for the various categories. Each relative frequency is the proportion (fraction) of responses that is in the corresponding category. Often there are only two possible responses (a **dichotomy**)—for example, male or female, does or does not have a driver's license, did or did not vote in the last election. It is convenient in such situations to label one of the two possible responses S (for success) and the other F (for failure). As long as further analysis is consistent with the labeling, it does not matter which category is assigned the S label. When the data set is a sample, the fraction of S's in the sample is called the **sample proportion of successes.**

DEFINITION

The **sample proportion of successes**, denoted by $\hat{p}$, is

$$\hat{p} = \text{sample proportion of successes} = \frac{\text{number of S's in the sample}}{n}$$

where S is the label used for the response designated as success.

EXAMPLE 4.6 Can You Hear Me Now?

Getty Images

It is not uncommon for a cell phone user to complain about the quality of his or her service provider. Suppose that each person in a sample of $n = 15$ cell phone users is asked if he or she is satisfied with the cell phone service. Each response is classified as S (satisfied) or F (not satisfied). The resulting data are

S	F	S	S	S	F	F	S	S	F
S	S	S	F	F					

This sample contains nine S's, so

$$\hat{p} = \frac{9}{15} = .60$$

That is, 60% of the sample responses are S's. Of those surveyed, 60% are satisfied with their cell phone service.

The letter p is used to denote the **population proportion of S's.*** We will see later how the value of $\hat{p}$ from a particular sample can be used to make inferences about p.

*Note that this is one situation in which we will not use a Greek letter to denote a population characteristic. Some statistics books use the symbol π for the population proportion and p for the sample proportion. We will not use π in this context so there is no confusion with the mathematical constant $\pi = 3.14\ldots$

EXERCISES 4.1 - 4.16

4.1 ● The Insurance Institute for Highway Safety (www.iihs.org, June 11, 2009) published data on repair costs for cars involved in different types of accidents. In one study, seven different 2009 models of mini- and micro-cars were driven at 6 mph straight into a fixed barrier. The following table gives the cost of repairing damage to the bumper for each of the seven models.

Model	Repair Cost
Smart Fortwo	$1,480
Chevrolet Aveo	$1,071
Mini Cooper	$2,291
Toyota Yaris	$1,688
Honda Fit	$1,124
Hyundai Accent	$3,476
Kia Rio	$3,701

Compute the values of the mean and median. Why are these values so different? Which of the two—mean or median—appears to be better as a description of a typical value for this data set?

4.2 ● The article "Caffeinated Energy Drinks—A Growing Problem" (*Drug and Alcohol Dependence* [2009]: 1–10) gave the following data on caffeine concentration (mg/ounce) for eight top-selling energy drinks:

Energy Drink	Caffeine Concentration (mg/oz)
Red Bull	9.6
Monster	10.0
Rockstar	10.0
Full Throttle	9.0
No Fear	10.9
Amp	8.9
SoBe Adrenaline Rush	9.5
Tab Energy	9.1

a. What is the value of the mean caffeine concentration for this set of top-selling energy drinks?
b. Coca-Cola has 2.9 mg/ounce of caffeine and Pepsi Cola has 3.2 mg/ounce of caffeine. Write a sentence explaining how the caffeine concentration of top-selling energy drinks compares to that of these colas.

4.3 ● Consumer Reports Health (www.consumerreports.org/health) reported the accompanying caffeine concentration (mg/cup) for 12 brands of coffee:

Coffee Brand	Caffeine Concentration (mg/cup)
Eight O'Clock	140
Caribou	195
Kickapoo	155
Starbucks	115
Bucks Country Coffee Co.	195
Archer Farms	180
Gloria Jean's Coffees	110
Chock Full o'Nuts	110
Peet's Coffee	130
Maxwell House	55
Folgers	60
Millstone	60

Use at least one measure of center to compare caffeine concentration for coffee with that of the energy drinks of the previous exercise. (Note: 1 cup = 8 ounces)

4.4 ● Consumer Reports Health (www.consumerreports.org/health) reported the sodium content (mg) per 2 tablespoon serving for each of 11 different peanut butters:

120	50	140	120	150	150	150	65
170	250	110					

a. Display these data using a dotplot. Comment on any unusual features of the plot.
b. Compute the mean and median sodium content for the peanut butters in this sample.
c. The values of the mean and the median for this data set are similar. What aspect of the distribution of sodium content—as pictured in the dotplot from Part (a)—provides an explanation for why the values of the mean and median are similar?

4.5 In August 2009, Harris Interactive released the results of the "Great Schools" survey. In this survey, 1086 parents of children attending a public or private school were asked approximately how much time they spent volunteering at school per month over the last school year. For this sample, the mean number of hours per month was 5.6 hours and the median number of hours was 1.0. What does the large difference between the mean and median tell you about this data set?

4.6 ● The accompanying data on number of minutes used for cell phone calls in one month was generated to be consistent with summary statistics published in a report of a marketing study of San Diego residents (TeleTruth, March 2009):

189	0	189	177	106	201	0	212	0	306
0	0	59	224	0	189	142	83	71	165
236	0	142	236	130					

a. Would you recommend the mean or the median as a measure of center for this data set? Give a brief explanation of your choice. (Hint: It may help to look at a graphical display of the data.)
b. Compute a trimmed mean by deleting the three smallest observations and the three largest observations in the data set and then averaging the remaining 19 observations. What is the trimming percentage for this trimmed mean?
c. What trimming percentage would you need to use in order to delete all of the 0 minute values from the data set? Would you recommend a trimmed mean with this trimming percentage? Explain why or why not.

4.7 ● *USA Today* (May 9, 2006) published the accompanying average weekday circulation for the 6-month period ending March 31, 2006, for the top 20 newspapers in the country:

2,272,815	2,049,786	1,142,464	851,832	724,242
708,477	673,379	579,079	513,387	438,722
427,771	398,329	398,246	397,288	365,011
362,964	350,457	345,861	343,163	323,031

a. Do you think the mean or the median will be larger for this data set? Explain.
b. Compute the values of the mean and the median of this data set.
c. Of the mean and median, which does the best job of describing a typical value for this data set?
d. Explain why it would not be reasonable to generalize from this sample of 20 newspapers to the population of all daily newspapers in the United States.

4.8 ● The chapter introduction gave the accompanying data on the percentage of those eligible for a low-income subsidy who had signed up for a Medicare drug plan in each of 49 states (information was not available for Vermont) and the District of Columbia (*USA Today*, May 9, 2006).

24	27	12	38	21	26	23	33
19	19	26	28	16	21	28	20
21	41	22	16	29	26	22	16
27	22	19	22	22	22	30	20
21	34	26	20	25	19	17	21
27	19	27	34	20	30	20	21
14	18						

a. Compute the mean for this data set.
b. The article stated that nationwide, 24% of those eligible had signed up. Explain why the mean of this data set from Part (a) is not equal to 24. (No information was available for Vermont, but that is not the reason that the mean differs—the 24% was calculated excluding Vermont.)

4.9 ● The U.S. Department of Transportation reported the number of speeding-related crash fatalities for the 20 days of the year that had the highest number of these fatalities between 1994 and 2003 (*Traffic Safety Facts*, July 2005).

Date	Speeding-Related Fatalities	Date	Speeding-Related Fatalities
Jan 1	521	Aug 17	446
Jul 4	519	Dec 24	436
Aug 12	466	Aug 25	433
Nov 23	461	Sep 2	433
Jul 3	458	Aug 6	431
Dec 26	455	Aug 10	426
Aug 4	455	Sept 21	424
Aug 31	446	Jul 27	422
May 25	446	Sep 14	422
Dec 23	446	May 27	420

a. Compute the mean number of speeding-related fatalities for these 20 days.
b. Compute the median number of speeding-related fatalities for these 20 days.
c. Explain why it is not reasonable to generalize from this sample of 20 days to the other 345 days of the year.

4.10 The ministry of Health and Long-Term Care in Ontario, Canada, publishes information on its web site (www.health.gov.on.ca) on the time that patients must wait for various medical procedures. For two cardiac procedures completed in fall of 2005, the following information was provided:

	Number of Completed Procedures	Median Wait Time (days)	Mean Wait Time (days)	90% Completed Within (days)
Angioplasty	847	14	18	39
Bypass surgery	539	13	19	42

a. The median wait time for angioplasty is greater than the median wait time for bypass surgery but the mean wait time is shorter for angioplasty than for bypass surgery. What does this suggest about the distribution of wait times for these two procedures?
b. Is it possible that another medical procedure might have a median wait time that is greater than the time reported for "90% completed within"? Explain.

4.11 Houses in California are expensive, especially on the Central Coast where the air is clear, the ocean is blue, and the scenery is stunning. The median home price in San Luis Obispo County reached a new high in July 2004, soaring to \$452,272 from \$387,120 in March 2004. (*San Luis Obispo Tribune*, April 28, 2004). The article included two quotes from people attempting to explain why the median price had increased. Richard Watkins, chairman of the Central Coast Regional Multiple Listing Services was quoted as saying, "There have been some fairly expensive houses selling, which pulls the median up." Robert Kleinhenz, deputy chief economist for the California Association of Realtors explained the volatility of house prices by stating: "Fewer sales means a relatively small number of very high or very low home prices can more easily skew medians." Are either of these statements correct? For each statement that is incorrect, explain why it is incorrect and propose a new wording that would correct any errors in the statement.

4.12 Consider the following statement: More than 65% of the residents of Los Angeles earn less than the average wage for that city. Could this statement be correct? If so, how? If not, why not?

4.13 ✦ A sample consisting of four pieces of luggage was selected from among those checked at an airline counter, yielding the following data on x = weight (in pounds):

$$x_1 = 33.5,\ x_2 = 27.3,\ x_3 = 36.7,\ x_4 = 30.5$$

Suppose that one more piece is selected and denote its weight by x_5. Find a value of x_5 such that $\bar{x}$ = sample median.

4.14 Suppose that 10 patients with meningitis received treatment with large doses of penicillin. Three days later, temperatures were recorded, and the treatment was considered successful if there had been a reduction in a patient's temperature. Denoting success by S and failure by F, the 10 observations are

S S F S S S F F S S

a. What is the value of the sample proportion of successes?
b. Replace each S with a 1 and each F with a 0. Then calculate $\bar{x}$ for this numerically coded sample. How does $\bar{x}$ compare to $\hat{p}$?
c. Suppose that it is decided to include 15 more patients in the study. How many of these would have to be S's to give $\hat{p} = .80$ for the entire sample of 25 patients?

4.15 An experiment to study the lifetime (in hours) for a certain brand of light bulb involved putting 10 light bulbs into operation and observing them for 1000 hours. Eight of the light bulbs failed during that period, and those lifetimes were recorded. The lifetimes of the two light bulbs still functioning after 1000 hours are recorded as 1000+. The resulting sample observations were

480 790 1000+ 350 920 860 570 1000+
170 290

Which of the measures of center discussed in this section can be calculated, and what are the values of those measures?

4.16 An instructor has graded 19 exam papers submitted by students in a class of 20 students, and the average so far is 70. (The maximum possible score is 100.) How high would the score on the last paper have to be to raise the class average by 1 point? By 2 points?

4.2 Describing Variability in a Data Set

Reporting a measure of center gives only partial information about a data set. It is also important to describe how much the observations differ from one another. The three different samples displayed in Figure 4.5 all have mean = median = 45. There is a lot of variability in the first sample compared to the third sample. The second sample shows less variability than the first and more variability than the third; most of the variability in the second sample is due to the two extreme values being so far from the center.

Sample

1. 20, 40, 50, 30, 60, 70

2. 47, 43, 44, 46, 20, 70

3. 44, 43, 40, 50, 47, 46

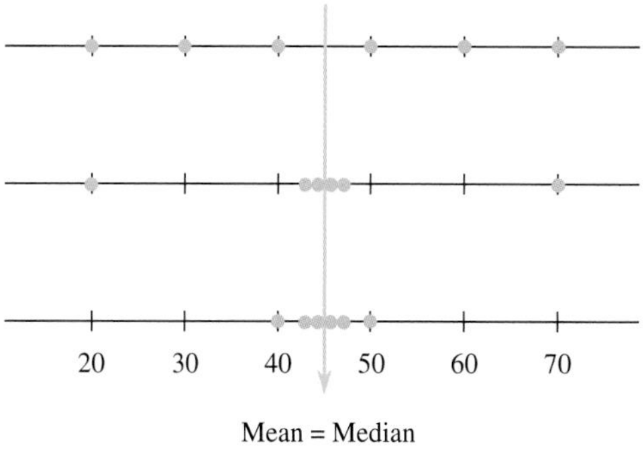

FIGURE 4.5
Three samples with the same center and different amounts of variability.

The simplest numerical measure of variability is the range.

DEFINITION

The **range** of a data set is defined as

range = largest observation − smallest observation

In general, more variability will be reflected in a larger range. However, variability is a characteristic of the entire data set, and each observation contributes to variability. The first two samples plotted in Figure 4.5 both have a range of 70 − 20 = 50, but there is less variability in the second sample.

Deviations from the Mean

The most widely used measures of variability describe the extent to which the sample observations deviate from the sample mean $\bar{x}$. Subtracting $\bar{x}$ from each observation gives a set of deviations from the mean.

DEFINITION

The ***n* deviations from the sample mean** are the differences

$$(x_1 - \bar{x}), (x_2 - \bar{x}), \ldots, (x_n - \bar{x})$$

A particular deviation is positive if the corresponding x value is greater than $\bar{x}$ and negative if the x value is less than $\bar{x}$.

EXAMPLE 4.7 The Big Mac Index

● McDonald's fast-food restaurants are now found in many countries around the world. But the cost of a Big Mac varies from country to country. Table 4.2 shows data on the cost of a Big Mac (converted to U.S. dollars based on the July 2009 exchange rates) taken from the article "Cheesed Off" (*The Economist*, July 18, 2009).

TABLE 4.2 Big Mac Prices for 7 Countries

Country	Big Mac Price in U.S. Dollars
Argentina	3.02
Brazil	4.67
Chile	3.28
Colombia	3.51
Costa Rica	3.42
Peru	2.76
Uruguay	2.87

Notice that there is quite a bit of variability in the Big Mac prices.

For this data set, $\sum x = 23.53$ and $\bar{x} = \$3.36$. Table 4.3 displays the data along with the corresponding deviations, formed by subtracting $\bar{x} = 3.36$ from each observation. Three of the deviations are positive because three of the observations are larger than $\bar{x}$. The negative deviations correspond to observations that are smaller than $\bar{x}$. Some of the deviations are quite large in magnitude (1.31 and −0.60, for example), indicating observations that are far from the sample mean.

TABLE 4.3 Deviations from the Mean for the Big Mac Data

Country	Big Mac Price in U.S. Dollars	Deviations from Mean
Argentina	3.02	−0.34
Brazil	4.67	1.31
Chile	3.28	−0.08
Colombia	3.51	0.15
Costa Rica	3.42	0.06
Peru	2.76	−0.60
Uruguay	2.87	−0.49

In general, the greater the amount of variability in the sample, the larger the magnitudes (ignoring the signs) of the deviations. We now consider how to combine the deviations into a single numerical measure of variability. A first thought might be to calculate the average deviation, by adding the deviations together (this sum can be denoted compactly by $\sum(x - \bar{x})$) and then dividing by n. This does not work, though, because negative and positive deviations counteract one another in the summation.

As a result of rounding, the value of the sum of the seven deviations in Example 4.7 is $\sum(x - \bar{x}) = 0.01$. If we used even more decimal accuracy in computing $\bar{x}$ the sum would be even closer to zero.

● Data set available online

Except for the effects of rounding in computing the deviations, it is always true that

$$\sum(x - \bar{x}) = 0$$

Since this sum is zero, the average deviation is always zero and so it cannot be used as a measure of variability.

The Variance and Standard Deviation

The customary way to prevent negative and positive deviations from counteracting one another is to square them before combining. Then deviations with opposite signs but with the same magnitude, such as +2 and −2, make identical contributions to variability. The squared deviations are $(x_1 - \bar{x})^2, (x_2 - \bar{x})^2, \ldots, (x_n - \bar{x})^2$ and their sum is

$$(x_1 - \bar{x})^2 + (x_2 - \bar{x})^2 + \cdots + (x_n - \bar{x})^2 = \sum(x - \bar{x})^2$$

Common notation for $\sum(x - \bar{x})^2$ is S_{xx}. Dividing this sum by the sample size n gives the average squared deviation. Although this seems to be a reasonable measure of variability, we use a divisor slightly smaller than n. (The reason for this will be explained later in this section and in Chapter 9.)

AP* EXAM TIP

Center and variability are two important aspects of a distribution. The sample mean and sample standard deviation are the most widely used descriptive measures of center and variability.

DEFINITION

The **sample variance**, denoted by s^2, is the sum of squared deviations from the mean divided by $n - 1$. That is,

$$s^2 = \frac{\sum(x - \bar{x})^2}{n - 1} = \frac{S_{xx}}{n - 1}$$

The **sample standard deviation** is the positive square root of the sample variance and is denoted by **s**.

A large amount of variability in the sample is indicated by a relatively large value of s^2 or s, whereas a value of s^2 or s close to zero indicates a small amount of variability. Notice that whatever unit is used for x (such as pounds or seconds), the squared deviations and therefore s^2 are in squared units. Taking the square root gives a measure expressed in the same units as x. Thus, for a sample of heights, the standard deviation might be $s = 3.2$ inches, and for a sample of textbook prices, it might be $s = \$12.43$.

EXAMPLE 4.8 Big Mac Revisited

Let's continue using the Big Mac data and the computed deviations from the mean given in Example 4.7 to calculate the sample variance and standard deviation. Table 4.4 shows the observations, deviations from the mean, and squared deviations. Combining the squared deviations to compute the values of s^2 and s gives

$$\sum(x - \bar{x}) = S_{xx} = 2.4643$$

and

$$s^2 = \frac{\sum(x - \bar{x})^2}{n - 1} = \frac{2.4643}{7 - 1} = \frac{2.4643}{6} = 0.4107$$

$$s = \sqrt{0.4107} = 0.641$$

Step-by-Step technology instructions available online

TABLE 4.4 Deviations and Squared Deviations for the Big Mac Data

Big Mac Price in U.S. Dollars	Deviations from Mean	Squared Deviations
3.02	−0.34	0.1156
4.67	1.31	1.7161
3.28	−0.08	0.0064
3.51	0.15	0.0225
3.42	0.06	0.0036
2.76	−0.60	0.3600
2.87	−0.49	0.2401
		$\sum(x - \bar{x})^2 = 2.4643$

The computation of s^2 can be a bit tedious, especially if the sample size is large. Fortunately, many calculators and computer software packages compute the variance and standard deviation upon request. One commonly used statistical computer package is Minitab. The output resulting from using the Minitab Describe command with the Big Mac data follows. Minitab gives a variety of numerical descriptive measures, including the mean, the median, and the standard deviation.

Descriptive Statistics: Big Mac Price in U.S. Dollars

Variable	N	Mean	SE Mean	StDev	Minimum	Q1	Median
Big Mac Price	7	3.361	0.242	0.641	2.760	2.870	3.280

Variable	Q3	Maximum
Big Mac Price	3.510	4.670

The standard deviation can be informally interpreted as the size of a "typical" or "representative" deviation from the mean. Thus, in Example 4.8, a typical deviation from $\bar{x}$ is about 0.641; some observations are closer to $\bar{x}$ than 0.641 and others are farther away. We computed $s = 0.641$ in Example 4.8 without saying whether this value indicated a large or a small amount of variability. At this point, it is better to use s for comparative purposes than for an absolute assessment of variability. If Big Mac prices for a different group of countries resulted in a standard deviation of $s = 1.25$ (this is the standard deviation for all 45 countries for which Big Mac data was available) then we would conclude that our original sample has much less variability than the data set consisting of all 45 countries.

There are measures of variability for the entire population that are analogous to s^2 and s for a sample. These measures are called the **population variance** and the **population standard deviation** and are denoted by σ^2 and σ, respectively. (We again use a lowercase Greek letter for a population characteristic.)

Notation

s^2	sample variance
σ^2	population variance
s	sample standard deviation
σ	population standard deviation

In many statistical procedures, we would like to use the value of σ, but unfortunately it is not usually known. Therefore, in its place we must use a value computed from the sample that we hope is close to σ (i.e., a good *estimate* of σ). We use the divisor $(n - 1)$ in s^2 rather than n because, on average, the resulting value tends to be a bit closer to σ^2. We will say more about this in Chapter 9.

An alternative rationale for using $(n - 1)$ is based on the property $\sum(x - \bar{x}) = 0$. Suppose that $n = 5$ and that four of the deviations are

$$x_1 - \bar{x} = -4 \quad x_2 - \bar{x} = 6 \quad x_3 - \bar{x} = 1 \quad x_5 - \bar{x} = -8$$

Then, because the sum of these four deviations is -5, the remaining deviation must be $x_4 - \bar{x} = 5$ (so that the sum of all five is zero). Although there are five deviations, only four of them contain independent information about variability. More generally, once any $(n - 1)$ of the deviations are available, the value of the remaining deviation is determined. The n deviations actually contain only $(n - 1)$ independent pieces of information about variability. Statisticians express this by saying that s^2 and s are based on $(n - 1)$ *degrees of freedom* (df).

The Interquartile Range

As with $\bar{x}$, the value of s can be greatly affected by the presence of even a single unusually small or large observation. The *interquartile range* is a measure of variability that is resistant to the effects of outliers. It is based on quantities called *quartiles.* The *lower quartile* separates the bottom 25% of the data set from the upper 75%, and the *upper quartile* separates the top 25% from the bottom 75%. The *middle quartile* is the median, and it separates the bottom 50% from the top 50%. Figure 4.6 illustrates the locations of these quartiles for a smoothed histogram.

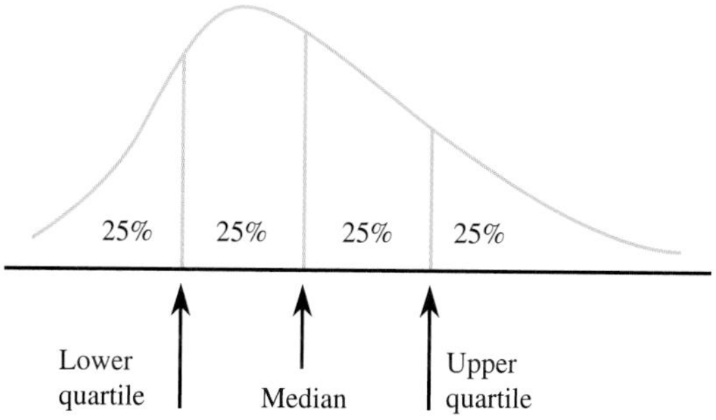

FIGURE 4.6
The quartiles for a smoothed histogram.

The quartiles for sample data are obtained by dividing the n ordered observations into a lower half and an upper half; if n is odd, the median is excluded from both halves. The two extreme quartiles are then the medians of the two halves. (Note: The median is only temporarily excluded for the purpose of computing quartiles. It is not excluded from the data set.)

DEFINITION*

lower quartile = median of the lower half of the sample
upper quartile = median of the upper half of the sample
(If n is odd, the median of the entire sample is excluded from both halves when computing quartiles.)

The **interquartile range (iqr)**, a measure of variability that is not as sensitive to the presence of outliers as the standard deviation, is given by

iqr = upper quartile − lower quartile

*There are several other sensible ways to define quartiles. Some calculators and software packages use an alternative definition.

The resistant nature of the interquartile range follows from the fact that up to 25% of the smallest sample observations and up to 25% of the largest sample observations can be made more extreme without affecting the value of the interquartile range.

EXAMPLE 4.9 Higher Education

● *The Chronicle of Higher Education* (Almanac Issue, 2009–2010) published the accompanying data on the percentage of the population with a bachelor's or higher degree in 2007 for each of the 50 U.S. states and the District of Columbia. The 51 data values are

21	27	26	19	30	35	35	26	47	26	27	30
24	29	22	24	29	20	20	27	35	38	25	31
19	24	27	27	23	34	34	25	32	26	26	24
22	28	26	30	23	25	22	25	29	33	34	30
17	25	23									

N = 51
Leaf Unit = 1.0

1	7
1	99
2	001
2	222333
2	444455555
2	66666677777
2	8999
3	00001
3	23
3	444555
3	
3	8
4	
4	
4	
4	7

FIGURE 4.7
Stem-and-leaf display: Percent with bachelor's or higher degree

Figure 4.7 gives a stem-and-leaf display (using repeated stems) of the data. The smallest value in the data set is 17% (West Virginia), and two values stand out on the high end—38% (Massachusetts) and 47% (District of Columbia).

To compute the quartiles and the interquartile range, we first order the data and use the median to divide the data into a lower half and an upper half. Because there is an odd number of observations ($n = 51$), the median is excluded from both the upper and lower halves when computing the quartiles.

Ordered Data

Lower Half:	17	19	19	20	20	21	22	22	22	23
23	23	**24**	24	24	24	25	25	25	25	25
26	26	26	26							
Median:		**26**								
Upper Half:	26	27	27	27	27	27	28	29	29	29
30	30	**30**	30	31	32	33	34	34	34	35
35	35	38	47							

Each half of the sample contains 25 observations. The lower quartile is just the median of the lower half of the sample (24 for this data set), and the upper quartile is the median of the upper half (30 for this data set). This gives

lower quartile = 24
upper quartile = 30
iqr = 30 − 24 = 6

The sample mean and standard deviation for this data set are 27.18 and 5.53, respectively. If we were to change the two largest values from 38 and 47 to 58 and 67 (so that they still remain the two largest values), the median and interquartile range would not be affected, whereas the mean and the standard deviation would change to 27.96 and 8.40, respectively. The value of the interquartile range is not affected by a few extreme values in the data set.

● Data set available online

The **population interquartile range** is the difference between the upper and lower population quartiles. If a histogram of the data set under consideration (whether a population or a sample) can be reasonably well approximated by a normal curve, then the relationship between the standard deviation (sd) and the interquartile range is roughly sd = iqr/1.35. A value of the standard deviation much larger than iqr/1.35 suggests a distribution with heavier (or longer) tails than a normal curve. For the degree data of Example 4.9, we had $s = 5.53$, whereas iqr/1.35 = 6/1.35 = 4.44. This suggests that the distribution of data values in Example 4.9 is indeed heavy-tailed compared to a normal curve. This can be seen in the stem-and-leaf display of Figure 4.7.

EXERCISES 4.17 - 4.31

4.17 ● The following data are cost (in cents) per ounce for nine different brands of sliced Swiss cheese (www.consumerreports.org):

29	62	37	41	70	82	47	52	49

a. Compute the variance and standard deviation for this data set.

b. If a very expensive cheese with a cost per slice of 150 cents was added to the data set, how would the values of the mean and standard deviation change?

4.18 ● Cost per serving (in cents) for six high-fiber cereals rated very good and for nine high-fiber cereals rated good by *Consumer Reports* are shown below. Write a few sentences describing how these two data sets differ with respect to center and variability. Use summary statistics to support your statements.

Cereals Rated Very Good

46	49	62	41	19	77

Cereals Rated Good

71	30	53	53	67	43	48	28	54

4.19 ● Combining the cost-per-serving data for high-fiber cereals rated very good and those rated good from the previous exercise gives the following data set:

46	49	62	41	19	77	71	30
53	53	67	43	48	28	54	

a. Compute the quartiles and the interquartile range for this combined data set.

b. Compute the interquartile range for just the cereals rated good. Is this value greater than, less than, or about equal to the interquartile range computed in Part (a)?

4.20 ● The paper "Caffeinated Energy Drinks—A Growing Problem" (*Drug and Alcohol Dependence* [2009]: 1–10) gave the accompanying data on caffeine per ounce for eight top-selling energy drinks and for 11 high-caffeine energy drinks:

Top-Selling Energy Drinks

9.6	10.0	10.0	9.0	10.9	8.9	9.5	9.1

High-Caffeine Energy Drinks

21.0	25.0	15.0	21.5	35.7	15.0
33.3	11.9	16.3	31.3	30.0	

The mean caffeine per ounce is clearly higher for the high-caffeine energy drinks, but which of the two groups of energy drinks (top-selling or high-caffeine) is the most variable with respect to caffeine per ounce? Justify your choice.

4.21 ● The Insurance Institute for Highway Safety (www.iihs.org, June 11, 2009) published data on repair costs for cars involved in different types of accidents. In one study, seven different 2009 models of mini- and micro-cars were driven at 6 mph straight into a fixed barrier. The following table gives the cost of repairing damage to the bumper for each of the seven models:

Model	Repair Cost
Smart Fortwo	\$1,480
Chevrolet Aveo	\$1,071
Mini Cooper	\$2,291
Toyota Yaris	\$1,688
Honda Fit	\$1,124
Hyundai Accent	\$3,476
Kia Rio	\$3,701

a. Compute the values of the variance and standard deviation. The standard deviation is fairly large. What does this tell you about the repair costs?

b. The Insurance Institute for Highway Safety (referenced in the previous exercise) also gave bumper repair costs in a study of six models of minivans (December 30, 2007). Write a few sentences describing how mini- and micro-cars and minivans differ with respect to typical bumper repair cost and bumper repair cost variability.

Model	Repair Cost
Honda Odyssey	$1,538
Dodge Grand Caravan	$1,347
Toyota Sienna	$840
Chevrolet Uplander	$1,631
Kia Sedona	$1,176
Nissan Quest	$1,603

4.22 ● Consumer Reports Health (www.consumerreports.org/health) reported the accompanying caffeine concentration (mg/cup) for 12 brands of coffee:

Coffee Brand	Caffeine concentration (mg/cup)
Eight O'Clock	140
Caribou	195
Kickapoo	155
Starbucks	115
Bucks Country Coffee Co.	195
Archer Farms	180
Gloria Jean's Coffees	110
Chock Full o'Nuts	110
Peet's Coffee	130
Maxwell House	55
Folgers	60
Millstone	60

Compute the values of the quartiles and the interquartile range for this data set.

4.23 ● The accompanying data on number of minutes used for cell phone calls in 1 month was generated to be consistent with summary statistics published in a report of a marketing study of San Diego residents (TeleTruth, March 2009):

189 0 189 177 106 201 0 212 0 306
0 0 59 224 0 189 142 83 71 165
236 0 142 236 130

a. Compute the values of the quartiles and the interquartile range for this data set.
b. Explain why the lower quartile is equal to the minimum value for this data set. Will this be the case for every data set? Explain.

4.24 Give two sets of five numbers that have the same mean but different standard deviations, and give two sets of five numbers that have the same standard deviation but different means.

4.25 Going back to school can be an expensive time for parents—second only to the Christmas holiday season in terms of spending (*San Luis Obispo Tribune*, August 18, 2005). Parents spend an average of $444 on their children at the beginning of the school year stocking up on clothes, notebooks, and even iPods. Of course, not every parent spends the same amount of money and there is some variation. Do you think a data set consisting of the amount spent at the beginning of the school year for each student at a particular elementary school would have a large or a small standard deviation? Explain.

4.26 The article "Rethink Diversification to Raise Returns, Cut Risk" (*San Luis Obispo Tribune*, January 21, 2006) included the following paragraph:

> In their research, Mulvey and Reilly compared the results of two hypothetical portfolios and used actual data from 1994 to 2004 to see what returns they would achieve. The first portfolio invested in Treasury bonds, domestic stocks, international stocks, and cash. Its 10-year average annual return was 9.85% and its volatility—measured as the standard deviation of annual returns—was 9.26%. When Mulvey and Reilly shifted some assets in the portfolio to include funds that invest in real estate, commodities, and options, the 10-year return rose to 10.55% while the standard deviation fell to 7.97%. In short, the more diversified portfolio had a slightly better return and much less risk.

Explain why the standard deviation is a reasonable measure of volatility and why it is reasonable to interpret a smaller standard deviation as meaning less risk.

4.27 ● The U.S. Department of Transportation reported the accompanying data (see next page) on the number of speeding-related crash fatalities during holiday periods for the years from 1994 to 2003 (*Traffic Safety Facts*, July 20, 2005).

a. Compute the standard deviation for the New Year's Day data.
b. Without computing the standard deviation of the Memorial Day data, explain whether the standard deviation for the Memorial Day data would be larger

Data for Exercise 4.27

	Speeding-Related Fatalities									
Holiday Period	1994	1995	1996	1997	1998	1999	2000	2001	2002	2003
New Year's Day	141	142	178	72	219	138	171	134	210	70
Memorial Day	193	178	185	197	138	183	156	190	188	181
July 4th	178	219	202	179	169	176	219	64	234	184
Labor Day	183	188	166	179	162	171	180	138	202	189
Thanksgiving	212	198	218	210	205	168	187	217	210	202
Christmas	152	129	66	183	134	193	155	210	60	198

or smaller than the standard deviation of the New Year's Day data.

c. Memorial Day and Labor Day are holidays that always occur on Monday and Thanksgiving always occurs on a Thursday, whereas New Year's Day, July 4th and Christmas do not always fall on the same day of the week every year. Based on the given data, is there more or less variability in the speeding-related crash fatality numbers from year to year for same day of the week holiday periods than for holidays that can occur on different days of the week? Support your answer with appropriate measures of variability.

4.28 The Ministry of Health and Long-Term Care in Ontario, Canada, publishes information on the time that patients must wait for various medical procedures on its web site (www.health.gov.on.ca). For two cardiac procedures completed in fall of 2005, the following information was provided:

Procedure	Number of Completed Procedures	Median Wait Time (days)	Mean Wait Time (days)	90% Completed Within (days)
Angioplasty	847	14	18	39
Bypass surgery	539	13	19	42

a. Which of the following must be true for the lower quartile of the data set consisting of the 847 wait times for angioplasty?
   i. The lower quartile is less than 14.
   ii. The lower quartile is between 14 and 18.
   iii. The lower quartile is between 14 and 39.
   iv. The lower quartile is greater than 39.

b. Which of the following must be true for the upper quartile of the data set consisting of the 539 wait times for bypass surgery?
   i. The upper quartile is less than 13.
   ii. The upper quartile is between 13 and 19.
   iii. The upper quartile is between 13 and 42.
   iv. The upper quartile is greater than 42.

c. Which of the following must be true for the number of days for which only 5% of the bypass surgery wait times would be longer?
   i. It is less than 13.
   ii. It is between 13 and 19.
   iii. It is between 13 and 42.
   iv. It is greater than 42.

4.29 ● The accompanying table shows the low price, the high price, and the average price of homes sold in 15 communities in San Luis Obispo County between January 1, 2004, and August 1, 2004 (*San Luis Obispo Tribune*, September 5, 2004):

Community	Average Price	Number Sold	Low	High
Cayucos	$937,366	31	$380,000	$2,450,000
Pismo Beach	$804,212	71	$439,000	$2,500,000
Cambria	$728,312	85	$340,000	$2,000,000
Avila Beach	$654,918	16	$475,000	$1,375,000
Morro Bay	$606,456	114	$257,000	$2,650,000
Arroyo Grande	$595,577	214	$178,000	$1,526,000
Templeton	$578,249	89	$265,000	$2,350,000
San Luis Obispo	$557,628	277	$258,000	$2,400,000
Nipomo	$528,572	138	$263,000	$1,295,000
Los Osos	$511,866	123	$140,000	$3,500,000
Santa Margarita	$430,354	22	$290,000	$583,000
Atascadero	$420,603	270	$140,000	$1,600,000
Grover Beach	$416,405	97	$242,000	$720,000
Paso Robles	$412,584	439	$170,000	$1,575,000
Oceano	$390,354	59	$177,000	$1,350,000

a. Explain why the average price for the combined areas of Los Osos and Morro Bay is not just the average of $511,866 and $606,456.

b. Houses sold in Grover Beach and Paso Robles have very similar average prices. Based on the other information given, which is likely to have the higher standard deviation for price?

c. Consider houses sold in Grover Beach and Paso Robles. Based on the other information given, which is likely to have the higher median price?

4.30 ● In 1997, a woman sued a computer keyboard manufacturer, charging that her repetitive stress injuries were caused by the keyboard (*Genessey* v. *Digital Equipment Corporation*). The jury awarded about $3.5 million for pain and suffering, but the court then set aside that award as being unreasonable compensation. In making this determination, the court identified a "normative" group of 27 similar cases and specified a reasonable award as one within 2 standard deviations of the mean of the awards in the 27 cases. The 27 award amounts were (in thousands of dollars)

37	60	75	115	135	140	149	150
238	290	340	410	600	750	750	750
1050	1100	1139	1150	1200	1200	1250	1576
1700	1825	2000					

What is the maximum possible amount that could be awarded under the "2-standard deviations rule?"

4.31 ● The standard deviation alone does not measure relative variation. For example, a standard deviation of $1 would be considered large if it is describing the variability from store to store in the price of an ice cube tray. On the other hand, a standard deviation of $1 would be considered small if it is describing store-to-store variability in the price of a particular brand of freezer. A quantity designed to give a relative measure of variability is the *coefficient of variation*. Denoted by CV, the coefficient of variation expresses the standard deviation as a percentage of the mean. It is defined by the formula $CV = 100\left(\frac{s}{\bar{x}}\right)$.

Consider two samples. Sample 1 gives the actual weight (in ounces) of the contents of cans of pet food labeled as having a net weight of 8 ounces. Sample 2 gives the actual weight (in pounds) of the contents of bags of dry pet food labeled as having a net weight of 50 pounds. The weights for the two samples are

Sample 1	8.3	7.1	7.6	8.1	7.6
	8.3	8.2	7.7	7.7	7.5
Sample 2	52.3	50.6	52.1	48.4	48.8
	47.0	50.4	50.3	48.7	48.2

a. For each of the given samples, calculate the mean and the standard deviation.

b. Compute the coefficient of variation for each sample. Do the results surprise you? Why or why not?

4.3 Summarizing a Data Set: Boxplots

In Sections 4.1 and 4.2, we looked at ways of describing the center and variability of a data set using numerical measures. It would be nice to have a method of summarizing data that gives more detail than just a measure of center and spread and yet less detail than a stem-and-leaf display or histogram. A *boxplot* is one way to do this. A boxplot is compact, yet it provides information about the center, spread, and symmetry or skewness of the data. We will consider two types of boxplots: the skeletal boxplot and the modified boxplot.

Construction of a Skeletal Boxplot

1. Draw a horizontal (or vertical) measurement scale.
2. Construct a rectangular box with a left (or lower) edge at the lower quartile and a right (or upper) edge at the upper quartile. The box width is then equal to the iqr.
3. Draw a vertical (or horizontal) line segment inside the box at the location of the median.
4. Extend horizontal (or vertical) line segments, called whiskers, from each end of the box to the smallest and largest observations in the data set.

EXAMPLE 4.10 Revisiting the Degree Data

Let's reconsider the data on percentage of the population with a bachelor's or higher degree for the 50 U.S. states and the District of Columbia (Example 4.9). The ordered observations are

Ordered Data

Lower Half:	17	19	19	20	20	21	22	22	22	23
23	23	**24**	24	24	24	25	25	25	25	25
26	26	26	26							
Median:		**26**								
Upper Half:	26	27	27	27	27	27	28	29	29	29
30	30	**30**	30	31	32	33	34	34	34	35
35	35	38	47							

To construct a boxplot of these data, we need the following information: the smallest observation, the lower quartile, the median, the upper quartile, and the largest observation. This collection of summary measures is often referred to as a **five-number summary.** For this data set we have

smallest observation = 17
lower quartile = median of the lower half = 24
median = 26th observation in the ordered list = 26
upper quartile = median of the upper half = 30
largest observation = 47

Figure 4.8 shows the corresponding boxplot. The median line is somewhat closer to the lower edge of the box than to the upper edge, suggesting a concentration of values in the lower part of the middle half. The upper whisker is longer than the lower whisker. These observations are consistent with the stem-and-leaf display of Figure 4.7.

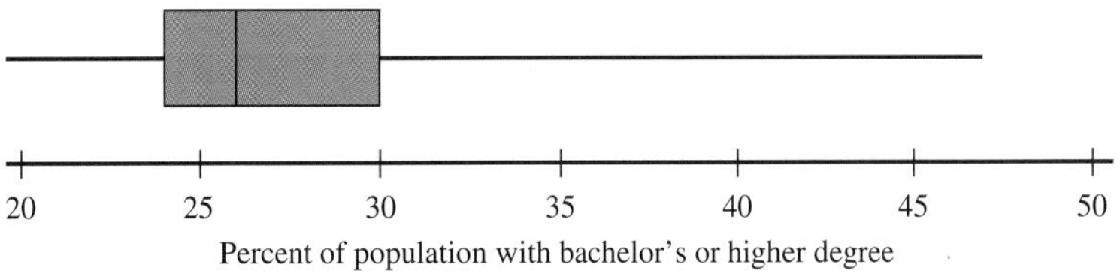

FIGURE 4.8 Skeletal boxplot for the degree data of Example 4.10.

The sequence of steps used to construct a skeletal boxplot is easily modified to give information about outliers.

DEFINITION

An observation is an **outlier** if it is more than 1.5(iqr) away from the nearest quartile (the nearest end of the box).

An outlier is **extreme** if it is more than 3(iqr) from the nearest quartile and it is **mild** otherwise.

A **modified boxplot** represents mild outliers by solid circles and extreme outliers by open circles, and the whiskers extend on each end to the most extreme observations that are *not* outliers.

Construction of a Modified Boxplot

1. Draw a horizontal (or vertical) measurement scale.
2. Construct a rectangular box with a left (or lower) edge at the lower quartile and right (or upper) edge at the upper quartile. The box width is then equal to the iqr.
3. Draw a vertical (or horizontal) line segment inside the box at the location of the median.
4. Determine if there are any mild or extreme outliers in the data set.
5. Draw whiskers that extend from each end of the box to the most extreme observation that is *not* an outlier.
6. Draw a solid circle to mark the location of any mild outliers in the data set.
7. Draw an open circle to mark the location of any extreme outliers in the data set.

AP* EXAM TIP

Outliers convey important information about a data set. For this reason, modified boxplots are usually preferred over skeletal boxplots.

EXAMPLE 4.11 Golden Rectangles

● The accompanying data came from an anthropological study of rectangular shapes (*Lowie's Selected Papers in Anthropology*, Cora Dubios, ed. [Berkeley, CA: University of California Press, 1960]: 137–142). Observations were made on the variable x = width/length for a sample of $n = 20$ beaded rectangles used in Shoshoni Indian leather handicrafts:

.553	.570	.576	.601	.606	.606	.609	.611	.615	.628
.654	.662	.668	.670	.672	.690	.693	.749	.844	.933

The quantities needed for constructing the modified boxplot follow:

median = .641	iqr = .681 − .606 = .075
lower quartile = .606	1.5(iqr) = .1125
upper quartile = .681	3(iqr) = .225

Thus,

$$(\text{upper quartile}) + 1.5(\text{iqr}) = .681 + .1125 = .7935$$
$$(\text{lower quartile}) - 1.5(\text{iqr}) = .606 - .1125 = .4935$$

So 0.844 and 0.933 are both outliers on the upper end (because they are larger than 0.7935), and there are no outliers on the lower end (because no observations are smaller than 0.4935). Because

$$(\text{upper quartile}) + 3(\text{iqr}) = 0.681 + 0.225 = 0.906$$

0.933 is an extreme outlier and 0.844 is only a mild outlier. The upper whisker extends to the largest observation that is not an outlier, 0.749, and the lower whisker extends to 0.553. The boxplot is shown in Figure 4.9. The median line is not at the center of the box, so there is a slight asymmetry in the middle half of the data. However, the most striking feature is the presence of the two outliers. These two x values considerably exceed the "golden ratio" of 0.618, used since antiquity as an aesthetic standard for rectangles.

Step-by-Step technology instructions available online

● Data set available online

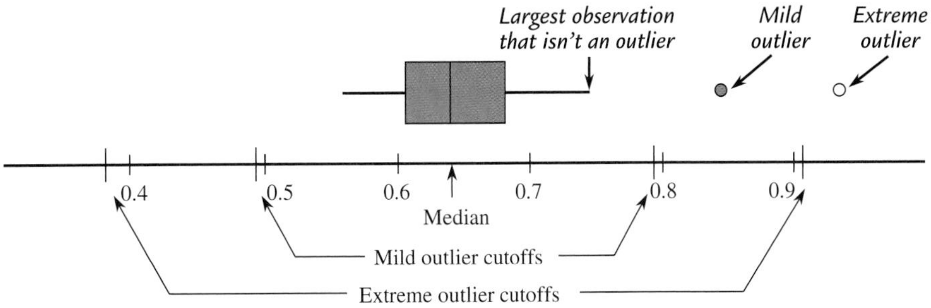

FIGURE 4.9
Boxplot for the rectangle data in Example 4.11.

EXAMPLE 4.12 Another Look at Big Mac Prices

Big Mac prices in U.S. dollars for 45 different countries were given in the article "Cheesed Off" first introduced in Example 4.7. The 45 Big Mac prices were:

3.57	3.01	3.97	4.67	3.80	3.64	3.28	1.83	3.51	3.42	3.92
5.89	3.04	2.36	4.92	1.72	3.89	5.20	2.21	3.98	3.54	3.24
3.06	1.99	2.48	3.54	7.03	2.28	2.76	2.09	2.66	2.31	2.93
3.03	2.37	2.91	1.83	5.57	6.39	2.31	1.93	3.80	2.72	1.70
2.87										

Figure 4.10 shows a Minitab boxplot for the Big Mac price data. Note that the upper whisker is longer than the lower whisker and that there are two outliers on the high end (Norway with a Big Mac price of \$7.04 and Switzerland with a price of \$6.29).

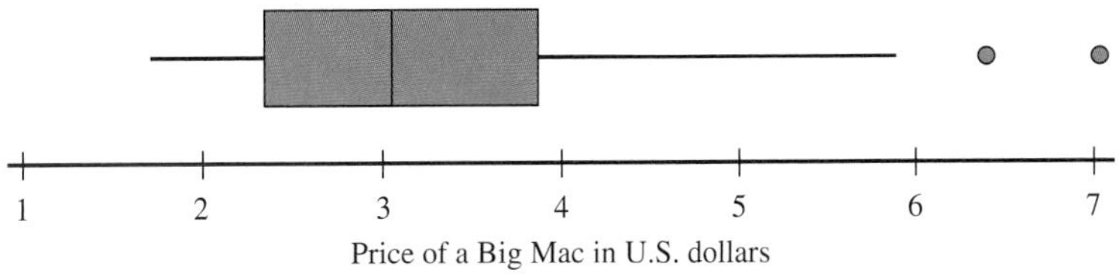

FIGURE 4.10
Minitab boxplot of the Big Mac price data of Example 4.12.

Note that Minitab does not distinguish between mild outliers and extreme outliers in the boxplot. For the Big Mac price data,

lower quartile = 2.335
upper quartile = 3.845
iqr = 3.845 − 2.335 = 1.510

Then

1.5(iqr) = 2.265
3(iqr) = 4.530

We can compute outlier boundaries as follows:

upper quartile + 1.5(iqr) = 3.845 + 2.265 = 6.110
upper quartile + 3(iqr) = 3.845 + 4.530 = 8.375

The observation for Switzerland (6.39) is a mild outlier because it is greater than 6.110 (the upper quartile + 1.5(iqr)) but less than 8.375 (the upper quartile + 3(iqr)). The observation for Norway is also a mild outlier. There are no extreme outliers in this data set.

With two or more data sets consisting of observations on the same variable (for example, fuel efficiencies for four types of car or weight gains for a control group and a treatment group), **comparative boxplots** (more than one boxplot drawn using the same scale) can tell us a lot about similarities and differences between the data sets.

EXAMPLE 4.13 NBA Salaries Revisited

The 2009–2010 salaries of NBA players published on the web site hoopshype.com were used to construct the comparative boxplot of the salary data for five teams shown in Figure 4.11.

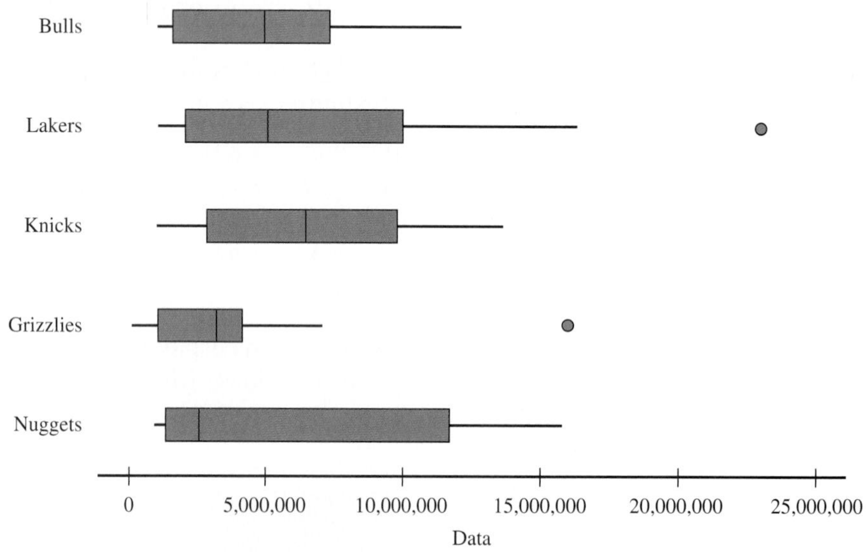

FIGURE 4.11
Comparative boxplot for salaries for five NBA teams.

The comparative boxplot reveals some interesting similarities and differences in the salary distributions of the five teams. The minimum salary is lower for the Grizzlies, but is about the same for the other four teams. The median salary was lowest for the Nuggets—in fact the median for the Nuggets is about the same as the lower quartile for the Knicks and the Lakers, indicating that half of the players on the Nuggets have salaries less than about \$2.5 million, whereas only about 25% of the Knicks and the Lakers have salaries less than about \$2.5 million. The Lakers had the player with by far the highest salary. The Grizzlies and the Lakers were the only teams that had any salary outliers. With the exception of one highly paid player, salaries for players on the Grizzlies team were noticeably lower than for the other four teams.

EXERCISES 4.32 - 4.37

4.32 Based on a large national sample of working adults, the U.S. Census Bureau reports the following information on travel time to work for those who do not work at home:

lower quartile = 7 minutes
median = 18 minutes
upper quartile = 31 minutes

Also given was the mean travel time, which was reported as 22.4 minutes.

a. Is the travel time distribution more likely to be approximately symmetric, positively skewed, or negatively skewed? Explain your reasoning based on the given summary quantities.
b. Suppose that the minimum travel time was 1 minute and that the maximum travel time in the sample was 205 minutes. Construct a skeletal boxplot for the travel time data.
c. Were there any mild or extreme outliers in the data set? How can you tell?

4.33 ● The report "Who Moves? Who Stays Put? Where's Home?" (*Pew Social and Demographic Trends*, December 17, 2008) gave the accompanying data for the 50 U.S. states on the percentage of the population that was born in the state and is still living there. The data values have been arranged in order from largest to smallest.

75.8	71.4	69.6	69.0	68.6	67.5	66.7	66.3	66.1	66.0	66.0
65.1	64.4	64.3	63.8	63.7	62.8	62.6	61.9	61.9	61.5	61.1
59.2	59.0	58.7	57.3	57.1	55.6	55.6	55.5	55.3	54.9	54.7
54.5	54.0	54.0	53.9	53.5	52.8	52.5	50.2	50.2	48.9	48.7
48.6	47.1	43.4	40.4	35.7	28.2					

a. Find the values of the median, the lower quartile, and the upper quartile.
b. The two smallest values in the data set are 28.2 (Alaska) and 35.7 (Wyoming). Are these two states outliers?
c. Construct a boxplot for this data set and comment on the interesting features of the plot.

4.34 ● The National Climate Data Center gave the accompanying annual rainfall (in inches) for Medford, Oregon, from 1950 to 2008 (www.ncdc.noaa.gov/oa/climate/research/cag3/city.html):

28.84	20.15	18.88	25.72	16.42	20.18	28.96	20.72	23.58
10.62	20.85	19.86	23.34	19.08	29.23	18.32	21.27	18.93
15.47	20.68	23.43	19.55	20.82	19.04	18.77	19.63	12.39
22.39	15.95	20.46	16.05	22.08	19.44	30.38	18.79	10.89
17.25	14.95	13.86	15.30	13.71	14.68	15.16	16.77	12.33
21.93	31.57	18.13	28.87	16.69	18.81	15.15	18.16	19.99
19.00	23.97	21.99	17.25	14.07				

a. Compute the quartiles and the interquartile range.
b. Are there outliers in this data set? If so, which observations are mild outliers? Which are extreme outliers?
c. Draw a boxplot for this data set that shows outliers.

4.35 ● The accompanying data on annual maximum wind speed (in meters per second) in Hong Kong for each year in a 45-year period were given in an article that appeared in the journal *Renewable Energy* (March 2007). Use the annual maximum wind speed data to construct a boxplot. Is the boxplot approximately symmetric?

30.3	39.0	33.9	38.6	44.6	31.4	26.7	51.9	31.9
27.2	52.9	45.8	63.3	36.0	64.0	31.4	42.2	41.1
37.0	34.4	35.5	62.2	30.3	40.0	36.0	39.4	34.4
28.3	39.1	55.0	35.0	28.8	25.7	62.7	32.4	31.9
37.5	31.5	32.0	35.5	37.5	41.0	37.5	48.6	28.1

4.36 ● Fiber content (in grams per serving) and sugar content (in grams per serving) for 18 high fiber cereals (www.consumerreports.com) are shown below.

Fiber Content

7	10	10	7	8	7	12	12	8
13	10	8	12	7	14	7	8	8

Sugar Content

11	6	14	13	0	18	9	10	19
6	10	17	10	10	0	9	5	11

a. Find the median, quartiles, and interquartile range for the fiber content data set.
b. Find the median, quartiles, and interquartile range for the sugar content data set.
c. Are there any outliers in the sugar content data set?
d. Explain why the minimum value for the fiber content data set and the lower quartile for the fiber content data set are equal.
e. Construct a comparative boxplot and use it to comment on the differences and similarities in the fiber and sugar distributions.

4.37 ● Shown here are the number of auto accidents per year for every 1000 people in each of 40 occupations (*Knight Ridder Tribune*, June 19, 2004):

Occupation	Accidents per 1000	Occupation	Accidents per 1000
Student	152	Social worker	98
Physician	109	Manual laborer	96
Lawyer	106	Analyst	95
Architect	105	Engineer	94
Real estate broker	102	Consultant	94
Enlisted military	99	Sales	93

(continued)

Occupation	Accidents per 1000	Occupation	Accidents per 1000
Military officer	91	Pharmacist	85
Nurse	90	Proprietor	84
School administrator	90	Teacher, professor	84
Skilled laborer	90	Accountant	84
Librarian	90	Law enforcement	79
Creative arts	90	Physical therapist	78
Executive	89	Veterinarian	78
Insurance agent	89	Clerical, secretary	77
Banking, finance	89	Clergy	76
Customer service	88	Homemaker	76
Manager	88	Politician	76
Medical support	87	Pilot	75
Computer-related	87	Firefighter	67
Dentist	86	Farmer	43

a. Would you recommend using the standard deviation or the iqr as a measure of variability for this data set?

b. Are there outliers in this data set? If so, which observations are mild outliers? Which are extreme outliers?

c. Draw a modified boxplot for this data set.

d. If you were asked by an insurance company to decide which, if any, occupations should be offered a professional discount on auto insurance, which occupations would you recommend? Explain.

4.4 Interpreting Center and Variability: Chebyshev's Rule, the Empirical Rule, and z Scores

The mean and standard deviation can be combined to make informative statements about how the values in a data set are distributed and about the relative position of a particular value in a data set. To do this, it is useful to be able to describe how far away a particular observation is from the mean in terms of the standard deviation. For example, we might say that an observation is 2 standard deviations above the mean or that an observation is 1.3 standard deviations below the mean.

EXAMPLE 4.14 Standardized Test Scores

Consider a data set of scores on a standardized test with a mean and standard deviation of 100 and 15, respectively. We can make the following statements:

1. Because $100 - 15 = 85$, we say that a score of 85 is "1 standard deviation *below* the mean." Similarly, $100 + 15 = 115$ is "1 standard deviation *above* the mean" (see Figure 4.12).

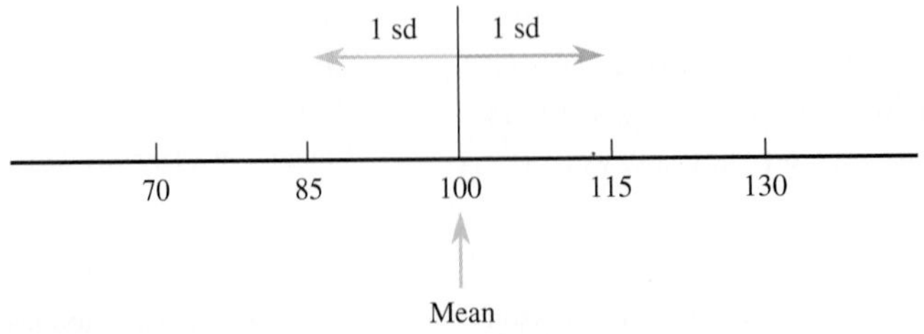

FIGURE 4.12
Values within 1 standard deviation of the mean (Example 4.14).

2. Because 2 times the standard deviation is $2(15) = 30$, and $100 + 30 = 130$ and $100 - 30 = 70$, scores between 70 and 130 are those *within* 2 standard deviations of the mean (see Figure 4.13).
3. Because $100 + (3)(15) = 145$, scores above 145 are greater than the mean by more than 3 standard deviations.

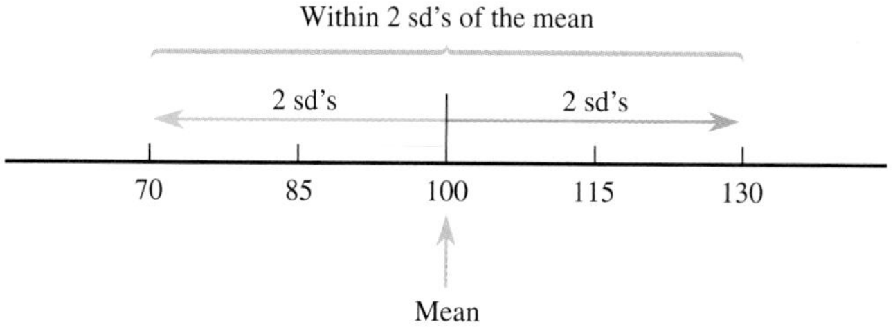

FIGURE 4.13
Values within 2 standard deviations of the mean (Example 4.14).

Sometimes in published articles, the mean and standard deviation are reported, but a graphical display of the data is not given. However, using a result called Chebyshev's Rule, it is possible to get a sense of the distribution of data values based on our knowledge of only the mean and standard deviation.

Chebyshev's Rule

Consider any number k, where $k \geq 1$. Then the percentage of observations that are within k standard deviations of the mean is at least $100\left(1 - \frac{1}{k^2}\right)\%$. Substituting selected values of k gives the following results.

Number of Standard Deviations, k	$1 - \frac{1}{k^2}$	**Percentage Within k Standard Deviations of the Mean**
2	$1 - \frac{1}{4} = .75$	at least 75%
3	$1 - \frac{1}{9} = .89$	at least 89%
4	$1 - \frac{1}{16} = .94$	at least 94%
4.472	$1 - \frac{1}{20} = .95$	at least 95%
5	$1 - \frac{1}{25} = .96$	at least 96%
10	$1 - \frac{1}{100} = .99$	at least 99%

EXAMPLE 4.15 Child Care for Preschool Kids

The article "Piecing Together Child Care with Multiple Arrangements: Crazy Quilt or Preferred Pattern for Employed Parents of Preschool Children?" (*Journal of Marriage and the Family* [1994]: 669–680) examined various modes of care for preschool children. For a sample of families with one preschool child, it was reported that the mean and standard deviation of child care time per week were approximately 36 hours and 12 hours, respectively. Figure 4.14 displays values that are 1, 2, and 3 standard deviations from the mean.

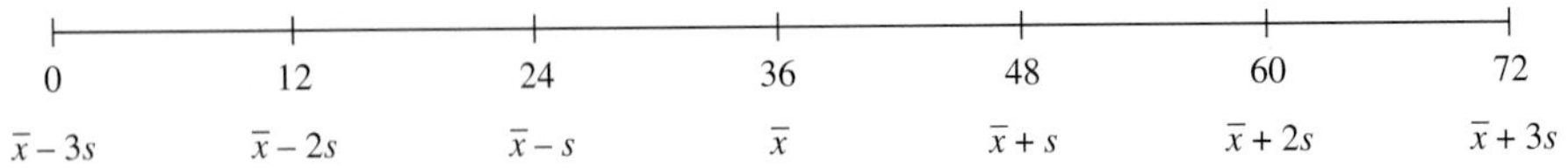

FIGURE 4.14
Measurement scale for child care time (Example 4.15).

Ariel Skelley/Blend Images/Jupiter Images

Chebyshev's Rule allows us to assert the following:

1. At least 75% of the sample observations must be between 12 and 60 hours (within 2 standard deviations of the mean).
2. Because at least 89% of the observations must be between 0 and 72, at most 11% are outside this interval. Time cannot be negative, so we conclude that at most 11% of the observations exceed 72.
3. The values 18 and 54 are 1.5 standard deviations to either side of $\bar{x}$, so using $k = 1.5$ in Chebyshev's Rule implies that at least 55.6% of the observations must be between these two values. Thus, at most 44.4% of the observations are less than 18—*not* at most 22.2%, because the distribution of values may not be symmetric.

Because Chebyshev's Rule is applicable to any data set (distribution), whether symmetric or skewed, we must be careful when making statements about the proportion above a particular value, below a particular value, or inside or outside an interval that is not centered at the mean. The rule must be used in a conservative fashion. There is another aspect of this conservatism. The rule states that *at least* 75% of the observations are within 2 standard deviations of the mean, but for many data sets substantially more than 75% of the values satisfy this condition. The same sort of understatement is frequently encountered for other values of k (numbers of standard deviations).

EXAMPLE 4.16 IQ Scores

Figure 4.15 gives a stem-and-leaf display of IQ scores of 112 children in one of the early studies that used the Stanford revision of the Binet–Simon intelligence scale (*The Intelligence of School Children*, L. M. Terman [Boston: Houghton-Mifflin, 1919]).

Summary quantities include

$$\bar{x} = 104.5 \quad s = 16.3 \quad 2s = 32.6 \quad 3s = 48.9$$

6	1
7	25679
8	0000124555668
9	0000112333446666778889
10	000112222233356666777778899999
11	00001122333344444477899
12	01111123445669
13	006
14	26
15	2

Stem: Tens
Leaf: Ones

FIGURE 4.15
Stem-and-leaf display of IQ scores used in Example 4.16.

In Figure 4.15, all observations that are within two standard deviations of the mean are shown in blue. Table 4.5 shows how Chebyshev's Rule can sometimes considerably understate actual percentages.

TABLE 4.5 Summarizing the Distribution of IQ Scores

k = Number of sd's	$\bar{x} \pm ks$	Chebyshev	Actual	
2	71.9 to 137.1	at least 75%	96% (108)	
2.5	63.7 to 145.3	at least 84%	97% (109)	← the blue leaves in Figure 4.15
3	55.6 to 153.4	at least 89%	100% (112)	

Empirical Rule

The fact that statements based on Chebyshev's Rule are frequently conservative suggests that we should look for rules that are less conservative and more precise. One useful rule is the **Empirical Rule**, which can be applied whenever the distribution of data values can be reasonably well described by a normal curve (distributions that are "mound" shaped).

The Empirical Rule

If the histogram of values in a data set can be reasonably well approximated by a normal curve, then

Approximately 68% of the observations are within 1 standard deviation of the mean.
Approximately 95% of the observations are within 2 standard deviations of the mean.
Approximately 99.7% of the observations are within 3 standard deviations of the mean.

The Empirical Rule makes "approximately" instead of "at least" statements, and the percentages for $k = 1$, 2, and 3 standard deviations are much higher than those of Chebyshev's Rule. Figure 4.16 illustrates the percentages given by the Empirical Rule. In contrast to Chebyshev's Rule, dividing the percentages in half is permissible, because a normal curve is symmetric.

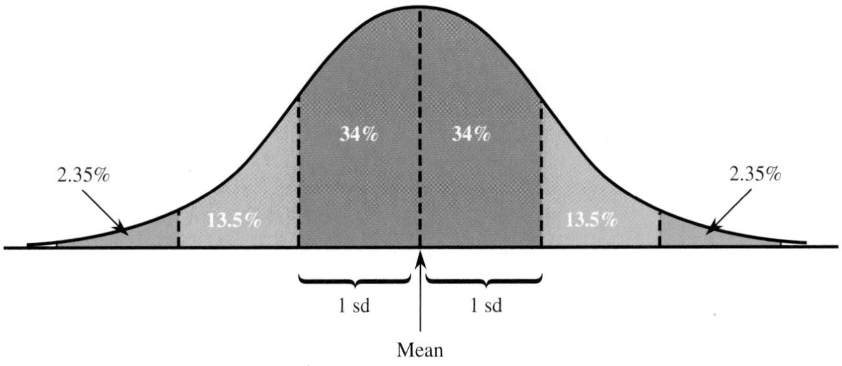

FIGURE 4.16
Approximate percentages implied by the Empirical Rule.

EXAMPLE 4.17 Heights of Mothers and the Empirical Rule

The Image Bank/Paul Thomas/
Getty Images

One of the earliest articles to argue for the wide applicability of the normal distribution was "On the Laws of Inheritance in Man. I. Inheritance of Physical Characters" (*Biometrika* [1903]: 375–462). Among the data sets discussed in the article was one consisting of 1052 measurements of the heights of mothers. The mean and standard deviation were

$$\bar{x} = 62.484 \text{ in.} \qquad s = 2.390 \text{ in.}$$

The data distribution was described as approximately normal. Table 4.6 contrasts actual percentages with those obtained from Chebyshev's Rule and the Empirical Rule.

TABLE 4.6 Summarizing the Distribution of Mothers' Heights

Number of sd's	Interval	Actual	Empirical Rule	Chebyshev Rule
1	60.094 to 64.874	72.1%	Approximately 68%	At least 0%
2	57.704 to 67.264	96.2%	Approximately 95%	At least 75%
3	55.314 to 69.654	99.2%	Approximately 99.7%	At least 89%

Clearly, the Empirical Rule is much more successful and informative in this case than Chebyshev's Rule.

Our detailed study of the normal distribution and areas under normal curves in Chapter 7 will enable us to make statements analogous to those of the Empirical Rule for values other than $k = 1, 2,$ or 3 standard deviations. For now, note that it is unusual to see an observation from a normally distributed population that is farther than 2 standard deviations from the mean (only 5%), and it is very surprising to see one that is more than 3 standard deviations away. If you encountered a mother whose height was 72 inches, you might reasonably conclude that she was not part of the population described by the data set in Example 4.17.

Measures of Relative Standing

When you obtain your score after taking a test, you probably want to know how it compares to the scores of others who have taken the test. Is your score above or below the mean, and by how much? Does your score place you among the top 5% of those who took the test or only among the top 25%? Questions of this sort are answered by finding ways to measure the position of a particular value in a data set relative to all values in the set. One measure of relative standing is a *z score.*

DEFINITION

The **z score** corresponding to a particular value is

$$z \text{ score} = \frac{\text{value} - \text{mean}}{\text{standard deviation}}$$

The z score tells us how many standard deviations the value is from the mean. It is positive or negative according to whether the value lies above or below the mean.

The process of subtracting the mean and then dividing by the standard deviation is sometimes referred to as *standardization,* and a z score is one example of what is called a *standardized score.*

EXAMPLE 4.18 Relatively Speaking, Which Is the Better Offer?

Suppose that two graduating seniors, one a marketing major and one an accounting major, are comparing job offers. The accounting major has an offer for \$45,000 per year, and the marketing student has an offer for \$43,000 per year. Summary information about the distribution of offers follows:

Accounting:	mean = 46,000	standard deviation = 1500
Marketing:	mean = 42,500	standard deviation = 1000

Then,

$$\text{accounting } z \text{ score} = \frac{45{,}000 - 46{,}000}{1500} = -.67$$

(so \$45,000 is .67 standard deviation below the mean), whereas

$$\text{marketing } z \text{ score} = \frac{43{,}000 - 42{,}500}{1000} = .5$$

Relative to the appropriate data sets, the marketing offer is actually more attractive than the accounting offer (although this may not offer much solace to the marketing major).

The z score is particularly useful when the distribution of observations is approximately normal. In this case, from the Empirical Rule, a z score outside the interval from -2 to $+2$ occurs in about 5% of all cases, whereas a z score outside the interval from -3 to $+3$ occurs only about 0.3% of the time.

Percentiles

A particular observation can be located even more precisely by giving the percentage of the data that fall at or below that observation. If, for example, 95% of all test scores are at or below 650, whereas only 5% are above 650, then 650 is called the *95th percentile* of the data set (or of the distribution of scores). Similarly, if 10% of all scores are at or below 400 and 90% are above 400, then the value 400 is the 10th percentile.

DEFINITION

For any particular number r between 0 and 100, the **rth percentile** is a value such that r percent of the observations in the data set fall at or below that value.

Figure 4.17 illustrates the 90th percentile. We have already met several percentiles in disguise. The median is the 50th percentile, and the lower and upper quartiles are the 25th and 75th percentiles, respectively.

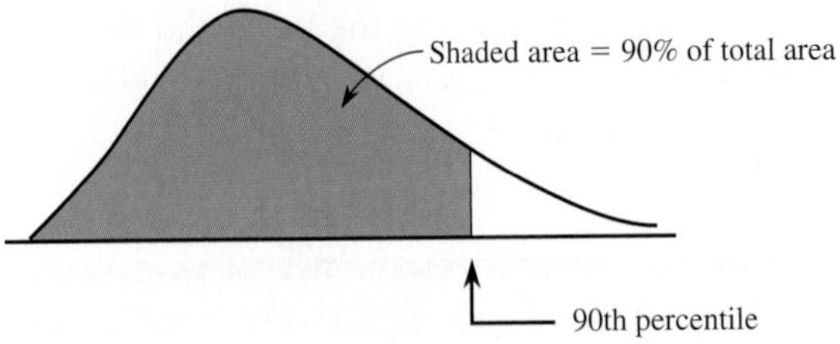

FIGURE 4.17
Ninetieth percentile for a smoothed histogram.

EXAMPLE 4.19 Head Circumference at Birth

In addition to weight and length, head circumference is another measure of health in newborn babies. The National Center for Health Statistics reports the following summary values for head circumference (in cm) at birth for boys (approximate values read from graphs on the Center for Disease Control web site):

Percentile	5	10	25	50	75	90	95
Head Circumference (cm)	32.2	33.2	34.5	35.8	37.0	38.2	38.6

Interpreting these percentiles, we know that half of newborn boys have head circumferences of less than 35.8 cm, because 35.8 is the 50th percentile (the median). The middle 50% of newborn boys have head circumferences between 34.5 cm and 37.0 cm, with about 25% of the head circumferences less than 34.5 cm and about 25% greater than 37.0 cm. We can tell that the head circumference distribution for newborn boys is not symmetric, because the 5th percentile is 3.6 cm below the median, whereas the 95th percentile is only 2.8 cm above the median. This suggests that the bottom part of the distribution stretches out more than the top part of the distribution. This would be consistent with a distribution that is negatively skewed, as shown in Figure 4.18.

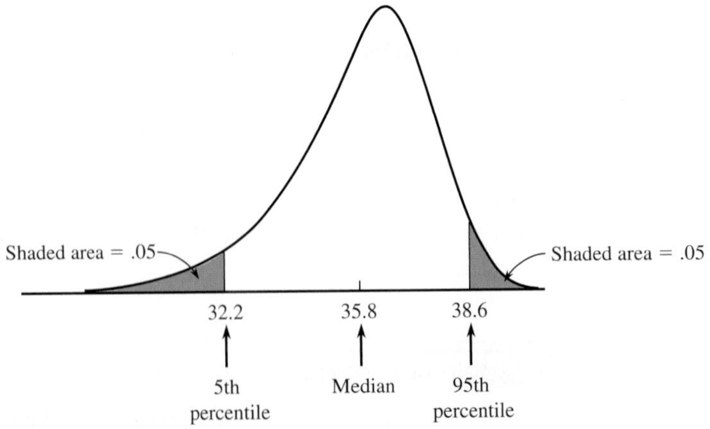

FIGURE 4.18
Negatively skewed distribution.

EXERCISES 4.38 - 4.52

4.38 The average playing time of compact discs in a large collection is 35 minutes, and the standard deviation is 5 minutes.

a. What value is 1 standard deviation above the mean? 1 standard deviation below the mean? What values are 2 standard deviations away from the mean?
b. Without assuming anything about the distribution of times, at least what percentage of the times is between 25 and 45 minutes?
c. Without assuming anything about the distribution of times, what can be said about the percentage of times that are either less than 20 minutes or greater than 50 minutes?
d. Assuming that the distribution of times is approximately normal, about what percentage of times are between 25 and 45 minutes? less than 20 minutes or greater than 50 minutes? less than 20 minutes?

4.39 ✦ In a study investigating the effect of car speed on accident severity, 5000 reports of fatal automobile accidents were examined, and the vehicle speed at impact was recorded for each one. For these 5000 accidents, the average speed was 42 mph and the standard deviation was 15 mph. A histogram revealed that the vehicle speed at impact distribution was approximately normal.

a. Roughly what proportion of vehicle speeds were between 27 and 57 mph?
b. Roughly what proportion of vehicle speeds exceeded 57 mph?

4.40 The U.S. Census Bureau (2000 census) reported the following relative frequency distribution for travel time to work for a large sample of adults who did not work at home:

Travel Time (minutes)	Relative Frequency
0 to <5	.04
5 to <10	.13
10 to <15	.16
15 to <20	.17
20 to <25	.14
25 to <30	.05
30 to <35	.12
35 to <40	.03
40 to <45	.03
45 to <60	.06
60 to <90	.05
90 or more	.02

a. Draw the histogram for the travel time distribution. In constructing the histogram, assume that the last interval in the relative frequency distribution (90 or more) ends at 200; so the last interval is 90 to <200. Be sure to use the density scale to determine the heights of the bars in the histogram because not all the intervals have the same width.
b. Describe the interesting features of the histogram from Part (a), including center, shape, and spread.
c. Based on the histogram from Part (a), would it be appropriate to use the Empirical Rule to make statements about the travel time distribution? Explain why or why not.
d. The approximate mean and standard deviation for the travel time distribution are 27 minutes and 24 minutes, respectively. Based on this mean and standard deviation and the fact that travel time cannot be negative, explain why the travel time distribution could not be well approximated by a normal curve.
e. Use the mean and standard deviation given in Part (d) and Chebyshev's Rule to make a statement about
   i. the percentage of travel times that were between 0 and 75 minutes
   ii. the percentage of travel times that were between 0 and 47 minutes
f. How well do the statements in Part (e) based on Chebyshev's Rule agree with the actual percentages for the travel time distribution? (Hint: You can estimate the actual percentages from the given relative frequency distribution.)

4.41 Mobile homes are tightly constructed for energy conservation. This can lead to a buildup of indoor pollutants. The paper "A Survey of Nitrogen Dioxide Levels Inside Mobile Homes" (*Journal of the Air Pollution Control Association* [1988]: 647–651) discussed various aspects of NO_2 concentration in these structures.

a. In one sample of mobile homes in the Los Angeles area, the mean NO_2 concentration in kitchens during the summer was 36.92 ppb, and the standard deviation was 11.34. Making no assumptions about the shape of the NO_2 distribution, what can be said about the percentage of observations between 14.24 and 59.60?
b. Inside what interval is it guaranteed that at least 89% of the concentration observations will lie?
c. In a sample of non–Los Angeles mobile homes, the average kitchen NO_2 concentration during the win-

ter was 24.76 ppb, and the standard deviation was 17.20. Do these values suggest that the histogram of sample observations did not closely resemble a normal curve? (Hint: What is $\bar{x} - 2s$?)

4.42 The article "Taxable Wealth and Alcoholic Beverage Consumption in the United States" (*Psychological Reports* [1994]: 813–814) reported that the mean annual adult consumption of wine was 3.15 gallons and that the standard deviation was 6.09 gallons. Would you use the Empirical Rule to approximate the proportion of adults who consume more than 9.24 gallons (i.e., the proportion of adults whose consumption value exceeds the mean by more than 1 standard deviation)? Explain your reasoning.

4.43 A student took two national aptitude tests. The national average and standard deviation were 475 and 100, respectively, for the first test and 30 and 8, respectively, for the second test. The student scored 625 on the first test and 45 on the second test. Use z scores to determine on which exam the student performed better relative to the other test takers.

4.44 Suppose that your younger sister is applying for entrance to college and has taken the SATs. She scored at the 83rd percentile on the verbal section of the test and at the 94th percentile on the math section of the test. Because you have been studying statistics, she asks you for an interpretation of these values. What would you tell her?

4.45 A sample of concrete specimens of a certain type is selected, and the compressive strength of each specimen is determined. The mean and standard deviation are calculated as $\bar{x} = 3000$ and $s = 500$, and the sample histogram is found to be well approximated by a normal curve.

a. Approximately what percentage of the sample observations are between 2500 and 3500?
b. Approximately what percentage of sample observations are outside the interval from 2000 to 4000?
c. What can be said about the approximate percentage of observations between 2000 and 2500?
d. Why would you not use Chebyshev's Rule to answer the questions posed in Parts (a)–(c)?

4.46 The paper "Modeling and Measurements of Bus Service Reliability" (*Transportation Research* [1978]: 253–256) studied various aspects of bus service and presented data on travel times (in minutes) from several different routes. The accompanying frequency distribution is for bus travel times from origin to destination on one particular route in Chicago during peak morning traffic periods:

Travel Time	Frequency	Relative Frequency
15 to <16	4	.02
16 to <17	0	.00
17 to <18	26	.13
18 to <19	99	.49
19 to <20	36	.18
20 to <21	8	.04
21 to <22	12	.06
22 to <23	0	.00
23 to <24	0	.00
24 to <25	0	.00
25 to <26	16	.08

a. Construct the corresponding histogram.
b. Compute (approximately) the following percentiles:
   i. 86th
   ii. 15th
   iii. 90th
   iv. 95th
   v. 10th

4.47 An advertisement for the "30 inch Wonder" that appeared in the September 1983 issue of the journal *Packaging* claimed that the 30 inch Wonder weighs cases and bags up to 110 pounds and provides accuracy to within 0.25 ounce. Suppose that a 50 ounce weight was repeatedly weighed on this scale and the weight readings recorded. The mean value was 49.5 ounces, and the standard deviation was 0.1. What can be said about the proportion of the time that the scale actually showed a weight that was within 0.25 ounce of the true value of 50 ounces? (Hint: Use Chebyshev's Rule.)

4.48 Suppose that your statistics professor returned your first midterm exam with only a z score written on it. She also told you that a histogram of the scores was approximately normal. How would you interpret each of the following z scores?

a. 2.2
b. 0.4
c. 1.8
d. 1.0
e. 0

4.49 The paper "Answer Changing on Multiple-Choice Tests" (*Journal of Experimental Education* [1980]: 18–21) reported that for a group of 162 college students, the average number of responses changed from the correct answer to an incorrect answer on a test containing 80 multiple-choice items was 1.4. The corresponding standard deviation was reported to be 1.5. Based on this mean and standard deviation, what can you tell about the shape of the distribution of the variable *number of answers changed from right to wrong?* What can you say about the number of students who changed at least six answers from correct to incorrect?

4.50 The average reading speed of students completing a speed-reading course is 450 words per minute (wpm). If the standard deviation is 70 wpm, find the z score associated with each of the following reading speeds.

a. 320 wpm
b. 475 wpm
c. 420 wpm
d. 610 wpm

4.51 ● The following data values are 2009 per capita expenditures on public libraries for each of the 50 U.S. states (from www.statemaster.com):

16.84	16.17	11.74	11.11	8.65	7.69	7.48
7.03	6.20	6.20	5.95	5.72	5.61	5.47
5.43	5.33	4.84	4.63	4.59	4.58	3.92
3.81	3.75	3.74	3.67	3.40	3.35	3.29
3.18	3.16	2.91	2.78	2.61	2.58	2.45
2.30	2.19	2.06	1.78	1.54	1.31	1.26
1.20	1.19	1.09	0.70	0.66	0.54	0.49
0.30	0.01					

a. Summarize this data set with a frequency distribution. Construct the corresponding histogram.
b. Use the histogram in Part (a) to find approximate values of the following percentiles:
i. 50th
ii. 70th
iii. 10th
iv. 90th
v. 40th

4.52 The accompanying table gives the mean and standard deviation of reaction times (in seconds) for each of two different stimuli:

	Stimulus 1	Stimulus 2
Mean	6.0	3.6
Standard deviation	1.2	0.8

If your reaction time is 4.2 seconds for the first stimulus and 1.8 seconds for the second stimulus, to which stimulus are you reacting (compared to other individuals) relatively more quickly?

4.5 Interpreting and Communicating the Results of Statistical Analyses

As was the case with the graphical displays of Chapter 3, the primary function of the descriptive tools introduced in this chapter is to help us better understand the variables under study. If we have collected data on the amount of money students spend on textbooks at a particular university, most likely we did so because we wanted to learn about the distribution of this variable (amount spent on textbooks) for the population of interest (in this case, students at the university). Numerical measures of center and spread and boxplots help to inform us, and they also allow us to communicate to others what we have learned from the data.

Communicating the Results of Statistical Analyses

When reporting the results of a data analysis, it is common to start with descriptive information about the variables of interest. It is always a good idea to start with a graphical display of the data, and, as we saw in Chapter 3, graphical displays of numerical data are usually described in terms of center, variability, and shape. The numerical measures of this chapter can help you to be more specific in describing the center and spread of a data set.

When describing center and spread, you must first decide which measures to use. Common choices are to use either the sample mean and standard deviation or the sample median and interquartile range (and maybe even a boxplot) to describe center and spread. Because the mean and standard deviation can be sensitive to extreme values in the data set, they are best used when the distribution shape is approximately symmetric and when there are few outliers. If the data set is noticeably skewed or if there are outliers, then the observations are more spread out in one part of the distribution than in the others. In this situation, a five-number summary or a boxplot conveys more information than the mean and standard deviation do.

Interpreting the Results of Statistical Analyses

It is relatively rare to find raw data in published sources. Typically, only a few numerical summary quantities are reported. We must be able to interpret these values and understand what they tell us about the underlying data set.

For example, a university conducted an investigation of the amount of time required to enter the information contained in an application for admission into the university computer system. One of the individuals who performs this task was asked to note starting time and completion time for 50 randomly selected application forms. The resulting entry times (in minutes) were summarized using the mean, median, and standard deviation:

$$\bar{x} = 7.854$$
$$\text{median} = 7.423$$
$$s = 2.129$$

What do these summary values tell us about entry times? The average time required to enter admissions data was 7.854 minutes, but the relatively large standard deviation suggests that many observations differ substantially from this mean. The median tells us that half of the applications required less than 7.423 minutes to enter. The fact that the mean exceeds the median suggests that some unusually large values in the data set affected the value of the mean. This last conjecture is confirmed by the stem-and-leaf display of the data given in Figure 4.19.

4	8
5	02345679
6	00001234566779
7	223556688
8	23334
9	002
10	011168
11	134
12	2
13	
14	3

Stem: Ones
Leaf: Tenths

FIGURE 4.19 Stem-and-leaf display of data entry times.

The administrators conducting the data-entry study looked at the outlier 14.3 minutes and at the other relatively large values in the data set; they found that the five largest values came from applications that were entered before lunch. After talking with the individual who entered the data, the administrators speculated that morning entry times might differ from afternoon entry times because there tended to be more distractions and interruptions (phone calls, etc.) during the morning hours, when the admissions office generally was busier. When morning and afternoon entry times were separated, the following summary statistics resulted:

Morning (based on $n = 20$ applications):	$\bar{x} = 9.093$	median = 8.743	$s = 2.329$
Afternoon (based on $n = 30$ applications):	$\bar{x} = 7.027$	median = 6.737	$s = 1.529$

Clearly, the average entry time is higher for applications entered in the morning; also, the individual entry times differ more from one another in the mornings than in the afternoons (because the standard deviation for morning entry times, 2.329, is about 1.5 times as large as 1.529, the standard deviation for afternoon entry times).

What to Look for in Published Data

Here are a few questions to ask yourself when you interpret numerical summary measures.

- Is the chosen summary measure appropriate for the type of data collected? In particular, watch for inappropriate use of the mean and standard deviation with categorical data that has simply been coded numerically.
- If both the mean and the median are reported, how do the two values compare? What does this suggest about the distribution of values in the data set? If only the mean or the median was used, was the appropriate measure selected?
- Is the standard deviation large or small? Is the value consistent with your expectations regarding variability? What does the value of the standard deviation tell you about the variable being summarized?
- Can anything of interest be said about the values in the data set by applying Chebyshev's Rule or the Empirical Rule?

For example, consider a study that investigated whether people tend to spend more money when they are paying with a credit card than when they are paying with cash. The authors of the paper "Monopoly Money: The Effect of Payment Coupling and Form on Spending Behavior" (*Journal of Experimental Psychology: Applied* [2008]: 213–225) randomly assigned each of 114 volunteers to one of two experimental groups. Participants were given a menu for a new restaurant that showed nine menu items. They were then asked to estimate the amount they would be willing to pay for each item. A price index was computed for each participant by averaging the nine prices assigned. The difference between the two experimental groups was that the menu viewed by one group showed a credit card logo at the bottom of the menu while there was no credit card logo on the menu that those in the other group viewed. The following passage appeared in the results section of the paper:

> On average, participants were willing to pay more when the credit card logo was present (M = \$4.53, SD = 1.15) than when it was absent (M = \$4.11, SD = 1.06). Thus, even though consumers were not explicitly informed which payment mode they would be using, the mere presence of a credit card logo increased the price that they were willing to pay.

The price index data was also described as mound shaped with no outliers for each of the two groups. Because price index (the average of the prices that a participant assigned to the nine menu items) is a numerical variable, the mean and standard deviation are reasonable measures for summarizing center and spread in the data set. Although the mean for the credit-card-logo group is higher than the mean for the no-logo group, the two standard deviations are similar, indicating similar variability in price index from person to person for the two groups.

Because the distribution of price index values was mound shaped for each of the two groups, we can use the Empirical Rule to tell us a bit more about the distribution. For example, for those in the group who viewed the menu with a credit card logo, approximately 95% of the price index values would have been between

$$4.53 - 2(1.15) = 4.53 - 2.3 = 2.23$$

and

$$4.53 + 2(1.15) = 4.53 + 2.30 = 6.83.$$

A Word to the Wise: Cautions and Limitations

When computing or interpreting numerical descriptive measures, you need to keep in mind the following:

1. Measures of center don't tell all. Although measures of center, such as the mean and the median, do give us a sense of what might be considered a typical value for a variable, this is only one characteristic of a data set. Without additional information about variability and distribution shape, we don't really know much about the behavior of the variable.
2. Data distributions with different shapes can have the same mean and standard deviation. For example, consider the following two histograms:

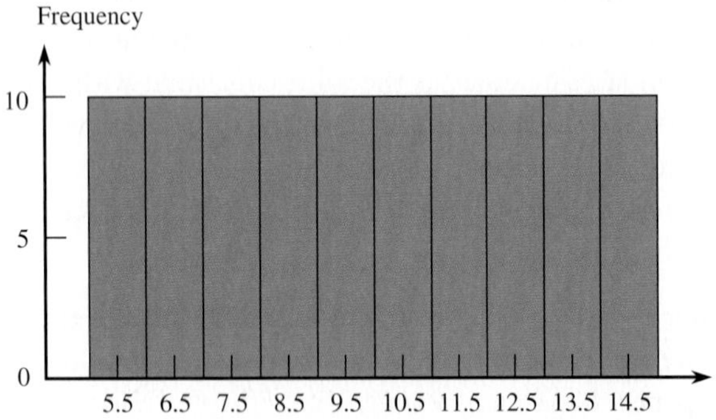

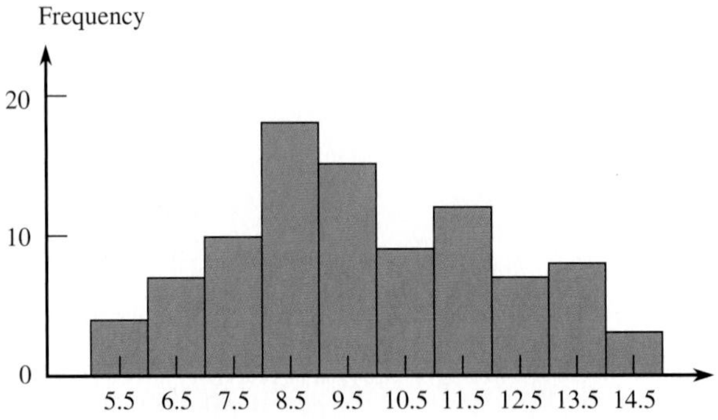

   Both histograms summarize data sets that have a mean of 10 and a standard deviation of 2, yet they have different shapes.
3. Both the mean and the standard deviation are sensitive to extreme values in a data set, especially if the sample size is small. If a data distribution is skewed or if the data set has outliers, the median and the interquartile range may be a better choice for describing center and spread.
4. Measures of center and variability describe the values of the variable studied, not the frequencies in a frequency distribution or the heights of the bars in a histogram. For example, consider the following two frequency distributions and histograms:

FREQUENCY DISTRIBUTION A		FREQUENCY DISTRIBUTION B	
Value	Frequency	Value	Frequency
1	10	1	5
2	10	2	10
3	10	3	20
4	10	4	10
5	10	5	5

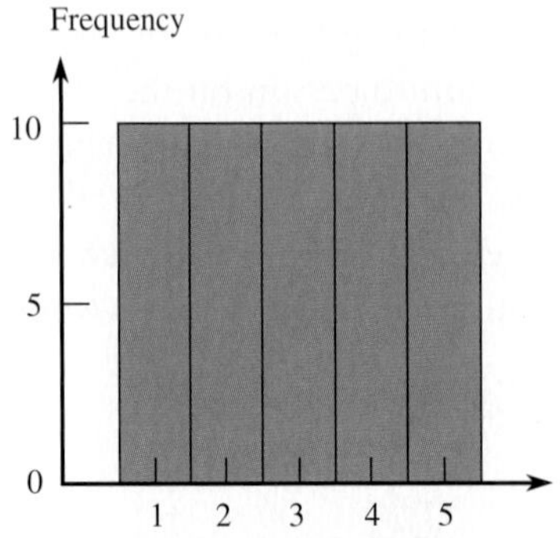

Histogram A

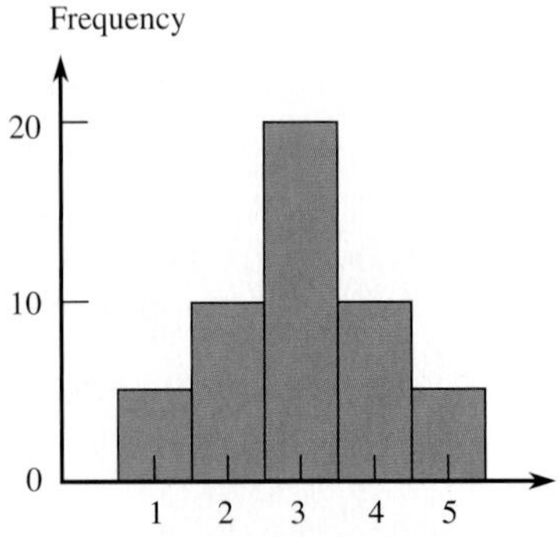

Histogram B

There is more variability in the data summarized by Frequency Distribution and Histogram A than in the data summarized by Frequency Distribution and Histogram B. This is because the values of the variable described by Histogram and Frequency Distribution B are more concentrated near the mean than are the values for the variable described by Histogram and Frequency Distribution A. Don't be misled by the fact that there is no variability in the frequencies in Frequency Distribution A or the heights of the bars in Histogram A.

5. Be careful with boxplots based on small sample sizes. Boxplots convey information about center, variability, and shape, but when the sample size is small, you should be hesitant to overinterpret shape information. It is really not possible to decide whether a data distribution is symmetric or skewed if only a small sample of observations from the distribution is available.
6. Not all distributions are normal (or even approximately normal). Be cautious in applying the Empirical Rule in situations in which you are not convinced that the data distribution is at least approximately normal. Using the Empirical Rule in such situations can lead to incorrect statements.
7. Watch out for outliers! Unusual observations in a data set often provide important information about the variable under study, so it is important to consider outliers in addition to describing what is typical. Outliers can also be problematic—both because the values of some descriptive measures are influenced by outliers and because some of the methods for drawing conclusions from data may not be appropriate if the data set has outliers.

EXERCISES 4.53 - 4.54

4.53 The authors of the paper "Delayed Time to Defibrillation after In-Hospital Cardiac Arrest" (*New England Journal of Medicine* [2008]: 9–16) described a study of how survival is related to the length of time it takes from the time of a heart attack to the administration of defibrillation therapy. The following is a statement from the paper:

> We identified 6789 patients from 369 hospitals who had in-hospital cardiac arrest due to ventricular fibrillation (69.7%) or pulseless ventricular trachycardia (30.3%). Overall, the median time to defibrillation was 1 minute (interquartile range [was] 3 minutes).

Data from the paper on time to defibrillation (in minutes) for these 6789 patients was used to produce the following Minitab output and boxplot.

a. Why is there no lower whisker in the given boxplot?

b. How is it possible for the median, the lower quartile, and the minimum value in the data set to all be equal? (Note—this is why you do not see a median line in the box part of the boxplot.)

c. The authors of the paper considered a time to defibrillation of greater than 2 minutes as unacceptable. Based on the given boxplot and summary statistics, is it possible that the percentage of patients having an unacceptable time to defibrillation is greater than 50%? Greater than 25%? Less than 25%? Explain.

Descriptive Statistics: Time to Defibrillation

Variable	N	Mean	StDev	Minimum	Q1	Median	Q3	Maximum
Time	6789	2.3737	2.0713	1.0000	1.0000	1.0000	3.0000	7.0000

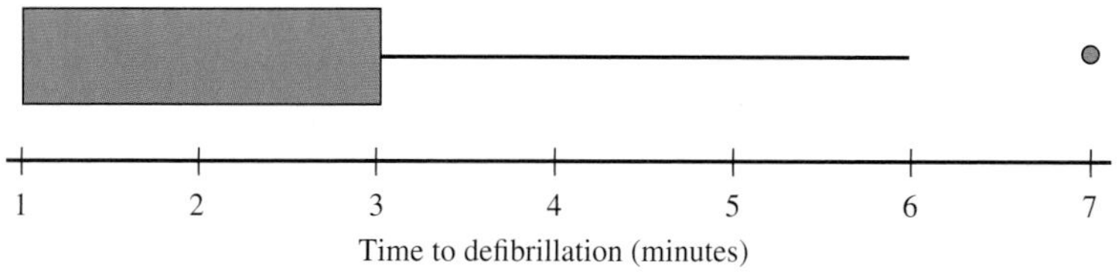

d. Is the outlier shown at 7 a mild outlier or an extreme outlier?

4.54 The paper "Portable Social Groups: Willingness to Communicate, Interpersonal Communication Gratifications, and Cell Phone Use among Young Adults" (*International Journal of Mobile Communications* [2007]: 139–156) describes a study of young adult cell phone use patterns.

a. Comment on the following quote from the paper. Do you agree with the authors?

Seven sections of an Introduction to Mass Communication course at a large southern university were surveyed in the spring and fall of 2003. The sample was chosen because it offered an excellent representation of the population under study—young adults.

b. Below is another quote from the paper. In this quote, the author reports the mean number of minutes of cell phone use per week for those who participated in the survey. What additional information would have been provided about cell phone use behavior if the author had also reported the standard deviation?

Based on respondent estimates, users spent an average of 629 minutes (about 10.5 hours) per week using their cell phone on or off line for any reason.

ACTIVITY 4.1 Collecting and Summarizing Numerical Data

In this activity, you will work in groups to collect data that will provide information about how many hours per week, on average, students at your school spend engaged in a particular activity. You will use the sampling plan designed in Activity 2.1 to collect the data.

1. With your group, pick one of the following activities to be the focus of your study:
   i. Surfing the web
   ii. Studying or doing homework
   iii. Watching TV
   iv. Exercising
   v. Sleeping

   or you may choose a different activity, *subject to the approval of your instructor.*
2. Use the plan developed in Activity 2.1 to collect data on the variable you have chosen for your study.
3. Summarize the resulting data using both numerical and graphical summaries. Be sure to address both center and variability.
4. Write a short article for your school paper summarizing your findings regarding student behavior. Your article should include both numerical and graphical summaries.

ACTIVITY 4.2 Airline Passenger Weights

The article "Airlines Should Weigh Passengers, Bags, NTSB Says" (*USA Today*, February 27, 2004) states that the National Transportation Safety Board recommended that airlines weigh passengers and their bags to prevent overloaded planes from attempting to take off. This recommendation was the result of an investigation into the crash of a small commuter plane in 2003, which determined that too much weight contributed to the crash.

Rather than weighing passengers, airlines currently use estimates of average passenger and luggage weights. After the 2003 accident, this estimate was increased by 10 pounds for passengers and 5 pounds for luggage. Although an airplane can fly if it is somewhat overweight if all systems are working properly, if one of the plane's engines fails an overweight plane becomes difficult for the pilot to control.

Assuming that the new estimate of the average passenger weight is accurate, discuss the following questions with a partner and then write a paragraph that answers these questions.

1. What role does variability in passenger weights play in creating a potentially dangerous situation for an airline?
2. Would an airline have a lower risk of a potentially dangerous situation if the variability in passenger weight is large or if it is small?

ACTIVITY 4.3 Boxplot Shapes

In this activity, you will investigate the relationship between boxplot shapes and the corresponding five-number summary. The accompanying figure shows four boxplots, labeled A–D. Also given are 4 five-number summaries, labeled I–IV. Match each five-number summary to the appropriate boxplot. Note that scales are not included on the boxplots, so you will have to think about what the five-number summary implies about characteristics of the boxplot.

Five-Number Summaries

	I	II	III	IV
Minimum	40	4	0.0	10
Lower quartile	45	8	0.1	34
Median	71	16	0.9	44
Upper quartile	88	25	2.2	82
Maximum	106	30	5.1	132

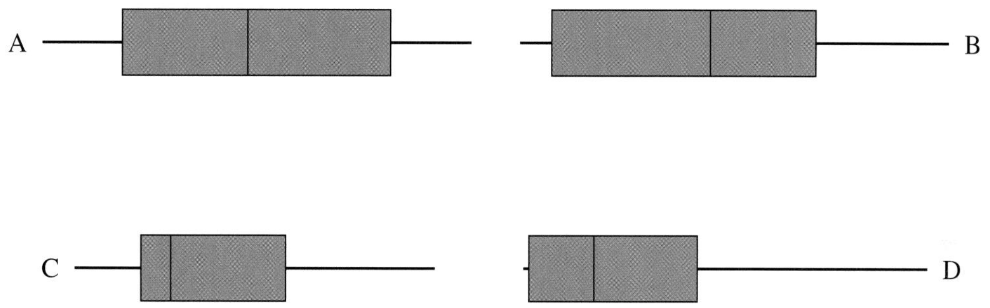

Summary of Key Concepts and Formulas

TERM OR FORMULA	COMMENT
$x_1, x_2, \ldots, x_n$	Notation for sample data consisting of observations on a variable *x*, where *n* is the sample size.
Sample mean, $\bar{x}$	The most frequently used measure of center of a sample. It can be very sensitive to the presence of even a single outlier (unusually large or small observation).
Population mean, μ	The average *x* value in the entire population.
Sample median	The middle value in the ordered list of sample observations. (For *n* even, the median is the average of the two middle values.) It is very insensitive to outliers.
Trimmed mean	A measure of center in which the observations are first ordered from smallest to largest, one or more observations are deleted from each end, and the remaining ones are averaged. In terms of sensitivity to outliers, it is a compromise between the mean and the median.
Deviations from the mean: $x_1 - \bar{x}, x_2 - \bar{x}, \ldots, x_n - \bar{x}$	Quantities used to assess variability in a sample. Except for rounding effects, $\sum(x - \bar{x}) = 0$.
The sample variance $s^2 = \dfrac{\sum(x - \bar{x})^2}{n - 1}$ and standard deviation $s = \sqrt{s^2}$	The most frequently used measures of variability for sample data.

TERM OR FORMULA	COMMENT
The population variance σ^2 and standard deviation σ	Measures of variability for the entire population.
Quartiles and the interquartile range	The lower quartile separates the smallest 25% of the data from the remaining 75%, and the upper quartile separates the largest 25% from the smallest 75%. The interquartile range (iqr), a measure of variability less sensitive to outliers than *s*, is the difference between the upper and lower quartiles.
Chebyshev's Rule	This rule states that for any number $k \geq 1$, *at least* $100\left(1 - \frac{1}{k^2}\right)\%$ of the observations in *any* data set are within *k* standard deviations of the mean. It is typically conservative in that the actual percentages often considerably exceed the stated lower bound.
Empirical Rule	This rule gives the approximate percentage of observations within 1 standard deviation (68%), 2 standard deviations (95%), and 3 standard deviations (99.7%) of the mean when the histogram is well approximated by a normal curve.
z score	This quantity gives the distance between an observation and the mean expressed as a certain number of standard deviations. It is positive (negative) if the observation lies above (below) the mean.
*r*th percentile	The value such that *r*% of the observations in the data set fall at or below that value.
Five-number summary	A summary of a data set that includes the minimum, lower quartile, median, upper quartile, and maximum.
Boxplot	A picture that conveys information about the most important features of a numerical data set: center, spread, extent of skewness, and presence of outliers.

Chapter Review Exercises 4.55 - 4.73

4.55 Research by the Food and Drug Administration (FDA) shows that acrylamide (a possible cancer-causing substance) forms in high-carbohydrate foods cooked at high temperatures and that acrylamide levels can vary widely even within the same brand of food (Associated Press, December 6, 2002). FDA scientists analyzed McDonald's French fries purchased at seven different locations and found the following acrylamide levels:

497 193 328 155 326 245 270

a. Compute the mean acrylamide level and the seven deviations from the mean.

b. Verify that, except for the effect of rounding, the sum of the deviations from mean is equal to 0 for this data set. (If you rounded the sample mean or the deviations, your sum may not be exactly zero, but it should be close to zero if you have computed the deviations correctly.)

c. Calculate the variance and standard deviation for this data set.

4.56 ● The technical report "Ozone Season Emissions by State" (U.S. Environmental Protection Agency, 2002) gave the following nitrous oxide emissions (in thousands of tons) for the 48 states in the continental U.S. states:

76	22	40	7	30	5	6	136	72	33	0
89	136	39	92	40	13	27	1	63	33	60
27	16	63	32	20	2	15	36	19	39	130
40	4	85	38	7	68	151	32	34	0	6
43	89	34	0							

Use these data to construct a boxplot that shows outliers. Write a few sentences describing the important characteristics of the boxplot.

4.57 The *San Luis Obispo Telegram-Tribune* (October 1, 1994) reported the following monthly salaries for supervisors from six different counties: \$5354 (Kern), \$5166 (Monterey), \$4443 (Santa Cruz), \$4129 (Santa Barbara), \$2500 (Placer), and \$2220 (Merced). San Luis Obispo County supervisors are supposed to be paid the average of the two counties among these six in the middle of the salary range. Which measure of center determines this salary, and what is its value? Why is the other measure of center featured in this section not as favorable to these supervisors (although it might appeal to taxpayers)?

4.58 ● A sample of 26 offshore oil workers took part in a simulated escape exercise, resulting in the accompanying data on time (in seconds) to complete the escape ("Oxygen Consumption and Ventilation During Escape from an Offshore Platform," *Ergonomics* [1997]: 281–292):

389	356	359	363	375	424	325	394	402
373	373	370	364	366	364	325	339	393
392	369	374	359	356	403	334	397	

a. Construct a stem-and-leaf display of the data. Will the sample mean or the sample median be larger for this data set?
b. Calculate the values of the sample mean and median.
c. By how much could the largest time be increased without affecting the value of the sample median? By how much could this value be decreased without affecting the sample median?

4.59 Because some homes have selling prices that are much higher than most, the median price is usually used to describe a "typical" home price for a given location. The three accompanying quotes are all from the *San Luis Obispo Tribune*, but each gives a different interpretation of the median price of a home in San Luis Obispo County. Comment on each of these statements. (Look carefully. At least one of the statements is incorrect.)

a. "So we have gone from 23% to 27% of county residents who can afford the median priced home at \$278,380 in SLO County. That means that half of the homes in this county cost less than \$278,380 and half cost more." (October 11, 2001)

b. "The county's median price rose to \$285,170 in the fourth quarter, a 9.6% increase from the same period a year ago, the report said. (The median represents the midpoint of a range.)" (February 13, 2002)

c. "'Your median is going to creep up above \$300,000 if there is nothing available below \$300,000,' Walker said." (February 26, 2002)

4.60 ● Although bats are not known for their eyesight, they are able to locate prey (mainly insects) by emitting high-pitched sounds and listening for echoes. A paper appearing in *Animal Behaviour* ("The Echolocation of Flying Insects by Bats" [1960]: 141–154) gave the following distances (in centimeters) at which a bat first detected a nearby insect:

62	23	27	56	52	34	42	40	68	45	83

a. Compute the sample mean distance at which the bat first detects an insect.
b. Compute the sample variance and standard deviation for this data set. Interpret these values.

4.61 For the data in Exercise 4.60, subtract 10 from each sample observation. For the new set of values, compute the mean and the deviations from the mean. How do these deviations compare to the deviations from the mean for the original sample? How does s^2 for the new values compare to s^2 for the old values? In general, what effect does subtracting (or adding) the same number to each observation have on s^2 and s? Explain.

4.62 For the data of Exercise 4.60, multiply each data value by 10. How does s for the new values compare to s for the original values? More generally, what happens to s if each observation is multiplied by the same positive constant c?

4.63 ● The percentage of juice lost after thawing for 19 different strawberry varieties appeared in the article "Evaluation of Strawberry Cultivars with Different Degrees of Resistance to Red Scale" (*Fruit Varieties Journal* [1991]: 12–17):

46 51 44 50 33 46 60 41 55 46 53 53
42 44 50 54 46 41 48

a. Are there any observations that are mild outliers? Extreme outliers?
b. Construct a boxplot, and comment on the important features of the plot.

4.64 ● The risk of developing iron deficiency is especially high during pregnancy. Detecting such a deficiency is complicated by the fact that some methods for determining iron status can be affected by the state of pregnancy itself. Consider the following data on transferrin receptor concentration for a sample of women with laboratory evidence of overt iron-deficiency anemia ("Serum Transferrin Receptor for the Detection of Iron Deficiency in Pregnancy," *American Journal of Clinical Nutrition* [1991]: 1077–1081):

15.2	9.3	7.6	11.9	10.4	9.7
20.4	9.4	11.5	16.2	9.4	8.3

Compute the values of the sample mean and median. Why are these values different here? Which one do you regard as more representative of the sample, and why?

4.65 ● The paper "The Pedaling Technique of Elite Endurance Cyclists" (*International Journal of Sport Biomechanics* [1991]: 29–53) reported the following data on single-leg power at a high workload:

244 191 160 187 180 176 174 205 211
183 211 180 194 200

a. Calculate and interpret the sample mean and median.
b. Suppose that the first observation had been 204, not 244. How would the mean and median change?
c. Calculate a trimmed mean by eliminating the smallest and the largest sample observations. What is the corresponding trimming percentage?
d. Suppose that the largest observation had been 204 rather than 244. How would the trimmed mean in Part (c) change? What if the largest value had been 284?

4.66 The paper cited in Exercise 4.65 also reported values of single-leg power for a low workload. The sample mean for $n = 13$ observations was $\bar{x} = 119.8$ (actually 119.7692), and the 14th observation, somewhat of an outlier, was 159. What is the value of $\bar{x}$ for the entire sample?

4.67 ● The amount of aluminum contamination (in parts per million) in plastic was determined for a sample of 26 plastic specimens, resulting in the following data ("The Log Normal Distribution for Modeling Quality Data When the Mean Is Near Zero," *Journal of Quality Technology* [1990]: 105–110):

30	30	60	63	70	79	87	90	101
102	115	118	119	119	120	125	140	145
172	182	183	191	222	244	291	511	

Construct a boxplot that shows outliers, and comment on the interesting features of this plot.

4.68 ● The article "Can We Really Walk Straight?" (*American Journal of Physical Anthropology* [1992]: 19–27) reported on an experiment in which each of 20 healthy men was asked to walk as straight as possible to a target 60 m away at normal speed. Consider the following data on cadence (number of strides per second):

0.95 0.85 0.92 0.95 0.93 0.86 1.00 0.92
0.85 0.81 0.78 0.93 0.93 1.05 0.93 1.06
1.06 0.96 0.81 0.96

Use the methods developed in this chapter to summarize the data; include an interpretation or discussion whenever appropriate. (Note: The author of the paper used a rather sophisticated statistical analysis to conclude that people cannot walk in a straight line and suggested several explanations for this.)

4.69 ● The article "Comparing the Costs of Major Hotel Franchises" (*Real Estate Review* [1992]: 46–51) gave the following data on franchise cost as a percentage of total room revenue for chains of three different types:

Budget	2.7	2.8	3.8	3.8	4.0	4.1	5.5
	5.9	6.7	7.0	7.2	7.2	7.5	7.5
	7.7	7.9	7.9	8.1	8.2	8.5	
Midrange	1.5	4.0	6.6	6.7	7.0	7.2	7.2
	7.4	7.8	8.0	8.1	8.3	8.6	9.0
First-class	1.8	5.8	6.0	6.6	6.6	6.6	7.1
	7.2	7.5	7.6	7.6	7.8	7.8	8.2
	9.6						

Construct a boxplot for each type of hotel, and comment on interesting features, similarities, and differences.

4.70 ● The accompanying data on milk volume (in grams per day) were taken from the paper "Smoking During Pregnancy and Lactation and Its Effects on Breast Milk Volume" (*American Journal of Clinical Nutrition* [1991]: 1011–1016):

Smoking	621	793	593	545	753	655
mothers	895	767	714	598	693	
Nonsmoking	947	945	1086	1202	973	981
mothers	930	745	903	899	961	

Compare and contrast the two samples

4.71 The *Los Angeles Times* (July 17, 1995) reported that in a sample of 364 lawsuits in which punitive damages were awarded, the sample median damage award was $50,000, and the sample mean was $775,000. What does this suggest about the distribution of values in the sample?

4.72 ● Age at diagnosis for each of 20 patients under treatment for meningitis was given in the paper "Penicillin in the Treatment of Meningitis" (*Journal of the American Medical Association* [1984]: 1870–1874). The ages (in years) were as follows:

18 18 25 19 23 20 69 18 21 18 20 18
18 20 18 19 28 17 18 18

a. Calculate the values of the sample mean and the standard deviation.
b. Calculate the 10% trimmed mean. How does the value of the trimmed mean compare to that of the sample mean? Which would you recommend as a measure of center? Explain.
c. Compute the upper quartile, the lower quartile, and the interquartile range.
d. Are there any mild or extreme outliers present in this data set?
e. Construct the boxplot for this data set.

4.73 Suppose that the distribution of scores on an exam is closely described by a normal curve with mean 100. The 16th percentile of this distribution is 80.

a. What is the 84th percentile?
b. What is the approximate value of the standard deviation of exam scores?
c. What z score is associated with an exam score of 90?
d. What percentile corresponds to an exam score of 140?
e. Do you think there were many scores below 40? Explain.

Bold exercises answered in back ● Data set available online ✦ Video Solution available

Graphing Calculator Explorations

EXPLORATION 4.1 Quartiles

In this exploration, we bring up a delicate statistical point. Statisticians are not in complete agreement about the best way to calculate quartiles, and because of this, you may encounter calculators or computer software packages that calculate quartiles differently. These different methods lead to potentially different values for the quartiles computed by calculators and computer software, and therefore to potentially different results for the interquartile range. It is possible that this *may* result in different observations being identified as outliers. This is a good news/bad news situation. The bad news: you may be confused by your textbook, software, and calculator giving you different answers when you make boxplots. The good news outweighs the bad: unless you have a very small data set the differences among the different methods for calculating quartiles are of little practical importance.

However, you should be aware of what your calculator and software actually do. With this knowledge you will be more comfortable in deciding when an observed discrepancy is likely to be due to the differing definitions and not an error in data entry. To check your calculator and computer software, use the following sets of data, designed to highlight any differences. The answers using the definitions in the text are in parentheses.

Test Data Set #1: 10, 20, 30, 40
(lower quartile = 15, median = 25, upper quartile = 35)

Test Data Set #2: 10, 20, 30, 40, 50
(lower quartile = 15, median = 30, upper quartile = 45)

Test Data Set #3: 10, 20, 30, 40, 50, 60
(lower quartile = 20, median = 35, upper quartile = 50)

Test Data Set #4: 10, 20, 30, 40, 50, 60, 70
(lower quartile = 20, median = 40, upper quartile = 60)

Did you obtain the same values using your calculator? If so, we and your calculator are using the same definitions. But, what if your calculator gives different quartiles? In that case, do not worry—remember, when analyzing real data, the method used to compute quartiles is not of great concern.

EXPLORATION 4.2 Boxplots

Calculators differ in their boxplot capabilities. Your calculator may graph a skeletal boxplot only, a modified boxplot only, or it may offer you a choice. If your calculator presents a modified boxplot and you need to sketch a skeletal boxplot you can simply extend the whiskers of the modified boxplot to include all the outliers.

If your calculator plots only a skeletal boxplot, you are still OK. Your calculator will have already calculated the quartiles and the median of the data. To sketch a modified boxplot, you need only locate this information and then decide which, if any, of the data values are outliers.

Your calculator will have a screen that displays a statistical summary for the data. Such quantities as the minimum and maximum data element, the mean, median, and standard deviation, and the lower and upper quartile will be shown. Using this information you can do the math and see if there are any outliers. You will need to calculate the following boundaries by hand.

$$\text{upper quartile} + 1.5 \text{ iqr} = \text{upper quartile} + 1.5\,(\text{upper quartile} - \text{lower quartile})$$
$$\text{lower quartile} - 1.5 \text{ iqr} = \text{lower quartile} - 1.5\,(\text{upper quartile} - \text{lower quartile})$$

Now look to see if any of the observations lie above or below the computed boundaries. If so, they are outliers.

If there are no outliers you are done! The skeletal boxplot and the modified boxplot will be the same. If your calculations indicate there are outliers in your data, find the largest observation that is not an outlier, and the smallest observation that is not an outlier. Any observations larger and smaller than these, respectively, will be outliers. Finding the outliers "by inspection"—that is, by scanning up and down the list—is tedious and error-laden. Use your calculator to sort the data, making it very easy to spot outliers by looking at either end of the data list.

Your calculator will sort the data from small to large or large to small; for the purpose of identifying outliers, it does not matter which you choose. The keystroke sequence for sorting data on your particular calculator can be found in your calculator manual; look in the chapter on "lists" or in the index under "sorting." Once the data is sorted, finding the outliers by inspection is very easy. A final suggestion before you do this: copy the numbers to a separate list and work with that list. Then, if you inadvertently mess something up, you still have the original data.

EXPLORATION 4.3 z scores

Despite the usefulness of standardized scores in general and z scores in particular, there will not be a z score function on your calculator. Suppose that you wanted to compute the z scores corresponding to each observation in a data set consisting of 20 values. You might worry that this would require mind-numbing and repetitious calculations—subtracting the mean from every value and then dividing each result by the standard deviation. Fortunately, this is not the case. Instead of 20 sets of calculations, you can perform one calculation on the whole list of data! Moreover, the keystrokes that will work for lists mirror the keystrokes for working with individual observations.

To demonstrate how this is done, enter the data in Figure 4.20(a). After entering the data, we need to find the mean and sample standard deviation. These values are $\bar{x} = 3.0$, $s = 1.58113883$. (Your calculator may not display all these digits, but it knows they are there!)

At this point, you can convert all the raw scores to z scores by performing arithmetic on the whole list. You can also store the results in another list without losing your original data. Again, your required keystrokes may differ, but they will accomplish the following:

1. Subtract the mean from each value in List1 to get the deviations.
2. Divide the deviations by the standard deviation.
3. Store the results of these calculations in List2.

The sequence of keystrokes will probably be very similar to this:

$$(\text{List1} - 3.0) \div 1.58113883 \rightarrow \text{List2}$$

Some calculators may use the slash "/" to indicate division, and some may use the equal sign "=" to indicate that the results should be stored in a second list. After performing the keystrokes appropriate for your calculator, you should see the results shown in List2 of Figure 4.20(b). If the lists you have chosen are next to each other on the screen, you can easily compare the raw data with the z scores.

List1
1.0
2.0
3.0
4.0
5.0

(a)

List2
−1.265
−0.6325
0.0
0.63246
1.2649

(b)

FIGURE 4.20
Original data and z scores.

You may be able to save a few more keystrokes by "recalling" the mean and standard deviation from the calculator memory, although this is probably a matter of style and individual taste. If you have not done any intervening statistical calculations since you calculated the mean and standard deviation, these values are still stored in the calculator memory. If you wish, you may recall those values from the calculator's memory rather than key in the numbers. These values can be inserted in your calculations in place of the actual numbers by pressing the appropriate keystroke sequence.

This capability typically involves using a "VARS" key, short for "variables." (The Texas Instruments TI-8x series calculators use VARS, as does the Casio CFX-9850Ga+. This capability may exist under different names with different calculators; consult your manual!) For example, on the Texas Instruments TI-84, you would press

VARS . . . Statistics . . . S_x . . . ENTER

to recall the sample standard deviation. In the discussion to follow, the keystroke VARS$\bar{x}$ will stand for the particular sequence to recall the sample mean, and VARSs will stand for the particular sequence to recall the sample standard deviation.

With this symbolism in mind, the sequence of keystrokes using the recall capabilities of your calculator would transform

(List1 − 3.0) ÷ 1.58113883 → List2

into a keystroke sequence like this:

(List1 − VARS$\bar{x}$) ÷ VARSs → List2.

The recall capability is a very nice feature, but we have found that individuals differ in their preferences about whether to use the VARS capabilities or just key in the digits when performing arithmetic operations with lists. We encourage you to try both ways and use the method with which you are more comfortable.

AP* Review Questions for Chapter 4

1. A study has been carried out to compare the effectiveness of four different diets on weight loss. Each of 200 people are randomly assigned to one of the four diets for a period of 6 weeks. The distributions of the amounts of weight lost for each diet are summarized in the histograms at the bottom of the page.

   One way to compare the diets would be to compare the mean weight loss for each diet. Order the diets from *largest* to *smallest* using the mean weight lost.

   (A) 2, 1, 4, 3
   (B) 3, 2, 4, 1
   (C) 2, 4, 1, 3
   (D) 2, 1, 3, 4
   (E) 3, 2, 1, 4

2. The commute times (in minutes) for a sample of 23 commuters in a metropolitan area are summarized in the stem-and-leaf display below.

   Leaf Unit = 1.0

0	6
1	258
2	235
3	01257
4	01224455678

   Determine the mean and median commute time for this sample.

   (A) $\bar{x} = 2$, median $= 2$
   (B) $\bar{x} = 3.91$, median $= 2$
   (C) $\bar{x} = 3.91$, median $= 4$
   (D) $\bar{x} = 33.48$, median $= 37$
   (E) $\bar{x} = 37$, median $= 37$

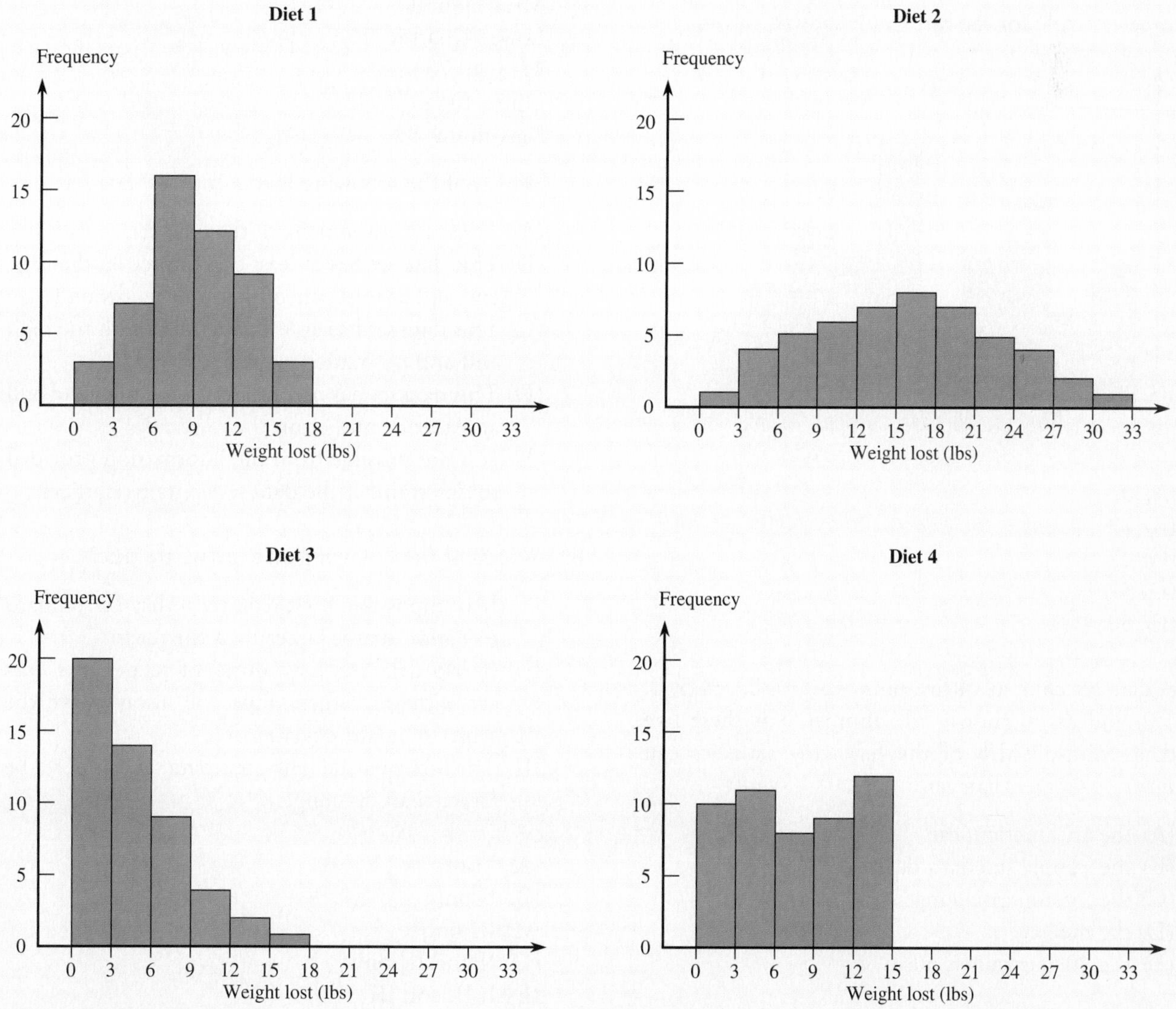

*AP and the Advanced Placement Program are registered trademarks of the College Entrance Examination Board, which was not involved in the production of, and does not endorse, this product.

3. California fishermen fishing for spiny lobster are allowed to keep only lobsters with a carapace length of 3.25 inches or longer. (The carapace length is measured from the rear edge of the eye socket to the rear edge of the body shell.) Any lobster smaller than 3.25 inches must be returned to the sea. Suppose that lobster carapace lengths have a distribution that is approximately normal with a mean of 5.50 inches and a standard deviation of 2.25 inches. Approximately what proportion of lobsters will have to be returned to the sea?

(A) 16%
(B) 32%
(C) 50%
(D) 68%
(E) 84%

4. Which of the following is closest to the value of the upper quartile for the histogram shown?

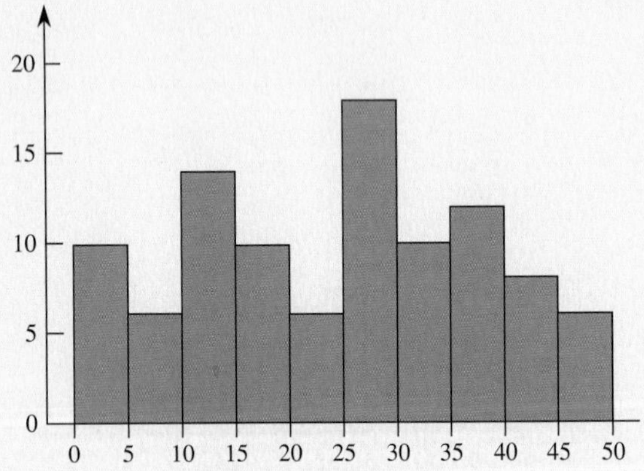

(A) 0
(B) 12
(C) 27
(D) 37
(E) 50

5. A data set consists of five numbers: −6.0, −4.5, 0, 5.0, and an unknown 5th number. For these five data points, which of the following statistics can *never* be greater than zero?

(A) the arithmetic mean
(B) the sample standard deviation
(C) the interquartile range
(D) the median
(E) the 20% trimmed mean

6. The values shown are observations on the number of cars rented at a rental car facility on 20 randomly selected days last year.

0	2	6	9	10
10	18	22	22	23
24	25	25	25	28
30	33	37	40	42

Which observations would be displayed as outliers in a boxplot of these data?

(A) 0 only
(B) 42 only
(C) 0 and 42 are the only outliers
(D) 0, 2, 40, and 42 are the only outliers
(E) None of the observations is an outlier.

7. The five-number summary for a data set is

Minimum: 60
Lower Quartile: 75
Median: 78
Upper Quartile: 82
Maximum: 89

Which of the following is true for this data set?

(A) There are no outliers in the data set.
(B) This data set has at least one outlier on the high end and at least one outlier on the low end.
(C) This data set has at least one outlier on the high end and no outliers on the low end.
(D) This data set has no outliers on the high end and at least one outlier on the low end.
(E) It is not possible from the information provided to determine if the data set contains outliers.

8. Which of the following statements are true?

I. It is impossible for a data set to have a standard deviation that is larger than the mean.
II. If two data sets have different ranges, the data set with the larger range will always have the larger standard deviation.
III. The interquartile range of a data set can never be larger than the range.

(A) I only
(B) II only
(C) III only
(D) II and III only
(E) I, II, and III

9. Which of the five boxplots shown in Figure 9 at the bottom of the page corresponds to a data set with the 5-number summary below?

Minimum: 55
Lower Quartile: 66
Median: 74
Upper Quartile: 83
Maximum: 94

(A) Boxplot 1
(B) Boxplot 2
(C) Boxplot 3
(D) Boxplot 4
(E) Boxplot 5

10. Each person in a sample of 75 unemployed people who were looking for work was asked how many weeks they had been unemployed. The data are summarized in the accompanying frequency distribution.

Weeks Unemployed	Frequency
1–3	22
4–6	31
7–9	11
10–12	8
13–15	1
>15	2

Which of the following could have been the median of the data set?

(A) 2
(B) 5
(C) 8
(D) 11
(E) 16

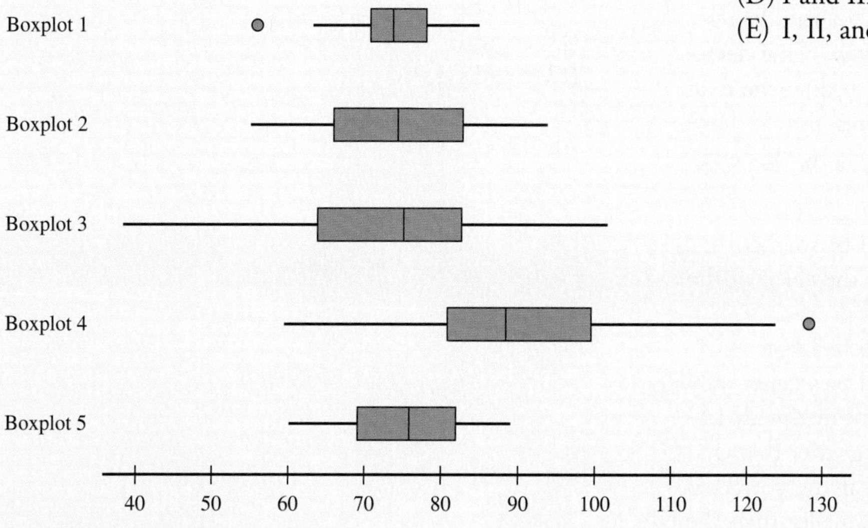

FIGURE 9

11. Consider the two sets of rectangles shown below:

Set 1:

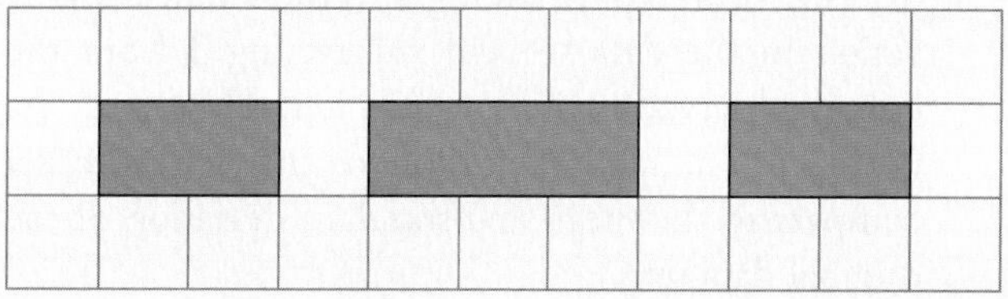

Set 2:

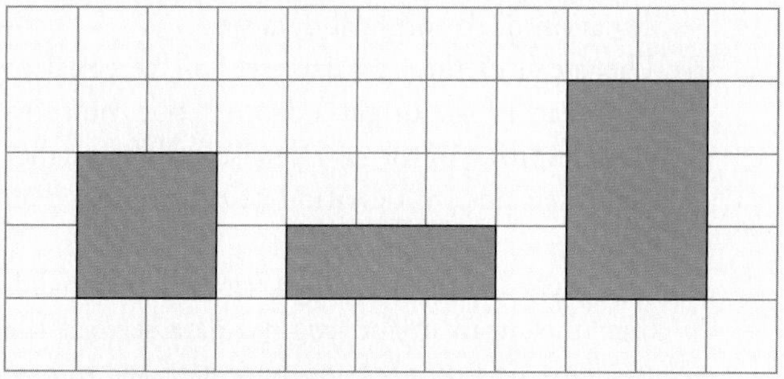

Which of the following statements are true?

I. The standard deviation of horizontal length for the rectangles in Set 1 is equal to the standard deviation of horizontal length for the rectangles in Set 2.
II. The standard deviation of vertical length for the rectangles in Set 1 is 0.
III. The standard deviation of vertical length is greater than the standard deviation of horizontal length for the rectangles of Set 2.

(A) I only
(B) II only
(C) III only
(D) I and III only
(E) I, II, and III

12. The mean and standard deviation of a data set with 50 observations are 47 and 10, respectively. A new data set is formed by adding 3 to the smallest observation in the data set and subtracting 3 from the largest observation in the data set. How will the mean and standard deviation of the new data set compare to the mean and standard deviation of the original data set?

(A) The mean and standard deviation of the new data set will be equal to the mean and standard deviation of the original data set.
(B) The mean of the new data set will be equal to the mean of the original data set but the standard deviation of the new data set will be smaller than the standard deviation of the original data set.
(C) The mean of the new data set will be smaller than the mean of the original data set but the standard deviation of the new data set will be equal to the standard deviation of the original data set.
(D) The mean of the new data set will be larger than the mean of the original data set but the standard deviation of the new data set will be smaller than the standard deviation of the original data set.
(E) The mean of the new data set will be smaller than the mean of the original data set and the standard deviation of the new data set will be smaller than the standard deviation of the original data set.

13. Fifty observations on waiting time (rounded to the nearest minute) for patients at a walk-in medical clinic were used to compute a sample mean waiting time. The two largest observations in the data set were 75 minutes and 120 minutes. It was later determined that there was an error in recording the data and the observation of 120 minutes should have been 12 minutes. How would correcting this error affect the sample mean?

(A) The corrected sample mean will be smaller.
(B) The correction will not change the value of the sample mean.
(C) The corrected sample mean will be larger.
(D) The corrected sample mean will be smaller only if the original sample mean (computed with 120 as one of the observations) was greater than 12.
(E) It is not possible to determine if the corrected sample mean will be larger or smaller than the original sample mean.

14. Each student in a sample of size 40 selected at random from those attending a particular university was asked how much they spent on housing per week. The smallest value in the data set was $70 and the largest was $620. If this data set were summarized using a stem-and-leaf display, which of the following would be the most appropriate choice of stems?

(A) 6, 7
(B) 0, 1, 2, ... , 6
(C) 70, 71, 71, ... , 619, 620
(D) 07, 08, 09, ... , 61, 62
(E) 0 to <75, 75 to <150, 150 to <225, ... , 525 to <675

15. A data set consisting of 100 observations was used to construct the following boxplot:

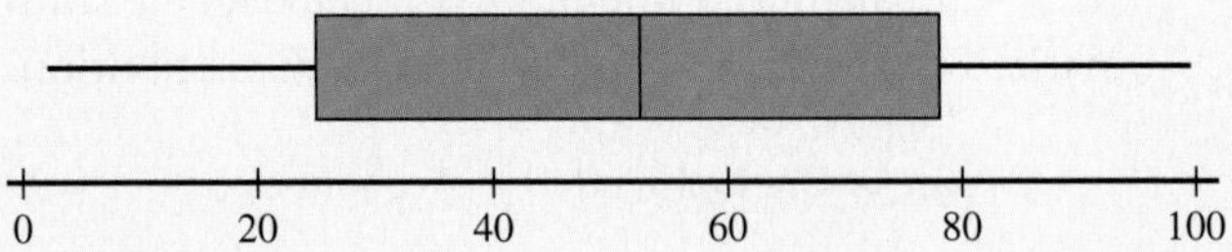

Based only on this boxplot, which of the following can be concluded about the shape of the sample distribution?

I. The sample distribution is approximately symmetric.
II. The sample distribution is approximately normal.
III. The sample distribution is extremely skewed to the right (positively skewed).

(A) I only
(B) II only
(C) III only
(D) I and II
(E) I and III

CHAPTER 5

© Spencer Platt/Getty Images

Summarizing Bivariate Data

Unusually large brain size at age 2 to 5 years is one indicator that a child may be at risk for autism. The authors of a paper that appeared in the *Journal of the American Medical Association* (July 2003) investigated whether head circumference at age 6 to 14 months could serve as a predictor of cerebral grey matter at age 2 to 5 years. Data on head circumference (measured at age 6 to 14 months) and cerebral grey matter (measured at age 2 to 5 years) for 18 male children with autism were used to explore the relationship between these two variables.

Questions of interest are: Is there a relationship between head circumference at age 6 to 14 months and the cerebral grey matter measurement at age 2 to 5 years? If so, can a head circumference measurement taken at an early age be used to predict what the grey matter measurement will be, potentially allowing doctors to detect autism at a younger age? How accurate are such predictions of grey matter?

In this chapter, we introduce methods for describing relationships between two numerical variables and for assessing the strength of a relationship. These methods allow us to answer questions such as the ones just posed regarding the relationship between head circumference at age 6 to 14 months and the grey matter measurement at age 2 to 5 years.

Make the most of your study time by accessing everything you need to succeed online with CourseMate.
Visit http://www.cengagebrain.com where you will find:

- An interactive eBook, which allows you to take notes, highlight, bookmark, search the text, and use in-context glossary definitions
- Step-by-step instructions for Minitab, Excel, TI-83/84, SPSS, and JMP
- Video solutions to selected exercises
- Data sets available for selected examples and exercises
- Online quizzes
- Flashcards
- Videos

In Chapter 13, methods for drawing conclusions from this type of data are developed. The techniques introduced in this chapter are also important stepping stones for analyzing data consisting of observations on three or more variables, the topic of Chapter 14.

5.1 Correlation

An investigator is often interested in how two or more variables are related to one another. For example, an environmental researcher might wish to know how the lead content of soil varies with distance from a major highway. Researchers in early childhood education might investigate how vocabulary size is related to age. College admissions officers, who must try to predict whether an applicant will succeed in college, might use a model relating college grade point average to high school grades, and ACT or SAT scores.

Recall that a scatterplot of bivariate numerical data gives a visual impression of how strongly x values and y values are related. However, to make precise statements and draw conclusions from data, we must go beyond pictures. A **correlation coefficient** (from *co-* and *relation*) is a numerical assessment of the strength of relationship between the x and y values in a bivariate data set consisting of (x, y) pairs. In this section, we introduce the most commonly used correlation coefficient.

Figure 5.1 displays several scatterplots that show different relationships between the x and y values. The plot in Figure 5.1(a) suggests a strong *positive relationship* between x and y; for every pair of points in the plot, the one with the larger x value also has the larger y value. That is, an increase in x is paired with an increase in y. The plot in Figure 5.1(b) shows a strong tendency for y to increase as x does, but there are a few exceptions. For example, the x and y values of the two points with the largest x values (shown in a different color) go in opposite directions (for this pair of points, x increases but y decreases in value). Nevertheless, a plot like this still indicates a fairly strong positive relationship. Figure 5.1(c) suggests that x and y are *negatively related*—as x increases, y tends to decrease. The

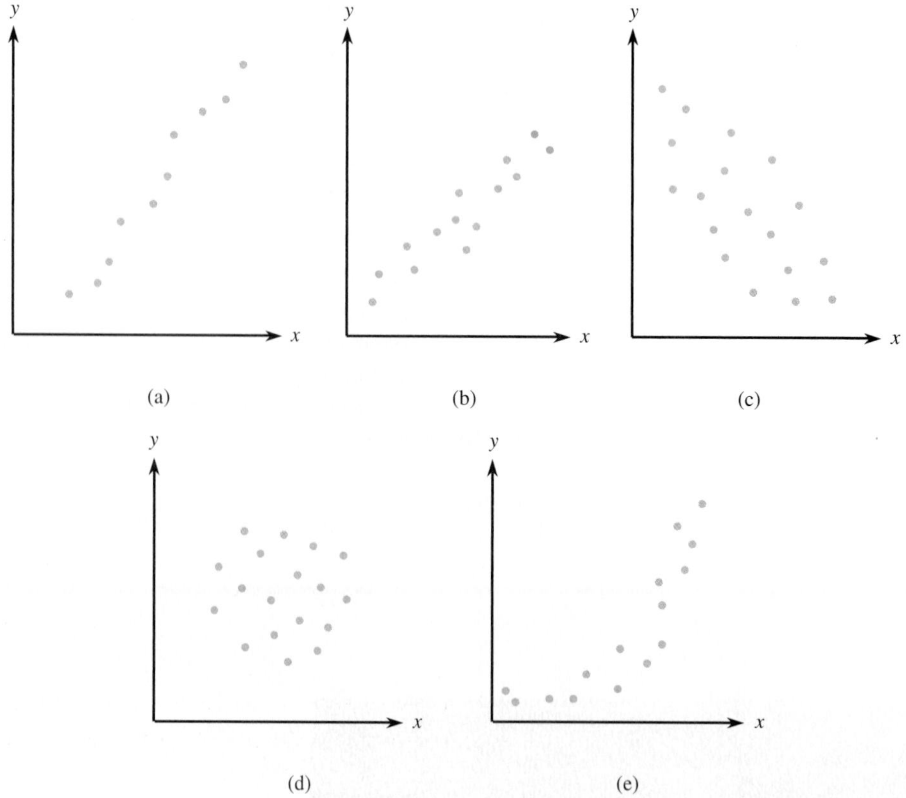

FIGURE 5.1
Scatterplots illustrating various types of relationships: (a) positive linear relationship; (b) another positive linear relationship; (c) negative linear relationship; (d) no relationship; (e) curved relationship.

negative relationship in this plot is not as strong as the positive relationship in Figure 5.1(b), although both plots show a well-defined linear pattern. The plot of Figure 5.1(d) indicates that there is not a strong relationship between x and y; there is no tendency for y either to increase or to decrease as x increases. Finally, as illustrated in Figure 5.1(e), a scatterplot can show evidence of a strong relationship that is curved rather than linear.

Pearson's Sample Correlation Coefficient

Pearson's sample correlation coefficient measures the strength of any linear relationship between two numerical variables. It does this by using z scores in a clever way. Consider replacing each x value by the corresponding z score, z_x (by subtracting $\bar{x}$ and then dividing by s_x) and similarly replacing each y value by its z score. Note that x values that are larger than $\bar{x}$ will have positive z scores and those smaller than $\bar{x}$ will have negative z scores. Also y values larger than $\bar{y}$ will have positive z scores and those smaller will have negative z scores. Pearson's sample correlation coefficient is based on the sum of the products of z_x and z_y for each observation in the bivariate data set. In algebraic notation, this is $\sum z_x z_y$.

To see how this works, let's look at some scatterplots. The scatterplot in Figure 5.2(a) indicates a strong positive relationship. A vertical line through $\bar{x}$ and a horizontal line through $\bar{y}$ divide the plot into four regions. In Region I, both x and y exceed their mean values, so the z score for x and the z score for y are both positive numbers. It follows that $z_x z_y$ is positive. The product of the z scores is also positive for any point in Region III, because both z scores are negative in Region III and multiplying two negative numbers gives a positive number. In each of the other two regions, one z score is positive and the other is negative, so $z_x z_y$ is negative. But because the points generally fall in Regions I and III, the products of z scores tend to be positive. Thus, the *sum* of the products will be a relatively large positive number.

Similar reasoning for the data displayed in Figure 5.2(b), which exhibits a strong negative relationship, implies that $\sum z_x z_y$ will be a relatively large (in magnitude) negative number. When there is no strong relationship, as in Figure 5.2(c), positive and negative products tend to counteract one another, producing a value of $\sum z_x z_y$ that is close to zero. In summary, $\sum z_x z_y$ seems to be a reasonable measure of the degree of association between x and y; it can be a large positive number, a large negative number, or a number close to 0, depending on whether there is a strong positive, a strong negative, or no strong linear relationship.

Pearson's sample correlation coefficient, denoted r, is obtained by dividing $\sum z_x z_y$ by $(n - 1)$.

DEFINITION

Pearson's sample correlation coefficient r is given by

$$r = \frac{\sum z_x z_y}{n - 1}$$

Although there are several different correlation coefficients, Pearson's correlation coefficient is by far the most commonly used, and so the name "Pearson's" is often omitted and it is referred to as simply the **correlation coefficient.**

Hand calculation of the correlation coefficient is quite tedious. Fortunately, all statistical software packages and most scientific calculators can compute r once the x and y values have been input.

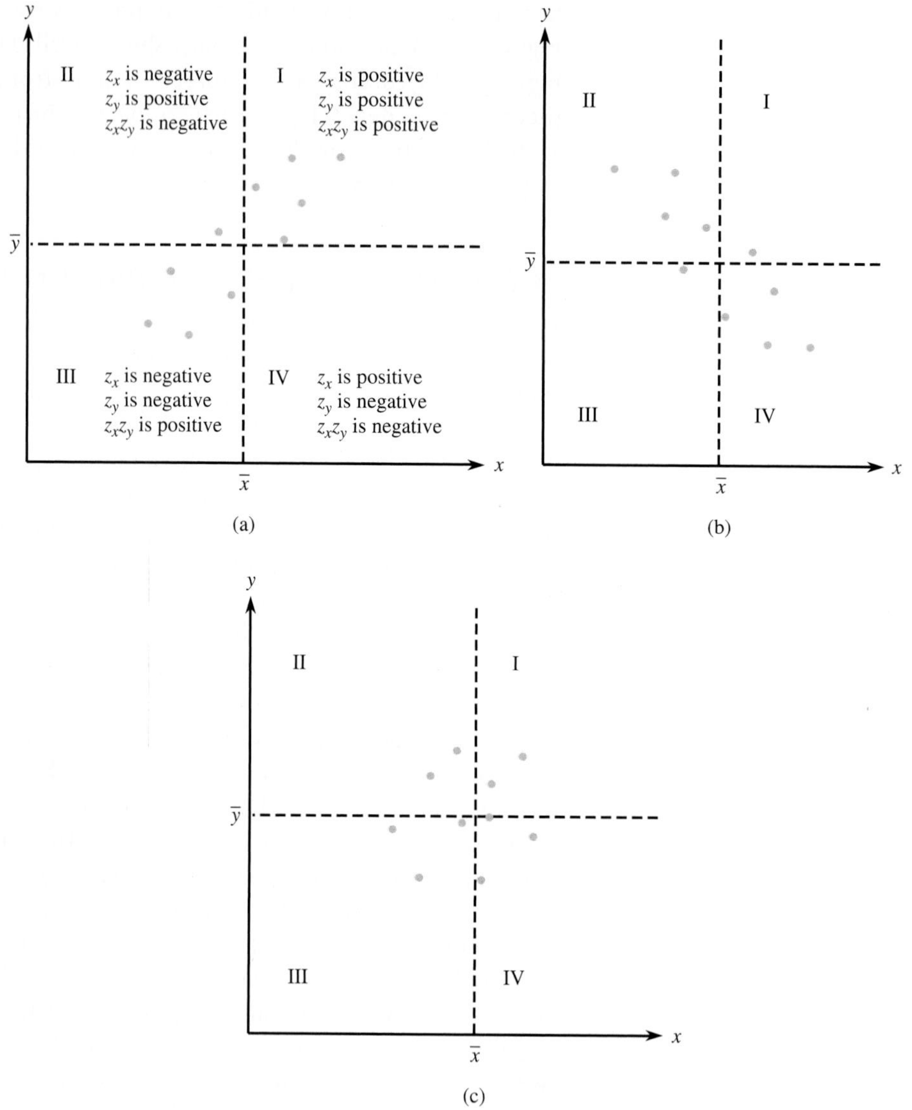

FIGURE 5.2
Viewing a scatterplot according to the signs of z_x and z_y: (a) a positive relation; (b) a negative relation; (c) no strong relation.

EXAMPLE 5.1 Graduation Rates and Student-Related Expenditures

● The web site www.collegeresults.org (The Education Trust) publishes data on U.S. colleges and universities. For the seven primarily undergraduate public universities in California with enrollments between 10,000 and 20,000, six-year graduation rates and student-related expenditures per full-time student for 2007 were reported as follows:

Observation	Graduation Rate (percent)	Student-Related Expenditure (dollars)
1	66.1	8,810
2	52.4	7,780
3	48.9	8,112
4	48.1	8,149
5	42.0	8,477
6	38.3	7,342
7	31.3	7,984

● Data set available online

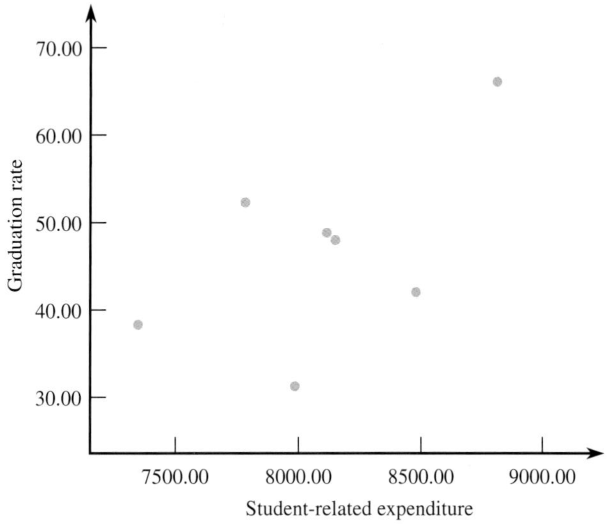

FIGURE 5.3
SPSS scatterplot for the data of Example 5.1.

Figure 5.3 is a scatterplot of these data generated using SPSS, a widely used statistics package.

Let x denote the student-related expenditure per full-time student and y denote the six-year graduation rate. It is easy to verify that

$$\bar{x} = 8093.43 \quad s_x = 472.39 \quad \bar{y} = 46.73 \quad s_y = 11.15$$

To illustrate the calculation of the correlation coefficient, we begin by computing z scores for each (x, y) pair in the data set. For example, the first observation is (8810, 66.1). The corresponding z scores are

$$z_x = \frac{8810 - 8093.43}{472.39} = 1.52 \qquad z_y = \frac{66.1 - 46.73}{11.15} = 1.74$$

The following table shows the z scores and the product $z_x z_y$ for each observation:

y	x	z_x	z_y	$z_x z_y$
66.1	8810	1.52	1.74	2.65
52.4	7780	−0.66	0.51	−0.34
48.9	8112	0.04	0.19	0.01
48.1	8149	0.12	0.12	0.01
42.0	8477	0.81	−0.42	−0.34
38.3	7342	−1.59	−0.76	1.21
31.3	7984	−0.23	−1.38	0.32

$$\sum z_x z_y = 3.52$$

Then, with $n = 7$

$$r = \frac{\sum z_x z_y}{n - 1} = \frac{3.52}{6} = .587$$

SPSS was used to compute the correlation coefficient, producing the following computer output.

Correlations

Gradrate Pearson Correlation .583

The difference between the correlation coefficient reported by SPSS and what we obtained is the result of rounding in the z scores when carrying out the calculations by hand. Based on the scatterplot and the properties of the correlation coefficient presented in the discussion that follows this example, we conclude that there is a moderate positive linear relationship between student-related expenditure and graduation rate for these seven universities.

Properties of r

AP* EXAM TIP

Interpretation of the value of the correlation coefficient contributes to understanding of the relationship between two numerical variables. These properties of the correlation coefficient can help guide your interpretation.

1. *The value of r does not depend on the unit of measurement for either variable.* For example, if x is height, the corresponding z score is the same whether height is expressed in inches, meters, or miles, and thus the value of the correlation coefficient is not affected. The correlation coefficient measures the inherent strength of the linear relationship between two numerical variables.
2. *The value of r does not depend on which of the two variables is considered x.* Thus, if we had let x = graduation rate and y = student-related expenditure in Example 5.1, the same value, $r = 0.587$, would have resulted.
3. *The value of r is between -1 and $+1$.* A value near the upper limit, $+1$, indicates a strong positive relationship, whereas an r close to the lower limit, -1, suggests a strong negative relationship. Figure 5.4 shows a useful way to describe the strength of relationship based on r. It may seem surprising that a value of r as extreme as $-.5$ or $.5$ should be in the weak category; an explanation for this is given later in the chapter. Even a weak correlation can indicate a meaningful relationship.

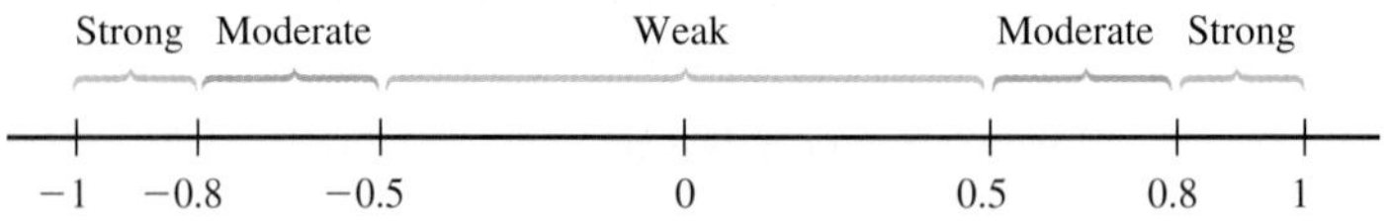

FIGURE 5.4 Describing the strength of a linear relationship.

4. *A correlation coefficient of $r = 1$ occurs only when all the points in a scatterplot of the data lie exactly on a straight line that slopes upward. Similarly, $r = -1$ only when all the points lie exactly on a downward-sloping line.* Only when there is a perfect linear relationship between x and y in the sample does r take on one of its two possible extreme values.
5. *The value of r is a measure of the extent to which x and y are linearly related*—that is, the extent to which the points in the scatterplot fall close to a straight line. A value of r close to 0 does not rule out *any* strong relationship between x and y; there could still be a strong relationship that is not linear.

EXAMPLE 5.2 Tannin Concentration in Wine

● Astringency is the characteristic of a wine that makes the wine drinker's mouth feel dry and puckery. The paper "Analysis of Tannins in Red Wine Using Multiple Methods: Correlation with Perceived Astringency" (*American Journal of Enology and Viticulture* [2006]: 481–485) describes a study to determine if there is a relation-

● Data set available online

ship between astringency and the concentration of tannins (chemical compounds found in the bark and fruit of some plants) in the wine. The accompanying data on x = tannin concentration and y = perceived astringency as determined by a panel of tasters for 32 red wines was provided by the authors.

x	y	x	y	x	y
0.72	0.43	0.76	0.19	0.52	−0.65
0.81	0.48	0.67	0.07	0.69	−0.15
0.92	0.49	0.56	−0.22	0.91	1.01
1.00	0.99	0.38	−0.90	0.64	−0.09
0.67	0.32	0.78	0.84	0.23	−1.13
0.53	0.30	0.67	0.13	0.78	0.54
0.51	−0.22	0.85	0.30	0.33	−1.10
0.56	0.20	0.41	−0.58	0.43	−0.58
0.77	0.33	0.93	0.78	0.32	−0.86
0.47	−0.34	0.31	−0.71	0.24	−0.55
0.73	0.77	0.32	−0.61		

Minitab was used to construct a scatterplot of the data (Figure 5.5) and to compute the value of the correlation coefficient for these data with the following result:

Correlations: x, y

Pearson correlation of x and y = 0.916

The correlation coefficient of $r = .916$ indicates a strong positive relationship between tannin concentration and astringency rating. This indicates that higher astringency ratings are associated with higher tannin concentrations. We will return to this data set again in Section 5.2 to see how the relationship between tannin concentration and astringency can be described in a way that will allow us to predict what the astringency rating will be for a given tannin concentration.

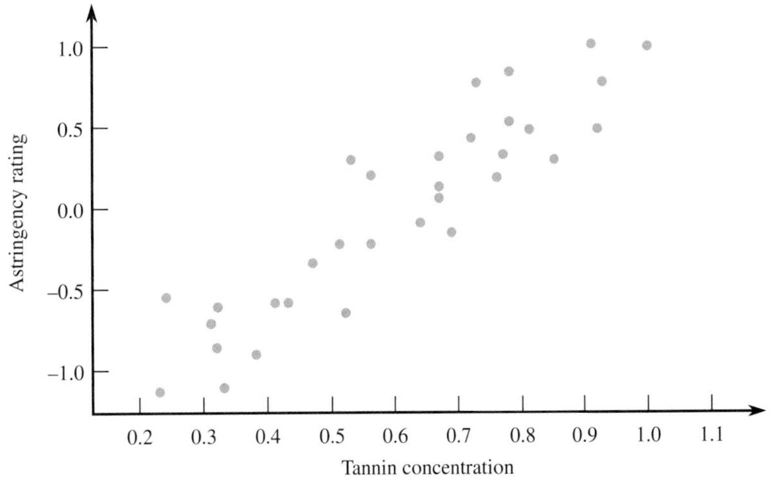

FIGURE 5.5
Minitab scatterplot for the wine data of Example 5.2.

EXAMPLE 5.3 Does It Pay to Pay More for a Bike Helmet?

● Are more expensive bike helmets safer than less expensive ones? The accompanying data on x = price and y = quality rating for 12 different brands of bike helmets appeared on the *Consumer Reports* web site (www.consumerreports.org/health). Quality rating was a number from 0 (the worst possible rating) to 100, and was determined based on factors that included how well the helmet absorbed the force of an impact, the strength of the helmet, ventilation, and ease of use. Figure 5.6 shows a scatterplot of the data.

Price	Quality Rating
35	65
20	61
30	60
40	55
50	54
23	47
30	47
18	43
40	42
28	41
20	40
25	32

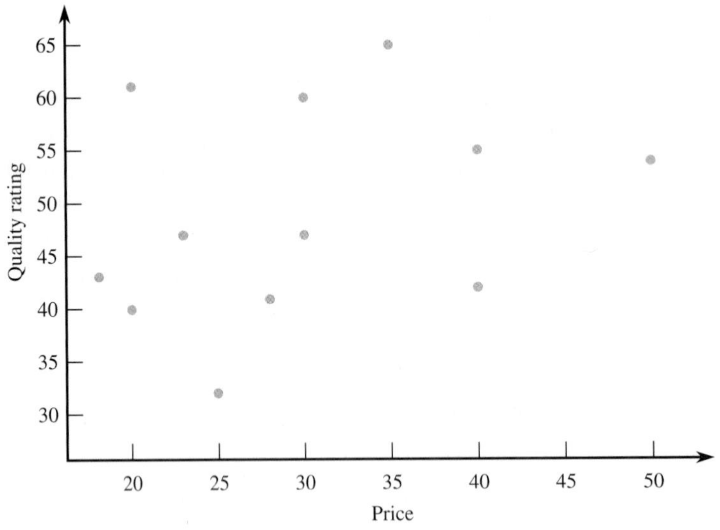

FIGURE 5.6
Minitab scatterplot for the bike helmet data of Example 5.3.

From the scatterplot, it appears that there is only a weak positive relationship between price and quality rating. The correlation coefficient, obtained using Minitab, is

Correlations: Price, Quality Rating

Pearson correlation of Price and Quality Rating = 0.303

A correlation coefficient of $r = .303$ confirms that there is a tendency for higher quality ratings to be associated with higher priced helmets, but that the relationship is not very strong. In fact, the highest quality rating was for a helmet priced near the middle of the price values.

● Data set available online

EXAMPLE 5.4 Age and Marathon Times

● The article "Master's Performance in the New York City Marathon" (*British Journal of Sports Medicine* [2004]: 408–412) gave the following data on the average finishing time by age group for female participants in the New York City marathon.

Age Group	Representative Age	Average Finish Time
10–19	15	302.38
20–29	25	193.63
30–39	35	185.46
40–49	45	198.49
50–59	55	224.30
60–69	65	288.71

The scatterplot of average finish time versus representative age is shown in Figure 5.7.

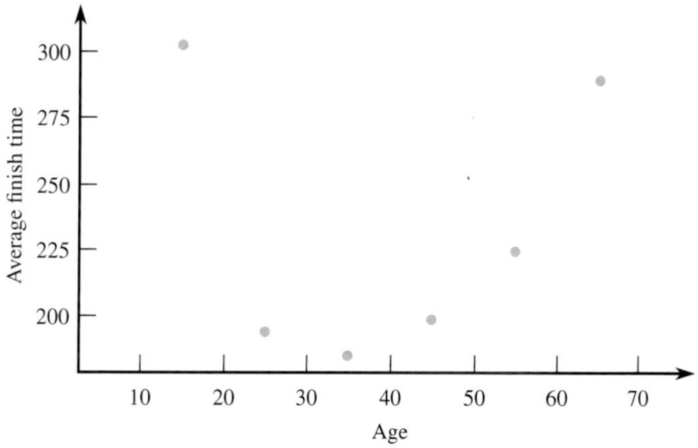

FIGURE 5.7
Scatterplot of y = average finish time and x = age for the data of Example 5.4.

Using Minitab to compute Pearson's correlation coefficient between age and average finish time results in the following:

Correlations: Age, Average Finish Time

Pearson correlation of Age and Average Finish Time = 0.038

This example shows the importance of interpreting r as a measure of the strength of a *linear* association. Here, r is not large, but there is a strong nonlinear relationship between age and average finish time. This is an important point—we should not conclude that there is no relationship whatsoever simply because the value of r is small in absolute value. Be sure to look at the scatterplot of the data before concluding that there is no relationship between two variables based on a correlation coefficient with a value near 0.

● Data set available online

The Population Correlation Coefficient

The sample correlation coefficient r measures how strongly the x and y values in a *sample* of pairs are linearly related to one another. There is an analogous measure of how strongly x and y are related in the entire population of pairs from which the sample was obtained. It is called the **population correlation coefficient** and is denoted ρ. (Notice again the use of a Greek letter for a population characteristic and a Roman letter for a sample characteristic.) We will never have to calculate ρ from an entire population of pairs, but it is important to know that ρ satisfies properties paralleling those of r:

1. ρ is a number between -1 and $+1$ that does not depend on the unit of measurement for either x or y, or on which variable is labeled x and which is labeled y.
2. $\rho = +1$ or -1 if and only if all (x, y) pairs in the population lie exactly on a straight line, so ρ measures the extent to which there is a linear relationship in the population.

In Chapter 13, we show how the sample correlation coefficient r can be used to draw conclusions about the value of the population correlation coefficient ρ.

Correlation and Causation

A value of r close to 1 indicates that the larger values of one variable tend to be associated with the larger values of the other variable. This is far from saying that a large value of one variable *causes* the value of the other variable to be large. Correlation measures the extent of association, but *association does not imply causation.* It frequently happens that two variables are highly correlated not because one is causally related to the other but because they are both strongly related to a third variable. Among all elementary school children, the relationship between the number of cavities in a child's teeth and the size of his or her vocabulary is strong and positive. Yet no one advocates eating foods that result in more cavities to increase vocabulary size (or working to decrease vocabulary size to protect against cavities). Number of cavities and vocabulary size are both strongly related to age, so older children tend to have higher values of both variables than do younger ones. In the ABCNews.com series "Who's Counting?" (February 1, 2001), John Paulos reminded readers that correlation does not imply causation and gave the following example: Consumption of hot chocolate is negatively correlated with crime rate (high values of hot chocolate consumption tend to be paired with lower crime rates), but both are responses to cold weather.

Scientific experiments can frequently make a strong case for causality by carefully controlling the values of all variables that might be related to the ones under study. Then, if y is observed to change in a "smooth" way as the experimenter changes the value of x, a plausible explanation would be that there is a causal relationship between x and y. In the absence of such control and ability to manipulate values of one variable, we must admit the possibility that an unidentified underlying third variable is influencing both the variables under investigation. A high correlation in many uncontrolled studies carried out in different settings can also marshal support for causality—as in the case of cigarette smoking and cancer—but proving causality is an elusive task.

EXERCISES 5.1 - 5.13

5.1 For each of the following pairs of variables, indicate whether you would expect a positive correlation, a negative correlation, or a correlation close to 0. Explain your choice.

a. Maximum daily temperature and cooling costs
b. Interest rate and number of loan applications
c. Incomes of husbands and wives when both have full-time jobs
d. Height and IQ
e. Height and shoe size

f. Score on the math section of the SAT exam and score on the verbal section of the same test

g. Time spent on homework and time spent watching television during the same day by elementary school children

h. Amount of fertilizer used per acre and crop yield (Hint: As the amount of fertilizer is increased, yield tends to increase for a while but then tends to start decreasing.)

5.2 Is the following statement correct? Explain why or why not.

A correlation coefficient of 0 implies that no relationship exists between the two variables under study.

5.3 Draw two scatterplots, one for which $r = 1$ and a second for which $r = -1$.

5.4 The article "That's Rich: More You Drink, More You Earn" (*Calgary Herald*, April 16, 2002) reported that there was a positive correlation between alcohol consumption and income. Is it reasonable to conclude that increasing alcohol consumption will increase income? Give at least two reasons or examples to support your answer.

5.5 ● The accompanying data are x = cost (cents per serving) and y = fiber content (grams per serving) for 18 high-fiber cereals rated by *Consumer Reports* (www.consumerreports.org/health).

Cost per serving	Fiber per serving
33	7
46	10
49	10
62	7
41	8
19	7
77	12
71	12
30	8
53	13
53	10
67	8
43	12
48	7
28	14
54	7
27	8
58	8

a. Compute and interpret the correlation coefficient for this data set.

b. The serving size differed for the different cereals, with serving sizes varying from ½ cup to 1¼ cups. Converting price and fiber content to "per cup" rather than "per serving" results in the accompanying data. Is the correlation coefficient for the per cup data greater than or less than the correlation coefficient for the per serving data?

Cost per Cup	Fiber per Cup
9.3	44
10	46
10	49
7	62
6.4	32.8
7	19
12	77
9.6	56.8
8	30
13	53
10	53
8	67
12	43
7	48
28	56
7	54
16	54
10.7	77.3

5.6 The authors of the paper "Flat-footedness is Not a Disadvantage for Athletic Performance in Children Aged 11 to 15 Years" (*Pediatrics* [2009]: e386–e392) studied the relationship between y = arch height and scores on a number of different motor ability tests for 218 children. They reported the following correlation coefficients:

Motor Ability Test	Correlation between Test Score and Arch Height
Height of counter movement jump	−0.02
Hopping: average height	−0.10
Hopping: average power	−0.09
Balance, closed eyes, one leg	0.04
Toe flexion	0.05

a. Interpret the value of the correlation coefficient between average hopping height and arch height. What does the fact that the correlation coefficient is negative say about the relationship? Do higher arch heights tend to be paired with higher or lower average hopping heights?

b. The title of the paper suggests that having a small value for arch height (flat-footedness) is not a disadvantage when it comes to motor skills. Do the given correlation coefficients support this conclusion? Explain.

5.7 In a study of 200 Division I athletes, variables related to academic performance were examined. The paper "Noncognitive Predictors of Student Athletes' Academic Performance" (*Journal of College Reading and Learning* [2000]: e167) reported that the correlation coefficient for college GPA and a measure of academic self-worth was $r = 0.48$. Also reported were the correlation coefficient for college GPA and high school GPA ($r = 0.46$) and the correlation coefficient for college GPA and a measure of tendency to procrastinate ($r = -0.36$). Higher scores on the measure of self-worth indicate higher self-worth, and higher scores on the measure of procrastination indicate a higher tendency to procrastinate. Write a few sentences summarizing what these correlation coefficients tell you about the academic performance of the 200 athletes in the sample.

5.8 The following time-series plot is based on data from the article "Bubble Talk Expands: Corporate Debt Is Latest Concern Turning Heads" (*San Luis Obispo Tribune*, September 13, 2002) and shows how household debt and corporate debt have changed over the time period from 1991 (year 1 in the graph) to 2002:

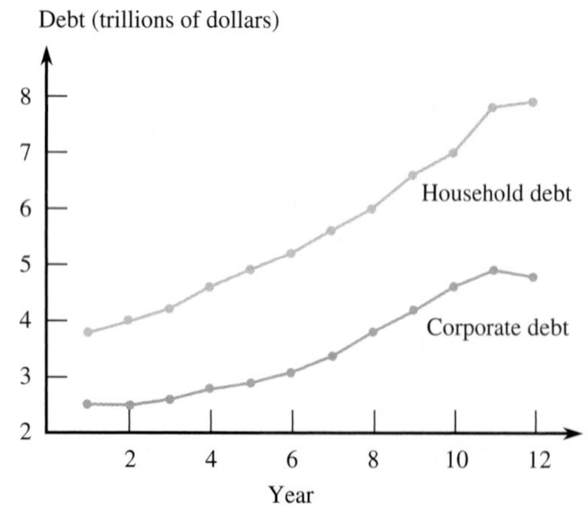

Based on the time-series plot, would the correlation coefficient between household debt and corporate debt be positive or negative? Weak or strong? What aspect of the time-series plot supports your answer?

5.9 ● Data from the U.S. Federal Reserve Board (Household Debt Service Burden, 2002) on the percentage of disposable personal income required to meet consumer loan payments and mortgage payments for selected years are shown in the following table:

Consumer Debt	Household Debt	Consumer Debt	Household Debt
7.88	6.22	6.24	5.73
7.91	6.14	6.09	5.95
7.65	5.95	6.32	6.09
7.61	5.83	6.97	6.28
7.48	5.83	7.38	6.08
7.49	5.85	7.52	5.79
7.37	5.81	7.84	5.81
6.57	5.79		

a. What is the value of the correlation coefficient for this data set?

b. Is it reasonable to conclude in this case that there is no strong relationship between the variables (linear or otherwise)? Use a graphical display to support your answer.

5.10 ● ✦ The accompanying data were read from graphs that appeared in the article "Bush Timber Proposal Runs Counter to the Record" (*San Luis Obispo Tribune*, September 22, 2002). The variables shown are the number of acres burned in forest fires in the western United States and timber sales.

Year	Number of Acres Burned (thousands)	Timber Sales (billions of board feet)
1945	200	2.0
1950	250	3.7
1955	260	4.4
1960	380	6.8
1965	80	9.7
1970	450	11.0
1975	180	11.0
1980	240	10.2
1985	440	10.0
1990	400	11.0
1995	180	3.8

a. Is there a correlation between timber sales and acres burned in forest fires? Compute and interpret the value of the correlation coefficient.

b. The article concludes that "heavier logging led to large forest fires." Do you think this conclusion is justified based on the given data? Explain.

5.11 It may seem odd, but one of the ways biologists can tell how old a lobster is involves measuring the concentration of a pigment called neurolipofuscin in the eyestalk of a lobster. (We are not making this up!) The authors of the paper "Neurolipofuscin is a Measure of Age in *Panulirus argus*, the Caribbean Spiny Lobster, in Florida" (*Biological Bulletin* [2007]: 55–66) wondered if it was sufficient to measure the pigment in just one eye stalk, which would be the case if there is a strong relationship between the concentration in the right and left eyestalks. Pigment concentration (as a percentage of tissue sample) was measured in both eyestalks for 39 lobsters, resulting is the following summary quantities (based on data read from a graph that appeared in the paper):

$$n = 39 \qquad \sum x = 88.8 \qquad \sum y = 86.1$$
$$\sum xy = 281.1 \qquad \sum x^2 = 288.0 \qquad \sum y^2 = 286.6$$

An alternative formula for computing the correlation coefficient that is based on raw data and is algebraically equivalent to the one given in the text is

$$r = \frac{\sum xy - \frac{(\sum x)(\sum y)}{n}}{\sqrt{\sum x^2 - \frac{(\sum x)^2}{n}}\sqrt{\sum y^2 - \frac{(\sum y)^2}{n}}}$$

Use this formula to compute the value of the correlation coefficient, and interpret this value.

5.12 An auction house released a list of 25 recently sold paintings. Eight artists were represented in these sales. The sale price of each painting also appears on the list. Would the correlation coefficient be an appropriate way to summarize the relationship between artist (x) and sale price (y)? Why or why not?

5.13 A sample of automobiles traversing a certain stretch of highway is selected. Each one travels at roughly a constant rate of speed, although speed does vary from auto to auto. Let x = speed and y = time needed to traverse this segment of highway. Would the sample correlation coefficient be closest to .9, .3, −.3, or −.9? Explain.

5.2 Linear Regression: Fitting a Line to Bivariate Data

The objective of *regression analysis* is to use information about one variable, x, to draw some sort of conclusion concerning a second variable, y. For example, we might want to predict y = product sales during a given period when the amount spent on advertising is x = \$10,000. The two variables in a regression analysis play different roles: y is called the **dependent** or **response variable**, and x is referred to as the **independent**, **predictor**, or **explanatory variable**.

Scatterplots frequently exhibit a linear pattern. When this is the case, it makes sense to summarize the relationship between the variables by finding a line that is as close as possible to the points in the plot. Before seeing how this is done, let's review some elementary facts about lines and linear relationships.

The equation of a line is $y = a + bx$. A particular line is specified by choosing values of a and b. For example, one line is $y = 10 + 2x$; another is $y = 100 - 5x$. If we choose some x values and compute $y = a + bx$ for each value, the points in the plot of the resulting (x, y) pairs will fall exactly on a straight line.

DEFINITION

The equation of a line is

Intercept

$$y = a + bx$$

Slope

The value of b, called the **slope** of the line, is the amount by which y increases when x increases by 1 unit. The value of a, called the **intercept** (or sometimes the **y-intercept** or **vertical intercept**) of the line, is the height of the line above the value $x = 0$.

The line $y = 10 + 2x$ has slope $b = 2$, so each 1-unit increase in x is paired with an increase of 2 in y. When $x = 0$, $y = 10$, so the height at which the line crosses the vertical axis (where $x = 0$) is 10. This is illustrated in Figure 5.8(a). The slope of the line $y = 100 - 5x$ is -5, so y increases by -5 (or equivalently, decreases by 5) when x increases by 1. The height of the line above $x = 0$ is $a = 100$. The resulting line is pictured in Figure 5.8(b).

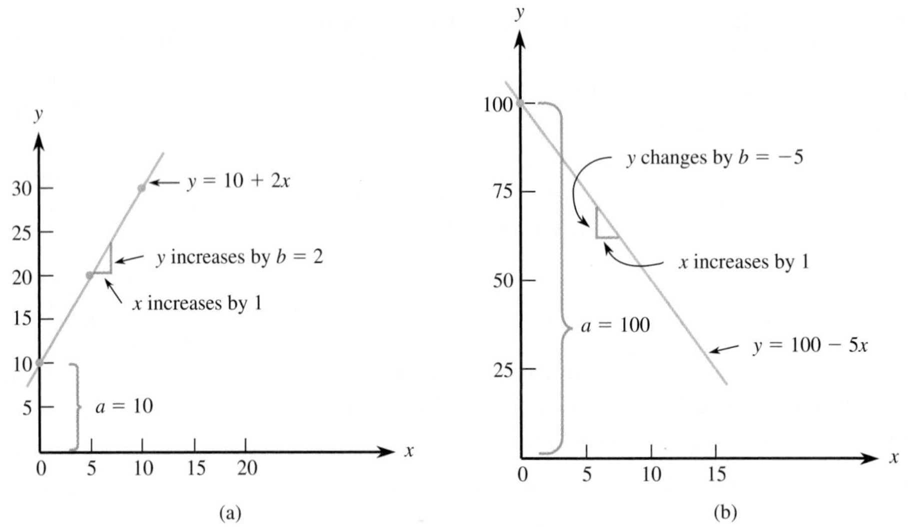

FIGURE 5.8
Graphs of two lines: (a) slope $b = 2$, intercept $a = 10$; (b) slope $b = -5$, intercept $a = 100$.

It is easy to draw the line corresponding to any particular linear equation. Choose any two x values and substitute them into the equation to obtain the corresponding y values. Then plot the resulting two (x, y) pairs as two points. The desired line is the one passing through these points. For the equation $y = 10 + 2x$, substituting $x = 5$ yields $y = 20$, whereas using $x = 10$ gives $y = 30$. The resulting two points are then (5, 20) and (10, 30). The line in Figure 5.8(a) passes through these points.

Fitting a Straight Line: The Principle of Least Squares

Figure 5.9 shows a scatterplot with two lines superimposed on the plot. Line II is a better fit to the data than Line I is. In order to measure the extent to which a particular line provides a good fit to data, we focus on the vertical deviations from the line. For example, Line II in Figure 5.9 has equation $y = 10 + 2x$, and the third and fourth points from the left in the scatterplot are (15, 44) and (20, 45). For these two points, the vertical deviations from this line are

$$\begin{aligned}\text{3rd deviation} &= y_3 - \text{height of the line above } x_3 \\ &= 44 - [10 + 2(15)] \\ &= 4\end{aligned}$$

and

$$\text{4th deviation} = 45 - [10 + 2(20)] = -5$$

A positive vertical deviation results from a point that lies above the chosen line, and a negative deviation results from a point that lies below this line. A particular line is said to be a good fit to the data if the deviations from the line are small in magnitude. Line I in Figure 5.9 fits poorly, because all deviations from that line are larger in magnitude (some are much larger) than the corresponding deviations from Line II.

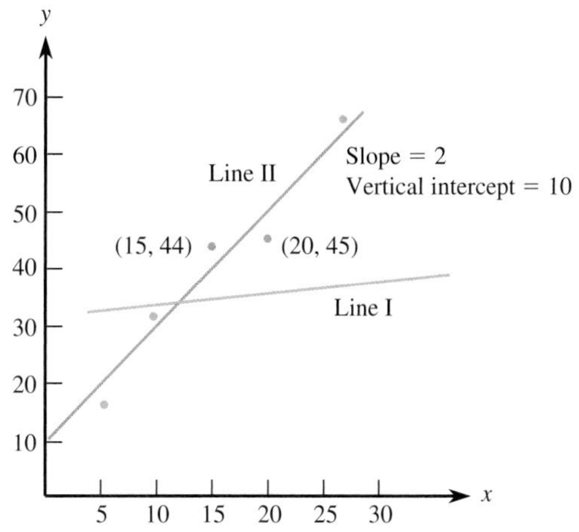

FIGURE 5.9
Line I gives a poor fit and Line II gives a good fit to the data.

To assess the overall fit of a line, we need a way to combine the n deviations into a single measure of fit. The standard approach is to square the deviations (to obtain nonnegative numbers) and then to sum these squared deviations.

DEFINITION

The most widely used measure of the goodness of fit of a line $y = a + bx$ to bivariate data $(x_1, y_1), \ldots, (x_n, y_n)$ is the **sum of the squared deviations** about the line

$$\Sigma[y - (a + bx)]^2 = [y_1 - (a + bx_1)]^2 + [y_2 - (a + bx_2)]^2 + \cdots + [y_n - (a + bx_n)]^2$$

The **least-squares line**, also called the **sample regression line**, is the line that minimizes this sum of squared deviations.

Fortunately, the equation of the least-squares line can be obtained without having to calculate deviations from any particular line. The accompanying box gives relatively simple formulas for the slope and intercept of the least-squares line.

The slope of the least-squares line is

$$b = \frac{\Sigma(x - \bar{x})(y - \bar{y})}{\Sigma(x - \bar{x})^2}$$

and the y intercept is

$$a = \bar{y} - b\bar{x}$$

We write the equation of the least-squares line as

$$\hat{y} = a + bx$$

where the ˆ above y indicates that $\hat{y}$ (read as y-hat) is the prediction of y that results from substituting a particular x value into the equation.

Statistical software packages and many calculators can compute the slope and intercept of the least-squares line. If the slope and intercept are to be computed by hand, the following computational formula can be used to reduce the amount of time required to perform the calculations.

Calculating Formula for the Slope of the Least-Squares Line

$$b = \frac{\sum xy - \frac{(\sum x)(\sum y)}{n}}{\sum x^2 - \frac{(\sum x)^2}{n}}$$

EXAMPLE 5.5 Pomegranate Juice and Tumor Growth

● Pomegranate, a fruit native to Persia, has been used in the folk medicines of many cultures to treat various ailments. Researchers are now studying pomegranate's antioxidant properties to see if it might have any beneficial effects in the treatment of cancer. One such study, described in the paper "Pomegranate Fruit Juice for Chemoprevention and Chemotherapy of Prostate Cancer" (*Proceedings of the National Academy of Sciences* [October 11, 2005]: 14813–14818), investigated whether pomegranate fruit extract (PFE) was effective in slowing the growth of prostate cancer tumors. In this study, 24 mice were injected with cancer cells. The mice were then randomly assigned to one of three treatment groups. One group of eight mice received normal drinking water, the second group of eight mice received drinking water supplemented with .1% PFE, and the third group received drinking water supplemented with .2% PFE. The average tumor volume for the mice in each group was recorded at several points in time. The accompanying data on y = average tumor volume (in mm^3) and x = number of days after injection of cancer cells for the mice that received plain drinking water was approximated from a graph that appeared in the paper:

x	11	15	19	23	27
y	150	270	450	580	740

A scatterplot of these data (Figure 5.10) shows that the relationship between number of days after injection of cancer cells and average tumor volume could reasonably be summarized by a straight line.

● Data set available online

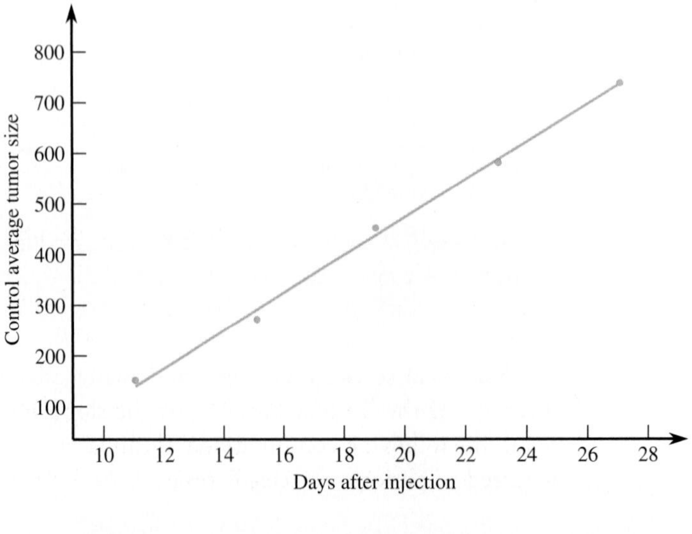

FIGURE 5.10
Minitab scatterplot for the data of Example 5.5.

The summary quantities necessary to compute the equation of the least-squares line are

$$\sum x = 95 \qquad \sum x^2 = 1965 \qquad \sum xy = 47{,}570$$
$$\sum y = 2190 \qquad \sum y^2 = 1{,}181{,}900$$

From these quantities, we compute

$$\bar{x} = 19 \qquad \bar{y} = 438$$

$$b = \frac{\sum xy - \frac{(\sum x)(\sum y)}{n}}{\sum x^2 - \frac{(\sum x)^2}{n}} = \frac{47{,}570 - \frac{(95)(2190)}{5}}{1965 - \frac{(95)^2}{5}} = \frac{5960}{160} = 37.25$$

and

$$a = \bar{y} - b\bar{x} = 438 - (37.25)(19) = -269.75$$

The least-squares line is then

$$\hat{y} = -269.75 + 37.25x$$

This line is also shown on the scatterplot of Figure 5.10.

If we wanted to predict average tumor volume 20 days after injection of cancer cells, we could use the y value of the point on the least-squares line above $x = 20$:

$$\hat{y} = -269.75 + 37.25(20) = 475.25$$

AP* EXAM TIP

A scatterplot can give you a visual sense of how far away an x value is from the range of x values in the data set.

Predicted average tumor volume for other numbers of days after injection of cancer cells could be computed in a similar way.

But, be careful in making predictions—the least-squares line should not be used to predict average tumor volume for times much outside the range 11 to 27 days (the range of x values in the data set) because we do not know whether the linear pattern observed in the scatterplot continues outside this range. This is sometimes referred to as the **danger of extrapolation.**

In this example, we can see that using the least-squares line to predict average tumor volume for fewer than 10 days after injection of cancer cells can lead to nonsensical predictions. For example, if the number of days after injection is five the predicted average tumor volume is negative:

$$\hat{y} = -269.75 + 37.25(5) = -83.5$$

Because it is impossible for average tumor volume to be negative, this is a clear indication that the pattern observed for x values in the 11 to 27 range does not continue outside this range. Nonetheless, the least-squares line can be a useful tool for making predictions for x values within the 11- to 27-day range.

Figure 5.11 shows a scatterplot for average tumor volume versus number of days after injection of cancer cells for both the group of mice that drank only water and the group that drank water supplemented by .2% PFE. Notice that the tumor growth seems to be much slower for the mice that drank water supplemented with PFE. For the .2% PFE group, the relationship between average tumor volume and number of days after injection of cancer cells appears to be curved rather than linear. We will see in Section 5.4 how a curve (rather than a straight line) can be used to summarize this relationship.

Calculations involving the least-squares line can obviously be tedious. This is when the computer or a graphing calculator comes to our rescue. All the standard statistical packages can fit a straight line to bivariate data.

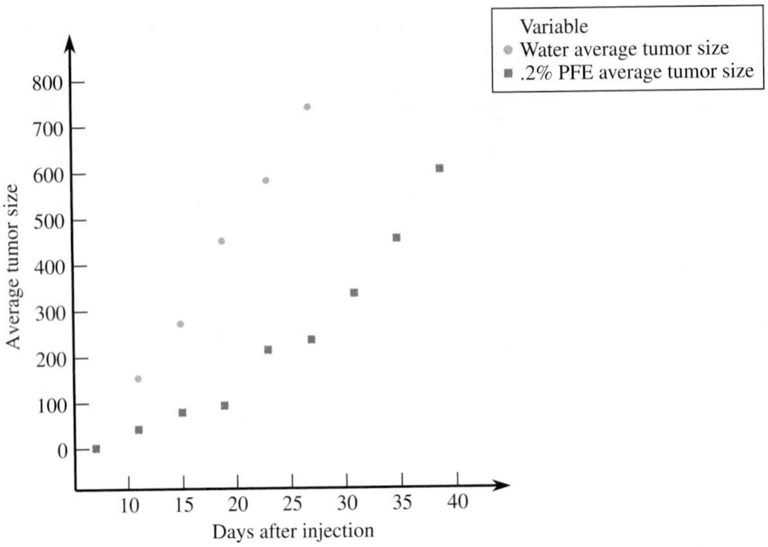

FIGURE 5.11
Scatterplot of average tumor volume versus number of days after injection of cancer cells for the water group and the .2% PFE group.

USE CAUTION—The Danger of Extrapolation

The least-squares line should not be used to make predictions outside the range of the x values in the data set because we have no evidence that the linear relationship continues outside this range.

EXAMPLE 5.6 Revisiting the Tannin Concentration Data

Data on x = tannin concentration and y = perceived astringency for n = 32 red wines was given in Example 5.2. In that example, we saw that the correlation coefficient was 0.916, indicating a strong positive linear relationship. This linear relationship can be summarized using the least-squares line, as shown in Figure 5.12.

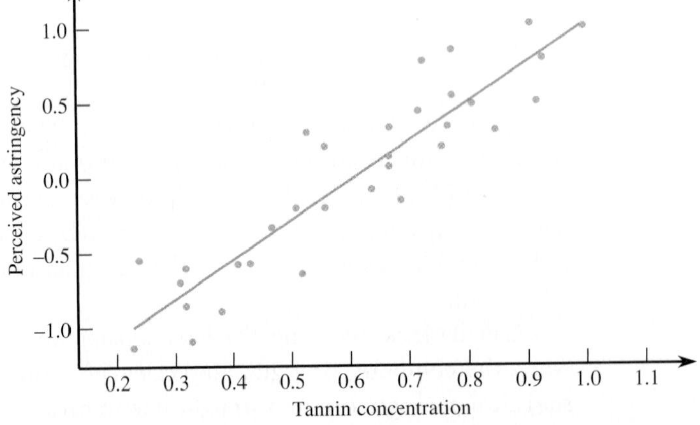

FIGURE 5.12
Scatterplot and least-squares line for the data of Example 5.6.

AP* EXAM TIP

Computer software will vary slightly in the way regression output is presented. Familiarity with the quantities usually included in the output and how they are computed will make it easier to read output from different packages.

Minitab was used to fit the least-squares line, and Figure 5.13 shows part of the resulting output. Instead of x and y, the variable labels "Perceived Astringency" and "Tannin Concentration" are used. The equation at the top is that of the least-squares line. In the rectangular table just below the equation, the first row gives information about the intercept, a, and the second row gives information concerning the slope, b. In particular, the coefficient column labeled "Coef" contains the values of a and b using more digits than in the rounded values that appear in the equation.

The regression equation is
Perceived Astringency = – 1.59 + 2.59 Tannin concentration ← *Equation $\hat{y} = a + bx$*

Predictor	Coef	SE Coef	T	P
Constant	–1.5908	0.1339	–11.88	0.000
Tannin concentration	2.5946	0.2079	12.48	0.000

Value of a *Value of b*

FIGURE 5.13
Partial Minitab output for Example 5.6.

The least-squares line should not be used to predict the perceived astringency for wines with tannin concentrations such as $x = 0.10$ or $x = 0.15$. These x values are well outside the range of the data, and we do not know if the linear relationship continues outside the observed range.

Regression

The least-squares line is often called the **sample regression line.** This terminology comes from the relationship between the least-squares line and Pearson's correlation coefficient. To understand this relationship, we first need alternative expressions for the slope b and the equation of the line itself. With s_x and s_y denoting the sample standard deviations of the x's and y's, respectively, a bit of algebraic manipulation gives

$$b = r\left(\frac{s_y}{s_x}\right)$$

$$\hat{y} = \bar{y} + r\left(\frac{s_y}{s_x}\right)(x - \bar{x})$$

You do not need to use these formulas in any computations, but several of their implications are important for appreciating what the least-squares line does.

1. When $x = \bar{x}$ is substituted in the equation of the line, $\hat{y} = \bar{y}$ results. That is, the least-squares line passes through the *point of averages* $(\bar{x}, \bar{y})$.
2. Suppose for the moment that $r = 1$, so that all points lie exactly on the line whose equation is

   $$\hat{y} = \bar{y} + \frac{s_y}{s_x}(x - \bar{x})$$

   Now substitute $x = \bar{x} + s_x$, which is 1 standard deviation above $\bar{x}$:

   $$\hat{y} = \bar{y} + \frac{s_y}{s_x}(\bar{x} + s_x - \bar{x}) = \bar{y} + s_y$$

That is, with $r = 1$, when x is 1 standard deviation above its mean, we predict that the associated y value will be 1 standard deviation above its mean. Similarly, if $x = \bar{x} - 2s_x$ (2 standard deviations below its mean), then

$$\hat{y} = \bar{y} + \frac{s_y}{s_x}(\bar{x} - 2s_x - \bar{x}) = \bar{y} - 2s_y$$

which is also 2 standard deviations below the mean. If $r = -1$, then $x = \bar{x} + s_x$ results in $\hat{y} = \bar{y} - s_y$, so the predicted y is also 1 standard deviation from its mean but on the opposite side of $\bar{y}$ from where x is relative to $\bar{x}$. In general, if x and y are perfectly correlated, the predicted y value associated with a given x value will be the same number of standard deviations (of y) from its mean $\bar{y}$ as x is from its mean $\bar{x}$.

3. Now suppose that x and y are not perfectly correlated. For example, suppose $r = .5$, so the least-squares line has the equation

$$\hat{y} = \bar{y} + .5\left(\frac{s_y}{s_x}\right)(x - \bar{x})$$

Then substituting $x = \bar{x} + s_x$ gives

$$\hat{y} = \bar{y} + .5\left(\frac{s_y}{s_x}\right)(\bar{x} + s_x - \bar{x}) = \bar{y} + .5s_y$$

That is, for $r = .5$, when x lies 1 standard deviation above its mean, we predict that y will be only 0.5 standard deviation above its mean. Similarly, we can predict y when r is negative. If $r = -.5$, then the predicted y value will be only half the number of standard deviations from $\bar{y}$ that x is from $\bar{x}$ but x and the predicted y will now be on opposite sides of their respective means.

Consider using the least-squares line to predict the value of y associated with an x value some specified number of standard deviations away from $\bar{x}$. Then the predicted y value will be only r times this number of standard deviations from $\bar{y}$. In terms of standard deviations, except when $r = 1$ or -1, the predicted y will always be closer to $\bar{y}$ than x is to $\bar{x}$.

Using the least-squares line for prediction results in a predicted y that is pulled back in, or regressed, toward the mean of y compared to where x is relative to the mean of x. This regression effect was first noticed by Sir Francis Galton (1822–1911), a famous biologist, when he was studying the relationship between the heights of fathers and their sons. He found that predicted heights of sons whose fathers were above average in height were also above average (because r is positive here) but not by as much as the father's height; he found a similar relationship for fathers whose heights were below average. This regression effect has led to the term **regression analysis** for the collection of methods involving the fitting of lines, curves, and more complicated functions to bivariate and multivariate data.

The alternative form of the regression (least-squares) line emphasizes that predicting y from knowledge of x is not the same problem as predicting x from knowledge of y. The slope of the least-squares line for predicting x is $r(s_x/s_y)$ rather than $r(s_y/s_x)$ and the intercepts of the lines are almost always different. For purposes of prediction, it makes a difference whether y is regressed on x, as we have done, or x is regressed on y. *The regression line of y on x should not be used to predict x, because it is not the line that minimizes the sum of squared deviations in the x direction.*

EXERCISES 5.14 - 5.28

5.14 ● ✦ The article "Air Pollution and Medical Care Use by Older Americans" (*Health Affairs* [2002]: 207–214) gave data on a measure of pollution (in micrograms of particulate matter per cubic meter of air) and the cost of medical care per person over age 65 for six geographical regions of the United States:

Region	Pollution	Cost of Medical Care
North	30.0	915
Upper South	31.8	891
Deep South	32.1	968
West South	26.8	972
Big Sky	30.4	952
West	40.0	899

a. Construct a scatterplot of the data. Describe any interesting features of the scatterplot.
b. Find the equation of the least-squares line describing the relationship between y = medical cost and x = pollution.
c. Is the slope of the least-squares line positive or negative? Is this consistent with your description of the relationship in Part (a)?
d. Do the scatterplot and the equation of the least-squares line support the researchers' conclusion that elderly people who live in more polluted areas have higher medical costs? Explain.

5.15 ● The authors of the paper "Evaluating Existing Movement Hypotheses in Linear Systems Using Larval Stream Salamanders" (*Canadian Journal of Zoology* [2009]: 292–298) investigated whether water temperature was related to how far a salamander would swim and whether it would swim upstream or downstream. Data for 14 streams with different mean water temperatures where salamander larvae were released are given (approximated from a graph that appeared in the paper). The two variables of interest are x = mean water temperature (°C) and y = net directionality, which was defined as the difference in the relative frequency of the released salamander larvae moving upstream and the relative frequency of released salamander larvae moving downstream. A positive value of net directionality means a higher proportion were moving upstream than downstream. A negative value of net directionality means a higher proportion were moving downstream than upstream.

Mean Temperature (x)	Net Directionality (y)
6.17	−0.08
8.06	0.25
8.62	−0.14
10.56	0.00
12.45	0.08
11.99	0.03
12.50	−0.07
17.98	0.29
18.29	0.23
19.89	0.24
20.25	0.19
19.07	0.14
17.73	0.05
19.62	0.07

a. Construct a scatterplot of the data. How would you describe the relationship between x and y?
b. Find the equation of the least-squares line describing the relationship between y = net directionality and x = mean water temperature.
c. What value of net directionality would you predict for a stream that had mean water temperature of 15 °C?
d. The authors state that "when temperatures were warmer, more larvae were captured moving upstream, but when temperatures were cooler, more larvae were captured moving downstream." Do the scatterplot and least-squares line support this statement?
e. Approximately what mean temperature would result in a prediction of the same number of salamander larvae moving upstream and downstream?

5.16 ● The article "California State Parks Closure List Due Soon" (*The Sacramento Bee*, August 30, 2009) gave the following data on x = number of visitors in fiscal year 2007–2008 and y = percentage of operating costs covered by park revenues for the 20 state park districts in California:

Number of Visitors	Percentage of Operating Costs Covered by Park Revenues
2,755,849	37
1,124,102	19
1,802,972	32

(continued)

Number of Visitors	Percentage of Operating Costs Covered by Park Revenues
1,757,386	80
1,424,375	17
1,524,503	34
1,943,208	36
819,819	32
1,292,942	38
3,170,290	40
3,984,129	53
1,575,668	31
1,383,898	35
14,519,240	108
3,983,963	34
14,598,446	97
4,551,144	62
10,842,868	36
1,351,210	36
603,938	34

a. Use a statistical software package or a graphing calculator to construct a scatterplot of the data. Describe any interesting features of the scatterplot.
b. Find the equation of the least-squares regression line (use software or a graphing calculator).
c. Is the slope of the least-squares line positive or negative? Is this consistent with your description in Part (a)?
d. Based on the scatterplot, do you think that the correlation coefficient for this data set would be less than 0.5 or greater than 0.5? Explain.

5.17 A sample of 548 ethnically diverse students from Massachusetts were followed over a 19-month period from 1995 and 1997 in a study of the relationship between TV viewing and eating habits (*Pediatrics* [2003]: 1321–1326). For each additional hour of television viewed per day, the number of fruit and vegetable servings per day was found to decrease on average by 0.14 serving.

a. For this study, what is the dependent variable? What is the predictor variable?
b. Would the least-squares line for predicting number of servings of fruits and vegetables using number of hours spent watching TV as a predictor have a positive or negative slope? Explain.

5.18 The relationship between hospital patient-to-nurse ratio and various characteristics of job satisfaction and patient care has been the focus of a number of research studies. Suppose x = patient-to-nurse ratio is the predictor variable. For each of the following potential dependent variables, indicate whether you expect the slope of the least-squares line to be positive or negative and give a brief explanation for your choice.

a. y = a measure of nurse's job satisfaction (higher values indicate higher satisfaction)
b. y = a measure of patient satisfaction with hospital care (higher values indicate higher satisfaction)
c. y = a measure of patient quality of care.

5.19 ● ✦ The accompanying data on x = head circumference z score (a comparison score with peers of the same age—a positive score suggests a larger size than for peers) at age 6 to 14 months and y = volume of cerebral grey matter (in ml) at age 2 to 5 years were read from a graph in the article described in the chapter introduction (*Journal of the American Medical Association* [2003]).

Cerebral Grey Matter (ml) 2–5 yr	Head Circumference z Scores at 6–14 Months
680	−.75
690	1.2
700	−.3
720	.25
740	.3
740	1.5
750	1.1
750	2.0
760	1.1
780	1.1
790	2.0
810	2.1
815	2.8
820	2.2
825	.9
835	2.35
840	2.3
845	2.2

a. Construct a scatterplot for these data.
b. What is the value of the correlation coefficient?
c. Find the equation of the least-squares line.
d. Predict the volume of cerebral grey matter at age 2 to 5 years for a child whose head circumference z score at age 12 months was 1.8.
e. Explain why it would not be a good idea to use the least-squares line to predict the volume of grey matter for a child whose head circumference z score was 3.0.

5.20 Studies have shown that people who suffer sudden cardiac arrest have a better chance of survival if a defibrillator shock is administered very soon after cardiac arrest. How is survival rate related to the time between when cardiac arrest occurs and when the defibrillator shock is delivered? This question is addressed in the paper "Improving Survival from Sudden Cardiac Arrest: The Role of Home Defibrillators" (by J. K. Stross, University of Michigan, February 2002; available at www.heartstarthome.com). The accompanying data give y = survival rate (percent) and x = mean call-to-shock time (minutes) for a cardiac rehabilitation center (in which cardiac arrests occurred while victims were hospitalized and so the call-to-shock time tended to be short) and for four communities of different sizes:

Mean call-to-shock time, *x*	2	6	7	9	12
Survival rate, *y*	90	45	30	5	2

a. Construct a scatterplot for these data. How would you describe the relationship between mean call-to-shock time and survival rate?
b. Find the equation of the least-squares line.
c. Use the least-squares line to predict survival rate for a community with a mean call-to-shock time of 10 minutes.

5.21 The data given in the previous exercise on x = call-to-shock time (in minutes) and y = survival rate (percent) were used to compute the equation of the least-squares line, which was

$$\hat{y} = 101.33 - 9.30x$$

The newspaper article "FDA OKs Use of Home Defibrillators" (*San Luis Obispo Tribune*, November 13, 2002) reported that "every minute spent waiting for paramedics to arrive with a defibrillator lowers the chance of survival by 10 percent." Is this statement consistent with the given least-squares line? Explain.

5.22 An article on the cost of housing in California that appeared in the *San Luis Obispo Tribune* (March 30, 2001) included the following statement: "In Northern California, people from the San Francisco Bay area pushed into the Central Valley, benefiting from home prices that dropped on average $4000 for every mile traveled east of the Bay area." If this statement is correct, what is the slope of the least-squares regression line, $\hat{y} = a + bx$, where y = house price (in dollars) and x = distance east of the Bay (in miles)? Explain.

5.23 ● The following data on sale price, size, and land-to-building ratio for 10 large industrial properties appeared in the paper "Using Multiple Regression Analysis in Real Estate Appraisal" (*Appraisal Journal* [2002]: 424–430):

Property	Sale Price (millions of dollars)	Size (thousands of sq. ft.)	Land-to-Building Ratio
1	10.6	2166	2.0
2	2.6	751	3.5
3	30.5	2422	3.6
4	1.8	224	4.7
5	20.0	3917	1.7
6	8.0	2866	2.3
7	10.0	1698	3.1
8	6.7	1046	4.8
9	5.8	1108	7.6
10	4.5	405	17.2

a. Calculate and interpret the value of the correlation coefficient between sale price and size.
b. Calculate and interpret the value of the correlation coefficient between sale price and land-to-building ratio.
c. If you wanted to predict sale price and you could use either size or land-to-building ratio as the basis for making predictions, which would you use? Explain.
d. Based on your choice in Part (c), find the equation of the least-squares regression line you would use for predicting y = sale price.

5.24 ● Representative data read from a plot that appeared in the paper "Effect of Cattle Treading on Erosion from Hill Pasture: Modeling Concepts and Analysis of Rainfall Simulator Data" (*Australian Journal of Soil Research* [2002]: 963–977) on runoff sediment concentration for plots with varying amounts of grazing damage, measured by the percentage of bare ground in the plot, are given for gradually sloped plots and for steeply sloped plots.

Gradually Sloped Plots

Bare ground (%)	5	10	15	25
Concentration	50	200	250	500
Bare ground (%)	30	40		
Concentration	600	500		

(continued)

Steeply Sloped Plots

Bare ground (%)	5	5	10	15
Concentration	100	250	300	600
Bare ground (%)	20	25	20	30
Concentration	500	500	900	800
Bare ground (%)	35	40	35	
Concentration	1100	1200	1000	

a. Using the data for steeply sloped plots, find the equation of the least-squares line for predicting y = runoff sediment concentration using x = percentage of bare ground.
b. What would you predict runoff sediment concentration to be for a steeply sloped plot with 18% bare ground?
c. Would you recommend using the least-squares equation from Part (a) to predict runoff sediment concentration for gradually sloped plots? If so, explain why it would be appropriate to do so. If not, provide an alternative way to make such predictions.

5.25 Explain why it can be dangerous to use the least-squares line to obtain predictions for x values that are substantially larger or smaller than those contained in the sample.

5.26 The sales manager of a large company selected a random sample of $n = 10$ salespeople and determined for each one the values of x = years of sales experience and y = annual sales (in thousands of dollars). A scatterplot of the resulting (x, y) pairs showed a linear pattern.

a. Suppose that the sample correlation coefficient is $r = .75$ and that the average annual sales is $\bar{y} = 100$. If a particular salesperson is 2 standard deviations above the mean in terms of experience, what would you predict for that person's annual sales?
b. If a particular person whose sales experience is 1.5 standard deviations below the average experience is predicted to have an annual sales value that is 1 standard deviation below the average annual sales, what is the value of r?

5.27 Explain why the slope b of the least-squares line always has the same sign (positive or negative) as does the sample correlation coefficient r.

5.28 ● The accompanying data resulted from an experiment in which weld diameter x and shear strength y (in pounds) were determined for five different spot welds on steel. A scatterplot shows a strong linear pattern. With $\sum(x-\bar{x})^2 = 1000$ and $\sum(x-\bar{x})(y-\bar{y}) = 8577$, the least-squares line is $\hat{y} = -936.22 + 8.577x$.

x	200.1	210.1	220.1	230.1	240.0
y	813.7	785.3	960.4	1118.0	1076.2

a. Because 1 lb = 0.4536 kg, strength observations can be re-expressed in kilograms through multiplication by this conversion factor: new y = 0.4536(old y). What is the equation of the least-squares line when y is expressed in kilograms?
b. More generally, suppose that each y value in a data set consisting of n (x, y) pairs is multiplied by a conversion factor c (which changes the units of measurement for y). What effect does this have on the slope b (i.e., how does the new value of b compare to the value before conversion), on the intercept a, and on the equation of the least-squares line? Verify your conjectures by using the given formulas for b and a. (Hint: Replace y with cy, and see what happens—and remember, this conversion will affect $\bar{y}$.)

5.3 Assessing the Fit of a Line

Once the least-squares regression line has been obtained, the next step is to examine how effectively the line summarizes the relationship between x and y. Important questions to consider are

1. Is a line an appropriate way to summarize the relationship between the two variables?
2. Are there any unusual aspects of the data set that we need to consider before proceeding to use the regression line to make predictions?
3. If we decide that it is reasonable to use the regression line as a basis for prediction, how accurate can we expect predictions based on the regression line to be?

In this section, we look at graphical and numerical methods that will allow us to answer these questions. Most of these methods are based on the vertical deviations of the data points from the regression line. These vertical deviations are called *residuals*, and each represents the difference between an actual y value and the corresponding predicted value, $\hat{y}$, that would result from using the regression line to make a prediction.

Predicted Values and Residuals

The predicted value corresponding to the first observation in a data set is obtained by substituting that value, x_1, into the regression equation to obtain $\hat{y}_1$, where

$$\hat{y}_1 = a + bx_1$$

The difference between the actual y value for the first observation, y_1, and the corresponding predicted value is

$$y_1 - \hat{y}_1$$

This difference, called a *residual*, is the vertical deviation of a point in the scatterplot from the regression line.

An observation falling above the line results in a positive residual, whereas a point falling below the line results in a negative residual. This is shown in Figure 5.14.

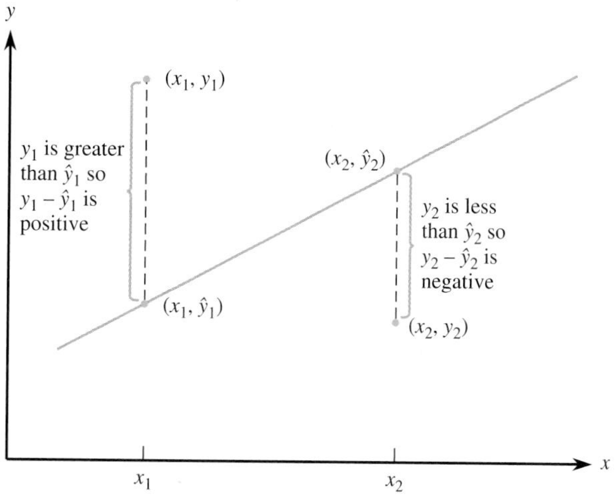

FIGURE 5.14
Positive and negative deviations from the least-squares line (residuals).

DEFINITION

The **predicted** or **fitted values** result from substituting each sample x value in turn into the equation for the least-squares line. This gives

$$\begin{aligned}\hat{y}_1 &= \textit{first predicted value} = a + bx_1\\ \hat{y}_2 &= \textit{second predicted value} = a + bx_2\\ &\vdots\\ \hat{y}_n &= \textit{nth predicted value} = a + bx_n\end{aligned}$$

The **residuals** from the least-squares line are the n quantities

$$\begin{aligned}y_1 - \hat{y}_1 &= \textit{first residual}\\ y_2 - \hat{y}_2 &= \textit{second residual}\\ &\vdots\\ y_n - \hat{y}_n &= \textit{nth residual}\end{aligned}$$

Each residual is the difference between an observed y value and the corresponding predicted y value.

EXAMPLE 5.7 It May Be a Pile of Debris to You, but It Is Home to a Mouse

● The accompanying data is a subset of data read from a scatterplot that appeared in the paper "Small Mammal Responses to fine Woody Debris and Forest Fuel Reduction in Southwest Oregon" (*Journal of Wildlife Management* [2005]: 625–632). The authors of the paper were interested in how the distance a deer mouse will travel for food is related to the distance from the food to the nearest pile of fine woody debris. Distances were measured in meters. The data are given in Table 5.1.

● Data set available online

TABLE 5.1 Predicted Values and Residuals for the Data of Example 5.7

Distance From Debris (x)	Distance Traveled (y)	Predicted Distance Traveled ($\hat{y}$)	Residual ($y - \hat{y}$)
6.94	0.00	14.76	−14.76
5.23	6.13	9.23	−3.10
5.21	11.29	9.16	2.13
7.10	14.35	15.28	−0.93
8.16	12.03	18.70	−6.67
5.50	22.72	10.10	12.62
9.19	20.11	22.04	−1.93
9.05	26.16	21.58	4.58
9.36	30.65	22.59	8.06

Minitab was used to fit the least-squares regression line. Partial computer output follows:

Regression Analysis: Distance Traveled versus Distance to Debris

The regression equation is

Distance Traveled = −7.7 + 3.23 Distance to Debris

Predictor	Coef	SE Coef	T	P
Constant	−7.69	13.33	−0.58	0.582
Distance to Debris	3.234	1.782	1.82	0.112

S = 8.67071 R-Sq = 32.0% R-Sq(adj) = 22.3%

The resulting least-squares line is $\hat{y} = -7.69 + 3.234x$.

A plot of the data that also includes the regression line is shown in Figure 5.15. The residuals for this data set are the signed vertical distances from the points to the line.

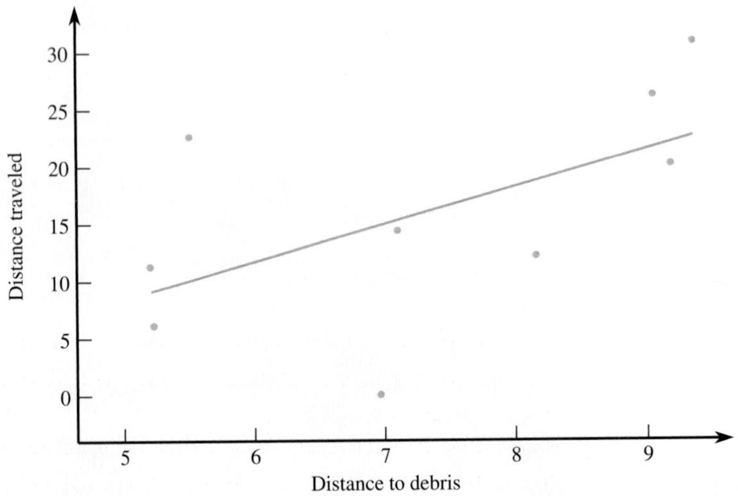

FIGURE 5.15
Scatterplot for the data of Example 5.7.

For the mouse with the smallest x value (the third observation with $x_3 = 5.21$ and $y_3 = 11.29$), the corresponding predicted value and residual are

$$\text{predicted value} = \hat{y}_3 = -7.69 + 3.234(x_3) = -7.69 + 3.234(5.21) = 9.16$$

$$\text{residual} = y_3 - \hat{y}_3 = 11.29 - 9.16 = 2.13$$

The other predicted values and residuals are computed in a similar manner and are included in Table 5.1.

Computing the predicted values and residuals by hand can be tedious, but Minitab and other statistical software packages, as well as many graphing calculators, include them as part of the output, as shown in Figure 5.16. The predicted values and residuals can be found in the table at the bottom of the Minitab output in the columns labeled "Fit" and "Residual," respectively.

The regression equation is
Distance Traveled = – 7.7 + 3.23 Distance to Debris

Predictor	Coef	SE Coef	T	P
Constant	–7.69	13.33	–0.58	0.582
Distance to Debris	3.234	1.782	1.82	0.112

S = 8.67071 R-Sq = 32.0% R-Sq(adj) = 22.3%

Analysis of Variance

Source	DF	SS	MS	F	P
Regression	1	247.68	247.68	3.29	0.112
Residual Error	7	526.27	75.18		
Total	8	773.95			

Obs	Distance to Debris	Distance Traveled	Fit	SE Fit	Residual	St Resid
1	6.94	0.00	14.76	2.96	–14.76	–1.81
2	5.23	6.13	9.23	4.69	–3.10	–0.42
3	5.21	11.29	9.16	4.72	2.13	0.29
4	7.10	14.35	15.28	2.91	–0.93	–0.11
5	8.16	12.03	18.70	3.27	–6.67	–0.83
6	5.50	22.72	10.10	4.32	12.62	1.68
7	9.19	20.11	22.04	4.43	–1.93	–0.26
8	9.05	26.16	21.58	4.25	4.58	0.61
9	9.36	30.65	22.59	4.67	8.06	1.10

FIGURE 5.16
Minitab output for the data of Example 5.7.

Plotting the Residuals

A careful look at residuals can reveal many potential problems. A *residual plot* is a good place to start when assessing the appropriateness of the regression line.

DEFINITION

A **residual plot** is a scatterplot of the (x, residual) pairs. Isolated points or a pattern of points in the residual plot indicate potential problems.

A desirable residual plot is one that exhibits no particular pattern, such as curvature. Curvature in the residual plot is an indication that the relationship between x and y is not linear and that a curve would be a better choice than a line for describing the relationship between x and y. This is sometimes easier to see in a residual plot than in a scatterplot of y versus x, as illustrated in Example 5.8.

EXAMPLE 5.8 Heights and Weights of American Women

● Consider the accompanying data on x = height (in inches) and y = average weight (in pounds) for American females, age 30–39 (from *The World Almanac and Book of Facts*). The scatterplot displayed in Figure 5.17(a) appears rather straight. However, when the residuals from the least-squares line ($\hat{y} = 98.23 + 3.59x$) are plotted (Figure 5.17(b)), substantial curvature is apparent (even though $r \approx .99$). It is not accurate to say that weight increases in direct proportion to height (linearly with height). Instead, average weight increases somewhat more rapidly for relatively large heights than it does for relatively small heights.

● Data set available online

x	58	59	60	61	62	63	64	65
y	113	115	118	121	124	128	131	134

x	66	67	68	69	70	71	72
y	137	141	145	150	153	159	164

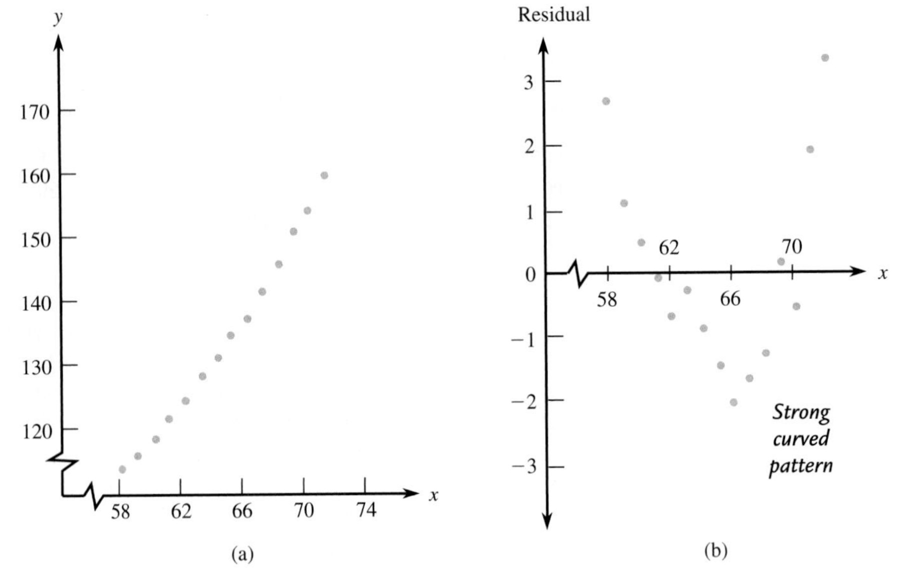

FIGURE 5.17
Plots for the data of Example 5.8: (a) scatterplot; (b) residual plot.

There is another common type of residual plot—one that plots the residuals versus the corresponding $\hat{y}$ values rather than versus the x values. Because $\hat{y} = a + bx$ is simply a linear function of x, the only real difference between the two types of residual plots is the scale on the horizontal axis. The pattern of points in the residual plots will be the same, and it is this pattern of points that is important, not the scale. Thus the two plots give equivalent information, as can be seen in Figure 5.18, which gives both plots for the data of Example 5.7.

It is also important to look for unusual values in the scatterplot or in the residual plot. A point falling far above or below the horizontal line at height 0 corresponds to a large residual, which may indicate some type of unusual behavior, such as a recording error, a nonstandard experimental condition, or an atypical experimental subject. A point whose x value differs greatly from others in the data set may have exerted excessive influence in determining the fitted line. One method for assessing the impact of such an isolated point on the fit is to delete it from the data set, recompute the best-fit line, and evaluate the extent to which the equation of the line has changed.

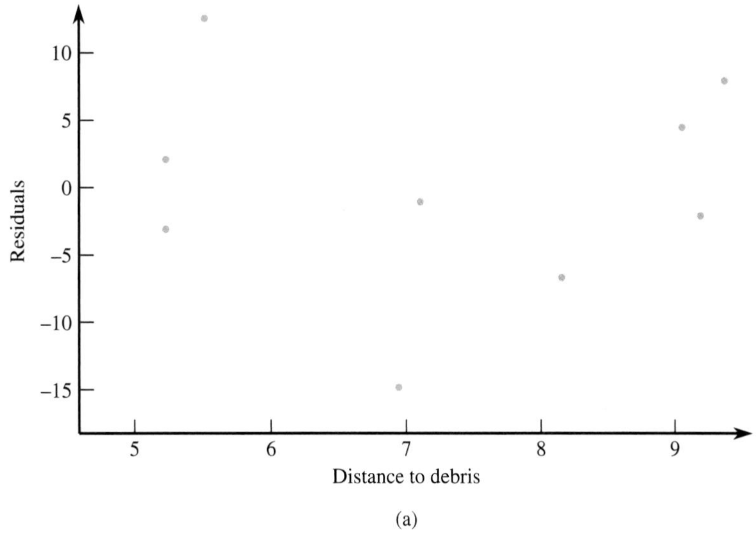

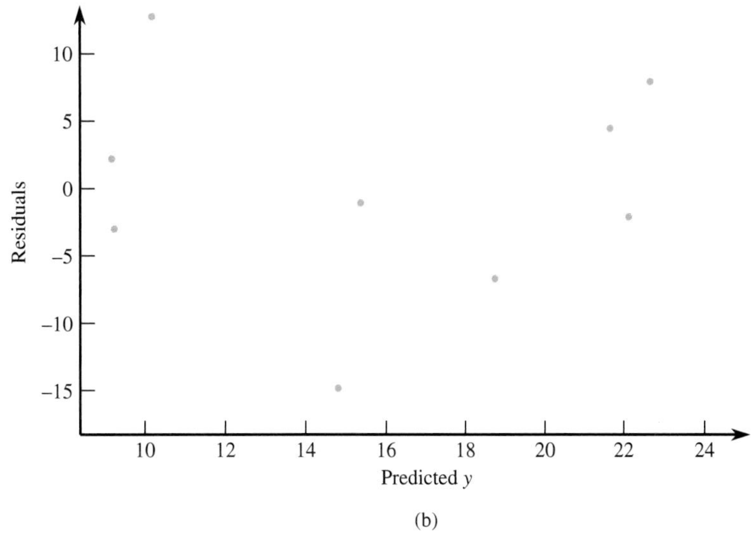

FIGURE 5.18
Plots for the data of Example 5.7.
(a) Plot of residuals versus x;
(b) plot of residuals versus $\hat{y}$.

EXAMPLE 5.9 Older Than Your Average Bear

● The accompanying data on x = age (in years) and y = weight (in kg) for 12 black bears appeared in the paper "Habitat Selection by Black Bears in an Intensively Logged Boreal Forest" (*Canadian Journal of Zoology* [2008]: 1307–1316).

A scatterplot and residual plot are shown in Figures 5.19(a) and 5.19(b), respectively. One bear in the sample was much older than the other bears (bear 3 with an age of $x = 28.5$ years and a weight of $y = 62.00$ kg). This results in a point in the scatterplot that is far to the right of the other points in the scatterplot. Because the least-squares line minimizes the sum of squared residuals, the line is pulled toward this observation. This single observation plays a big role in determining the slope of the least-squares line, and it is therefore called an *influential observation.* Notice that this influential observation is not necessarily one with a large residual, because the least-squares line actually passes near this point. Figure 5.20 shows what happens when the influential observation is removed from the data set. Both the slope and intercept of the least-squares line are quite different from the slope and intercept of the line with this influential observation included.

● Data set available online

Bear	Age	Weight
1	10.5	54
2	6.5	40
3	28.5	62
4	10.5	51
5	6.5	55
6	7.5	56
7	6.5	62
8	5.5	42
9	7.5	40
10	11.5	59
11	9.5	51
12	5.5	50

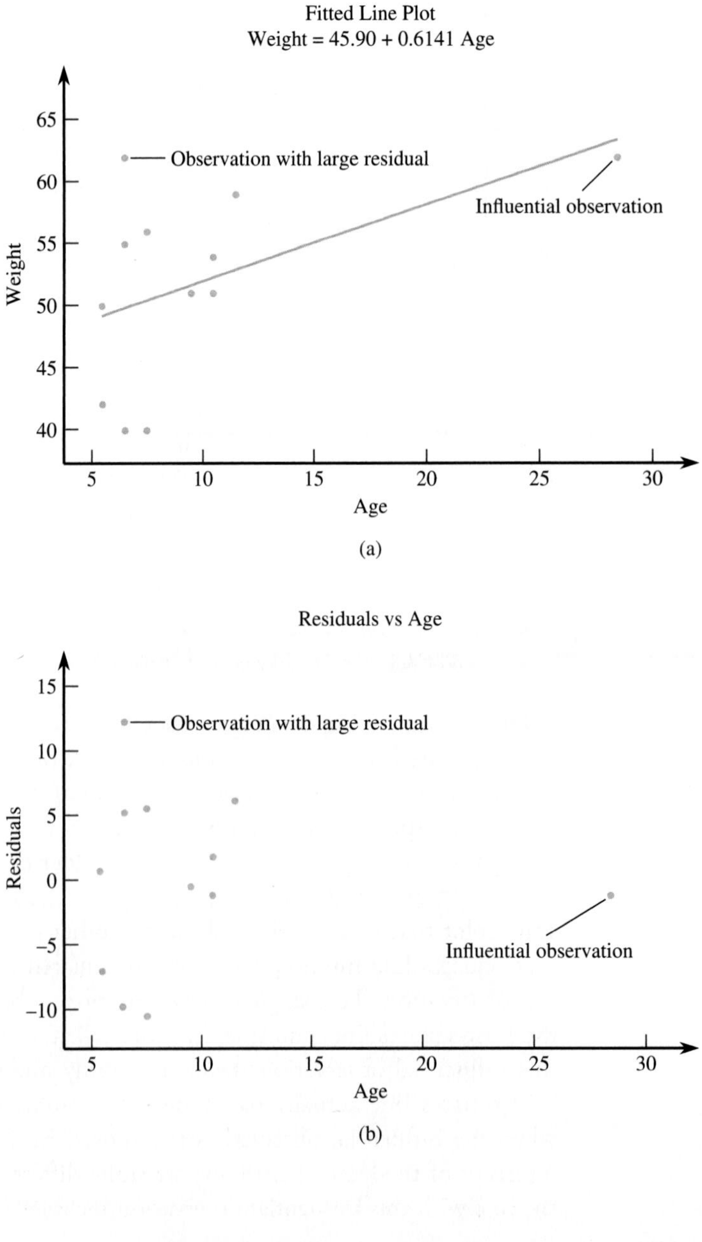

FIGURE 5.19
Minitab plots for the bear data of Example 5.9: (a) scatterplot; (b) residual plot.

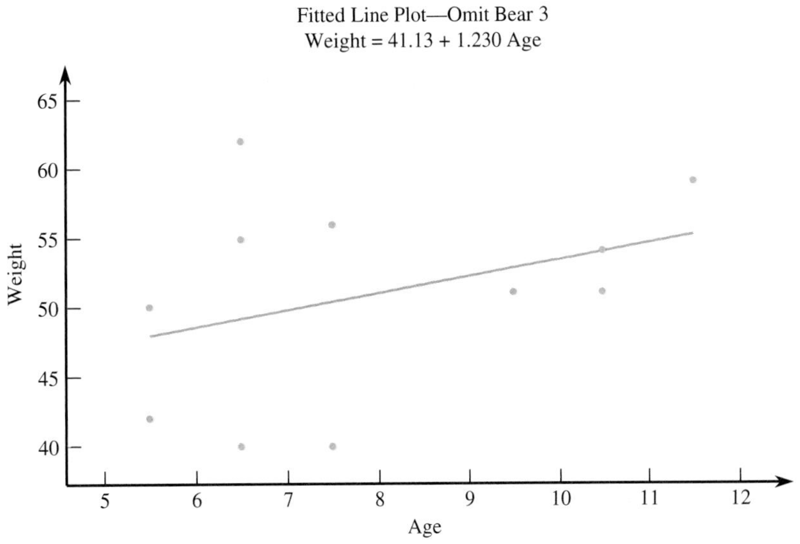

FIGURE 5.20
Scatterplot and least-squares line with bear 3 removed from data set.

Some points in the scatterplot may fall far from the least-squares line in the y direction, resulting in a large residual. These points are sometimes referred to as outliers. In this example, the observation with the largest residual is bear 7 with an age of $x = 6.5$ years and a weight of $y = 62.00$ kg. This observation is labeled in Figure 5.19. Even though this observation has a large residual, this observation is not influential. The equation of the least-squares line for the data set consisting of all 12 observations is $\hat{y} = 45.90 + 0.6141x$, which is not much different from the equation that results from deleting bear 7 from the data set ($\hat{y} = 43.81 + 0.7131x$).

Unusual points in a bivariate data set are those that fall away from most of the other points in the scatterplot in either the x direction or the y direction.

An observation is potentially an **influential observation** if it has an x value that is far away from the rest of the data (separated from the rest of the data in the x direction). To determine if the observation is in fact influential, we assess whether removal of this observation has a large impact on the value of the slope or intercept of the least-squares line.

An observation is an **outlier** if it has a large residual. Outlier observations fall far away from the least-squares line in the y direction.

Careful examination of a scatterplot and a residual plot can help us determine the appropriateness of a line for summarizing a relationship. If we decide that a line is appropriate, the next step is to think about assessing the accuracy of predictions based on the least-squares line and whether these predictions (based on the value of x) are better in general than those made without knowledge of the value of x. Two numerical measures that are helpful in this assessment are the coefficient of determination and the standard deviation about the regression line.

Coefficient of Determination

Suppose that we would like to predict the price of homes in a particular city. A random sample of 20 homes that are for sale is selected, and $y =$ price and $x =$ size (in square feet) are recorded for each house in the sample. There will be variability in house price (the houses will differ with respect to price), and it is this variability that makes accurate prediction of price a challenge. How much of the variability in house price can be explained by the fact that price is related to house size and that houses differ in size? If differences in size account for a large proportion of the variability in price, a price prediction that takes house size into account is a big improvement over a prediction that is not based on size.

The **coefficient of determination** is a measure of the proportion of variability in the y variable that can be "explained" by a linear relationship between x and y.

DEFINITION

The **coefficient of determination**, denoted by r^2, gives the proportion of variation in y that can be attributed to an approximate linear relationship between x and y.

The value of r^2 is often converted to a percentage (by multiplying by 100) and interpreted as the percentage of variation in y that can be explained by an approximate linear relationship between x and y.

To understand how r^2 is computed, we first consider variation in the y values. Variation in y can effectively be explained by an approximate straight-line relationship when the points in the scatterplot fall close to the least-squares line—that is, when the residuals are small in magnitude. A natural measure of variation about the least-squares line is the sum of the squared residuals. (Squaring before combining prevents negative and positive residuals from counteracting one another.) A second sum of squares assesses the total amount of variation in observed y values by considering how spread out the y values are from the mean y value.

DEFINITION

The **total sum of squares**, denoted by **SSTo**, is defined as

$$\text{SSTo} = (y_1 - \bar{y})^2 + (y_2 - \bar{y})^2 + \cdots + (y_n - \bar{y})^2 = \sum(y - \bar{y})^2$$

The **residual sum of squares** (sometimes referred to as the error sum of squares), denoted by **SSResid**, is defined as

$$\text{SSResid} = (y_1 - \hat{y}_1)^2 + (y_2 - \hat{y}_2)^2 + \cdots + (y_n - \hat{y}_n)^2 = \sum(y - \hat{y})^2$$

These sums of squares can be found as part of the regression output from most standard statistical packages or can be obtained using the following computational formulas:

$$\text{SSTo} = \sum y^2 - \frac{(\sum y)^2}{n}$$

$$\text{SSResid} = \sum y^2 - a\sum y - b\sum xy$$

EXAMPLE 5.10 Revisiting the Deer Mice Data

Figure 5.21 displays part of the Minitab output that results from fitting the least-squares line to the data on y = distance traveled for food and x = distance to nearest woody debris pile from Example 5.7. From the output,

$$\text{SSTo} = 773.95 \text{ and } \text{SSResid} = 526.27$$

Notice that SSResid is fairly large relative to SSTo.

Regression Analysis: Distance Traveled versus Distance to Debris

The regression equation is
Distance Traveled = – 7.7 + 3.23 Distance to Debris

Predictor	Coef	SE Coef	T	P
Constant	–7.69	13.33	–0.58	0.582
Distance to Debris	3.234	1.782	1.82	0.112

S = 8.67071 R-Sq = 32.0% R-Sq(adj) = 22.3%

Analysis of Variance

Source	DF	SS	MS	F	P
Regression	1	247.68	247.68	3.29	0.112
Residual Error	7	526.27	75.18		
Total	8	773.95			

SSTo SSResid

FIGURE 5.21
Minitab output for the data of Example 5.10.

The residual sum of squares is the sum of squared vertical deviations from the least-squares line. As Figure 5.22 illustrates, SSTo is also a sum of squared vertical deviations from a line—the horizontal line at height $\bar{y}$. The least-squares line is, by definition, the one having the smallest sum of squared deviations. It follows that SSResid $\leq$ SSTo. The two sums of squares are equal only when the least-squares line *is* the horizontal line.

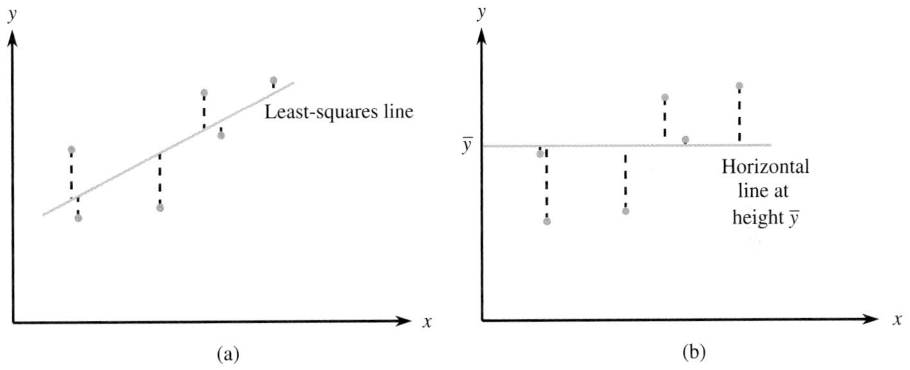

FIGURE 5.22
Interpreting sums of squares: (a) SSResid = sum of squared vertical deviations from the least-squares line; (b) SSTo = sum of squared vertical deviations from the horizontal line at height $\bar{y}$.

SSResid is often referred to as a measure of unexplained variation—the amount of variation in y that cannot be attributed to the linear relationship between x and y. The more the points in the scatterplot deviate from the least-squares line, the larger the value of SSResid and the greater the amount of y variation that cannot be explained by the approximate linear relationship. Similarly, SSTo is interpreted as a measure of total variation. The larger the value of SSTo, the greater the amount of variability in $y_1, y_2, \ldots, y_n$.

The ratio SSResid/SSTo is the fraction or proportion of total variation that is unexplained by a straight-line relation. Subtracting this ratio from 1 gives the proportion of total variation that *is* explained:

The coefficient of determination is computed as

$$r^2 = 1 - \frac{\text{SSResid}}{\text{SSTo}}$$

Multiplying r^2 by 100 gives the percentage of y variation attributable to the approximate linear relationship. The closer this percentage is to 100%, the more successful is the relationship in explaining variation in y.

EXAMPLE 5.11 r^2 for the Deer Mice Data

For the data on distance traveled for food and distance to nearest debris pile from Example 5.10, we found SSTo = 773.95 and SSResid = 526.27. Thus

$$r^2 = 1 - \frac{\text{SSResid}}{\text{SSTo}} = 1 - \frac{526.27}{773.95} = .32$$

This means that only 32% of the observed variability in distance traveled for food can be explained by an approximate linear relationship between distance traveled for food and distance to nearest debris pile. Note that the r^2 value can be found in the Minitab output of Figure 5.21, labeled "R-Sq."

The symbol r was used in Section 5.1 to denote Pearson's sample correlation coefficient. It is not coincidental that r^2 is used to represent the coefficient of determination. The notation suggests how these two quantities are related:

$$(\text{correlation coefficient})^2 = \text{coefficient of determination}$$

Thus, if $r = .8$ or $r = -.8$, then $r^2 = .64$, so 64% of the observed variation in the dependent variable can be explained by the linear relationship. Because the value of r does not depend on which variable is labeled x, the same is true of r^2. The coefficient of determination is one of the few quantities computed in a regression analysis whose value remains the same when the roles of dependent and independent variables are interchanged. When $r = .5$, we get $r^2 = .25$, so only 25% of the observed variation is explained by a linear relation. This is why a value of r between $-.5$ and $.5$ is not considered evidence of a strong linear relationship.

EXAMPLE 5.12 Lead Exposure and Brain Volume

The authors of the paper "Decreased Brain Volume in Adults with Childhood Lead Exposure" (*Public Library of Science Medicine* [May 27, 2008]: e112) studied the relationship between childhood environmental lead exposure and a measure of brain volume change in a particular region of the brain. Data on x = mean childhood blood lead level (μg/dL) and y = brain volume change (percent) read from a graph that appeared in the paper was used to produce the scatterplot in Figure 5.23. The least-squares line is also shown on the scatterplot.

Figure 5.24 displays part of the Minitab output that results from fitting the least-squares line to the data. Notice that although there is a slight tendency for smaller y values (corresponding to a brain volume decrease) to be paired with higher values of mean blood lead levels, the relationship is weak. The points in the plot are widely scattered around the least-squares line.

From the computer output, we see that $100r^2 = 13.6\%$, so $r^2 = .136$. This means that differences in childhood mean blood lead level explain only 13.6% of the variability in adult brain volume change. Because the coefficient of determination is the square of the correlation coefficient, we can compute the value of the correlation

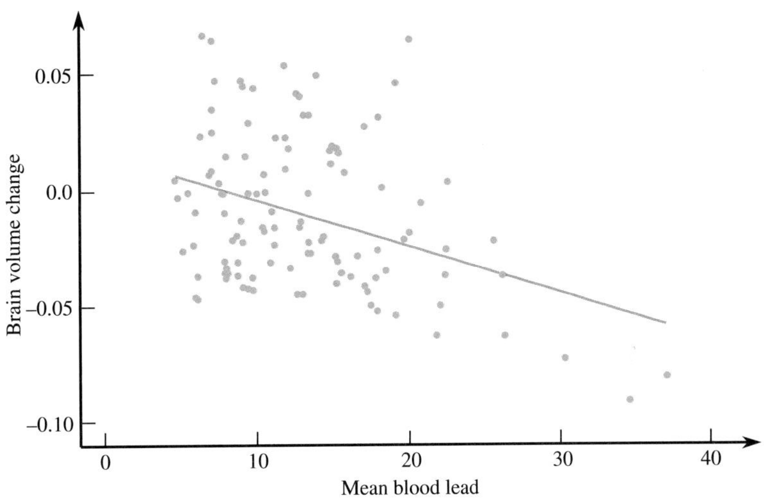

FIGURE 5.23
Scatterplot and least-squares line for the data of Example 5.12.

Regression Analysis: Brain Volume Change versus Mean Blood Lead

The regression equation is
Brain Volume Change = 0.01559 – 0.001993 Mean Blood Lead

S = 0.0310931 R-Sq = 13.6% R-Sq(adj) = 12.9%

Analysis of Variance

Source	DF	SS	MS	F	P
Regression	1	0.016941	0.0169410	17.52	0.000
Error	111	0.107313	0.0009668		
Total	112	0.124254			

FIGURE 5.24
Minitab output for the data of Example 5.12.

coefficient by taking the square root of r^2. In this case, we know that the correlation coefficient will be negative (because there is a negative relationship between x and y), so we want the negative square root:

$$r = -\sqrt{.136} = -.369$$

Based on the values of the correlation coefficient and the coefficient of determination, we would conclude that there is a weak negative linear relationship and that childhood mean blood lead level explains only about 13.6% of adult change in brain volume.

AP* EXAM TIP

Assessing the fit of a line involves looking at all of the evidence—both graphical and numerical. The first step should be to examine the residual plot for any suspicious patterns. If nothing troubling is found, then consider both the value of the coefficient of determination and the value of the standard deviation about the regression line.

Standard Deviation About the Least-Squares Line

The coefficient of determination measures the extent of variation about the best-fit line *relative* to overall variation in y. A high value of r^2 does not by itself promise that the deviations from the line are small in an absolute sense. A typical observation could deviate from the line by quite a bit, yet these deviations might still be small relative to overall y variation.

Recall that in Chapter 4 the sample standard deviation

$$s = \sqrt{\frac{\sum(x - \bar{x})^2}{n - 1}}$$

was used as a measure of variability in a single sample; roughly speaking, s is the typical amount by which a sample observation deviates from the mean. There is an analogous measure of variability when a least-squares line is fit.

DEFINITION

The **standard deviation about the least-squares line** is given by

$$s_e = \sqrt{\frac{\text{SSResid}}{n - 2}}$$

Roughly speaking, s_e is the typical amount by which an observation deviates from the least-squares line. Justification for division by $(n - 2)$ and the use of the subscript e is given in Chapter 13.

EXAMPLE 5.13 Predicting Graduation Rates

● Consider the accompanying data from 2007 on six-year graduation rate (%), student-related expenditure per full-time student, and median SAT score for the 38 primarily undergraduate public universities and colleges in the United States with enrollments between 10,000 and 20,000 (Source: College Results Online, The Education Trust).

Graduation Rate	Expenditure	Median SAT
81.2	7462	1160
66.8	7310	1115
66.4	6959	1070
66.1	8810	1205
64.9	7657	1135
63.7	8063	1060
62.6	8352	1130
62.5	7789	1200
61.2	8106	1015
59.8	7776	1100
56.6	8515	990
54.8	7037	1085
52.7	8715	1040
52.4	7780	1040
52.4	7198	1105
50.5	7429	975
49.9	7551	1030
48.9	8112	1030
48.1	8149	950
46.5	6744	1010
45.3	8842	1223
45.2	7743	990
43.7	5587	1010
43.5	7166	1010
42.9	5749	950
42.1	6268	955
42.0	8477	985
38.9	7076	990
38.8	8153	990
38.3	7342	910
35.9	8444	1075

● Data set available online

Graduation Rate	Expenditure	Median SAT
32.8	7245	885
32.6	6408	1060
32.3	4981	990
31.8	7333	970
31.3	7984	905
31.0	5811	1010
26.0	7410	1005

Figure 5.25 displays scatterplots of graduation rate versus student-related expenditure and graduation rate versus median SAT score. The least-squares lines and the values of r^2 and s_e are also shown.

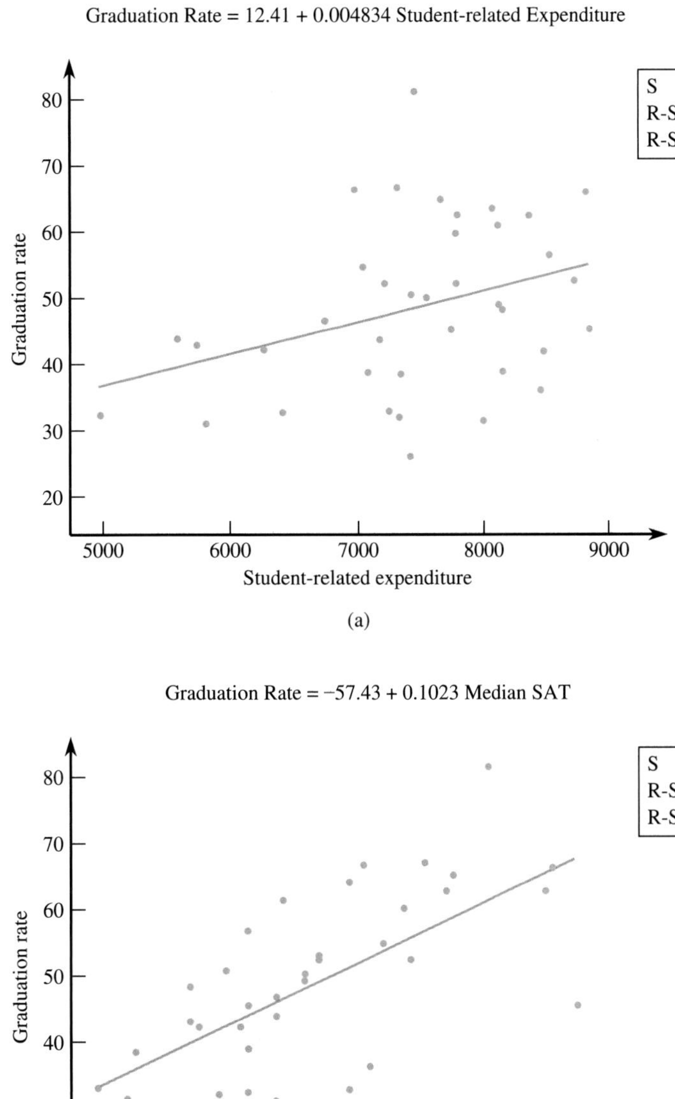

FIGURE 5.25
Scatterplots for the data of Example 5.13: (a) graduation rate versus student-related expenditure; (b) graduation rate versus median SAT.

Notice that while there is a positive linear relationship between student-related expenditure and graduation rate, the relationship is weak. The value of r^2 is only .119 (11.9%), indicating that only about 11.9% of the variability in graduation rate from university to university can be explained by student-related expenditures. The standard deviation about the regression line is $s_e = 12.2846$, which is larger than s_e for the predictor median SAT, a reflection of the fact that the points in the scatterplot of graduation rate versus student-related expenditure tend to fall farther from the regression line than is the case for the line that describes graduation rate versus median SAT. The value of r^2 for graduation rate versus median SAT is .421 (42.1%) and $s_e = 9.95214$, indicating that the predictor median SAT does a better job of explaining variability in graduation rates and the corresponding least-squares line would be expected to produce more accurate estimates of graduation rates than would be the case for the predictor student-related expenditure.

Based on the values of r^2 and s_e, median SAT would be a better choice for predicting graduation rates than student-related expenditures. It is also possible to develop a prediction equation that would incorporate both potential predictors—techniques for doing this are introduced in Chapter 14.

EXERCISES 5.29 - 5.43

5.29 ● The data in the accompanying table is from the paper "Six-Minute Walk Test in Children and Adolescents" (*The Journal of Pediatrics* [2007]: 395–399). Two hundred and eighty boys completed a test that measures the distance that the subject can walk on a flat, hard surface in 6 minutes. For each age group shown in the table, the median distance walked by the boys in that age group is also given.

Age Group	Representative Age (Midpoint of Age Group)	Median Six-minute Walk Distance (meters)
3–5	4	544.3
6–8	7	584.0
9–11	10	667.3
12–15	13.5	701.1
16–18	17	727.6

a. With x = representative age and y = median distance walked in 6 minutes, construct a scatterplot. Does the pattern in the scatterplot look linear?

b. Find the equation of the least-squares regression line that describes the relationship between median distance walked in 6 minutes and representative age.

c. Compute the five residuals and construct a residual plot. Are there any unusual features in the plot?

5.30 ● The paper referenced in the previous exercise also gave the 6-minute walk distances for 248 girls age 3 to 18 years. The median 6-minute walk times for girls for the five age groups were

492.4 578.3 655.8 657.6 660.9

a. With x = representative age and y = median distance walked in 6 minutes, construct a scatterplot. How does the pattern in the scatterplot for girls differ from the pattern in the scatterplot for boys from Exercise 5.29?

b. Find the equation of the least-squares regression line that describes the relationship between median distance walked in 6 minutes and representative age for girls.

c. Compute the five residuals and construct a residual plot. The authors of the paper decided to use a curve rather than a straight line to describe the relationship between median distance walked in 6 minutes and age for girls. What aspect of the residual plot supports this decision?

5.31 ● Data on pollution and cost of medical care for elderly people were given in Exercise 5.14 and are also shown here. The accompanying data are a measure of pollution (micrograms of particulate matter per cubic meter of air) and the cost of medical care per person over age 65 for six geographic regions of the United States.

Region	Pollution	Cost of Medical Care
North	30.0	915
Upper South	31.8	891
Deep South	32.1	968
West South	26.8	972
Big Sky	30.4	952
West	40.0	899

The equation of the least-squares regression line for this data set is $\hat{y} = 1082.2 - 4.691x$, where y = medical cost and x = pollution.

a. Compute the six residuals.

b. What is the value of the correlation coefficient for this data set? Does the value of r indicate that the linear relationship between pollution and medical cost is strong, moderate, or weak? Explain.

c. Construct a residual plot. Are there any unusual features of the plot?

d. The observation for the West, (40.0, 899), has an x value that is far removed from the other x values in the sample. Is this observation influential in determining the values of the slope and/or intercept of the least-squares line? Justify your answer.

5.32 ● Northern flying squirrels eat lichen and fungi, which makes for a relatively low quality diet. The authors of the paper "Nutritional Value and Diet Preference of Arboreal Lichens and Hypogeous Fungi for Small Mammals in the Rocky Mountain" (*Canadian Journal of Zoology* [2008]: 851–862) measured nitrogen intake and nitrogen retention in six flying squirrels that were fed the fungus *Rhizopogon*. Data read from a graph that appeared in the paper are given in the table below. (The negative value for nitrogen retention for the first squirrel represents a net loss in nitrogen.)

Nitrogen Intake, x (grams)	Nitrogen Retention, y (grams)
0.03	−0.04
0.10	0.00
0.07	0.01
0.06	0.01
0.07	0.04
0.25	0.11

a. Construct a scatterplot of these data.

b. Find the equation of the least-squares regression line. Based on this line, what would you predict nitrogen retention to be for a flying squirrel whose nitrogen intake is 0.06 grams? What is the residual associated with the observation (0.06, 0.01)?

c. Look again at the scatterplot from Part (a). Which observation is potentially influential? Explain the reason for your choice.

d. When the potentially influential observation is deleted from the data set, the equation of the least-squares regression line fit to the remaining five observations is $\hat{y} = -0.037 + 0.627x$. Use this equation to predict nitrogen retention for a flying squirrel whose nitrogen intake is 0.06. Is this prediction much different than the prediction made in Part (b)?

5.33 ● The relationship between x = total number of salmon in a creek and y = percentage of salmon killed by bears that were transported away from the stream prior to the bear eating the salmon was examined in the paper "Transportation of Pacific Salmon Carcasses from Streams to Riparian Forests by Bears" (*Canadian Journal of Zoology* [2009]: 195–203). Data for the 10 years from 1999 to 2008 is given in the accompanying table.

Total Number	Percentage Transported
19,504	77.8
3,460	28.7
1,976	28.9
8,439	27.9
11,142	55.3
3,467	20.4
3,928	46.8
20,440	76.3
7,850	40.3
4,134	24.1

a. Construct a scatterplot of the data. Does there appear to be a relationship between the total number of salmon in the stream and the percentage of salmon killed by bears that are transported away from the stream?

b. Find the equation of the least-squares regression line. Draw the regression line for the scatterplot from Part (a).

c. The residuals from the least-squares line are shown in the accompanying table. The observation (3928, 46.8) has a large residual. Is this data point also an influential observation?

Total Number	Percent Transported	Residual
19,504	77.8	3.43
3,460	28.7	0.30
1,976	28.9	4.76
8,439	27.9	−14.76
11,142	55.3	4.89
3,467	20.4	−8.02
3,928	46.8	17.06
20,440	76.3	−0.75
7,850	40.3	−0.68
4,134	24.1	−6.23

d. The two points with unusually large x values (19,504 and 20,440) were not thought to be influential observations even though they are far removed in the x direction from the rest of the points in the scatterplot. Explain why these two points are not influential.

e. Partial Minitab output resulting from fitting the least-squares line is shown here. What is the value of s_e? Write a sentence interpreting this value.

Regression Analysis: Percent Transported versus Total Number

The regression equation is

Percent Transported = 18.5 + 0.00287 Total Number

Predictor	Coef	SE Coef	T	P
Constant	18.483	4.813	3.84	0.005
Total Number	0.0028655	0.0004557	6.29	0.000

S = 9.16217 R-Sq = 83.2% R-Sq(adj) = 81.1%

f. What is the value of r^2 for this data set (see Minitab output in Part (e))? Is the value of r^2 large or small? Write a sentence interpreting the value of r^2.

5.34 ● The paper "Effects of Age and Gender on Physical Performance" (*Age* [2007]: 77–85) describes a study of the relationship between age and 1-hour swimming performance. Data on age and swim distance for over 10,000 men participating in a national long-distance 1-hour swimming competition are summarized in the accompanying table.

Age Group	Representative Age (Midpoint of Age Group)	Average Swim Distance (meters)
20–29	25	3913.5
30–39	35	3728.8
40–49	45	3579.4
50–59	55	3361.9
60–69	65	3000.1
70–79	75	2649.0
80–89	85	2118.4

(continued)

a. Find the equation of the least-squares line with x = representative age and y = average swim distance.

b. Compute the seven residuals and use them to construct a residual plot. What does the residual plot suggest about the appropriateness of using a line to describe the relationship between representative age and swim distance?

c. Would it be reasonable to use the least-squares line from Part (a) to predict the average swim distance for women age 40 to 49 by substituting the representative age of 45 into the equation of the least-squares line? Explain.

5.35 Data on x = representative age and y = 6-minute walk time for boys were given in Exercise 5.29. Compute the values of s_e and r^2 for these data. What do these values tell you about the fit of the least-squares line?

5.36 ● Cost-to-charge ratio (the percentage of the amount billed that represents the actual cost) for inpatient and outpatient services at 11 Oregon hospitals is shown in the following table (Oregon Department of Health Services, 2002). A scatterplot of the data is also shown.

	Cost-to-Charge Ratio	
Hospital	Outpatient Care	Inpatient Care
1	62	80
2	66	76
3	63	75
4	51	62
5	75	100
6	65	88
7	56	64
8	45	50
9	48	54
10	71	83
11	54	100

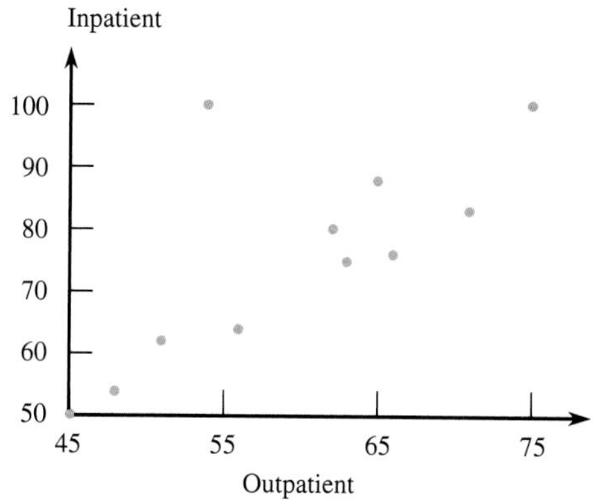

The least-squares regression line with y = inpatient cost-to-charge ratio and x = outpatient cost-to-charge ratio is $\hat{y} = -1.1 + 1.29x$.

a. Is the observation for Hospital 11 an influential observation? Justify your answer.
b. Is the observation for Hospital 11 an outlier? Explain.
c. Is the observation for Hospital 5 an influential observation? Justify your answer.
d. Is the observation for Hospital 5 an outlier? Explain.

5.37 The article "Examined Life: What Stanley H. Kaplan Taught Us About the SAT" (*The New Yorker* [December 17, 2001]: 86–92) included a summary of findings regarding the use of SAT I scores, SAT II scores, and high school grade point average (GPA) to predict first-year college GPA. The article states that "among these, SAT II scores are the best predictor, explaining 16 percent of the variance in first-year college grades. GPA was second at 15.4 percent, and SAT I was last at 13.3 percent."

a. If the data from this study were used to fit a least-squares line with y = first-year college GPA and x = high school GPA, what would be the value of r^2?
b. The article stated that SAT II was the best predictor of first-year college grades. Do you think that predictions based on a least-squares line with y = first-year college GPA and x = SAT II score would be very accurate? Explain why or why not.

5.38 ● The paper "Accelerated Telomere Shortening in Response to Life Stress" (*Proceedings of the National Academy of Sciences* [2004]: 17312–17315) described a study that examined whether stress accelerates aging at a cellular level. The accompanying data on a measure of perceived stress (x) and telomere length (y) were read from a scatterplot that appeared in the paper. Telomere length is a measure of cell longevity.

Perceived Stress	Telomere Length	Perceived Stress	Telomere Length
5	1.25	20	1.22
6	1.32	20	1.30
6	1.5	20	1.32
7	1.35	21	1.24
10	1.3	21	1.26
11	1	21	1.30
12	1.18	22	1.18
13	1.1	22	1.22
14	1.08	22	1.24
14	1.3	23	1.18
15	0.92	24	1.12
15	1.22	24	1.50
15	1.24	25	0.94
17	1.12	26	0.84
17	1.32	27	1.02
17	1.4	27	1.12
18	1.12	28	1.22
18	1.46	29	1.30
19	0.84	33	0.94

a. Compute the equation of the least-squares line.
b. What is the value of r^2?
c. Does the linear relationship between perceived stress and telomere length account for a large or small proportion of the variability in telomere length? Justify your answer.

5.39 ● The article "California State Parks Closure List Due Soon" (*The Sacramento Bee*, August 30, 2009) gave the following data on y = number of employees in fiscal year 2007–2008 and x = total size of parks (in acres) for the 20 state park districts in California:

Number of Employees, y	Total Park Size, x
95	39,334
95	324
102	17,315
69	8,244
67	620,231
77	43,501
81	8,625
116	31,572
51	14,276
36	21,094
96	103,289
71	130,023
76	16,068
112	3,286
43	24,089

Continued

Number of Employees, y	Total Park Size, x
87	6,309
131	14,502
138	62,595
80	23,666
52	35,833

a. Construct a scatterplot of the data.

b. Find the equation of the least-squares line. Do you think the least-squares line gives accurate predictions? Explain.

c. Delete the observation with the largest x value from the data set and recalculate the equation of the least-squares line. Does this observation greatly affect the equation of the line?

5.40 ● The article referenced in the previous exercise also gave data on the percentage of operating costs covered by park revenues for the 2007–2008 fiscal year.

Number of Employees, x	Percent of Operating Cost Covered by Park Revenues, y
95	37
95	19
102	32
69	80
67	17
77	34
81	36
116	32
51	38
36	40
96	53
71	31
76	35
112	108
43	34
87	97
131	62
138	36
80	36
52	34

(continued)

a. Find the equation of the least-squares line relating y = percent of operating costs covered by park revenues and x = number of employees.

b. Based on the values of r^2 and s_e, do you think that the least-squares regression line does a good job of describing the relationship between y = percent of operating costs covered by park revenues and x = number of employees? Explain.

c. The graph in Figure EX5.40 is a scatterplot of y = percent of operating costs covered by park revenues and x = number of employees. The least-squares line is also shown. Which observations are outliers? Do the observations with the largest residuals correspond to the park districts with the largest number of employees?

5.41 A study was carried out to investigate the relationship between the hardness of molded plastic (y, in Brinell units) and the amount of time elapsed since termination of the molding process (x, in hours). Summary quantities include n = 15, SSResid = 1235.470, and

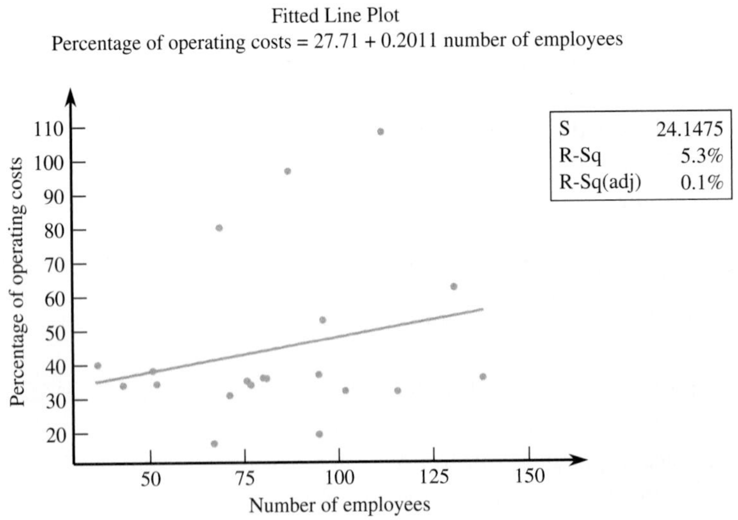

FIGURE EX5.40

SSTo = 25,321.368. Calculate and interpret the coefficient of determination.

5.42 Both r^2 and s_e are used to assess the fit of a line.

a. Is it possible that both r^2 and s_e could be large for a bivariate data set? Explain. (A picture might be helpful.)

b. Is it possible that a bivariate data set could yield values of r^2 and s_e that are both small? Explain. (Again, a picture might be helpful.)

c. Explain why it is desirable to have r^2 large and s_e small if the relationship between two variables x and y is to be described using a straight line.

5.43 With a bit of algebra, we can show that

$$\text{SSResid} = (1 - r^2)\Sigma(y - \bar{y})^2$$

from which it follows that

$$s_e = \sqrt{\frac{n-1}{n-2}}\sqrt{1 - r^2}\, s_y$$

Unless n is quite small, $(n - 1)/(n - 2) \approx 1$, so

$$s_e \approx \sqrt{1 - r^2}\, s_y$$

a. For what value of r is s_e as large as s_y? What is the least-squares line in this case?

b. For what values of r will s_e be much smaller than s_y?

c. A study by the Berkeley Institute of Human Development (see the book *Statistics* by Freedman et al., listed in the back of the book) reported the following summary data for a sample of $n = 66$ California boys:

$r \approx .80$

At age 6, average height $\approx$ 46 inches, standard deviation $\approx$ 1.7 inches.

At age 18, average height $\approx$ 70 inches, standard deviation $\approx$ 2.5 inches.

What would s_e be for the least-squares line used to predict 18-year-old height from 6-year-old height?

d. Referring to Part (c), suppose that you wanted to predict the past value of 6-year-old height from knowledge of 18-year-old height. Find the equation for the appropriate least-squares line. What is the corresponding value of s_e?

5.4 Nonlinear Relationships and Transformations

As we have seen in previous sections, when the points in a scatterplot exhibit a linear pattern and the residual plot does not reveal any problems with the linear fit, the least-squares line is a sensible way to summarize the relationship between x and y. A linear relationship is easy to interpret, departures from the line are easily detected, and using the line to predict y from our knowledge of x is straightforward. Often, though, a scatterplot or residual plot exhibits a curved pattern, indicating a more complicated relationship between x and y. In this case, finding a curve that fits the observed data well is a more complex task. In this section, we consider two common approaches to fitting nonlinear relationships: polynomial regression and transformations.

Polynomial Regression

Let's reconsider the data first introduced in Example 5.4 on x = age and y = average marathon finish time:

Age Group	x = Representative Age	y = Average Finish Time
10–19	15	302.38
20–29	25	193.63
30–39	35	185.46
40–49	45	198.49
50–59	55	224.30
60–69	65	288.71

The scatterplot of these data is reproduced here as Figure 5.26. Because this plot shows a marked curved pattern, it is clear that no straight line can do a reasonable job of describing the relationship between x and y. However, the relationship can be described by a curve, and in this case the curved pattern in the scatterplot looks like a parabola (the graph of a quadratic function). This suggests trying to find a quadratic function of the form

$$\hat{y} = a + b_1x + b_2x^2$$

that would reasonably describe the relationship. That is, the values of the coefficients a, b_1, and b_2 in this function must be selected to obtain a good fit to the data.

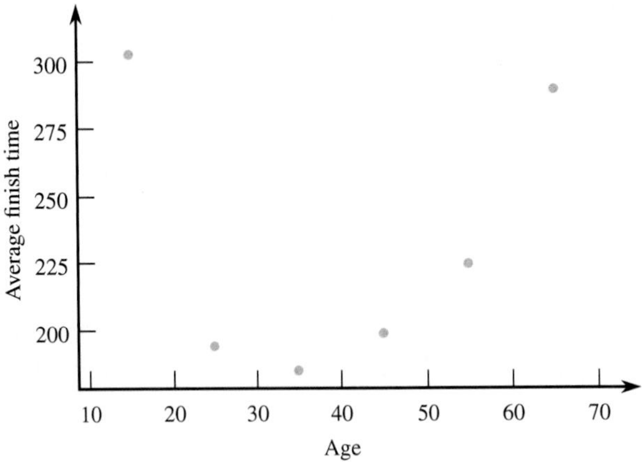

FIGURE 5.26
Scatterplot for the marathon data.

What are the best choices for the values of a, b_1, and b_2? In fitting a line to data, we used the principle of least squares to guide our choice of slope and intercept. Least squares can be used to fit a quadratic function as well. The deviations, $y - \hat{y}$, are still represented by vertical distances in the scatterplot, but now they are vertical distances from the points to a parabola (the graph of a quadratic function) rather than to a line, as shown in Figure 5.27. We then choose values for the coefficients in the quadratic function so that the sum of squared deviations is as small as possible.

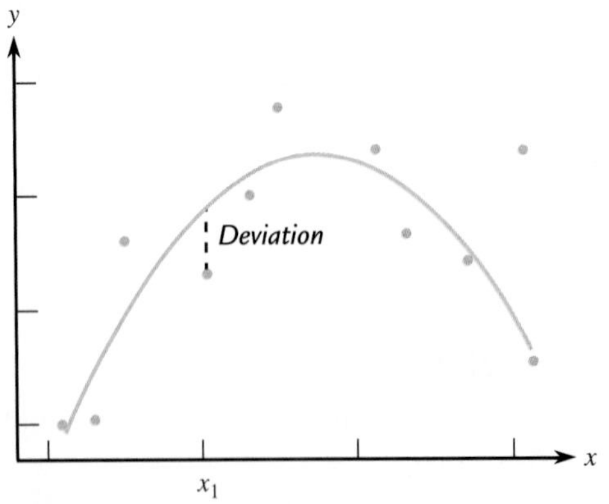

FIGURE 5.27
Deviation for a quadratic function.

For a quadratic regression, the least squares estimates of a, b_1, and b_2 are those values that minimize the sum of squared deviations $\sum(y - \hat{y})^2$ where $\hat{y} = a + b_1x + b_2x^2$.

For quadratic regression, a measure that is useful for assessing fit is

$$R^2 = 1 - \frac{\text{SSResid}}{\text{SSTo}}$$

where SSResid $= \sum(y - \hat{y})^2$. The measure R^2 is defined in a way similar to r^2 for simple linear regression and is interpreted in a similar fashion. The notation r^2 is used only with linear regression to emphasize the relationship between r^2 and the correlation coefficient, r, in the linear case.

The general expressions for computing the least-squares estimates are somewhat complicated, so we rely on a statistical software package or graphing calculator to do the computations for us.

EXAMPLE 5.14 Marathon Data Revisited: Fitting a Quadratic Model

For the marathon data, the scatterplot (see Figure 5.26) showed a marked curved pattern. If the least-squares line is fit to these data, it is no surprise that the line does not do a good job of describing the relationship ($r^2 = .001$ or .1% and $s_e = 56.9439$), and the residual plot shows a distinct curved pattern as well (Figure 5.28).

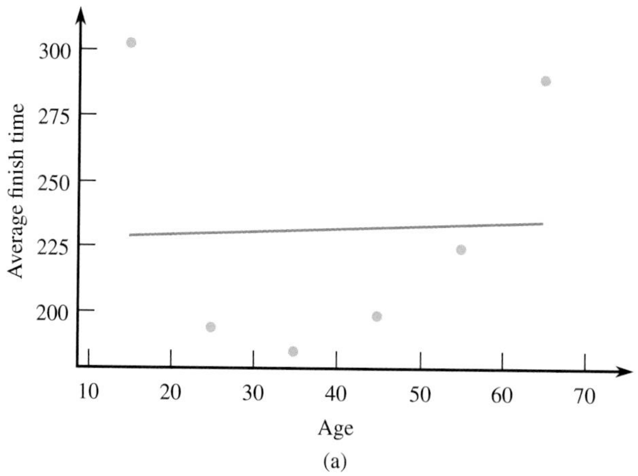

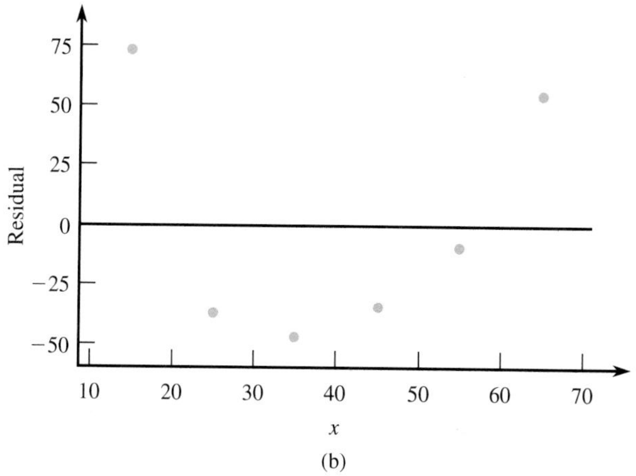

FIGURE 5.28
Plots for the marathon data of Example 5.14: (a) least-square regression line; (b) residual plot.

Part of the Minitab output from fitting a quadratic regression function to these data is as follows:

The regression equation is

y = 462 − 14.2 x + 0.179 x-squared

Predictor	Coef	SE Coef	T	P
Constant	462.00	43.99	10.50	0.002
x	−14.205	2.460	−5.78	0.010
x-squared	0.17888	0.03025	5.91	0.010

S = 18.4813 R-Sq = 92.1% R-Sq(adj) = 86.9%

Analysis of Variance

Source	DF	SS	MS	F	P
Regression	2	11965.0	5982.5	17.52	0.022
Residual Error	3	1024.7	341.6		
Total	5	12989.7			

The least-squares coefficients are

$$a = 462.00 \qquad b_1 = -14.205 \qquad b_2 = 0.17888$$

and the least-squares quadratic is

$$\hat{y} = 462.00 - 14.205x + 0.17888x^2$$

A plot showing the curve and the corresponding residual plot for the quadratic regression are given in Figure 5.29. Notice that there is no strong pattern in the residual plot for the quadratic case, as there was in the linear case. For the quadratic regression, $R^2 = .921$ (as opposed to .001 for the least-squares line), which means that 92.1% of the variability in average marathon finish time can be explained by an approximate quadratic relationship between average finish time and age.

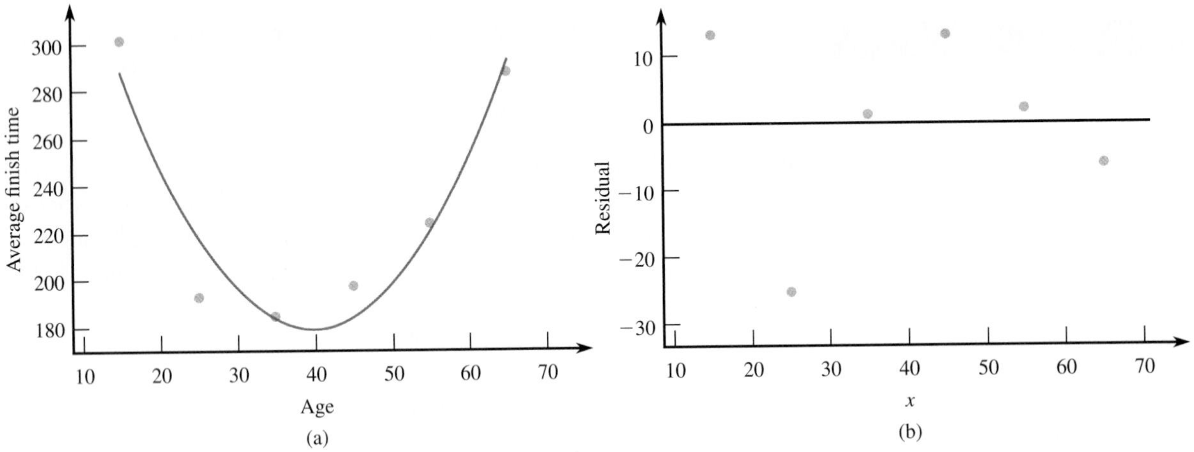

FIGURE 5.29
Quadratic regression of Example 5.13: (a) scatterplot; (b) residual plot.

Linear and quadratic regression are special cases of polynomial regression. A polynomial regression curve is described by a function of the form

$$\hat{y} = a + b_1x + b_2x^2 + b_3x^3 + \cdots + b_kx^k$$

which is called a kth-degree polynomial. The case of $k = 1$ results in linear regression ($\hat{y} = a + b_1x$) and $k = 2$ yields a quadratic regression ($\hat{y} = a + b_1x + b_2x^2$). A quadratic curve has only one bend (see Figure 5.30(a) and (b)). A less frequently encountered special case is for $k = 3$, where $\hat{y} = a + b_1x + b_2x^2 + b_3x^3$, which is called a cubic regression curve. Cubic curves have two bends, as shown in Figure 5.30(c).

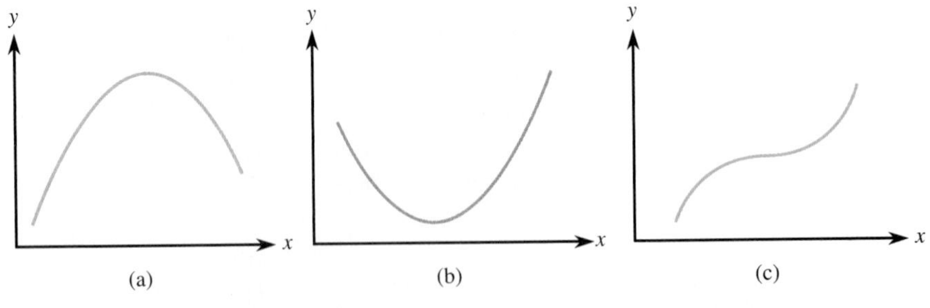

FIGURE 5.30
Polynomial regression curves: (a) quadratic curve with $b_2 < 0$; (b) quadratic curve with $b_2 > 0$; (c) cubic curve.

EXAMPLE 5.15 Fish Food

● Sea bream are one type of fish that are often raised in large fish farming enterprises. These fish are usually fed a diet consisting primarily of fish meal. The authors of the paper "Growth and Economic Profit of Gilthead Sea Bream (Sparus aurata, L.) Fed Sunflower Meal (*Aquaculture* [2007]: 528–534) describe a study to investigate

● Data set available online

whether it would be more profitable to substitute plant protein in the form of sunflower meal for some of the fish meal in the sea bream's diet.

The accompanying data are consistent with summary quantities given in the paper for x = percent of sunflower meal in the diet and y = average weight (in grams) of fish after 248 days.

Sunflower Meal (%)	Average Fish Weight
0	432
6	450
12	455
18	445
24	427
30	422
36	421

Figure 5.31 shows a scatterplot of these data. The relationship between x and y does not appear to be linear, so we might try using a quadratic regression to describe the relationship between sunflower meal content and average fish weight.

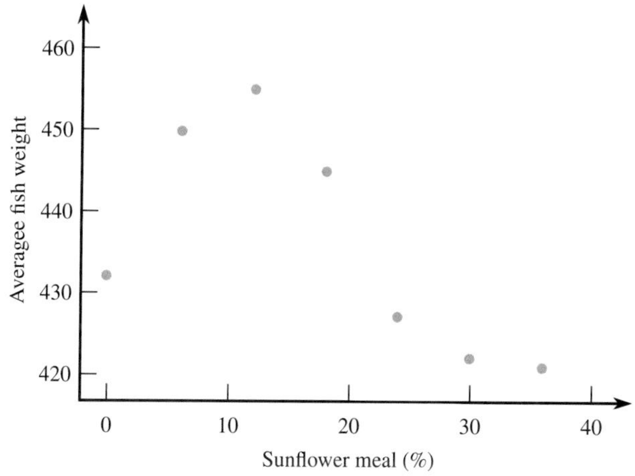

FIGURE 5.31
Scatterplot of average fish weight versus sunflower meal content for the data of Example 5.15.

Minitab was used to fit a quadratic regression function and to compute the corresponding residuals. The least-squares quadratic regression is

$$\hat{y} = 439 + 1.22x - 0.053x^2$$

A plot of the quadratic regression curve and the corresponding residual plot are shown in Figure 5.32.

Notice that the residual plot in Figure 5.32(b) shows a curved pattern (cubic)—not something we like to see in a residual plot. This suggests that we may want to consider something other than a quadratic curve to describe the relationship between x and y. Looking again at the scatterplot of Figure 5.31, we see that a cubic function might be a better choice because there appear to be two "bends" in the curved relationship—one at around $x = 12$ and another at the far right hand side of the scatterplot.

Using the given data, Minitab was used to fit a cubic regression, resulting in the curve shown in Figure 5.33(a). The cubic regression is then

$$\hat{y} = 431.5 + 5.39x - 0.37x^2 + 0.006x^3$$

The corresponding residual plot, shown in Figure 5.33(b), does not reveal any troublesome patterns that would suggest a choice other than the cubic regression.

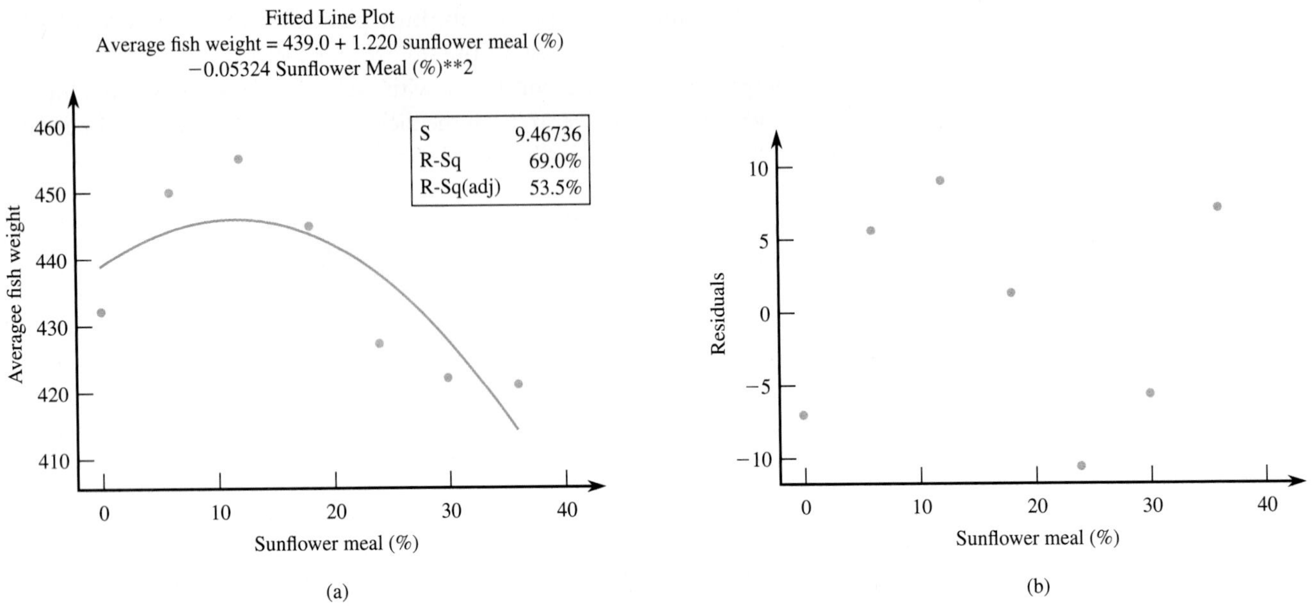

FIGURE 5.32
Quadratic regression plots for the fish food data of Example 5.15: (a) least-squares quadratic regression; (b) residual plot for quadratic regression.

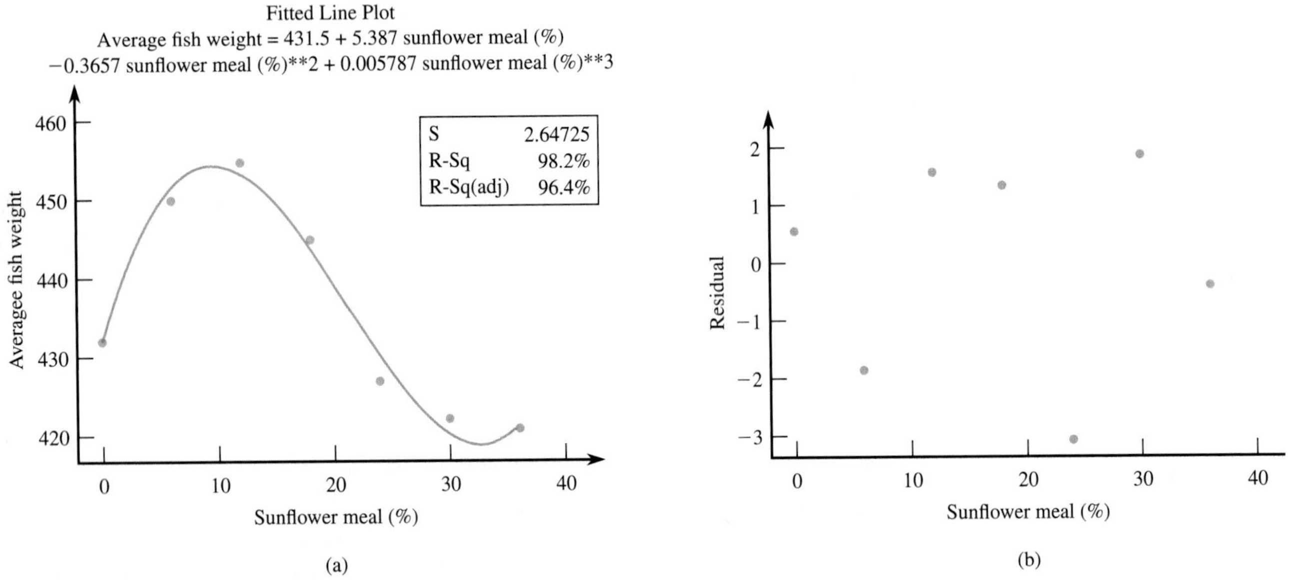

FIGURE 5.33
Cubic regression plots for the fish food data of Example 5.15:
(a) least-squares cubic regression;
(b) residual plot for cubic regression.

Based on analysis of these data, we might recommend using sunflower meal for about 12% of the diet. Sunflower meal is less costly than fish meal, but using more than about 12% sunflower meal is associated with a decrease in the average fish weight. It is not clear what happens to average fish weight when sunflower meal is used for more than 36% of the diet, the largest x value in the data set.

Transformations

An alternative to finding a curve to fit the data is to find a way to transform the x values and/or y values so that a scatterplot of the transformed data has a linear appearance. A **transformation** (sometimes called a reexpression) involves using a simple function of a variable in place of the variable itself. For example, instead of trying to describe the relationship between x and y, it might be easier to describe the relationship between $\sqrt{x}$ and y or between x and $\log(y)$. And, if we can describe the relationship between, say, $\sqrt{x}$ and y, we will still be able to predict the value of y for a given x value. Common transformations involve taking square roots, logarithms, or reciprocals.

EXAMPLE 5.16 River Water Velocity and Distance from Shore

● As fans of white-water rafting know, a river flows more slowly close to its banks (because of friction between the river bank and the water). To study the nature of the relationship between water velocity and the distance from the shore, data were gathered on velocity (in centimeters per second) of a river at different distances (in meters) from the bank. Suppose that the resulting data were as follows:

Distance	.5	1.5	2.5	3.5	4.5	5.5	6.5	7.5	8.5	9.5
Velocity	22.00	23.18	25.48	25.25	27.15	27.83	28.49	28.18	28.50	28.63

A graph of the data exhibits a curved pattern, as seen in both the scatterplot and the residual plot from a linear fit (see Figures 5.34(a) and 5.34(b)).

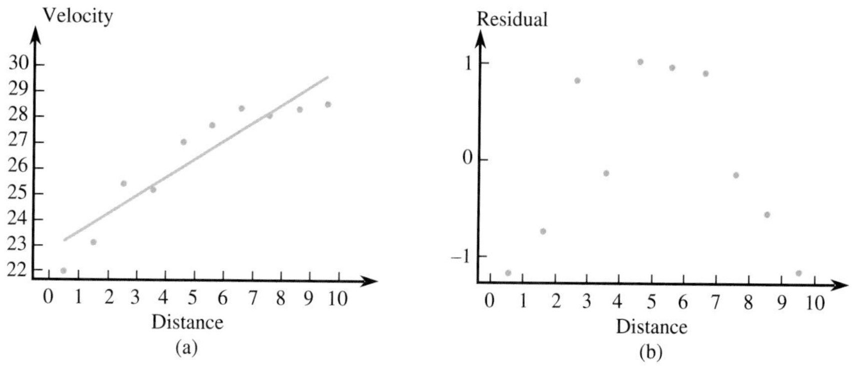

FIGURE 5.34
Plots for the data of Example 5.16: (a) scatterplot of the river data; (b) residual plot from linear fit.

Let's try transforming the x values by replacing each x value by its square root. We define

$$x' = \sqrt{x}$$

The resulting transformed data are given in Table 5.2.

TABLE 5.2 Original and Transformed Data of Example 5.16

Original Data		Transformed Data	
x	y	x'	y
0.5	22.00	0.7071	22.00
1.5	23.18	1.2247	23.18
2.5	25.48	1.5811	25.48
3.5	25.25	1.8708	25.25
4.5	27.15	2.1213	27.15
5.5	27.83	2.3452	27.83
6.5	28.49	2.5495	28.49
7.5	28.18	2.7386	28.18
8.5	28.50	2.9155	28.50
9.5	28.63	3.0822	28.63

● Data set available online

Figure 5.35(a) shows a scatterplot of y versus x' (or equivalently y versus $\sqrt{x}$). The pattern of points in this plot looks linear, and so we can fit a least-squares line using the transformed data. The Minitab output from this regression appears below.

Regression Analysis

The regression equation is
Velocity = 20.1 + 3.01 sqrt distance

Predictor	Coef	StDev	T	P
Constant	20.1102	0.6097	32.99	0.000
Sqrt dis	3.0085	0.2726	11.03	0.000

S = 0.6292 R-Sq = 93.8% R-Sq(adj) = 93.1%

Analysis of Variance

Source	DF	SS	MS	F	P
Regression	1	48.209	48.209	121.76	0.000
Residual Error	8	3.168	0.396		
Total	9	51.376			

The residual plot in Figure 5.35(b) shows no indication of a pattern. The resulting regression equation is

$$\hat{y} = 20.1 + 3.01x'$$

An equivalent equation is

$$\hat{y} = 20.1 + 3.01\sqrt{x}$$

The values of r^2 and s_e (see the Minitab output) indicate that a line is a reasonable way to describe the relationship between y and x'. To predict velocity of the river at a distance of 9 meters from shore, we first compute $x' = \sqrt{x} = \sqrt{9} = 3$ and then use the sample regression line to obtain a prediction of y:

$$\hat{y} = 20.1 + 3.01x' = 20.1 + (3.01)(3) = 29.13$$

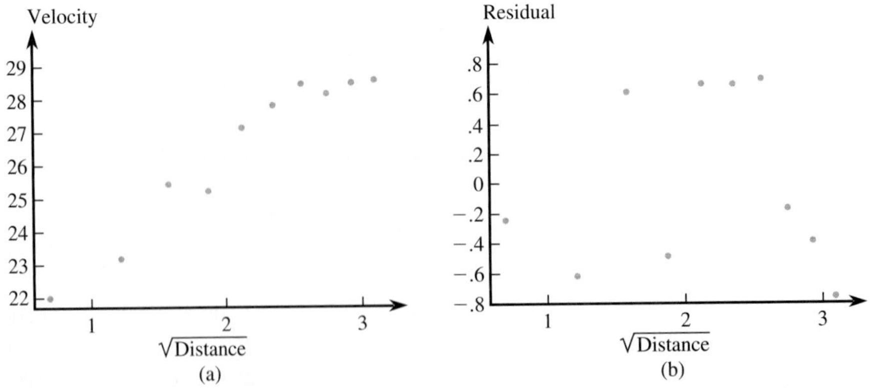

FIGURE 5.35 Plots for the transformed data of Example 5.16: (a) scatterplot of y versus x'; (b) residual plot resulting from a linear fit to the transformed data.

In Example 5.16, transforming the x values using the square root function worked well. In general, how can we choose a transformation that will result in a linear pattern? Table 5.3 gives some guidance and summarizes some of the properties of the most commonly used transformations.

TABLE 5.3 Commonly Used Transformations

Transformation	Mathematical Description	Try This Transformation When
No transformation	$\hat{y} = a + bx$	The change in y is constant as x changes. A 1-unit increase in x is associated with, on average, an increase of b in the value of y.
Square root of x	$\hat{y} = a + b\sqrt{x}$	The change in y is not constant. A 1-unit increase in x is associated with smaller increases or decreases in y for larger x values.
Log of x*	$\hat{y} = a + b\log_{10}(x)$ or $\hat{y} = a + b\ln(x)$	The change in y is not constant. A 1-unit increase in x is associated with smaller increases or decreases in the value of y for larger x values.
Reciprocal of x	$\hat{y} = a + b\left(\frac{1}{x}\right)$	The change in y is not constant. A 1-unit increase in x is associated with smaller increases or decreases in the value of y for larger x values. In addition, y has a limiting value of a as x increases.
Log of y* (Exponential growth or decay)	$\log_{10}(\hat{y}) = a + bx$ or $\ln(\hat{y}) = a + bx$	The change in y is not constant. A 1-unit increase in x is associated with larger increases or decreases in the value of y for larger x values.

*The values of a and b in the regression equation will depend on whether $\log_{10}$ or ln is used, but the $\hat{y}$'s and r^2 values will be identical.

EXAMPLE 5.17 Loons on Acidic Lakes

● A study of factors that affect the survival of loon chicks is described in the paper "Does Prey Biomass or Mercury Exposure Affect Loon Chick Survival in Wisconsin?" (*The Journal of Wildlife Management* [2005]: 57–67). In this study, a relationship between the pH of lake water and blood mercury level in loon chicks was observed. The researchers thought that this might be because the pH of the lake water might be related to the type of fish that the loons ate. The accompanying data (read from a graph in the paper and shown in Table 5.4) is x = lake pH and y = blood

TABLE 5.4 Data and Transformed Data from Example 5.17

Lake pH (x)	Blood Mercury Level (y)	Log(y)
5.28	1.10	0.0414
5.69	0.76	−0.1192
5.56	0.74	−0.1308
5.51	0.60	−0.2218
4.90	0.48	−0.3188
5.02	0.43	−0.3665
5.02	0.29	−0.5376
5.04	0.09	−1.0458
5.30	0.10	−1.0000
5.33	0.20	−0.6990
5.64	0.28	−0.5528
5.83	0.17	−0.7696
5.83	0.18	−0.7447
6.17	0.55	−0.2596
6.22	0.43	−0.3665
6.15	0.40	−0.3979

(continued)

● Data set available online

TABLE 5.4 Data and Transformed Data from Example 5.17—cont'd

Lake pH (x)	Blood Mercury Level (y)	Log(y)
6.05	0.33	−0.4815
6.04	0.26	−0.5850
6.24	0.18	−0.7447
6.30	0.16	−0.7959
6.80	0.45	−0.3468
6.58	0.30	−0.5229
6.65	0.28	−0.5528
7.06	0.22	−0.6576
6.99	0.21	−0.6778
6.97	0.13	−0.8861
7.03	0.12	−0.9208
7.20	0.15	−0.8239
7.89	0.11	−0.9586
7.93	0.11	−0.9586
7.99	0.09	−1.0458
7.99	0.06	−1.2218
8.30	0.09	−1.0458
8.42	0.09	−1.0458
8.42	0.04	−1.3979
8.95	0.12	−0.9208
9.49	0.14	−0.8539

mercury level (μg/g) for 37 loon chicks from different lakes in Wisconsin. A scatterplot is shown in Figure 5.36(a).

The pattern in this scatterplot is typical of exponential decay, with the change in y as x increases much smaller for large x values than for small x values. You can see that a change of 1 in pH is associated with a much larger change in blood mercury level in the part of the plot where the x values are small than in the part of the plot where the x values are large. Table 5.3 suggests transforming the y values (blood mercury level in this example) by taking their logarithms.

Two standard logarithmic functions are commonly used for such transformations—the common logarithm (log base 10, denoted by log or $\log_{10}$) and the natural logarithm (log base e, denoted ln). Either the common or the natural logarithm can be used; the only difference in the resulting scatterplots is the scale of the transformed y variable. This can be seen in Figures 5.36(b) and 5.36(c). These two scatterplots show the same pattern, and it looks like a line would be appropriate to describe this relationship.

Table 5.4 displays the original data along with the transformed y values using $y' = \log(y)$. The following Minitab output shows the result of fitting the least-squares line to the transformed data:

Regression Analysis: Log(y) versus Lake pH

```
The regression equation is
Log(y) = 0.458 - 0.172 Lake pH

Predictor        Coef     SE Coef       T       P
Constant       0.4582      0.2404    1.91   0.065
Lake Ph      -0.17183     0.03589   -4.79   0.000
S = 0.263032    R-Sq = 39.6%    R-Sq(adj) = 37.8%
```

(continued)

Analysis of Variance

Source	DF	SS	MS	F	P
Regression	1	1.5856	1.5856	22.92	0.000
Residual Error	35	2.4215	0.0692		
Total	36	4.0071			

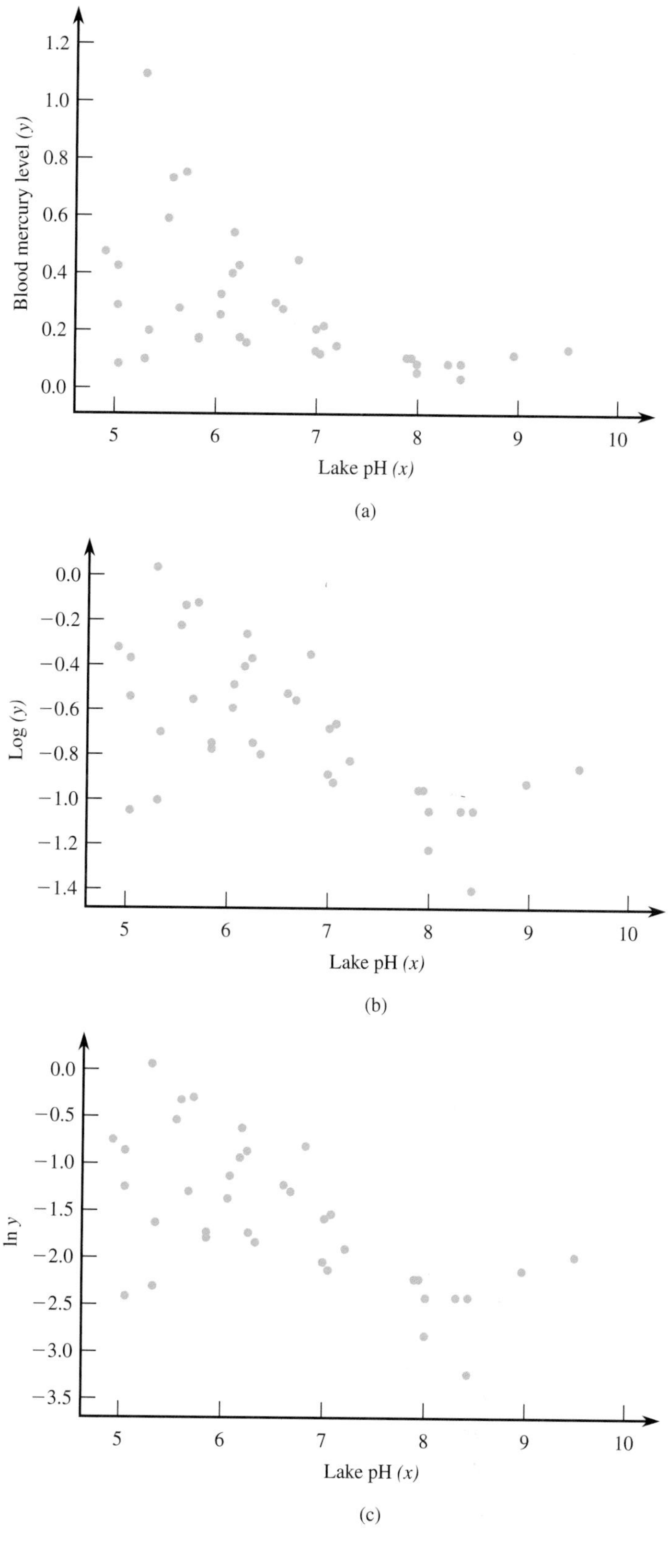

FIGURE 5.36
Plots for the data of Example 5.17: (a) scatterplot of the loon data; (b) scatterplot of the transformed data with $y' = \log(y)$; (c) scatterplot of transformed data with $y' = \ln(y)$.

The resulting regression equation is

$$y' = 0.458 - 0.172x$$

or, equivalently

$$\log(y) = 0.458 - 0.172x$$

Fitting a Curve Using Transformations The objective of a regression analysis is usually to describe the approximate relationship between x and y with an equation of the form y = some function of x.

If we have transformed only x, fitting a least-squares line to the transformed data results in an equation of the desired form, for example,

$$\hat{y} = 5 + 3x' = 5 + 3\sqrt{x} \quad \textit{where } x' = \sqrt{x}$$

or

$$\hat{y} = 4 + .2x' = 4 + .2\frac{1}{x} \quad \textit{where } x' = \frac{1}{x}$$

These functions specify lines when graphed using y and x', and they specify curves when graphed using y and x, as illustrated in Figure 5.37 for the square root transformation.

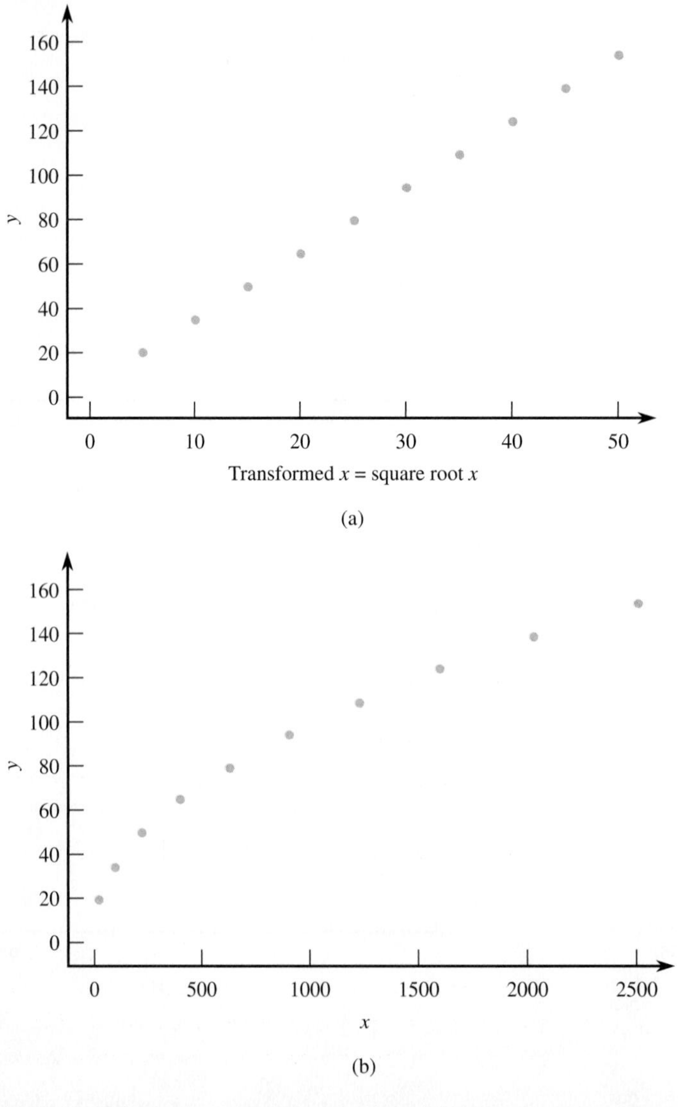

FIGURE 5.37
(a) A plot of $\hat{y} = 5 + 3x'$ where $x' = \sqrt{x}$; (b) a plot of $\hat{y} = 5 + 3\sqrt{x}$.

If the y values have been transformed, after obtaining the least-squares line the transformation can be undone to yield an expression of the form y = some function of x (as opposed to y' = some function of x). For example, to reverse a logarithmic transformation $(y' = \log(y))$, we can take the antilogarithm of each side of the equation. To reverse a square root transformation $(y' = \sqrt{y})$, we can square both sides of the equation, and to reverse a reciprocal transformation $(y' = 1/y)$, we can take the reciprocal of each side of the equation. This is illustrated in Example 5.18.

EXAMPLE 5.18 Revisiting the Loon Data

For the loon data of Example 5.17, $y' = \log(y)$ and the least-squares line relating y' and x was

$$y' = 0.458 - 0.172x$$

or, equivalently

$$\log(y) = 0.458 - 0.172x$$

To reverse this transformation, we take the antilog log of both sides of the equation:

$$10^{\log(y)} = 10^{0.458 - 0.172x}$$

Using properties of logs and exponents we know that

$$10^{\log(y)} = y$$

and

$$10^{0.458 - 0.172x} = (10^{0.458})(10^{-0.172x})$$

Finally, we get

$$\hat{y} = (10^{0.458})(10^{-0.172x}) = 2.8708(10^{-0.172x})$$

This equation can now be used to predict the y value (blood mercury level) for a given x (lake pH). For example, the predicted blood mercury level when lake pH is 6 is

$$\hat{y} = 2.8708(10^{-0.172x}) = 2.8708(10^{-0.172(6)}) = (2.8708)(0.0929) = 0.2667$$

It should be noted that the process of transforming data, fitting a line to the transformed data, and then undoing the transformation to get an equation for a curved relationship between x and y usually results in a curve that provides a reasonable fit to the sample data, but it is not the least-squares curve for the data. For example, in Example 5.18, a transformation was used to fit the curve $y = (10^{0.458})(10^{-0.172x})$. However, there may be another equation of the form $\hat{y} = a(10^{bx})$ that has a smaller sum of squared residuals for the *original* data than the one we obtained using transformations. Finding the least-squares estimates for a and b in an equation of this form is complicated. Fortunately, the curves found using transformations usually provide reasonable predictions of y.

Power Transformations Frequently, an appropriate transformation is suggested by the data. One type of transformation that statisticians have found useful for straightening a plot is a **power transformation**. A power (exponent) is first selected, and each original value is raised to that power to obtain the corresponding transformed value. Table 5.5 displays a "ladder" of the most frequently used power transformations. The power 1 corresponds to no transformation at all. Using the power 0 would transform every value to 1, which is certainly not informative, so statisticians use the logarithmic transformation in its place in the ladder of transformations. Other powers intermediate to or more extreme than those listed can be used, of course, but they are not used as frequently as those on the ladder. Notice that all the transformations previously presented are included in this ladder.

Figure 5.38 is designed to suggest where on the ladder we should go to find an appropriate transformation. The four curved segments, labeled 1, 2, 3, and 4, represent shapes of curved scatterplots that are commonly encountered. Suppose that a scatterplot looks like the curve labeled 1. Then, to straighten the plot, we should use a power of x that is up the ladder from the no-transformation row (x^2 or x^3) and/or a power on y that is also up the ladder from the power 1. Thus, we might be led to squaring each x value, cubing each y, and plotting the transformed pairs. If the curvature looks like curved segment 2, a power up the ladder from no transformation for x and/or a power down the ladder for y (e.g., $\sqrt{y}$ or $\log(y)$) should be used.

TABLE 5.5 Power Transformation Ladder

Power	Transformed Value	Name
3	$(\text{Original value})^3$	Cube
2	$(\text{Original value})^2$	Square
1	**(Original value)**	**No transformation**
$\frac{1}{2}$	$\sqrt{\text{Original value}}$	Square root
$\frac{1}{3}$	$\sqrt[3]{\text{Original value}}$	Cube root
0	Log(Original value)	Logarithm
-1	$\frac{1}{\text{Original value}}$	Reciprocal

The scatterplot for the loon data (Figure 5.36(a)) has the pattern of segment 3 in Figure 5.38. This suggests going down the ladder of transformations for x and/or for y. We found that transforming the y values in this data set by taking logarithms worked well, and this is consistent with the suggestion of going down the ladder of transformations for y.

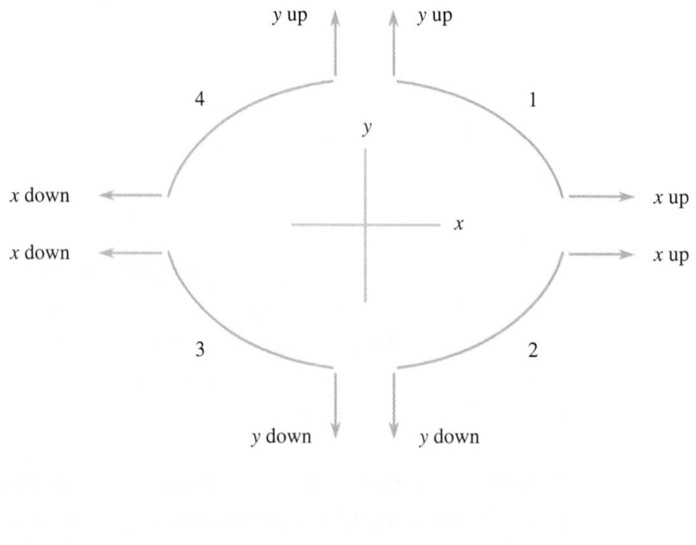

FIGURE 5.38
Scatterplot shapes and where to go on the transformation ladder to straighten the plot.

EXAMPLE 5.19 How Old Is That Lobster?

● Can you tell how old a lobster is by its size? This question was investigated by the authors of a paper that appeared in the *Biological Bulletin* (August 2007). Researchers measured carapace (the exterior shell) length (in mm) of 27 laboratory-raised lobsters of known age. The data on x = carapace length and y = age (in years) in Table 5.6 were read from a graph that appeared in the paper.

● Data set available online

TABLE 5.6 Original and Transformed Data for Example 5.19

y	x	$\sqrt{y}$	x^2
1.00	63.32	1.00	4,009.4
1.00	67.50	1.00	4,556.3
1.00	69.58	1.00	4,841.4
1.00	73.41	1.00	5,389.0
1.42	79.32	1.19	6,291.7
1.42	82.80	1.19	6,855.8
1.42	85.59	1.19	7,325.7
1.82	105.07	1.35	11,039.7
1.82	107.16	1.35	11,483.3
1.82	117.25	1.35	13,747.6
2.18	109.24	1.48	11,933.4
2.18	110.64	1.48	12,241.2
2.17	118.99	1.47	14,158.6
2.17	122.81	1.47	15,082.3
2.33	138.47	1.53	19,173.9
2.50	133.95	1.58	17,942.6
2.51	125.25	1.58	15,687.6
2.50	123.51	1.58	15,254.7
2.93	146.82	1.71	21,556.1
2.92	139.17	1.71	19,368.3
2.92	136.73	1.71	18,695.1
2.92	122.81	1.71	15,082.3
3.17	142.30	1.78	20,249.3
3.41	152.73	1.85	23,326.5
3.42	145.78	1.85	21,251.8
3.75	148.21	1.94	21,966.2
4.08	152.04	2.02	23,116.2

The scatterplot of the data in Figure 5.39 shows a clear curved pattern, which resembles the curved segment 2 in Figure 5.38. This suggests that we should consider transforming x using a power up the ladder (such as (x^2 or x^3)) or transforming y using a power down the ladder (such as $\sqrt{y}$ or $\log(y)$).

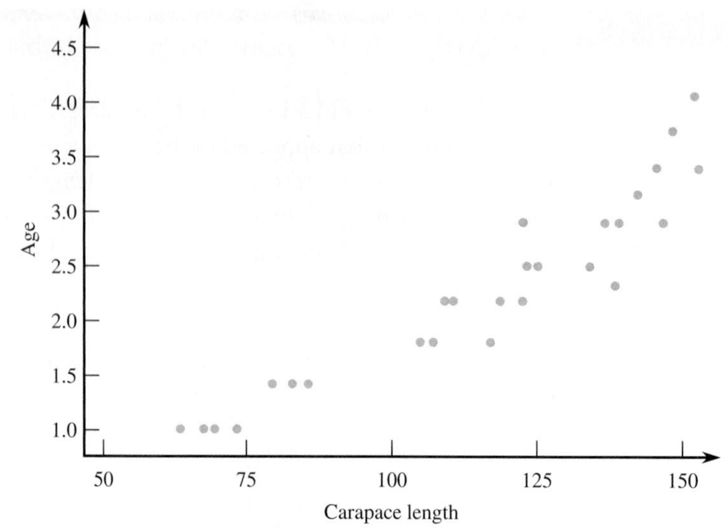

FIGURE 5.39
Scatterplot of age versus carapace length.

Figure 5.40 shows scatterplots of $\sqrt{y}$ versus x (Figure 5.40(a)), of y versus x^2 (Figure 5.40(b)), and of $\sqrt{y}$ versus x^2 (Figure 5.40(c)). The relationship in the scatterplot of Figure 5.40(c) is more nearly linear than in the other two plots, so we can fit a line to the transformed data with $y' = \sqrt{y}$ and $x' = x^2$.

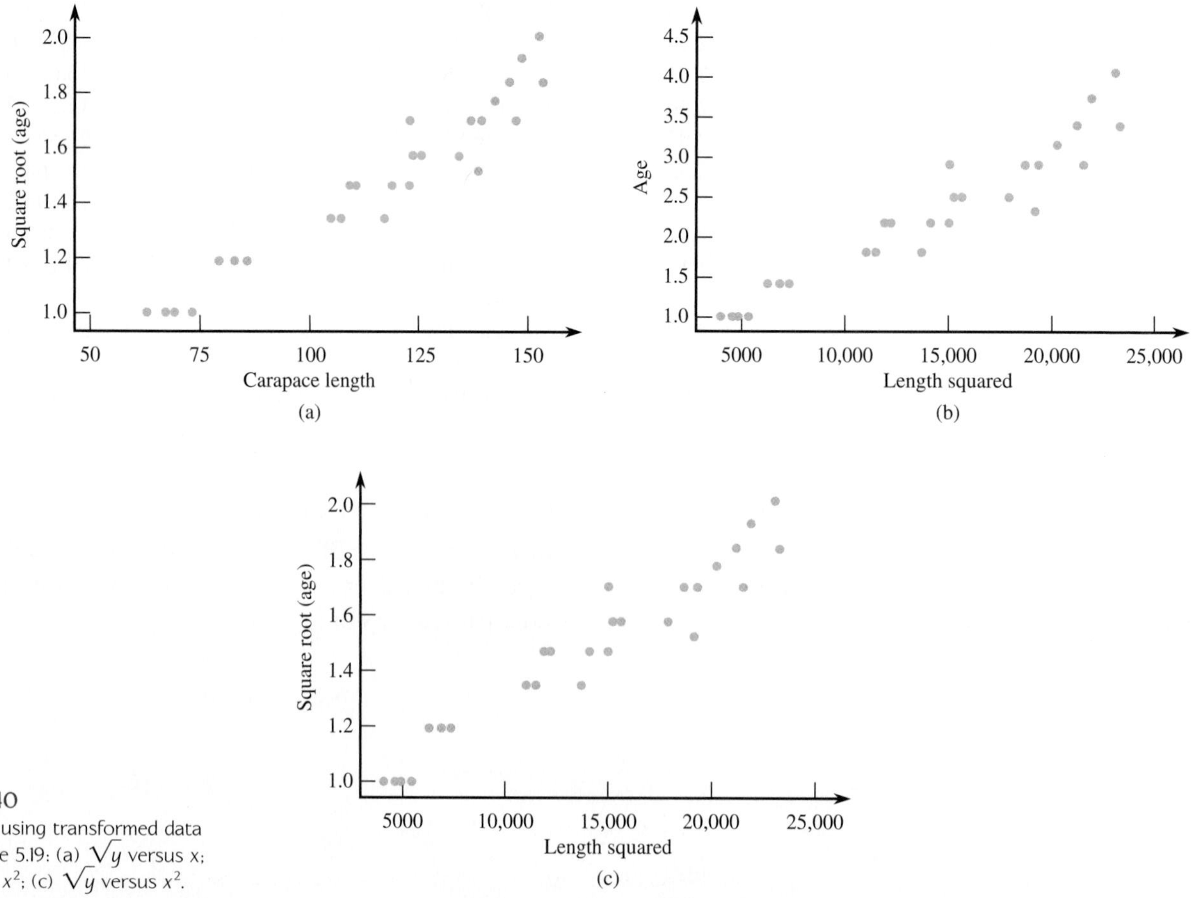

FIGURE 5.40
Scatterplots using transformed data from example 5.19: (a) $\sqrt{y}$ versus x; (b) y versus x^2; (c) $\sqrt{y}$ versus x^2.

Using Minitab to fit a least-squares line to the transformed data results in the following output:

Regression Analysis: Sqrt(Age) versus Length Squared

The regression equation is
Sqrt(Age) = 0.829 + 0.000046 Length Squared

Predictor	Coef	SE Coef	T	P
Constant	0.82867	0.04022	20.60	0.000
Length Squared	0.00004637	0.00000261	17.75	0.000

S = 0.0828744 R-Sq = 92.6% R-Sq(adj) = 92.4%

The least-squares line is

$$y' = 0.829 + 0.000046x'$$

or equivalently

$$\sqrt{y} = 0.829 + 0.000046x^2$$

This transformation can be reversed by squaring both sides to obtain an equation of the form y = some function of x:

$$(y')^2 = (0.829 + 0.000046x')^2$$

Since $(y')^2 = y$ and $x' = x^2$, we get

$$\hat{y} = (0.829 + 0.000046x^2)^2$$

To predict the age of a lobster with a carapace length of 100 mm, we substitute 100 into the equation to obtain a predicted value $\hat{y}$:

$$\hat{y} = (0.829 + 0.000046x^2)^2 = (0.829 + 0.000046(100)^2)^2 = (1.289)^2 = 1.66 \text{ years}$$

EXERCISES 5.44 - 5.55

5.44 ● Example 5.5 described a study of the effectiveness of pomegranate fruit extract (PFE) in slowing the growth of prostate cancer tumors (*Proceedings of the National Academy of Sciences* [October 11, 2005]: 14813–14818). Figure 5.11 from that example is reproduced here. Based on this figure, we noted that for the .2% PFE group, the relationship between average tumor volume and number of days after injection of cancer cells appears curved rather than linear.

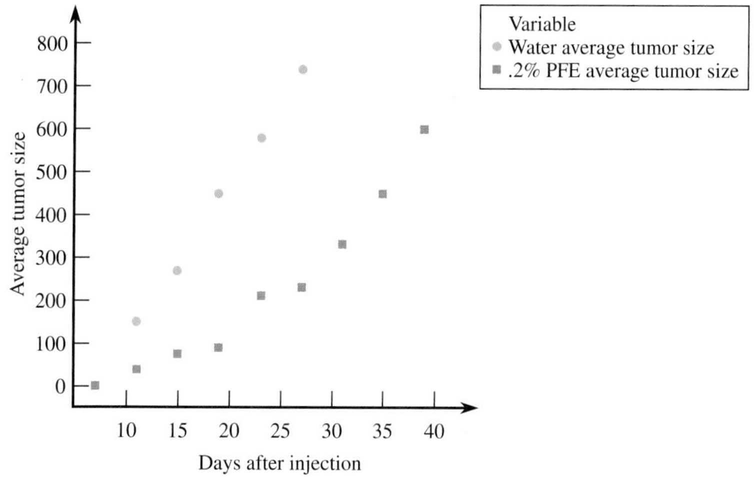

a. One transformation that might result in a relationship that is more nearly linear is log(y). The values of x = number of days since injection of cancer cells, y = average tumor volume (in mm^3), and $y' = \log(y)$ for the 0.2% PFE group are given in the accompanying table. Construct a scatterplot of y' versus x. Does this scatterplot look more nearly linear than the plot of the original data?

Days After Injection x	0.2% PFE Average Tumor Size y	Log(y)
11	40	1.60
15	75	1.88
19	90	1.95
23	210	2.32
27	230	2.36
31	330	2.52
35	450	2.65
39	600	2.78

b. Based on the accompanying Minitab output, does the least-squares line effectively summarize the relationship between y' and x?

The regression equation is
log(average tumor size) = 1.23 + 0.0413 Days After Injection

Predictor	Coef	SE Coef	T	P
Constant	1.22625	0.07989	15.35	0.000
Days After Injection	0.041250	0.003000	13.75	0.000

S = 0.0777817 R-Sq = 96.9% R-Sq(adj) = 96.4%

c. Use the Minitab output to predict average tumor size 30 days after injection of cancer cells for a mouse that received water supplemented with 0.2% PFE.

d. Residual plots of the residuals from the least-squares line using the untransformed data and using y' and x are shown at the bottom of the page in Figure EX5.44. What feature of the residual plot for the original data suggests that the least-squares line is not the best way to describe the relationship between y and x? In what way does the residual plot for the transformed data suggest that a line is a reasonable description of the relationship for the transformed data (y' and x)?

5.45 ● Example 5.15 described a study that involved substituting sunflower meal for a portion of the usual diet of farm-raised sea breams (*Aquaculture* [2007]: 528–534). This paper also gave data on y = feed intake (in grams per 100 grams of fish per day) and x = percentage sunflower meal in the diet (read from a graph in the paper).

x	0	6	12	18	24	30	36
y	0.86	0.84	0.82	0.86	0.87	1.00	1.09

A scatterplot of these data is curved and the pattern in the plot resembles a quadratic curve.

a. Using a statistical software package or a graphing calculator, find the equation of the least-squares quadratic curve that can be used to describe the relationship between percentage sunflower meal and feed intake.

b. Use the least-squares equation from Part (a) to predict feed intake for fish fed a diet that included 20% sunflower meal.

5.46 ● The paper "Commercially Available Plant Growth Regulators and Promoters Modify Bulk Tissue Abscisic Acid Concentrations in Spring Barley, but not Root Growth and Yield Response to Drought" (*Ap-*

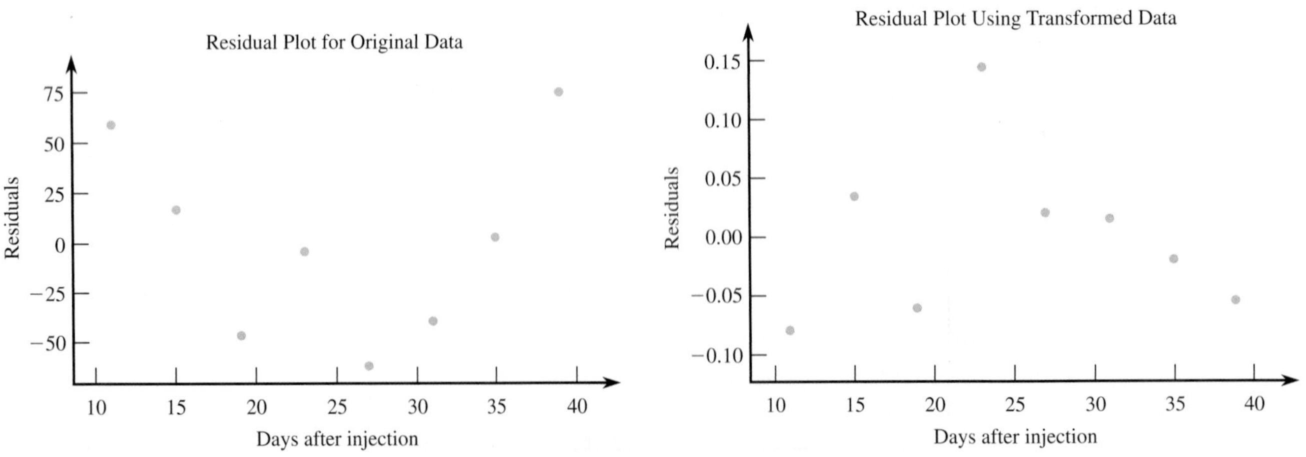

FIGURE EX5.44

plied Biology [2006]: 291–304) describes a study of the drought response of barley. The accompanying data on x = days after sowing and y = soil moisture deficit (in mm) was read from a graph that appeared in the paper.

Days After Sowing	Soil Moisture Deficit
37	0.00
63	69.36
68	79.15
75	85.11
82	93.19
98	104.26
104	108.94
111	112.34
132	115.74

a. Construct a scatterplot of y = soil moisture deficit versus x = days after sowing. Does the relationship between these two variables appear to be linear or nonlinear?
b. Fit a least-squares line to the given data and construct a residual plot. Does the residual plot support your conclusion in Part (a)? Explain.
c. Consider transforming the data by leaving y unchanged and using either $x' = \sqrt{x}$ or $x'' = \frac{1}{x}$. Which of these transformations would you recommend? Justify your choice using appropriate graphical displays.
d. Using the transformation you recommend in Part (c), find the equation of the least-squares line that describes the relationship between y and the transformed x.
e. What would you predict for soil moisture deficit 50 days after sowing? For 100 days after sowing?
f. Explain why it would not be reasonable to predict soil moisture deficit 200 days after sowing.

5.47 ● Is electromagnetic radiation from phone antennae associated with declining bird populations? This is one of the questions addressed by the authors of the paper "The Urban Decline of the House Sparrow (*Passer domesticus*): A Possible Link with Electromagnetic Radiation" (*Electromagnetic Biology and Medicine* [2007]: 141–151). The accompanying data on x = electromagnetic field strength (V/m) and y = sparrow density (birds/hectare) was read from a graph that appeared in the paper.

Field Strength	Sparrow Density
0.11	41.71
0.20	33.60
0.29	24.74
0.40	19.50
0.50	19.42
0.61	18.74
1.01	24.23
1.10	22.04
0.70	16.29
0.80	14.69
0.90	16.29
1.20	16.97
1.30	12.83
1.41	13.17
1.50	4.64
1.80	2.11
1.90	0.00
3.01	0.00
3.10	14.69
3.41	0.00

a. Construct a scatterplot of y = sparrow density versus x = field strength. Does the relationship between these two variables appear to be linear or nonlinear?
b. Consider transforming the data by leaving y unchanged and using either $x' = \sqrt{x}$ or $x'' = \log(x)$. The $\log(x)$ values given in the same order as the x values in the table above are

−0.96	−0.70	−0.54	−0.40	−0.30	−0.21
0.00	0.04	−0.15	−0.10	−0.05	0.08
0.11	0.15	0.18	0.26	0.28	0.48
0.49	0.53				

Which of these transformations would you recommend? Justify your choice using appropriate graphical displays.
c. Using the transformation you recommend in Part (b), find the equation of the least-squares line that describes the relationship between y and the transformed x.
d. What would you predict for sparrow density if the field strength is 0.5? What would you predict for sparrow density if the field strength is 2.5?

5.48 ● The paper "Effects of Age and Gender on Physical Performance" (*Age* [2007]: 77–85) describes a study of the relationship between age and 1-hour swimming performance. Data on age and swim distance for over 10,000 men participating in a national long-distance 1-hour swimming competition are summarized in the accompanying table. In Exercise 5.34 from Section 5.3, a plot of the residuals from the least-squares line showed a curved pattern that suggested that a quadratic curve would do a better job of summarizing the relationship between x = representative age and y = average swim distance. Find the equation of the least-squares quadratic curve and use it to predict average swim distance at 40 years of age.

Age Group	Representative Age (Midpoint of Age Group)	Average Swim Distance (meters)
20–29	25	3913.5
30–39	35	3728.8
40–49	45	3579.4
50–59	55	3361.9
60–69	65	3000.1
70–79	75	2649.0
80–89	85	2118.4

5.49 The paper "Feeding Ecology of the Great Basin Rattlesnake" (*Canadian Journal of Zoology* [2008]: 723–734) investigated whether there was a relationship between the size of a rattlesnake and the size of the unsuspecting rodent the snake would hunt. The authors collected data on x = snake body mass (in grams) and prey body mass (in grams) for 22 snakes and their prey. Because the relationship between snake mass and prey mass was not linear, the authors transformed both x and y by taking natural logarithms. The transformed data was used to construct the following scatterplot, which shows a linear pattern. If a scatterplot had been constructed using the untransformed data, which of the four curved segments in Figure 5.38 do you think it would most resemble? Explain your choice.

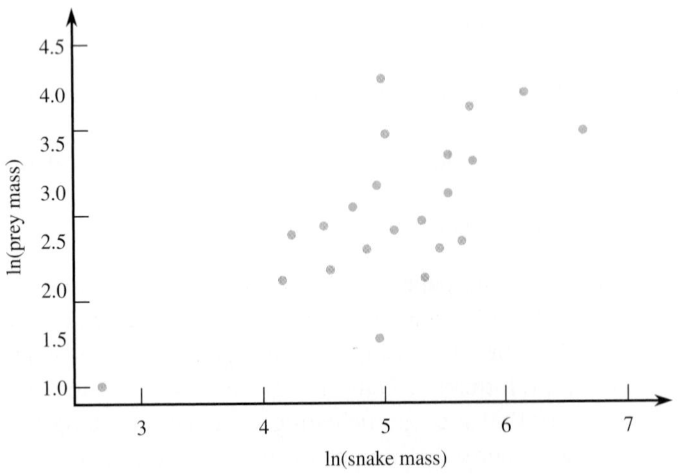

5.50 ● The paper "Developmental and Individual Differences in Pure Numerical Estimation" (*Developmental Psychology* [2006]: 189–201) describes a study of how young children develop the ability to estimate lengths. Children were shown a piece of paper with two lines. One line was a short line labeled as having length 1 *zip*. The second line was a much longer line labeled as having length 1000 *zips*. The child was then asked to draw a line that had a length of a specified number of *zips*, such as 438 *zips*. The data in the accompanying table gives the length requested and the average of the actual lengths of the lines drawn by 30 second graders.

Requested Length	Second Grade Average Length Drawn
3	37.15
7	92.88
19	207.43
52	272.45
103	458.20
158	442.72
240	371.52
297	467.49
346	487.62
391	530.96
438	482.97
475	544.89
502	515.48
586	595.98
613	575.85
690	605.26
721	637.77
760	674.92
835	701.24
874	662.54
907	758.51
962	749.23

a. Construct a scatterplot of y = second grade average length drawn versus x = requested length.
b. Based on the scatterplot in Part (a), would you suggest using a line, a quadratic curve, or a cubic curve to describe the relationship between x and y? Explain your choice.
c. Using a statistical software package or a graphing calculator, fit a cubic curve to this data and use it to predict average length drawn for a requested length of 500 *zips*.

5.51 ● Researchers have examined a number of climatic variables in an attempt to understand the mechanisms that govern rainfall runoff. The paper "The Applicability of Morton's and Penman's Evapotranspiration Estimates in Rainfall-Runoff Modeling" (*Water Resources Bulletin* [1991]: 611–620) reported on a study that examined the relationship between x = cloud cover index and y = sunshine index. The cloud cover index can have values between 0 and 1. The accompanying data are consistent with summary quantities in the article. The authors of the article used a cubic regression to describe the relationship between cloud cover and sunshine.

Cloud Cover Index (x)	Sunshine Index (y)
0.2	10.98
0.5	10.94
0.3	10.91
0.1	10.94
0.2	10.97
0.4	10.89
0.0	10.88
0.4	10.92
0.3	10.86

a. Construct a scatterplot of the data. What characteristics of the plot suggest that a cubic regression would be more appropriate for summarizing the relationship between sunshine index and cloud cover index than a linear or quadratic regression?

b. Find the equation of the least-squares cubic function.

c. Construct a residual plot by plotting the residuals from the cubic regression model versus x. Are there any troubling patterns in the residual plot that suggest that a cubic regression is not an appropriate way to summarize the relationship?

d. Use the cubic regression to predict sunshine index when the cloud cover index is 0.25.

e. Use the cubic regression to predict sunshine index when the cloud cover index is 0.45.

f. Explain why it would not be a good idea to use the cubic regression equation to predict sunshine index for a cloud cover index of 0.75.

5.52 ● ✦ The report "Older Driver Involvement in Injury Crashes in Texas" (Texas Transportation Institute, 2004) included a scatterplot of y = fatality rate (percentage of drivers killed in injury crashes) versus x = driver age. The accompanying data are approximate values read from the scatterplot.

Age	Fatality Rate	Age	Fatality Rate
40	0.75	70	1.30
45	0.75	75	1.65
50	0.95	80	2.20
55	1.05	85	3.00
60	1.15	90	3.20
65	1.20		

a. Construct a scatterplot of these data.

b. Using Table 5.5 and the ladder of transformations in Figure 5.38, suggest a transformation that might result in variables for which the scatterplot would exhibit a pattern that was more nearly linear.

c. Reexpress x and/or y using the transformation you recommended in Part (b). Construct a scatterplot of the transformed data.

d. Does the scatterplot in Part (c) suggest that the transformation was successful in straightening the plot?

e. Using the transformed variables, fit the least-squares line and use it to predict the fatality rate for 78-year-old drivers.

5.53 ● The article "Organ Transplant Demand Rises Five Times as Fast as Existing Supply" (*San Luis Obispo Tribune*, February 23, 2001) included a graph that showed the number of people waiting for organ transplants each year from 1990 to 1999. The following data are approximate values and were read from the graph in the article:

Year	Number Waiting for Transplant (in thousands)
1 (1990)	22
2	25
3	29
4	33
5	38
6	44
7	50
8	57
9	64
10 (1999)	72

a. Construct a scatterplot of the data with y = number waiting for transplant and x = year. Describe how the number of people waiting for transplants has changed over time from 1990 to 1999.

b. The scatterplot in Part (a) is shaped like segment 2 in Figure 5.38. Find a transformation of x and/or y that straightens the plot. Construct a scatterplot for your transformed variables.

c. Using the transformed variables from Part (b), fit a least-squares line and use it to predict the number waiting for an organ transplant in 2000 (Year 11).

d. The prediction made in Part (c) involves prediction for an x value that is outside the range of the x values in the sample. What assumption must you be willing to make for this to be reasonable? Do you think this assumption is reasonable in this case? Would your answer be the same if the prediction had been for the year 2010 rather than 2000? Explain.

5.54 ● Penicillin was administered orally to five different horses, and the concentration of penicillin in the blood was determined after five different lengths of time. The following data on x = elapsed time (in hours) and y = penicillin concentration (in mg/ml) appeared in the paper "Absorption and Distribution Patterns of Oral Phenoxymethyl Penicillin in the Horse" (*Cornell Veterinarian* [1983]: 314–323):

x	1	2	3	6	8
y	1.8	1.0	0.5	0.1	0.1

Construct scatterplots using the following variables. Which transformation, if any, would you recommend?

a. x and y
b. $\sqrt{x}$ and y
c. x and $\sqrt{y}$
d. $\sqrt{x}$ and $\sqrt{y}$
e. x and $\log(y)$ (values of $\log(y)$ are 0.26, 0, −0.30, −1, and −1).

5.55 ● Determining the age of an animal can sometimes be a difficult task. One method of estimating the age of harp seals is based on the width of the pulp canal in the seal's canine teeth. To investigate the relationship between age and the width of the pulp canal, researchers measured age and canal width in seals of known age. The following data on x = age (in years) and y = canal length (in millimeters) are a portion of a larger data set that appeared in the paper "Validation of Age Estimation in the Harp Seal Using Dentinal Annuli" (*Canadian Journal of Fisheries and Aquatic Science* [1983]: 1430–1441):

x	0.25	0.25	0.50	0.50	0.50	0.75	0.75	1.00
y	700	675	525	500	400	350	300	300
x	1.00	1.00	1.00	1.00	1.25	1.25	1.50	1.50
y	250	230	150	100	200	100	100	125
x	2.00	2.00	2.50	2.75	3.00	4.00	4.00	5.00
y	60	140	60	50	10	10	10	10
x	5.00	5.00	5.00	6.00	6.00			
y	15	10	10	15	10			

Construct a scatterplot for this data set. Would you describe the relationship between age and canal length as linear? If not, suggest a transformation that might straighten the plot.

Bold exercises answered in back ● Data set available online ✦ Video Solution available

5.5 Logistic Regression (Optional)

The correlation and regression techniques we have seen up to this point require that both variables of interest be numerical. But what if the dependent variable in a study is not numerical? This situation requires a different approach. For a dependent variable that is categorical with just two possible values (a binary variable), logistic regression can be used to describe the way in which such a dependent variable is related to a numerical predictor variable.

EXAMPLE 5.20 Look Out for Those Wolf Spiders

● The paper "Sexual Cannibalism and Mate Choice Decisions in Wolf Spiders: Influence of Male Size and Secondary Sexual Characteristics" (*Animal Behaviour* [2005]: 83–94) described a study in which researchers were interested in what variables might be related to a female wolf spider's decision to kill and consume her part-

● Data set available online

ner during courtship or mating. The accompanying data (approximate values read from a graph in the paper) are values of x = difference in body width (female – male) and y = cannibalism, coded as 0 for no cannibalism and 1 for cannibalism for 52 pairs of courting wolf spiders.

Size Difference (mm)	Cannibalism	Size Difference (mm)	Cannibalism
−1	0	0.4	0
−1	0	0.4	0
−0.8	0	0.4	0
−0.8	0	0.4	0
−0.6	0	0.4	1
−0.6	0	0.6	0
−0.4	0	0.6	0
−0.4	0	0.6	0
−0.4	0	0.6	0
−0.4	0	0.6	0
−0.2	0	0.6	1
−0.2	0	0.6	1
−0.2	0	0.8	0
−0.2	0	0.8	0
0.0	0	0.8	1
0.0	0	0.8	1
0.0	0	0.8	1
0.0	0	1.0	0
0.0	0	1.0	0
0.0	0	1.0	1
0.2	0	1.0	1
0.2	0	1.2	0
0.2	0	1.4	0
0.2	0	1.6	1
0.2	0	1.8	1
0.2	0	2.0	1

A Minitab scatterplot of the data is shown in Figure 5.41. Note that the plot was constructed so that if two points fell in exactly the same position, one was offset a bit so that all observations would be visible. (This is called jittering.)

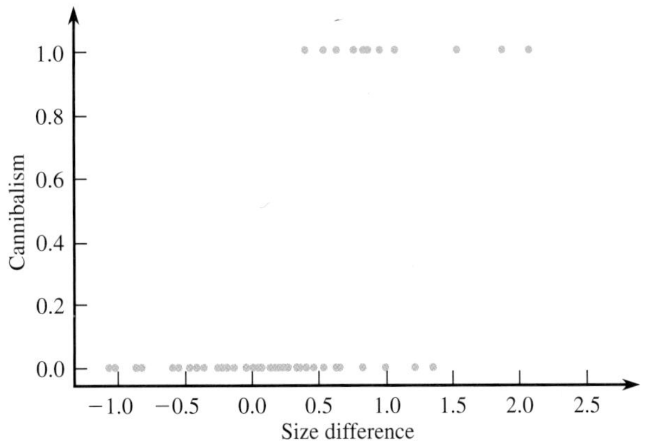

FIGURE 5.41
Scatterplot of the wolf spider data.

The scatterplot doesn't look like others we have seen before—its odd appearance is due to the fact that all y values are either 0 or 1. But, we can see from the plot that there are more occurrences of cannibalism for large x values (where the female is bigger than the male) than for smaller x values. In this situation, it makes sense to consider the probability of cannibalism (or equivalently, the proportion of the time cannibalism would occur) as being related to size difference. For example, we might focus on a single x value, say $x = 0$ where the female and male are the same size. Based on the data at hand, what can we say about the cannibalism proportion for pairs where the size difference is 0? We will return to this question after introducing the logistic regression equation.

A logistic regression equation is used to describe how the probability of "success" (for example, cannibalism in the wolf spider example) changes as a numerical predictor variable, x, changes.

With p denoting the probability of success, the **logistic regression function** is

$$p = \frac{e^{a+bx}}{1 + e^{a+bx}}$$

where a and b are constants.

The logistic regression equation looks complicated, but it has some very convenient properties. For any x value, the value of $e^{a+bx}/(1 + e^{a+bx})$ is between 0 and 1. As x changes, the graph of this equation has an "S" shape. Consider the two S-shaped curves of Figure 5.42. The blue curve starts near 0 and increases to 1 as x increases. This is the type of behavior exhibited by $p = e^{a+bx}/(1 + e^{a+bx})$ when $b > 0$. The red curve starts near 1 for small x values and then decreases as x increases. This happens when $b < 0$ in the logistic regression equation. The steepness of the curve—how quickly it rises or falls—also depends on the value of b. The farther b is from 0, the steeper the curve.

Most statistics packages, such as Minitab and SPSS, have the capability of using sample data to compute values for a and b in the logistic regression equation to produce an equation relating the probability of success to the predictor x. An explanation of an alternate method for computing reasonable values of a and b is given later in this section.

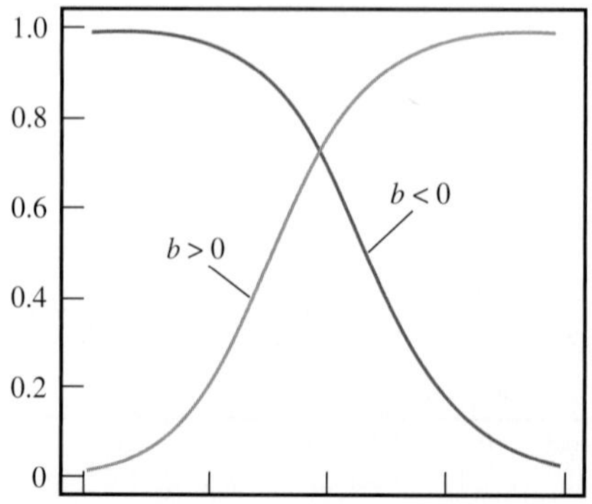

FIGURE 5.42
Two logistic regression curves.

EXAMPLE 5.21 Cannibal Spiders II

Minitab was used to fit a logistic regression equation to the wolf spider data of Example 5.20. The resulting Minitab output is given in Figure 5.43, and Figure 5.44 shows a scatterplot of the original data with the logistic regression curve superimposed.

Response Information

Variable	Value	Count	
Cannibalism	1	11	(Event)
	0	41	
	Total	52	

Logistic Regression Table

Predictor	Coef	SE Coef	Z	P	Odds Ratio	95% CI Lower	95% CI Upper
Constant	−3.08904	0.828780	−3.73	0.000			
Size difference	3.06928	1.00407	3.06	0.002	21.53	3.01	154.05

FIGURE 5.43
Minitab output for the data of Example 5.21.

With $a = -3.08904$ and $b = 3.06928$, the equation of the logistic regression function is

$$p = \frac{e^{-3.08904+3.06928x}}{1 + e^{-3.08904+3.06928x}}$$

To predict or estimate the probability of cannibalism when the size difference between the female and male = 0, we substitute 0 into the logistic regression equation to obtain

$$p = \frac{e^{-3.08904+3.06928(0)}}{1 + e^{-3.08904+3.06928(0)}} = \frac{e^{-3.08904}}{1 + e^{-3.08904}} = .044$$

The probabilities of cannibalism for other values of x = size difference can be computed in a similar manner.

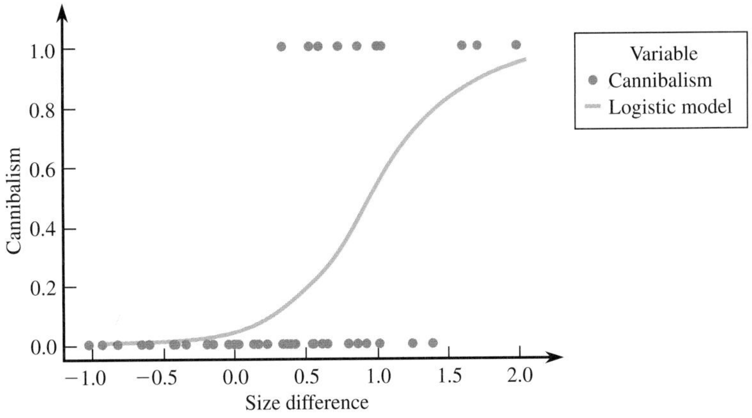

FIGURE 5.44
Scatterplot and logistic regression curve for data of Example 5.21.

Relating Logistic Regression to Data Transformation

Consider an important question in drug development—what strength of dose of a drug is needed to elicit a response? For example, suppose that we are marketing a poison, RatRiddance, to be used to eradicate rats. We want to use enough of the toxic agent to dispose of the little critters, but for safety and ecological reasons we don't want to use more poison than necessary. Imagine that an experiment is conducted to assess the toxicity of RatRiddance, where the amount of the active ingredient is varied. Eleven different concentrations are tested, with about 500 rats in each treatment. The results of the experiment are given in Table 5.7. A plot of the data is shown in Figure 5.45.

TABLE 5.7 Mortality Data for RatRiddance

Concentration	20	40	60	80	100	120	140	160	180	200	240
Number Exposed	440	462	500	467	515	561	469	550	542	479	497
Mortality Rate	.225	.236	.398	.628	.678	.795	.853	.860	.921	.940	.968

The original data consisted of about 5000 observations; for each individual rat there was a (dose, response) pair, where the response was categorical—survived or did not survive. The data were then summarized in Table 5.7 by computing the proportion that did not survive (the mortality rate) for each dose. It is these proportions that were plotted in the scatterplot of Figure 5.45 and that exhibit the typical "S" shape of the logistic regression equation.

Let's use the logistic regression equation to describe the relationship between the proportion of rats who did not survive (mortality rate) and dose. The model is then

$$p = \frac{e^{a+bx}}{1 + e^{a+bx}}$$

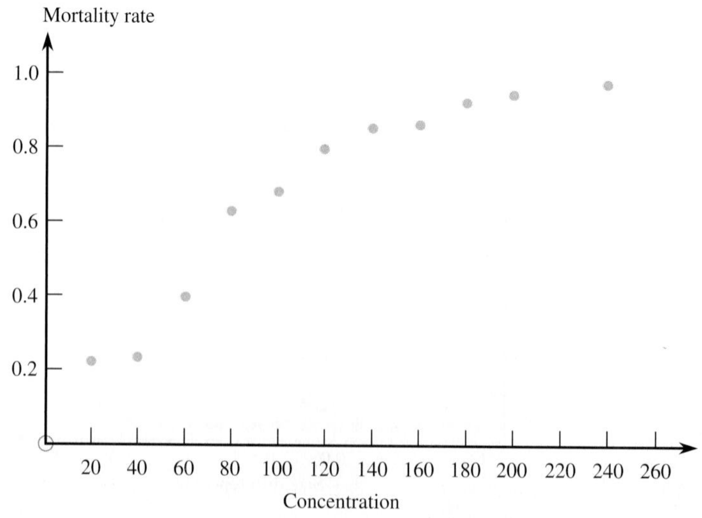

FIGURE 5.45
Scatterplot of mortality versus dose.

For data that has been converted into proportions, some tedious but straightforward algebra demonstrates how we can use a transformation to calculate values for a and b in the logistic regression equation:

$$p = \frac{e^{a+bx}}{1 + e^{a+bx}}$$ multiply both sides by $1 + e^{a+bx}$

$$p(1 + e^{a+bx}) = e^{a+bx}$$ complete the multiplication on the left hand side of the equation

$$p + pe^{a+bx} = e^{a+bx}$$ subtract pe^{a+bx} from each side

$$p = e^{a+bx} - pe^{a+bx}$$ factor out e^{a+bx} in the right hand side of the equation

$$p = e^{a+bx}(1 - p)$$ divide both sides of the equation by $(1 - p)$

$$\frac{p}{1 - p} = e^{a+bx}$$ take the natural log of both sides

$$\ln\left(\frac{p}{1 - p}\right) = a + bx$$

This means that if the logistic regression curve is a reasonable way to describe the relationship between p and x, the relationship between $\ln\left(\frac{p}{1-p}\right)$ and x is linear. A consequence of this is that if we transform p using

$$y' = \ln\left(\frac{p}{1 - p}\right)$$

we can use least squares to fit a line to the (x, y') data.

For the RatRiddance example, the transformed data are

x	p	$\frac{p}{1-p}$	$y' = \ln\left(\frac{p}{1-p}\right)$
20	0.225	0.290	−1.237
40	0.236	0.309	−1.175
60	0.398	0.661	−0.414
80	0.628	1.688	0.524
100	0.678	2.106	0.745
120	0.795	3.878	1.355
140	0.853	5.803	1.758
160	0.860	6.143	1.815
180	0.921	11.658	2.456
200	0.940	15.667	2.752

The resulting best fit line is

$$\begin{aligned} y' &= a + bx \\ &= -1.6033 + 0.221x \end{aligned}$$

We can check the transformed linear model fit in the customary way, checking the scatterplot and the residual plot, as shown in Figure 5.46(a) and (b). Although there seems to be an ever-so-slight hint of curvature in the data, the linear model appears to fit quite well. In fact, the linear fit accounts for about 97% of the variation in y'.

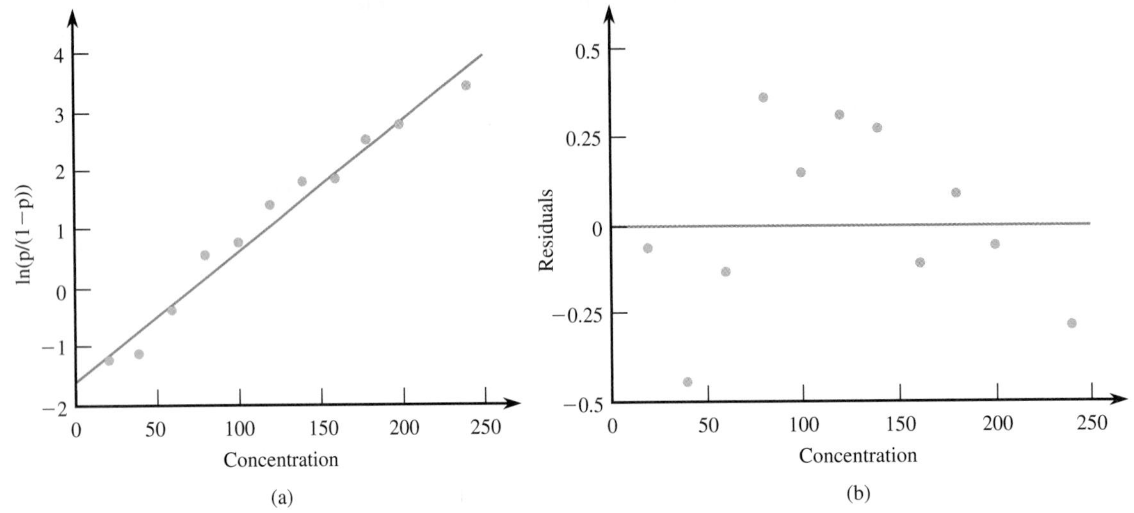

FIGURE 5.46
Scatterplot (a) and residual plot (b) for the transformed mortality data.

EXAMPLE 5.22 The Call of the Wild Amazonian . . . Frog

Alan and Sandy Carey/Photodisc/Getty Images

● The Amazonian tree frog uses vocal communication to call for a mate. In a study of the relationship between calling behavior and the amount of rainfall ("How, When, and Where to Perform Visual Displays: The Case of the Amazonian Frog *Hyla parviceps*," *Herpetologica* [2004]: 420–429), the daily rainfall (in mm) was recorded as well as observations of calling behavior by male Amazonian frogs. Calling behavior was used to compute the call rate, which is the proportion of frogs exhibiting calling behavior. Data consistent with the article are given in Table 5.8.

TABLE 5.8 Proportion Calling versus Daily Rainfall (mm)

Rainfall	0.2	0.3	0.4	0.5	0.7	0.8
Call rate	.17	.19	.20	.21	.27	.28
Rainfall	0.9	1.1	1.2	1.3	1.5	1.6
Call rate	.29	.34	.39	.41	.46	.49
Rainfall	1.7	2.0	2.2	2.4	2.6	2.8
Call rate	.53	.60	.67	.71	.75	.82
Rainfall	2.9	3.2	3.5	4.2	4.9	5.0
Call rate	.84	.88	.90	.97	.98	.98

Inspection of the scatterplot in Figure 5.47(a) reveals a pattern that is consistent with a logistic relationship between the daily rainfall and the proportion of frogs exhibiting calling behavior. The transformed data in Figure 5.47(b) show a clearly linear pattern. For these data the least-squares line is given by the equation $y' = -1.871 + 1.177(\text{Rainfall})$.

To predict calling proportion for a location with daily rainfall of 4.0 mm, we use the computed values of a and b in the logistic regression equation:

$$p = \frac{e^{-1.871+1.177x}}{1 + e^{-1.871+1.177x}} = \frac{e^{-1.871+1.177(4.0)}}{1 + e^{-1.871+1.177(4.0)}} = .945$$

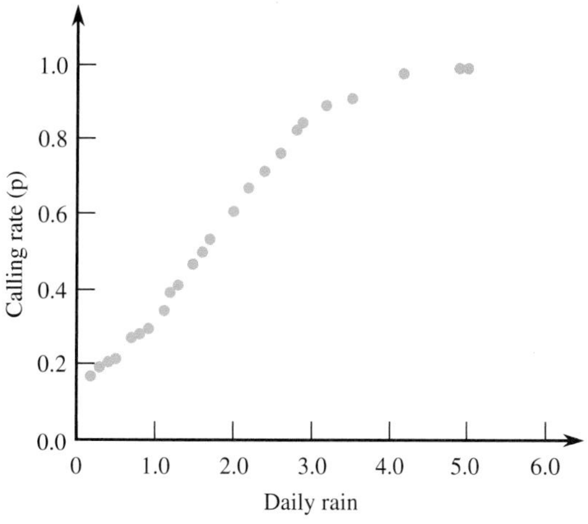

(a)

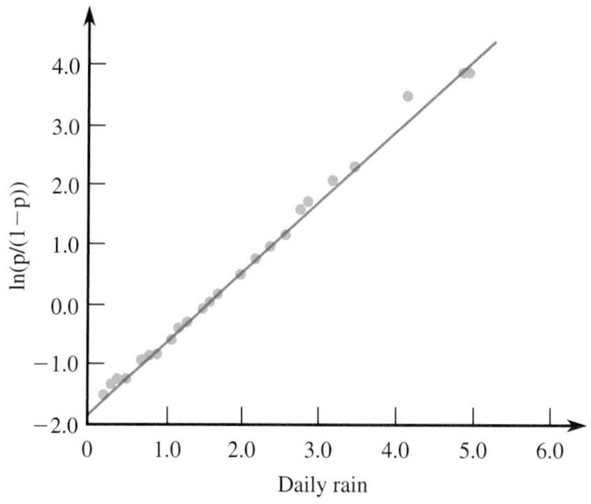

Linear Fit

ln(p/(1−p)) = −1.871 + 1.177 Daily Rain

Summary of Fit

RSquare	0.996
RSquare Adj	0.996
s	0.103

(b)

FIGURE 5.47
Scatterplot of original and transformed data of Example 5.22.

EXERCISES 5.56 - 5.62

5.56 ● Anabolic steroid abuse has been increasing despite increased press reports of adverse medical and psychiatric consequences. In a recent study, medical researchers studied the potential for addiction to testosterone in hamsters (*Neuroscience* [2004]: 971–981). Hamsters were allowed to self-administer testosterone over a period of days, resulting in the death of some of the animals. The data below show the proportion of hamsters surviving versus the peak self-administration of testosterone (μg). Fit a logistic regression equation and use the equation to predict the probability of survival for a hamster with a peak intake of 40μg.

Peak Intake (micrograms)	Survival Proportion (p)	$\frac{p}{1-p}$	$y' = \ln\left(\frac{p}{1-p}\right)$
10	0.980	49.0000	3.8918
30	0.900	9.0000	2.1972
50	0.880	7.3333	1.9924
70	0.500	1.0000	0.0000
90	0.170	0.2048	−1.5856

5.57 ● Does high school GPA predict success in first-year college English? The proportion with a grade of C or better in freshman English for students with various high school GPAs for freshmen at Cal Poly, San Luis Obispo, in fall of 2007 is summarized in the accompanying table. Fit a logistic regression equation that would allow you to predict the probability of passing freshman English based on high school GPA. Use the resulting equation to predict the probability of passing freshman English for students with a high school GPA of 2.2.

High School GPA	Proportion C or Better	$\frac{p}{1-p}$	$y' = \ln\left(\frac{p}{1-p}\right)$
3.36	0.95	19.00	2.94
2.94	0.90	9.00	2.20
2.68	0.85	5.67	1.73
2.49	0.80	4.00	1.39
2.33	0.75	3.00	1.10
2.19	0.70	2.33	0.85
2.06	0.65	1.86	0.62

(continued)

High School GPA	Proportion C or Better	$\frac{p}{1-p}$	$y' = \ln\left(\frac{p}{1-p}\right)$
1.94	0.60	1.50	0.41
1.83	0.55	1.22	0.20
1.72	0.50	1.00	0.00
1.61	0.45	0.82	−0.20
1.49	0.40	0.67	−0.41
1.38	0.34	0.52	−0.66
1.25	0.30	0.43	−0.85
1.11	0.25	0.33	−1.10
0.95	0.20	0.25	−1.39
0.75	0.15	0.18	−1.73
0.05	0.10	0.11	−2.20
0.08	0.05	0.05	−2.94

5.58 Some plant viruses are spread by insects and tend to spread from the edges of a field inward. The data on x = distance from the edge of the field (in meters) and y = proportion of plants with virus symptoms that appeared in the paper "Patterns of Spread of Two Non-Persistently Aphid-Borne Viruses in Lupin Stands" (*Annals of Applied Biology* [2005]: 337–350) was used to fit a least-squares regression line to describe the relationship between x and $y' = \ln\left(\frac{p}{1-p}\right)$. Minitab output resulting from fitting the least-squares line is given below.

```
The regression equation is
ln(p/(1-p)) = −0.917 − 0.107 Distance to Crop Edge

Predictor                  Coef    SE Coef       T      P
Constant                −0.9171     0.1249   −7.34  0.000
Distance to Crop Edge  −0.10716    0.01062  −10.09  0.000
S = 0.387646   R-Sq = 72.8%   R-Sq(adj) = 72.1%
```

a. What is the logistic regression function relating x and the proportion of plants with virus symptoms?
b. What would you predict for the proportion of plants with virus symptoms at a distance of 15 meters from the edge of the field? (Note: the x values in the data set ranged from 0 to 20.)

5.59 ● The paper "The Shelf Life of Bird Eggs: Testing Egg Viability Using a Tropical Climate Gradient" (*Ecology* [2005]: 2164–2175) investigated the effect of altitude and length of exposure on the hatch rate of thrasher eggs. Data consistent with the estimated probabilities of hatching after a number of days of exposure given in the paper are shown here.

Probability of Hatching

Exposure (days)	1	2	3	4	5	6	7	8
Proportion (lowland)	0.81	0.83	0.68	0.42	0.13	0.07	0.04	0.02
Proportion (mid-elevation)	0.73	0.49	0.24	0.14	0.037	0.040	0.024	0.030
Proportion (cloud forest)	0.75	0.67	0.36	0.31	0.14	0.09	0.06	0.07

a. Plot the data for the low- and mid-elevation experimental treatments versus exposure. Are the plots generally the shape you would expect from "logistic" plots?
b. Using the techniques introduced in this section, calculate $y' = \ln\left(\frac{p}{1-p}\right)$ for each of the exposure times in the cloud forest and fit the line $y' = a + b(\text{Days})$. What is the significance of a negative slope to this line?
c. Using your best-fit line from Part (b), what would you estimate the proportion of eggs that would, on average, hatch if they were exposed to cloud forest conditions for 3 days? 5 days?
d. At what point in time does the estimated proportion of hatching for cloud forest conditions seem to cross from greater than 0.5 to less than 0.5?

5.60 ● As part of a study of the effects of timber management strategies (*Ecological Applications* [2003]: 1110–1123) investigators used satellite imagery to study abundance of the lichen *Lobaria oregano* at different elevations. Abundance of a species was classified as "common" if there were more than 10 individuals in a plot of land. In the table below, approximate proportions of plots in which *Lobaria oregano* were common are given.

Proportions of Plots Where *Lobaria oregano* Are Common

Elevation (m)	400	600	800	1000	1200	1400	1600
Prop. of plots with lichen common	0.99	0.96	0.75	0.29	0.077	0.035	0.01

a. As elevation increases, does the proportion of plots for which lichen is common become larger or smaller? What aspect(s) of the table support your answer?

b. Using the techniques introduced in this section, calculate $y' = \ln\left(\frac{p}{1-p}\right)$ for each of the elevations and fit the line $y' = a + b(\text{Elevation})$. What is the equation of the best-fit line?
c. Using the best-fit line from Part (b), estimate the proportion of plots of land on which *Lobaria oregano* are classified as "common" at an elevation of 900 m.

5.61 ● The hypothetical data below are from a toxicity study designed to measure the effectiveness of different doses of a pesticide on mosquitoes. The table below summarizes the concentration of the pesticide, the sample sizes, and the number of critters dispatched.

Concentration (g/cc)	0.10	0.15	0.20	0.30	0.50	0.70	0.95
Number of mosquitoes	48	52	56	51	47	53	51
Number killed	10	13	25	31	39	51	49

a. Make a scatterplot of the proportions of mosquitoes killed versus the pesticide concentration.
b. Using the techniques introduced in this section, calculate $y' = \ln\left(\frac{p}{1-p}\right)$ for each of the concentrations and fit the line $y' = a + b(\text{Concentration})$. What is the significance of a positive slope for this line?
c. The point at which the dose kills 50% of the pests is sometimes called LD50, for "Lethal dose 50%." What would you estimate to be LD50 for this pesticide when used on mosquitoes?

5.62 ● In the study of textiles and fabrics, the strength of a fabric is a very important consideration. Suppose that a significant number of swatches of a certain fabric are subjected to different "loads" or forces applied to the fabric. The data from such an experiment might look as follows:

Hypothetical Data on Fabric Strength

Load (lb/sq in.)	5	15	35	50	70	80	90
Proportion failing	0.02	0.04	0.20	0.23	0.32	0.34	0.43

a. Make a scatterplot of the proportion failing versus the load on the fabric.
b. Using the techniques introduced in this section, calculate $y' = \ln\left(\frac{p}{1-p}\right)$ for each of the loads and fit the line $y' = a + b(\text{Load})$. What is the significance of a positive slope for this line?
c. What proportion of the time would you estimate this fabric would fail if a load of 60 lb/sq in. were applied?
d. In order to avoid a "wardrobe malfunction," one would like to use fabric that has less than a 5% chance of failing. Suppose that this fabric is our choice for a new shirt. To have less than a 5% chance of failing, what would you estimate to be the maximum "safe" load in lb/sq in.?

Bold exercises answered in back ● Data set available online ✦ Video Solution available

5.6 Interpreting and Communicating the Results of Statistical Analyses

Using either a least-squares line to summarize a linear relationship or a correlation coefficient to describe the strength of a linear relationship is common in investigations that focus on more than a single variable. In fact, the methods described in this chapter are among the most widely used of all statistical tools. When numerical bivariate data are analyzed in journal articles and other published sources, it is common to find a scatterplot of the data and a least-squares line or a correlation coefficient.

Communicating the Results of Statistical Analyses

When reporting the results of a data analysis involving bivariate numerical data, it is important to include graphical displays as well as numerical summaries. Including a scatterplot and providing a description of what the plot reveals about the form of the relationship between the two variables under study establish the context in which numerical summary measures, such as the correlation coefficient or the equation of the least-squares line, can be interpreted.

In general, the goal of an analysis of bivariate data is to give a quantitative description of the relationship, if any, between the two variables. If there is a relationship, you can describe how strong or weak the relationship is or model the relationship in a way that allows various conclusions to be drawn. If the goal of the study is to describe the strength of the relationship and the scatterplot shows a linear pattern, you can report the value of the correlation coefficient or the coefficient of determination as a measure of the strength of the linear relationship.

When you interpret the value of the correlation coefficient, it is a good idea to relate the interpretation to the pattern observed in the scatterplot. This is especially important before making a statement of no relationship between two variables, because a correlation coefficient near 0 does not necessarily imply that there is no relationship of any form. Similarly, a correlation coefficient near 1 or -1, by itself, does not guarantee that the relationship is linear. A curved pattern, such as the one we saw in Figure 5.17, can produce a correlation coefficient that is near 1.

If the goal of a study is prediction, then, when you report the results of the study, you should not only give a scatterplot and the equation of the least-squares line but also address how well the linear prediction model fits the data. At a minimum, you should include both the values of s_e (the standard deviation about the regression line) and r^2 (the coefficient of determination). Including a residual plot can also provide support for the appropriateness of the linear model for describing the relationship between the two variables.

What to Look for in Published Data

Here are a few things to consider when you read an article that includes an analysis of bivariate data:

- What two variables are being studied? Are they both numerical? Is a distinction made between a dependent variable and an independent variable?
- Does the article include a scatterplot of the data? If so, does there appear to be a relationship between the two variables? Can the relationship be described as linear, or is some type of nonlinear relationship a more appropriate description?
- Does the relationship between the two variables appear to be weak or strong? Is the value of a correlation coefficient reported?
- If the least-squares line is used to summarize the relationship between the dependent and independent variables, is any measure of goodness of fit reported, such as r^2 or s_e? How are these values interpreted, and what do they imply about the usefulness of the least-squares line?
- If a correlation coefficient is reported, is it interpreted properly? Be cautious of interpretations that claim a causal relationship.

The authors of the paper "Recycling and Ambivalence: Quantitative and Qualitative Analyses of Household Recycling Among Young Adults" (*Environment and Behavior* [2008]: 777–797) describe a study of recycling among young adults in Sweden. They considered $y =$ a numerical measure of recycling behavior that was based on how often six types of household waste (newspapers, glass, hard plastic, soft plastic, metal, and paper) were recycled and x = distance to the nearest recycling facility. They reported that "a check of a plot between the variables recycling behavior and distance to the nearest recycling facility showed an approximately linear association between the two variables." Based on this observation, a least-squares regression line is an appropriate way to summarize the relationship between recycling behavior and distance to nearest recycling facility.

A related article, "Rubbish Regression and the Census Undercount" (*Chance* [1992]: 33), describes work done by the Garbage Project at the University of Arizona. Project researchers had analyzed different categories of garbage for a number of households. They were asked by the Census Bureau to see whether any of the garbage data variables were related to household size. They reported that "the weight data for different categories of garbage were plotted on graphs against data on household size, dwelling by dwelling, and the resulting scatterplots were analyzed to see in which categories the weight showed a steady, monotonic rise relative to household size."

The researchers determined that the strongest linear relationship appeared to be that between the amount of plastic discarded and household size. The line used to summarize this relationship was stated to be $\hat{y} = 0.2815x$, where y = household size and x = weight (in pounds) of plastic during a 5-week collection. Note that this line has an intercept of 0. Scientists at the Census Bureau believed that this relationship would extend to entire neighborhoods, and so the amount of plastic discarded by a neighborhood could be measured (rather than having to measure house by house) and then used to approximate the neighborhood size.

An example of the use of the correlation coefficient is found in a paper describing a study of nightingales (a species of bird known for its song). For male songbirds, both physical characteristics and the quality of the song play a role in a female's choice of a mate. The authors of the article "Song Repertoire Is Correlated with Body Measures and Arrival Date in Common Nightingales" (*Animal Behaviour* [2005]: 211–217) used data from $n = 20$ nightingales to reach the conclusion that there was a positive correlation between the number of different songs in a nightingale's repertoire and both body weight ($r = .53$) and wing length ($r = .47$), and a negative correlation between repertoire size and arrival date ($r = -.47$). This means that heavier birds tend to know more songs, as do birds with longer wings. The authors of the paper indicated that the observed correlation between repertoire size and body characteristics was unlikely to be due solely to the age of the bird, since all nightingales in the study were more than 3 years old and prior research indicates that repertoire size does not continue to increase with age after the third year. The negative correlation between repertoire size and arrival date was interpreted as meaning that male nightingales who knew more songs tended to arrive at their breeding habitats earlier than those who knew fewer songs.

A nonlinear regression was used by the authors of the paper "Maternal Blood Manganese Levels and Infant Birth Weight" (*Epidemiology* [2009]: 367–373) to describe the relationship between y = birth weight and x = maternal blood-manganese level at delivery for 470 mother-infant pairs. The paper states:

> In this cross-sectional study, there was an inverted U-shaped association between maternal blood-manganese levels at delivery and birth weight in full-term infants. This suggests that both lower and higher manganese exposures are associated with lower birth weight, although the association of higher manganese with lower weight was rather weak and imprecise. This is the first epidemiologic study to provide clear evidence of a nonlinear association between maternal manganese exposure and birth weight.

The paper goes on to suggest why the relationship may be best described by a quadratic rather than a linear equation:

> One possible explanation for this effect would be oxidative stress caused by high manganese levels, leading to impairment of cellular function and growth. Manganese, like iron, is a transitional metal and can catalyze oxidative cellular reactions. Exposure to high levels of iron, a metal with overlapping chemical properties to manganese, has been associated with low birth weight.

A Word to the Wise: Cautions and Limitations

There are a number of ways to get into trouble when analyzing bivariate numerical data! Here are some of the things you need to keep in mind when conducting your own analyses or when reading reports of such analyses:

1. Correlation does not imply causation. A common media blunder is to infer a cause-and-effect relationship between two variables simply because there is a strong correlation between them. Don't fall into this trap! A strong correlation implies only that the two variables tend to vary together in a predictable way, but there are many possible explanations for why this is occurring besides one variable causing changes in the other.

   For example, the article "Ban Cell Phones? You May as Well Ban Talking Instead" (*USA Today*, April 27, 2000) gave data that showed a strong negative correlation between the number of cell phone subscribers and traffic fatality rates. During the years from 1985 to 1998, the number of cell phone subscribers increased from 200,000 to 60,800,000, and the number of traffic deaths per 100 million miles traveled decreased from 2.5 to 1.6 over the same period. However, based on this correlation alone, the conclusion that cell phone use improves road safety is not reasonable!

   Similarly, the *Calgary Herald* (April 16, 2002) reported that heavy and moderate drinkers earn more than light drinkers or those who do not drink. Based on the correlation between number of drinks consumed and income, the author of the study concluded that moderate drinking "causes" higher earnings. This is obviously a misleading statement, but at least the article goes on to state that "there are many possible reasons for the correlation. It could be because better-off men simply choose to buy more alcohol. Or it might have something to do with stress: Maybe those with stressful jobs tend to earn more after controlling for age, occupation, etc., and maybe they also drink more in order to deal with the stress."
2. A correlation coefficient near 0 does not necessarily imply that there is no relationship between two variables. Before such an interpretation can be given, it is important to examine a scatterplot of the data carefully. Although it may be true that the variables are unrelated, there may in fact be a strong but nonlinear relationship.
3. The least-squares line for predicting y from x is not the same line as the least-squares line for predicting x from y. The least-squares line is, by definition, the line that has the smallest possible sum of squared deviations of points from the line *in the y direction* (it minimizes $\sum(y - \hat{y})^2$). The line that minimizes the sum of squared deviations in the y direction is not generally the same as the line that minimizes the sum of the squared deviations in the x direction. So, for example, it is not appropriate to fit a line to data using y = house price and x = house size and then use the resulting least-squares line Price $= a + b$(Size) to predict the size of a house by substituting in a price and then solving for size. Make sure that

the dependent and independent variables are clearly identified and that the appropriate line is fit.

4. Beware of extrapolation. It is dangerous to assume that a linear model fit to data is valid over a wider range of x values. Using the least-squares line to make predictions outside the range of x values in the data set often leads to poor predictions.
5. Be careful in interpreting the value of the slope and intercept in the least-squares line. In particular, in many instances interpreting the intercept as the value of y that would be predicted when $x = 0$ is equivalent to extrapolating way beyond the range of the x values in the data set, and this should be avoided unless $x = 0$ is within the range of the data.
6. Remember that the least-squares line may be the "best" line (in that it has a smaller sum of squared deviations than any other line), but that doesn't necessarily mean that the line will produce good predictions. Be cautious of predictions based on a least-squares line without any information about the adequacy of the linear model, such as s_e and r^2.
7. It is not enough to look at just r^2 or just s_e when assessing a linear model. These two measures address different aspects of the fit of the line. In general, we would like to have a small value for s_e (which indicates that deviations from the line tend to be small) and a large value for r^2 (which indicates that the linear relationship explains a large proportion of the variability in the y values). It is possible to have a small s_e combined with a small r^2 or a large r^2 combined with a large s_e. Remember to consider both values.
8. The value of the correlation coefficient as well as the values for the intercept and slope of the least-squares line can be sensitive to influential observations in the data set, particularly if the sample size is small. Because potentially influential observations are those whose x values are far away from most of the x values in the data set, it is important to look for such observations when examining the scatterplot. (Another good reason for *always* starting with a plot of the data!)
9. If the relationship between two variables is nonlinear, it is preferable to model the relationship using a nonlinear model rather than fitting a line to the data. A plot of the residuals from a linear fit is particularly useful in determining whether a nonlinear model would be a more appropriate choice.

EXERCISES 5.63 - 5.66

5.63 The "Admitted Students Highlights Report 2009" prepared by The College Board for Cal Poly San Luis Obispo summarizes responses to a survey completed by 2001 new students who enrolled at Cal Poly in fall 2008 and by 2000 students who were admitted to Cal Poly for the fall 2008 term but who enrolled at other universities. One question in the survey presented a list of "college images" (such as career-oriented and friendly) and asked students to indicate for each image whether or not they associated that image with Cal Poly. The percentage that associated an image with Cal Poly was recorded for enrolling students and for non-enrolling students for each image. For example, 61% of enrolling students but only 46% of non-enrolling students associated the image "career-oriented" with Cal Poly. The resulting data were used to construct a scatterplot that appeared in the report. The scatterplot is reproduced as Figure EX5.63 at the bottom of the following page.

a. What do you think the two dashed lines in the scatterplot represent?
b. Write a short article appropriate for a student newspaper commenting on what can be learned from this scatterplot. You can assume that the scatterplot will appear with the article.

5.64 The following is an excerpt from a letter to the editor written by Roger Cleary that appeared in the *San Luis Obispo Tribune* (September 16, 2008):

> The causes of poor fuel economy have nothing to do with higher highway speeds, notwithstanding all the press hoopla, including the July 19 Miami Herald claim that "There is no question that slower speeds will save gasoline," and the July 3 statement by Drive Smarter Challenge vehicle director Deron Lovaas that, "I'm not sure whether most people make the connection between how fast they drive and how much fuel they use."
>
> I decided to gather the speed facts for myself using my Chevy, which comes equipped with a fuel usage driver information center, real-time read out. At a road speed of 17.5 mph, it averages 10 mpg; at 35 mph, it averages 20 mpg; and at 65 mph, it averages 30 mpg, all testing done with engine speed standardized at 2000 rpm.
>
> The higher the speed, the better the fuel economy. The faster you drive, the more fuel efficient you become and the more gasoline you save.

Notice that the only speeds that the letter writer provides data for are 17.5, 35, and 65 mpg. Studies of the relationship between y = gas mileage and x = speed have suggested that the relationship is not linear, and some have used a quadratic curve to describe the relationship between gas mileage and speed.

Write a response to Mr. Cleary that explains how his three observed data points could still be consistent with the statement that higher highway speeds lead to reduced fuel efficiency. Include a graph to support your explanation.

5.65 The paper "How Lead Exposure Relates to Temporal Changes in IQ, Violent Crime, and Unwed Pregnancy" (*Environmental Research* [2000]: 1–22) investigated whether childhood lead exposure is related to criminal behavior in young adults. Using historical data, the author paired y = assault rate (assaults per 100,000 people) for each year from 1964 to 1997 with a measure of lead exposure (tons of gasoline lead per 1000 people) 23 years earlier. For example, the lead exposure from 1974 was paired with the assault rate from 1997. The author chose to go back 23 years for lead exposure

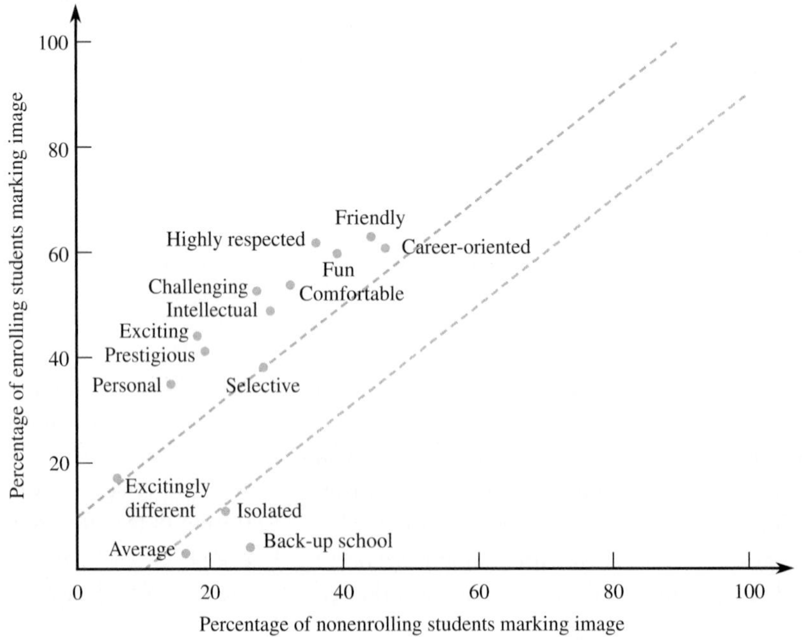

FIGURE EX5.63

because the highest number of assaults are committed by people in their early twenties, and 23 years earlier would represent a time when those in this age group were infants.

A least-squares regression line was used to describe the relationship between assault rate and lead exposure 23 years prior. Summary statistics given in the paper are

intercept:	−24.08
slope	327.41
r^2	0.89

Use the information provided to answer the following questions.

a. What is the value of the correlation coefficient for x = lead exposure 23 years prior and y = assault rate? Interpret this value. Is it reasonable to conclude that increased lead exposure is the cause of increased assault rates? Explain.

b. What is the equation of the least-squares regression line? Use the line to predict assault rate in a year in which gasoline lead exposure 23 years prior was 0.5 tons per 1000 people.

c. What proportion of year-to-year variability in assault rates can be explained by the relationship between assault rate and gasoline lead exposure 23 years earlier?

d. The graph below appeared in the paper. Note that this is not a scatterplot of the (x, y) pairs—it is two separate time series plots. The time scale 1941, 1942, ..., 1986 is the time scale used for the lead exposure data and the time scale 1964, 1965, ..., 2009 is used for the assault rate data. Also note that at the time the graph was constructed, assault rate data was only available through 1997. Spend a few minutes thinking about the information contained in this graph and then briefly explain what aspect of this graph accounts for the reported positive correlation between assault rate and lead exposure 23 years prior.

5.66 The following quote is from the paper "Evaluation of the Accuracy of Different Methods Used to Estimate Weights in the Pediatric Population" (*Pediatrics* [2009]: e1045–e1051):

> As expected, the model demonstrated that weight increased with age, but visual inspection of an age versus weight plot demonstrated a nonlinear relationship unless infants and children were analyzed separately. The linear coefficient for age as a predictor of weight was 6.93 in infants and 3.1 to 3.48 in children.

This quote suggests that when a scatterplot of weight versus age was constructed for all 1011 children in the study described in the paper, the relationship between y = weight and x = age was not linear. When the 1011 children were separated into two groups—infants (age birth to 1 year) and children (age 1 to 10 years)—and separate scatterplots were constructed, the relationship between weight and age appeared linear in each scatterplot. The slopes reported in the given quote (referred to as "the linear coefficient") are expressed in kg/year. Briefly explain why the relationship between weight and age in the scatterplot for the combined group would appear nonlinear.

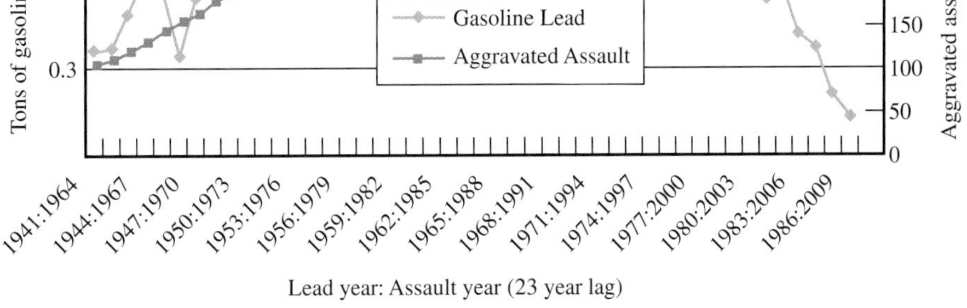

ACTIVITY 5.1 Exploring Correlation and Regression Technology Activity (Applets)

Open the applet (available in CengageNOW at www.cengage.com/login) called CorrelationPoints. You should see a screen like the one shown below.

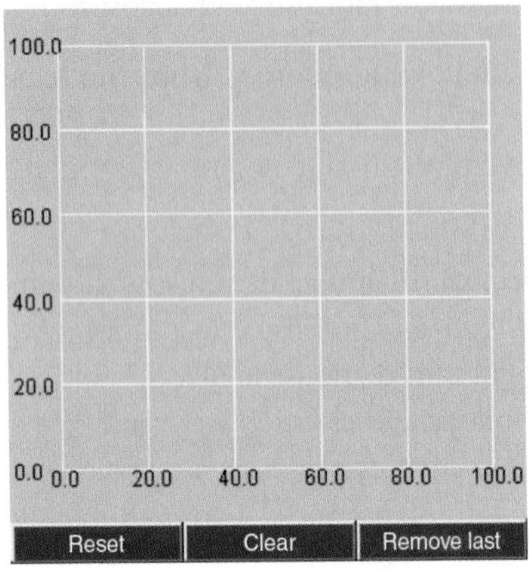

1. Using the mouse, you can click to add points to form a scatterplot. The value of the correlation coefficient for the data in the plot at any given time (once you have two or more points in the plot) will be displayed at the top of the screen. Try to add points to obtain a correlation coefficient that is close to −0.8. Briefly describe the factors that influenced where you placed the points.
2. Reset the plot (by clicking on the Reset bar in the lower left corner of the screen) and add points trying to produce a data set with a correlation that is close to +0.4. Briefly describe the factors that influenced where you placed the points.

Now open the applet called RegDecomp. You should see a screen that looks like the one shown at the top of the next column.

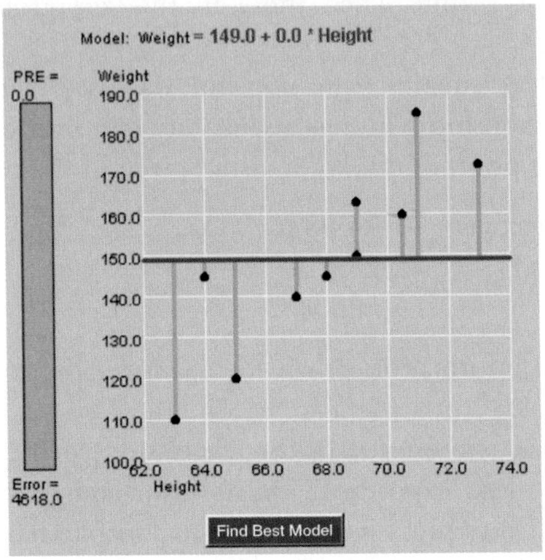

The black points in the plot represent the data set, and the blue line represents a possible line that might be used to describe the relationship between the two variables shown. The pink lines in the graph represent the deviations of points from the line, and the pink bar on the left-hand side of the display depicts the sum of squared errors for the line shown.

3. Using your mouse, you can move the line and see how the deviations from the line and the sum of squared errors change as the line changes. Try to move the line into a position that you think is close to the least-squares regression line. When you think you are close to the line that minimizes the sum of squared errors, you can click on the bar that says "Find Best Model" to see how close you were to the actual least-squares line.

ACTIVITY 5.2 Age and Flexibility

Materials needed: Yardsticks.

In this activity, you will investigate the relationship between age and a measure of flexibility. Flexibility will be measured by asking a person to bend at the waist as far as possible, extending his or her arms toward the floor. Using a yardstick, measure the distance from the floor to the fingertip closest to the floor.

1. Age and the measure of flexibility just described will be measured for a group of individuals. Our goal is to determine whether there is a relationship between age and this measure of flexibility. What are two reasons why it would not be a good idea to use just the students in your class as the subjects for your study?
2. Working as a class, decide on a reasonable way to collect data on the two variables of interest.
3. After your class has collected appropriate data, use them to construct a scatterplot. Comment on the interesting features of the plot. Does it look like there is a relationship between age and flexibility?
4. If there appears to be a relationship between age and flexibility, fit a model that is appropriate for describing the relationship.
5. *In the context of this activity,* write a brief description of the danger of extrapolation.

Summary of Key Concepts and Formulas

TERM OR FORMULA	COMMENT
Scatterplot	A graph of bivariate numerical data in which each observation (x, y) is represented as a point located with respect to a horizontal x axis and a vertical y axis.
Pearson's sample correlation coefficient $r = \frac{\sum z_x z_y}{n - 1}$	A measure of the extent to which sample x and y values are linearly related; $-1 \le r \le 1$, so values close to 1 or -1 indicate a strong linear relationship.
Principle of least squares	The method used to select a line that summarizes an approximate linear relationship between x and y. The least-squares line is the line that minimizes the sum of the squared errors (vertical deviations) for the points in the scatterplot.
$b = \frac{\sum(x - \bar{x})(y - \bar{y})}{\sum(x - \bar{x})^2} = \frac{\sum xy - \frac{(\sum x)(\sum y)}{n}}{\sum x^2 - \frac{(\sum x)^2}{n}}$	The slope of the least-squares line.
$a = \bar{y} - b\bar{x}$	The intercept of the least-squares line.
Predicted (fitted) values $\hat{y}_1, \hat{y}_2, \ldots, \hat{y}_n$	Obtained by substituting the x value for each observation in the data set into the least-squares line; $\hat{y}_1 = a + bx_1, \ldots, \hat{y}_n = a + bx_n$
Residuals	Obtained by subtracting each predicted value from the corresponding observed y value: $y_1 - \hat{y}_1, \ldots, y_n - \hat{y}_n$. These are the vertical deviations from the least-squares line.
Residual plot	Scatterplot of the (x, residual) pairs. Isolated points or a pattern of points in a residual plot are indicative of potential problems.
Residual (error) sum of squares $\text{SSResid} = \sum(y - \hat{y})^2$	The sum of the squared residuals is a measure of y variation that cannot be attributed to an approximate linear relationship (unexplained variation).
Total sum of squares $\text{SSTo} = \sum(y - \bar{y})^2$	The sum of squared deviations from the sample mean is a measure of total variation in the observed y values.
Coefficient of determination $r^2 = 1 - \frac{\text{SSResid}}{\text{SSTo}}$	The proportion of variation in observed y's that can be explained by an approximate linear relationship.
Standard deviation about the least-squares line $s_e = \sqrt{\frac{\text{SSResid}}{n - 2}}$	The size of a "typical" deviation from the least-squares line.
Transformation	A simple function of the x and/or y variable, which is then used in a regression.
Power transformation	An exponent, or power, p, is first specified, and then new (transformed) data values are calculated as *transformed value* = (original value)^p. A logarithmic transformation is identified with $p = 0$. When the scatterplot of original data exhibits curvature, a power transformation of x and/or y will often result in a scatterplot that has a linear appearance.
Logistic regression function $p = \frac{e^{a+bx}}{1 + e^{a+bx}}$	The graph of this function is an S-shaped curve. The logistic regression function is used to describe the relationship between probability of success and a numerical predictor variable.

Chapter Review Exercises 5.67 - 5.79

5.67 ● The accompanying data represent x = amount of catalyst added to accelerate a chemical reaction and y = resulting reaction time:

x	1	2	3	4	5
y	49	46	41	34	25

a. Calculate r. Does the value of r suggest a strong linear relationship?

b. Construct a scatterplot. From the plot, does the word *linear* provide the most effective description of the relationship between x and y? Explain.

5.68 ● The paper "A Cross-National Relationship Between Sugar Consumption and Major Depression?" (*Depression and Anxiety* [2002]: 118–120) concluded that there was a correlation between refined sugar consumption (calories per person per day) and annual rate of major depression (cases per 100 people) based on data from six countries. The following data were read from a graph that appeared in the paper:

Country	Sugar Consumption	Depression Rate
Korea	150	2.3
United States	300	3.0
France	350	4.4
Germany	375	5.0
Canada	390	5.2
New Zealand	480	5.7

a. Compute and interpret the correlation coefficient for this data set.

b. Is it reasonable to conclude that increasing sugar consumption leads to higher rates of depression? Explain.

c. Do you have any concerns about this study that would make you hesitant to generalize these conclusions to other countries?

5.69 ● The following data on x = score on a measure of test anxiety and y = exam score for a sample of $n = 9$ students are consistent with summary quantities given in the paper "Effects of Humor on Test Anxiety and Performance" (*Psychological Reports* [1999]: 1203–1212):

x	23	14	14	0	17	20	20	15	21
y	43	59	48	77	50	52	46	51	51

Higher values for x indicate higher levels of anxiety.

a. Construct a scatterplot, and comment on the features of the plot.

b. Does there appear to be a linear relationship between the two variables? How would you characterize the relationship?

c. Compute the value of the correlation coefficient. Is the value of r consistent with your answer to Part (b)?

d. Is it reasonable to conclude that test anxiety caused poor exam performance? Explain.

5.70 ● Researchers asked each child in a sample of 411 school-age children if they were more or less likely to purchase a lottery ticket at a store if lottery tickets were visible on the counter. The percentage that said that they were *more* likely to purchase a ticket by grade level are as follows (R&J Child Development Consultants, Quebec, 2001):

Grade	Percentage That Said They Were More Likely to Purchase
6	32.7
8	46.1
10	75.0
12	83.6

a. Construct a scatterplot of y = percentage who said they were more likely to purchase and x = grade. Does there appear to be a linear relationship between x and y?

b. Find the equation of the least-squares line.

5.71 ● Percentages of public school students in fourth grade in 1996 and in eighth grade in 2000 who were at or above the proficient level in mathematics were given in the article "Mixed Progress in Math" (*USA Today*, August 3, 2001) for eight western states:

State	4th grade (1996)	8th grade (2000)
Arizona	15	21
California	11	18
Hawaii	16	16
Montana	22	37
New Mexico	13	13
Oregon	21	32
Utah	23	26
Wyoming	19	25

a. Construct a scatterplot, and comment on any interesting features.
b. Find the equation of the least-squares line that summarizes the relationship between x = 1996 fourth-grade math proficiency percentage and y = 2000 eighth-grade math proficiency percentage.
c. Nevada, a western state not included in the data set, had a 1996 fourth-grade math proficiency of 14%. What would you predict for Nevada's 2000 eighth-grade math proficiency percentage? How does your prediction compare to the actual eighth-grade value of 20 for Nevada?

5.72 ● The following table gives the number of organ transplants performed in the United States each year from 1990 to 1999 (The Organ Procurement and Transplantation Network, 2003):

Year	Number of Transplants (in thousands)
1 (1990)	15.0
2	15.7
3	16.1
4	17.6
5	18.3
6	19.4
7	20.0
8	20.3
9	21.4
10 (1999)	21.8

a. Construct a scatterplot of these data, and then find the equation of the least-squares regression line that describes the relationship between y = number of transplants performed and x = year. Describe how the number of transplants performed has changed over time from 1990 to 1999.
b. Compute the 10 residuals, and construct a residual plot. Are there any features of the residual plot that indicate that the relationship between year and number of transplants performed would be better described by a curve rather than a line? Explain.

5.73 The paper "Effects of Canine Parvovirus (CPV) on Gray Wolves in Minnesota" (*Journal of Wildlife Management* [1995]: 565–570) summarized a regression of y = percentage of pups in a capture on x = percentage of CPV prevalence among adults and pups. The equation of the least-squares line, based on n = 10 observations, was $\hat{y} = 62.9476 - 0.54975x$, with $r^2 = .57$.

a. One observation was (25, 70). What is the corresponding residual?
b. What is the value of the sample correlation coefficient?
c. Suppose that SSTo = 2520.0 (this value was not given in the paper). What is the value of s_e?

5.74 ● The paper "Aspects of Food Finding by Wintering Bald Eagles" (*The Auk* [1983]: 477–484) examined the relationship between the time that eagles spend aerially searching for food (indicated by the percentage of eagles soaring) and relative food availability. The accompanying data were taken from a scatterplot that appeared in this paper. Let x denote salmon availability and y denote the percentage of eagles in the air.

x	0	0	0.2	0.5	0.5	1.0
y	28.2	69.0	27.0	38.5	48.4	31.1
x	1.2	1.9	2.6	3.3	4.7	6.5
y	26.9	8.2	4.6	7.4	7.0	6.8

a. Draw a scatterplot for this data set. Would you describe the pattern in the plot as linear or curved?
b. One possible transformation that might lead to a straighter plot involves taking the square root of both the x and y values. Use Figure 5.38 to explain why this might be a reasonable transformation.
c. Construct a scatterplot using the variables $\sqrt{x}$ and $\sqrt{y}$. Is this scatterplot more nearly linear than the scatterplot in Part (a)?
d. Using Table 5.5, suggest another transformation that might be used to straighten the original plot.

5.75 Data on salmon availability (x) and the percentage of eagles in the air (y) were given in the previous exercise.
a. Calculate the correlation coefficient for these data.
b. Because the scatterplot of the original data appeared curved, transforming both the x and y values by taking square roots was suggested. Calculate the correlation coefficient for the variables $\sqrt{x}$ and $\sqrt{y}$. How does this value compare with that calculated in Part (a)? Does this indicate that the transformation was successful in straightening the plot?

5.76 No tortilla chip lover likes soggy chips, so it is important to find characteristics of the production process that produce chips with an appealing texture. The accompanying data on x = frying time (in seconds) and y = moisture content (%) appeared in the paper, "Thermal and Physical Properties of Tortilla Chips as a

Function of Frying Time" (*Journal of Food Processing and Preservation* [1995]: 175–189):

Frying time (x):	5	10	15	20	25	30	45	60
Moisture content (y):	16.3	9.7	8.1	4.2	3.4	2.9	1.9	1.3

a. Construct a scatterplot of these data. Does the relationship between moisture content and frying time appear to be linear?
b. Transform the y values using $y' = \log(y)$ and construct a scatterplot of the (x, y') pairs. Does this scatterplot look more nearly linear than the one in Part (a)?
c. Find the equation of the least-squares line that describes the relationship between y' and x.
d. Use the least-squares line from Part (c) to predict moisture content for a frying time of 35 minutes.

5.77 ● The article "Reduction in Soluble Protein and Chlorophyll Contents in a Few Plants as Indicators of Automobile Exhaust Pollution" (*International Journal of Environmental Studies* [1983]: 239–244) reported the following data on x = distance from a highway (in meters) and y = lead content of soil at that distance (in parts per million):

x	0.3	1	5	10	15	20
y	62.75	37.51	29.70	20.71	17.65	15.41
x	25	30	40	50	75	100
y	14.15	13.50	12.11	11.40	10.85	10.85

a. Use a statistical computer package to construct scatterplots of y versus x, y versus $\log(x)$, $\log(y)$ versus $\log(x)$, and $\frac{1}{y}$ versus $\frac{1}{x}$.
b. Which transformation considered in Part (a) does the best job of producing an approximately linear relationship? Use the selected transformation to predict lead content when distance is 25 m.

5.78 ● An accurate assessment of oxygen consumption provides important information for determining energy expenditure requirements for physically demanding tasks. The paper "Oxygen Consumption During Fire Suppression: Error of Heart Rate Estimation" (*Ergonomics* [1991]: 1469–1474) reported on a study in which x = oxygen consumption (in milliliters per kilogram per minute) during a treadmill test was determined for a sample of 10 firefighters. Then y = oxygen consumption at a comparable heart rate was measured for each of the 10 individuals while they performed a fire-suppression simulation. This resulted in the following data and scatterplot:

Firefighter	1	2	3	4	5
x	51.3	34.1	41.1	36.3	36.5
y	49.3	29.5	30.6	28.2	28.0

Firefighter	6	7	8	9	10
x	35.4	35.4	38.6	40.6	39.5
y	26.3	33.9	29.4	23.5	31.6

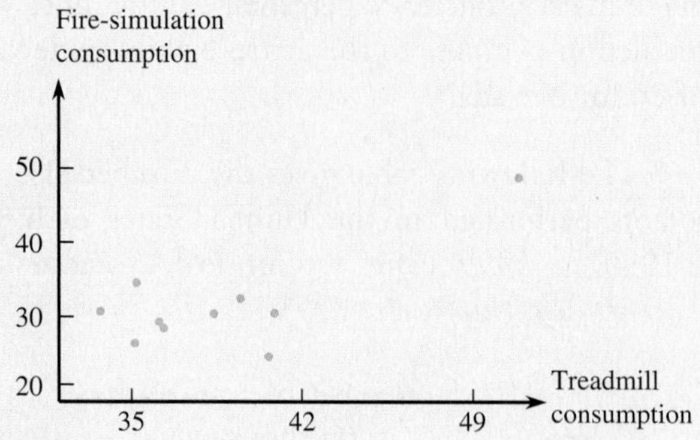

a. Does the scatterplot suggest an approximate linear relationship?
b. The investigators fit a least-squares line. The resulting Minitab output is given in the following:

```
The regression equation is
firecon = -11.4 + 1.09 treadcon

Predictor     Coef     Stdev    t-ratio       p
Constant    -11.37     12.46      -0.91   0.388
treadcon    1.0906    0.3181       3.43   0.009
s = 4.70    R-sq = 59.5%    R-sq(adj) = 54.4%
```

Predict fire-simulation consumption when treadmill consumption is 40.
c. How effectively does a straight line summarize the relationship?
d. Delete the first observation, (51.3, 49.3), and calculate the new equation of the least-squares line and the value of r^2. What do you conclude? (Hint: For the original data, $\sum x = 388.8$, $\sum y = 310.3$, $\sum x^2 = 15{,}338.54$, $\sum xy = 12{,}306.58$, and $\sum y^2 = 10{,}072.41$.)

5.79 Consider the four (x, y) pairs (0, 0), (1, 1), (1, −1), and (2, 0).
a. What is the value of the sample correlation coefficient r?
b. If a fifth observation is made at the value $x = 6$, find a value of y for which $r > 0.5$.
c. If a fifth observation is made at the value $x = 6$, find a value of y for which $r < 0.5$.

Graphing Calculator Explorations

EXPLORATION 5.1 Linear Regression

The scatterplot is a versatile graph, not limited to its use in fitting a model to data. Thus, your calculator will most likely separate the scatterplot and the regression procedures, and you may have to perform two distinct procedures as you perform a regression and plot the results. The construction of scatterplots was considered in a previous Graphing Calculator Exploration. Here we will point out some of the things you will encounter as you find a regression line.

In general, you will need to perform three tasks to get the regression line:

1. Prepare for the plotting of the scatterplot, as discussed previously.
2. Navigate the menu to select linear regression.
3. Transfer the regression equation information back to the graphing screen.

Navigating your calculator's menu system means yet another session with your calculator manual. The procedure should end with a choice that looks like "Linear Regression," or possibly "LinReg" for short. When you arrive at that menu option, just press the appropriate key, and—voilà!—the regression line will be calculated for you. When you type the final keystroke or select the final menu item, you see

LinReg

What your calculator sees, however, is,

LinReg, List1, List2

which it interprets as "*find the regression line assuming that the x values are in List1, and the y values are in List2.*" If you set up your data in different lists, possibly because you wish to save the data from a previous analysis, you will need to key in the "complete" LinReg command to override the default lists, possibly something like this:

LinReg, List3, List4

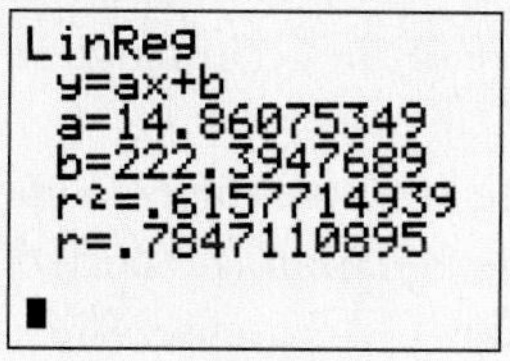

FIGURE 5.48
Linear regression output.

Again, you will need to check your manual for the exact syntax, especially to see which variable is assigned the first list in the command. Figure 5.48 shows the output from a linear regression.

Now that we have calculated the regression line, we want to show it on the scatterplot. There are two ways to do this—one easy and one even easier. The easy way is to simply enter the equation as you would any other function. Then, when the graph is made, the line will appear along with the scatterplot. This is because the "data plotting screen" and the "function plotting screen" share the same memory and the same coordinate system. The easier way will differ from calculator to calculator but will, in general, be one of these three possibilities:

1. There may be a "draw" menu option on the screen with the scatterplot. Pressing this will cause the regression line to be drawn.
2. You may be able to "copy and paste" the equation stored by the regression procedure. This would be similar to the copy-and-paste operation on computers.
3. On many calculators, this copy-and-paste operation can be entered directly on the LinReg line when you specify the regression. For example, the LinReg line might look like:

   LinReg List1, List2, Y1

   which your calculator would interpret as "*find the regression line assuming that the x values are in List1, and the y values are in List2. Then, paste that regression line into function Y1 for graphing purposes.*"

EXPLORATION 5.2 The Calculator as Communicator

As many aficionados of both movies and television are aware, when movies are later shown on television there are some compromises made because of the space limitations of TV. *King Kong* simply doesn't look the same on television! There are similar compromises made when the designers of calculators create displays on calculator screens.

When we do "mathematical" work on paper, our instructors usually have certain requirements, which will vary from instructor to instructor. These requirements usually assume access to 8.5-by-11-inch paper. It can safely be said that not very many calculators will have a screen that large, and this creates problems for calculator manufacturers. What is the best way to present information on a calculator screen? Calculator screens have limited space for effective display of text characters, and limited space for graphics. Although the designers of the calculators are very knowledgeable about how mathematics is written, they cannot work miracles and convert from 8.5-by-11-inch paper to a much smaller area. And in any case they cannot anticipate what each instructor will want shown for responses to different questions.

In general, it is our belief that how you solve a problem and report your method of solution should closely mirror what you would write if you were not using a calculator. When answering a question, your fundamental task is not just to provide an answer, but also to communicate your method. The calculator, because of the compromises discussed above, is unable to communicate methods effectively. We would like to use the context of regression to discuss some of the differences between what the calculator gives you and what you should include as part of your solution. (You should check with your instructor to make sure what his or her requirements are—we will merely point out that there may well be a mismatch between instructors' requirements and a calculator's screen.)

The data we will use for our regression example is taken from "The Ball-on-Three-Ball Test for Tensile Strength: Refined Methodology and Results for Three Hohokam Ceramic Types" (*American Antiquity* [2002]: 558–569). The anthropologist Margaret Beck was interested in the force (load, in kg) it would take to break 11th-century pot shards. Such strength is regarded as a measure of the technological advancement of a society.

```
LinReg
 y=a+bx
 a=-12.39347029
 b=3.870529721
 r²=.6419808409
 r=.8012370691
```

FIGURE 5.49
Linear regression output.

Consider first the regression output in Figure 5.49. Notice all those digits? You probably don't want to report all of them! Also, notice that the equation is reported very generically. To the designer of the calculator screen this makes perfect sense. With a generic presentation the amount of screen area needed remains constant, irrespective of what variables you are using. However, in your work you should indicate what the variables are. We recommend presenting the regression information as follows:

$$\text{Load} = -12.39 + 3.87 \cdot \text{Thickness}$$

or

$$\hat{L} = -12.39 + 3.87T$$

where L and T have been previously defined. Also, report $r = -0.80$, or $r = -0.801$, a more reasonable choice of significant digits.

Suppose you were asked to predict the breaking force of a shard 5.0 mm thick. Here is a possible template with our notes about what each line is saying:

$\hat{L} = -12.39 + 3.87T$ ← *("Here's the formula I'm using.")*

$= -12.39 + 3.87(5.0)$ ← *("Here are numbers I'm substituting.")*

$\hat{L} = 6.96 \text{ kg}$ ← *("Here's my result.")*

The advantages of this presentation are

1. If you err in your keystrokes, your instructor can still evaluate your method and assess your understanding.
2. If your answer differs from that of your fellow statistics students, you can easily tell whether you made a conceptual error or a keystroke error without having to take time to duplicate your work.
3. Most important, you are communicating in the language of statistics, where reliable communication demands a standard symbolism.

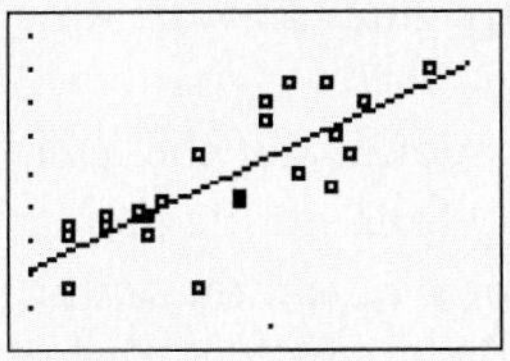

FIGURE 5.50
Scatterplot of load versus thickness.

Now consider the scatterplot as it appears on the calculator screen in Figure 5.50. The most serious omission is the scale on the two axes. From looking at the graph, one cannot tell how large or small the numbers are. Also, there is no indication of what the variables are. This is certainly understandable on a calculator screen, where all this information would take up precious space. However, this is not how to present such a plot. We recommend that every graph include a scale on each axis, indicate units, and show any other relevant information, as in Figure 5.51.

Load $= -12.39 + 3.87 \cdot$ Thickness or
$r = 0.8$

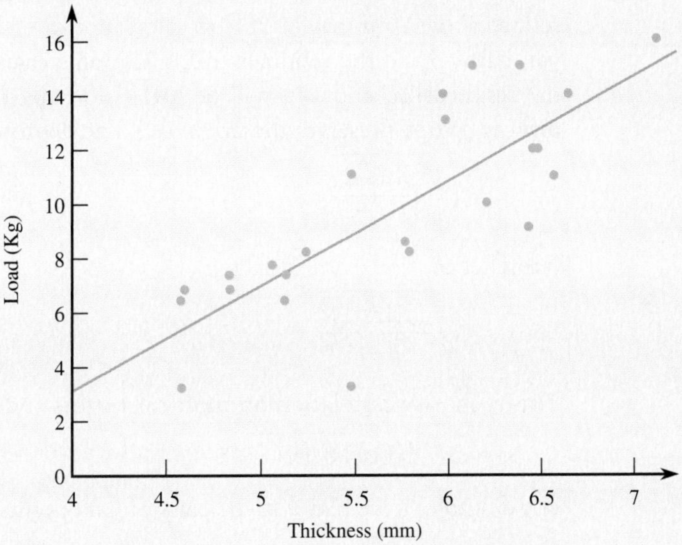

FIGURE 5.51
Regression line and scatterplot.

The message to the student using a graphing calculator is really very simple: You must realize not only the power of the calculator to save you time and effort, but also its limitations in communication.

EXPLORATION 5.3 In the Matter of Residuals

Different calculators handle residuals in different ways. Calculator A may store the residuals but not let you work with them; calculator B may not even store the residuals. In this Graphing Calculator Exploration we will offer several "workarounds" related to residuals. We assume that your calculator is list-based, and that you can perform calculations using those lists.

First, suppose that your calculator does not store the residuals. Let's see how we might get around this problem. We will suppose that the x-variable data have been stored in List1, and the y variable data in List2, and that you have successfully performed the appropriate regression calculations, giving you a regression line: $\hat{y} = a + bx$.

Once you have the regression line you can calculate the residuals and put them in a list (for example, List3) as follows:

$$\text{List2} - (a + b * (\text{List1})) \rightarrow \text{List3}$$

As you have probably already noticed, we are simply using the definition of the residuals for these calculations. This "List algebra" corresponds to our usual algebra, which would be

$$y_i - \hat{y}_i \rightarrow \text{residual list} \quad \text{or} \quad y_i - (a + bx_i) \rightarrow \text{residual list}$$

Once the residuals are stored in this list we can plot them and use them in other ways as well.

A second problem is the calculation of the standard deviation about the least-squares line, $s_e = \sqrt{\text{SSResid}/(n - 2)}$. You can obtain s_e directly from information at hand: the number of points, n, the sample standard deviation of y, s_y, and the sample correlation coefficient, r. We will skip the straightforward but slightly tedious algebra and cut directly to the chase:

$$s_e = \sqrt{\frac{n - 1}{n - 2}}\left(\sqrt{1 - r^2}\right) s_y$$

If your calculator is list-based and you have stored the residuals in a list as described above, you may be able to calculate s_e directly from the formula. Suppose that you have copied the residuals to List1. (Some calculators will not let you work with the residual list, and you will be forced to copy them to another list. In any case, making a copy preserves the originals.) The defining formula,

$$s_e = \sqrt{\frac{\text{SSResid}}{n - 2}}$$

translates to

$$s_e = \sqrt{\frac{\Sigma(\text{List1})^2}{n - 2}}$$

This is an easy calculation on most calculators and might look something like this:

$$s_e = \sqrt{\Sigma(\text{List1})^2/(n - 2)}$$

For example, if we had $n = 10$ pairs of data points, we would calculate

$$s_e = \sqrt{\Sigma(\text{List1})^2/8}$$

With these two workarounds, you should be able to circumvent a slightly statistically challenged calculator and work with residuals just as if you had one of those fancy statistical calculators!

EXPLORATION 5.4 How Does Your Calculator Perform Nonlinear Regression?

Scientific graphing calculators come with built-in statistical capability, including linear regression. Some calculators will also have options for nonlinear regression, such as exponential regression ($\hat{y} = ab^x$), power regression ($\hat{y} = ax^b$), and logarithmic regression ($\hat{y} = a + b\ln(x)$), as well as polynomial regression. The process of transforming data, fitting a line to the transformed data, and then "undoing" the transformation is used to get a good—though not "best" in the least-squares sense—fit of a function to the data.

Your calculator may transform variable(s) and fit a line to the transformed data, or it may use more complicated methods to estimate the least-squares solution. It is also possible that your calculator may produce unusual residual plots. This is not necessarily a bad thing, but does place some responsibility on your shoulders. Although your calculator does the arithmetic, *you* are responsible for understanding and interpreting the calculator output.

We will use exponential regression to illustrate how you might explore the calculator's regression output. We will compare two approaches to the regression: using linear regression on the transformed data, and using the "exp reg" button on the calculator. Since your calculator may differ from ours, we will continue to avoid specific keystrokes. You should be able to reproduce this analysis for different nonlinear regressions. If you choose to do reexpression "by hand" (transforming the data, fitting a line to the transformed data, and then back-transforming), you do not need to worry about what the calculator "button" does. This analysis needs to be done only if you wish to get quicker answers by using your calculator's built-in nonlinear regression capabilities.

The strategy we will use is to pick pairs of points with the same x values, and choose y values on either side of our model, $f(x) - k$ and $f(x) + k$. Choosing points in this manner will produce data that will force a least-squares solution through $f(x)$. Generating data using the function $f(x) = e^x$, x values from 2 to 5, and $k = 5$ results in the data shown in the x and y columns of the accompanying table. Because of the way the data were generated, the least-squares exponential function is $\hat{y} = e^x$.

x	y (formula)	y (decimal)	$\ln(y)$	Residual (calculator)	Residual (formula)
2	$e^2 + 5$	12.3890561	2.51681351	.744216305	6.5029351
2	$e^2 - 5$	2.3890561	.87089835	−.901698854	−3.4970648
3	$e^3 + 5$	25.0855369	3.22229146	.355243875	7.5005137
3	$e^3 - 5$	15.0855369	2.71373646	−.153311121	−2.4994863
4	$e^4 + 5$	59.5981500	4.08762453	.126126565	7.0621858
4	$e^4 - 5$	49.5981500	3.90395353	−.057544433	−2.9378142
5	$e^5 + 5$	153.4131591	5.03313466	−.022813682	−3.5401474
5	$e^5 - 5$	143.4131591	4.96572968	−.090218662	−13.5401474

Let's transform the data, fit a line, back-transform, and then compare the result to the calculator output when an exponential regression is requested. If the relationship between x and y is exponential (as it is here because of the way in which the data were generated), a log transformation would be an appropriate transformation to create a linear relationship. Taking the natural logarithm of y results in the transformed y values in the $\ln(y)$ column of the table. Using the calculator to fit a line to the $(x, \ln(y))$ data gives

$$\ln y = -0.416303559 + 1.094450382x$$

with $r^2 = 0.885784757$. Back-transforming gives the nonlinear relationship

$$y = 0.659480049(2.987540226)^x.$$

Notice this is different from the least-squares solution of $y = e^x$, but it still provides a reasonable fit to the data.

Figure 5.52(a) shows a scatterplot of $\ln(y)$ versus x and Figure 5.52(b) a plot of the residuals for the linear fit to the transformed data. The residual plot certainly does not look "random," but for our present purposes this is not a problem. The calculator reports the residuals from this regression and we have reproduced these in the Residual (calculator) column in the previous table.

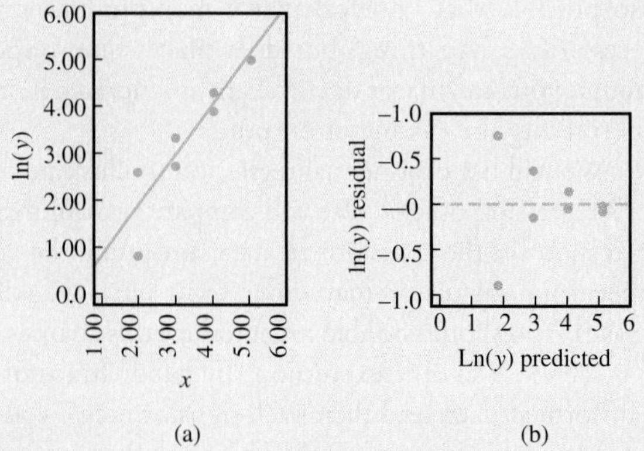

FIGURE 5.52
Plots using transformed data: (a) plot of ln(y) versus x; (b) plot of ln(y) residuals versus ln(y) predicted values.

Now try the "exp reg" function on your calculator. You should find that the reported regression is $y = 0.659480049 \cdot 2.987540226^x$ with $r^2 = 0.886$, the same values that were obtained by transforming and then fitting a linear function to the transformed data. Note that the calculator did not produce the least-squares fit of $y = e^x$. If you now request a scatterplot and a residual plot, you will see something like the plots in Figures 5.53(a) and 5.53(b).

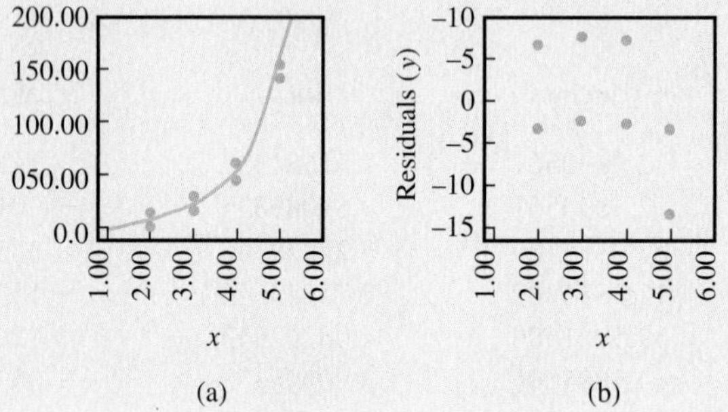

FIGURE 5.53
Plots using untransformed data: (a) scatterplot; (b) residual plot.

The scatterplots look different, which would be expected because the second plot is of the untransformed data. However, the pattern of residuals is very different, which suggests that the calculator is using a different procedure to calculate the residuals. It appears that the calculator is using the back-transformed equation to get a predicted y and then computing residual $= y -$ predicted y rather than using the residuals from the linear fit to the transformed data, ln(y) − predicted ln(y). Another fact to note is that the r^2 reported by the exp reg button analysis is the r^2 for the *transformed* fit, even though the residuals reported are in the *untransformed* scale. The calculator is doing the transformations for us, which seems reasonable. However, the residuals from the linear regression are not the ones presented; moreover, the residuals that are reported have a very different pattern than those from the linear regression of the transformed data.

The lesson from all these calculations is a simple one: If you wish to use the built-in capabilities of the calculator, you need to understand what it is actually doing. Remember, *you* are ultimately responsible for your analyses. Your calculator can only perform really quick arithmetic—you, the analyst, must provide the careful thinking and clear understanding of the results of that arithmetic.

Cumulative Review Exercises CR5.1 - CR5.19

CR5.1 The article "Rocker Shoe Put to the Test: Can it Really Walk the Walk as a Way to Get in Shape?" (*USA Today*, October 12, 2009) describes claims made by Skechers about Shape-Ups, a shoe line introduced in 2009. These curved-sole sneakers are supposed to help you "get into shape without going to the gym" according to a Skechers advertisement. Briefly describe how you might design a study to investigate this claim. Include how you would select subjects and what variables you would measure. Is the study you designed an observational study or an experiment?

CR5.2 Data from a survey of 1046 adults age 50 and older were summarized in the *AARP Bulletin* (November 2009). The following table gives relative frequency distributions of the responses to the question, "How much do you plan to spend for holiday gifts this year?" for respondents age 50 to 64 and for respondents age 65 and older. Construct a histogram for each of the two age groups and comment on the differences between the two age groups. (Notice that the interval widths in the relative frequency distribution are not the same, so you shouldn't use relative frequency on the *y*-axis for your histograms.)

Amount Plan to Spend	Relative Frequency for Age Group 50 to 64	Relative Frequency for Age Group 65 and Older
less than $100	.20	.36
$100 to <$200	.13	.11
$200 to <$300	.16	.16
$300 to <$400	.12	.10
$400 to <$500	.11	.05
$500 to <$1000	.28	.22

CR5.3 The graph in Figure CR5.3 appeared in the report "Testing the Waters 2009" (Natural Resources Defense Council). Spend a few minutes looking at the graph and reading the caption that appears with the graph. Briefly explain how the graph supports the claim that discharges of polluted storm water may be responsible for increased illness levels.

CR5.4 The cost of Internet access was examined in the report "Home Broadband Adoption 2009" (pewinternet.org). In 2009, the mean and median amount paid monthly for service for broadband users was reported as $39.00 and $38.00, respectively. For

FIGURE CR5.3 Influence of Heavy Rainfall on Occurrence of *E. Coli* Infections

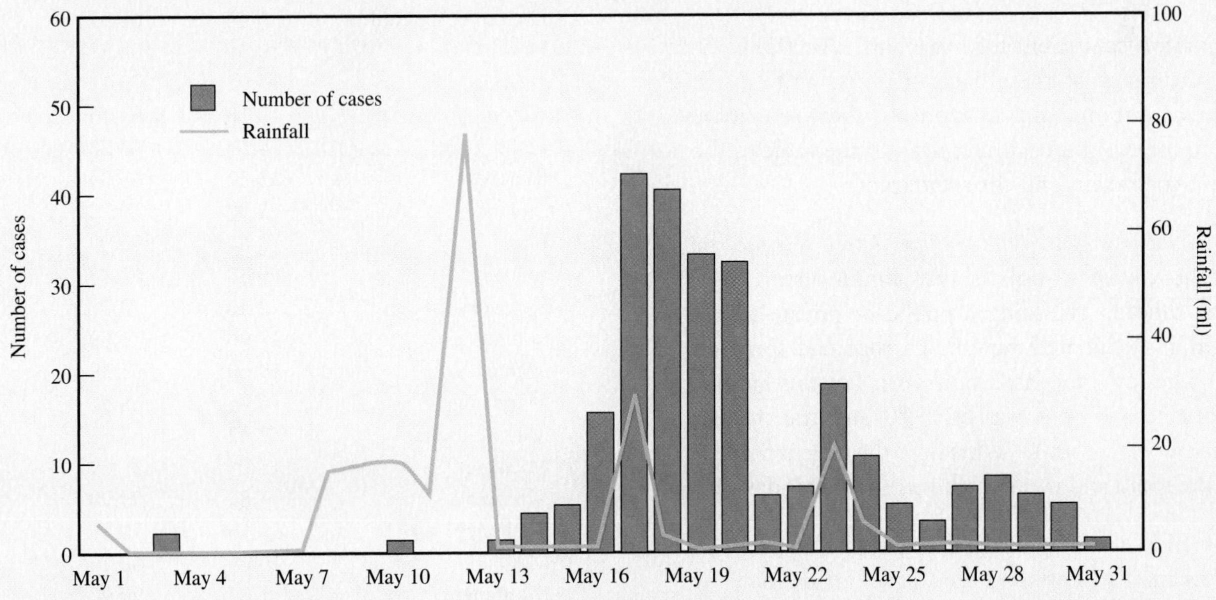

The graph shows the relationship between unusually heavy rainfall and the number of confirmed cases of *E. coli* infection that occurred during a massive disease outbreak in Ontario, Quebec, in May 2000. The incubation period for *E.Coli* is usually 3 to 4 days, which is consistent with the lag between extreme precipitation events and surges in the number of cases.

dial-up users, the mean and median amount paid monthly were $26.60 and $20.00, respectively. What do the values of the mean and median tell you about the shape of the distribution of monthly amount paid for broadband users? For dial-up users?

CR5.5 ● Foal weight at birth is an indicator of health, so it is of interest to breeders of thoroughbred horses. Is foal weight related to the weight of the mare (mother)? The accompanying data are from the paper "Suckling Behaviour Does Not Measure Milk Intake in Horses" (*Animal Behaviour* [1999]: 673–678):

Observation	Mare Weight (x, in kg)	Foal weight (y, in kg)
1	556	129
2	638	119
3	588	132
4	550	123.5
5	580	112
6	642	113.5
7	568	95
8	642	104
9	556	104
10	616	93.5
11	549	108.5
12	504	95
13	515	117.5
14	551	128
15	594	127.5

The correlation coefficient for these data is 0.001. Construct a scatterplot of these data and then write a few sentences describing the relationship between mare weight and foal weight that refer both to the value of the correlation coefficient and the scatterplot.

CR5.6 In August 2009, Harris Interactive released the results of the "Great Schools" survey. In this survey, 1086 parents of children attending a public or private school were asked approximately how much they had spent on school supplies over the last school year. For this sample, the mean amount spent was $235.20 and the median amount spent was $150.00. What does the large difference between the mean and median tell you about this data set?

CR5.7 ● Bidri is a popular and traditional art form in India. Bidri articles (bowls, vessels, and so on) are made by casting from an alloy containing primarily zinc along with some copper. Consider the following observations on copper content (%) for a sample of Bidri artifacts in London's Victoria and Albert Museum ("Enigmas of Bidri," *Surface Engineering* [2005]: 333–339), listed in increasing order:

2.0	2.4	2.5	2.6	2.6	2.7	2.7	2.8	3.0
3.1	3.2	3.3	3.3	3.4	3.4	3.6	3.6	3.6
3.6	3.7	4.4	4.6	4.7	4.8	5.3	10.1	

a. Construct a dotplot for these data.
b. Calculate the mean and median copper content.
c. Will an 8% trimmed mean be larger or smaller than the mean for this data set? Explain your reasoning.

CR5.8 ● ✦ Medicare's new medical plans offer a wide range of variations and choices for seniors when picking a drug plan (*San Luis Obispo Tribune*, November 25, 2005). The monthly cost for a stand-alone drug plan can vary from a low of $1.87 in Montana, Wyoming, North Dakota, South Dakota, Nebraska, Minnesota, and Iowa to a high of $104.89. Here are the lowest and highest monthly premiums for stand-alone Medicare drug plans for each state:

State	$ Low	$ High
Alabama	14.08	69.98
Alaska	20.05	61.93
Arizona	6.14	64.86
Arkansas	10.31	67.98
California	5.41	66.08
Colorado	8.62	65.88
Connecticut	7.32	65.58
Delaware	6.44	68.91
District of Columbia	6.44	68.91
Florida	10.35	104.89
Georgia	17.91	73.17
Hawaii	17.18	64.43
Idaho	6.33	68.88
Illinois	13.32	65.04
Indiana	12.30	70.72
Iowa	1.87	99.90
Kansas	9.48	67.88
Kentucky	12.30	70.72
Louisiana	17.06	70.59
Maine	19.60	65.39
Maryland	6.44	68.91
Massachusetts	7.32	65.58
Michigan	13.75	65.69
Minnesota	1.87	99.90
Mississippi	11.60	70.59
Missouri	10.29	68.26
Montana	1.87	99.90
Nebraska	1.87	99.90
Nevada	6.42	64.63

(continued)

State	$ Low	$ High
New Hampshire	19.60	65.39
New Jersey	4.43	66.53
New Mexico	10.65	62.38
New York	4.10	85.02
North Carolina	13.27	65.03
North Dakota	1.87	99.90
Ohio	14.43	68.05
Oklahoma	10.07	70.79
Oregon	6.93	64.99
Pennsylvania	10.14	68.61
Rhode Island	7.32	65.58
South Carolina	16.57	69.72
South Dakota	1.87	99.90
Tennessee	14.08	69.98
Texas	10.31	68.41
Utah	6.33	68.88
Vermont	7.32	65.58
Virginia	8.81	68.61
Washington	6.93	64.99
West Virginia	10.14	68.61
Wisconsin	11.42	63.23
Wyoming	1.87	99.90

Which of the following can be determined from the data? If it can be determined, calculate the requested value. If it cannot be determined, explain why not.

a. the median premium cost in Colorado
b. the number of plan choices in Virginia
c. the state(s) with the largest difference in cost between plans
d. the state(s) with the choice with the highest premium cost
e. the state for which the minimum premium cost is greatest
f. the mean of the minimum cost of all states beginning with the letter "M"

CR5.9 *Note: This exercise requires the use of a computer.* Refer to the Medicare drug plan premium data of Exercise 5.8.

a. Construct a dotplot or a stem-and-leaf display of the lowest premium cost data.
b. Based on the display in Part (a), which of the following would you expect to be the case for the lowest cost premium data?
   i. the mean will be less than the median
   ii. the mean will be approximately equal to the median
   iii. the mean will be greater than the median
c. Compute the mean and median for the lowest cost premium data.
d. Construct an appropriate graphical display for the highest cost premium data.
e. Compute the mean and median for the highest cost premium data.

CR5.10 ● ✦ The paper "Total Diet Study Statistics on Element Results" (Food and Drug Administration, April 25, 2000) gave information on sodium content for various types of foods. Twenty-six tomato catsups were analyzed. Data consistent with summary quantities given in the paper were

Sodium content (mg/kg)

12,148	10,426	10,912	9116	13,226	11,663
11,781	10,680	8457	10,788	12,605	10,591
11,040	10,815	12,962	11,644	10,047	10,478
10,108	12,353	11,778	11,092	11,673	8758
11,145	11,495				

Compute the values of the quartiles and the interquartile range.

CR5.11 ● The paper referenced in Exercise 5.10 also gave data on sodium content (in milligrams per kilogram) of 10 chocolate puddings made from instant mix:

3099 3112 2401 2824 2682 2510 2297
3959 3068 3700

a. Compute the mean, the standard deviation, and the interquartile range for sodium content of these chocolate puddings.
b. Based on the interquartile range, is there more or less variability in sodium content for the chocolate pudding data than for the tomato catsup data of Cumulative Exercise 5.10?

CR5.12 ● ✦ A report from Texas Transportation Institute (Texas A&M University System, 2005) on congestion reduction strategies looked into the extra travel time (due to traffic congestion) for commute travel per traveler per year in hours for different urban areas. Below are the data for urban areas that had a population of over 3 million for the year 2002.

Urban Area	Extra Hours per Traveler per Year
Los Angeles	98
San Francisco	75
Washington DC	66
Atlanta	64

(continued)

Urban Area	Extra Hours per Traveler per Year
Houston	65
Dallas, Fort Worth	61
Chicago	55
Detroit	54
Miami	48
Boston	53
New York	50
Phoenix	49
Philadelphia	40

a. Compute the mean and median values for extra travel hours. Based on the values of the mean and median, is the distribution of extra travel hours likely to be approximately symmetric, positively skewed, or negatively skewed?
b. Construct a modified boxplot for these data and comment on any interesting features of the plot.

CR5.13 ● ✦ The paper "Relationship Between Blood Lead and Blood Pressure Among Whites and African Americans" (a technical report published by Tulane University School of Public Health and Tropical Medicine, 2000) gave summary quantities for blood lead level (in micrograms per deciliter) for a sample of whites and a sample of African Americans. Data consistent with the given summary quantities follow:

Whites	8.3	0.9	2.9	5.6	5.8	5.4	1.2
	1.0	1.4	2.1	1.3	5.3	8.8	6.6
	5.2	3.0	2.9	2.7	6.7	3.2	
African	4.8	1.4	0.9	10.8	2.4	0.4	5.0
Americans	5.4	6.1	2.9	5.0	2.1	7.5	3.4
	13.8	1.4	3.5	3.3	14.8	3.7	

a. Compute the values of the mean and the median for blood lead level for the sample of African Americans. Which of the mean or the median is larger? What characteristic of the data set explains the relative values of the mean and the median?
b. Construct a comparative boxplot for blood lead level for the two samples. Write a few sentences comparing the blood lead level distributions for the two samples.

CR5.14 ● Cost-to-charge ratios (the percentage of the amount billed that represents the actual cost) for 11 Oregon hospitals of similar size were reported separately for inpatient and outpatient services. The data are shown in the table at the top of the next column.

Hospital	Cost-to-Charge Ratio Inpatient	Outpatient
Blue Mountain	80	62
Curry General	76	66
Good Shepherd	75	63
Grande Ronde	62	51
Harney District	100	54
Lake District	100	75
Pioneer	88	65
St. Anthony	64	56
St. Elizabeth	50	45
Tillamook	54	48
Wallowa Memorial	83	71

a. Does there appear to be a strong linear relationship between the cost-to-charge ratio for inpatient and outpatient services? Justify your answer based on the value of the correlation coefficient and examination of a scatterplot of the data.
b. Are any unusual features of the data evident in the scatterplot?
c. Suppose that the observation for Harney District was removed from the data set. Would the correlation coefficient for the new data set be greater than or less than the one computed in Part (a)? Explain.

CR5.15 The accompanying scatterplot shows observations on hemoglobin level, determined both by the standard spectrophotometric method (y) and by a new, simpler method based on a color scale (x) ("A Simple and Reliable Method for Estimating Hemoglobin," *Bulletin of the World Health Organization* [1995]: 369–373):

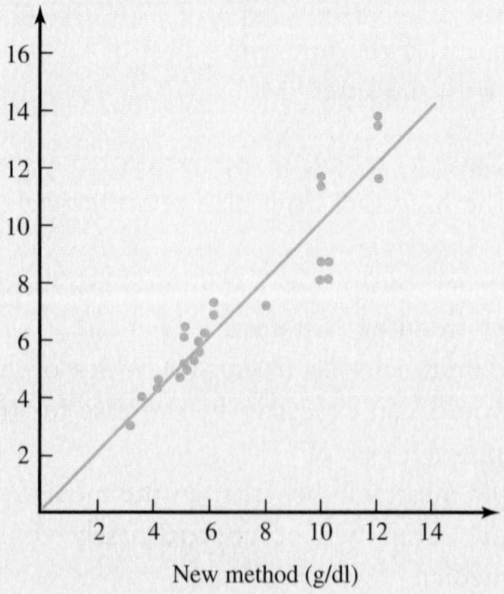

a. Does it appear that x and y are highly correlated?
b. The paper reported that $r = .9366$. How would you describe the relationship between the two variables?
c. The line pictured in the scatterplot has a slope of 1 and passes through (0, 0). If x and y were always identical, all points would lie exactly on this line. The authors of the paper claimed that perfect correlation ($r = 1$) would result in this line. Do you agree? Explain your reasoning.

CR5.16 In the article "Reproductive Biology of the Aquatic Salamander *Amphiuma tridactylum* in Louisiana" (*Journal of Herpetology* [1999]: 100–105), 14 female salamanders were studied. Using regression, the researchers predicted y = clutch size (number of salamander eggs) from x = snout-vent length (in centimeters) as follows:

$$\hat{y} = -147 + 6.175x$$

For the salamanders in the study, the range of snout-vent lengths was approximately 30 to 70 cm.
a. What is the value of the y intercept of the least-squares line? What is the value of the slope of the least-squares line? Interpret the slope in the context of this problem.
b. Would you be reluctant to predict the clutch size when snout-vent length is 22 cm? Explain.

CR5.17 Exercise CR5.16 gave the least-squares regression line for predicting y = clutch size from x = snout-vent length ("Reproductive Biology of the Aquatic Salamander *Amphiuma tridactylum* in Louisiana," *Journal of Herpetology* [1999]: 100–105). The paper also reported $r^2 = .7664$ and SSTo = 43,951.
a. Interpret the value of r^2.
b. Find and interpret the value of s_e (the sample size was $n = 14$).

CR5.18 ● A study, described in the paper "Prediction of Defibrillation Success from a Single Defibrillation Threshold Measurement" (*Circulation* [1988]: 1144–1149) investigated the relationship between defibrillation success and the energy of the defibrillation shock (expressed as a multiple of the defibrillation threshold) and presented the following data:

Energy of Shock	Success (%)
0.5	33.3
1.0	58.3
1.5	81.8
2.0	96.7
2.5	100.0

a. Construct a scatterplot of y = success percentage and x = energy of shock. Does the relationship appear to be linear or nonlinear?
b. Fit a least-squares line to the given data, and construct a residual plot. Does the residual plot support your conclusion in Part (a)? Explain.
c. Consider transforming the data by leaving y unchanged and using either $x' = \sqrt{x}$ or $x'' = \log(x)$. Which of these transformations would you recommend? Justify your choice by appealing to appropriate graphical displays.
d. Using the transformation you recommended in Part (c), find the equation of the least-squares line that describes the relationship between y and the transformed x.
e. What would you predict success percentage to be when the energy of shock is 1.75 times the threshold level? When it is 0.8 times the threshold level?

CR5.19 ● The paper "Population Pressure and Agricultural Intensity" (*Annals of the Association of American Geographers* [1977]: 384–396) reported a positive association between population density and agricultural intensity. The following data consist of measures of population density (x) and agricultural intensity (y) for 18 different subtropical locations:

x	1.0	26.0	1.1	101.0	14.9	134.7
y	9	7	6	50	5	100
x	3.0	5.7	7.6	25.0	143.0	27.5
y	7	14	14	10	50	14
x	103.0	180.0	49.6	140.6	140.0	233.0
y	50	150	10	67	100	100

a. Construct a scatterplot of y versus x. Is the scatterplot compatible with the statement of positive association made in the paper?

b. The scatterplot in Part (a) is curved upward like segment 2 in Figure 5.38, suggesting a transformation that is up the ladder for x or down the ladder for y. Try a scatterplot that uses y and x^2. Does this transformation straighten the plot?

c. Draw a scatterplot that uses $\log(y)$ and x. The $\log(y)$ values, given in order corresponding to the y values, are 0.95, 0.85, 0.78, 1.70, 0.70, 2.00, 0.85, 1.15, 1.15, 1.00, 1.70, 1.15, 1.70, 2.18, 1.00, 1.83, 2.00, and 2.00. How does this scatterplot compare with that of Part (b)?

d. Now consider a scatterplot that uses transformations on both x and y: $\log(y)$ and x^2. Is this effective in straightening the plot? Explain.

AP* Review Questions for Chapter 5

1. Which of the following three scatterplots displays a data set that would have a correlation coefficient farthest from 0?

(A)

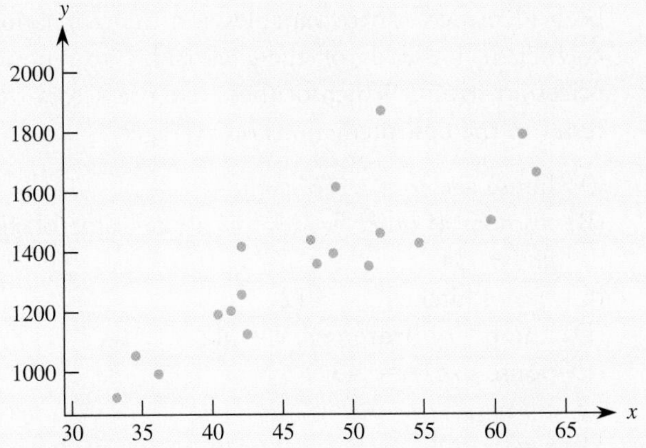

(B)

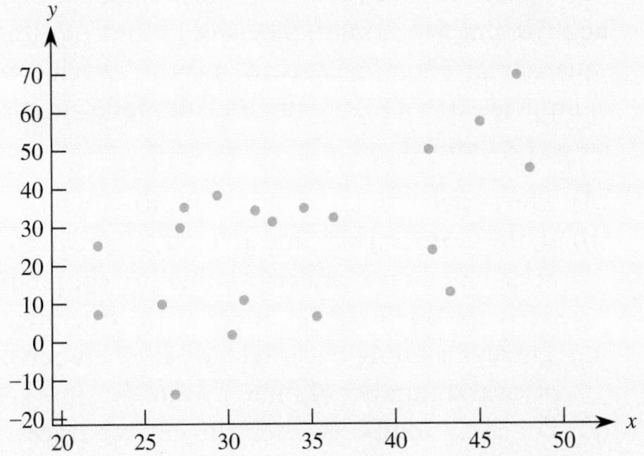

(C)

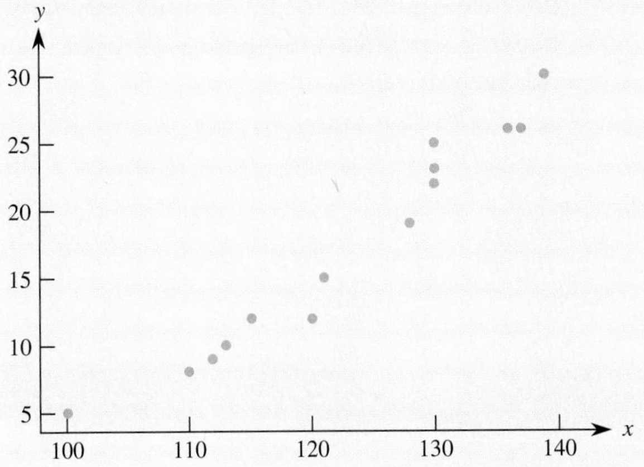

(D)

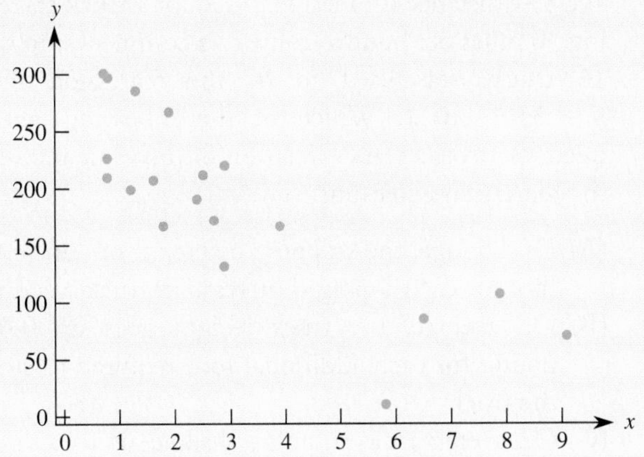

(E)

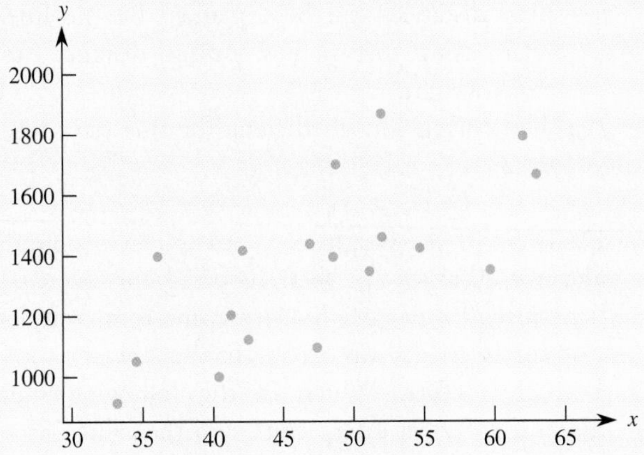

2. Data on x = weight (in ounces) and y = overnight shipping cost (dollars) for 20 items was used to fit the regression line, $\hat{y} = 22 + 1.50x$. Which of the following statements about a different line, $y = 10 + 0.75x$, is true?

(A) The line $y = 10 + 0.75x$ will have a smaller sum of squared deviations than the regression line.

(B) The line $y = 10 + 0.75x$ will have the same sum of squared deviations as the regression line.

(C) The line $y = 10 + 0.75x$ will have a larger sum of squared deviations than the regression line.

(D) The line $y = 10 + 1.5x$ will have the same sum of deviations as the regression line.

(E) It is not possible to tell how the sum of squared deviations for the line $y = 10 + 0.75x$ will compare to the sum of squared deviations for the regression line.

*AP and the Advanced Placement Program are registered trademarks of the College Entrance Examination Board, which was not involved in the production of, and does not endorse, this product.

3. Data on x = the weight of a pickup truck (pounds) and y = distance (in feet) required for a truck traveling 30 miles per hour to come to a complete stop for 16 trucks was used to fit the regression line $\hat{y} = 23 + 0.02x$. Which of the following statements is a correct interpretation of the value 0.02 in the regression equation?

(A) On average, the stopping distance goes up 0.02 foot for each 1-pound increase in truck weight.
(B) On average, the truck weight goes up 0.02 pound for each additional foot required to stop the truck.
(C) On average, the stopping distance is 0.02 foot when the truck weight is 0.
(D) Approximately 2% of the variation in the stopping distances can be explained by the linear relationship between stopping distance and truck weight.
(E) The correlation coefficient for this data set is 0.02.

4. Data on x = the weight of a pickup truck (pounds) and y = distance (in feet) required for the truck traveling 30 miles per hour to come to a complete stop for 16 trucks was used to fit the regression line, $\hat{y} = 23 + 0.02x$. Which of the following statements is a correct interpretation of the value 23?

(A) On average, the stopping distance increases by 23 feet for each 1-pound increase in truck weight.
(B) On average, the truck weight increases by 23 pounds for each additional foot in stopping distance.
(C) On average, the stopping distance is 23 feet when the car weight is 0.
(D) Approximately 2% of the variation in the stopping distances can be explained by the linear relationship between stopping distance and truck weight.
(E) It is not reasonable to interpret the intercept in this setting because a weight of 0 is outside the range of the data used to fit the regression line.

5. A realtor is interested in being able to predict the selling price of houses in a particular city. She plans to choose one predictor variable and then find the least-squares regression line and use it to make her predictions. Five possible predictor variables have been identified. These variables and the correlation coefficient for each of these variables and house prices are given. Which of these five predictors will result in the best predictions on average?

(A) house age, $r = -.46$
(B) number of other homes for sale on same block, $r = -.34$
(C) size of kitchen, $r = .12$
(D) number of bedrooms, $r = .42$
(E) house size, $r = .45$

6. Data were collected on y = price of car (in dollars) and x = age of car (in years) for each car in a sample of 50 used Toyota Camrys. A scatterplot showed a negative linear relationship between x and y. A least-squares regression line was fit and the r^2 value was computed. If $r^2 = .25$, which of the following is a correct statement?

(A) The correlation coefficient is positive, $r = .5$.
(B) If the least-squares line is used to predict car price based on number of miles driven, predictions should be within \$0.25 of the true price.
(C) There is a strong linear relationship between car price and number of miles driven.
(D) For each additional mile driven, car price increases by approximately \$0.25.
(E) Approximately 25% of the variability in car price can be explained by the linear relationship between car price and number of miles the car has been driven.

7. Consider the following three scatterplots. All three scatterplots are drawn to the same scale on both the x and y axes. Which of the following correctly orders these from smallest to largest based on the value of the correlation coefficient?

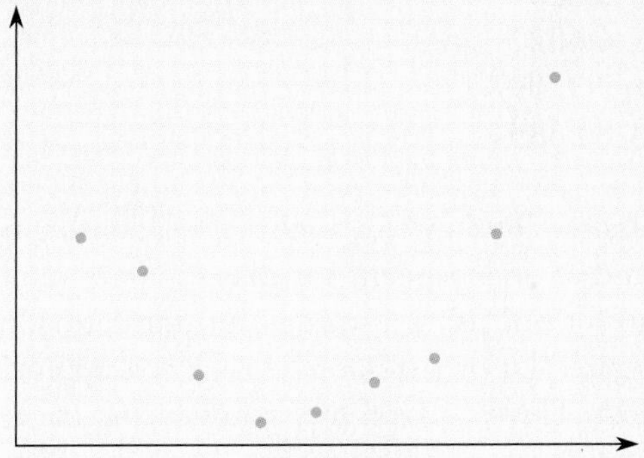

Scatterplot I
(I)

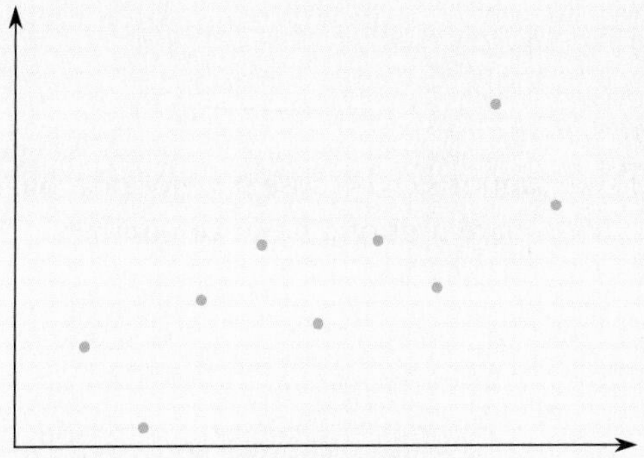

Scatterplot II
(II)

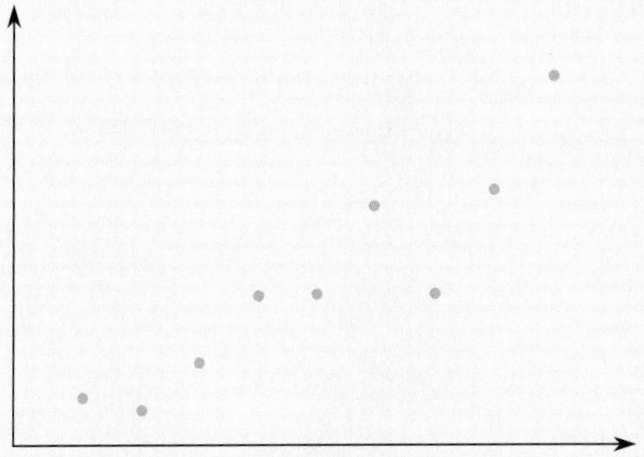

Scatterplot III
(III)

(A) I, II, III
(B) II, III, I
(C) III, II, I
(D) II, I, III
(E) III, I, II

8. Consider the following five scatterplots. All are drawn to the same scale on both the x and y axes. For which scatterplot is the standard deviation about the least-squares regression line the smallest?

(A)

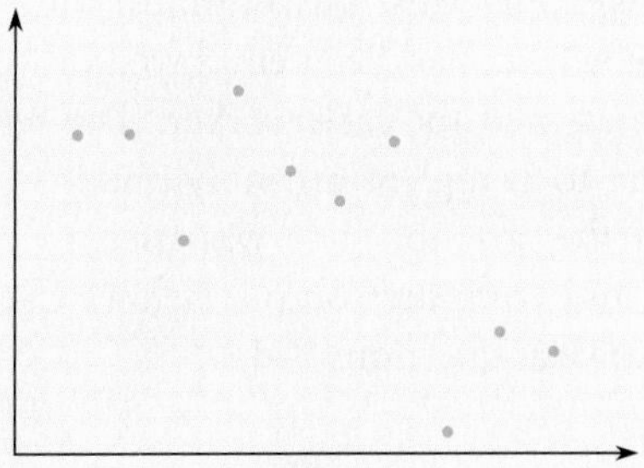

Scatterplot A

(B)

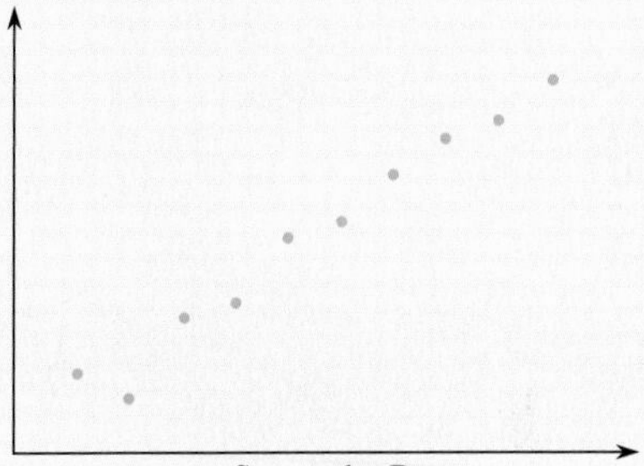

Scatterplot B

(C)

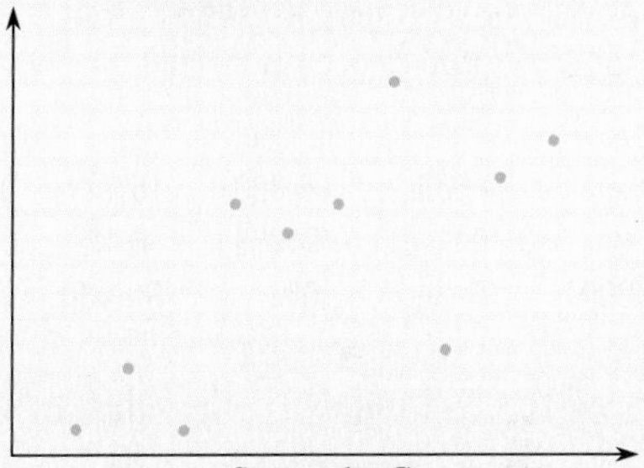

Scatterplot C

(D)

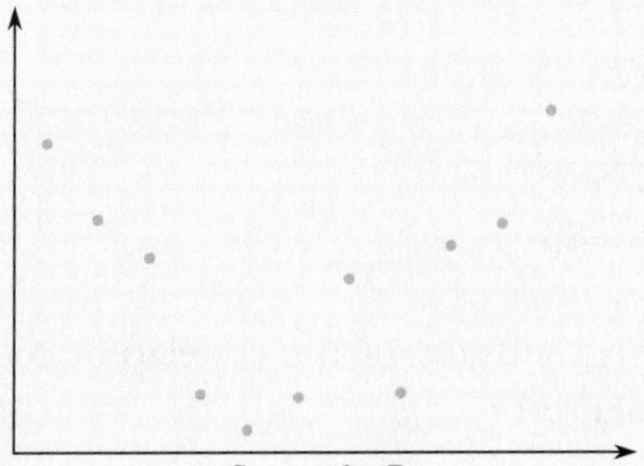

Scatterplot D

(E)

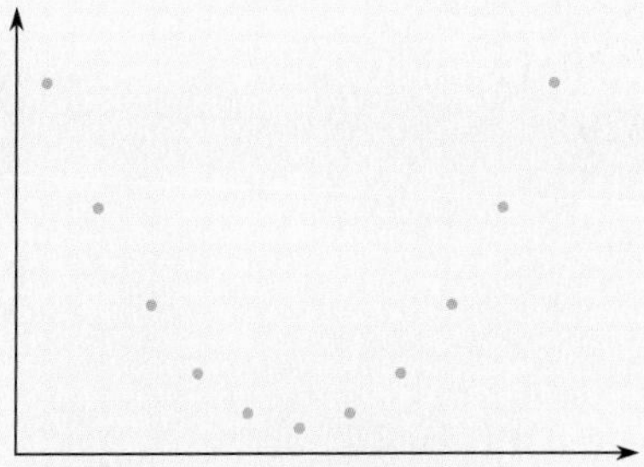

Scatterplot E

The following applies to questions 9–11:
Twenty-five assembly line workers participated in a study to investigate the relationship between experience and the amount of time required to complete an assembly task. Assembly time (in minutes) and number of months the worker had been employed on the assembly line were measured for each worker. The resulting data on y = time to complete assembly and x = number of months on the assembly line was used to produce the scatterplot and computer output below. Use this information to answer questions 9–11.

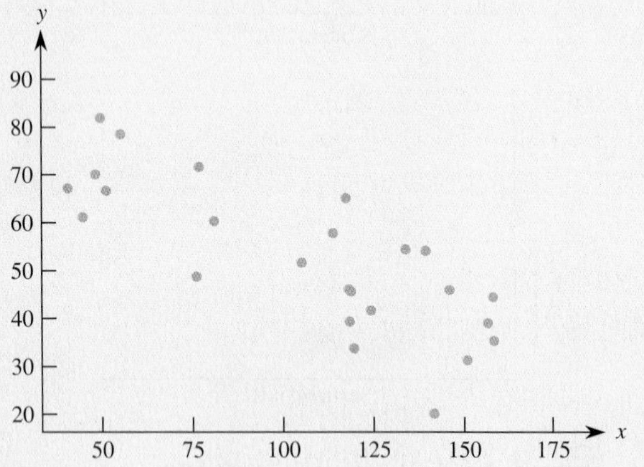

Predictor	Coef	SE Coef	T	P
Constant	84.683	5.602	15.12	0.000
x	-0.30411	0.04963	-6.13	0.000

S = 9.79097 R-Sq = 62.0% R-Sq(adj) = 60.4%

9. Which of the following is the value of the slope of the least-squares regression line?

(A) −0.30411
(B) 0.04963
(C) 0.620
(D) 9.79097
(E) 84.683

10. What is the value of the correlation coefficient for this data set?

(A) −0.787
(B) −0.620
(C) −0.30411
(D) 0.620
(E) 0.787

11. What proportion of variability in assembly time can be explained by the linear relationship between assembly time and number of months on the assembly line?

(A) 0.4963
(B) 0.620
(C) 6.602
(D) 9.97097
(E) 84.683

12. A scatterplot showed a nonlinear relationship between y and an independent variable x. The x values were transformed using a square-root transformation, and a scatterplot of y versus $x' = \sqrt{x}$ was approximately linear. The regression line summarizing the relationship between y and x' was $\hat{y} = 14 - 2x'$. What is the predicted value of y when $x = 9$?

(A) −4
(B) $\sqrt{-4}$
(C) 8
(D) $\sqrt{8}$
(E) We cannot say, because it is not possible to take the square root of a negative number.

13. A study was carried out to investigate the relationship between $x =$ time spent working each week (hours) and $y =$ time spent on math homework on a typical weekday (in minutes) for a random sample of 20 students in a first-quarter calculus course. The scatterplot of the data is shown below.

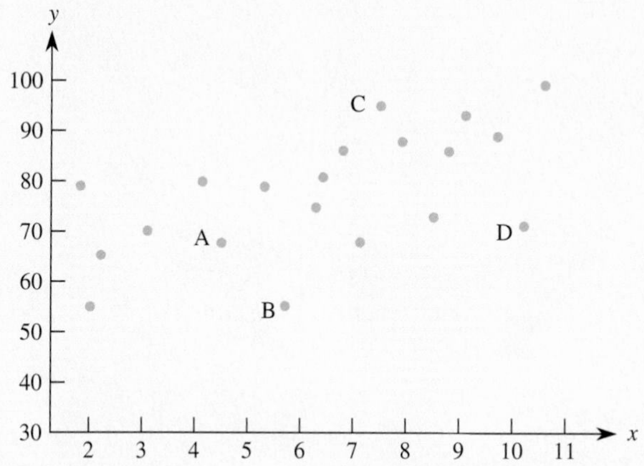

When the simple linear regression model is fit to the sample data, which point will have the smallest (in magnitude) residual?

(A) A
(B) B
(C) C
(D) D
(E) All four points will have the same positive value for the residual.

14. From March 1980 to April 1981, data were gathered on the amount of lead sold in gasoline (metric tons) in Massachusetts vs. the amount of lead found in umbilical blood in Boston (micrograms per deciliter). A summary of the analysis is presented below, and a least-squares regression line has been fit to the data.

$r = 0.673$ $\quad r^2 = 0.453$ $\quad \hat{U} = 4.108 + 0.01489{*}G$

Variable	Mean	St. Dev.
Gasoline Lead	124.21	36.22
Umbilical Lead	5.9571	8.8007

The residual associated with the observation that has a gasoline lead value of 82 metric tons and 4.5 micrograms per deciliter is in which interval below?

(A) $-1.0 \leq$ residual < -0.5
(B) $-0.5 \leq$ residual < 0.0
(C) $0.0 \leq$ residual $< +0.5$
(D) $+0.5 \leq$ residual $< +1.0$
(E) $+1.0 \leq$ residual $< +1.5$

15. Of the following, which is *not* true of r?

(A) r is independent of the units of y and x.
(B) r is always between 0 and 1.
(C) r measures the strength of the linear relation between x and y.
(D) r does not depend on which of two variables is labeled x.
(E) $|r|$ is less than 1.0 unless the points on a scatterplot line up exactly.

CHAPTER 6

Probability

© Doug Menuez/Photodisc/Getty Images

We make decisions based on uncertainty every day. Should you buy an extended warranty for your new iPod? It depends on the likelihood that it will fail during the warranty period. Should you allow 45 minutes to get to your 8 A.M. class, or is 35 minutes enough? From experience, you may know that most mornings you can drive to school and park in 25 minutes or less. Most of the time, the walk from your parking space to class is 5 minutes or less. But how often will the drive to school or the walk to class take longer than you expect? When it takes longer than usual to drive to campus, is it more likely that it will also take longer to walk to class? less likely? Or are the driving and walking times unrelated? Some questions involving uncertainty are more serious: If an artificial heart has four key parts, how likely is each one to fail? How likely is it that at least one will fail? We can answer questions like these using the ideas and methods of probability, the systematic study of uncertainty.

6.1 Chance Experiments and Events

The basic ideas and terminology of probability are most easily introduced in situations that are both familiar and reasonably simple. Because of this, some of our initial examples involve such elementary activities as tossing a coin, selecting cards from a deck, and rolling a die. However, after considering a few of these simplistic examples, we will move on to more interesting and realistic situations.

Chance Experiments

When a single coin is tossed, there are two possible outcomes. The coin can land with its heads side up or its tails side up. The selection of a single card from a well-mixed standard deck may result in the ace of spades, the five of diamonds, or any one of the other 50 possibilities. Consider rolling both a red die and a green die. One possible outcome is the red die lands with four dots facing up and the green die shows one dot on its upturned face. Another outcome is the red die lands with three dots facing up and the green die also shows three dots on its upturned face. There are 36 possible outcomes in all, and we do not know in advance what the result of a particular roll will be. Situations such as these are referred to as *chance experiments.*

DEFINITION

A **chance experiment** is any activity or situation in which there is uncertainty about which of two or more possible outcomes will result.

When the term *chance experiment* is used in a probability setting, we mean something different from what was meant by the term *experiment* in Chapter 2 (where experiments investigated the effect of two or more treatments on a response). For example, in an opinion poll or survey, there is uncertainty about whether an individual selected at random from the population of interest supports a school bond, and when a die is rolled, there is uncertainty about which face will land upturned. Both of these situations fit the definition of a chance experiment.

Consider a chance experiment to investigate whether men or women are more likely to choose a hybrid car over a traditional internal combustion engine car when purchasing a Honda Civic at a particular car dealership. The Honda Civic is available with either a hybrid or a traditional engine. In this experiment, a customer will be selected at random from those who purchased a Honda Civic. The type of vehicle purchased (hybrid or traditional) will be determined and the customer's gender will be recorded. Before the customer is selected the outcome of this chance experiment is unknown to us. We do know, however, what the possible outcomes are. This set of possible outcomes is called the *sample space.*

DEFINITION

The collection of all possible outcomes of a chance experiment is the **sample space** for the experiment.

The sample space of a chance experiment can be represented in many ways. An obvious representation is a simple list of all the possible outcomes. For the car-purchase chance experiment, the possible outcomes are:

1. A male buying hybrid
2. A female buying hybrid
3. A male buying traditional
4. A female buying traditional

For brevity, we can use set notation and ordered pairs. A male purchasing a hybrid is represented as (male, hybrid). The sample space is then

$$\text{sample space} = \left\{ \begin{array}{l} \text{(male, hybrid), (female, hybrid),} \\ \text{(male, traditional), (female, traditional)} \end{array} \right\}$$

Another representation of the sample space is a tree diagram. A tree diagram (shown in Figure 6.1) for the outcomes of the car-purchase chance experiment has two sets of branches corresponding to the two pieces of information that were gathered. To identify any particular element of the sample space, you traverse the tree by first selecting a branch corresponding to gender and then a branch identified with a type of car.

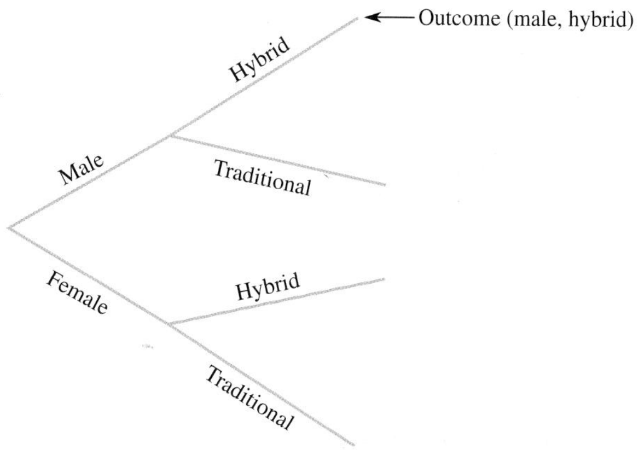

FIGURE 6.1
Tree diagram for the car purchase example.

In the tree diagram of Figure 6.1, there is no particular reason for having the gender as the first generation branch and the type of car as the second generation branch. Some chance experiments involve making observations in a particular order, in which case the order of the branches in the tree does matter. In this example, however, it would be acceptable to represent the sample space with the tree diagram shown in Figure 6.2.

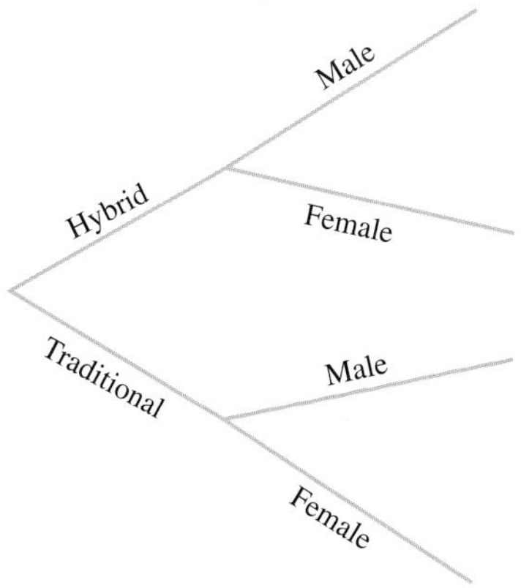

FIGURE 6.2
Another tree diagram for the car purchase example.

As we have seen, the sample space can be represented in several ways, but the representations all have one thing in common: *Every* element of the sample space is included in the representation.

Events

In the car-purchase chance experiment, we might be interested in which particular outcome will result. Or we might focus on a group of outcomes that involve the purchase of a hybrid—the group consisting of (male, hyrid) and (female, hybrid).

When we combine one or more individual outcomes in a collection, we are creating what is known as an *event.*

DEFINITION

An **event** is any collection of outcomes from the sample space of a chance experiment.

A **simple event** is an event consisting of exactly one outcome.

We usually represent an event by an uppercase letter, such as A, B, C, and so on. On some occasions, the same letter with different numerical subscripts, such as E_1, E_2, E_3, ... may be used for this purpose.

EXAMPLE 6.1 Car Preferences

Reconsider the situation in which a person who purchased a Honda Civic was categorized by gender (M or F) and type of car purchased (H = hybrid, T = traditional). Using this notation, one possible representation of the sample space is

sample space = {MH, FH, MT, FT}

Because there are four outcomes, there are four simple events:

E_1 = MH E_2 = FH E_3 = MT E_4 = FT

One event of interest might be the event consisting of all outcomes for which a hybrid was purchased. A symbolic description of the event *hybrid* is

hybrid = {MH, FH}

Another event is the event that the purchaser is male,

male = {MH, MT}

EXAMPLE 6.2 Losing at Golf

Suppose you believe that after losing a game to an opponent, a golfer is more likely to lose the next game. You conduct a chance experiment that consists of watching two consecutive games for a particular player and observing whether the player won, tied, or lost each of the two games. In this case (using W, T, and L to represent win, tie, and loss, respectively), the sample space can be represented as

sample space = {WW, WT, WL, TW, TT, TL, LW, LT, LL}

The event *lose exactly one of the two games*, denoted by L_1, could then be defined as

L_1 = {WL, TL, LW, LT}

Only one outcome—and thus one simple event—occurs when a chance experiment is performed. We say that a given event occurs whenever one of the outcomes making up the event occurs. If the outcome in Example 6.1 is MH, then the simple event *male purchasing a hybrid* has occurred, and so has the nonsimple event *hybrid purchased.*

Forming New Events Once some events have been specified, they can be manipulated in several useful ways to create new events. Some new events are presented in the following definition.

DEFINITION

Let A and B denote two events.

1. The event ***not A*** consists of all experimental outcomes that are not in event A. *Not A* is sometimes called the *complement* of A and is usually denoted by A^C, A', or $\bar{A}$.
2. The event ***A or B*** consists of all experimental outcomes that are in at least one of the two events, that is, in A or in B or in both of these. *A or B* is called the *union* of the two events and is denoted by $A \cup B$.
3. The event ***A and B*** consists of all experimental outcomes that are in both of the events A and B. *A and B* is called the *intersection* of the two events and is denoted by $A \cap B$.

EXAMPLE 6.3 Turning Directions

Grant Faint/The image Bank/Getty Images

An observer will stand at the bottom of a freeway off-ramp and record the turning direction (L = left or R = right) of each of three successive vehicles. The sample space contains eight outcomes:

all 3 cars turn left (→ LLL) *the 1st car turns left and the next 2 turn right* (→ LRR)

{LLL, RLL, LRL, LLR, RRL, RLR, LRR, RRR}

Each of these outcomes determines a simple event. Other events include

A = event that exactly one of the cars turns right = {RLL, LRL, LLR}
B = event that at most one of the cars turns right = {LLL, RLL, LRL, LLR}
C = event that all cars turn in the same direction = {LLL, RRR}

Some other events that can be formed from those just defined are

not C = C^C = event that not all cars turn in the same direction
= {RLL, LRL, LLR, RRL, RLR, LRR}
A or C = $A \cup C$ = event that exactly one of the cars turns right or all cars turn in the same direction
= {RLL, LRL, LLR, LLL, RRR}
B and C = $B \cap C$ = event that at most one car turns right and all cars turn in the same direction
= {LLL}

EXAMPLE 6.4 More Losing at Golf

In Example 6.2, in addition to the event that a golfer loses exactly one of the two games, L_1 = {WL, TL, LW, LT}, we could also define events corresponding to L_0 = neither game is lost and L_2 = both games are lost. Then L_0 = {WW, WT, TW, TT} and L_2 = {LL}.

Some other events that can be formed from those just defined include

$$\begin{aligned} L_2^C &= \text{event that at most one game was lost} \\ &= \{\text{WW, WT, WL, TW, TT, TL, LW, LT}\} \\ L_1 \cup L_2 &= \text{event that at least one game was lost} \\ &= \{\text{WL, TL, LW, LT, LL}\} \\ L_1 \cap L_2 &= \text{event that exactly one game was lost } \textit{and} \text{ two games were lost} \\ &= \text{the empty set} \end{aligned}$$

AP* EXAM TIP

Probability problems are often counterintuitive. Often, the key to solving a probability problem is to go back to basics: what is the sample space and what are the outcomes?

It frequently happens that two events have no common outcomes, as was the case for events L_1 and L_2 in the golf example. Such situations are described by special terminology.

DEFINITION

Two events that have no common outcomes are said to be **disjoint** or **mutually exclusive.**

Two events are disjoint if their intersection is the empty set, so any two *simple* events are disjoint.

It is sometimes useful to draw an informal picture of events to visualize relationships. In a **Venn diagram**, the collection of all possible outcomes is typically shown as the interior of a rectangle. Other events are then identified by specified regions inside this rectangle. Figure 6.3 illustrates several Venn diagrams.

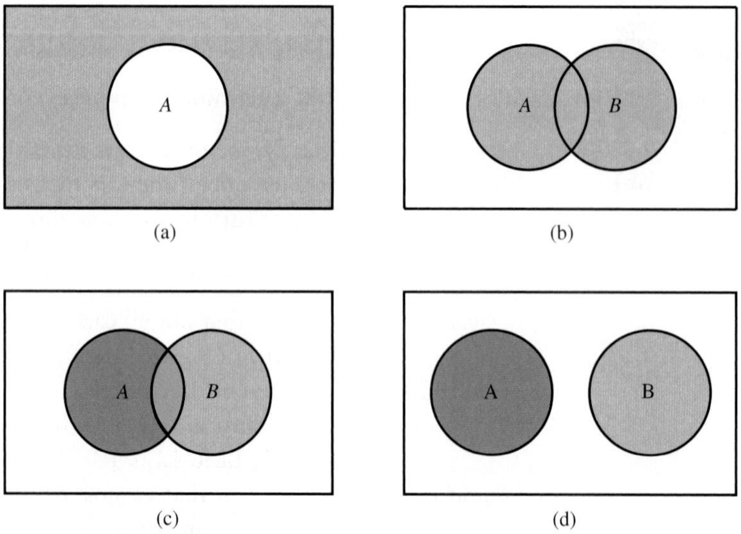

FIGURE 6.3
Venn diagrams: (a) gold region = *not A*; (b) gold region = *A or B*; (c) green region = *A and B*; (d) two disjoint events.

The use of the *or* and *and* operations can be extended to form new events from more than two initially specified events (as illustrated in Figure 6.4).

DEFINITION

Let $A_1, A_2, \ldots, A_k$ denote k events.

1. The event A_1 *or* A_2 *or* ... *or* A_k consists of all outcomes in at least one of the individual events $A_1, A_2, \ldots, A_k$.
2. The event A_1 *and* A_2 *and* ... *and* A_k consists of all outcomes that are simultaneously in every one of the individual events $A_1, A_2, \ldots, A_k$.

These k events are disjoint if no two of them have any common outcomes.

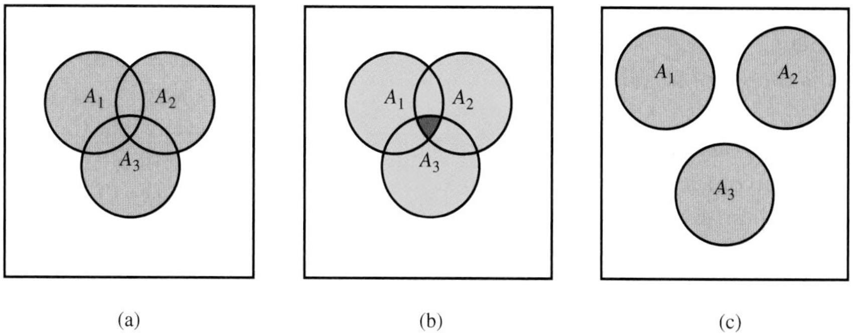

FIGURE 6.4
Venn diagrams: (a) gold region = A_1 *or* A_2 *or* A_3; (b) blue region = A_1 *and* A_2 *and* A_3; (c) three disjoint events.

EXAMPLE 6.5 Asking Questions

The instructor in a seminar class consisting of four students has an unusual way of asking questions. Four slips of paper numbered 1, 2, 3, and 4 are placed in a box. The instructor determines the student to whom any particular question is to be addressed by selecting one of these four slips. Suppose that one question is to be posed during each of the next two class meetings. One possible outcome could be represented as (3, 1)—the first question is addressed to Student 3 and the second question to Student 1. There are 15 other possibilities. Consider the following events:

the event that the same student is asked both questions → $A = \{(1,1), (2,2), (3,3), (4,4)\}$

the event that Student 1 is asked at least one of the two questions → $B = \{(1,1), (1,2), (1,3), (1,4), (2,1), (3,1), (4,1)\}$

$C = \{(3,1), (2,2), (1,3)\}$

$D = \{(3,3), (3,4), (4,3)\}$

$E = \{(1,1), (1,3), (2,2), (3,1), (4,2), (3,3), (2,4), (4,4)\}$

$F = \{(1,1), (1,2), (2,1)\}$

Then

$$A \text{ or } C \text{ or } D = \{(1,1), (2,2), (3,3), (4,4), (3,1), (1,3), (3,4), (4,3)\}$$

The outcome (3,1) is contained in each of the events B, C, and E, as is the outcome (1,3). These are the only two common outcomes, so

$$B \text{ and } C \text{ and } E = \{(3,1), (1,3)\}$$

The events C, D, and F are disjoint because no outcome in any one of these events is contained in either of the other two events.

EXERCISES 6.1 - 6.12

6.1 Define the term *chance experiment,* and give an example of a chance experiment with four possible outcomes.

6.2 Define the term *sample space,* and then give the sample space for the chance experiment you described in Exercise 6.1.

6.3 Consider the chance experiment in which the type of transmission—automatic (A) or manual (M)—is recorded for each of the next two cars purchased from a certain dealer.

a. What is the set of all possible outcomes (the sample space)?

b. Display the possible outcomes in a tree diagram.

c. List the outcomes in each of the following events. Which of these events are simple events?

i. *B* the event that at least one car has an automatic transmission

ii. *C* the event that exactly one car has an automatic transmission

iii. *D* the event that neither car has an automatic transmission

d. What outcomes are in the event *B and C*? In the event *B or C*?

6.4 A tennis shop sells five different brands of rackets, each of which comes in either a midsize version or an oversize version. Consider the chance experiment in which brand and size are noted for the next racket purchased. One possible outcome is Head midsize, and another is Prince oversize. Possible outcomes correspond to cells in the following table:

	Head	Prince	Slazenger	Wimbledon	Wilson
Midsize					
Oversize					

a. Let *A* denote the event that an oversize racket is purchased. List the outcomes in *A*.

b. Let *B* denote the event that the name of the brand purchased begins with a W. List the outcomes in *B*.

c. List the outcomes in the event *not B*.

d. Head, Prince, and Wilson are U.S. companies. Let *C* denote the event that the racket purchased is made by a U.S. company. List the outcomes in the event *B or C*.

e. List outcomes in *B and C*.

f. Display the possible outcomes on a tree diagram, with a first-generation branch for each brand.

6.5 A new model of laptop computer can be ordered with one of three screen sizes (10 inches, 12 inches, 15 inches) and one of four hard drive sizes (50 GB, 100 GB, 150 GB, and 200 GB). Consider the chance experiment in which a laptop order is selected and the screen size and hard drive size are recorded.

a. Display possible outcomes using a tree diagram.

b. Let *A* be the event that the order is for a laptop with a screen size of 12 inches or smaller. Let *B* be the event that the order is for a laptop with a hard drive size of at most 100 GB. What outcomes are in A^C? In $A \cup B$? In $A \cap B$?

c. Let *C* denote the event that the order is for a laptop with a 200 GB hard drive. Are *A* and *C* disjoint events? Are *B* and *C* disjoint?

6.6 A college library has four copies of a certain book; the copies are numbered 1, 2, 3, and 4. Two of these are selected at random. The first selected book is placed on 2-hour reserve, and the second book can be checked out overnight.

a. Construct a tree diagram to display the 12 outcomes in the sample space.

b. Let *A* denote the event that at least one of the books selected is an even-numbered copy. What outcomes are in *A*?

c. Suppose that copies 1 and 2 are first printings, whereas copies 3 and 4 are second printings. Let *B* denote the event that exactly one of the copies selected is a first printing. What outcomes are contained in *B*?

6.7 A library has five copies of a certain textbook on reserve of which two copies (1 and 2) are first printings and the other three (3, 4, and 5) are second printings. A student examines these books in random order, stopping only when a second printing has been selected.

a. Display the possible outcomes in a tree diagram.

b. What outcomes are contained in the event *A*, that exactly one book is examined before the chance experiment terminates?

c. What outcomes are contained in the event *C*, that the chance experiment terminates with the examination of book 5?

6.8 Suppose that, starting at a certain time, batteries coming off an assembly line are examined one by one to see whether they are defective (let D = defective and N = not defective). The chance experiment terminates as soon as a nondefective battery is obtained.

a. Give five possible experimental outcomes.
b. What can be said about the number of outcomes in the sample space?
c. What outcomes are in the event E, that the number of batteries examined is an even number?

6.9 Refer to Exercise 6.8, and now suppose that the chance experiment terminates only when two nondefective batteries have been obtained.

a. Let A denote the event that at most three batteries must be examined to terminate the chance experiment. What outcomes are contained in A?
b. Let B be the event that exactly four batteries must be examined before the chance experiment terminates. What outcomes are in B?
c. What can be said about the number of possible outcomes for this chance experiment?

6.10 A family consisting of three people—P_1, P_2, and P_3—belongs to a medical clinic that always has a physician at each of stations 1, 2, and 3. During a certain week, each member of the family visits the clinic exactly once and is randomly assigned to a station. One experimental outcome is (1, 2, 1), which means that P_1 is assigned to station 1, P_2 to station 2, and P_3 to station 1.

a. List the 27 possible outcomes. (Hint: First list the nine outcomes in which P_1 goes to station 1, then the nine in which P_1 goes to station 2, and finally the nine in which P_1 goes to station 3; a tree diagram might help.)
b. List all outcomes in the event A, that all three people go to the same station.
c. List all outcomes in the event B, that all three people go to different stations.
d. List all outcomes in the event C, that no one goes to station 2.
e. Identify outcomes in each of the following events: B^C, C^C, $A \cup B$, $A \cap B$, $A \cap C$.

6.11 An engineering construction firm is currently working on power plants at three different sites. Define events E_1, E_2, and E_3 as follows:

E_1 = the plant at Site 1 is completed by the contract date
E_2 = the plant at Site 2 is completed by the contract date
E_3 = the plant at Site 3 is completed by the contract date

The following Venn diagram pictures the relationships among these events:

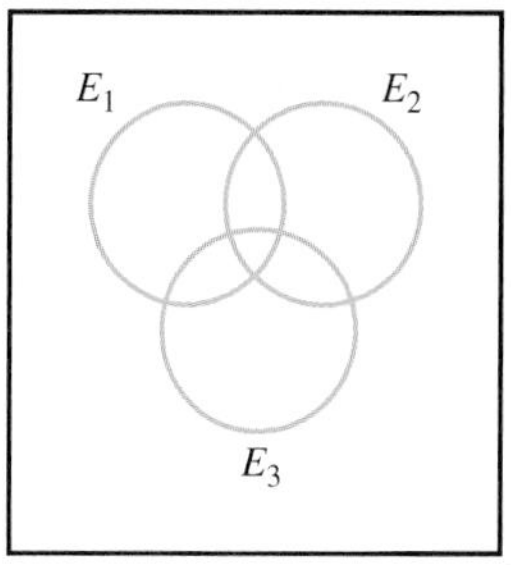

Shade the region in the Venn diagram corresponding to each of the following events (redraw the Venn diagram for each part of the problem):

a. At least one plant is completed by the contract date.
b. All plants are completed by the contract date.
c. None of the plants are completed by the contract date.
d. Only the plant at Site 1 is completed by the contract date.
e. Exactly one of the three plants is completed by the contract date.
f. Either the plant at Site 1 or both of the other two plants are completed by the contract date.

6.12 Consider a Venn diagram picturing two events A and B that are not disjoint.

a. Shade the event $(A \cup B)^C$. On a separate Venn diagram shade the event $A^C \cap B^C$. How are these two events related?
b. Shade the event $(A \cap B)^C$. On a separate Venn diagram shade the event $A^C \cup B^C$. How are these two events related? (Note: These two relationships together are called DeMorgan's laws.)

6.2 Definition of Probability

Reasoning about games of chance and probabilistic thinking share a long history. Archeologists have found evidence that Egyptians used a small bone in mammals, the astragalus, as a sort of four-sided die as early as 3500 B.C. Games of chance were common in Greek and Roman times and during the Renaissance of Western Europe. Girolamo Cardano, a character of some ill-repute in early mathematical circles, wrote about such games and did some calculations of odds in the 16th century; Galileo mentioned dice in his writings in the early 17th century.

The formal study of probability began with the correspondence between Blaise Pascal (1623–62) and Pierre de Fermat (1601–65) in 1654. Their letters discussed some problems related to gambling that were posed by the French nobleman Chevalier de Mère. The methods and solutions that resulted from this exchange, especially techniques of combinatorics (advanced counting), greatly enhanced the study of probability.

From this early work, new interpretations of probability have evolved, including an empirical approach preferred by many statisticians today. We begin our discussion of probability with a look at some of the different approaches to probability: the classical, relative frequency, and subjective approaches.

Classical Approach to Probability

Early mathematicians' development of the theory of probability was primarily in the context of gambling and reflected the peculiarities of games of chance. A characteristic common to most games of chance is a physical device used to generate different outcomes. In children's games, a "spinner" might be used to create chance outcomes. In other games, the sequence of events is determined by playing cards. In the 17th century, the most popular gaming devices were dice. Dice were constructed so that the physical characteristics of each face were alike (except, of course, for the number of dots), ensuring that the different outcomes for an individual die were very close to equally likely. Therefore, it seemed quite natural for mathematicians of the time to assume, for example, that the probability of getting a five when a single six-sided die was rolled was one-sixth (1 chance in 6). In general, if there are N *equally likely* outcomes in a game of chance, the probability of each of the outcomes would be $1/N$. The early probabilists often referred to honest dice or fair coins as physical devices that seemed to obey this assumption of equal probabilities. These early efforts led to what is known as the classical definition of probability.

Classical Approach to Probability for Equally Likely Outcomes

When the outcomes in the sample space of a chance experiment are equally likely, the **probability of an event E,** denoted by $P(E)$, is the ratio of the number of outcomes favorable to E to the total number of outcomes in the sample space:

$$P(E) = \frac{\text{number of outcomes favorable to E}}{\text{number of outcomes in the sample space}}$$

According to this definition, the calculation of a probability consists of counting the number of outcomes that make up an event, counting the number of outcomes in the sample space, and then dividing.

Chance experiments that involve tossing fair coins, rolling fair dice, or selecting cards from a well-mixed deck have equally likely outcomes. For example, if a fair die is rolled once, each outcome (simple event) has probability 1/6. With E denoting the event that the number rolled is even, $P(E) = 3/6$. This is just the number of outcomes in E divided by the total number of possible outcomes.

EXAMPLE 6.6 Calling the Toss

On some football teams, the honor of calling the toss at the beginning of a football game is determined by random selection. Suppose that this week a member of the offensive team will call the toss. There are 5 interior linemen on the 11-player offensive team. If we define the event L as the event that an interior lineman is selected to call the toss, 5 of the 11 possible outcomes are included in L. The probability that an interior lineman will be selected is then

$$P(L) = \frac{5}{11}$$

EXAMPLE 6.7 Math Contest

Four students (Adam, Betina, Carlos, and Debra) submitted correct solutions to a math contest with two prizes. The contest rules specify that if more than two correct responses are submitted, the winners will be selected at random from those submitting correct responses. In this case, the set of possible outcomes for the chance experiment that consists of selecting the two winners from the four correct responses is

$$\{(A, B), (A, C), (A, D), (B, C), (B, D), (C, D)\}$$

Because the winners are selected at random, the six outcomes are equally likely and the probability of each individual outcome is 1/6.

Let E be the event that both selected winners are the same gender. Then

$$E = \{(A, C), (B, D)\}$$

Because E contains two outcomes, $P(E) = 2/6 = .333$. If F denotes the event that at least one of the selected winners is female, then F consists of all outcomes except (A, C) and $P(F) = 5/6 = .833$.

Limitations of the Classical Approach to Probability The classical approach to probability works well with games of chance or other situations with a finite set of outcomes that can be regarded as equally likely. However, some situations that are clearly probabilistic in nature do not fit the classical model. Consider the accident rates of young adults driving cars. Information of this kind is used by insurance companies to set car insurance rates. Suppose that we have two individuals, one 18 years old and one 28 years old. A person purchasing a standard accident insurance policy at age 28 should have a lower annual premium than a person purchasing the same policy at age 18, because the 28-year-old has a much lower chance of an accident, based on prior experience. However, the classical probabilist, playing by the classical rules, would have to consider that there are two outcomes for a policy year—having one or more accidents or not having an accident—*and would consider those outcomes equally likely for both the 28-year-old and the 18-year-old.* This certainly seems to defy reason and experience.

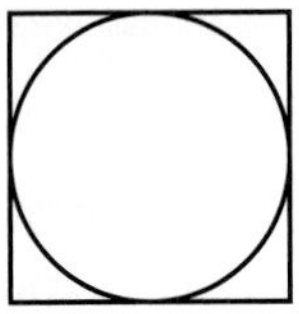

Another example of a situation that cannot be handled using the classical approach has a geometric flavor. Suppose that you have a square that is 8 inches on each side and that a circle with a diameter of 8 inches is drawn inside the square, touching the square on all four sides, as shown.

This drawing will be used as a target in a dart game. A dart will be thrown at the target and any dart that completely misses the square is a "do-over" and will be thrown again. It seems reasonable to think about the probability of a dart landing in the circle as a ratio of the area of the circle to the area of the square. That ratio is

$$\frac{\text{area of circle}}{\text{area of square}} = \frac{\pi r^2}{s^2} = \frac{\pi(4)^2}{8^2} = \frac{\pi}{4} = .785$$

A practiced dart player who is aiming for the center of the target might have an even greater probability of hitting the inside of the circle. In any case, it is not reasonable to think that the two outcomes *inside the circle* and *not inside the circle* are equally likely, so the classical approach to probability will not help here.

From the standpoint of statistics, a major limitation of the classical approach to probability is that there seems to be no way to allow past experience to inform our expectation of the future. To return to the car insurance example, suppose that in the experience of the insurance companies, 0.5% of 18-year-olds have accidents during their 19th year. It seems reasonable that, all things being equal, we could expect this percentage to be stable enough to set the prices for an insurance policy. Although the classical approach's assumption of equal probabilities is based on and consistent with the experience with dice, it cannot accommodate using an observed proportion in real life to estimate a probability. For a statistician, this is a problem. Without an understanding of probability that allows such a generalization, statistical inference would be impossible.

Relative Frequency Approach to Probability

After the revolutionary writings of Sir Isaac Newton (1642–1727), modern science became solidly based on observation and the recording of data. Early scientific investigators were aware that chance experiments and observations do not always give the same results when repeated and that even in the most carefully replicated chance experiment, there is variation. Early on, it was noticed that the unpredictability of an individual chance experiment gave rise to a dependably stable regularity when a chance experiment was repeated many times. This became the basis for fair wagering in games of chance. For example, suppose that two friends, Chris and Jay, meet to play a game. A fair coin is flipped. If it lands heads up, Chris pays Jay \$1; otherwise, Jay pays the same amount to Chris. After many repetitions, the proportion of the time that Chris wins will be close to one-half, and the two friends will have simply enjoyed the pleasure of each other's company for a few hours. This happy circumstance occurs because *in the long run* (i.e., over many repetitions) the proportion of heads is .5. In the long run, half the time Chris wins, and half the time Jay wins.

When any given chance experiment is performed, some events are relatively likely to occur, whereas others are not so likely to occur. For a specified event E, we want to assign a probability that gives a precise indication of how likely it is that E will occur. In the relative frequency approach to probability, the probability describes how frequently E occurs when the chance experiment is performed repeatedly.

EXAMPLE 6.8 Tossing a Coin

Frequently, we hear a coin described as fair, or we are told that there is a 50% chance of a coin landing heads up. What might be the meaning of the expression *fair*? Such a description cannot refer to the result of a single toss, because a single toss cannot result in both a head and a tail. Might "fairness" and "50%" refer to 10 successive tosses yielding exactly five heads and five tails? Not really, because it is easy to imagine a fair coin landing heads up on only 3 or 4 of the 10 tosses.

Consider the chance experiment of tossing a coin just once. Define the simple events

H = event that the coin lands with its heads side facing up
T = event that the coin lands with its tails side facing up

Now suppose that we take a fair coin and begin to toss it over and over. After each toss, we compute the relative frequency of heads observed so far. This calculation gives the value of the ratio

$$\frac{\text{number of times event } H \text{ occurs}}{\text{number of tosses}}$$

The results of the first ten tosses might be as follows:

Toss	1	2	3	4	5	6	7	8	9	10
Cumulative number of H's	0	1	2	3	3	3	4	5	5	5
Relative frequency of H's	0	.5	.667	.75	.6	.5	.571	.625	.556	.5

Figure 6.5 illustrates how the relative frequency of heads fluctuates during a sample sequence of 50 tosses. *As the number of tosses increases, the relative frequency of heads does not continue to fluctuate wildly but instead stabilizes and approaches some fixed number (the limiting value).* This stabilization is illustrated for a sequence of 1000 tosses in Figure 6.6.

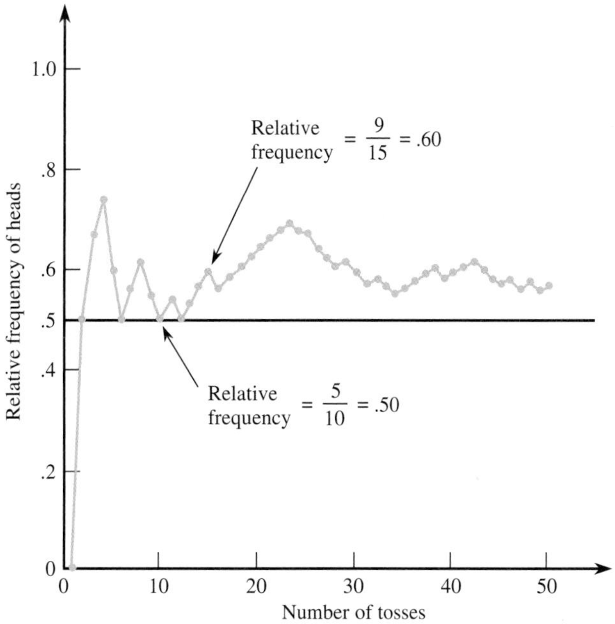

FIGURE 6.5
Relative frequency of heads in the first 50 of a long series of coin tosses.

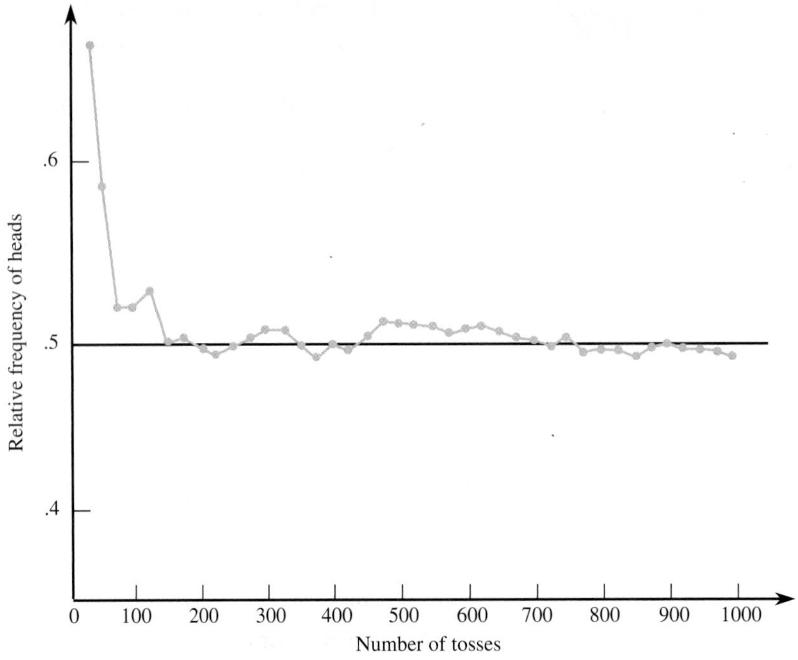

FIGURE 6.6
Stabilization of the relative frequency of heads in coin tossing.

It may seem natural to you that the proportion of H's would get closer and closer to the "real" probability of .5. That an empirically observed proportion could behave like this in real life also seemed reasonable to James Bernoulli in the early 18th century. He focused his considerable mathematical power on this topic and was able to prove mathematically what we now know as the law of large numbers.*

A Law of Large Numbers

As the number of repetitions of a chance experiment increases, the chance that the relative frequency of occurrence for an event will differ from the true probability of the event by more than any small number approaches 0.

Note that, as the number of repetitions of the chance experiment increases, the proportion of H's gets closer and closer to the real probability of H occurring in a single chance experiment *even if the value of this probability is not known*. This means that we can observe the outcomes of repetitions of a chance experiment and then use the observed outcomes to estimate probabilities.

Relative Frequency Approach To Probability

The **probability of an event *E*,** denoted by ***P*(*E*),** is defined to be the value approached by the relative frequency of occurrence of E in a very long series of trials of a chance experiment. Thus, if the number of trials is quite large,

$$P(E) \approx \frac{\text{number of times } E \text{ occurs}}{\text{number of trials}}$$

*Technically, this should be referred to more specifically as the weak law of large numbers for Bernoulli trials. After Bernoulli's proof, mathematical statisticians proved more general laws of large numbers.

The relative frequency definition of probability depends on being able to repeat a chance experiment under identical conditions. Suppose that we perform a chance experiment that consists of flipping a cap from a 20-ounce bottle of soda and noting whether the cap lands with the open side up or down. The crucial difference from the previous coin-tossing chance experiment is that there is no particular reason to believe the cap is equally likely to land top up or top down. If we assume that the chance experiment can be repeated under similar conditions (which seems reasonable), then we can flip the cap a number of times and compute the relative frequency of the event *top up* observed so far:

$$\frac{\text{number of times the event } \textit{top up} \text{ occurs}}{\text{number of flips}}$$

The results of the first 10 flips, with U indicating top up and D indicating top down, might be:

Flip	1	2	3	4	5	6	7	8	9	10
Outcome	U	U	D	U	D	D	U	D	U	U
Cumulative number of *ups*	1	2	2	3	3	3	4	4	5	6
Relative frequency of *ups*	1.0	1.0	.67	.75	.6	.5	.57	.5	.56	.6

Figure 6.7 illustrates how the relative frequency of the event *top up* fluctuates during a sample sequence of 100 flips. Based on these results and faith in the law of large numbers, it is reasonable to think that the probability of the cap landing top up is about .7.

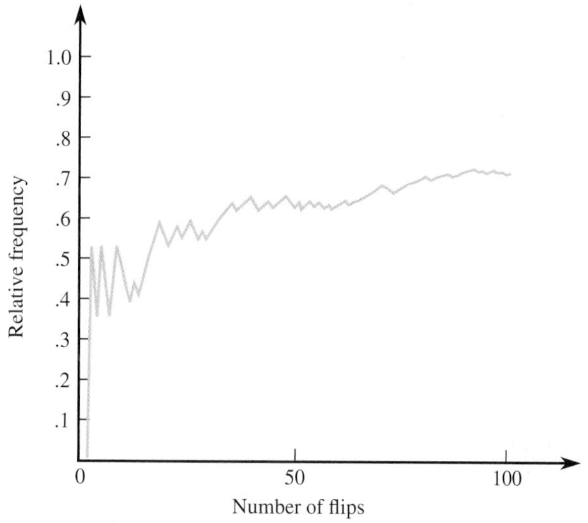

FIGURE 6.7
Stabilization of the relative frequency of a bottle cap landing top up.

The relative frequency approach to probability is based on observation. From repeated observation, we can obtain stable relative frequencies that will, in the long run, provide good estimates of the probabilities of different events. The relative frequency interpretation of probability is intuitive, widely used, and most relevant for the inferential procedures introduced in later chapters.

Subjective Approach to Probability

A third distinct approach to probability is based on subjective judgments. In this view, probability can be interpreted as a personal measure of the strength of belief that a particular outcome will occur. A probability of 1 represents a belief that the outcome will certainly occur. A probability of 0 represents a belief that the outcome will certainly not occur—that it is impossible. Other probabilities are placed somewhere between 0 and 1, based on the strength of one's beliefs. For example, an airline passenger might report her subjective assessment of the probability of being denied a seat as a result of overbooking on a particular flight as .01. Because this probability is close to 0, she believes it is very unlikely that she will be denied a seat.

The subjective interpretation of probability presents some difficulties. For one thing, different people may assign different probabilities to the same outcome, because each could have a different subjective belief. Although subjective probabilities are useful in studying and analyzing decision making, they are of limited use because they are personal and not generally replicable by others.

How Are Probabilities Determined?

Probability statements are frequently encountered in newspapers and magazines (and, of course, in this textbook). What is the basis for these probability statements? In most cases, research allows reasonable estimates based on observation and analysis. In general, if a probability is stated, it is based on one of the following approaches:

1. *The classical approach:* This approach is appropriate only for modeling chance experiments with equally likely outcomes.
2. *The subjective approach:* In this case, the probability represents an individual's judgment based on facts combined with personal evaluation of other information.
3. *The relative frequency approach:* An estimate is based on an accumulation of experimental results. This estimate, usually derived empirically, presumes a replicable chance experiment.

When you see probabilities in this book and in other published sources, you should consider how the probabilities were produced. Be particularly cautious in the case of subjective probabilities.

6.3 Basic Properties of Probability

The view of a probability as a long-run relative frequency that can be approximated empirically has some limitations when it comes to calculating probabilities in real life. The most obvious problem is time. If computing probabilities even for simple chance experiments were to require hundreds or thousands of repeated trials, even the most ardent statistics students would avoid this task! An alternative approach that simplifies things in some situations is to study fundamental properties of probability that can be used to find probabilities of complex events. These fundamental properties are given in the accompanying box, and then a discussion of each property follows.

Fundamental Properties of Probability

1. For any event E, $0 \leq P(E) \leq 1$.
2. If S is the sample space for an experiment, $P(S) = 1$.
3. If two events E and F are disjoint, then $P(E \text{ or } F) = P(E) + P(F)$.
4. For any event E, $P(E) + P(\text{not } E) = 1$. Therefore

$$P(\text{not } E) = 1 - P(E)$$

and

$$P(E) = 1 - P(\text{not } E).$$

Property 1: For any event E, $0 \leq P(E) \leq 1$. To understand the first property of probability, recall the previous bottle cap chance experiment. You may remember that we were keeping track of the number of flips landing with the inside of the bottle cap facing up. Suppose that, after flipping the bottle cap N times, we have observed x occurrences of top up. What are the possible values of x? The fewest that could have been counted is 0, and the most that could have been counted is N. Therefore, the relative frequency falls between two numbers:

$$\frac{0}{N} \leq \text{relative frequency} \leq \frac{N}{N}$$

Thus, $0 \leq$ relative frequency ≤ 1. As N increases, the long-run value of the relative frequency, which defines the probability, must also lie between 0 and 1.

Property 2: If S is the sample space for a chance experiment, $P(S) = 1$. Because the probability of any event is the proportion of time an outcome in the event will occur in the long run and because the sample space consists of all possible outcomes for a chance experiment, in the long run an outcome that is in S must occur 100% of the time, resulting in $P(S) = 1$.

Property 3: If two events E and F are disjoint, then $P(E \text{ or } F) = P(E) + P(F)$. This is one of the most important properties of probability because it provides a method for computing probabilities if the number of possible outcomes (simple events) in the sample space is finite. Any nonsimple event is just a collection of outcomes from the sample space—some outcomes are in the event and others are not. Because simple events are disjoint, any event can be viewed as a union of disjoint events. For example, suppose that a chance experiment has a sample space that consists of six outcomes, $O_1, O_2, \ldots, O_6$. Then $P(O_1)$ can be interpreted as the long run proportion of times that the outcome O_1 will occur, and the probabilities of the other outcomes can be interpreted in a similar way. Suppose that an event E is made up of outcomes O_1, O_2, and O_4. Because E will occur whenever O_1, O_2, or O_4 occurs and because O_1, O_2, and O_4 are disjoint, the long-run proportion of time that E will occur is just the sum of the proportion of time that each of the outcomes O_1, O_2, and O_4 will occur. Because it is always possible to express any event as a collection of disjoint simple events in this way, finding the probability of an event can be reduced to finding the probabilities of the simple events (outcomes) that make up the event and then adding. If the probabilities of all the simple events are known, it is then easy to compute the probability of more complex events constructed from the simple events.

Property 4: For any event E, $P(E) + P(\textit{not } E) = 1$. Therefore $P(\textit{not } E) = 1 - P(E)$ and $P(E) = 1 - P(\textit{not } E)$. Property 4 follows from Properties 2 and 3. Property 2 tells us that $P(E)$ is the sum of the probabilities in E and that $P(\textit{not } E)$ is the sum of the probabilities for simple events corresponding to outcomes in *not* E. Every outcome in the sample space is in either E or *not* E, and we know from Property 3 that the sum of the probabilities of all the simple events is 1. It follows that $P(E) + P(\textit{not } E)$ must equal 1. The implication of Property 4, namely, that $P(E) = 1 - P(\textit{not } E)$ is surprisingly useful. There are many situations in which calculation of $P(\textit{not } E)$ is much easier than direct determination of $P(E)$.

EXAMPLE 6.9 Medical Errors

Diagnostic errors in medical settings are of concern because they often lead to serious consequences and sometimes even death. The paper "Diagnostic Error in Internal Medicine" (*Archives of Internal Medicine* [2005]: 1493–1499) describes possible outcomes when a doctor reaches a diagnosis for a patient seen by a specialist in internal medicine. The possible diagnostic outcomes are

- O_1 Correct diagnosis
- O_2 No-fault diagnostic error (a misdiagnosis due to unusual symptoms or due to an uncooperative or deceptive patient)
- O_3 System-related diagnostic error (a misdiagnosis due to equipment failure, faulty lab results, etc.)
- O_4 Cognitive diagnostic error (a misdiagnosis due to faulty or inadequate doctor knowledge or failure to synthesize available information correctly)
- O_5 Misdiagnosis resulting from a combination of system-related error and cognitive error

Based on a study of a large number of patients, the paper suggests that 85% of patients are correctly diagnosed, 1% are misdiagnosed because of a no-fault error, 3% are misdiagnosed because of a system-related error, 4% are misdiagnosed because of a cognitive error, and 7% are misdiagnosed because of a combination of system and cognitive errors.

The following table displays the probabilities of the simple events for the chance experiment in which the diagnostic outcome is observed for a randomly selected patient:

Simple Event (Outcome)	O_1	O_2	O_3	O_4	O_5
Probability	.85	.01	.03	.04	.07

Let's create event E, the event that *a randomly selected patient is misdiagnosed.* This event consists of the outcomes O_2, O_3, O_4, and O_5. Therefore

$$P(E) = P(O_2 \cup O_3 \cup O_4 \cup O_5) = P(O_2) + P(O_3) + P(O_4) + P(O_5) = .01 + .03 + .04 + .07 = .15$$

That is, in the long run, 15% of all patients seen by internal medicine specialists are misdiagnosed. Another way to compute this probability is to notice that the event *not E* consists only of the outcome O_1. As an alternative, we could have computed

$$P(E) = 1 - P(\textit{not } E) = 1 - P(O_1) = 1 - .85 = .15$$

If we were interested in the probability of a misdiagnosis that involved a cognitive error in some way, we could define the event F, where F is the event that *a randomly selected patient is misdiagnosed in a way that involved a cognitive error.* Then

$$F = O_4 \cup O_5$$

and

$$P(F) = P(O_4 \cup O_5) = P(O_4) + P(O_5) = .04 + .07 = .11$$

This means that, in the long run, cognitive errors play a role in the misdiagnosis of about 11% of patients.

We have kept the discussion of the fundamental properties of probability nonmathematical. Students interested in a more formal mathematical treatment of these properties in particular and of probability in general are encouraged to consult a more advanced textbook (see the references by Devore or Mostellar, Rourke and Thomas listed in the back of the book).

Having established the fundamental properties of probability, we now present some practical probability rules that can be used to evaluate probabilities in some situations. An important aspect of each rule is the set of conditions necessary in order to use the rule. A common error for beginning statistics students is to believe that the rules can be used in *any* probability calculation. This is *not* the case. You must be careful to use the rules only after verifying that any necessary conditions are met.

Equally Likely Outcomes

The first probability rule that we consider applies only when events are equally likely; it is *not* always true for all events in all situations. Chance experiments involving tossing fair coins, rolling fair dice, or selecting cards from a well-mixed deck are examples of chance experiments that have equally likely outcomes. If a fair die is rolled once, each possible outcome (1, 2, 3, 4, 5, and 6) has probability 1/6. With E denoting the event that the outcome is an even number,

$$P(E) = P(2 \text{ } or \text{ } 4 \text{ } or \text{ } 6) = P(2) + P(4) + P(6) = \frac{1}{6} + \frac{1}{6} + \frac{1}{6} = \frac{3}{6}$$

This is just the ratio of the number of outcomes in E to the total number of possible outcomes. The following box presents the generalization of this result.

Calculating Probabilities When Outcomes Are Equally Likely

Consider an experiment that can result in any one of N possible outcomes. Denote the corresponding simple events by $O_1, O_2, \ldots, O_N$. If these simple events are equally likely to occur, then

1. $P(O_1) = \frac{1}{N}, P(O_2) = \frac{1}{N}, \ldots, P(O_N) = \frac{1}{N}$
2. For *any* event E,

$$P(E) = \frac{\text{number of outcomes in } E}{N}$$

Addition Rule for Disjoint Events

We have seen previously that the probability of an event can be calculated by adding together probabilities of the simple events that correspond to the outcomes making up the event. This addition process is also legitimate when calculating the probability of the union of two events that are disjoint (mutually exclusive) but not necessarily simple.

The Addition Rule for Disjoint (Mutually Exclusive) Events

Let E and F be two disjoint events. One of the basic properties (axioms) of probability is

$$P(E \text{ or } F) = P(E \cup F) = P(E) + P(F)$$

This property of probability is known as the addition rule for disjoint events. More generally, if events $E_1, E_2, \ldots, E_k$ are disjoint, then

$$P(E_1 \text{ or } E_2 \text{ or} \ldots \text{or } E_k) = P(E_1 \cup E_2 \cup \cdots \cup E_k) = P(E_1) + P(E_2) + \cdots + P(E_k)$$

In words, the probability that any of these k disjoint events occurs is the sum of the probabilities of the individual events.

Consider the chance experiment that consists of rolling a pair of fair dice. There are 36 possible outcomes for this chance experiment, such as (1, 1), (1, 2), and so on. Because these outcomes are equally likely, we can compute the probability of observing a total of 5 on the two dice by counting the number of outcomes that result in a total of 5. There are four such outcomes—(1, 4), (2, 3), (3, 2), and (4, 1)—giving

$$P(\text{total of } 5) = \frac{4}{36}$$

The probabilities for the other totals can be computed in a similar fashion; they are shown in the following table:

Total	Probability	Total	Probability
2	1/36	8	5/36
3	2/36	9	4/36
4	3/36	10	3/36
5	4/36	11	2/36
6	5/36	12	1/36
7	6/36		

What is the probability of getting a total of 3 or 5? Consider the two events E = *total is 3* and F = *total is 5*. Clearly E and F are disjoint because the sum cannot simultaneously be both 3 and 5. Notice also that neither of these events is simple, because neither consists of only a single outcome from the sample space. We can apply the addition rule for disjoint events as follows:

$$P(E \text{ or } F) = P(E \cup F) = P(E) + P(F) = \frac{2}{36} + \frac{4}{36} = \frac{6}{36}$$

EXAMPLE 6.10 Car Choices

A large auto center sells cars made by a number of different manufacturers. Three of these manufacturers are Japanese: Honda, Nissan, and Toyota. Consider a chance experiment that consists of observing the make and model of the next car purchased at this auto center. The outcomes in the sample space would then be simple events such as Nissan Altima and Toyota Prius. Let's define events E_1, E_2, and E_3 by E_1 = Honda, E_2 = Nissan, and E_3 = Toyota. Notice that E_1 is not a simple event because there is more than one model Honda (for example, Civic, Accord, and Insight).

Based on several years of sales data, the probabilities of these three events have been estimated empirically as $P(E_1) = .25$, $P(E_2) = .18$, and $P(E_3) = .14$. Because E_1, E_2, and E_3 are disjoint, the addition rule gives

$$\begin{aligned} P(\text{Honda } or \text{ Nissan } or \text{ Toyota}) &= P(E_1 \cup E_2 \cup E_3) \\ &= P(E_1) + P(E_2) + P(E_3) \\ &= .25 + .18 + .14 = .57 \end{aligned}$$

The probability that the next car purchased is *not* made by one of these three manufacturers is

$$P(not(E_1 \text{ } or \text{ } E_2 \text{ } or \text{ } E_3)) = P((E_1 \cup E_2 \cup E_3)^C) = 1 - .57 = .43$$

In Section 6.6, we will show how $P(E \cup F)$ can be calculated when the two events E and F are not disjoint.

EXERCISES 6.13 - 6.29

6.13 A large department store offers online ordering. When a purchase is made online, the customer can select one of four different delivery options: expedited overnight delivery, expedited second-business-day delivery, standard delivery, or delivery to the nearest store for customer pick-up. Consider the chance experiment that consists of observing the selected delivery option for a randomly selected online purchase.

a. What are the simple events that make up the sample space for this experiment?

b. Suppose that the probability of an overnight delivery selection is .1, the probability of a second-day delivery selection is .3, and the probability of a standard-delivery selection is .4. Find the following probabilities:

i. the probability that a randomly selected online purchase selects delivery to the nearest store for customer pick-up.

ii. the probability that the customer selects a form of expedited delivery.

iii. the probability that either standard delivery or delivery to the nearest store is selected.

6.14 The manager of a music store has kept records of the number of CDs bought in a single transaction by customers who make a purchase at the store. The accompanying table gives six possible outcomes and the estimated probability associated with each of these outcomes for the chance experiment that consists of observing the number of CDs purchased by the next customer at the store.

Number of CDs purchased	1	2	3	4	5	6 or more
Estimated probability	.45	.25	.10	.10	.07	.03

a. What is the estimated probability that the next customer purchases three or fewer CDs?

b. What is the estimated probability that the next customer purchases at most three CDs? How does this compare to the probability computed in Part (a)?

c. What is the estimated probability that the next customer purchases five or more CDs?

d. What is the estimated probability that the next customer purchases one or two CDs?

e. What is the estimated probability that the next customer purchases more than two CDs? Show two different ways to compute this probability that use the probability rules of this section.

6.15 A bookstore sells two types of books (fiction and nonfiction) in several formats (hardcover, paperback, digital, and audio). For the chance experiment that consists of observing the type and format of a single-book purchase, two possible outcomes are a hardcover fiction book and an audio nonfiction book.

a. There are eight outcomes in the sample space for this experiment. List these possible outcomes.

b. Do you think it is reasonable to think that the outcomes for this experiment would be equally likely? Explain.

c. For customers who purchase a single book, the estimated probabilities for the different possible outcomes are given in the cells of the accompanying table. What is the probability that a randomly selected single-book purchase will be for a book in print format (hardcover or paperback)?

	Hardcover	Paperback	Digital	Audio
Fiction	.15	.45	.10	.10
Nonfiction	.08	.04	.02	.06

d. Show two different ways to compute the probability that a randomly selected single-book purchase will be for a book that is not in a print format.

e. Find the probability that a randomly selected single-book purchase will be for a work of fiction.

6.16 ✦ Medical insurance status—covered (C) or not covered (N)—is determined for each individual arriving for treatment at a hospital's emergency room. Consider the chance experiment in which this determination is made for two randomly selected patients. The simple events are O_1 = (C, C), meaning that the first patient selected was covered and the second patient selected was also covered, O_2 = (C, N), O_3 = (N, C), and O_4 = (N, N). Suppose that probabilities are $P(O_1) = .81$, $P(O_2) = .09$, $P(O_3) = .09$, and $P(O_4) = .01$.

a. What outcomes are contained in A, the event that at most one patient is covered, and what is $P(A)$?

b. What outcomes are contained in B, the event that the two patients have the same status with respect to coverage, and what is $P(B)$?

6.17 "N.Y. Lottery Numbers Come Up 9-1-1 on 9/11" was the headline of an article that appeared in the *San Francisco Chronicle* (September 13, 2002). More than 5600 people had selected the sequence 9-1-1 on that date, many more than is typical for that sequence. A professor at the University of Buffalo is quoted as saying, "I'm a bit surprised, but I wouldn't characterize it as bizarre. It's randomness. Every number has the same chance of coming up."

a. The New York state lottery uses balls numbered 0–9 circulating in three separate bins. To select the winning sequence, one ball is chosen at random from each bin. What is the probability that the sequence 9-1-1 is the sequence selected on any particular day? (Hint: It may be helpful to think about the chosen sequence as a three-digit number.)

b. What approach (classical, relative frequency, or subjective) did you use to obtain the probability in Part (a)? Explain.

6.18 An article in the *New York Times* (March 2, 1994) reported that people who suffer cardiac arrest in New York City have only a 1 in 100 chance of survival. Using probability notation, an equivalent statement would be $P(\text{survival}) = .01$ for people who suffer a cardiac arrest in New York City. (The article attributed this poor survival rate to factors common in large cities: traffic congestion and the difficulty of finding victims in large buildings.)

a. Give a relative frequency interpretation of the given probability.

b. The research that was the basis for the *New York Times* article was a study of 2329 consecutive cardiac arrests in New York City. To justify the "1 in 100 chance of survival" statement, how many of the 2329 cardiac arrest sufferers do you think survived? Explain.

6.19 The article "Anxiety Increases for Airline Passengers After Plane Crash" (*San Luis Obispo Tribune*, November 13, 2001) reported that air passengers have a 1 in 11 million chance of dying in an airplane crash. This probability was then interpreted as "You could fly every day for 26,000 years before your number was up." Comment on why this probability interpretation is misleading.

6.20 Refer to the following information on births in the United States over a given period of time:

Type of Birth	Number of Births
Single birth	41,500,000
Twins	500,000
Triplets	5,000
Quadruplets	100

Use this information to approximate the probability that a randomly selected pregnant woman who reaches full term

a. Delivers twins

b. Delivers quadruplets

c. Gives birth to more than a single child

6.21 Consider the chance experiment in which both tennis racket head size and grip size are noted for a randomly selected customer at a particular store. The six possible outcomes (simple events) and their probabilities are displayed in the following table:

	Grip Size		
Head size	$4\frac{3}{8}$ in.	$4\frac{1}{2}$ in.	$4\frac{5}{8}$ in.
Midsize	O_1 (.10)	O_2 (.20)	O_3 (.15)
Oversize	O_4 (.20)	O_5 (.15)	O_6 (.20)

a. The probability that grip size is $4\frac{1}{2}$ inches (event A) is $P(A) = P(O_2 \text{ or } O_5) = .20 + .15 = .35$. How would you interpret this probability?

b. Use the result of Part (a) to calculate the probability that grip size is not $4\frac{1}{2}$ inches

c. What is the probability that the racket purchased has an oversize head (event B), and how would you interpret this probability?

d. What is the probability that grip size is *at least* $4\frac{1}{2}$ inches?

6.22 ✦ A mutual fund company offers its customers several different funds: a money market fund, three different bond funds, two stock funds, and a balanced fund. Among customers who own shares in just one fund, the percentages of customers in the different funds are as follows:

Money market	20%
Short-term bond	15%
Intermediate-term bond	10%
Long-term bond	5%
High-risk stock	18%
Moderate-risk stock	25%
Balanced fund	7%

A customer who owns shares in just one fund is to be selected at random.

a. What is the probability that the selected individual owns shares in the balanced fund?

b. What is the probability that the individual owns shares in a bond fund?

c. What is the probability that the selected individual does not own shares in a stock fund?

6.23 A radio station that plays classical music has a "by request" program each Saturday evening. The percentages of requests for composers on a particular night are as follows:

Bach	5%
Beethoven	26%
Brahms	9%
Dvorak	2%
Mendelssohn	3%
Mozart	21%
Schubert	12%
Schumann	7%
Tchaikovsky	14%
Wagner	1%

Suppose that one of these requests is to be selected at random.

a. What is the probability that the request is for one of the three B's (Bach, Beethoven, or Brahms)?

b. What is the probability that the request is not for one of the two S's?

c. All of the listed composers wrote at least one symphony except Bach and Wagner. What is the probability that the request is for a composer who wrote at least one symphony?

6.24 Refer to Exercise 6.21. Adding probabilities in the first row of the given table yields $P(\text{midsize}) = .45$, whereas from the first column, $P(4\frac{3}{8} \text{ in. grip}) = .30$. Is the following true?

$$P(\text{midsize } or \ 4\tfrac{3}{8} \text{ in. grip}) = .45 + .30 = .75$$

Explain.

6.25 A deck of 52 cards is mixed well, and 5 cards are dealt.

a. It can be shown that (disregarding the order in which the cards are dealt) there are 2,598,960 possible five-card hands, of which only 1287 are hands consisting entirely of spades. What is the probability that a hand will consist entirely of spades? What is the probability that a hand will consist entirely of a single suit?

b. It can be shown that exactly 63,206 hands contain only spades and clubs, with both suits represented. What is the probability that a hand consists entirely of spades and clubs with both suits represented?

c. Using the result of Part (b), what is the probability that a hand contains cards from exactly two suits?

6.26 After all students have left the classroom, a statistics professor notices that four copies of the text were left under desks. At the beginning of the next lecture, the professor distributes the four books at random to the four students (1, 2, 3, and 4) who claim to have left books. One possible outcome is that 1 receives 2's book, 2 receives 4's book, 3 receives his or her own book, and 4 receives 1's book. This outcome can be abbreviated (2, 4, 3, 1).

a. List the 23 other possible outcomes.
b. Which outcomes are contained in the event that exactly two of the books are returned to their correct owners? Assuming equally likely outcomes, what is the probability of this event?
c. What is the probability that exactly one of the four students receives his or her own book?
d. What is the probability that exactly three receive their own books?
e. What is the probability that at least two of the four students receive their own books?

6.27 The student council for a school of science and math has one representative from each of the five academic departments: biology (B), chemistry (C), mathematics (M), physics (P), and statistics (S). Two of these students are to be randomly selected for inclusion on a university-wide student committee (by placing five slips of paper in a bowl, mixing, and drawing out two of them).

a. What are the 10 possible outcomes (simple events)?
b. From the description of the selection process, all outcomes are equally likely. What is the probability of each simple event?
c. What is the probability that one of the committee members is the statistics department representative?
d. What is the probability that both committee members come from laboratory science departments?

6.28 A student placement center has requests from five students for interviews regarding employment with a particular consulting firm. Three of these students are math majors, and the other two students are statistics majors. Unfortunately, the interviewer has time to talk to only two of the students. These two will be randomly selected from among the five.

a. What is the probability that both selected students are statistics majors?
b. What is the probability that both students are math majors?
c. What is the probability that at least one of the students selected is a statistics major?
d. What is the probability that the selected students have different majors?

6.29 Suppose that a six-sided die is "loaded" so that any particular even-numbered face is twice as likely to land face up as any particular odd-numbered face. Consider the chance experiment that consists of rolling this die.

a. What are the probabilities of the six simple events? (Hint: Denote these events by $O_1, \ldots, O_6$. Then $P(O_1) = p$, $P(O_2) = 2p$, $P(O_3) = p, \ldots, P(O_6) = 2p$. Now use a condition on the sum of these probabilities to determine p.)
b. What is the probability that the number showing is an odd number? at most three?
c. Now suppose that the die is loaded so that the probability of any particular simple event is proportional to the number showing on the corresponding upturned face; that is, $P(O_1) = c$, $P(O_2) = 2c, \ldots,$ $P(O_6) = 6c$. What are the probabilities of the six simple events? Calculate the probabilities of Part (b) for this die.

6.4 Conditional Probability

Sometimes the knowledge that one event has occurred changes our assessment of the likelihood that another event occurs. For example, consider a population in which 0.1% of all individuals have a certain disease. The presence of the disease cannot be discerned from outward appearances, but there is a diagnostic test available. Unfortunately, the test is not infallible: 80% of those with positive test results actually have the disease; the other 20% who show positive test results are false-positives. To put this in probability terms, consider the chance experiment in which an individual is randomly selected from the population. Define the following events:

E = event that the individual has the disease
F = event that the individual's diagnostic test is positive

Let $P(E|F)$ denote the probability of the event E *given that* the event F is known to have occurred. A new symbol has been used to indicate that a probability calculation has been made conditional on the occurrence of another event. The standard symbol for this is a vertical line, and it is read "given." We would say, "the probability that an individual has the disease *given* that the diagnostic test is positive," and represent this symbolically as $P(\text{has disease}|\text{positive test})$ or $P(E|F)$. This probability is called a **conditional probability**.

The information provided then implies that

$$P(E) = .001$$
$$P(E|F) = .8$$

That is, before we have diagnostic test information, the occurrence of E is unlikely, whereas once it is known that the test result is positive, the likelihood of the disease increases dramatically. (If this were not so, the diagnostic test would not be very useful!)

EXAMPLE 6.11 After-School Activities

At the fictional George Washington High School (GWHS), after-school activities can be classified into three types: athletics, fine arts, and other. The following table gives the number of students participating in each of these types of activities by grade:

	9th	10th	11th	12th	Total
Athletics	150	160	140	150	**600**
Fine arts	100	90	120	125	**435**
Other	125	140	150	150	**565**
Total	**375**	**390**	**410**	**425**	**1600**

For the purposes of this example, we will assume that every student at the school is in exactly one of these after-school activities. Consider each of the following statements, and make sure that you see how each follows from the information in the table:

1. There are 160 10th-grade students participating in athletics.
2. The number of seniors participating in fine arts activities is 125.
3. There are 435 students in fine arts activities.
4. GWHS has 410 juniors.
5. The total number of students is 1600.

The principal at GWHS selects students at random and invites them to have lunch with her to discuss various issues that might be of concern to them. She feels that random selection will give her the greatest chance of hearing from a cross-section of the student body. What is the probability that a randomly selected student is a senior athlete? Assuming that each student is equally likely to be selected, we can calculate this probability as follows:

$$P(\text{senior athlete}) = \frac{\text{number of senior athletes}}{\text{total number of students}} = \frac{150}{1600} = .09375$$

Now suppose that the principal's secretary records not only the student's name but also the student's grade level. The secretary has indicated that the selected student is a senior. Does this information change our assessment of the likelihood that the selected student is an athlete? Because 150 of the 425 seniors participate in athletics, this suggests that

$$P(\text{athlete}|\text{senior}) = \frac{\text{number of senior athletes}}{\text{total number of seniors}} = \frac{150}{425} = .3529$$

The probability is calculated in this way because we know that the selected student is one of 425 seniors, each of whom is equally likely to have been the one selected. The interpretation of this conditional probability is that if we were to repeat the chance experiment of selecting a student at random, about 35.29% of the trials that resulted in a senior being selected would also result in the selection of someone who participates in athletics.

EXAMPLE 6.12 GFI Switches

A GFI (ground fault interrupt) switch turns off power to a system in the event of an electrical malfunction. A spa manufacturer currently has 25 spas in stock, each equipped with a single GFI switch. Two different companies supply the switches, and some of the switches are defective, as summarized in the following table:

	Nondefective	Defective	Total
Company 1	10	5	**15**
Company 2	8	2	**10**
Total	**18**	7	

A spa is randomly selected for testing. Let

E = event that GFI switch in selected spa is from Company 1
F = event that GFI switch in selected spa is defective

The tabulated information implies that

$$P(E) = \frac{15}{25} = .60 \quad P(F) = \frac{7}{25} = .28 \quad P(E \text{ and } F) = P(E \cap F) = \frac{5}{25} = .20$$

Now suppose that testing reveals a defective switch. (Thus the chosen spa is one of the seven in the "defective" column.) How likely is it that the switch came from the first company? Because five of the seven defective switches are from Company 1,

$$P(E|F) = P(\text{company } 1|\text{defective}) = \frac{5}{7} = .714$$

Notice that this is larger than the unconditional probability $P(E)$. This is because Company 1 has a much higher defective rate than does Company 2.

An alternative expression for the conditional probability is

$$P(E|F) = \frac{5}{7} = \frac{5/25}{7/25} = \frac{P(E \text{ and } F)}{P(F)} = \frac{P(E \cap F)}{P(F)}$$

That is, $P(E|F)$ is a ratio of two previously specified probabilities: the probability that both events occur divided by the probability of the "conditioning event" F. Additional insight comes from the Venn diagram of Figure 6.8. Once it is known that the outcome lies in F, the likelihood of E (also) occurring is the "size" of (E *and* F) relative to the size of F.

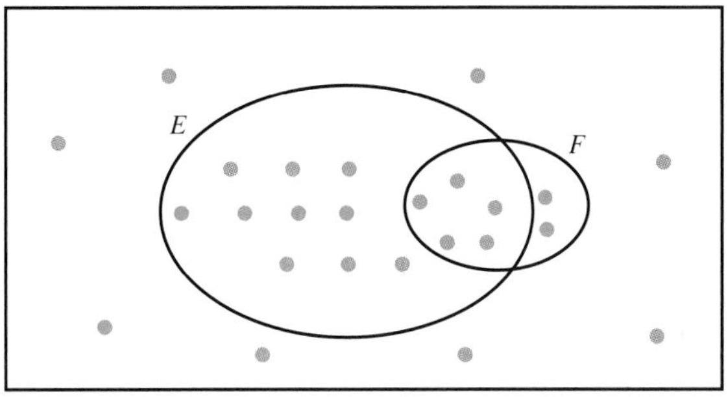

FIGURE 6.8
Venn diagram for Example 6.12 (each dot represents one GFI switch).

The results of the previous example lead us to a general definition of conditional probability.

DEFINITION

Let E and F be two events with $P(F) > 0$. The conditional probability of the event E given that the event F has occurred, denoted by $P(E|F)$, is

$$P(E|F) = \frac{P(E \cap F)}{P(F)}$$

Notice the requirement that $P(F) > 0$. In addition to the standard warning about division by 0, there is another reason for requiring $P(F)$ to be positive. If the probability of F were 0, the event F would never occur; therefore, it would be unreasonable to calculate the probability of another event conditional on F having occurred.

EXAMPLE 6.13 Surviving a Heart Attack

Medical guidelines recommend that a hospitalized patient who suffers cardiac arrest should receive defibrillation (an electric shock to the heart) within 2 minutes. The paper "Delayed Time to Defibrillation After In-Hospital Cardiac Arrest" (*The New England Journal of Medicine* [2008]: 9–17) describes a study of the time to defibrillation for hospitalized patients in hospitals of various sizes. The authors examined medical records of 6716 patients who suffered cardiac arrest while hospitalized, recording the size of the hospital and whether or not defibrillation occurred in 2 minutes or less. Data from this study are reproduced here:

	Time to Defibrillation		
Hospital Size	2 minutes or less	More than 2 minutes	Total
Small (Less than 250 beds)	1124	576	**1700**
Medium (250–499 beds)	2178	886	**3064**
Large (500 or more beds)	1387	565	**1952**
Total	**4689**	**2027**	**6716**

We will assume that these data are representative of the larger group of all hospitalized patients who suffer a cardiac arrest. Suppose that a hospitalized patient who suffered a cardiac arrest is selected at random. The following events are of interest:

S = event that the selected patient is at a small hospital
M = event that the selected patient is at a medium-sized hospital
L = event that the selected patient is at a large hospital
D = event that the selected patient receives defibrillation in 2 minutes or less

We can use the information in the table to compute

$$P(D) = \frac{4689}{6716} = .698$$

This probability is interpreted as the proportion of hospitalized patients who suffer cardiac arrest that receive defibrillation in 2 minutes or less. That is, 69.8% of these patients receive timely defibrillation.

Now suppose it is known that the selected patient was at a small hospital. How likely is it that this patient received defibrillation in 2 minutes or less? To answer this question, we need to compute $P(D|S)$, the probability of defibrillation in 2 minutes or less given that the patient is at a small hospital. Using the formula for conditional probability, we know

$$P(D|S) = \frac{P(D \cap S)}{P(S)}$$

From the information in the table, we can compute

$$P(D \cap S) = \frac{1124}{6716} = .167$$

$$P(S) = \frac{1700}{6716} = .253$$

and so

$$P(D|S) = \frac{P(D \cap S)}{P(S)} = \frac{.167}{.253} = .660$$

Notice that this is smaller than the unconditional probability, $P(D) = .698$. This tells us that there is a smaller probability of timely defibrillation at a small hospital.

Two other conditional probabilities of interest are

$$P(D|M) = \frac{P(D \cap M)}{P(M)} = \frac{2178/6716}{3064/6716} = .711$$

and

$$P(D|L) = \frac{P(D \cap L)}{P(L)} = \frac{1387/6716}{1952/6716} = .711$$

From this, we see that the probability of timely defibrillation is the same for patients at medium-sized and large hospitals, and that this probability is higher than that for patients at small hospitals.

It is also possible to compute $P(L|D)$, the probability that a patient is at a large hospital given that the patient received timely defibrillation:

$$P(L|D) = \frac{P(L \cap D)}{P(D)} = \frac{1387/6716}{4689/6716} = .296$$

Let's look carefully at the interpretation of some of these probabilities:

1. $P(D) = .698$ is interpreted as the proportion of all hospitalized patients suffering cardiac arrest who would receive timely defibrillation. Approximately 69.8% of these patients would receive timely defibrillation.
2. $P(D \cap L) = \frac{1387}{6716} = .207$ gives the proportion of all hospitalized patients who suffer cardiac arrest who are at a large hospital *and* who would receive timely defibrillation.
3. $P(D|L) = .711$ is the proportion *of patients at large hospitals* suffering cardiac arrest who would receive timely defibrillation.
4. $P(L|D) = .296$ is the proportion *of patients who would receive timely defibrillation* who were at large hospitals.

Notice the difference between the unconditional probabilities in Interpretations 1 and 2 and the conditional probabilities in Interpretations 3 and 4. The reference point for the unconditional probabilities is the entire group of interest (all hospitalized patients suffering cardiac arrest), whereas the conditional probabilities are interpreted in a more restricted context defined by the "given" event.

Example 6.14 demonstrates the calculation of conditional probabilities and also makes the point that we must be careful when translating real-world problems—especially probability problems—into mathematical form. Not only are probability problems sometimes difficult to formulate precisely, but the answers are frequently nonintuitive and occasionally counterintuitive.

EXAMPLE 6.14 Two-Kid Families

Consider the population of all families with two children. Representing the gender of each child using G for girl and B for boy results in four possibilities: BB, BG, GB, GG. The gender information is sequential, with the first letter indicating the gender of the older sibling. Thus, a family having a girl first and then a boy is denoted GB. If we assume that a child is equally likely to be male or female, each of the four possibilities in the sample space for the chance experiment that selects at random from families with two children is equally likely. Consider the following two questions:

1. What is the probability that the selected family has two girls, given that the family has at least one girl?
2. What is the probability that the selected family has two girls, given that the older sibling is a girl?

To many people, these questions *appear* to be identical. However, by computing the appropriate probabilities, we can see that they are actually different.

For Question 1 we obtain

$$P(\text{family with two girls} \mid \text{family has at least one girl})$$

$$= \frac{P(\text{family with two girls and family with at least one girl})}{P(\text{family with at least one girl})}$$

$$= \frac{P(GG)}{P(GG \text{ or } BG \text{ or } GB)}$$

$$= \frac{1/4}{3/4} = \frac{.25}{.75} = .3333$$

For question 2 we calculate

$$P(\text{family with two girls} \mid \text{family with older sibling a girl})$$
$$= \frac{P(\text{family with two girls } \textit{and} \text{ family with older sibling a girl})}{P(\text{family with older sibling a girl})}$$
$$= \frac{P(GG)}{P(GB \text{ or } GG)}$$
$$= \frac{1/4}{1/2} = \frac{.25}{.50} = .50$$

The moral of this story is: Correct solutions to probability problems, especially conditional probability problems, are much more the result of careful consideration of the sample spaces and the probabilities than they are a product of what your intuition tells you!

As we mentioned in the opening paragraphs of this section, one of the most important practical uses of conditional probability is in making diagnoses. Your mechanic diagnoses your car by hooking it up to a machine and reading the pressures and speeds of the various components. A meteorologist diagnoses the weather by looking at temperatures, isobars, and wind speeds. And medical doctors diagnose the state of a person's health by performing various tests and gathering information, such as weight and blood pressure.

Doctors observe characteristics of their patients in an attempt to determine whether or not their patients have a certain disease. Many diseases are not actually observable—or at least not easily so—and often the doctor must make a probabilistic judgment. As we will see, conditional probability plays a large role in evaluating diagnostic techniques.

We begin with the commonsense notion that a randomly selected individual either has or does not have a particular disease, for example, toxoplasmosis. Toxoplasmosis is a parasitic disease that usually does not result in any symptoms, but it may pose a significant risk to the developing fetus of a pregnant woman. The problem here is that the patient feels no symptoms and the doctor observes no symptoms in a routine checkup; the disease must be detected by prenatal screening.

Normally, a criterion or standard exists by which it would be unequivocally decided whether a person has a disease; this criterion is colloquially known as the "gold standard." The gold standard might be an invasive surgical procedure, expensive and dangerous. Or, the gold standard might be a test that takes a long time to perform in the lab or that is costly. For a diagnostic test to be preferred over the gold standard, it would need to be faster, less expensive, or less invasive and yet still produce results that agree with the gold standard. In this context, *agreement* means (1) that the test generally comes out positive when the patient has the disease and (2) that the test generally comes out negative when the patient does not have the disease. These statements lead us to consideration of conditional probabilities, as illustrated in the following example.

EXAMPLE 6.15 Diagnosing Tuberculosis

To illustrate the calculations involved in evaluating a diagnostic test, we consider the case of tuberculosis (TB), an infectious disease that typically attacks lung tissue. Before 1998, culturing was the existing gold standard for diagnosing TB. This method took

10 to 15 days to yield a positive or negative result. In 1998, investigators evaluated a DNA technique that turned out to be much faster ("LCx: A Diagnostic Alternative for the Early Detection of *Mycobacterium tuberculosis* Complex," *Diagnostic Microbiology and Infectious Diseases* [1998]: 259–264). The DNA technique for detecting tuberculosis was evaluated by comparing results from the test to the existing gold standard, with the following results for 207 patients exhibiting symptoms:

	Has Tuberculosis (gold standard)	Does Not Have Tuberculosis (gold standard)
DNA Positive Indication	14	0
DNA Negative Indication	12	181

Converting these data to proportions and inserting the column and row totals into the table, we get the following information:

	Has TB	Does Not Have TB	Total
DNA+	.0676	.0000	**.0676**
DNA−	.0580	.8744	**.9324**
Total	**.1256**	**.8744**	**1.0000**

A cursory look at the table indicates that the DNA technique seems to be working in a manner consistent with what we expect from a diagnostic test. Samples that tested positive with the technique agreed with the gold standard in every case. Samples that tested negative were generally in agreement with the gold standard, but the table also indicates some false-negative results. Consider a randomly selected individual who is tested for TB. Define the following events:

T = event that the individual has tuberculosis
N = event that the DNA test is negative

Let $P(T|N)$ denote the probability of the event T given that the event N has occurred. We calculate this probability as follows:

$$
\begin{aligned}
P(T|N) &= P(\text{tuberculosis}\,|\,\text{negative DNA test}) \\
&= \frac{P(\text{tuberculosis} \cap \text{negative DNA test})}{P(\text{negative DNA test})} \\
&= \frac{.0580}{.9324} \\
&= .0622
\end{aligned}
$$

Notice that .1256 of those tested had tuberculosis. The added information provided by the diagnostic test has altered the probability—and provided some measure of relief for the patients who test negative. Once it is known that the test result is negative, the estimated likelihood of the disease is cut in half. If the diagnostic test did not significantly alter the probability, the test would not be very useful to the doctor or patient.

EXERCISES 6.30 - 6.42

6.30 Two different airlines have a flight from Los Angeles to New York that departs each weekday morning at a certain time. Let E denote the event that the first airline's flight is fully booked on a particular day, and let F denote the event that the second airline's flight is fully booked on that same day. Suppose that $P(E) = .7$, $P(F) = .6$, and $P(E \cap F) = .54$.

a. Calculate $P(E|F)$, the probability that the first airline's flight is fully booked given that the second airline's flight is fully booked.
b. Calculate $P(F|E)$.

6.31 The article "Chances Are You Know Someone with a Tattoo, and He's Not a Sailor" (*Associated Press*, June 11, 2006) included results from a survey of adults aged 18 to 50. The accompanying data are consistent with summary values given in the article.

	At Least One Tattoo	No Tattoo
Age 18–29	18	32
Age 30–50	6	44

Assuming these data are representative of adult Americans and that an adult American is selected at random, use the given information to estimate the following probabilities.

a. $P(tattoo)$
b. $P(tattoo | age\ 18\text{–}29)$
c. $P(tattoo | age\ 30\text{–}50)$
d. $P(age\ 18\text{–}29 | tattoo)$

6.32 The accompanying data are from the article "Characteristics of Buyers of Hybrid Honda Civic IMA: Preferences, Decision Process, Vehicle Ownership, and Willingness-to-Pay" (Institute for Environmental Decisions, November 2006). Each of 311 people who purchased a Honda Civic was classified according to gender and whether the car purchased had a hybrid engine or not.

	Hybrid	Not Hybrid
Male	77	117
Female	34	83

Suppose one of these 311 individuals is to be selected at random.

a. Find the following probabilities:
   i. $P(male)$
   ii. $P(hybrid)$
   iii. $P(hybrid | male)$
   iv. $P(hybrid | female)$
   v. $P(female | hybrid)$
b. For each of the probabilities calculated in Part (a), write a sentence interpreting the probability.
c. Are the probabilities $P(hybrid | male)$ and $P(male | hybrid)$ equal? If not, write a sentence or two explaining the difference between these two probabilities.

6.33 The following graphical display appeared in *USA Today* (January 8, 2010).

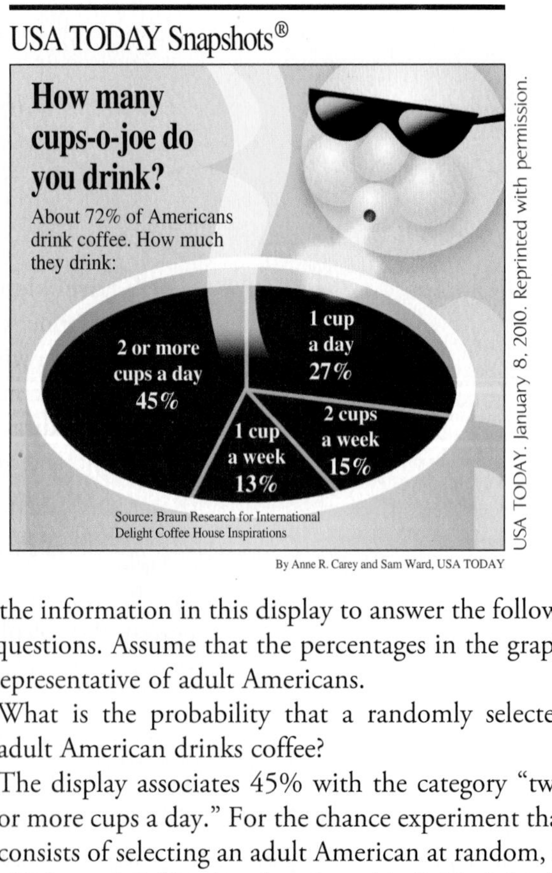

Use the information in this display to answer the following questions. Assume that the percentages in the graph are representative of adult Americans.

a. What is the probability that a randomly selected adult American drinks coffee?
b. The display associates 45% with the category "two or more cups a day." For the chance experiment that consists of selecting an adult American at random, is .45 the probability that the selected individual drinks two or more cups of coffee a day, or is it the conditional probability that the selected individual drinks two or more cups a day given that he or she drinks coffee? Explain.

6.34 Delayed diagnosis of cancer is a problem because it can delay the start of treatment. The paper "Causes of Physician Delay in the Diagnosis of Breast Cancer" (*Archives of Internal Medicine* [2002]: 1343–1348) examined possible causes for delayed diagnosis for women with breast cancer. The accompanying table summarizes data on the initial written mammogram report (benign or suspicious) and whether or not diagnosis was delayed for 433 women with breast cancer.

	Diagnosis Delayed	Diagnosis Not Delayed
Mammogram Report Benign	32	89
Mammogram Report Suspicious	8	304

Consider the following events:

B = the event that the mammogram report says benign

S = event that the mammogram report says suspicious

D = event that diagnosis is delayed

a. Assume that these data are representative of the larger group of all women with breast cancer. Use the data in the table to find and interpret the following probabilities:
   i. $P(B)$
   ii. $P(S)$
   iii. $P(D|B)$
   iv. $P(D|S)$
b. Remember that all of the 433 women in this study actually had breast cancer, so benign mammogram reports were, by definition, in error. Write a few sentences explaining whether this type of error in the reading of mammograms is related to delayed diagnosis of breast cancer.

6.35 The events E and T_i are defined as E = the event that someone who is out of work and actively looking for work will find a job within the next month and T_i = the event that someone who is currently out of work has been out of work for i months. For example, T_2 is the event that someone who is out of work has been out of work for 2 months. The following conditional probabilities are approximate and were read from a graph in the paper "The Probability of Finding a Job" (*American Economic Review: Papers & Proceedings* [2008]: 268–273):

$P(E|T_1) = .30$ $P(E|T_2) = .24$
$P(E|T_3) = .22$ $P(E|T_4) = .21$
$P(E|T_5) = .20$ $P(E|T_6) = .19$
$P(E|T_7) = .19$ $P(E|T_8) = .18$
$P(E|T_9) = .18$ $P(E|T_{10}) = .18$
$P(E|T_{11}) = .18$ $P(E|T_{12}) = .18$

a. Interpret the following two probabilities:
   i. $P(E|T_1) = .30$
   ii. $P(E|T_6) = .19$
b. Construct a graph of $P(E|T_i)$ versus i. That is, plot $P(E|T_i)$ on the y-axis and $i = 1, 2, \dots, 12$ on the x-axis.
c. Write a few sentences about how the probability of finding a job in the next month changes as a function of length of unemployment.

6.36 The newspaper article "Folic Acid Might Reduce Risk of Down Syndrome" (*USA Today*, September 29, 1999) makes the following statement: "Older women are at a greater risk of giving birth to a baby with Down Syndrome than are younger women. But younger women are more fertile, so most children with Down Syndrome are born to mothers under 30." Let D = event that a randomly selected baby is born with Down Syndrome and Y = event that a randomly selected baby is born to a young mother (under age 30). For each of the following probability statements, indicate whether the statement is consistent with the quote from the article, and if not, explain why not.

a. $P(D|Y) = .001,\ P(D|Y^C) = .004,\ P(Y) = .7$
b. $P(D|Y) = .001,\ P(D|Y^C) = .001,\ P(Y) = .7$
c. $P(D|Y) = .004,\ P(D|Y^C) = .004,\ P(Y) = .7$
d. $P(D|Y) = .001,\ P(D|Y^C) = .004,\ P(Y) = .4$
e. $P(D|Y) = .001,\ P(D|Y^C) = .001,\ P(Y) = .4$
f. $P(D|Y) = .004,\ P(D|Y^C) = .004,\ P(Y) = .4$

6.37 Suppose that an individual is randomly selected from the population of all adult males living in the United States. Let A be the event that the selected individual is over 6 feet in height, and let B be the event that the selected individual is a professional basketball player. Which do you think is larger, $P(A|B)$ or $P(B|A)$? Why?

6.38 ✦ Is ultrasound a reliable method for determining the gender of an unborn baby? The accompanying data on 1000 births are consistent with summary values that appeared in the online version of the *Journal of Statistics Education* ("New Approaches to Learning Probability in the First Statistics Course" [2001]).

	Ultrasound Predicted Female	Ultrasound Predicted Male
Actual Gender Is Female	432	48
Actual Gender Is Male	130	390

a. Use the given information to estimate the probability that a newborn baby is female, given that the ultrasound predicted the baby would be female.
b. Use the given information to estimate the probability that a newborn baby is male, given that the ultrasound predicted the baby would be male.
c. Based on your answers to Parts (a) and (b), do you think that a prediction that a baby is male and a prediction that a baby is female are equally reliable? Explain.

6.39 The table at the bottom of the page summarizes data on smoking status and perceived risk of smoking and is consistent with summary quantities obtained in a Gallup Poll conducted in November 2002. Assume that it is reasonable to consider these data as representative of the adult American population.
a. What is the probability that a randomly selected adult American is a former smoker?
b. What is the probability that a randomly selected adult American views smoking as very harmful?
c. What is the probability that a randomly selected adult American views smoking as very harmful given that the selected individual is a current smoker?
d. What is the probability that a randomly selected adult American views smoking as very harmful given that the selected individual is a former smoker?
e. What is the probability that a randomly selected adult American views smoking as very harmful given that the selected individual never smoked?
f. How do the probabilities computed in Parts (c), (d), and (e) compare? Does this surprise you? Explain.

6.40 *USA Today* (June 6, 2000) gave information on seat belt usage by gender. The proportions in the following table are based on a survey of a large number of adult men and women in the United States.

	Male	Female
Uses Seat Belts Regularly	.10	.175
Does Not Use Seat Belts Regularly	.40	.325

Assume that these proportions are representative of adult Americans and that an adult American is selected at random.
a. What is the probability that the selected adult regularly uses a seat belt?
b. What is the probability that the selected adult regularly uses a seat belt given that the individual selected is male?
c. What is the probability that the selected adult does not use a seat belt regularly given that the selected individual is female?
d. What is the probability that the selected individual is female given that the selected individual does not use a seat belt regularly?
e. Are the probabilities from Parts (c) and (d) equal? Write a couple of sentences explaining why this is so.

6.41 The *USA Today* article referenced in Exercise 6.40 also gave information on seat belt usage by age, which is summarized in the following table:

Age	Does Not Use Seat Belt Regularly	Uses Seat Belt Regularly
18–24	59	41
25–34	73	27
35–44	74	26
45–54	70	30
55–64	70	30
65 and older	82	18

	Perceived Risk			
Smoking Status	Very Harmful	Somewhat Harmful	Not Too Harmful	Not at All Harmful
Current Smoker	60	30	5	1
Former Smoker	78	16	3	2
Never Smoked	86	10	2	1

Consider the following events: S = event that a randomly selected individual uses a seat belt regularly, A_1 = event that a randomly selected individual is in age group 18–24, and A_6 = event that a randomly selected individual is in age group 65 and older.

a. Convert the counts to proportions and then use them to compute the following probabilities:

i. $P(A_1)$ ii. $P(A_1 \cap S)$ iii. $P(A_1 | S)$
iv. $P(\text{not } A_1)$ v. $P(S | A_1)$ vi. $P(S | A_6)$

b. Using the probabilities $P(S | A_1)$ and $P(S | A_6)$ computed in Part (a), comment on how 18–24-year-olds and seniors differ with respect to seat belt usage.

6.42 The paper "Good for Women, Good for Men, Bad for People: Simpson's Paradox and the Importance of Sex-Specific Analysis in Observational Studies" (*Journal of Women's Health and Gender-Based Medicine* [2001]: 867–872) described the results of a medical study in which one treatment was shown to be better for men and better for women than a competing treatment. However, if the data for men and women are combined, it appears as though the competing treatment is better. To see how this can happen, consider the accompanying data tables constructed from information in the paper. Subjects in the study were given either Treatment A or Treatment B, and survival was noted. Let S be the event that a patient selected at random survives, A be the event that a patient selected at random received Treatment A, and B be the event that a patient selected at random received Treatment B.

a. The following table summarizes data for men and women combined:

	Survived	Died	Total
Treatment A	215	85	**300**
Treatment B	241	59	**300**
Total	**456**	**144**	

i. Find $P(S)$.
ii. Find $P(S | A)$.
iii. Find $P(S | B)$.
iv. Which treatment appears to be better?

b. Now consider the summary data for the men who participated in the study:

	Survived	Died	Total
Treatment A	120	80	**200**
Treatment B	20	20	**40**
Total	**140**	**100**	

i. Find $P(S)$.
ii. Find $P(S | A)$.
iii. Find $P(S | B)$.
iv. Which treatment appears to be better?

c. Now consider the summary data for the women who participated in the study:

	Survived	Died	Total
Treatment A	95	5	**100**
Treatment B	221	39	**260**
Total	**316**	**144**	

i. Find $P(S)$.
ii. Find $P(S | A)$.
iii. Find $P(S | B)$.
iv. Which treatment appears to be better?

d. You should have noticed from Parts (b) and (c) that for both men and women, Treatment A appears to be better. But in Part (a), when the data for men and women are combined, it looks like Treatment B is better. This is an example of what is called Simpson's paradox. Write a brief explanation of why this apparent inconsistency occurs for this data set. (Hint: Do men and women respond similarly to the two treatments?)

6.5 Independence

In Section 6.4, we saw that knowledge of the occurrence of one event can alter our assessment of the likelihood that some other event has occurred. We also saw how information about conditional probabilities could be used in medical diagnosis to revise assessments of patients in light of the outcome of a diagnostic procedure. However, it is also possible that knowledge that one event has occurred will not change our assessment of the probability of occurrence of a second event.

EXAMPLE 6.16 Mortgage Choices

A large lending institution issues both adjustable-rate and fixed-rate mortgage loans on residential property, which it classifies into three categories: single-family houses, condominiums, and multifamily dwellings. The following table, sometimes called a *joint probability table*, displays probabilities based on the bank's long-run lending behavior:

	Single-Family	Condo	Multifamily	Total
Adjustable	.40	.21	.09	**.70**
Fixed	.10	.09	.11	**.30**
Total	**.50**	**.30**	**.20**	

From the table we see that 70% of all mortgages are adjustable rate, 50% of all mortgages are for single-family properties, 40% of all mortgages are adjustable rate for single-family properties (adjustable-rate *and* single-family), and so on. Define the events E and F by

E = event that a mortgage is adjustable rate
F = event that a mortgage is for a single-family house

Then

$$P(E|F) = \frac{P(E \text{ and } F)}{P(F)} = \frac{.40}{.50} = .80$$

That is, 80% of loans made for single-family houses are adjustable-rate loans. Notice that $P(E|F)$ is larger than the original (unconditional) probability $P(E) = .70$. Also,

$$P(F|E) = \frac{P(E \text{ and } F)}{P(E)} = \frac{.40}{.70} = .571$$

which is larger than the unconditional probability $P(F) = .5$. Knowing that E has occurred has changed our assessment of how likely it is that F has also occurred.

If we define another event C by

C = event that a mortgage is for a condominium

we have

$$P(E|C) = \frac{P(E \text{ and } C)}{P(C)} = \frac{.21}{.30} = .70$$

Notice that $P(E|C) = P(E)$. In this case, knowing that a mortgage is for a condominium doesn't change our assessment of the probability that the mortgage has an adjustable interest rate.

When two events E and F are such that $P(E|F) = P(E)$, the probability that event E has occurred is the same after we learn that F has occurred as it was before we had information about F's occurrence. We then say that E and F are independent of one another.

DEFINITION

Two events E and F are said to be **independent** if

$$P(E|F) = P(E)$$

If E and F are not independent, they are said to be **dependent** events.

If $P(E|F) = P(E)$, it is also true that $P(F|E) = P(F)$, and vice versa.

Independence of events E and F also implies the following additional three relationships:

$$P(\textit{not } E|F) = P(\textit{not } E)$$
$$P(E|\textit{not } F) = P(E)$$
$$P(\textit{not } E|\textit{not } F) = P(\textit{not } E)$$

That is, to say that E and F are independent implies that nothing we learn about F will change the likelihood of E or of *not* E.

Recall that the formula for conditional probability is

$$P(E|F) = \frac{P(E \cap F)}{P(F)}$$

which can be rearranged to give

$$P(E \cap F) = P(E|F)P(F)$$

When E and F are independent, $P(E|F) = P(E)$, so

$$P(E \cap F) = P(E|F)P(F) = P(E)P(F)$$

This result is called the multiplication rule for two independent events.

Multiplication Rule for Two Independent Events

The events E and F are independent if and only if

$$P(E \cap F) = P(E)P(F)$$

EXAMPLE 6.17 Hitchhiker's Thumb

In humans, there is a gene that controls a characteristic known as hitchhiker's thumb, the ability to bend the last joint of the thumb back at an angle of 60° or more. Whether an offspring has hitchhiker's thumb is determined by two random events: which of two alleles is contributed by the father and which of two alleles is contributed by the mother. (You can think of these alleles as a parental vote of yes or no on the hitchhiker's thumb gene. If the votes by the two parents disagree, the dominant allele wins.) These two random events, the results of cell division in two different biological parents, are independent of each other. Suppose that there is a .10 probability that a parent contributes a positive hitchhiker's thumb allele. Because the events are independent, the probability that each parent contributes a positive hitchhiker's thumb allele, H+, to the offspring is

$$\begin{aligned} &P(\textit{mother contributes } \mathrm{H+} \cap \textit{father contributes } \mathrm{H+}) \\ &\quad = P(\textit{mother contributes } \mathrm{H+})P(\textit{father contributes } \mathrm{H+}) \\ &\quad = (.10)(.10) \\ &\quad = .01 \end{aligned}$$

EXAMPLE 6.18 Curious Guppies

Maximillian Weinzier/Alamy

Let's look at another example, this time from the field of animal behavior, to illustrate how an investigator could judge whether two events are independent. In a number of fish species, including guppies, a phenomenon known as predator inspection has been reported. It is thought that predator inspection allows a guppy to assess the risk posed by a potential predator. In a typical inspection a guppy moves toward a predator, presumably to acquire information and then (hopefully) depart to inspect again another day.

Investigators have observed that guppies sometimes approach and inspect a predator in pairs. Suppose that it is not known whether these predator inspections are independent or whether the guppies are operating as a team. Denote the probability that an individual guppy will inspect a predator by p. Let event E_i be the event that guppy i will approach and inspect a predator. Then the probability of two guppies, i and j, approaching the predator by chance if they are acting *independently* is

$$P(E_i \cap E_j) = P(E_i)P(E_j) = p \cdot p = p^2$$

Based on our analysis, if the inspections are in fact independent, we would expect the proportion of times that two guppies happen to simultaneously inspect a predator to be equal to the square of the proportion of times that a single fish does so. For example, if the probability a single guppy inspects a predator is .3, we would expect the proportion of the time that two guppies would inspect a predator simultaneously to be $(.3)^2 = .09$. Based on observations of the inspection behavior of a large number of guppies, scientists have concluded that the inspection behavior of guppies does not appear to be independent.

The concept of independence extends to more than two events. Consider three events, E_1, E_2, and E_3. Then independence means not only that

$$P(E_1 | E_2) = P(E_1)$$
$$P(E_3 | E_2) = P(E_3)$$

and so on but also that

$$P(E_1 | E_2 \textit{ and } E_3) = P(E_1)$$
$$P(E_1 \textit{ and } E_3 | E_2) = P(E_1 \textit{ and } E_3)$$

and so on. There is also a multiplication rule for more than two independent events.

The independence of more than two events is an important concept in studying complex systems with many components. If these components are critical to the operation of a machine, an examination of the probability of the machine's failure is undertaken by analyzing the failure probabilities of the components.

Multiplication Rule for *k* Independent Events

Events $E_1, E_2, \ldots, E_k$ are **independent** if knowledge that some number of the events have occurred does not change the probabilities that any particular one or more of the other events has occurred.
Independence implies that

$$P(E_1 \cap E_2 \cap \cdots \cap E_k) = P(E_1)P(E_2)\cdots P(E_k)$$

Thus when events are independent, the probability that all occur together is the product of the individual probabilities. Furthermore, this relationship remains valid if one or more E_i is replaced by the event E_i^C.

In Example 6.19 we take a rather simplified view of a desktop computer to illustrate the use of the multiplication rule.

EXAMPLE 6.19 Computer Configurations

Suppose that a desktop computer system consists of a monitor, a mouse, a keyboard, the computer processor itself, and storage devices such as a disk drive. Most computer system problems due to manufacturing defects occur soon in the system's lifetime. Purchasers of new computer systems are advised to turn their computers on as soon as they are purchased and then to let them run for a few hours to see if any problems crop up.

Let

E_1 = event that a newly purchased monitor is not defective
E_2 = event that a newly purchased mouse is not defective
E_3 = event that a newly purchased disk drive is not defective
E_4 = event that a newly purchased computer processor is not defective

Suppose the four events are independent, with

$$P(E_1) = P(E_2) = .98 \qquad P(E_3) = .95 \qquad P(E_4) = .99$$

The probability that all these components are not defective and that the system will operate properly is then

$$\begin{aligned} P(E_1 \cap E_2 \cap E_3 \cap E_4) &= P(E_1)P(E_2)P(E_3)P(E_4) \\ &= (.98)(.98)(.94)(.99) \\ &= .89 \end{aligned}$$

We interpret this probability as follows: In the long run, 89% of such systems will run properly when tested shortly after purchase. (In reality, the reliability of these components is much higher than the numbers used in this example!) The probability that all components except the monitor will run properly is

$$\begin{aligned} P(E_1^C \cap E_2 \cap E_3 \cap E_4) &= P(E_1^C)P(E_2)P(E_3)P(E_4) \\ &= (1 - P(E_1))P(E_2)P(E_3)P(E_4) \\ &= (.02)(.98)(.94)(.99) \\ &= .018 \end{aligned}$$

Sampling With and Without Replacement

One area of statistics where the rules of probability are important is sampling. As we saw in Chapter 2, a well-designed sampling plan allows investigators to make inferences about a population based on information from a sample. Sampling methods can be classified into two categories: *sampling with replacement* and *sampling without replacement.* Most inferential methods presented in an introductory statistics course are based on the assumption of sampling *with* replacement, but when sampling from real populations, we almost always sample *without* replacement. This seemingly contradictory practice can be a source of confusion. Fortunately, in many circumstances, the distinction between sampling with and without replacement is unimportant for *practical* purposes.

DEFINITION

Sampling is **with replacement** if, once selected, an individual or object is put back into the population before the next selection. Sampling is **without replacement** if, once selected, an individual or object is not returned to the population prior to subsequent selections.

EXAMPLE 6.20 Selecting Cards

Consider the process of selecting three cards from a standard deck. This selection can be made in two ways. One method is to deal three cards off the top of the deck. This method would constitute sampling without replacement. A second method, rarely seen in real games, is to select a card at random, note which card is observed, replace it in the deck, and shuffle before selecting the next card. This method is sampling with replacement. From the standpoint of probability, these procedures are analyzed differently. To see this, consider these events:

H_1 = event that the first card is a heart
H_2 = event that the second card is a heart
H_3 = event that the third card is a heart

For sampling with replacement, the probability of H_3 is .25, regardless of whether either H_1 or H_2 occurs, because replacing selected cards gives the same deck for the third selection as for the first two selections. Whether either of the first two cards is a heart has no bearing on the third card selected, so the three events, H_1, H_2, and H_3, are independent.

When sampling is without replacement, the chance of getting a heart on the third draw does depend on the results of the first two draws. If both H_1 and H_2 occur, only 11 of the 50 remaining cards are hearts. Because any one of these 50 has the same chance of being selected, the probability of H_3 in this case is

$$P(H_3 | H_1 \text{ and } H_2) = \frac{11}{50} = .22$$

Alternatively, if neither of the first 2 cards is a heart, then all 13 hearts remain in the deck for the third draw, so

$$P(H_3 | \text{ not } H_1 \text{ and not } H_2) = \frac{13}{50} = .26$$

Information about the occurrence of H_1 and H_2 affects the chance that H_3 has occurred; for sampling without replacement, the events are not independent.

In opinion polls and other types of surveys, sampling is virtually always done without replacement. For this method of sampling, the results of successive selections are not independent of one another. However, Example 6.21 suggests that, *under certain circumstances*, the fact that selections in sampling without replacement are not independent is not a cause for concern.

EXAMPLE 6.21 Independence and Sampling Without Replacement

A lot of 10,000 computer chips used in graphing calculators consists of 2500 manufactured by one firm and 7500 manufactured by a second firm, all mixed together. Three of the chips will be selected at random without replacement. Let

E_1 = event that first chip selected was manufactured by Firm 1
E_2 = event that second chip selected was manufactured by Firm 1
E_3 = event that third chip selected was manufactured by Firm 1

Following the reasoning we used in Example 6.20, we get

$$P(E_3 | E_1 \text{ and } E_2) = \frac{2498}{9998} = .24985$$

$$P(E_3 | \text{not } E_1 \text{ and not } E_2) = \frac{2500}{9998} = .25005$$

Although these two probabilities differ slightly, when rounded to three decimal places they are both .250. We conclude that the occurrence or nonoccurrence of E_1 or E_2 has virtually no effect on the chance that E_3 will occur. *For practical purposes*, the three events can be considered independent.

The essential difference between the situations of Example 6.20 and Example 6.21 is the size of the sample relative to the size of the population. In Example 6.20 a relatively large proportion of the population was sampled (3 out of 52), whereas in Example 6.21 the proportion of the population sampled was quite small (only 3 out of 10,000).

Usually the sample size is small compared to the size of the population. The theory of sampling with replacement required for many inferential methods can coexist with the practice of sampling without replacement because of the following principle:

If a random sample of size *n* is taken from a population of size *N*, the theoretical probabilities of successive selections calculated on the basis of sampling with replacement and on the basis of sampling without replacement differ by insignificant amounts when *n* is small compared to *N*. In practice, independence can be assumed for the purpose of calculating probabilities as long as *n* is not larger than 5% of *N*.

This principle justifies the assumption of independence in many statistical problems. The phrase *assumption of independence* does not signify that the investigators are in some sense fooling themselves; they are recognizing that, for all practical purposes, the results will not differ from the "right" answers.

In some sampling situations, the sample size might be a significant fraction of the population. For example, a school newspaper editor might easily sample more than

5% of the student body. In that instance, the editors would be wise to consult a statistician before proceeding. Does this mean that an investigator should not sample more than 5% of a population? Certainly not! Except for the time and resources used in sampling a population, it is almost always the case that a larger sample results in better inferences about the population. The only disadvantage of sampling more than 5% of the population is that the analysis of the resulting data is slightly more complicated.

EXERCISES 6.43 - 6.58

6.43 Many fire stations handle emergency calls for medical assistance as well as calls requesting firefighting equipment. A particular station says that the probability that an incoming call is for medical assistance is .85. This can be expressed as *P*(*call is for medical assistance*) = .85.

a. Give a relative frequency interpretation of the given probability.

b. What is the probability that a call is not for medical assistance?

c. Assuming that successive calls are independent of one another, calculate the probability that two successive calls will both be for medical assistance.

d. Still assuming independence, calculate the probability that for two successive calls, the first is for medical assistance and the second is not for medical assistance.

e. Still assuming independence, calculate the probability that exactly one of the next two calls will be for medical assistance. (Hint: There are two different possibilities. The one call for medical assistance might be the first call, or it might be the second call.)

f. Do you think that it is reasonable to assume that the requests made in successive calls are independent? Explain.

6.44 The paper "Predictors of Complementary Therapy Use Among Asthma Patients: Results of a Primary Care Survey" (*Health and Social Care in the Community* [2008]: 155–164) included the accompanying table. The table summarizes the responses given by 1077 asthma patients to two questions:

Question 1: Do conventional asthma medications usually help your asthma symptoms?

Question 2: Do you use complementary therapies (such as herbs, acupuncture, aroma therapy) in the treatment of your asthma?

	Doesn't Use Complementary Therapies	Does Use Complementary Therapies
Conventional Medications Usually Help	816	131
Conventional Medications Usually Do Not Help	103	27

Consider a chance experiment that consists of randomly selecting one of the 1077 survey participants.

a. Construct a joint probability table (similar to the one in Example 6.16) by dividing the count in each cell of the table by the sample size $n = 1077$.

b. The joint probability in the upper left cell of the table from Part (a) is $\frac{816}{1077} = .758$. This represents the probability of conventional medications usually help *and* does not use complementary therapies. Interpret the other three probabilities in the joint probability table of Part (a).

c. Are the events

CH = event that the selected participant reports that conventional medications usually help

and

CT = event that the selected participant reports using complementary therapies

independent events?

Use a probability argument to justify your choice.

6.45 The report "TV Drama/Comedy Viewers and Health Information" (www.cdc.gov/Healthmarketing) describes the results of a large survey involving approximately 3500 people that was conducted for the Center for Disease Control. The sample was selected in a way that the Center for Disease Control believed would result in a sample that was representative of adult Americans. One question on the survey asked respondents if they had learned something new about a health issue or disease from a TV show in the previous 6 months. Data from the survey was used to estimate the following probabilities, where

L = event that a randomly selected adult American reports learning something new about a health issue or disease from a TV show in the previous 6 months

and

F = event that a randomly selected adult American is female

$P(L) = .58 \qquad P(L \cap F) = .31$

Assume that $P(F) = .5$. Are the events L and F independent events? Use probabilities to justify your answer.

6.46 The article "SUVs Score Low in New Federal Rollover Ratings" (*San Luis Obispo Tribune*, January 6, 2001) gave information on death rates for various kinds of accidents by vehicle type for accidents reported to the police. Suppose that we randomly select an accident reported to the police and consider the following events: R = event that the selected accident is a single-vehicle rollover, F = event that the selected accident is a frontal collision, and D = event that the selected accident results in a death. Information in the article indicates that the following probability estimates are reasonable: $P(R) = .06$, $P(F) = .60$, $P(R|D) = .30$, $P(F|D) = .54$.

a. Interpret the value of $P(R|D)$.
b. Interpret the value of $P(F|D)$.
c. Are the events R and D independent? Justify your answer.
d. Is $P(F \cap D) = P(F)P(D)$? Explain why or why not.
e. Is $F = R^C$? Explain how you can tell.

6.47 A Gallup survey of 2002 adults found that 46% of women and 37% of men experience pain daily (*San Luis Obispo Tribune*, April 6, 2000). Suppose that this information is representative of adult Americans. If an adult American is selected at random, are the events *selected adult is male* and *selected adult experiences pain daily* independent or dependent? Explain.

6.48 In a small city, approximately 15% of those eligible are called for jury duty in any one calendar year. People are selected for jury duty at random from those eligible, and the same individual cannot be called more than once in the same year. What is the probability that a particular eligible person in this city is selected in each of the next 2 years? In each of the next 3 years?

6.49 Jeanie is a bit forgetful, and if she doesn't make a "to do" list, the probability that she forgets something she is supposed to do is .1. Tomorrow she intends to run three errands, and she fails to write them on her list.

a. What is the probability that Jeanie forgets all three errands? What assumptions did you make to calculate this probability?
b. What is the probability that Jeanie remembers at least one of the three errands?
c. What is the probability that Jeanie remembers the first errand but not the second or third?

6.50 ✦ Approximately 30% of the calls to an airline reservation phone line result in a reservation being made.

a. Suppose that an operator handles 10 calls. What is the probability that none of the 10 calls result in a reservation?
b. What assumption did you make to calculate the probability in Part (a)?
c. What is the probability that at least one call results in a reservation being made?

6.51 Consider a system consisting of four components, as pictured in the following diagram:

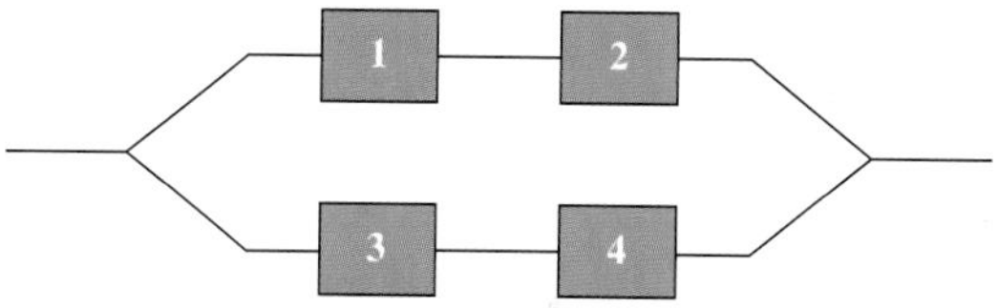

Components 1 and 2 form a series subsystem, as do Components 3 and 4. The two subsystems are connected in parallel. Suppose that $P(1 \text{ works}) = .9$, $P(2 \text{ works}) = .9$, $P(3 \text{ works}) = .9$, and $P(4 \text{ works}) = .9$ and that the four components work independently of one another.

a. The 1–2 subsystem works only if both components work. What is the probability of this happening?
b. What is the probability that the 1–2 subsystem doesn't work? that the 3–4 subsystem doesn't work?
c. The system won't work if the 1–2 subsystem doesn't work and if the 3–4 subsystem also doesn't work. What is the probability that the system won't work? that it will work?
d. How would the probability of the system working change if a 5–6 subsystem were added in parallel with the other two subsystems?
e. How would the probability that the system works change if there were three components in series in each of the two subsystems?

6.52 Information from a poll of registered voters in Cedar Rapids, Iowa, to assess voter support for a new school tax was the basis for the following statements (*Cedar Rapids Gazette*, August 28, 1999):

> The poll showed 51% of the respondents in the Cedar Rapids school district are in favor of the tax. The approval rating rises to 56% for those with children in public schools. It falls to 45% for those with no children in public schools. The older the respondent, the less favorable the view of the proposed tax: 36% of those over age 56 said they would vote for the tax compared with 72% of 18- to 25-year-olds.

Suppose that a registered voter from Cedar Rapids is selected at random, and define the following events: F = event that the selected individual favors the school tax, C = event that the selected individual has children in the public schools, O = event that the selected individual is over 56 years old, and Y = event that the selected individual is 18–25 years old.

a. Use the given information to estimate the values of the following probabilities:
   i. $P(F)$
   ii. $P(F|C)$
   iii. $P(F|C^C)$
   iv. $P(F|O)$
   v. $P(F|Y)$
b. Are F and C independent? Justify your answer.
c. Are F and O independent? Justify your answer.

6.53 The following case study was reported in the article "Parking Tickets and Missing Women," which appeared in an early edition of the book *Statistics: A Guide to the Unknown*. In a Swedish trial on a charge of overtime parking, a police officer testified that he had noted the position of the two air valves on the tires of a parked car: To the closest hour, one was at the one o'clock position and the other was at the six o'clock position. After the allowable time for parking in that zone had passed, the policeman returned, noted that the valves were in the same position, and ticketed the car. The owner of the car claimed that he had left the parking place in time and had returned later. The valves just happened by chance to be in the same positions. An "expert" witness computed the probability of this occurring as (1/12)(1/12) = 1/144.

a. What reasoning did the expert use to arrive at the probability of 1/144?

b. Can you spot the error in the reasoning that leads to the stated probability of 1/144? What effect does this error have on the probability of occurrence? Do you think that 1/144 is larger or smaller than the correct probability of occurrence?

6.54 Three friends (A, B, and C) will participate in a round-robin tournament in which each one plays both of the others. Suppose that P(A beats B) = .7, P(A beats C) = .8, P(B beats C) = .6, and that the outcomes of the three matches are independent of one another.

a. What is the probability that A wins both her matches and that B beats C?
b. What is the probability that A wins both her matches?
c. What is the probability that A loses both her matches?
d. What is the probability that each person wins one match? (Hint: There are two different ways for this to happen.)

6.55 A shipment of 5000 printed circuit boards contains 40 that are defective. Two boards will be chosen at random, without replacement. Consider the two events E_1 = event that the first board selected is defective and E_2 = event that the second board selected is defective.

a. Are E_1 and E_2 dependent events? Explain in words.

b. Let *not* E_1 be the event that the first board selected is not defective (the event E_1^C). What is $P(not\ E_1)$?

c. How do the two probabilities $P(E_2|E_1)$ and $P(E_2|not\ E_1)$ compare?

d. Based on your answer to Part (c), would it be reasonable to view E_1 and E_2 as approximately independent?

6.56 A store sells two different brands of dishwasher soap, and each brand comes in three different sizes: small (S), medium (M), and large (L). The proportions of the two brands and of the three sizes purchased are displayed as marginal totals in the following table.

		Size S	Size M	Size L	
Brand	B_1				.40
Brand	B_2				.60
		.30	.50	.20	

Suppose that any event involving brand is independent of any event involving size. What is the probability of the event that a randomly selected purchaser buys the small size of Brand B_1 (the event $B_1 \cap S$)? What are the probabilities of the other brand–size combinations?

6.57 The National Public Radio show *Car Talk* has a feature called "The Puzzler." Listeners are asked to send in answers to some puzzling questions—usually about cars but sometimes about probability (which, of course, must account for the incredible popularity of the program!). Suppose that for a car question, 800 answers are submitted, of which 50 are correct.

a. Suppose that the hosts randomly select two answers from those submitted *with replacement*. Calculate the probability that both selected answers are correct. (For purposes of this problem, keep at least five digits to the right of the decimal.)

b. Suppose now that the hosts select the answers at random but *without replacement*. Use conditional probability to evaluate the probability that both answers selected are correct. How does this probability compare to the one computed in Part (a)?

6.58 Refer to Exercise 6.57. Suppose now that for a probability question, 100 answers are submitted, of which 50 are correct. Calculate the probabilities in Parts (a) and (b) of Exercise 6.57 for the probability question.

6.6 Some General Probability Rules

In previous sections, we saw how the probability of $P(E \cup F)$ could be easily computed when E and F are disjoint (mutually exclusive) and how $P(E \cap F)$ could be computed when E and F are independent. In this section, we develop more general rules: an addition rule that can be used even when events are not disjoint and a multiplication rule that can be used even when events are not independent.

General Addition Rule

The computation of $P(E \cup F)$ when the two events are not disjoint is a bit more complicated than in the case of disjoint events. Consider Figure 6.9, in which E and F overlap. The area of the colored region $(E \cup F)$ is not the sum of the area of E and the area of F, because when the two individual areas are added, the area of the intersection $(E \cap F)$ is counted twice. Similarly, $P(E) + P(F)$ includes $P(E \cap F)$ twice, so this intersection probability must then be subtracted from the sum to obtain $P(E \cup F)$. This reasoning leads to the general addition rule.

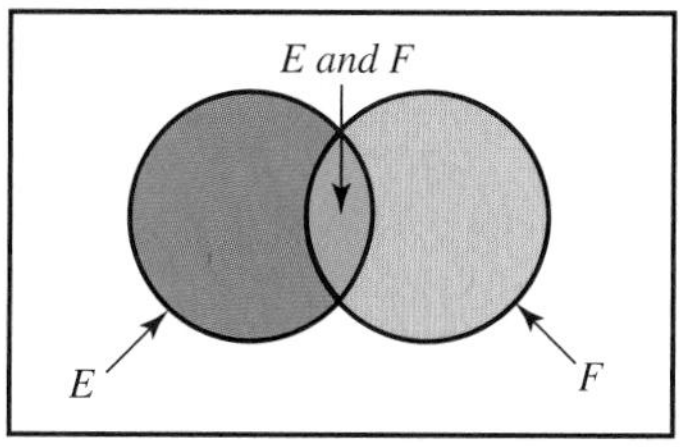

FIGURE 6.9
The colored region is $P(E \cup F)$, and $P(E \cup F) \neq P(E) + P(F)$.

General Addition Rule for Two Events

For any two events E and F,

$$P(E \cup F) = P(E) + P(F) - P(E \cap F)$$

When E and F are disjoint, the general addition rule simplifies to the previous rule for disjoint events. This is because when E and F are disjoint, $E \cap F$ contains no outcomes and $P(E \cap F) = 0$. The general addition rule can be used to determine any one of the four probabilities $P(E)$, $P(F)$, $P(E \cap F)$, or $P(E \cup F)$ provided that the other three probabilities are known.

EXAMPLE 6.22 Cable Services

Suppose that 60% of all customers of a large cable company subscribe to Internet service, 40% subscribe to phone service, and 25% have both types of services. If a customer is selected at random, what is the probability that he or she has at least one of these two types of service? Let

E = event that a selected customer has Internet service
F = event that a selected customer has phone service

AP* EXAM TIP

When solving problems using the general addition rule, it is helpful to write out the rule and then substitute in the values that are given in the context of the problem.

The given information implies that

$$P(E) = .60 \quad P(F) = .40 \quad P(E \cap F) = .25$$

from which we obtain

$$\begin{aligned} &P(\text{customer has at least one of the two types of services}) \\ &= P(E \cup F) \\ &= P(E) + P(F) - P(E \cap F) \\ &= .60 + .40 - .25 \\ &= .75 \end{aligned}$$

The event that the customer has neither type of service is $(E \cup F)^C$, so

$$P(\text{customer has neither type of service}) = 1 - P(E \cup F) = .25$$

Now let's determine the probability that the selected customer has exactly one type of service. Referring to the Venn diagram in Figure 6.10, we see that the event *at least one* can be thought of as consisting of two disjoint parts: *exactly one* and *both*. Thus

$$\begin{aligned} P(E \cup F) &= P(\text{at least one}) \\ &= P(\text{exactly one} \cup \text{both}) \\ &= P(\text{exactly one}) + P(\text{both}) \\ &= P(\text{exactly one}) + P(E \cap F) \end{aligned}$$

Then

$$\begin{aligned} P(\text{exactly one}) &= P(E \cup F) - P(E \cap F) \\ &= .75 - .25 \\ &= .50 \end{aligned}$$

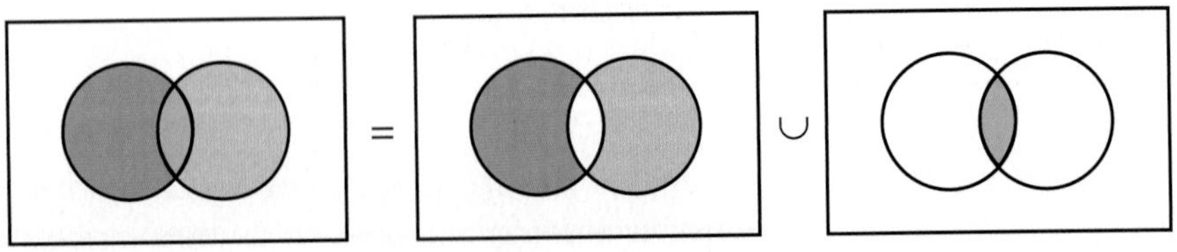

FIGURE 6.10
Representing $P(E \cup F)$ as the union of two disjoint events.

The general addition rule for more than two nondisjoint events is rather complicated. For example, in the case of three events,

$$\begin{aligned} P(E \cup F \cup G) = {} & P(E) + P(F) + P(G) - P(E \cap F) - P(E \cap G) \\ & - P(F \cap G) + P(E \cap F \cap G) \end{aligned}$$

A more advanced treatment of probability can be consulted for examples and extensions of these methods.

General Multiplication Rule

Recall the definition of conditional probability: When $P(F) > 0$,

$$P(E|F) = \frac{P(E \cap F)}{P(F)}$$

Up to this point, we have used this formula to compute conditional probabilities when $P(E \cap F)$ is known. Sometimes, however, conditional probabilities are known or can be estimated. When this is the case, they can be used to calculate the probability of the intersection of two events. Multiplying both sides of the conditional probability formula by $P(F)$ gives a useful expression for the probability that both events will occur.

General Multiplication Rule for Two Events

For any two events E and F,

$$P(E \cap F) = P(E|F)P(F)$$

EXAMPLE 6.23 Traffic School

Suppose that 20% of all teenage drivers in a certain county received a citation for a moving violation within the past year. Assume in addition that 80% of those receiving such a citation attended traffic school so that the citation would not appear on their permanent driving record. If a teenage driver from this county is randomly selected, what is the probability that he or she received a citation and attended traffic school?

Let's define two events E and F as follows:

E = selected driver attended traffic school
F = selected driver received such a citation

The question posed can then be answered by calculating $P(E \cap F)$. The percentages given in the problem imply that $P(F) = .20$ and $P(E|F) = .80$. Notice the difference between $P(E)$, which is the proportion in the entire population who attended traffic school (not given), and $P(E|F)$ which is the proportion of those receiving a citation that attended traffic school. Using the multiplication rule, we calculate

$$\begin{aligned} P(E \textit{ and } F) &= P(E|F)P(F) \\ &= (.80)(.20) \\ &= .16 \end{aligned}$$

Thus 16% of all teenage drivers in this county received a citation *and* attended traffic school.

EXAMPLE 6.24 DVD Player Warranties

The following table gives information on DVD players sold by a certain electronics store:

	Percentage of Customers Purchasing	Of Those Who Purchase, Percentage Who Purchase Extended Warranty
Brand 1	70	20
Brand 2	30	40

A purchaser is randomly selected from among all those who bought a DVD player from the store. What is the probability that the selected customer purchased a Brand 1 model and an extended warranty?

To answer this question, we first define the following events:

B_1 = event that Brand 1 is purchased
B_2 = event that Brand 2 is purchased
E = event that an extended warranty is purchased

The tabulated information implies that

$$P(\text{Brand 1 purchased}) = P(B_1) = .70$$
$$P(\text{extended warranty} \mid \text{Brand 1 purchased}) = P(E \mid B_1) = .20$$

Notice that the 20% is identified with a *conditional* probability; *among purchasers of Brand 1*, this is the percentage opting for an extended warranty. Substituting these numbers into the general multiplication rule yields

$$\begin{aligned} P(B_1 \text{ and } E) &= P(E \mid B_1)P(B_1) \\ &= (.20)(.70) \\ &= .14 \end{aligned}$$

The tree diagram of Figure 6.11 gives a nice visual display of how the general multiplication rule is used here. The two first-generation branches are labeled with events B_1 and B_2 along with their probabilities. Two second-generation branches extend from each first-generation branch; these correspond to the two events E and *not* E. The *conditional* probabilities $P(E \mid B_1)$, $P(\text{not } E \mid B_1)$, $P(E \mid B_2)$, and $P(\text{not } E \mid B_2)$, appear on these branches. Application of the multiplication rule then consists of multiplying probabilities across the branches of the tree diagram. For example,

$$\begin{aligned} P(\text{Brand 2 and warranty purchased}) &= P(B_2 \text{ and } E) \\ &= P(B_2 \cap E) \\ &= P(E \mid B_2)P(B_2) \\ &= (.4)(.3) \\ &= .12 \end{aligned}$$

and this probability is displayed to the right of the E branch that comes from the B_2 branch.

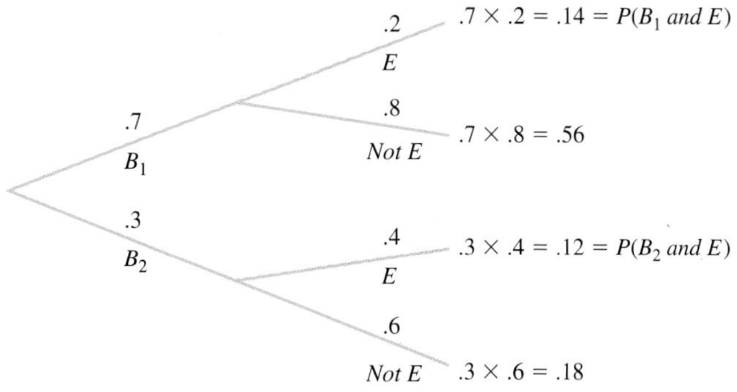

FIGURE 6.11
A tree diagram for the probability calculations of Example 6.24.

We can now easily calculate $P(E)$, the probability that an extended warranty is purchased. The event E can occur in two different ways: Buy Brand 1 *and* warranty, or buy Brand 2 *and* warranty. Symbolically, these events are $B_1 \cap E$ and $B_2 \cap E$. Furthermore, if each customer purchased a single DVD player, he or she could not have simultaneously purchased both Brand 1 and Brand 2, so the two events $B_1 \cap E$ and $B_2 \cap E$ are disjoint.

Thus

$$\begin{aligned} P(E) &= P(B_1 \cap E) + P(B_2 \cap E) \\ &= P(E|B_1)P(B_1) + P(E|B_2)P(B_2) \\ &= (.2)(.7) + (.4)(.3) \\ &= .14 + .12 \\ &= .26 \end{aligned}$$

This probability is the sum of two of the probabilities shown on the right-hand side of the tree diagram. Thus 26% of all DVD player purchasers selected an extended warranty.

The general multiplication rule can be extended to give an expression for the probability that several events occur together. In the case of three events E, F, and G, we have

$$P(E \cap F \cap G) = P(E|F \cap G)P(F|G)P(G)$$

When the events are all independent, $P(E|F \cap G) = P(E)$ and $P(F|G) = P(F)$ so the right-hand side of the equation for $P(E \cap F \cap G)$ is simply the product of the three unconditional probabilities.

EXAMPLE 6.25 Lost Luggage

Twenty percent of all passengers who fly from Los Angeles (LA) to New York (NY) do so on Airline G. This airline misplaces luggage for 10% of its passengers, and 90% of this lost luggage is subsequently recovered. If a passenger who has flown from LA to NY is randomly selected, what is the probability that the selected individual flew on Airline G (event G), had luggage misplaced (event F), and subsequently recovered the misplaced luggage (event E)? The given information implies that

$$P(G) = .20 \quad P(F|G) = .10 \quad P(E|F \cap G) = .90$$

Then

$$P(E \cap F \cap G) = P(E|F \cap G)P(F|G)P(G) = (.90)(.10)(.20) = .018$$

That is, about 1.8% of passengers flying from LA to NY fly on Airline G, have their luggage misplaced, and subsequently recover the lost luggage.

Law of Total Probability

Let's reconsider the information on DVD player sales from Example 6.24. In this example, the following events were defined:

$$B_1 = \text{event that Brand 1 is purchased}$$
$$B_2 = \text{event that Brand 2 is purchased}$$
$$E = \text{event that an extended warranty is purchased}$$

Based on the information given in Example 6.24, the following probabilities are known:

$$P(B_1) = .7 \quad P(B_2) = .3 \quad P(E|B_1) = .2 \quad P(E|B_2) = .4$$

Notice that the conditional probabilities $P(E|B_1)$ and $P(E|B_2)$ are known but that the unconditional probability $P(E)$ is not known.

To find $P(E)$ we note that the event E can occur in two ways: (1) A customer purchases an extended warranty *and* buys Brand 1 $(E \cap B_1)$; or (2) a customer purchases an extended warranty *and* buys Brand 2 $(E \cap B_2)$. Because these are the only ways in which E can occur, we can write the event E as

$$E = (E \cap B_1) \cup (E \cap B_2)$$

Again, the two events $(E \cap B_1)$ and $(E \cap B_2)$ are disjoint (since B_1 and B_2 are disjoint), so using the addition rule for disjoint events gives

$$\begin{aligned} P(E) &= P((E \cap B_1) \cup (E \cap B_2)) \\ &= P(E \cap B_1) + P(E \cap B_2) \end{aligned}$$

Finally, using the general multiplication rule to evaluate $P(E \cap B_1)$ and $P(E \cap B_2)$ results in

$$\begin{aligned} P(E) &= P(E \cap B_1) + P(E \cap B_2) \\ &= P(E|B_1)P(B_1) + P(E|B_2)P(B_2) \end{aligned}$$

Substituting in the known probabilities gives

$$\begin{aligned} P(E) &= P(E|B_1)P(B_1) + P(E|B_2)P(B_2) \\ &= (.2)(.7) + (.4)(.3) \\ &= .26 \end{aligned}$$

We conclude that 26% of the DVD player customers purchased an extended warranty.

As we have just illustrated, when conditional probabilities are known, they can sometimes be used to compute unconditional probabilities. The **law of total probability** formalizes this use of conditional probabilities.

The Law of Total Probability

If B_1 and B_2 are disjoint events with $P(B_1) + P(B_2) = 1$, then for any event E

$$\begin{aligned} P(E) &= P(E \cap B_1) + P(E \cap B_2) \\ &= P(E|B_1)P(B_1) + P(E|B_2)P(B_2) \end{aligned}$$

More generally, if $B_1, B_2, \ldots, B_k$ are disjoint events with $P(B_1) + P(B_2) + \cdots + P(B_k) = 1$, then for any event E

$$\begin{aligned} P(E) &= P(E \cap B_1) + P(E \cap B_2) + \cdots + P(E \cap B_k) \\ &= P(E|B_1)P(B_1) + P(E|B_2)P(B_2) + \cdots + P(E|B_k)P(B_k) \end{aligned}$$

EXAMPLE 6.26 Which Way to Jump?

The paper "Action Bias among Elite Soccer Goalkeepers: The Case of Penalty Kicks" (*Journal of Economic Psychology* [2007]: 606–621) presents an interesting analysis of 286 penalty kicks in televised championship soccer games from around the world. In a penalty kick, the only players involved are the kicker and the goalkeeper from the opposing team. The kicker tries to kick a ball into the goal from a point located 11 meters away. The goalkeeper tries to block the ball from reaching the goal. For each penalty kick analyzed, the researchers recorded the direction that the goalkeeper moved (jumped to the left, stayed in the center, or jumped to the right) and whether or not the penalty kick was successfully blocked.

Consider the following events:

L = the event that the goalkeeper jumps to the left
C = the event that the goalkeeper stays in the center
R = the event that the goalkeeper jumps to the right
B = the event that the penalty kick is blocked

Based on their analysis of the penalty kicks, the authors of the paper gave the following probability estimates:

$$P(B|L) = .142 \qquad P(B|C) = .333 \qquad P(B|R) = .126$$
$$P(L) = .493 \qquad P(C) = .063 \qquad P(R) = .444$$

What proportion of penalty kicks were blocked? We can use the law of total probability to answer this question. Here, the three events L, C, and R play the role of B_1, B_2, and B_3 and B plays the role of E in the formula for the law of total probability.

Substituting into the formula, we get

$$\begin{aligned} P(B) &= P(B \cap L) + P(B \cap C) + P(B \cap R) \\ &= P(B|L)P(L) + P(B|C)P(C) + P(B|R)P(R) \\ &= (.142)(.493) + (.333)(.063) + (.126)(.444) \\ &= .070 + .021 + .056 \\ &= .147 \end{aligned}$$

This means that only 14.7% of penalty kicks were successfully blocked. Two other interesting findings of this study were

1. The direction that the goalkeeper moves appears to be independent of whether the kicker kicked the ball to the left, center, or right of the goal. This was attributed to the fact that goalkeepers have to choose their action before they can clearly observe the direction of the kick.

2. Based on the three conditional probabilities—$P(B|L) = .142$, $P(B|C) = .333$, and $P(B|R) = .126$—the optimal strategy for a goalkeeper appears to be to stay in the center of the goal. However, staying in the center was only chosen 6.3% of the time—much less often that jumping left or right. The authors believe that this is because a goalkeeper does not feel as bad about not successfully blocking a kick if some action (jumping left or right) is taken compared to if no action (staying in the center) is taken. This is the "action bias" referred to in the title of the paper.

Bayes' Rule

We conclude our discussion of probability rules by considering a formula discovered by the Reverend Thomas Bayes (1702–1761), an English Presbyterian minister. He discovered what is now known as Bayes' rule (or Bayes' theorem). Bayes' rule is a solution to what Bayes called the converse problem. To see what he meant by this, we return to the field of medical diagnosis.

EXAMPLE 6.27 Lyme Disease

Lyme disease is the leading tick-borne disease in the United States and Europe. Diagnosis of the disease is difficult and is aided by a test that detects particular antibodies in the blood. The article "Laboratory Considerations in the Diagnosis and Management of Lyme Borreliosis" (*American Journal of Clinical Pathology* [1993]: 168–174) used the following notation:

$+$	represents a positive result on the blood test
$-$	represents a negative result on the blood test
L	represents the event that the patient actually has Lyme disease
L^C	represents the event that the patient actually does not have Lyme disease

The following probabilities were reported in the article:

$P(L) = .00207$	The prevalence of Lyme disease in the population; .207% of the population actually has Lyme disease.
$P(L^C) = .99793$	99.793% of the population does not have Lyme disease.
$P(+\|L) = .937$	93.7% of those with Lyme disease test positive.
$P(-\|L) = .063$	6.3% of those with Lyme disease test negative.
$P(+\|L^C) = .03$	3% of those who do not have Lyme disease test positive.
$P(-\|L^C) = .97$	97% of those who do not have Lyme disease test negative.

Notice the form of the known conditional probabilities; for example, $P(+|L)$ is the probability of a positive test given that a person selected at random from the population actually has Lyme disease. Bayes' converse problem poses a question of a different form: Given that a person tests positive for the disease, what is the probability that he or she actually has Lyme disease? This converse problem is the one that is of primary interest in medical diagnosis problems.

Bayes reasoned as follows to obtain the answer to the converse problem of finding $P(L|+)$. We know from the definition of conditional probability that

$$P(L|+) = \frac{P(L \cap +)}{P(+)}$$

Because $P(L \cap +) = P(+ \cap L)$, we can use the general multiplication rule to get

$$P(L \cap +) = P(+ \cap L) = P(+ \mid L)P(L)$$

This helps, because both $P(+ \mid L)$ and $P(L)$are known. We now have

$$P(L \mid +) = \frac{P(+ \mid L)P(L)}{P(+)}$$

The denominator $P(+)$ can be evaluated using the law of total probability, because L and L^C are disjoint with $P(L) + P(L^C) = 1$. Applying the law of total probability to the denominator, we obtain

$$\begin{aligned} P(+) &= P(+ \cap L) + P(+ \cap L^C) \\ &= P(+ \mid L)P(L) + P(+ \mid L^C)P(L^C) \end{aligned}$$

We now have all we need to answer the converse problem:

$$\begin{aligned} P(L \mid +) &= \frac{P(+ \mid L)P(L)}{P(+ \mid L)P(L) + P(+ \mid L^C)P(L^C)} \\ &= \frac{(.937)(.00207)}{(.937)(.00207) + (.03)(.99793)} = \frac{.0019}{.0319} = .0596 \end{aligned}$$

The probability $P(L \mid +)$ is a conditional probability and can be interpreted as such. $P(L \mid +) = .0596$ means that, in the long run, only 5.96% of those who test positive actually have the disease. Note the difference between $P(L \mid +)$ and the previously reported conditional probability $P(+ \mid L) = .937$, which means that 93.7% of those with Lyme disease test positive.

AP* EXAM TIP

Although Bayes' Rule is not in the AP Statistics Course syllabus, solving "Bayes-like" problems (that is, complex conditional probability problems) *is* expected of AP Statistics students. You don't need to memorize the formula—Bayes-like problems can also be solved using tree diagrams or tables.

The accompanying box formalizes this reasoning in the statement of Bayes' rule.

Bayes' Rule

If B_1 and B_2 are disjoint events with $P(B_1) + P(B_2) = 1$, then for any event E

$$P(B_1 \mid E) = \frac{P(E \mid B_1)P(B_1)}{P(E \mid B_1)P(B_1) + P(E \mid B_2)P(B_2)}$$

More generally, if $B_1, B_2, \ldots, B_k$ are disjoint events with $P(B_1) + P(B_2) + \cdots + P(B_k) = 1$ then for any event E,

$$P(B_i \mid E) = \frac{P(E \mid B_i)P(B_i)}{P(E \mid B_1)P(B_1) + P(E \mid B_2)P(B_2) + \cdots + P(E \mid B_k)P(B_k)}$$

EXAMPLE 6.28 Internet Addiction

Internet addiction has been defined by researchers as a disorder characterized by excessive time and effort spent on the Internet, impaired judgment and decision-making ability, social withdrawal, and depression. The paper "The Association between Aggressive Behaviors and Internet Addiction and Online Activities in Adolescents" (*Journal of Adolescent Health* [2009]: 598–605) reported on a study of more than 9400 adolescents. Each participant in the study was assessed using the

Chen Internet Addiction Scale to determine if he or she suffered from Internet addiction. The following statements are based on the survey results:

1. 51.8% of the study participants were female and 48.2% were male.
2. 13.1% of the females suffered from Internet addiction.
3. 24.8% of the males suffered from Internet addiction.

Consider the chance experiment that consists of selecting a study participant at random. Let's define the following events:

F = the event that the selected participant is female
M = the event that the selected participant is male
I = the event that the selected participant suffers from Internet addiction

The three statements from the paper define the following probabilities:

$P(F) = .518 \qquad P(M) = .482$
$P(I|F) = .131 \qquad P(I|M) = .248$

Suppose that we want to know the proportion of those who suffer from Internet addiction who are female. This is equivalent to $P(F|I)$.

Notice that we know $P(I|F)$ but not $P(F|I)$. We can use Bayes' rule to evaluate $P(F|I)$ as follows (with F and M playing the role of B_1 and B_2 and I playing the role of E in the formula for Bayes' rule):

$$P(F|I) = \frac{P(I|F)P(F)}{P(I|F)P(F) + P(I|M)P(M)}$$

$$= \frac{(.131)(.518)}{(.131)(.518) + (.482)(.248)}$$

$$= \frac{.068}{.068 + .120}$$

$$= \frac{068}{.188}$$

$$= .362$$

This tells us that 36.2% of those who suffered from Internet addiction were female.

EXERCISES 6.59 - 6.77

6.59 ✦ A certain university has 10 vehicles available for use by faculty and staff. Six of these are vans and four are cars. On a particular day, only two requests for vehicles have been made. Suppose that the two vehicles to be assigned are chosen in a completely random fashion from among the 10.

a. Let E denote the event that the first vehicle assigned is a van. What is $P(E)$?

b. Let F denote the event that the second vehicle assigned is a van. What is $P(F|E)$?

c. Use the results of Parts (a) and (b) to calculate $P(E \text{ and } F)$ (Hint: Use the definition of $P(F|E)$.)

6.60 A construction firm bids on two different contracts. Let E_1 be the event that the bid on the first contract is successful, and define E_2 analogously for the second contract. Suppose that $P(E_1) = .4$ and $P(E_2) = .3$ and that E_1 and E_2 are independent events.

a. Calculate the probability that both bids are successful (the probability of the event E_1 *and* E_2).

b. Calculate the probability that neither bid is successful (the probability of the event (*not* E_1) *and* (*not* E_2)).

c. What is the probability that the firm is successful in at least one of the two bids?

6.61 There are two traffic lights on the route used by a certain individual to go from home to work. Let E denote the event that the individual must stop at the first light, and define the event F in a similar manner for the second light. Suppose that $P(E) = .4$, $P(F) = .3$, and $P(E \cap F) = .15$.

a. What is the probability that the individual must stop at at least one light; that is, what is the probability of the event $E \cup F$?

b. What is the probability that the individual needn't stop at either light?

c. What is the probability that the individual must stop at exactly one of the two lights?

d. What is the probability that the individual must stop just at the first light? (Hint: How is the probability of this event related to $P(E)$ and $P(E \cap F)$? A Venn diagram might help.)

6.62 Let F denote the event that a randomly selected registered voter in a certain city has signed a petition to recall the mayor. Also, let E denote the event that the randomly selected registered voter actually votes in the recall election. Describe the event $E \cap F$ in words. If $P(F) = .10$ and $P(E|F) = .80$, determine $P(E \cap F)$.

6.63 The accompanying probabilities are from the report "Estimated Probability of Competing in Athletics Beyond the High School Interscholastic Level" (www.ncaa.org). The probability that a randomly selected high school basketball player plays NCAA basketball as a freshman in college is .0303; the probability that someone who plays NCAA basketball as a freshman will be playing NCAA basketball in his senior year is .7776; and the probability that a college senior NCAA basketball player will play professionally after college is .0102. Suppose that a high school senior basketball player is chosen at random. Define the events F, S, and D as

F = the event that the player plays as a college freshman
S = the event that the player also plays as a senior
D = the event that the player plays professionally after college

a. Based on the information given, what are the values of $P(F)$, $P(S|F)$, and $P(D|S \cap F)$?

b. What is the probability that a senior high school basketball player plays college basketball as a freshman and as a senior and then plays professionally? (Hint: This is $P(F \cap S \cap D)$.)

6.64 A large cable company reports the following:

- 80% of its customers subscribe to cable TV service
- 42% of its customers subscribe to Internet service
- 32% of its customers subscribe to telephone service
- 25% of its customers subscribe to both cable TV and Internet service
- 21% of its customers subscribe to both cable TV and phone service
- 23% of its customers subscribe to both Internet and phone service
- 15% of its customers subscribe to all three services

Consider the chance experiment that consists of selecting one of the cable company customers at random. Find and interpret the following probabilities:

a. P(cable TV only)
b. P(Internet | cable TV)
c. P(exactly two services)
d. P(Internet and cable TV only)

6.65 Refer to the information given in Exercise 6.64 about customers of a large cable company.

a. Suppose two customers are to be selected at random. Would it be reasonable to consider the events C_1 = event that the first customer selected subscribes to cable TV and C_2 = the event that the second customer selected subscribes to cable TV as independent events? Explain.

b. With C_1 and C_2 as defined in Part (a), find $P(C_1 \cap C_2)$.

6.66 The authors of the paper "Do Physicians Know when Their Diagnoses Are Correct?" (*Journal of General Internal Medicine* [2005]: 334–339) presented detailed case studies to medical students and to faculty at medical schools. Each participant was asked to provide a diagnosis in the case and also to indicate whether his or her confidence in the correctness of the diagnosis was high or low. Define the events C, I, and H as follows:

C = event that diagnosis is correct
I = event that diagnosis is incorrect
H = event that confidence in the correctness of the diagnosis is high

a. Data appearing in the paper were used to estimate the following probabilities for medical students:

$P(C) = .261$ $P(I) = .739$
$P(H|C) = .375$ $P(H|I) = .073$

Use Bayes' rule to compute the probability of a correct diagnosis given that the student's confidence level in the correctness of the diagnosis is high.

b. Data from the paper were also used to estimate the following probabilities for medical school faculty:

$P(C) = .495$ $P(I) = .505$
$P(H|C) = .537$ $P(H|I) = .252$

Compute $P(C|H)$ for medical school faculty. How does the value of this probability compare to the value of $P(C|H)$ for students computed in Part (a)?

6.67 The following statement is from a letter to the editor that appeared in *USA Today* (September 3, 2008):

> Among Notre Dame's current undergraduates, our ethnic minority students (21%) and international students (3%) alone equal the percentage of students who are children of alumni (24%). Add the 43% of our students who receive need-based financial aid (one way to define working-class kids), and more than 60% of our student body is composed of minorities and students from less affluent families.

Do you think that the statement that more than 60% of the student body is composed of minorities and students from less affluent families could be correct? Explain.

6.68 A study of how people are using online services for medical consulting is described in the paper "Internet Based Consultation to Transfer Knowledge for Patients Requiring Specialized Care" (*British Medical Journal* [2003]: 696–699). Patients using a particular online site could request any combination of three services: specialist opinion, assessment of imaging studies (such as X-ray and MRI), and assessment of pathology results. The accompanying table shows the combinations of services that were requested by 79 patients in their online consultations.

Combination of Services Provided	Number of Patients
Specialist opinion only	37
Assessment of pathology results only	1
Specialist opinion and assessment of pathology results only	11
Specialist opinion and assessment of imaging studies only	14
Specialist opinion, assessment of imaging studies, and assessment of pathology results	16

For a randomly selected patient from this study, define the events O, I, and A as follows:

O = event that the online consultation involves a specialist opinion
I = event that the online consultation involves the assessment of imaging studies
A = event that the online consultation involves the assessment of pathology results

Use the given information to find the following probabilities:

a. $P(O)$
b. $P(not A)$
c. $P(O \cap I)$
d. $P(I|O)$
e. $P(O|I)$

6.69 The report "Twitter in Higher Education: Usage Habits and Trends of Today's College Faculty" (*Magna Publications*, September 2009) describes results of a survey of nearly 2000 college faculty. The report indicates the following:

- 30.7% reported that they use Twitter and 69.3% said that they did not use Twitter.
- Of those who use Twitter, 39.9% said they sometimes use Twitter to communicate with students.
- Of those who use Twitter, 27.5% said that they sometimes use Twitter as a learning tool in the classroom.

Consider the chance experiment that selects one of the study participants at random and define the following events:

T = event that selected faculty member uses Twitter
C = event that selected faculty member sometimes uses Twitter to communicate with students
L = event that selected faculty member sometimes uses Twitter as a learning tool in the classroom

a. Use the given information to determine the following probabilities:
i. $P(T)$
ii. $P(T^C)$
iii. $P(C|T)$
iv. $P(L|T)$
v. $P(C \cap T)$

b. Interpret each of the probabilities computed in Part (a).

c. What proportion of the faculty surveyed sometimes use Twitter to communicate with students? [Hint: Use the law of total probability to find $P(C)$.]

d. What proportion of faculty surveyed sometimes use Twitter as a learning tool in the classroom?

6.70 The accompanying table summarizes data from a medical expenditures survey carried out by the National Center for Health Statistics ("Assessing the Effects of Race and Ethnicity on Use of Complementary and Alternative Therapies in the USA," *Ethnicity and Health* [2005]: 19–32).

Use of Alternative Therapies by Education

Education Level	Percent Using Alternative Therapies
High school or less	4.3%
College—1 to 4 years	8.2%
College—5 years or more	11.0%

These percentages were based on data from 7320 people whose education level was high school or less, 4793 people with 1 to 4 years of college, and 1095 people with 5 or more years of college.

a. Use the information given to determine the *number* of respondents falling into each of the six cells of the table below.

	Uses Alternative Therapies	Does Not Use Alternative Therapies	Total
HS/less			**7,320**
College: 1–4 yrs			**4,793**
College: ≥5 yrs			**1,095**

b. Construct a table of joint relative frequencies by dividing the count in each of the six table cells by the total sample size, $n = 13{,}208$.

c. The authors of the study indicated that the sample was selected in a way that makes it reasonable to regard the joint relative frequencies in the table from Part (b) as representative of the adult population in the United States. Use the information in that table to estimate the following probabilities for adults in the United States.

i. The probability that a randomly selected individual has 5 or more years of college.

ii. The probability that a randomly selected individual uses alternative therapies.

iii. The probability that a randomly selected individual uses alternative therapies given that he or she has 5 or more years of college.

iv. The probability that a randomly selected individual uses alternative therapies given that he or she has an education level of high school or less.

v. The probability that a randomly selected individual who uses alternative therapies has an education level of high school or less.

vi. The probability that a randomly selected individual with some college uses alternative therapies.

d. Are the events H = event that a randomly selected individual has an education level of high school or less and A = event that a randomly selected individual uses alternative therapies independent events? Explain.

6.71 Suppose that we define the following events: C = event that a randomly selected driver is observed to be using a cell phone, A = event that a randomly selected driver is observed driving a passenger automobile, V = event that a randomly selected driver is observed driving a van or SUV, and T = event that a randomly selected driver is observed driving a pickup truck. Based on the article "Three Percent of Drivers on Hand-Held Cell Phones at Any Given Time" (*San Luis Obispo Tribune*, July 24, 2001), the following probability estimates are reasonable: $P(C) = .03$, $P(C|A) = .026$, $P(C|V) = .048$, and $P(C|T) = .019$. Explain why $P(C)$ is not just the average of the three given conditional probabilities.

6.72 The article "Checks Halt over 200,000 Gun Sales" (*San Luis Obispo Tribune*, June 5, 2000) reported that required background checks blocked 204,000 gun sales in 1999. The article also indicated that state and local police reject a higher percentage of would-be gun buyers than does the FBI, stating, "The FBI performed 4.5 million of the 8.6 million checks, compared with 4.1 million by state and local agencies. The rejection rate among state and local agencies was 3%, compared with 1.8% for the FBI."

a. Use the given information to estimate $P(F)$, $P(S)$, $P(R|F)$, and $P(R|S)$, where F = event that a randomly selected gun purchase background check is performed by the FBI, S = event that a randomly selected gun purchase background check is performed by a state or local agency, and R = event that a randomly selected gun purchase background check results in a blocked sale.

b. Use the probabilities from Part (a) to evaluate $P(S|R)$, and write a sentence interpreting this value in the context of this problem.

6.73 In an article that appears on the web site of the American Statistical Association (www.amstat.org), Carlton Gunn, a public defender in Seattle, Washington, wrote about how he uses statistics in his work as an attorney. He states:

> I personally have used statistics in trying to challenge the reliability of drug testing results. Suppose the chance of a mistake in the taking and processing of a urine sample for a drug test is just 1 in 100. And your client has a "dirty" (i.e., positive) test result. Only a 1 in 100 chance that it could be wrong? Not necessarily. If the vast majority of all tests given—say 99 in 100—are truly clean, then you get one false dirty and one true dirty in every 100 tests, so that half of the dirty tests are false.

Define the following events as TD = event that the test result is dirty, TC = event that the test result is clean, D = event that the person tested is actually dirty, and C = event that the person tested is actually clean.

a. Using the information in the quote, what are the values of
   i. $P(TD|D)$
   ii. $P(TD|C)$
   iii. $P(C)$
   iv. $P(D)$

b. Use the law of total probability to find $P(TD)$.

c. Use Bayes' rule to evaluate $P(C|TD)$. Is this value consistent with the argument given in the quote? Explain.

6.74 The article "Birth Beats Long Odds for Leap Year Mom, Baby" (*San Luis Obispo Tribune*, March 2, 1996) reported that a leap year baby (someone born on February 29) became a leap year mom when she gave birth to a baby on February 29, 1996. The article stated that a hospital spokesperson said that only about 1 in 2.1 million births is a leap year baby born to a leap year mom (a probability of approximately .00000047).

a. In computing the given probability, the hospital spokesperson used the fact that a leap day occurs only once in 1461 days. Write a few sentences explaining how the hospital spokesperson computed the stated probability.

b. To compute the stated probability, the hospital spokesperson had to assume that the birth was equally likely to occur on any of the 1461 days in a four-year period. Do you think that this is a reasonable assumption? Explain.

c. Based on your answer to Part (b), do you think that the probability given by the hospital spokesperson is too small, about right, or too large? Explain.

6.75 According to a study released by the federal Substance Abuse and Mental Health Services Administration (*Knight Ridder Tribune*, September 9, 1999), approximately 8% of all adult full-time workers are drug users and approximately 70% of adult drug users are employed full-time.

a. Is it possible for both of the reported percentages to be correct? Explain.

b. Define the events D and E as D = event that a randomly selected adult is a drug user and E = event that a randomly selected adult is employed full-time. What are the estimated values of $P(D|E)$ and $P(E|D)$?

c. Is it possible to determine $P(D)$, the probability that a randomly selected adult is a drug user, from the information given? If not, what additional information would be needed?

6.76 ✦ A friend who works in a big city owns two cars, one small and one large. Three-quarters of the time he drives the small car to work, and one-quarter of the time he takes the large car. If he takes the small car, he usually has little trouble parking and so is at work on time with probability .9. If he takes the large car, he is on time to work with probability .6. Given that he was at work on time on a particular morning, what is the probability that he drove the small car?

6.77 Only 0.1% of the individuals in a certain population have a particular disease (an incidence rate of .001). Of those who have the disease, 95% test positive when a certain diagnostic test is applied. Of those who do not have the disease, 90% test negative when the test is applied. Suppose that an individual from this population is randomly selected and given the test.

a. Construct a tree diagram having two first-generation branches, for *has disease* and *doesn't have disease*, and two second-generation branches leading out from each of these, for *positive test* and *negative test*. Then enter appropriate probabilities on the four branches.

b. Use the general multiplication rule to calculate P(has disease *and* positive test).

c. Calculate P(positive test).

d. Calculate P(has disease | positive test). Does the result surprise you? Give an intuitive explanation for the size of this probability.

6.7 Estimating Probabilities Empirically Using Simulation

In the examples presented so far, reaching conclusions required knowledge of the probabilities of various outcomes. In some cases, this is reasonable, and we know the true long-run proportion of the time that each outcome will occur. In other situations, these probabilities are not known and must be determined. Sometimes probabilities can be determined analytically, by using mathematical rules and probability properties, including the basic ones introduced in this chapter. When an analytical approach is impossible, impractical, or just beyond the limited probability tools of the introductory course, we can *estimate* probabilities empirically through observation or by simulation.

Estimating Probabilities Empirically

It is fairly common practice to use observed long-run proportions to estimate probabilities. The process of estimating probabilities is simple:

1. Observe a very large number of chance outcomes under controlled circumstances.
2. Estimate the probability of an event to be the observed proportion of occurrence by appealing to the interpretation of probability as a long-run relative frequency and to the law of large numbers.

This process is illustrated in Examples 6.29 and 6.30.

EXAMPLE 6.29 Fair Hiring Practices

The Biology Department at a university plans to recruit a new faculty member and intends to advertise for someone with a Ph.D. in biology and at least 10 years of college-level teaching experience. A member of the department expresses the belief that the experience requirement will exclude many potential applicants and will exclude far more female applicants than male applicants. The Biology Department would like to determine the probability that an applicant with a Ph.D. in biology would be eliminated from consideration because of the experience requirement.

A similar university just completed a search in which there was no requirement for prior teaching experience, but the information about prior teaching experience was recorded. The 410 applications yielded the following data:

	Number of Applicants		
	Less Than 10 Years of Experience	10 Years of Experience or More	Total
Male	178	112	**290**
Female	99	21	**120**
Total	**277**	**133**	**410**

Let's assume that the populations of applicants for the two positions can be regarded as the same. We can use the available information to approximate the probability that an applicant will fall into each of the four gender–experience combinations.

The estimated probabilities (obtained by dividing the number of applicants for each gender–experience combination by 410) are given in Table 6.1. From Table 6.1, the estimate of P(candidate excluded because of the experience requirement) = .4341 + .2415 = .6756.

TABLE 6.1 Estimated Probabilities for Example 6.29

	Less Than 10 Years of Experience	10 Years of Experience or More
Male	.4341	.2732
Female	.2415	.0512

We can also assess the impact of the experience requirement separately for male and for female applicants. From the given information, the proportion of male applicants who have less than 10 years of experience is 178/290 = .6138, whereas the corresponding proportion for females is 99/120 = .8250. Therefore, approximately 61% of the male applicants would be eliminated by the experience requirement, and about 83% of the female applicants would be eliminated.

These subgroup proportions—.6138 for males and .8250 for females—are examples of *conditional probabilities*, which show how the original probability changes in light of new information. In this example, the probability that a potential candidate has less than 10 years of experience is .6756, but this probability changes to .8250 if we know that a candidate is female. These probabilities can be expressed as

$$P(\text{less than 10 years of experience}) = .6756 \quad \text{(an unconditional probability)}$$

and

$$P(\text{less than 10 years of experience} \mid \text{female}) = .8250 \quad \text{(a conditional probability)}$$

EXAMPLE 6.30 Who Has the Upper Hand?

Men and women frequently express intimacy through the simple act of holding hands. Some researchers have suggested that hand-holding is not only an expression of intimacy but also communicates status differences. For two people to hold hands, one must assume an overhand grip and one an underhand grip. Research in this area has shown that it is predominantly the male who assumes the overhand grip. In the view of some investigators, the overhand grip is seen to imply status or superiority. The authors of the paper "Men and Women Holding Hands: Whose Hand Is Uppermost?" (*Perceptual and Motor Skills* [1999]: 537–549) investigated an alternative explanation—perhaps the positioning of hands is a function of the heights of the individuals? Because men, on average, tend to be taller than women, maybe comfort, not status, dictates the positioning. Investigators at two separate universities observed hand-holding male–female pairs and recorded the data in the table at the top of the next page.

Assuming that these hand-holding couples are representative of hand-holding couples in general, we can use the available information to estimate various probabilities. For example, if a hand-holding couple is selected at random, then

$$\text{estimate of } P(\text{man's hand uppermost}) = \frac{3170}{3920} = 0.809$$

Number of Hand-Holding Couples

	Sex of Person with Uppermost Hand		
	Male	Female	Total
Man Taller	2149	299	**2448**
Equal Height	780	246	**1026**
Woman Taller	241	205	**446**
Total	**3170**	**750**	**3920**

For a randomly selected hand-holding couple, if the man is taller, then the probability that the male has the uppermost hand is

$$2149/2448 = 0.878.$$

On the other hand—so to speak—if the woman is taller, the probability that the female has the uppermost hand is

$$205/446 = 0.460.$$

Notice that these last two estimates are estimates of the conditional probabilities $P(\text{male uppermost} \mid \text{male taller})$ and $P(\text{female uppermost} \mid \text{female taller})$, respectively. Also, because $P(\text{male uppermost} \mid \text{male taller})$ is not equal to $P(\text{male uppermost})$, the events *male uppermost* and *male taller* are not independent events. But, even when the female is taller, the male is still more likely to have the upper hand!

Estimating Probabilities Using Simulation

Simulation provides a means of estimating probabilities when we are unable (or do not have the time or resources) to determine probabilities analytically and when it is impractical to estimate them empirically by observation. Simulation is a method that generates "observations" by performing a chance experiment that is as similar as possible in structure to the real situation of interest.

To illustrate the idea of simulation, consider the situation in which a professor wishes to estimate the probabilities of different possible scores on a 20-question true–false quiz when students are merely guessing at the answers. Because each question is a true–false question, a person who is guessing should be equally likely to answer correctly or incorrectly on any given question. Rather than asking a student to select true or false and then comparing the choice to the correct answer, an equivalent process would be to pick a ball at random from a box that contains half red balls and half blue balls, with a blue ball representing a correct answer. Making 20 selections from the box (with replacement) and then counting the number of correct choices (the number of times a blue ball is selected) is a physical substitute for an observation from a student who has guessed at the answers to 20 true–false questions. Any particular number of blue balls in 20 selections should have the same probability as the same number of correct responses to the quiz when a student is guessing.

For example, 20 selections of balls might yield the following results:

Selection	1	2	3	4	5	6	7	8	9	10
	R	R	B	R	B	B	R	R	R	B
Selection	**11**	**12**	**13**	**14**	**15**	**16**	**17**	**18**	**19**	**20**
	R	R	B	R	R	B	B	R	R	B

This would correspond to a quiz with eight correct responses, and it would provide us with one observation for estimating the probabilities of interest. This process could then be repeated a large number of times to generate additional observations. For example, we might find the following:

Repetition	Number of "Correct" Responses
1	8
2	11
3	10
4	12
⋮	⋮
1000	11

The 1000 simulated quiz scores could then be used to construct a table of estimated probabilities.

Taking this many balls out of a box and writing down the results would be cumbersome and tedious. The process can be simplified by using random digits to substitute for drawing balls from the box. For example, a single digit could be selected at random from the 10 digits 0, 1, 2, 3, 4, 5, 6, 7, 8, 9. When using random digits, each of the 10 possibilities is equally likely to occur, so we can use the even digits (including 0) to indicate a correct response and the odd digits to indicate an incorrect response. This would maintain the important property that a correct response and an incorrect response are equally likely, because correct and incorrect are each represented by 5 of the 10 digits.

To aid in carrying out such a simulation, tables of random digits (such as Appendix A Table 1) or computer-generated random digits can be used. The numbers in Appendix A Table 1 were generated using a computer's random number generator. You can think of the table as being produced by repeatedly drawing a chip from a box containing 10 chips numbered 0, 1, . . . , 9. After each selection, the result is recorded, the chip returned to the box, and the chips mixed. Thus, any of the digits is equally likely to occur on any of the selections.

To see how a table of random numbers can be used to carry out a simulation, let's reconsider the quiz example. We use a random digit to represent the guess on a single question, with an even digit representing a correct response. A series of 20 digits represents the answers to the 20 quiz questions. We pick an arbitrary starting point in Appendix A Table 1. Suppose that we start at row 10 and take the 20 digits in a row to represent one quiz. The first five "quizzes" and the corresponding number correct (number of even digits) are:

Quiz	Random Digits	Number Correct
1	9 4 6 0 6 9 7 8 8 2 5 2 9 6 0 1 4 6 0 5	**13**
2	6 6 9 5 7 4 4 6 3 2 0 6 0 8 9 1 3 6 1 8	**12**
3	0 7 1 7 7 7 2 9 7 8 7 5 8 8 6 9 8 4 1 0	**9**
4	6 1 3 0 9 7 3 3 6 6 0 4 1 8 3 2 6 7 6 8	**11**
5	2 2 3 6 2 1 3 0 2 2 6 6 9 7 0 2 1 2 5 8	**13**

This process would be repeated to generate a large number of observations, which would then be used to construct a table of estimated probabilities.

AP* EXAM TIP

Given today's technology, calculators and computers are used to carry out most simulations. However, in the non-real world of testing, random number tables are used so that student responses can be consistently evaluated. Make sure that you know how to use a random number table, as this skill may come in handy on the AP exam.

The method for generating observations must preserve the important characteristics of the actual process being considered if simulation is to be successful. For example, it would be easy to adapt the simulation procedure for the true–false quiz to one for a multiple-choice quiz. Suppose that each of the 20 questions on the quiz has five possible responses, only one of which is correct. For any particular question, we would expect a student to be able to guess the correct answer only one-fifth of the time in the long run. To simulate this situation, we could select at random from a box that contained four red balls and only one blue ball (or, more generally, four times as many red balls as blue balls). If we are using random digits for the simulation, we could use 0 and 1 to represent a correct response and 2, 3, . . . , 9 to represent an incorrect response.

Using Simulation to Approximate a Probability

1. Design a method that uses a random mechanism (such as a random number generator or table, the selection of a ball from a box, the toss of a coin, etc.) to represent an observation. Be sure that the important characteristics of the actual process are preserved.
2. Generate an observation using the method from Step 1, and determine whether the outcome of interest has occurred.
3. Repeat Step 2 a large number of times.
4. Calculate the estimated probability by dividing the number of observations for which the outcome of interest occurred by the total number of observations generated.

The simulation process is illustrated in Examples 6.31–6.33.

EXAMPLE 6.31 Building Permits

Many California cities limit the number of building permits that are issued each year. Because of limited water resources, one such city plans to issue permits for only 10 dwelling units in the upcoming year. The city will decide who is to receive permits by holding a lottery. Suppose that you are one of 39 individuals who apply for permits. Thirty of these individuals are requesting permits for a single-family home, eight are requesting permits for a duplex (which counts as two dwelling units), and one person is requesting a permit for a small apartment building with eight units (which counts as eight dwelling units). Each request will be entered into the lottery. Requests will be selected at random one at a time, and if there are enough permits remaining, the request will be granted. This process will continue until all 10 permits have been issued. If your request is for a single-family home, what are your chances of receiving a permit? Let's use simulation to estimate this probability. (It is not easy to determine analytically.)

To carry out the simulation, we can view the requests as being numbered from 1 to 39 as follows:

01–30	Requests for single-family homes
31–38	Requests for duplexes
39	Request for 8-unit apartment

For ease of discussion, let's assume that your request is number 01.

One method for simulating the permit lottery consists of these three steps:

1. Choose a random number between 01 and 39 to indicate which permit request is selected first, and grant this request.
2. Select another random number between 01 and 39 to indicate which permit request is considered next. Determine the number of dwelling units for the selected request. Grant the request only if there are enough permits remaining to satisfy the request.
3. Repeat Step 2 until permits for 10 dwelling units have been granted.

We used Minitab to generate random numbers between 01 and 39 to imitate the lottery drawing. (The random number table in Appendix A Table 1 could also be used by selecting two digits and ignoring 00 and any value over 39). For example, the first sequence generated by Minitab is

Random Number	Type of Request	Total Number of Units So Far
25	Single-family home	1
07	Single-family home	2
38	Duplex	4
31	Duplex	6
26	Single-family home	7
12	Single-family home	8
33	Duplex	10

We would stop at this point, because permits for 10 units would have been issued. In this simulated lottery, Request 01 was not selected, so you would not have received a permit.

The next simulated lottery (using Minitab to generate the selections) is as follows:

Ramdom Number	Type of Request	Total Number of Units So Far
38	Duplex	2
16	Single-family home	3
30	Single-family home	4
39	Apartment—not granted, since there are not 8 permits remaining	4
14	Single-family home	5
26	Single-family home	6
36	Duplex	8
13	Single-family home	9
15	Single-family home	10

Again, Request 01 was not selected, so you would not have received a permit in this simulated lottery.

Now that a strategy for simulating a lottery has been devised, the tedious part of the simulation begins. We would now have to simulate a large number of lottery drawings, determining for each whether Request 01 was granted. We simulated 500 such drawings and found that Request 01 was selected in 85 of the lotteries. This results in

$$\text{estimated probability of receiving a building permit} = \frac{85}{500} = .17$$

EXAMPLE 6.32 One-Boy Family Planning

Suppose that couples who wanted children were to continue having children until a boy is born. Assuming that each newborn child is equally likely to be a boy or a girl, would this behavior change the proportion of boys in the population? This question was posed in an article that appeared in *The American Statistician* ("What Some Puzzling Problems Teach About the Theory of Simulation and the Use of Resampling" [1994]: 290–293), and many people answered the question incorrectly. We will use simulation to estimate the long-run proportion of boys in the population if families were to continue to have children until they have a boy. This proportion is an estimate of the probability that a randomly selected child from this population is a boy. Note that every sibling group would have exactly one boy.

We use a single-digit random number to represent a child. The odd digits (1, 3, 5, 7, 9) represent a male birth, and the even digits represent a female birth. An observation is constructed by selecting a sequence of random digits. If the first random number obtained is odd (a boy), the observation is complete. If the first selected number is even (a girl), another digit is chosen. We continue in this way until an odd digit is obtained. For example, reading across row 15 of the random number table (Appendix A Table 1), the first 10 digits are

0 7 1 7 4 2 0 0 0 1

Using these numbers to simulate sibling groups, we get

Sibling group 1	0 7	girl, boy
Sibling group 2	1	boy
Sibling group 3	7	boy
Sibling group 4	4 2 0 0 0 1	girl, girl, girl, girl, girl, boy

Continuing along row 15 of the random number table,

Sibling group 5	3	boy
Sibling group 6	1	boy
Sibling group 7	2 0 4 7	girl, girl, girl, boy
Sibling group 8	8 4 1	girl, girl, boy

After simulating eight sibling groups, we have 8 boys among 19 children. The proportion of boys is 8/19, which is close to .5. Continuing the simulation to obtain a large number of observations suggests that the long-run proportion of boys in the population would still be .5, which is indeed the case.

EXAMPLE 6.33 ESP?

Can a close friend read your mind? Try the following chance experiment. Write the word *blue* on one piece of paper and the word *red* on another, and place the two slips of paper in a box. Select one slip of paper from the box, look at the word written on it, and then try to convey the word by sending a mental message to a friend who is seated in the same room. Ask your friend to select either red or blue, and record whether the response is correct. Repeat this 10 times and total the number of correct responses. How did your friend do? Is your friend receiving your mental messages or just guessing?

Let's investigate this issue by using simulation to get the approximate probabilities of the various possible numbers of correct responses for someone who is guessing. Someone who is guessing should have an equal chance of responding correctly or incorrectly. We can use a random digit to represent a response, with an even digit representing a correct response (C) and an odd digit representing an incorrect response (X). A sequence of 10 digits can be used to simulate performing the chance experiment one time.

For example, using the last 10 digits in row 25 of the random number table (Appendix A Table 1) gives

5	2	8	3	4	3	0	7	3	5
X	C	C	X	C	X	C	X	X	X

which is a simulated chance experiment resulting in four correct responses. We used Minitab to generate 150 sequences of 10 random digits and obtained the following results:

Sequence Number	Digits	Number Correct
1	3996285890	**5**
2	1690555784	**3**
3	9133190550	**2**
⋮	⋮	⋮
149	3083994450	**5**
150	9202078546	7

Table 6.2 summarizes the results of our simulation.

The estimated probabilities in Table 6.2 are based on the assumption that a correct and an incorrect response are equally likely (guessing). Evaluate your friend's performance in light of the information in Table 6.2. Is it likely that someone who is guessing would have been able to get as many correct as your friend did? Do you think your friend was receiving your mental messages? How are the estimated probabilities in Table 6.2 used to support your answer?

TABLE 6.2 Estimated Probabilities for Example 6.33

Number Correct	Number of Sequences	Estimated Probability
0	0	.0000
1	1	.0067
2	8	.0533
3	16	.1067
4	30	.2000
5	36	.2400
6	35	.2333
7	17	.1133
8	7	.0467
9	0	.0000
10	0	.0000
Total	**150**	**1.0000**

EXERCISES 6.78 - 6.86

6.78 The *Los Angeles Times* (June 14, 1995) reported that the U.S. Postal Service is getting speedier, with higher overnight on-time delivery rates than in the past. The Price Waterhouse accounting firm conducted an independent audit by seeding the mail with letters and recording on-time delivery rates for these letters. Suppose that the results were as follows (these numbers are fictitious but are compatible with summary values given in the article):

	Number of Letters Mailed	Number of Letters Arriving on Time
Los Angeles	500	425
New York	500	415
Washington, D.C.	500	405
Nationwide	6000	5220

Use the given information to estimate the following probabilities:

a. The probability of an on-time delivery in Los Angeles
b. The probability of late delivery in Washington, D.C.
c. The probability that two letters mailed in New York are both delivered on time
d. The probability of on-time delivery nationwide

6.79 Five hundred first-year students at a state university were classified according to both high school GPA and whether they were on academic probation at the end of their first semester. The data are

	High School GPA			
Probation	2.5 to <3.0	3.0 to <3.5	3.5 and Above	Total
Yes	50	55	30	**135**
No	45	135	185	**365**
Total	**95**	**190**	**215**	**500**

a. Construct a table of the estimated probabilities for each GPA–probation combination.
b. Use the table constructed in Part (a) to approximate the probability that a randomly selected first-year student at this university will be on academic probation at the end of the first semester.
c. What is the estimated probability that a randomly selected first-year student at this university had a high school GPA of 3.5 or above?
d. Are the two outcomes *selected student has a high school GPA of 3.5 or above* and *selected student is on academic probation at the end of the first semester* independent outcomes? How can you tell?
e. Estimate the proportion of first-year students with high school GPAs between 2.5 and 3.0 who are on academic probation at the end of the first semester.
f. Estimate the proportion of those first-year students with high school GPAs 3.5 and above who are on academic probation at the end of the first semester.

6.80 ✦ The table for Exercise 6.80 at the bottom of the page describes (approximately) the distribution of students by gender and college at a mid-sized public university in the West. If we were to randomly select one student from this university:

a. What is the probability that the selected student is a male?
b. What is the probability that the selected student is in the College of Agriculture?
c. What is the probability that the selected student is a male in the College of Agriculture?
d. What is the probability that the selected student is a male who is not from the College of Agriculture?

6.81 On April 1, 2000, the Bureau of the Census in the United States attempted to count every U.S. resident. Suppose that the counts in the table for Exercise 6.81 at the bottom of the page are obtained for four counties in one region.

a. If one person is selected at random from this region, what is the probability that the selected person is from Ventura County?
b. If one person is selected at random from Ventura County, what is the probability that the selected person is Hispanic?
c. If one Hispanic person is selected at random from this region, what is the probability that the selected individual is from Ventura County?
d. If one person is selected at random from this region, what is the probability that the selected person is an Asian from San Luis Obispo County?
e. If one person is selected at random from this region, what is the probability that the person is either Asian or from San Luis Obispo County?
f. If one person is selected at random from this region, what is the probability that the person is Asian or from San Luis Obispo County but not both?
g. If two people are selected at random from this region, what is the probability that both are Caucasians?
h. If two people are selected at random from this region, what is the probability that neither is Caucasian?
i. If two people are selected at random from this region, what is the probability that exactly one is a Caucasian?
j. If two people are selected at random from this region, what is the probability that both are residents of the same county?
k. If two people are selected at random from this region, what is the probability that both are from different racial/ethnic groups?

Table for Exercise 6.80

	College						
Gender	Education	Engineering	Liberal Arts	Science and Math	Agriculture	Business	Architecture
Male	200	3200	2500	1500	2100	1500	200
Female	300	800	1500	1500	900	1500	300

Table for Exercise 6.81

	Race/Ethnicity				
County	Caucasian	Hispanic	Black	Asian	American Indian
Monterey	163,000	139,000	24,000	39,000	4,000
San Luis Obispo	180,000	37,000	7,000	9,000	3,000
Santa Barbara	230,000	121,000	12,000	24,000	5,000
Ventura	430,000	231,000	18,000	50,000	7,000

6.82 A medical research team wishes to evaluate two different treatments for a disease. Subjects are selected two at a time, and then one of the pair is assigned to each of the two treatments. The treatments are applied, and each is either a success (S) or a failure (F). The researchers keep track of the total number of successes for each treatment. They plan to continue the chance experiment until the number of successes for one treatment exceeds the number of successes for the other treatment by 2. For example, they might observe the results in the table for Exercise 6.82 given below. The chance experiment would stop after the sixth pair, because Treatment 1 has 2 more successes than Treatment 2. The researchers would conclude that Treatment 1 is preferable to Treatment 2.

Suppose that Treatment 1 has a success rate of .7 (that is, *P*(success) = .7 for Treatment 1) and that Treatment 2 has a success rate of .4. Use simulation to estimate the probabilities in Parts (a) and (b). (Hint: Use a pair of random digits to simulate one pair of subjects. Let the first digit represent Treatment 1 and use 1–7 as an indication of a success and 8, 9, and 0 to indicate a failure. Let the second digit represent Treatment 2, with 1–4 representing a success. For example, if the two digits selected to represent a pair were 8 and 3, you would record failure for Treatment 1 and success for Treatment 2. Continue to select pairs, keeping track of the total number of successes for each treatment. Stop the trial as soon as the number of successes for one treatment exceeds that for the other by 2. This would complete one trial. Now repeat this whole process until you have results for at least 20 trials [more is better]. Finally, use the simulation results to estimate the desired probabilities.)

a. Estimate the probability that more than five pairs must be treated before a conclusion can be reached. (Hint: *P*(more than 5) = 1 − *P*(5 or fewer).)

b. Estimate the probability that the researchers will incorrectly conclude that Treatment 2 is the better treatment.

6.83 Many cities regulate the number of taxi licenses, and there is a great deal of competition for both new and existing licenses. Suppose that a city has decided to sell 10 new licenses for $25,000 each. A lottery will be held to determine who gets the licenses, and no one may request more than three licenses. Twenty individuals and taxi companies have entered the lottery. Six of the 20 entries are requests for 3 licenses, 9 are requests for 2 licenses, and the rest are requests for a single license. The city will select requests at random, filling as many of the requests as possible. For example, the city might fill requests for 2, 3, 1, and 3 licenses and then select a request for 3. Because there is only one license left, the last request selected would receive a license, but only one.

a. An individual has put in a request for a single license. Use simulation to approximate the probability that the request will be granted. Perform *at least* 20 simulated lotteries (more is better!).

b. Do you think that this is a fair way of distributing licenses? Can you propose an alternative procedure for distribution?

6.84 Four students must work together on a group project. They decide that each will take responsibility for a particular part of the project, as follows:

Person	Maria	Alex	Juan	Jacob
Task	Survey design	Data collection	Analysis	Report writing

Because of the way the tasks have been divided, one student must finish before the next student can begin work.

Table for Exercise 6.82

Pair	Treatment 1	Treatment 2	Total Number of Successes for Treatment 1	Total Number of Successes for Treatment 2
1	S	F	1	0
2	S	S	2	1
3	F	F	2	1
4	S	S	3	2
5	F	F	3	2
6	S	F	4	2

To ensure that the project is completed on time, a schedule is established, with a deadline for each team member. If any one of the team members is late, the timely completion of the project is jeopardized. Assume the following probabilities:

1. The probability that Maria completes her part on time is .8.
2. If Maria completes her part on time, the probability that Alex completes on time is .9, but if Maria is late, the probability that Alex completes on time is only .6.
3. If Alex completes his part on time, the probability that Juan completes on time is .8, but if Alex is late, the probability that Juan completes on time is only .5.
4. If Juan completes his part on time, the probability that Jacob completes on time is .9, but if Juan is late, the probability that Jacob completes on time is only .7.

Use simulation (with at least 20 trials) to estimate the probability that the project is completed on time. Think carefully about this one. For example, you might use a random digit to represent each part of the project (four in all). For the first digit (Maria's part), 1–8 could represent *on time* and 9 and 0 could represent *late*. Depending on what happened with Maria (late or on time), you would then look at the digit representing Alex's part. If Maria was on time, 1–9 would represent *on time* for Alex, but if Maria was late, only 1–6 would represent *on time*. The parts for Juan and Jacob could be handled similarly.

6.85 In Exercise 6.84, the probability that Maria completes her part on time was .8. Suppose that this probability is really only .6. Use simulation (with at least 20 trials) to estimate the probability that the project is completed on time.

6.86 Refer to Exercises 6.84 and 6.85. Suppose that the probabilities of timely completion are as in Exercise 6.84 for Maria, Alex, and Juan, but that Jacob has a probability of completing on time of .7 if Juan is on time and .5 if Juan is late.

a. Use simulation (with at least 20 trials) to estimate the probability that the project is completed on time.
b. Compare the probability from Part (a) to the one computed in Exercise 6.85. Which decrease in the probability of on-time completion (Maria's or Jacob's) made the bigger change in the probability that the project is completed on time?

ACTIVITY 6.1 Kisses

Background: The paper "What Is the Probability of a Kiss? (It's Not What You Think)" (*Journal of Statistics Education* (online) [2002]) posed the following question: What is the probability that a Hershey's Kiss will land on its base (as opposed to its side) if it is flipped onto a table? Unlike flipping a coin, there is no reason to believe that this probability would be .5.

Working as a class, develop a plan that would enable you to estimate this probability empirically.

Once you have an acceptable plan, carry it out and use the resulting data to produce an estimate of the desired probability. Do you think that a kiss is equally likely to land on its base or on its side? Explain.

ACTIVITY 6.2 A Crisis for European Sports Fans?

Background: The *New Scientist* (January 4, 2002) reported on a controversy surrounding the Euro coins that have been introduced as a common currency across Europe. Each country mints its own coins, but these coins are accepted in any of the countries that have adopted the Euro as their currency.

A group in Poland claims that the Belgium-minted Euro does not have an equal chance of landing heads or tails. This claim was based on 250 tosses of the Belgium-minted Euro, of which 140 (56%) came up heads. Should this be cause for alarm for European sports fans, who know that "important" decisions are made by the flip of a coin?

In this activity, we will investigate whether this should be cause for alarm by examining whether observing 140 heads out of 250 tosses is an unusual outcome if the coin is fair.

1. For this first step, you can either (a) flip a U.S. penny 250 times, keeping a tally of the number of heads and tails observed (this won't take as long as you think), or (b) simulate 250 coin tosses by using your calculator or a statistics software package to generate random numbers (if you choose this option, give a brief description of how you carried out the simulation).
2. For your sequence of 250 tosses, calculate the proportion of heads observed.
3. Form a data set that consists of the values for proportion of heads observed in 250 tosses of a fair coin for the entire class. Summarize this data set by constructing a graphical display.
4. Working with a partner, write a paragraph explaining why European sports fans should or should not be worried by the results of the Polish experiment. Your explanation should be based on the observed proportion of heads from the Polish experiment and the graphical display constructed in Step 3.

ACTIVITY 6.3 The "Hot Hand" in Basketball

Background: Consider a mediocre basketball player who has consistently made only 50% of his free throws over several seasons. If we were to examine his free throw record over the last 50 free throw attempts, is it likely that we would see a streak of 5 in a row where he is successful in making the free throw? In this activity, we will investigate this question. We will assume that the outcomes of successive free throw attempts are independent and that the probability that the player is successful on any particular attempt is .5.

1. Begin by simulating a sequence of 50 free throws for this player. Because this player has probability of success of .5 for each attempt and the attempts are independent, we can model a free throw by tossing a coin. Using heads to represent a successful free throw and tails to represent a missed free throw, simulate 50 free throws by tossing a coin 50 times, recording the outcome of each toss.
2. For your sequence of 50 tosses, identify the longest streak by looking for the longest string of heads in your sequence. Determine the length of this longest streak.
3. Combine your longest streak value with those from the rest of the class and construct a histogram or dotplot of these longest streak values.
4. Based on the graph from Step 3, does it appear likely that a player of this skill level would have a streak of 5 or more successes sometime during a sequence of 50 free throw attempts? Justify your answer based on the graph from Step 3.
5. Use the combined class data to estimate the probability that a player of this skill level has a streak of at least 5 somewhere in a sequence of 50 free throw attempts.
6. Using basic probability rules, we can calculate the probability that a player of this skill level is successful on the *next* 5 free throw attempts:

$$P(SSSSS) = \left(\frac{1}{2}\right)\left(\frac{1}{2}\right)\left(\frac{1}{2}\right)\left(\frac{1}{2}\right)\left(\frac{1}{2}\right) = \left(\frac{1}{2}\right)^5 = .031$$

   which is relatively small. At first this might seem inconsistent with your answer in Step 5, but the estimated probability from Step 5 and the computed probability of .031 are really considering different situations. Explain why it is plausible that both probabilities could be correct.
7. Do you think that the assumption that the outcomes of successive free throws are independent is reasonable? Explain. (This is a hotly debated topic among both sports fans and statisticians!)

Summary of Key Concepts and Formulas

TERM OR FORMULA	COMMENT
Chance experiment	Any experiment for which there is uncertainty concerning the resulting outcome.
Sample space	The collection of all possible outcomes from a chance experiment.
Event	Any collection of possible outcomes from a chance experiment.
Simple event	An event that consists of a single outcome.
Events	
1. *not A*, A^C	1. The event consisting of all outcomes not in A.
2. *A or B*, $A \cup B$	2. The event consisting of all outcomes in at least one of the two events.
3. *A and B*, $A \cap B$	3. The event consisting of outcomes common to both events.
Disjoint (mutually exclusive) events	Events that have no outcomes in common.
Fundamental properties of probability	Fundamental properties of probability 1. The probability of any event must be a number between 0 and 1. 2. If S is the sample space for a chance experiment, $P(S) = 1$ 3. If E and F are disjoint events, $P(E \cup F) = P(E) + P(F)$ 4. $P(E) + P(E^C) = 1$
$P(E) = \dfrac{\text{number of outcomes in } E}{N}$	$P(E)$ when the outcomes are *equally likely* and where N is the number of outcomes in the sample space.
$P(E \cup F) = P(E) + P(F)$ $P(E_1 \cup \cdots \cup E_k) = P(E_1) + \cdots + P(E_k)$	Addition rules when events are *disjoint.*
$P(E \mid F) = \dfrac{P(E \cap F)}{P(F)}$	The conditional probability of the event E given that the event F has occurred.
Independence of events E and F $P(E \mid F) = P(E)$	Events E and F are independent if the probability that E has occurred given F is the same as the probability that E will occur with no knowledge of F.
$P(E \cap F) = P(E)P(F)$ $P(E_1 \cap \cdots \cap E_k) = P(E_1)P(E_2)\cdots P(E_k)$	Multiplication rules for *independent* events.
$P(E \cup F) = P(E) + P(F) - P(E \cap F)$	The general addition rule for two events.
$P(E \cap F) = P(E \mid F)P(F)$	The general multiplication rule for two events.
$P(E) = P(E \mid B_1)P(B_1) + P(E \mid B_2)P(B_2) + \cdots + P(E \mid B_k)P(B_k)$	The law of total probability, where $B_1, B_2, \ldots, B_k$ are disjoint events with $P(B_1) + P(B_2) + \cdots + P(B_k) = 1$
$P(B_i \mid E) = \dfrac{P(E \mid B_i)P(B_i)}{P(E \mid B_1)P(B_1) + P(E \mid B_2)P(B_2) + \cdots + P(E \mid B_k)P(B_k)}$	Bayes' rule, where $B_1, B_2, \ldots, B_k$ are disjoint events with $P(B_1) + P(B_2) + \cdots + P(B_k) = 1$

Chapter Review Exercises 6.87 - 6.103

6.87 A company uses three different assembly lines—A_1, A_2, and A_3—to manufacture a particular component. Of those manufactured by A_1, 5% need rework to remedy a defect, whereas 8% of A_2's components and 10% of A_3's components need rework. Suppose that 50% of all components are produced by A_1, whereas 30% are produced by A_2 and 20% come from A_3.

a. Construct a tree diagram with first-generation branches corresponding to the three lines. Leading from each branch, draw one branch for rework (R) and another for no rework (N). Then enter appropriate probabilities on the branches.

b. What is the probability that a randomly selected component came from A_1 and needed rework?

c. What is the probability that a randomly selected component needed rework?

6.88 A certain company sends 40% of its overnight mail parcels by means of express mail service A_1. Of these parcels, 2% arrive after the guaranteed delivery time (use L to denote the event *late delivery*). If a record of an overnight mailing is randomly selected from the company's files, what is the probability that the parcel went by means of A_1 and was late?

6.89 Online chat rooms allow people from all over the world to exchange opinions on various topics of interest. A side effect of such conversations is "flaming," which is negative criticism of others' contributions to the conversation. The paper "Criticism on the Internet: An Analysis of Participant Reactions" (*Communication Research Reports* [1998]:180–187) investigated the effect that personal criticism has on an individual. Data from a survey of 193 chat room users from this study are reproduced here:

	Have Been Personally Criticized	Have Not Been Personally Criticized	Total
Have Criticized Others	19	8	**27**
Have Not Criticized Others	23	143	**166**
Total	**42**	**151**	**193**

Assume that this data is representative of the larger group of all chat room users and that the frequencies in the table are indicative of the long-run behavior of chat room users. Suppose that a chat room user is selected at random, and define events

C = event that the selected individual has criticized others

O = event that the selected individual has been personally criticized by others

Find and interpret each of the following probabilities:

a. $P(C)$

b. $P(O)$

c. $P(C \cap O)$

d. $P(C|O)$

e. $P(O|C)$

6.90 The Associated Press (*San Luis Obispo Telegram-Tribune*, August 23, 1995) reported on the results of mass screening of schoolchildren for tuberculosis (TB). For Santa Clara County, California, the proportion of all tested kindergartners who were found to have TB was .0006. The corresponding proportion for recent immigrants (thought to be a high-risk group) was .0075. Suppose that a Santa Clara County kindergartner is selected at random. Are the events *selected student is a recent immigrant* and *selected student has TB* independent or dependent events? Justify your answer using the given information.

6.91 The Australian newspaper *The Mercury* (May 30, 1995) reported that, based on a survey of 600 reformed and current smokers, 11.3% of those who had attempted to quit smoking in the previous 2 years had used a nicotine aid (such as a nicotine patch). It also reported that 62% of those who quit smoking without a nicotine aid began smoking again within 2 weeks and 60% of those who used a nicotine aid began smoking again within 2 weeks. If a smoker who is trying to quit smoking is selected at random, are the events *selected smoker who is trying to quit uses a nicotine aid* and *selected smoker who has attempted to quit begins smoking again within 2 weeks* independent or dependent events? Justify your answer using the given information.

6.92 Consider the following information about travelers on vacation: 40% check work e-mail, 30% use a cell phone to stay connected to work, 25% bring a laptop with them on vacation, 23% both check work e-mail and use a cell phone to stay connected, and 51% neither check work e-mail nor use a cell phone to stay connected nor bring a laptop. In addition 88% of those who bring a laptop also check work e-mail and 70% of those who use a cell phone to stay connected also bring a laptop. With E = event that a traveler on vacation checks work e-mail, C = event that a traveler on vacation uses a cell phone to stay connected, and L = event that a traveler on vacation brought a laptop, use the given information to determine the following probabilities. A Venn diagram may help.

a. $P(E)$
b. $P(C)$
c. $P(L)$
d. $P(E \text{ and } C)$
e. $P(E^C \text{ and } C^C \text{ and } L^C)$
f. $P(E \text{ and } C \text{ or } L)$
g. $P(E|L)$
h. $P(L|C)$
i. $P(E \text{ and } C \text{ and } L)$
j. $P(E \text{ and } L)$
k. $P(C \text{ and } L)$
l. $P(C|E \text{ and } L)$

6.93 Return to Exercise 6.88, and suppose that 50% of the overnight parcels are sent by means of express mail service A_2 and the remaining 10% are sent by means of A_3. Of those sent by means of A_2, only 1% arrived late, whereas 5% of the parcels handled by A_3 arrived late.

a. What is the probability that a randomly selected parcel arrived late? (Hint: A tree diagram should help.)

b. Suppose that the selected record shows that the parcel arrived late, but the name of the service does not appear on the record. What is the probability that the parcel was handled by A_1? That is, what is the probability of A_1 given L, denoted $P(A_1|L)$? What is $P(A_2|L)$? $P(A_3|L)$?

6.94 Two individuals, A and B, are finalists for a chess championship. They will play a sequence of games, each of which can result in a win for A, a win for B, or a draw. Suppose that the outcomes of successive games are independent, with $P(\text{A wins game}) = .3$, $P(\text{B wins game}) = .2$, and $P(\text{draw}) = .5$. Each time a player wins a game, he earns 1 point and his opponent earns no points. The first player to win 5 points wins the championship. For the sake of simplicity, assume that the championship will end in a draw if both players obtain 5 points at the same time.

a. What is the probability that A wins the championship in just five games?
b. What is the probability that it takes just five games to obtain a champion?
c. If a draw earns a half-point for each player, describe how you would perform a simulation to estimate P(A wins the championship).
d. If neither player earns any points from a draw, would the simulation in Part (c) take longer to perform? Explain your reasoning.

6.95 A single-elimination tournament with four players is to be held. In Game 1, the players seeded (rated) first and fourth play. In Game 2, the players seeded second and third play. In Game 3, the winners of Games 1 and 2 play, with the winner of Game 3 declared the tournament winner. Suppose that the following probabilities are given:

$P(\text{seed 1 defeats seed 4}) = .8$
$P(\text{seed 1 defeats seed 2}) = .6$
$P(\text{seed 1 defeats seed 3}) = .7$
$P(\text{seed 2 defeats seed 3}) = .6$
$P(\text{seed 2 defeats seed 4}) = .7$
$P(\text{seed 3 defeats seed 4}) = .6$

a. Describe how you would use a selection of random digits to simulate Game 1 of this tournament.
b. Describe how you would use a selection of random digits to simulate Game 2 of this tournament.
c. How would you use a selection of random digits to simulate Game 3 in the tournament? (This will depend on the outcomes of Games 1 and 2.)
d. Simulate one complete tournament, giving an explanation for each step in the process.
e. Simulate 10 tournaments, and use the resulting information to estimate the probability that the first seed wins the tournament.
f. Ask four classmates for their simulation results. Along with your own results, this should give you information on 50 simulated tournaments. Use this information to estimate the probability that the first seed wins the tournament.
g. Why do the estimated probabilities from Parts (e) and (f) differ? Which do you think is a better estimate of the true probability? Explain.

6.96 In a school machine shop, 60% of all machine breakdowns occur on lathes and 15% occur on drill presses. Let E denote the event that the next machine breakdown is on a lathe, and let F denote the event that a drill press is the next machine to break down. With $P(E) = .60$ and $P(F) = .15$, calculate:

a. $P(E^C)$
b. $P(E \cup F)$
c. $P(E^C \cap F^C)$

6.97 There are five faculty members in a certain academic department. These individuals have 3, 6, 7, 10, and 14 years of teaching experience. Two of these individuals are randomly selected to serve on a personnel review committee. What is the probability that the chosen representatives have a total of at least 15 years of teaching experience? (Hint: Consider all possible committees.)

6.98 The general addition rule for three events states that

$$P(A \text{ or } B \text{ or } C) = P(A) + P(B) + P(C) - P(A \text{ and } B) - P(A \text{ and } C) - P(B \text{ and } C) + P(A \text{ and } B \text{ and } C)$$

A new magazine publishes columns entitled "Art" (A), "Books" (B), and "Cinema" (C). Suppose that 14% of all subscribers read A, 23% read B, 37% read C, 8% read A and B, 9% read A and C, 13% read B and C, and 5% read all three columns. What is the probability that a randomly selected subscriber reads at least one of these three columns?

6.99 A theater complex is currently showing four R-rated movies, three PG-13 movies, two PG movies, and one G movie. The following table gives the number of people at the first showing of each movie on a certain Saturday:

Theater	Rating	Number of Viewers
1	R	600
2	PG-13	420
3	PG-13	323
4	R	196
5	G	254
6	PG	179
7	PG-13	114
8	R	205
9	R	139
10	PG	87

Suppose that a single one of these viewers is randomly selected.

a. What is the probability that the selected individual saw a PG movie?
b. What is the probability that the selected individual saw a PG or a PG-13 movie?
c. What is the probability that the selected individual did not see an R movie?

6.100 Refer to Exercise 6.99, and suppose that two viewers are randomly selected (without replacement). Let R_1 and R_2 denote the events that the first and second individuals, respectively, watched an R-rated movie. Are R_1 and R_2 independent events? Explain. From a practical point of view, can these events be regarded as independent? Explain.

6.101 Suppose that a box contains 25 light bulbs, of which 20 are good and the other 5 are defective. Consider randomly selecting three bulbs without replacement. Let E denote the event that the first bulb selected is good, F be the event that the second bulb is good, and G represent the event that the third bulb selected is good.

a. What is $P(E)$?
b. What is $P(F|E)$?
c. What is $P(G|E \cap F)$?
d. What is the probability that all three selected bulbs are good?

6.102 Return to Exercise 6.101, and suppose that 4 bulbs are randomly selected from the 25, what is the probability that all 4 are good? What is the probability that at least 1 selected bulb is bad?

6.103 A transmitter is sending a message using a binary code, namely, a sequence of 0's and 1's. Each transmitted bit (0 or 1) must pass through three relays to reach the receiver. At each relay, the probability is .20 that the bit sent on is different from the bit received (a reversal). Assume that the relays operate independently of one another:

transmitter → relay 1 → relay 2 → relay 3 → receiver

a. If a 1 is sent from the transmitter, what is the probability that a 1 is sent on by all three relays?
b. If a 1 is sent from the transmitter, what is the probability that a 1 is received by the receiver? (Hint: The eight experimental outcomes can be displayed on a tree diagram with three generations of branches, one generation for each relay.)

Graphing Calculator Explorations

EXPLORATION 6.1 Probabilities as Long-Run Relative Frequencies

Your calculator is a very effective tool for simulating chance experiments. Recall that the long-run behavior of a chance event is stable, with the relative frequency of occurrence approaching a number that is by definition the probability of the event. We will use a calculator to simulate flipping a coin; that is, the calculator will produce behavior that mimics the behavior of a coin flip. Graphing Calculator Exploration 2.2 illustrated the process of generating a random number between 0 and 1 using a sequence of keystrokes defined as *rand.* We will use this process now to flip some virtual coins. Define the probability of success, S, for the event of interest to be equal to p.

One characteristic of the *rand* process is that for any number, p, the probability of generating a number between 0 and p is equal to p. Using this fact we can perform the chance experiment as follows: Generate a uniform random number between 0 and 1 using your *rand* keystroke sequence. If the number generated is less than or equal to p, count that as a "success." If the number generated is greater than p, count that as a "failure." For a fair coin, p is equal to .5, and therefore any number generated by *rand* that is less than or equal to .5 will count as a success. The following table shows the beginning of such a simulation:

Toss	*rand*	S/F	Cumulative Successes	Cumulative Relative Frequency of Successes
1	.9351587791	F	0	0/1 = .0000
2	.1080114624	S	1	1/2 = .5000
3	.0062633066	S	2	2/3 = .6667
4	.5489861799	F	2	2/4 = .5000
5	.8555803143	F	2	2/5 = .4000

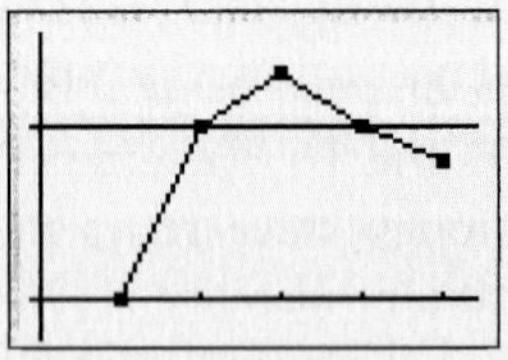
FIGURE 6.12

To see how the cumulative relative frequency of success behaves, plot toss number on the horizontal axis and cumulative relative frequency of success on the vertical axis of a scatterplot. A plot from the table above is shown in Figure 6.12.

To be more convinced that the relative frequency settles down and gets close to the true probability of success, we would need to simulate a very large number of tosses. This is a relatively slow process if you are flipping coins by hand, but fast on a calculator. Your calculator can perform this experiment many times and store the results, using some of its list commands. These commands will, of course, be different from calculator to calculator but the logic will be very similar. You will need to look up the correct syntax for the list commands in your calculator manual. (You may wish to refer to Graphing Calculator Exploration 3.1.) Here is a typical sequence of instructions to perform this simulation:

Step	Generic Keystrokes	Description
1	Sequence(x, x, 1, 100) → List1	Generate a sequence of numbers from 1 to 100, and store this sequence in List1.
2	Sequence(*rand*, x, 1, 100) → List 2	Create a sequence of random numbers and store them in List2.
3	Int(p − List2) +1 → List 3	Convert the random numbers from List2 into 0's and 1's in List3.
4	CumSum(List3) → List 4	Store the cumulative frequency from List3 to List4.
5	List4/List1 → List 5	Convert the cumulative frequency to a relative frequency "so far" and store in List5.

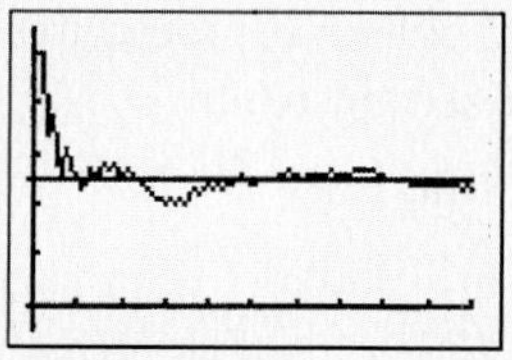

FIGURE 6.13
Continuation of the simulation.

Now make a scatterplot using the numbers in List1 and the cumulative relative frequencies in List5. Figure 6.13 shows you what a typical screen might look like after performing the procedure. We used a $p = .5$ for our coin so we added the horizontal line corresponding to *cumulative relative frequency* = .5 for reference.

EXPLORATION 6.2 Simulating Events That Are Independent

As noted earlier your calculator has a sequence of keystrokes that we have collectively referred to as "*rand*." The numbers generated by *rand* can be used to construct simulations that involve independent events.

The *rand* function automatically generates "independent" random numbers. This means that, for example, the probability of *rand* returning a number between .5 and 1.0 is unaffected by the value of the previously returned random number. The practical effect of this is that pressing the *rand* button repeatedly generates a sequence of independently generated numbers. Technically, this isn't quite true. Your calculator actually generates what are known as pseudo-random numbers. The algorithm that generates the numbers is really generating a sequence of numbers that are *for our practical simulation purposes* "random." Let's see how we can use this capability in a simulation. We will consider a simplified version of an important problem from meteorology: In a world where a photon of light may be absorbed or deflected in its path, how far will it travel in its original direction? Safety when driving in fog depends on enough light from our headlights reaching an oncoming car for that driver to be aware of our presence.

For purposes of our simulation we will assume that (1) an absorbed photon of light is no longer visible, (2) a photon once deflected does *not* return to its original path, and (3) there are constant probabilities of deflection and absorption. Furthermore the probability of the fate of the photon one second from now is independent of its status now. It is this real-life independence that requires us to generate "independent" random numbers to faithfully mirror the situation being modeled by our simulation.

Our model of a photon's travel will be a point traveling from left to right in the grid below, starting at square one. (*Note*: The probabilities we will use are for illustrative purposes and do not represent real probabilities in actual fog.)

1	2	3	4	5	6	7	8	9	10

At each position, the photon has three possible fates:

1. From square x it will go on to square $x + 1$ with probability .90.
2. From square x it will be absorbed with probability 0.05.
3. From square x it may be deflected "up" or "down," each with probability .025.

We arbitrarily define square 10 to be the position at which we would like an oncoming driver to be aware of our presence. We wish to find the probability a photon will get all the way to square 10. To estimate this probability via simulation, we need to link the probabilities of the fates listed above with random numbers generated by *rand*.

Photon Fate	Probability	*rand* Interval
Continue on path	.9	$0 \leq \text{rand} < .9$
Be absorbed	.05	$.9 \leq \text{rand} < .95$
Be deflected	.05	$.95 \leq \text{rand} < .1.0$

Here are two rows of five random numbers generated by our *rand* procedure. A trial proceeds by reading across the first row, then across the second row.

.812788	.710859	.704518	.146311	.956130
.050035	.126108	.330590	.390195	.114339

In this trial, the photon of light would go straight for 4 intervals and then—according to the interpretation of the random number .956130—be deflected. Here is a second trial:

.576809	.715678	.404556	.635070	.811570
.062257	.490527	.285129	.758026	.231308

In this second trial, the simulated photon makes it all the way to the oncoming car; all the random numbers are less than .90.

Forty trials were carried out with the following results, where Success is defined as a photon making it to square 10 and Failure is defined as being absorbed or deflected en route.

FSSFFFSFFFSSSFFFFSSSFFFFSFFSFFFSFFFFSSFF

Based on these 40 simulated trials, we estimate the probability of a photon arriving uninterrupted at square 10 to be approximately 14/40, or 0.35.

Here we have considered only whether the photon arrives successfully at square 10. This is not the only simulation we could consider, nor is it the most interesting. We could, for example, consider the typical distance a photon travels before it is absorbed or deflected. We might ask the question, At least how far do 50% of the photons travel on average? To address this question we would want to know the median of the distribution of photon travel distances. The outcome of a trial would not be success or failure, but the actual number of squares traveled by the photon before being absorbed or deflected. In the long run, the distribution of simulation results should look more and more like the "true" distribution of photon distances traveled, and the median of our simulation results should get closer and closer to the true median of photon travel distance.

EXPLORATION 6.3 Simulating Events That Are Not Independent

To simulate nonindependent events we must use the definition of conditional probability and consider the outcome of one event before we can simulate the second event. We can simulate the outcome of an event by generating a random number; simulating two dependent events will require generating at least two random numbers, depending on the complexity of the simulation.

To illustrate, consider the following example. Burglaries occur about once a month in a neighborhood troubled by crime. Suppose the neighborhood decides to get a watchdog, whose function would be to bark loudly and scare away burglars. They have rescued an elderly (but vicious looking!) German shepherd from the local animal shelter. Unfortunately his bark is very much worse than his bite. Much of his time is spent sleeping, and there is some concern about his hearing. But he *does* have a relatively ferocious bark, and they got him cheap. From actual trial runs using local neighbors disguised as burglars (i.e., a simulation!), it was discovered that Herr Rover noticed the simulated burglars 90% of the time. When he noticed the simulated burglars he emitted a ferocious bark 75% of the time. The question the neighbors now have is when can they expect a payoff from Rover? On average, how many months will go by before a burglar is noticed by Rover *and* frightened by Rover's ferocious bark?

Basic probability rules could be used to calculate the probability that Rover notices a burglar *and* barks, but it is not obvious how to determine the number of months that will go by before this event occurs using only basic rules. A simulation is an alternative method for modeling this problem, and is a lot less complicated to set up!

A particular burglar event can be modeled using the definition of conditional probability and two random numbers generated by *rand*:

1. If the first random number is less than or equal to .90, this will count as detected the burglar.
2. If the burglar is detected, we will use the second random number to determine whether Rover alerts the neighborhood as desired. A value less than or equal to .75 will indicate a "ferocious bark."
3. The first two steps represent the burglar event for one month. We will repeat Steps 1 and 2 until we get a "ferocious bark," thus completing a trial of the simulation. We note the number of months required to get an occurrence of "detected *and* ferocious bark."
4. Many repetitions (trials) would generate a distribution of times until a ferocious burglar-scaring bark occurs, and we could examine this distribution to find a "typical" number of months between successful burglar scarings.

Here is a record of five trials of this experiment, using random numbers generated by the calculator:

First Random Number	Detection?	Second Random Number	Ferocious Bark?
.8767844333	Yes	.7900592279	No
.9546136582	No	.5215775123	(not detected)
.5329329133	Yes	.2805102664	Yes—a 3-month wait
.1320755632	Yes	.7338039727	Yes—a 1-month wait
.6958584068	Yes	.5688014123	Yes—a 1-month wait
.9961435487	No	.6002686874	(not detected)
.7286825076	Yes	.3887292922	Yes—a 2-month wait
.4319389989	Yes	.0143592629	Yes—a 1-month wait

With only five trials, we cannot reach any reliable conclusions, but after many repetitions we would be able to estimate the probability that a burglar would be detected and scared away after 1, 2, 3, or any other number of months.

You should notice that we were led to simulation because our basic probability rules alone were not adequate to solve the problem of interest. Of course, an analytic solution is preferable—if one can be found!—because it gives a correct answer quickly. Simulation and an appeal to the law of large numbers can only give an approximate answer and may take considerable time and bookkeeping to execute, but it DOES work!

EXPLORATION 6.4 Simulations and the seq Function

Our examples of simulations have been fairly small so far. Usually simulations are undertaken with a large number of trials. Just as more data give us more information about the data distribution, more trials in a simulation will yield a more reliable picture of the distribution of outcomes.

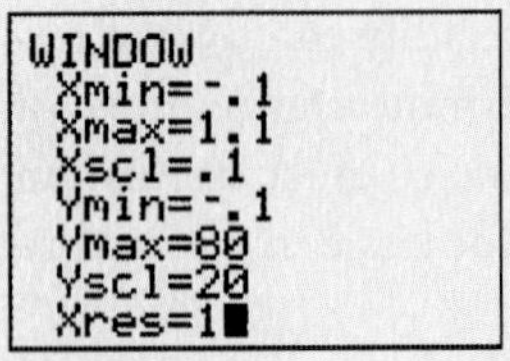

FIGURE 6.14
Window settings.

If a simulation is not too complicated, it is possible to use an interesting calculator function called a "Sequence" function, or "seq" for short. This function can be used with the list capability of your calculator to perform simulations and analyze the results graphically. The sequence command will allow a sequence of operations to be performed repetitiously, with results then stored in a list. If one random number is desired, you can just use *rand*; if 200 random numbers in a list are desired, the seq command can be used to fill the list. For example, the command

seq(*rand*, x, 1, 200) → List1

stores 200 random numbers in List1. As always, you should check your calculator manual to see what the syntax of the corresponding command is on your calculator.

Now we will perform a simulation that illustrates this command. Here's a question about random numbers generated using *rand*: Will the distribution of the average of random numbers look like the distribution of random numbers used to calculate the average? We will use the seq command to put 200 numbers generated by *rand*, in each of five lists.

Seq(*rand*, x, 1, 200) → List1
Seq(*rand*, x, 1, 200) → List2
Seq(*rand*, x, 1, 200) → List3
Seq(*rand*, x, 1, 200) → List4
Seq(*rand*, x, 1, 200) → List5

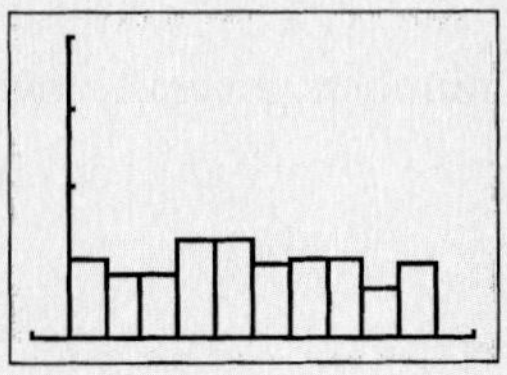

FIGURE 6.15
Histogram of data in List2.

Now we'll add the results, store them in List6, divide their sum by 5 to get the averages, and store in List6:

(List1 + List2 + List3 + List4 + List5)/5 → List6

The settings in the window shown in Figure 6.14 were used to generate the histograms in Figures 6.15 and 6.16. The histogram in Figure 6.15 is of the data in List2, and is typical of the histograms in Lists 1–5. The histogram in Figure 6.16 is a histogram of List6, the sum of the first 5 lists, divided by 5 (the average of five numbers). Do they have the same shape? It doesn't look like it.

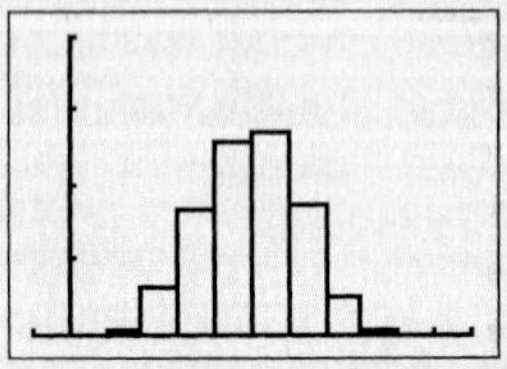

FIGURE 6.16
Histogram of data in List6.

This simulation illustrates the effect of averaging numbers. As you continue the study of statistics you will find that the Central Limit Theorem, an important result in statistics, governs the behavior of a sum or average. Our point here is that a calculator, together with data analysis skills, can be used to perform nontrivial simulations and analyze the results statistically.

AP* Review Questions for Chapter 6

1. A die is weighted so that when it is rolled, an odd number will come up twice as often as an even number in the long run. Which of the following is a legitimate assignment of probabilities to the outcomes in the sample space that is consistent with the description of the die?

(A)

Outcome	1	2	3	4	5	6
Probability	1/6	1/6	1/6	1/6	1/6	1/6

(B)

Outcome	1	2	3	4	5	6
Probability	1/6	2/6	1/6	2/6	1/6	2/6

(C)

Outcome	1	2	3	4	5	6
Probability	1/9	2/9	1/9	2/9	1/9	2/9

(D)

Outcome	1	2	3	4	5	6
Probability	2/9	1/9	2/9	1/9	2/9	1/9

(E) None of the above

Use the following to answer questions 2 and 3.

In a survey of 100 students selected at random from those enrolled at a small liberal arts college, the following data was obtained. Each student was asked how much time he or she spent on the Internet during a typical day, and gender was also noted.

	None	Less than 1 hour	1 hour or more	Total
Male	15	20	30	**65**
Female	10	15	10	**35**
Total	**25**	**35**	**40**	**100**

Assume that this data is representative of students at this college.

2. What is the approximate probability that a randomly selected student at this college is a female that spends no time on the Internet in a typical day?

(A) 10/10
(B) 10/15
(C) 10/25
(D) 10/35
(E) 10/100

3. If a randomly selected student is male, what is the approximate probability that he spends 1 hour or more on the Internet in a typical day?

(A) 30/30
(B) 30/40
(C) 30/65
(D) 35/65
(E) 30/100

4. Under what conditions is it true that P(A *or* B) = P(A) + P(B)

(A) A and B must be mutually exclusive
(B) A and B cannot be mutually exclusive
(C) A and B must be independent
(D) A and B must be both mutually exclusive and independent
(E) No conditions are required. It is always true that P(A or B) = P(A) + P(B)

5. Under what conditions is it true that P(A and B) = P(B|A)P(A)

(A) A and B must be mutually exclusive
(B) A and B cannot be mutually exclusive
(C) A and B must be independent
(D) A and B must be both mutually exclusive and independent
(E) No conditions are required. It is always true that P(A and B) = P(B|A)P(A)

6. A statistics class consists of 30 males and 20 females. Ten of the males and 10 of the females are also currently enrolled in a science course. If a student is selected at random from those enrolled in this statistics class, what is the probability that a female is selected?

(A) 0.1
(B) 0.2
(C) 0.4
(D) 0.5
(E) 0.6

7. Sixty percent of the students at an urban university carry more than one credit card. Selecting a student at random from the students at this university can be viewed as an experiment with two possible outcomes: *has more than one credit card* and *does not have more than one credit card.* Which of the following would be a correct assignment of random digits to the outcomes in order to simulate selecting a student at random from the students enrolled at the university?

   (A) 0 represents more than one credit card, 1 represents not more than one credit card, ignore all other digits.
   (B) Odd digits represent more than one credit card, and even digits represent not more than one credit card.
   (C) 0, 1, 2, and 3 represent more than one credit card, and 4, 5, 6, 7, 8, and 9 represent not more than one credit card.
   (D) 0, 1, 2, 3, 4, and 5 represent more than one credit card, and 6, 7, 8, and 9 represent not more than one credit card.
   (E) C and D both represent correct assignments.

8. A statistics class consists of 30 males and 20 females. Ten of the males and ten of the females are also currently enrolled in a science course. If a student is selected at random from those enrolled in this statistics class, what is the probability that the selected student is a male who is also enrolled in a science course?

   (A) .1
   (B) .2
   (C) .4
   (D) .5
   (E) .6

9. A statistics class consists of 30 males and 20 females. Ten of the males and ten of the females are also currently enrolled in a science course. A student is selected at random from those enrolled in this statistics class. Given that the selected student is female, what is the probability that the selected student is enrolled in a science course?

   (A) .1
   (B) .2
   (C) .4
   (D) .5
   (E) .6

10. Which of the following would be a correct assignment of random digits to the outcomes of heads and tails in order to simulate the flip of a fair coin?

    (A) 0 represents heads, 1 represents tails; ignore all other digits.
    (B) Odd digits represent heads, even digits represent tails.
    (C) 0, 1, 2, 3, and 4 represent heads, and 5, 6, 7, 8, and 9 represent tails.
    (D) Only B and C above are correct.
    (E) A, B, and C above are all correct.

11. Which of the following statements is true for two events, each with probability greater than 0?

    (A) If the events are mutually exclusive, they must be independent.
    (B) If the events are independent, they must be mutually exclusive.
    (C) If the events are not mutually exclusive, they must be independent.
    (D) If the events are not independent, they must be mutually exclusive.
    (E) If the events are mutually exclusive, they cannot be independent.

12. The Air Force receives 20% of its parachutes from Company C1, 55% from Company C2, and the rest from Company C3. The probability that a randomly selected parachute will fail to open is 0.0025, 0.002, and 0.0022, depending on whether it is from Company C1, C2, or C3, respectively. If a randomly chosen parachute fails to open, what is the probability it is from company C3?

    (A) .00055
    (B) .00215
    (C) .0022
    (D) .250
    (E) .256

13. A and B are events with $P(A) = .6$, $P(B) = .7$, and $P(A \cap B) = .4$. Which of the following is true?

    (A) A and B are mutually exclusive.
    (B) A and B are independent.
    (C) $P(A \cup B) = .6 + .7$
    (D) $P(A|B) = P(A)$
    (E) None of the above is true.

14. Two coins—a nickel and a dime—are to be flipped. Consider the following two events:

A = the event that the nickel lands with the head side up

B = the event that the dime lands with the head side up

Which of the following is true?

(A) The events A and B are independent and mutually exclusive.
(B) The events A and B are neither independent nor mutually exclusive.
(C) The events A and B are independent but not mutually exclusive.
(D) The events A and B are mutually exclusive but not independent.
(E) The events A and B are independent only if the coins are fair.

15. A chance experiment involves selecting a person at random from those who purchased a new car at a particular dealership during 2010 and noting both the gender and whether or not the selected person purchased a hybrid vehicle. The sample space for this experiment is {male who purchased a hybrid, male who did not purchase a hybrid, female who purchased a hybrid, female who did not purchase a hybrid}. Under what conditions would the four outcomes in the sample space be equally likely?

(A) No conditions are necessary—they are always equally likely.
(B) There must be an equal number of males and females who purchased cars from this dealership during 2010.
(C) 50% of the males must have purchased a hybrid.
(D) 50% of the males must have purchased a hybrid and 50% of the females must have purchased a hybrid.
(E) Both conditions B and D above are necessary.

CHAPTER 7

Random Variables and Probability Distributions

© Walter Bibikow/Getty Images

This chapter is the first of two chapters that together link the basic ideas of probability explored in Chapter 6 with the techniques of statistical inference. Chapter 6 used probability to describe the long-run relative frequency of occurrence of various types of outcomes. In this chapter we introduce probability models that can be used to describe the distribution of values of a variable. In Chapter 8, we will see how these same probability models can be used to describe the behavior of sample statistics. Such models play an important role in drawing conclusions based on sample data.

In a chance experiment, we often focus on some numerical aspect of the outcome. An environmental scientist who obtains an air sample from a specified location might be especially concerned with the concentration of ozone (a major constituent of smog). A quality control inspector who must decide whether to accept a large shipment of components may base the decision on the number of defective components in a group of 20 components randomly selected from the shipment.

Make the most of your study time by accessing everything you need to succeed online with CourseMate.
Visit http://www.cengagebrain.com where you will find:

- An interactive eBook, which allows you to take notes, highlight, bookmark, search the text, and use in-context glossary definitions
- Step-by-step instructions for Minitab, Excel, TI-83/84, SPSS, and JMP
- Video solutions to selected exercises
- Data sets available for selected examples and exercises
- Online quizzes
- Flashcards
- Videos

Before selection of the air sample, the value of the ozone concentration is uncertain. Similarly, the number of defective components among the 20 selected might be any whole number between 0 and 20. Because the value of a variable quantity such as ozone concentration or number of defective components is subject to uncertainty, such variables are called *random variables.*

In this chapter we begin by distinguishing between discrete and continuous numerical random variables. We show how variation in both discrete and continuous numerical random variables can be described by a probability distribution. This distribution can then be used to make probability statements about values of the random variable. Special emphasis is given to three commonly encountered probability distributions: the binomial, geometric, and normal distributions.

7.1 Random Variables

In most chance experiments, an investigator focuses attention on one or more variable quantities. For example, consider a management consultant who is studying the operation of a supermarket. The chance experiment might involve randomly selecting a customer leaving the store. One interesting numerical variable might be the number of items purchased by the customer. We can denote this variable using a letter, such as x. Possible values of this variable are 0 (a frustrated customer), 1, 2, 3, and so on. Until a customer is selected and the number of items counted, the value of x is uncertain. Another variable of potential interest might be the time y (in minutes) spent in a checkout line. One possible value of y is 3.0 minutes and another is 4.0 minutes, but *any* other number between 3.0 and 4.0 is also a possibility. In this example, the possible values of x are isolated points on the number line and the possible y values form an entire interval (a continuum) on the number line.

AP* EXAM TIP

Your calculator may have capabilities that will make working with random variables much less arithmetic-intensive. Periodically check out the Graphing Calculator Explorations at the end of the chapters for technological alternatives to hand calculations.

DEFINITION

Random variable: a numerical variable whose value depends on the outcome of a chance experiment. A random variable associates a numerical value with each outcome of a chance experiment.

A random variable is **discrete** if its set of possible values is a collection of isolated points along the number line.

A random variable is **continuous** if its set of possible values includes an entire interval on the number line.

We use lowercase letters, such as x and y, to represent random variables.* Figure 7.1 shows a set of possible values for each type of random variable. In practice, a discrete random variable almost always arises in connection with counting (for example, the number of items purchased, the number of gas pumps in use, or the number of broken eggs in a carton). A continuous random variable is one whose value is typically obtained by measurement (temperature in a freezer compartment, weight

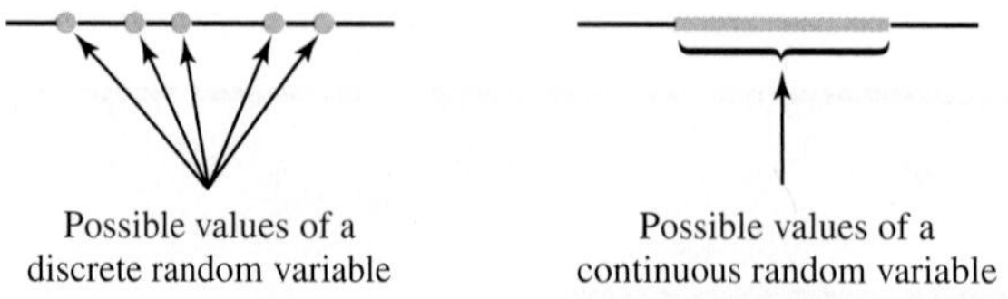

FIGURE 7.1
Two different types of random variables.

*In some books, uppercase letters are used to name random variables, with lowercase letters representing a particular value that the variable might assume. We have chosen to use a simpler and less formal notation.

of a pineapple, amount of time spent in the store, etc.). Because there is a limit to the accuracy of any measuring instrument, such as a watch or a scale, it may seem that any variable should be regarded as discrete. For example, when weight is measured to the nearest pound, the observed values appear to be isolated points along the number line, such as 2 pounds, 3 pounds, etc. But this is just a function of the accuracy with which weight is recorded and not because a weight between 2 and 3 pounds is impossible. In this case, the variable is continuous.

EXAMPLE 7.1 Book Sales

Consider an experiment in which the type of book, print (P) or digital (D), chosen by each of three successive customers making a purchase from on an online bookstore is noted. Define a random variable x by

$x =$ number of customers purchasing a book in digital format

The experimental outcome in which the first and third customers purchase a digital book and the second customer purchases a print book can be abbreviated DPD. The associated x value is 2, because two of the three customers selected a digital book. Similarly, the x value for the outcome DDD (all three purchase a digital book) is 3. We display each of the eight possible experimental outcomes and the corresponding value of x in the following table:

Outcome	PPP	DPP	PDP	PPD	DDP	DPD	PDD	DDD
x value	0	1	1	1	2	2	2	3

There are only four possible x values—0, 1, 2, and 3—and these are isolated points on the number line. Thus, x is a discrete random variable.

In some situations, the random variable of interest is discrete, but the number of possible values is not finite. This is illustrated in Example 7.2.

EXAMPLE 7.2 This Could Be a Long Game . . .

Two friends agree to play a game that consists of a sequence of trials. The game continues until one player wins two trials in a row. One random variable of interest might be

$x =$ number of trials required to complete the game

Let A denote a win for Player 1 and B denote a win for Player 2. The simplest possible experimental outcomes are AA (the case in which Player 1 wins the first two trials and the game ends) and BB (the case in which Player 2 wins the first two trials). With either of these two outcomes, $x = 2$. There are also two outcomes for which $x = 3$: ABB and BAA. Some other possible outcomes and associated x values are

Outcomes	x value
AA, BB	2
BAA, ABB	3
ABAA, BABB	4
ABABB, BABAA	5
⋮	⋮
ABABABABAA, BABABABABB	10

and so on.

Any positive integer that is at least 2 is a possible value. Because the values 2, 3, 4, ... are isolated points on the number line (x is determined by counting), x is a discrete random variable even though there is no upper limit to the number of possible values.

EXAMPLE 7.3 Stress

In an engineering stress test, pressure is applied to a thin 1-foot-long bar until the bar snaps. The precise location where the bar will snap is uncertain. Let x be the distance from the left end of the bar to the break. Then $x = 0.25$ is one possibility, $x = 0.9$ is another, and in fact any number between 0 and 1 is a possible value of x. (Figure 7.2 shows the case of the outcome $x = 0.6$.) The set of possible values is an entire interval on the number line, so x is a continuous random variable.

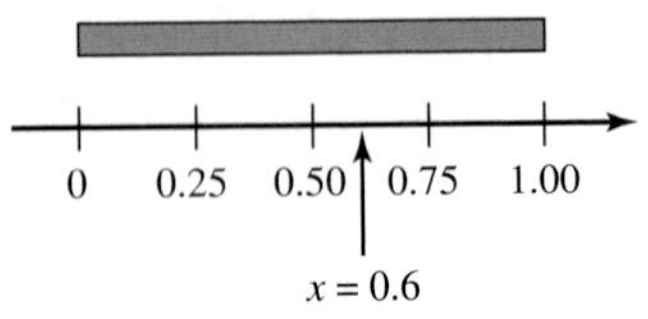

FIGURE 7.2
The bar for Example 7.3 and the outcome $x = 0.6$.

Even though in practice we may be able to measure the distance only to the nearest tenth of an inch or hundredth of an inch, the *actual* distance could be any number between 0 and 1. So, even though the recorded values might be rounded because of the accuracy of the measuring instrument, the variable is still continuous.

In data analysis, random variables often arise in the context of summarizing sample data when a sample is selected from some population. This is illustrated in Example 7.4.

EXAMPLE 7.4 College Plans

Suppose that a counselor plans to select a random sample of 50 seniors at a large high school and to ask each student in the sample whether he or she plans to attend college after graduation. The process of sampling is a chance experiment. The sample space for this experiment consists of all the different possible random samples of size 50 that might result (there is a very large number of these), and for simple random sampling, each of these outcomes is equally likely. Let

x = number of successes in the sample

where a success in this instance is defined as a student who plans to attend college. Then x is a random variable, because it associates a numerical value with each of the possible outcomes (random samples) that might occur. Possible values of x are 0, 1, 2, . . . , 50, and x is a discrete random variable.

EXERCISES 7.1 - 7.7

7.1 State whether each of the following random variables is discrete or continuous:
a. The number of defective tires on a car
b. The body temperature of a hospital patient
c. The number of pages in a book
d. The number of draws (with replacement) from a deck of cards until a heart is selected
e. The lifetime of a lightbulb

7.2 Classify each of the following random variables as either discrete or continuous:

a. The fuel efficiency (mpg) of an automobile
b. The amount of rainfall at a particular location during the next year
c. The distance that a person throws a baseball
d. The number of questions asked during a 1-hour lecture
e. The tension (in pounds per square inch) at which a tennis racket is strung
f. The amount of water used by a household during a given month
g. The number of traffic citations issued by the highway patrol in a particular county on a given day

7.3 Starting at a particular time, each car entering an intersection is observed to see whether it turns left (L) or right (R) or goes straight ahead (S). The experiment terminates as soon as a car is observed to go straight. Let y denote the number of cars observed. What are possible y values? List five different outcomes and their associated y values.

7.4 A point is randomly selected from the interior of the square pictured.

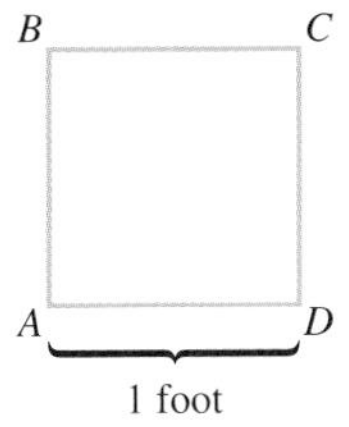

Let x denote the distance from the lower left-hand corner A of the square to the selected point. What are possible values of x? Is x a discrete or a continuous variable?

7.5 A point is randomly selected on the surface of a lake that has a maximum depth of 100 feet. Let y be the depth of the lake at the randomly chosen point. What are possible values of y? Is y discrete or continuous?

7.6 A person stands at the corner marked A of the square pictured in Exercise 7.4 and tosses a coin. If it lands heads up, the person moves one corner clockwise, to B. If the coin lands tails up, the person moves one corner counterclockwise, to D. This process is then repeated until the person arrives back at A. Let y denote the number of coin tosses. What are possible values of y? Is y discrete or continuous?

7.7 A box contains four slips of paper marked 1, 2, 3, and 4. Two slips are selected without replacement. List the possible values for each of the following random variables:

a. x = sum of the two numbers
b. y = difference between the first and second numbers
c. z = number of slips selected that show an even number
d. w = number of slips selected that show a 4

7.2 Probability Distributions for Discrete Random Variables

The probability distribution for a random variable is a model that describes the long-run behavior of the variable. For example, suppose that the Department of Animal Regulation in a particular county is interested in studying the variable x = number of licensed dogs or cats for a household. County regulations prohibit more than five dogs or cats per household. If we consider the chance experiment of randomly selecting a household in this county, then x is a discrete random variable because it associates a numerical value (0, 1, 2, 3, 4, or 5) with each of the possible outcomes (households) in the sample space. Although we know what the possible values for x are, it would also be useful to know how this variable behaves in repeated observation. What would be the most common value? What proportion of the time would $x = 5$ be observed? $x = 3$? A probability distribution provides this type of information about the long-run behavior of a random variable.

DEFINITION

The **probability distribution of a discrete random variable x** gives the probability associated with each possible *x* value. Each probability is the long-run relative frequency of occurrence of the corresponding *x* value when the chance experiment is performed a very large number of times.

Common ways to display a probability distribution for a discrete random variable are a table, a probability histogram, or a formula.

If one possible value of x is 2, we often write $p(2)$ in place of $P(x = 2)$. Similarly, $p(5)$ denotes the probability that $x = 5$, and so on.

EXAMPLE 7.5 Energy Efficient Refrigerators

Suppose that each of four randomly selected customers purchasing a refrigerator at a large appliance store chooses either an energy efficient model (E) or one from a less expensive group of models (G) that do not have an energy efficient rating. Assume that these customers make their choices independently of one another and that 40% of all customers select an energy efficient model. This implies that for any particular one of the four customers, $P(\text{E}) = .4$ and $P(\text{G}) = .6$. One possible experimental outcome is EGGE, where the first and fourth customers select energy efficient models and the other two choose less expensive models. Because the customers make their choices independently, the multiplication rule for independent events implies that

$$\begin{aligned} P(\text{EGGE}) &= P(\text{1st chooses E } \textit{and} \text{ 2nd chooses G } \textit{and} \text{ 3rd chooses G } \textit{and} \text{ 4th chooses E}) \\ &= P(E)P(G)P(G)P(E) \\ &= (.4)(.6)(.6)(.4) \\ &= .0576 \end{aligned}$$

Similarly,

$$\begin{aligned} P(\text{EGEG}) &= P(E)P(G)P(E)P(G) \\ &= (.4)(.6)(.4)(.6) \\ &= .0576 \quad (\text{identical to } P(\text{EGGE})) \end{aligned}$$

and

$$P(\text{GGGE}) = (.6)(.6)(.6)(.4) = .0864$$

The number among the four customers who purchase an energy efficient model is a random variable. Let

x = the number of energy efficient refrigerators purchased by the four customers

Table 7.1 displays the 16 possible experimental outcomes, the probability of each outcome, and the value of the random variable x that is associated with each outcome.

The probability distribution of x is easily obtained from this information. Consider the smallest possible x value, 0. The only outcome for which $x = 0$ is GGGG, so

$$p(0) = P(x = 0) = P(\text{GGGG}) = .1296$$

TABLE 7.1 Outcomes and Probabilities for Example 7.5

Outcome	Probability	x Value	Outcome	Probability	x Value
GGGG	.1296	0	GEEG	.0576	2
EGGG	.0864	1	GEGE	.0576	2
GEGG	.0864	1	GGEE	.0576	2
GGEG	.0864	1	GEEE	.0384	3
GGGE	.0864	1	EGEE	.0384	3
EEGG	.0576	2	EEGE	.0384	3
EGEG	.0576	2	EEEG	.0384	3
EGGE	.0576	2	EEEE	.0256	4

There are four different outcomes for which $x = 1$, so $p(1)$ results from adding the four corresponding probabilities:

$$\begin{aligned} p(1) &= P(x = 1) = P(\text{EGGG } or \text{ GEGG } or \text{ GGEG } or \text{ GGGE}) \\ &= P(\text{EGGG}) + P(\text{GEGG}) + P(\text{GGEG}) + P(\text{GGGE}) \\ &= .0864 + .0864 + .0864 + .0864 \\ &= 4(.0864) \\ &= .3456 \end{aligned}$$

Similarly,

$$\begin{aligned} p(2) &= P(\text{EEGG}) + \cdots + P(\text{GGEE}) = 6(.0576) = .3456 \\ p(3) &= 4(.0384) = .1536 \\ p(4) &= .0256 \end{aligned}$$

The probability distribution of x is summarized in the following table:

x Value	0	1	2	3	4
$p(x)$ = Probability of Value	.1296	.3456	.3456	.1536	.0256

To interpret $p(3) = .1536$, think of performing the chance experiment repeatedly, each time with a new group of four customers. In the long run, 15.36% of these groups will have exactly three customers purchasing an energy efficient refrigerator.

The probability distribution can be used to determine probabilities of various events involving x. For example, the probability that at least two of the four customers choose energy efficient models is

$$\begin{aligned} P(x \geq 2) &= P(x = 2 \text{ or } x = 3 \text{ or } x = 4) \\ &= p(2) + p(3) + p(4) \\ &= .5248 \end{aligned}$$

Thus, in the long run, 52.48% of the time a group of four refrigerator purchasers will include at least two who select energy efficient models.

A probability distribution table for a discrete variable shows the possible x values and also $p(x)$ for each possible x value. Because $p(x)$ is a probability, it must be a number between 0 and 1, and because the probability distribution lists all possible

x values, the sum of all the $p(x)$ values must equal 1. These properties of discrete probability distributions are summarized in the following box.

Properties of Discrete Probability Distributions

Properties of Discrete Probability Distributions

1. For every possible x value, $0 \leq p(x) \leq 1$.
2. $\sum_{\text{all } x \text{ values}} p(x) = 1$

A pictorial representation of a discrete probability distribution is called a *probability histogram*. The picture has a rectangle centered above each possible value of x, and the area of each rectangle is proportional to the probability of the corresponding value. Figure 7.3 displays the probability histogram for the probability distribution of Example 7.5.

AP* EXAM TIP

Probability histograms help us understand probability distributions in the same way that graphical displays help us understand data distributions.

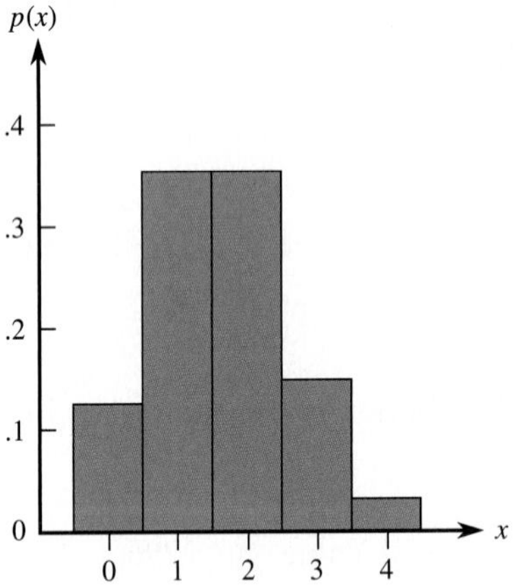

FIGURE 7.3
Probability histogram for the distribution of Example 7.5.

In Example 7.5, the probability distribution was derived by starting with a chance experiment and applying probability rules. When a derivation from fundamental probabilities is not possible because of the complexity of the experimental situation, an investigator often proposes an approximate probability distribution consistent with empirical evidence and prior knowledge. Probability distributions based on empirical evidence must still be consistent with rules of probability. Specifically,

1. $p(x) \geq 0$ for every x value.
2. $\sum_{\text{all } x \text{ values}} p(x) = 1$

This is illustrated in Examples 7.6 and 7.7

EXAMPLE 7.6 Paint Flaws

In automobile manufacturing, one of the last steps in the process of assembling a new car is painting. Some minor blemishes in the paint surface are considered acceptable, but if there are too many, it becomes noticeable to a potential customer and the car must be repainted. Cars coming off the assembly line are carefully inspected and the number of minor blemishes in the paint surface is determined. Let x denote the number of minor blemishes on a randomly selected car from a particular manufacturing plant. A large number of automobiles were evaluated, and a probability distribution consistent with these observations is

x	0	1	2	3	4	5	6	7	8	9	10
$p(x)$	.041	.010	.209	.223	.178	.114	.061	.028	.011	.004	.001

The corresponding probability histogram appears in Figure 7.4. The probabilities in this distribution reflect the car manufacturer's experience. For example, $p(3) = .223$ indicates that 22.3% of new automobiles had 3 minor paint blemishes. The probability that the number of minor paint blemishes is between 2 and 5 inclusive is

$$P(2 \leq x \leq 5) = p(2) + p(3) + p(4) + p(5) = .724$$

If car after car of this type were examined, in the long run, 72.4% would have 2, 3, 4, or 5 minor paint blemishes.

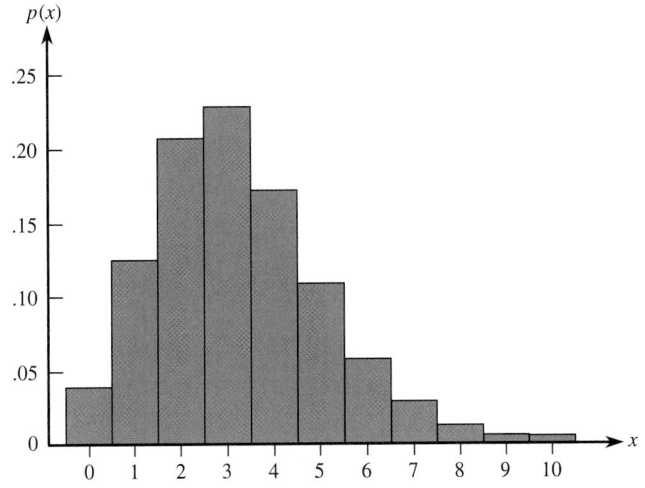

FIGURE 7.4
Probability histogram for the distribution of the number of minor paint blemishes on a randomly selected car.

EXAMPLE 7.7 iPod Shuffles

The paper "Does Your iPod *Really* Play Favorites?" (*American Statistician* [2009]: 263–268) investigated the shuffle feature of the iPod. The shuffle feature takes a group of songs, called a playlist, and plays them in a random order. Some have questioned the "randomness" of the shuffle, citing examples of situations where several songs from the same artist were played in close proximity to each other. One such example appeared in a *Newsweek* article in 2005, where the author states that Steely Dan songs always seem to pop up in the first hour of play. (For those young readers unfamiliar with Steely Dan, see http://www.steelydan.com.) Is this consistent with a "random" shuffle?

To investigate the alleged non-randomness, suppose we create a playlist of 3000 songs that includes 50 songs by Steely Dan (this is the situation considered by the authors of the *American Statistician* paper). We could then carry out a simulation by creating a shuffle of 20 songs (about one hour of playing time) from the playlist and noting the number of songs by Steely Dan that were among the 20. This could be done by thinking of the songs in the playlist as being numbered from 1 to 3000, with numbers 1 to 50 representing the Steely Dan songs. A random number generator could then be used to select 20 random numbers between 1 and 3000. We would then count how many times a number between 1 and 50 was included in this list.

This would correspond to the number of Steely Dan songs in this particular shuffle of 20 songs. Repeating this process a large number of times would enable us to estimate the probabilities needed for the probability distribution of

x = number of Steely Dan songs in a random shuffle consisting of 20 songs

The probabilities in the accompanying probability distribution are from the *American Statistician* paper. Even though possible values of x are 0, 1, 2, . . . , 20, the probability of x taking on a value of 4 or greater is very small, and so 4, 5, . . . , 20 have been grouped into a single entry in the probability distribution table.

PROBABILITY DISTRIBUTION OF x = NUMBER OF STEELY DAN SONGS IN A 20-SONG SHUFFLE

x	$p(x)$
0	.7138
1	.2435
2	.0387
3	.0038
4 or more	.0002

Notice that $P(x \geq 1) = 1 - .7138 = .2862$. This means that about 28.6% of the time, at least one Steely Dan song would occur in a random shuffle of 20 songs. Given that there are only 50 Steely Dan songs in the playlist of 3000 songs, this result surprises many people!

We have seen examples in which the probability distribution of a discrete random variable has been given as a table or as a probability histogram. It is also possible to give a formula that allows calculation of the probability for each possible value of the random variable. Examples of this approach are given in Section 7.5.

EXERCISES 7.8 - 7.19

7.8 Let x be the number of courses for which a randomly selected student at a certain university is registered. The probability distribution of x appears in the following table:

x	1	2	3	4	5	6	7
$p(x)$	.02	.03	.09	.25	.40	.16	.05

a. What is $P(x = 4)$?
b. What is $P(x \leq 4)$?
c. What is the probability that the selected student is taking at most five courses?
d. What is the probability that the selected student is taking at least five courses? more than five courses?
e. Calculate $P(3 \leq x \leq 6)$ and $P(3 < x < 6)$. Explain in words why these two probabilities are different.

7.9 ✦ Let y denote the number of broken eggs in a randomly selected carton of one dozen eggs. Suppose that the probability distribution of y is as follows:

y	0	1	2	3	4
$p(y)$	.65	.20	.10	.04	?

a. Only y values of 0, 1, 2, 3, and 4 have positive probabilities. What is $p(4)$?
b. How would you interpret $p(1) = .20$?
c. Calculate $P(y \leq 2)$, the probability that the carton contains at most two broken eggs, and interpret this probability.
d. Calculate $P(y < 2)$, the probability that the carton contains *fewer than* two broken eggs. Why is this smaller than the probability in Part (c)?
e. What is the probability that the carton contains exactly 10 unbroken eggs?
f. What is the probability that at least 10 eggs are unbroken?

7.10 A restaurant has four bottles of a certain wine in stock. Unbeknownst to the wine steward, two of these bottles (Bottles 1 and 2) are bad. Suppose that two bottles are ordered, and let x be the number of good bottles among these two.
a. One possible experimental outcome is (1,2) (Bottles 1 and 2 are the ones selected) and another is (2,4). List all possible outcomes.
b. Assuming that the two bottles are randomly selected from among the four, what is the probability of each outcome in Part (a)?
c. The value of x for the (1,2) outcome is 0 (neither selected bottle is good), and $x = 1$ for the outcome (2,4). Determine the x value for each possible outcome. Then use the probabilities in Part (b) to determine the probability distribution of x.

7.11 Airlines sometimes overbook flights. Suppose that for a plane with 100 seats, an airline takes 110 reservations. Define the variable x as the number of people who actually show up for a sold-out flight. From past experience, the probability distribution of x is given in the following table:

x	95	96	97	98	99	100	101	102
$p(x)$	.05	.10	.12	.14	.24	.17	.06	.04

x	103	104	105	106	107	108	109	110
$p(x)$	.03	.02	.01	.005	.005	.005	.0037	.0013

a. What is the probability that the airline can accommodate everyone who shows up for the flight?
b. What is the probability that not all passengers can be accommodated?
c. If you are trying to get a seat on such a flight and you are number 1 on the standby list, what is the probability that you will be able to take the flight? What if you are number 3?

7.12 Suppose that a computer manufacturer receives computer boards in lots of five. Two boards are selected from each lot for inspection. We can represent possible outcomes of the selection process by pairs. For example, the pair (1,2) represents the selection of Boards 1 and 2 for inspection.
a. List the 10 different possible outcomes.
b. Suppose that Boards 1 and 2 are the only defective boards in a lot of five. Two boards are to be chosen at random. Define x to be the number of defective boards observed among those inspected. Find the probability distribution of x.

7.13 Simulate the chance experiment described in Exercise 7.12 using five slips of paper, with two marked *defective* and three marked *nondefective*. Place the slips in a box, mix them well, and draw out two. Record the number of defective boards. Replace the slips and repeat until you have 50 observations on the variable x. Construct a relative frequency distribution for the 50 observations, and compare this with the probability distribution obtained in Exercise 7.12.

7.14 Of all airline flight requests received by a certain discount ticket broker, 70% are for domestic travel (D) and 30% are for international flights (I). Let x be the number of requests among the next three requests received that are for domestic flights. Assuming independence of successive requests, determine the probability distribution of x. (Hint: One possible outcome is DID, with the probability $(.7)(.3)(.7) = .147$.)

7.15 Suppose that 20% of all homeowners in an earthquake-prone area of California are insured against earthquake damage. Four homeowners are selected at random; let x denote the number among the four who have earthquake insurance.
a. Find the probability distribution of x. (Hint: Let S denote a homeowner who has insurance and F one who does not. Then one possible outcome is SFSS, with probability $(.2)(.8)(.2)(.2)$ and associated x value of 3. There are 15 other outcomes.)
b. What is the most likely value of x?
c. What is the probability that at least two of the four selected homeowners have earthquake insurance?

7.16 A box contains five slips of paper, marked \$1, \$1, \$1, \$10, and \$25. The winner of a contest selects two slips of paper at random and then gets the larger of the dollar amounts on the two slips. Define a random variable w by w = amount awarded. Determine the probability distribution of w. (Hint: Think of the slips as numbered 1, 2, 3, 4, and 5, so that an outcome of the experiment consists of two of these numbers.)

7.17 Components coming off an assembly line are either free of defects (S, for success) or defective (F, for failure). Suppose that 70% of all such components are defect-free. Components are independently selected and tested one by one. Let y denote the number of components that must be tested until a defect-free component is obtained.

a. What is the smallest possible y value, and what experimental outcome gives this y value? What is the second smallest y value, and what outcome gives rise to it?

b. What is the set of all possible y values?

c. Determine the probability of each of the five smallest y values. You should see a pattern that leads to a simple formula for $p(y)$, the probability distribution of y.

7.18 A contractor is required by a county planning department to submit anywhere from one to five forms (depending on the nature of the project) in applying for a building permit. Let y be the number of forms required of the next applicant. The probability that y forms are required is known to be proportional to y; that is, $p(y) = ky$ for $y = 1, \ldots, 5$.

a. What is the value of k? (Hint: $\sum p(y) = 1$.)

b. What is the probability that at most three forms are required?

c. What is the probability that between two and four forms (inclusive) are required?

d. Could $p(y) = y^2/50$ for $y = 1, 2, 3, 4, 5$ be the probability distribution of y? Explain.

7.19 A library subscribes to two different weekly news magazines, each of which is supposed to arrive in Wednesday's mail. In actuality, each one could arrive on Wednesday (W), Thursday (T), Friday (F), or Saturday (S). Suppose that the two magazines arrive independently of one another and that for each magazine $P(W) = .4$, $P(T) = .3$, $P(F) = .2$, and $P(S) = .1$. Define a random variable y by y = the number of days beyond Wednesday that it takes for both magazines to arrive. For example, if the first magazine arrives on Friday and the second magazine arrives on Wednesday, then $y = 2$, whereas $y = 1$ if both magazines arrive on Thursday. Obtain the probability distribution of y. (Hint: Draw a tree diagram with two generations of branches, the first labeled with arrival days for Magazine 1 and the second for Magazine 2.)

7.3 Probability Distributions for Continuous Random Variables

A continuous random variable is one that has as its set of possible values an entire interval on the number line. An example is the weight x (in pounds) of a full-term newborn child. Suppose for the moment that weight is recorded only to the nearest pound. Then a reported weight of 7 pounds would be used for any weight greater than or equal to 6.5 pounds and less than 7.5 pounds. The probability distribution can be pictured as a probability histogram in which rectangles are centered at 4, 5, and so on. The area of each rectangle is the probability of the corresponding weight value. The total area of all the rectangles is 1, and the probability that a weight (to the nearest pound) is between two values, such as 6 and 8, is the sum of the corresponding rectangular areas. Figure 7.5(a) illustrates this.

Now suppose that weight is measured to the nearest tenth of a pound. There are many more possible reported weight values than before, such as 5.0, 5.1, 5.7, 7.3, and 8.9. As shown in Figure 7.5(b), the rectangles in the probability histogram are much narrower, and this histogram has a much smoother appearance than the first one. Again, this histogram can be drawn so that the area of each rectangle equals the corresponding probability, and the total area of all the rectangles is 1.

Figure 7.5(c) shows what happens as weight is measured to a greater and greater degree of accuracy. The sequence of probability histograms approaches a smooth

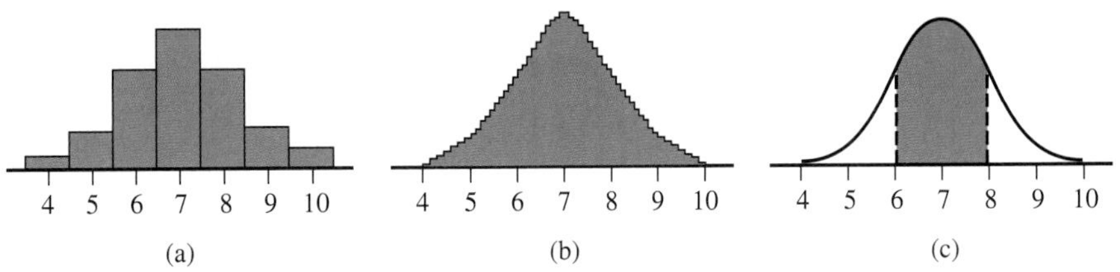

FIGURE 7.5
Probability distribution for birth weight: (a) weight measured to the nearest pound; (b) weight measured to the nearest tenth of a pound; (c) limiting curve as measurement accuracy increases; shaded area = $P(6 \leq \text{weight} \leq 8)$.

curve. The curve cannot go below the horizontal measurement scale, and the total area under the curve is 1 (because this is true of every probability histogram). The probability that x falls in an interval such as $6 \leq x \leq 8$ is the area under the curve and above that interval.

DEFINITION

A **probability distribution for a continuous random variable** x is specified by a curve called a **density curve.** The function that defines this curve is denoted by $f(x)$ and it is called the **density function.**

The following are properties of all continuous probability distributions:

1. $f(x) \geq 0$ (so that the curve cannot dip below the horizontal axis).
2. The total area under the density curve is equal to 1.

The probability that x falls in any particular interval is the area under the density curve and above the interval.

Many probability calculations for continuous random variables involve the following three events:

1. $a < x < b$, the event that the random variable x assumes a value between two given numbers, a and b
2. $x < a$, the event that the random variable x assumes a value less than a given number a
3. $x > b$, the event that the random variable x assumes a value greater than a given number b (this can also be written as $b < x$)

Figure 7.6 illustrates how the probabilities of these events are identified with areas under a density curve.

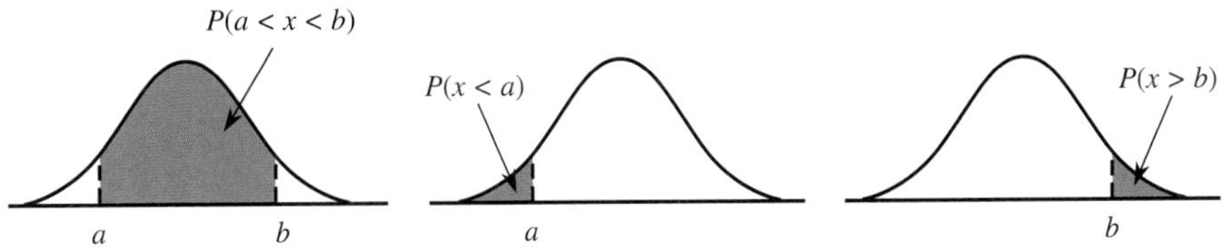

FIGURE 7.6
Probabilities as areas under a probability density curve.

EXAMPLE 7.8 Application Processing Times

Suppose x represents a continuous random variable x defined as amount of time (in minutes) taken by a clerk to process a certain type of application form. Suppose that x has a probability distribution with density function

$$f(x) = \begin{cases} .5 & 4 < x < 6 \\ 0 & \text{otherwise} \end{cases}$$

The graph of $f(x)$, the density curve, is shown in Figure 7.7(a). It is especially easy to use this density curve to calculate probabilities, because it just requires finding the area of rectangles using the formula

$$\text{area} = (\text{base})(\text{height})$$

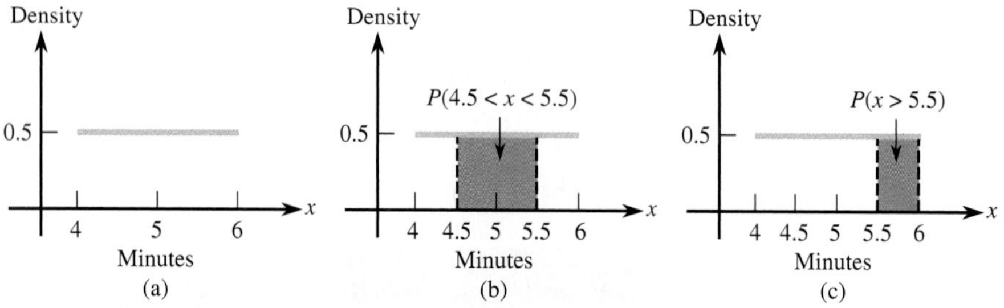

FIGURE 7.7
The uniform distribution for Example 7.8.

The curve has positive height, 0.5, only between $x = 4$ and $x = 6$. The total area under the curve is just the area of the rectangle with base extending from 4 to 6 and with height 0.5. This gives

$$\text{area} = (6 - 4)(0.5) = 1$$

as required.

When the density is constant over an interval (resulting in a horizontal density curve), the probability distribution is called a *uniform distribution.*

As illustrated in Figure 7.7(b), the probability that x is between 4.5 and 5.5 is

$$\begin{aligned} P(4.5 < x < 5.5) &= \text{area of shaded rectangle} \\ &= (\text{base width})(\text{height}) \\ &= (5.5 - 4.5)(.5) \\ &= .5 \end{aligned}$$

Similarly (see Figure 7.7(c)), because in this context $x > 5.5$ is equivalent to $5.5 < x \leq 6$, we have

$$P(x > 5.5) = (6 - 5.5)(.5) = .25$$

According to this model, in the long run, 25% of all forms that are processed will have processing times that exceed 5.5 min.

The probability that a *discrete* random variable x lies in the interval between two limits a and b depends on whether either limit is included in the interval. Suppose, for example, that x is the number of major defects on a new automobile. Then

$$P(3 \leq x \leq 7) = p(3) + p(4) + p(5) + p(6) + p(7)$$

whereas

$$P(3 < x < 7) = p(4) + p(5) + p(6)$$

However, if x is a *continuous* random variable, such as task completion time, then

$$P(3 \leq x \leq 7) = P(3 < x < 7)$$

because the area under a density curve and above a single value such as 3 or 7 is 0. Geometrically, we can think of finding the area above a single point as finding the area of a rectangle with width = 0. The area above an interval of values, therefore, does not depend on whether either endpoint is included.

If x is a continuous random variable, then for any two numbers a and b with $a < b$,

$$P(a \le x \le b) = P(a < x \le b) = P(a \le x < b) = P(a < x < b)$$

Probabilities for continuous random variables are often calculated using cumulative areas. A cumulative area is all of the area under the density curve to the left of a particular value. Figure 7.8 illustrates the cumulative area to the left of .5, which is $P(x < .5)$. The probability that x is in any particular interval, $P(a < x < b)$, is equal to the difference between two cumulative areas.

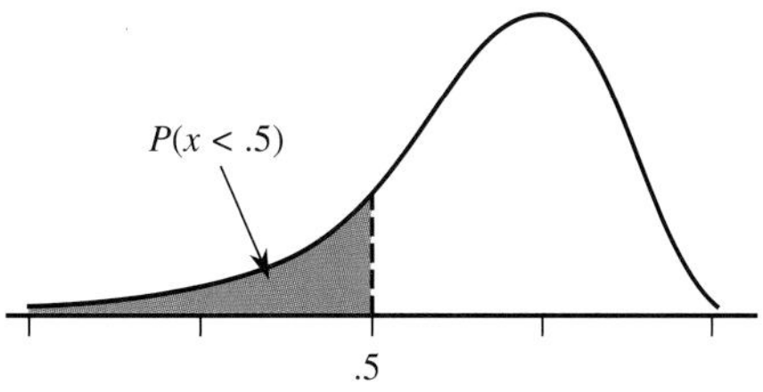

FIGURE 7.8
A cumulative area under a density curve.

The probability that a continuous random variable x lies between a lower limit a and an upper limit b is

$$\begin{aligned} P(a < x < b) &= (\text{cumulative area to the left of } b) - (\text{cumulative area to the left of } a) \\ &= P(x < b) - P(x < a) \end{aligned}$$

This property is illustrated in Figure 7.9 for the case of $a = .25$ and $b = .75$. We will use this result often in Section 7.6 when we calculate probabilities using the normal distribution.

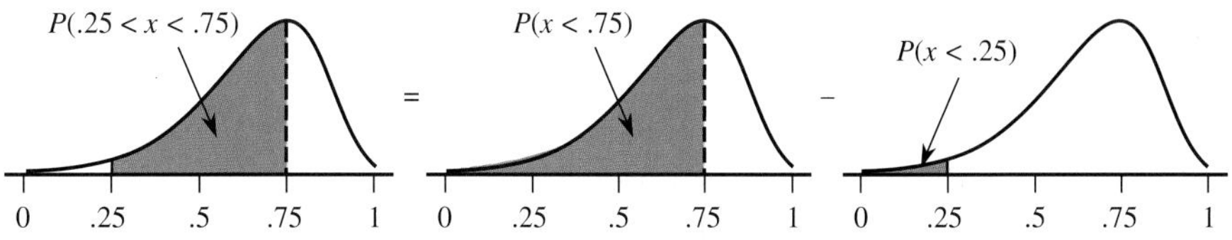

FIGURE 7.9
Calculation of $P(a < x < b)$ using cumulative areas.

For some continuous distributions, cumulative areas can be calculated using methods from the branch of mathematics called integral calculus. However, because we are not assuming knowledge of calculus, we will rely on tables that have been constructed for the commonly encountered continuous probability distributions. Most graphing calculators and statistical software packages will also compute areas for the most widely used continuous probability distributions.

EXERCISES 7.20 - 7.26

7.20 Let x denote the lifetime (in thousands of hours) of a certain type of fan used in diesel engines. The density curve of x is as pictured:

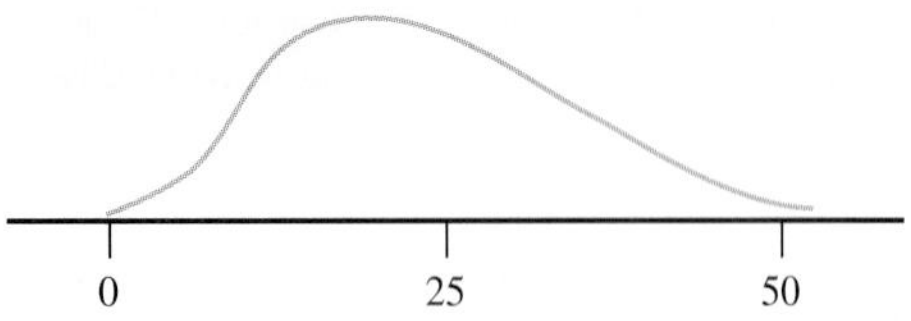

Shade the area under the curve corresponding to each of the following probabilities (draw a new curve for each part):

a. $P(10 < x < 25)$
b. $P(10 \leq x \leq 25)$
c. $P(x < 30)$
d. The probability that the lifetime is at least 25,000 hours
e. The probability that the lifetime exceeds 25,000 hours

7.21 A particular professor never dismisses class early. Let x denote the amount of time past the hour (minutes) that elapses before the professor dismisses class. Suppose that x has a uniform distribution on the interval from 0 to 10 minutes. The density curve is shown in the following figure:

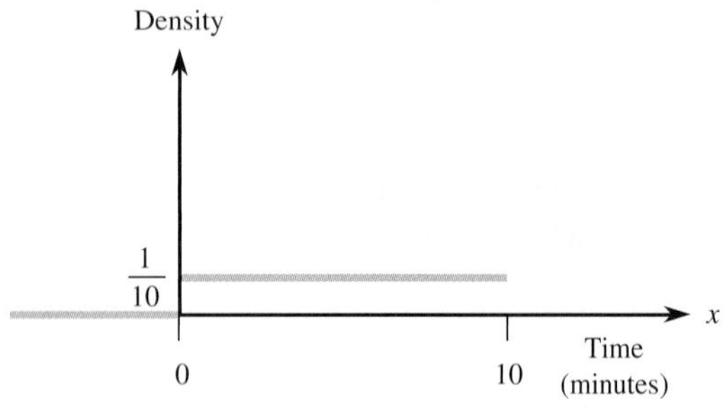

a. What is the probability that at most 5 minutes elapse before dismissal?
b. What is the probability that between 3 and 5 minutes elapse before dismissal?

7.22 Refer to the probability distribution given in Exercise 7.21. Put the following probabilities in order, from smallest to largest:

$$P(2 < x < 3),\ P(2 \leq x \leq 3),\ P(x < 2),\ P(x > 7)$$

Explain your reasoning.

7.23 The article "Modeling Sediment and Water Column Interactions for Hydrophobic Pollutants" (*Water Research* [1984]: 1169–1174) suggests the uniform distribution on the interval from 7.5 to 20 as a model for x = depth (in centimeters) of the bioturbation layer in sediment for a certain region.

a. Draw the density curve for x.
b. What is the height of the density curve?
c. What is the probability that x is at most 12?
d. What is the probability that x is between 10 and 15? Between 12 and 17? Why are these two probabilities equal?

7.24 Let x denote the amount of gravel sold (in tons) during a randomly selected week at a particular sales facility. Suppose that the density curve has height $f(x)$ above the value x, where

$$f(x) = \begin{cases} 2(1-x) & 0 \leq x \leq 1 \\ 0 & \text{otherwise} \end{cases}$$

The density curve (the graph of $f(x)$) is shown in the following figure:

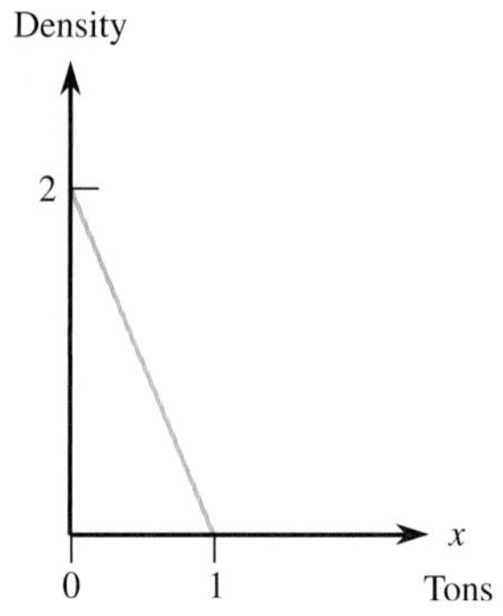

Use the fact that the area of a triangle $= \frac{1}{2}$ (base)(height) to calculate each of the following probabilities. (Hint: Drawing a picture and shading the appropriate area will help.)

a. $P\left(x < \frac{1}{2}\right)$
b. $P\left(x \leq \frac{1}{2}\right)$
c. $P\left(x < \frac{1}{4}\right)$
d. $P\left(\frac{1}{4} < x < \frac{1}{2}\right)$ (Hint: Use the results of Parts (a)–(c).)

e. The probability that gravel sold exceeds $\frac{1}{2}$ ton
f. The probability that gravel sold is at least $\frac{1}{4}$ ton

7.25 Let x be the amount of time (in minutes) that a particular San Francisco commuter must wait for a BART train. Suppose that the density curve is as pictured (a uniform distribution):

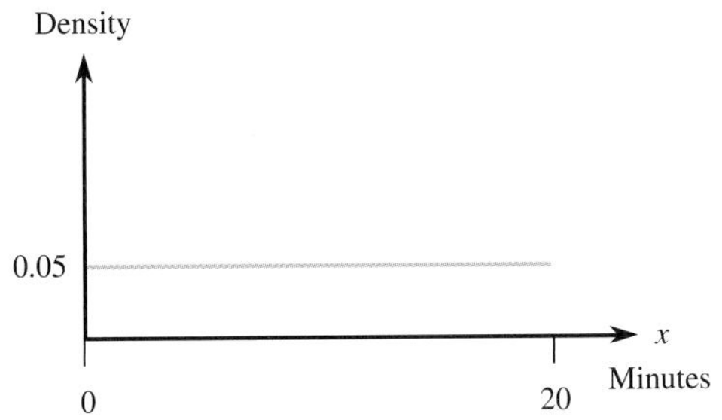

a. What is the probability that x is less than 10 minutes? more than 15 minutes?
b. What is the probability that x is between 7 and 12 minutes?
c. Find the value c for which $P(x < c) = .9$.

7.26 Referring to Exercise 7.25, let x and y be waiting times on two independently selected days. Define a new random variable w by $w = x + y$, the sum of the two waiting times. The set of possible values for w is the interval from 0 to 40 (because both x and y can range from 0 to 20). It can be shown that the density curve of w is as pictured (this curve is called a triangular distribution, for obvious reasons!):

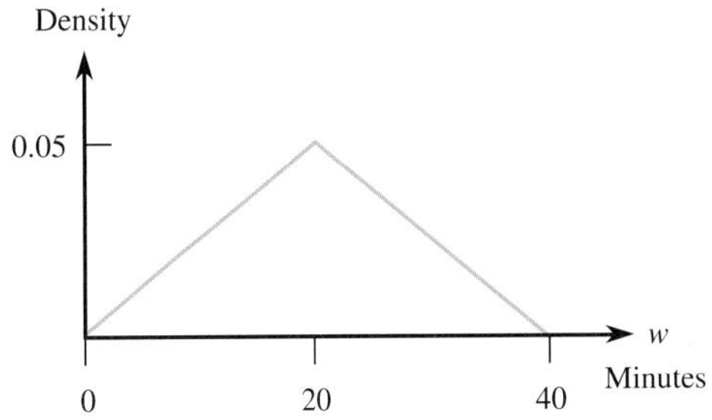

a. Verify that the total area under the density curve is equal to 1. (Hint: The area of a triangle is $= \frac{1}{2}$(base)(height).)
b. What is the probability that w is less than 20? less than 10? greater than 30?
c. What is the probability that w is between 10 and 30? (Hint: It might be easier first to find the probability that w is not between 10 and 30.)

7.4 Mean and Standard Deviation of a Random Variable

We study a random variable x, such as the number of insurance claims made by a homeowner (a discrete variable) or the birth weight of a baby (a continuous variable), to learn something about how its values are distributed along the measurement scale. The sample mean $\bar{x}$ and sample standard deviation s summarize center and spread for the values in a sample. Similarly, the mean value and standard deviation of a random variable describe where the variable's probability distribution is centered and the extent to which it spreads out about the center.

The **mean value of a random variable x**, denoted by μ_x, describes where the probability distribution of x is centered.

The **standard deviation of a random variable x**, denoted by σ_x, describes variability in the probability distribution. When the value of σ_x is small, observed values of x will tend to be close to the mean value (little variability). When the value of σ_x is large, there will be more variability in observed x values.

Figure 7.10(a) shows two discrete probability distributions with the same standard deviation (spread) but different means (center). One distribution has a mean of $\mu_x = 6$ and the other has $\mu_x = 10$. Which is which? Figure 7.10(b) shows two continuous probability distributions that have the same mean but different standard deviations. Which distribution—(i) or (ii)—has the larger standard deviation? Finally, Figure 7.10(c) shows three continuous distributions with different means and standard deviations. Which of the three distributions has the largest mean? Which has a mean of about 5? Which distribution has the smallest standard deviation? (The answers to these questions are the following: Figure 7.10(a)(ii) has a mean of 6, and Figure 7.10(a)(i) has a mean of 10; Figure 7.10(b)(ii) has the larger standard deviation; Figure 7.10(c)(iii) has the largest mean, Figure 7.10(c)(ii) has a mean of about 5, and Figure 7.10(c)(iii) has the smallest standard deviation.)

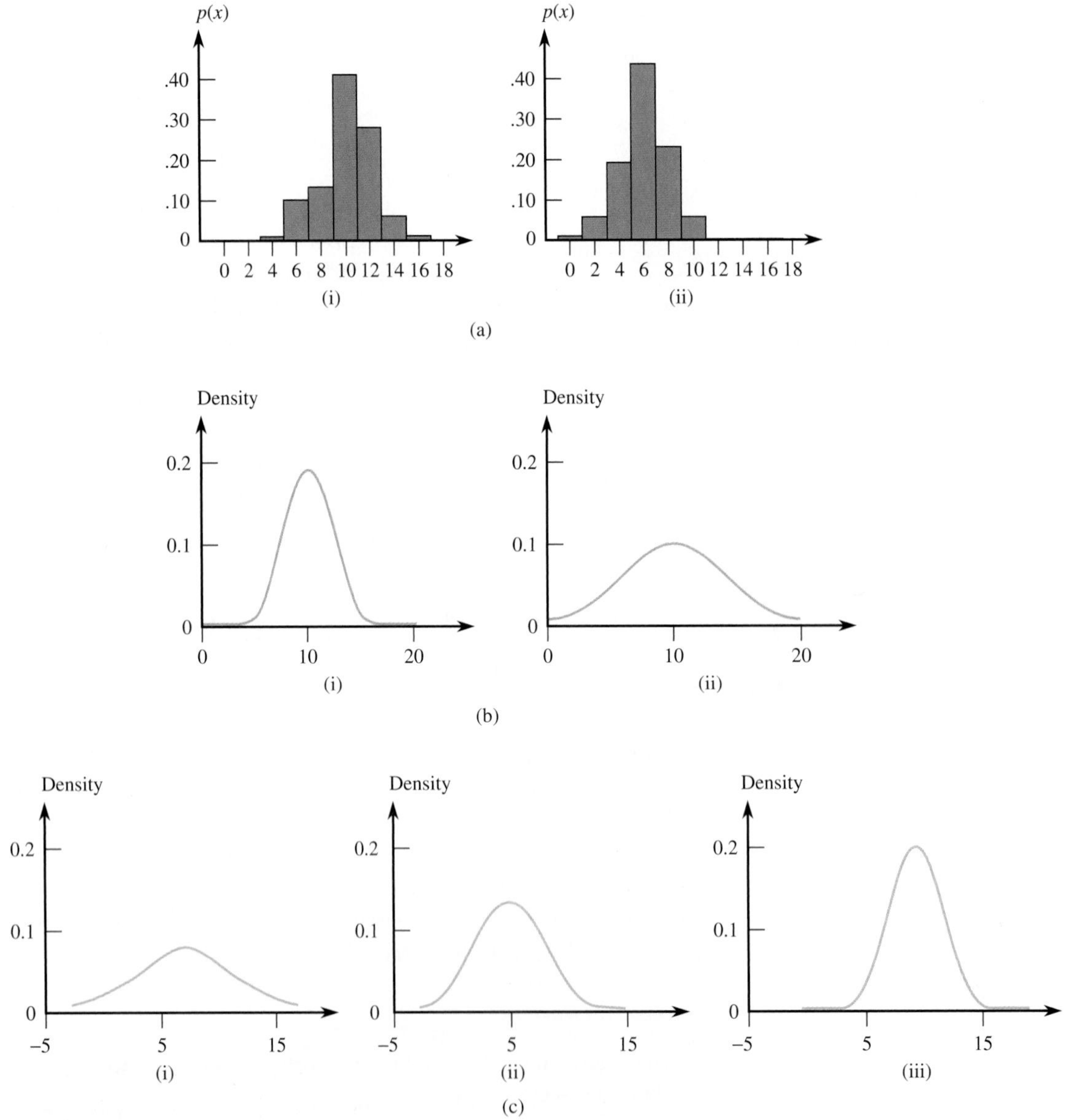

FIGURE 7.10
Some probability distributions: (a) different values of μ_x with the same value of σ_x; (b) different values of σ_x with the same value of μ_x; (c) different values of μ_x and σ_x.

It is customary to use the terms *mean of the random variable x* and *mean of the probability distribution of x* interchangeably. Similarly, the standard deviation of the random variable x and the standard deviation of the probability distribution of x refer to the same thing. Although the mean and standard deviation are computed differently for discrete and continuous random variables, the interpretation is the same in both cases.

Mean Value of a Discrete Random Variable

Consider an experiment consisting of randomly selecting an automobile licensed in a particular state. Let the discrete random variable x be the number of low-beam headlights on the selected car that need adjustment. Possible x values are 0, 1, and 2, and the probability distribution of x might be as follows:

x value	0	1	2
Probability	.5	.3	.2

The corresponding probability histogram appears in Figure 7.11. In a sample of 100 cars, the sample relative frequencies might differ somewhat from the given probabilities (which are the limiting relative frequencies). We might see:

x value	0	1	2
Frequency	46	33	21

The sample average value of x for these 100 observations is then the sum of 46 zeros, 33 ones, and 21 twos, all divided by 100:

$$\begin{aligned}\bar{x} &= \frac{(46)(0) + (33)(1) + (21)(2)}{100} \\ &= \left(\frac{46}{100}\right)(0) + \left(\frac{33}{100}\right)(1) + \left(\frac{21}{100}\right)(2) \\ &= (\text{rel. freq. of } 0)(0) + (\text{rel. freq. of } 1)(1) + (\text{rel. freq. of } 2)(2) \\ &= .75\end{aligned}$$

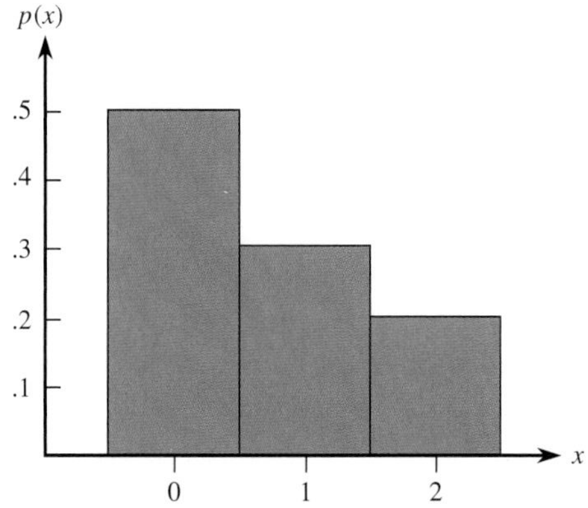

FIGURE 7.11
Probability histogram for the distribution of the number of headlights needing adjustments.

As the sample size increases, each relative frequency approaches the corresponding probability. In a very long sequence of experiments, the value of $\bar{x}$ approaches

$$\begin{aligned}&P(x = 0)(0) + P(x = 1)(1) + P(x = 2)(2) \\ &= (.5)(0) + (.3)(1) + (.2)(2) \\ &= .70 \\ &= \text{mean value of } x\end{aligned}$$

Notice that the expression for $\bar{x}$ is a weighted average of possible x values; the weight of each value is the observed relative frequency. Similarly, the mean value of the random variable x is a weighted average, but now the weights are the probabilities from the probability distribution.

DEFINITION

The **mean value of a discrete random variable x,** denoted by μ_x, is computed by first multiplying each possible x value by the probability of observing that value and then adding the resulting quantities. Symbolically,

$$\mu_x = \sum_{\text{all possible } x \text{ values}} x \cdot p(x)$$

The term **expected value** is sometimes used in place of mean value, and $E(x)$ is alternative notation for μ_x.

EXAMPLE 7.9 Exam Attempts

Individuals applying for a certain license are allowed up to four attempts to pass the licensing exam. Let x denote the number of attempts made by a randomly selected applicant. The probability distribution of x is as follows:

x	1	2	3	4
$p(x)$	.10	.20	.30	.40

Then x has mean value

$$\begin{aligned}\mu_x &= \sum_{x=1,2,3,4} x \cdot p(x) \\ &= (1)p(1) + (2)p(2) + (3)p(3) + (4)p(4) \\ &= (1)(.10) + (2)(.20) + (3)(.30) + (4)(.40) \\ &= .10 + .40 + .90 + 1.60 \\ &= 3.00\end{aligned}$$

It is no accident that the symbol μ_x for the mean value is the same symbol used previously for a population mean. When the probability distribution describes how x values are distributed among the members of a population (and therefore the probabilities are population relative frequencies), the mean value of x is exactly the average value of x in the population.

EXAMPLE 7.10 Apgar Scores

At 1 minute after birth and again at 5 minutes, each newborn child is given a numerical rating called an Apgar score. Possible values of this score are 0, 1, 2, . . . , 9, 10. A child's score is determined by five factors: muscle tone, skin color, respiratory effort, strength of heartbeat, and reflex, with a high score indicating a healthy infant. Let the random variable x denote the Apgar score (at 1 minute) of a randomly selected newborn infant at a particular hospital, and suppose that x has the following probability distribution:

x	0	1	2	3	4	5	6	7	8	9	10
$p(x)$	.002	.001	.002	.005	.02	.04	.17	.38	.25	.12	.01

The mean value of x is

$$\begin{aligned}\mu_x &= (0)p(0) + (1)p(1) + \cdots + (9)p(9) + (10)p(10)\\ &= (0)(.002) + (1)(.001) + \cdots + (9)(.12) + (10)(.01)\\ &= 7.16\end{aligned}$$

The average Apgar score for a *sample* of newborn children born at this hospital may be $\bar{x} = 7.05$, $\bar{x} = 8.30$, or any one of a number of other possible values between 0 and 10. However, as child after child is born and rated, the average score will approach the value 7.16. This value can be interpreted as the mean Apgar score for the population of all babies born at this hospital.

Standard Deviation of a Discrete Random Variable

The mean value μ_x provides only a partial summary of a probability distribution. Two different distributions can have the same value of μ_x, yet a long sequence of sample values from one distribution might exhibit considerably more variability than a long sequence of values from the other distribution.

EXAMPLE 7.11 Glass Panels

Flat screen TVs require high quality glass with very few flaws. A television manufacturer receives glass panels from two different suppliers. Let x and y denote the number of flaws in a randomly selected glass panel from the first and second suppliers, respectively. Suppose that the probability distributions for x and y are as follows:

x	0	1	2	3	4
$p(x)$	.4	.3	.2	.1	0

y	0	1	2	3	4
$p(y)$	.2	.6	.2	0	0

Probability histograms for x and y are given in Figure 7.12.

It is easy to verify that the mean values of both x and y are 1, so for either supplier the long-run average number of flaws per panel is 1. However, the two probability histograms show that the probability distribution for the second supplier is concentrated closer to the mean value than is the first supplier's distribution.

AP* EXAM TIP

Just as was true for data distributions, considering center, shape, and spread are central to understanding the behavior of random variables. Given a discrete probability distribution, you should be able to draw the probability histogram and to calculate the mean and standard deviation of the probability distribution.

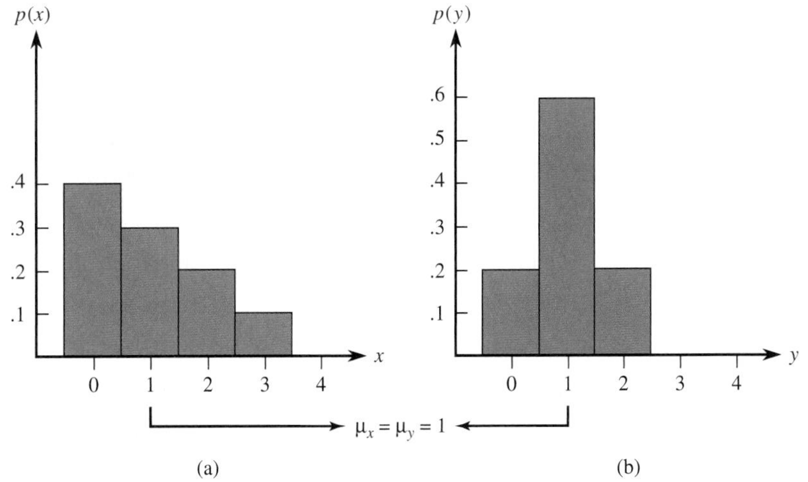

FIGURE 7.12
Probability distribution for the number of flaws in a glass panel in Example 7.11: (a) Supplier 1; (b) Supplier 2.

The greater spread of the first distribution implies that there will be more variability in a long sequence of observed x values than in an observed sequence of y values. For example, the y sequence will contain no 3's, whereas in the long run, 10% of the observed x values will be 3.

As with s^2 and s, the variance and standard deviation of x involve squared deviations from the mean. A value far from the mean results in a large squared deviation. However, such a value contributes substantially to variability in x only if the probability associated with that value is not too small. For example, if $\mu_x = 1$ and $x = 25$ is a possible value, then the squared deviation is $(25 - 1)^2 = 576$. If, however, $P(x = 25) = .000001$, the value 25 will hardly ever be observed, so it won't contribute much to variability in a long sequence of observations. This is why each squared deviation is multiplied by the probability associated with the value to obtain a measure of variability.

DEFINITION

The **variance of a discrete random variable x**, denoted by σ_x^2, is computed by first subtracting the mean from each possible x value to obtain the deviations, then squaring each deviation and multiplying the result by the probability of the corresponding x value, and finally adding these quantities. Symbolically,

$$\sigma_x^2 = \sum_{\text{all possible } x \text{ values}} (x - \mu_x)^2 p(x)$$

The **standard deviation of x**, denoted by σ_x, is the square root of the variance.

When the probability distribution describes how x values are distributed among members of a population (so that the probabilities are population relative frequencies), σ_x^2 and σ_x are the population variance and standard deviation (of x), respectively.

EXAMPLE 7.12 Glass Panels Revisited

For x = number of flaws in a glass panel from the first supplier in Example 7.11,

$$\begin{aligned}\sigma_x^2 &= (0 - 1)^2p(0) + (1 - 1)^2p(1) + (2 - 1)^2p(2) + (3 - 1)^2p(3)\\ &= (1)(.4) + (0)(.3) + (1)(.2) + (4)(.1)\\ &= 1.0\end{aligned}$$

Therefore $\sigma_x = 1.0$. For y = the number of flaws in a glass panel from the second supplier,

$$\sigma_y^2 = (0 - 1)^2(.2) + (1 - 1)^2(.6) + (2 - 1)^2(.2) = .4$$

Then $\sigma_y = \sqrt{.4} = .632$. The fact that $\sigma_x > \sigma_y$ confirms the impression conveyed by Figure 7.12 concerning the variability of x and y.

EXAMPLE 7.13 More on Apgar Scores

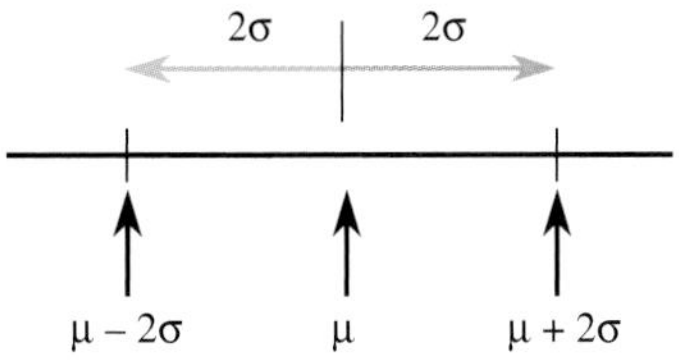

FIGURE 7.13
Values within 2 standard deviations of the mean.

Reconsider the distribution of Apgar scores for children born at a certain hospital, introduced in Example 7.10. What is the probability that a randomly selected child's score will be within 2 standard deviations of the mean score? As Figure 7.13 shows, values of x within 2 standard deviations of the mean are those for which

$$\mu - 2\sigma < x < \mu + 2\sigma.$$

From Example 7.10 we already have $\mu_x = 7.16$. The variance is

$$\begin{aligned}\sigma^2 &= \sum(x - \mu)^2p(x) = \sum(x - 7.16)^2p(x)\\ &= (0 - 7.16)^2(.002) + (1 - 7.16)^2(.001) + \cdots + (10 - 7.16)^2(.01)\\ &= 1.5684\end{aligned}$$

and the standard deviation is

$$\sigma = \sqrt{1.5684} = 1.25$$

This gives (using the probabilities given in Example 7.10)

$$\begin{aligned}P(\mu - 2\sigma < x < \mu + 2\sigma) &= P(7.16 - 2.50 < x < 7.16 + 2.50)\\ &= P(4.66 < x < 9.66)\\ &= p(5) + \cdots + p(9)\\ &= .96\end{aligned}$$

Mean and Standard Deviation When x Is Continuous

For continuous probability distributions, μ_x and σ_x can be defined and computed using methods from calculus. The details need not concern us; what is important is knowing that μ_x and σ_x play exactly the same role here as they did in the discrete case. The mean value μ_x locates the center of the continuous distribution and gives the approximate long-run average of many observed x values. The standard deviation σ_x measures the extent that the continuous distribution (density curve) spreads out about μ_x and gives information about the amount of variability that can be expected in a long sequence of observed x values.

EXAMPLE 7.14 A "Concrete" Example

A company receives concrete of a certain type from two different suppliers. Define random variables x and y as follows:

x = compressive strength of a randomly selected batch from Supplier 1
y = compressive strength of a randomly selected batch from Supplier 2

Suppose that

$\mu_x = 4650$ pounds/inch^2 $\quad \sigma_x = 200$ pounds/inch^2
$\mu_y = 4500$ pounds/inch^2 $\quad \sigma_y = 275$ pounds/inch^2

The long-run average strength per batch for many, many batches from Supplier 1 will be roughly 4650 pounds/inch^2. This is 150 pounds/inch^2 greater than the long-run average for batches from Supplier 2. In addition, a long sequence of batches from Supplier 1 will exhibit substantially less variability in compressive strength values than will a similar sequence from Supplier 2. The first supplier is preferred to the second both in terms of mean value and variability. Figure 7.14 displays density curves that are consistent with this information.

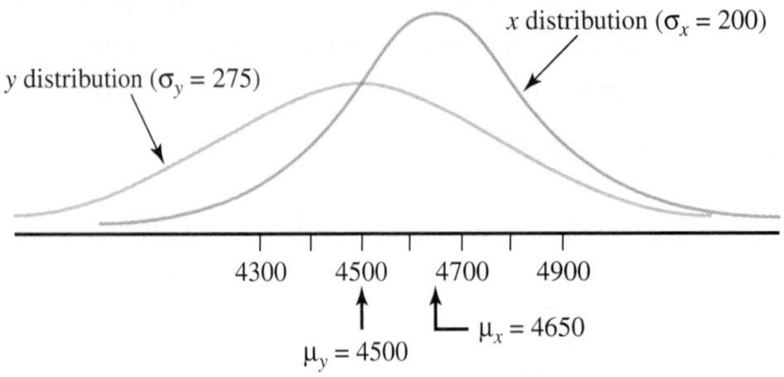

FIGURE 7.14
Density curves for Example 7.14.

Mean and Variance of Linear Functions and Linear Combinations

> **AP* EXAM TIP**
>
> Be sure to read homework and exam questions carefully. With probability in general, and the algebraic formulas for working with random variables in particular, deciding which rule applies in a given situation will be much easier if you read carefully!

We have seen how the mean and standard deviation of one or more random variables provide useful information about the variables' long-run behavior, but we might also be interested in the behavior of some function of these variables.

For example, consider the experiment in which a customer of a propane gas company is randomly selected. Suppose that the mean and standard deviation of the random variable

x = number of gallons required to fill a customer's propane tank

are known to be 318 gallons and 42 gallons, respectively. The company is considering two different pricing models:

Model 1: \$3 per gallon
Model 2: service charge of \$50 + \$2.80 per gallon

The company is interested in the variable

y = amount billed

For each of the two models, y can be expressed as a function of the random variable x:

Model 1: $y_{model\ 1} = 3x$
Model 2: $y_{model\ 2} = 50 + 2.8x$

Both of these equations are examples of a linear function of x. The mean and standard deviation of a linear function of x can be computed from the mean and standard deviation of x, as described in the following box.

The Mean, Variance, and Standard Deviation of a Linear Function

If x is a random variable with mean μ_x and variance σ_x and a and b are numerical constants, the random variable y defined by

$$y = a + bx$$

is called a **linear function of the random variable x.**

(continued)

The mean of $y = a + bx$ is

$$\mu_y = \mu_{a+bx} = a + b\mu_x$$

The variance of y is

$$\sigma_y^2 = \sigma_{a+bx}^2 = b^2\sigma_x^2$$

from which it follows that the standard deviation of y is

$$\sigma_y = \sigma_{a+bx} = |b|\sigma_x$$

We can use the results in the preceding box to compute the mean and standard deviation of the billing amount variable for the propane gas example, as follows:

For Model 1:

$$\mu_{model\ 1} = \mu_{3x} = 3\mu_x = 3(318) = 954$$
$$\sigma_{model\ 1}^2 = \sigma_{3x}^2 = 3^2\sigma_x^2 = 9(42)^2 = 15{,}876$$
$$\sigma_{model\ 1} = \sqrt{15{,}876} = 126 = 3(42)$$

For Model 2:

$$\mu_{model\ 2} = \mu_{50+2.8x} = 50 + 2.8\mu_x = 50 + 2.8(318) = 940.40$$
$$\sigma_{model\ 2}^2 = \sigma_{50+2.8x}^2 = 2.8^2\sigma_x^2 = (2.8)^2(42)^2 = 13{,}829.76$$
$$\sigma_{model\ 2} = \sqrt{13{,}829.76} = 117.60, \text{ which is equal to } 2.8(42)$$

The mean billing amount for Model 1 is a bit higher than for Model 2, as is the variability in billing amounts. Model 2 results in slightly more consistency from bill to bill in the amount charged.

Linear Combinations Now let's consider a different type of problem. Suppose that you have three tasks that you plan to complete on the way home from school: stop at the public library to return an overdue book for which you must pay a fine, deposit your most recent paycheck at the bank, and stop by the office supply store to purchase paper for your computer printer. Define the following variables:

x_1 = time required to return book and pay fine
x_2 = time required to deposit paycheck
x_3 = time required to buy printer paper

We can then define a new variable, y, to represent the total amount of time to complete these tasks:

$$y = x_1 + x_2 + x_3$$

Defined in this way, y is an example of a linear combination of random variables.

If $x_1, x_2, \ldots, x_n$ are random variables and $a_1, a_2, \ldots, a_n$ are numerical constants, the random variable y defined as

$$y = a_1x_1 + a_2x_2 + \cdots + a_nx_n$$

is a **linear combination of the** x_i**'s.**

For example, $y = 10x_1 - 5x_2 + 8x_3$ is a linear combination of x_1, x_2, and x_3 with $a_1 = 10$, $a_2 = -5$ and $a_3 = 8$. It is easy to compute the mean of a linear combination of x_i's if the individual means $\mu_1, \mu_2, \ldots, \mu_n$ are known. The variance and standard deviation of a linear combination of the x_i's are also easily computed *if the x_i's are independent.* Two random variables x_i and x_j are independent if any event defined solely by x_i is independent of any event defined solely by x_j. When the x_i's are not independent, computation of the variance and standard deviation of a linear combination of the x_i is more complicated; this case is not considered here.

Mean, Variance, and Standard Deviation for Linear Combinations

If $x_1, x_2, \dots, x_n$ are random variables with means $\mu_1, \mu_2, \dots, \mu_n$ and variances $\sigma_1^2, \sigma_2^2, \dots, \sigma_n^2$, respectively, and

$$y = a_1x_1 + a_2x_2 + \cdots + a_nx_n$$

then

1. $\mu_y = \mu_{a_1x_1+a_2x_2+\cdots+a_nx_n} = a_1\mu_1 + a_2\mu_2 + \cdots + a_n\mu_n$

This result is true regardless of whether the x_i's are independent.

2. When $x_1, x_2, \dots, x_n$ are *independent* random variables,

$$\sigma_y^2 = \sigma^2_{a_1x_1+a_2x_2+\cdots+a_nx_n} = a_1^2\sigma_1^2 + a_2^2\sigma_2^2 + \cdots + a_n^2\sigma_n^2$$

$$\sigma_y = \sigma_{a_1x_1+a_2x_2+\cdots+a_nx_n} = \sqrt{a_1^2\sigma_1^2 + a_2^2\sigma_2^2 + \cdots + a_n^2\sigma_n^2}$$

This result is true only when the x_i's are independent.

Examples 7.15–7.17 illustrate the use of these rules.

EXAMPLE 7.15 Freeway Traffic

Three different roads feed into a particular freeway entrance. Suppose that during a fixed time period, the number of cars coming from each road onto the freeway is a random variable with mean values as follows:

Road	1	2	3
Mean	800	1000	600

With x_i representing the number of cars entering from road i, we can define y, the total number of cars entering the freeway, as $y = x_1 + x_2 + x_3$, the total number of cars entering the freeway. The mean value of y is

$$\begin{aligned}\mu_y &= \mu_{x_1+x_2+x_3}\\ &= \mu_{x_1} + \mu_{x_2} + \mu_{x_3}\\ &= 800 + 1000 + 600\\ &= 2400\end{aligned}$$

EXAMPLE 7.16 Combining Exam Subscores

A nationwide standardized exam consists of a multiple-choice section and a free response section. For each section, the mean and standard deviation are reported to be

	Mean	Standard Deviation
Multiple Choice	38	6
Free Response	30	7

Let's define x_1 and x_2 as the multiple-choice score and the free-response score, respectively, of a student selected at random from those taking this exam. We are also interested in the variable y = overall exam score. Suppose that the free-response score is given twice the weight of the multiple-choice score in determining the overall exam score. Then the overall score is computed as $y = x_1 + 2x_2$. What are the mean and standard deviation of y?

Because $y = x_1 + 2x_2$ is a linear combination of x_1 and x_2, the mean of y is

$$\begin{aligned}\mu_y &= \mu_{x_1+2x_2} \\ &= \mu_{x_1} + 2\mu_{x_2} \\ &= 38 + 2(30) \\ &= 98\end{aligned}$$

What about the variance and standard deviation of y? To use Rule 2 in the preceding box, x_1 and x_2 must be independent. It is unlikely that the value of x_1 (a student's multiple-choice score) would be unrelated to the value of x_2 (the same student's free-response score), because it seems probable that students who score well on one section of the exam will also tend to score well on the other section. Therefore, it would not be appropriate to use the formulas mentioned above to calculate the variance and standard deviation.

EXAMPLE 7.17 Baggage Weights

A commuter airline flies small planes between San Luis Obispo and San Francisco. For small planes, the baggage weight is a concern, especially on foggy mornings, because the weight of the plane has an effect on how quickly the plane can ascend. Suppose that it is known that the variable x = weight (in pounds) of baggage checked by a randomly selected passenger has a mean and standard deviation of 42 and 16, respectively. Consider a flight on which 10 passengers, all traveling alone, are flying. If we use x_i to denote the baggage weight for passenger i (for i ranging from 1 to 10), the total weight of checked baggage, y, is then

$$y = x_1 + x_2 + \cdots + x_{10}$$

Note that y is a linear combination of the x_i's. The mean value of y is

$$\begin{aligned}\mu_y &= \mu_{x_1} + \mu_{x_2} + \cdots + \mu_{x_{10}} \\ &= 42 + 42 + \cdots + 42 \\ &= 420\end{aligned}$$

Since the 10 passengers are all traveling alone, it is reasonable to think that the 10 baggage weights are unrelated and that the x_i's are independent. (This would not be a reasonable assumption if the 10 passengers were not traveling alone.) Then the variance of y is

$$\begin{aligned}\sigma_y^2 &= \sigma_{x_1}^2 + \sigma_{x_2}^2 + \cdots + \sigma_{x_{10}}^2 \\ &= 16^2 + 16^2 + \cdots + 16^2 \\ &= 2560\end{aligned}$$

and the standard deviation of y is

$$\sigma_y = \sqrt{2650} = 50.596$$

One Last Note on Linear Functions and Linear Combinations

In Example 7.17, the random variable of interest was x = weight of baggage checked by a randomly selected airline passenger. However, when we considered a flight with multiple passengers, we added subscripts to create variables like

$$x_1 = \text{baggage weight for passenger 1}$$

and

$$x_2 = \text{baggage weight for passenger 2}$$

It is important to note that the sum of the baggage weights for two different passengers does not result in the same value as doubling the baggage weight of a single passenger. That is, the linear combination $x_1 + x_2$ is different from the linear function $2x$. Although the mean of $x_1 + x_2$ and the mean of $2x$ are the same, the variances and standard deviations are different. For example, for the baggage weight distribution described in Example 7.17 (mean of 42 and standard deviation of 16), the mean of $2x$ is

$$\mu_{2x} = 2\mu_x = 2(42) = 84$$

and the mean of $x_1 + x_2$ is

$$\mu_{x_1+x_2} = \mu_{x_1} + \mu_{x_2} = 42 + 42 = 84$$

However, the variance of $2x$ is

$$\sigma^2_{2x} = (2)^2\sigma^2_x = 4(16^2) = 1024$$

whereas the variance of $x_1 + x_2$ is

$$\sigma^2_{x_1+x_2} = \sigma^2_{x_1} + \sigma_{2x_2} = 16^2 + 16^2 = 256 + 256 = 512$$

This means that observations of $2x$ for randomly selected passengers will show more variability than observations of $x_1 + x_2$ for two randomly selected passengers. This may seem counterintuitive, but it is true! For example, each row of the first two columns of the accompanying table show simulated baggage weights for two passengers (an x_1 and an x_2 value) that were selected at random from a probability distribution with mean 42 and standard deviation 16. The third column of the table contains the value of $2x_1$ (two times the passenger 1 baggage weight) and the last column contains the values of $x_1 + x_2$ (the sum of the passenger 1 baggage weight and the passenger 2 baggage weight).

x_1	x_2	$2x_1$	$x_1 + x_2$
56	41	112	97
30	5	60	35
32	15	64	47
55	45	110	100
40	54	80	94
41	68	82	109
42	35	84	77
33	47	66	80
46	52	92	98
73	40	146	113
44	23	88	67

(continued)

x_1	x_2	$2x_1$	$x_1 + x_2$
48	54	96	102
52	69	104	121
56	63	112	119
79	35	158	114
18	34	36	52
8	71	16	79
51	58	102	109
18	49	36	67
41	46	82	87

Figure 7.15 shows dotplots of the 20 values of $2x_1$ and the 20 values of $x_1 + x_2$. You can see that there is less variability in the $x_1 + x_2$ values than in the values of $2x_1$.

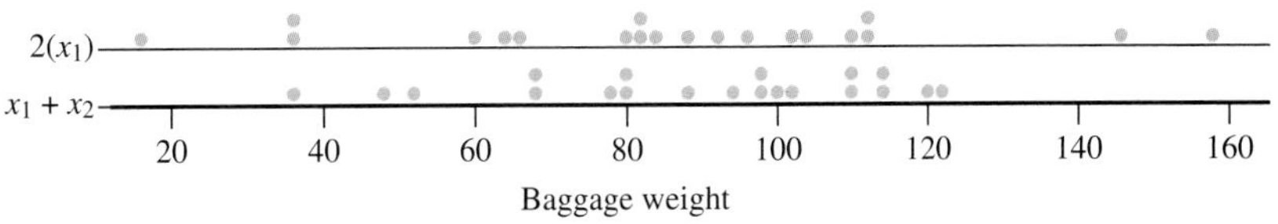

FIGURE 7.15
Dotplots of $2x_1$ and $x_1 + x_2$.

EXERCISES 7.27 - 7.42

7.27 An express mail service charges a special rate for any package that weighs less than 1 pound. Let x denote the weight of a randomly selected parcel that qualifies for this special rate. The probability distribution of x is specified by the following density curve:

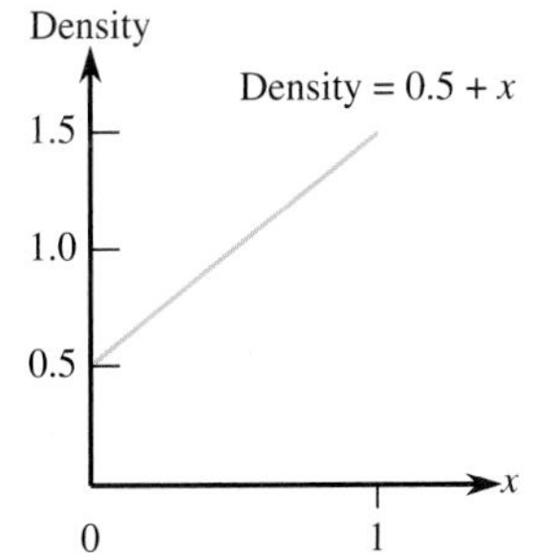

Use the fact that area of a trapezoid = (base)(average of two side lengths) to answer each of the following questions:

a. What is the probability that a randomly selected package of this type weighs at most 0.5 pound? between 0.25 and 0.5 pound? at least 0.75 pound?

b. It can be shown that $\mu_x = \frac{7}{12}$ and $\sigma_x^2 = \frac{11}{144}$. What is the probability that the value of x is more than 1 standard deviation from the mean value?

7.28 The probability distribution of x, the number of defective tires on a randomly selected automobile checked at a certain inspection station, is given in the following table:

x	0	1	2	3	4
$p(x)$	.54	.16	.06	.04	.20

a. Calculate the mean value of x.

b. What is the probability that x exceeds its mean value?

7.29 Exercise 7.9 introduced the following probability distribution for y = the number of broken eggs in a carton:

y	0	1	2	3	4
$p(y)$	.65	.20	.10	.04	.01

a. Calculate and interpret μ_y.

b. In the long run, for what percentage of cartons is the number of broken eggs less than μ_y? Does this surprise you?

c. Why doesn't $\mu_y = (0 + 1 + 2 + 3 + 4)/5 = 2.0$. Explain.

7.30 Referring to Exercise 7.29, use the result of Part (a) along with the fact that a carton contains 12 eggs to determine the mean value of z = the number of unbroken eggs. (Hint: z can be written as a linear function of y.)

7.31 Exercise 7.8 gave the following probability distribution for x = the number of courses for which a randomly selected student at a certain university is registered:

x	1	2	3	4	5	6	7
$p(x)$	.02	.03	.09	.25	.40	.16	.05

It can be easily verified that $\mu = 4.66$ and $\sigma = 1.20$.

a. Because $\mu - \sigma = 3.46$, the x values 1, 2, and 3 are more than 1 standard deviation below the mean. What is the probability that x is more than 1 standard deviation below its mean?

b. What x values are more than 2 standard deviations away from the mean value (either less than $\mu - 2\sigma$ or greater than $\mu + 2\sigma$)? What is the probability that x is more than 2 standard deviations away from its mean value?

7.32 Example 7.11 gave the probability distributions of x = number of flaws in a randomly selected glass panel for two suppliers of glass used in the manufacture of flat screen TVs. If the manufacturer wanted to select a single supplier for glass panels, which of these two suppliers would you recommend? Justify your choice based on consideration of both center and variability.

7.33 The states of Ohio, Iowa, and Idaho are often confused, probably because the names sound so similar. Each year, the State Tourism Directors of these three states drive to a meeting in one of the state capitals to discuss strategies for attracting tourists to their states so that the states will become better known. The location of the meeting is selected at random from the three state capitals. The shortest highway distance from Boise, Idaho to Columbus, Ohio passes through Des Moines, Iowa. The highway distance from Boise to Des Moines is 1350 miles, and the distance from Des Moines to Columbus is 650 miles. Let d_1 represent the driving distance from Columbus to the meeting, with d_2 and d_3 representing the distances from Des Moines and Boise, respectively.

a. Find the probability distribution of d_1 and display it in a table.

b. What is the expected value of d_1?

c. What is the value of the standard deviation of d_1?

d. Consider the probability distributions of d_2 and d_3. Is either probability distribution the same as the probability distribution of d_1? Justify your answer.

e. Define a new random variable $t = d_1 + d_2$. Find the probability distribution of t.

f. For each of the following statements, indicate if the statement is true or false and provide statistical evidence to support your answer.

i. $E(t) = E(d_1) + E(d_2)$ (Hint: $E(t)$ is the expected value of t and another way of denoting the mean of t.)

ii. $\sigma_t^2 = \sigma_{d_1}^2 + \sigma_{d_2}^2$

7.34 Suppose that for a given computer salesperson, the probability distribution of x = the number of systems sold in 1 month is given by the following table:

x	1	2	3	4	5	6	7	8
$p(x)$	.05	.10	.12	.30	.30	.11	.01	.01

a. Find the mean value of x (the mean number of systems sold).

b. Find the variance and standard deviation of x. How would you interpret these values?

c. What is the probability that the number of systems sold is within 1 standard deviation of its mean value?

d. What is the probability that the number of systems sold is more than 2 standard deviations from the mean?

7.35 A local television station sells 15-second, 30-second, and 60-second advertising spots. Let x denote the length of a randomly selected commercial appearing on this station, and suppose that the probability distribution of x is given by the following table:

x	15	30	60
$p(x)$	.1	.3	.6

a. Find the average length for commercials appearing on this station.

b. If a 15-second spot sells for \$500, a 30-second spot for \$800, and a 60-second spot for \$1000, find the average amount paid for commercials appearing on this station. (Hint: Consider a new variable, y = cost, and then find the probability distribution and mean value of y.)

7.36 An author has written a book and submitted it to a publisher. The publisher offers to print the book and gives the author the choice between a flat payment of \$10,000 and a royalty plan. Under the royalty plan the author would receive \$1 for each copy of the book sold. The author thinks that the following table gives the probability distribution of the variable x = the number of books that will be sold:

x	1000	5000	10,000	20,000
$p(x)$	.05	.30	.40	.25

Which payment plan should the author choose? Why?

7.37 A grocery store has an express line for customers purchasing at most five items. Let x be the number of items purchased by a randomly selected customer using this line. Give examples of two different assignments of probabilities such that the resulting distributions have the same mean but quite different standard deviations.

7.38 An appliance dealer sells three different models of upright freezers having 13.5, 15.9, and 19.1 cubic feet of storage space. Let x = the amount of storage space purchased by the next customer to buy a freezer. Suppose that x has the following probability distribution:

x	13.5	15.9	19.1
$p(x)$	.2	.5	.3

a. Calculate the mean and standard deviation of x.
b. If the price of the freezer depends on the size of the storage space, x, such that *Price* $= 25x - 8.5$, what is the mean value of the variable *Price* paid by the next customer?
c. What is the standard deviation of the price paid?

7.39 ✦ To assemble a piece of furniture, a wood peg must be inserted into a predrilled hole. Suppose that the diameter of a randomly selected peg is a random variable with mean 0.25 inch and standard deviation 0.006 inch and that the diameter of a randomly selected hole is a random variable with mean 0.253 inch and standard deviation 0.002 inch. Let x_1 = peg diameter, and let x_2 = denote hole diameter.

a. Why would the random variable y, defined as $y = x_2 - x_1$, be of interest to the furniture manufacturer?
b. What is the mean value of the random variable y?
c. Assuming that x_1 and x_2 are independent, what is the standard deviation of y?
d. Is it reasonable to think that x_1 and x_2 are independent? Explain.
e. Based on your answers to Parts (b) and (c), do you think that finding a peg that is too big to fit in the predrilled hole would be a relatively common or a relatively rare occurrence? Explain.

7.40 A multiple-choice exam consists of 50 questions. Each question has five choices, of which only one is correct. Suppose that the total score on the exam is computed as

$$y = x_1 - \frac{1}{4}x_2$$

where x_1 = number of correct responses and x_2 = number of incorrect responses. (Calculating a total score by subtracting a term based on the number of incorrect responses is known as a correction for guessing and is designed to discourage test takers from choosing answers at random.)

a. It can be shown that if a totally unprepared student answers all 50 questions by just selecting one of the five answers at random, then $\mu_{x_1} = 10$ and $\mu_{x_2} = 40$. What is the mean value of the total score, y? Does this surprise you? Explain.
b. Explain why it is unreasonable to use the formulas given in this section to compute the variance or standard deviation of y.

7.41 Consider a large ferry that can accommodate cars and buses. The toll for cars is \$3, and the toll for buses is \$10. Let x and y denote the number of cars and buses, respectively, carried on a single trip. Cars and buses are accommodated on different levels of the ferry, so the number of buses accommodated on any trip is independent of the number of cars on the trip. Suppose that x and y have the following probability distributions:

x	0	1	2	3	4	5
$p(x)$	.05	.10	.25	.30	.20	.10

y	0	1	2
$p(y)$	.50	.30	.20

a. Compute the mean and standard deviation of x.
b. Compute the mean and standard deviation of y.
c. Compute the mean and variance of the total amount of money collected in tolls from cars.
d. Compute the mean and variance of the total amount of money collected in tolls from buses.
e. Compute the mean and variance of z = total number of vehicles (cars and buses) on the ferry.
f. Compute the mean and variance of w = total amount of money collected in tolls.

7.42 Consider a game in which a red die and a blue die are rolled. Let x_R denote the value showing on the uppermost face of the red die, and define x_B similarly for the blue die.

a. The probability distribution of x_R is

x_R	1	2	3	4	5	6
$p(x_R)$	1/6	1/6	1/6	1/6	1/6	1/6

Find the mean, variance, and standard deviation of x_R.

b. What are the values of the mean, variance, and standard deviation of x_B? (You should be able to answer this question without doing any additional calculations.)

c. Suppose that you are offered a choice of the following two games:

Game 1: Costs \$7 to play, and you win y_1 dollars, where $y_1 = x_R + x_B$.

Game 2: Doesn't cost anything to play initially, but you "win" $3y_2$ dollars, where $y_2 = x_R - x_B$. If y_2 is negative, you must pay that amount; if it is positive, you receive that amount.

For Game 1, the net amount won in a game is $w_1 = y_1 - 7 = x_R + x_B - 7$. What are the mean and standard deviation of w_1?

d. For Game 2, the net amount won in a game is $w_2 = 3y_2 = 3(x_R - x_B)$. What are the mean and standard deviation of w_2?

e. Based on your answers to Parts (c) and (d), if you had to play, which game would you choose and why?

7.5 Binomial and Geometric Distributions

In this section, we introduce two of the more commonly encountered discrete probability distributions: the binomial distribution and the geometric distribution. These distributions arise when the experiment of interest consists of making a sequence of dichotomous observations (two possible values for each observation). The process of making a single such observation is called a *trial.* For example, one characteristic of blood type is Rh factor, which can be either positive or negative. We can think of an experiment that consists of noting the Rh factor for each of 25 blood donors as a sequence of 25 dichotomous trials, where each trial consists of observing the Rh factor (positive or negative) of a single donor.

We could also conduct a different experiment that consists of observing the Rh factor of blood donors until a donor who is Rh-negative is encountered. This second experiment can also be viewed as a sequence of dichotomous trials, but the total number of trials in this experiment is not predetermined, as it was in the previous example, in which we knew in advance that there would be 25 trials. Experiments of the two types just described are characteristic of those leading to the binomial and the geometric probability distributions, respectively.

Binomial Distributions

Suppose that we decide to record the gender of each of the next 25 newborn children at a particular hospital. What is the chance that at least 15 are female? What is the chance that between 10 and 15 are female? How many among the 25 can we expect to be female? These and other similar questions can be answered by studying the *binomial probability distribution.* This distribution arises when the experiment of interest is a *binomial experiment.* Binomial experiments have the properties listed in the following box.

Properties of a Binomial Experiment

A binomial experiment consists of a sequence of trials with the following conditions:

1. There are a fixed number of trials.
2. Each trial can result in one of only two possible outcomes, labeled success (*S*) and failure (*F*).
3. Outcomes of different trials are independent.
4. The probability that a trial results in a success is the same for each trial.

(continued)

The **binomial random variable *x*** is defined as

x = number of successes observed when a binomial experiment is performed

The probability distribution of x is called the *binomial probability distribution.*

The term *success* here does not necessarily have any of its usual connotations. Which of the two possible outcomes is labeled "success" is determined by the random variable of interest. For example, if the variable counts the number of female births among the next 25 births at a particular hospital, then a female birth would be labeled a success (because this is what the variable counts). If male births were counted instead, a male birth would be labeled a success and a female birth a failure.

One situation in which a binominal probability distribution arises was given in Example 7.5. In that example, we considered x = number among four customers who selected an energy efficient refrigerator (rather than a less expensive model). This is a binomial experiment with four trials, where the purchase of an energy efficient refrigerator is considered a success and $P(\text{success}) = P(E) = .4$. The 16 possible outcomes, along with the associated probabilities, were displayed in Table 7.1.

Consider now the case of five customers, a binomial experiment with five trials. The possible values of x = number who purchase an energy efficient refrigerator are 0, 1, 2, 3, 4, and 5. There are 32 possible outcomes of the binomial experiment, each one a sequence of five successes and failures. Five of these outcomes result in $x = 1$: *SFFFF, FSFFF, FFSFF, FFFSF,* and *FFFFS.*

Because the trials are independent, the first of these outcomes has probability

$$\begin{aligned} P(SFFFF) &= P(S)P(F)P(F)P(F)P(F) \\ &= (.4)(.6)(.6)(.6)(.6) \\ &= (.4)(.6)^4 \\ &= .05184 \end{aligned}$$

The probability calculation will be the same for any outcome with only one success ($x = 1$). It does not matter where in the sequence the single success occurs. Thus

$$\begin{aligned} p(1) &= P(x = 1) \\ &= P(SFFFF \text{ or } FSFFF \text{ or } FFSFF \text{ or } FFFSF \text{ or } FFFFS) \\ &= .05184 + .05184 + .05184 + .05184 + .05184 \\ &= (5)(.05184) \\ &= .25920 \end{aligned}$$

Similarly, there are 10 outcomes for which $x = 2$, because there are 10 ways to select two from among the five trials to be the *S*'s: *SSFFF, SFSFF,* . . . , and *FFFSS.* The probability of each results from multiplying together (.4) two times and (.6) three times. For example,

$$\begin{aligned} P(SSFFF) &= (.4)(.4)(.6)(.6)(.6) \\ &= (.4)^2(.6)^3 \\ &= .03456 \end{aligned}$$

and so

$$\begin{aligned} p(2) &= P(x = 2) \\ &= P(SSFFF) + \cdots + P(FFFSS) \\ &= (10)(.4)^2(.6)^3 \\ &= .34560 \end{aligned}$$

The general form of the formula for calculating the probabilities associated with the different possible values of x is

$$\begin{aligned} p(x) &= P(x\ S\text{'s among the five trials}) \\ &= (\text{number of outcomes with } x\ S\text{'s}) \cdot (\text{probability of any given outcome with } x\ S\text{'s}) \\ &= (\text{number of outcomes with } x\ S\text{'s}) \cdot (.4)^x(.6)^{5-x} \end{aligned}$$

This form was seen previously where $p(2) = 10(.4)^2(.6)^3$.

Let n denote the number of trials in the experiment. Then the number of outcomes with x S's is the number of ways of selecting x from among the n trials to be the success trials. A simple expression for this quantity is

$$\text{number of outcomes with } x \text{ successes} = \frac{n!}{x!(n-x)!}$$

where, for any positive whole number m, the symbol $m!$ (read "m factorial") is defined by

$$m! = m(m-1)(m-2)\cdots(2)(1)$$

and $0! = 1$.

The Binomial Distribution

Let

n = number of independent trials in a binomial experiment
p = constant probability that any particular trial results in a success

Then

$$\begin{aligned} p(x) &= P(x \text{ successes among } n \text{ trials}) \\ &= \frac{n!}{x!(n-x)!}p^x(1-p)^{n-x} \quad x = 0, 1, 2, \ldots, n \end{aligned}$$

The expressions $\binom{n}{x}$ or ${}_nC_x$ are sometimes used in place of $\frac{n!}{x!(n-x)!}$. Both are read as "n choose x" and represent the number of ways of choosing x items from a set of n. The binomial probability function can then be written as

$$p(x) = \binom{n}{x}p^x(1-p)^{n-x} \quad x = 0, 1, 2, \ldots, n$$

or

$$p(x) = {}_nC_x p^x(1-p)^{n-x} \quad x = 0, 1, 2, \ldots, n$$

Notice that the probability distribution is specified using a formula that allows calculation of the various probabilities rather than by giving a table or a probability histogram.

EXAMPLE 7.18 Recognizing Your Roommate's Scent

An interesting experiment was described in the paper "Sociochemosensory and Emotional Functions" (*Psychological Science* [2009]: 1118–1123). The authors of this paper wondered if college students could recognize their roommate by scent. They carried out an experiment in which female college students used fragrance-free soap, deodorant, shampoo, and laundry detergent for a period of time. Their bedding was also laundered using a fragrance-free detergent. Each person was then given a new t-shirt that she slept in for one night. The shirt was then collected and sealed in an airtight bag. Later, the roommate was presented with three identical t-shirts (one worn by her roommate and two worn by other women) and asked to pick the one that smelled most like her roommate. (Yes, hard to believe, but people really do research like this!) This process was repeated a second time, with the shirts refolded and rearranged before the second trial. The researchers recorded how many times (0, 1, or 2) that the shirt worn by the roommate was correctly identified.

This can be viewed as a binomial experiment consisting of $n = 2$ trials. Each trial results in either a correct identification or an incorrect identification. Because the researchers counted the number of correct identifications, a correct identification is considered a success. We can then define $x =$ number of correct identifications.

Suppose that a participant is not able to identify her roommate by smell. If this is the case, she is essentially just picking one of the three shirts at random and so the probability of success (picking the correct shirt) is 1/3. And, if a participant can't identify her roommate by smell, it is also reasonable to regard the two trials as independent. In this case, the experiment satisfies the conditions of a binomial experiment, and x is a binomial random variable with $n = 2$ and $p = 1/3$.

We can use the binomial probability distribution formula to compute the probability associated with each of the possible x values as follows:

$$p(0) = \binom{2}{0}\left(\frac{1}{3}\right)^0\left(\frac{2}{3}\right)^2 = \frac{2!}{0!2!}\left(\frac{1}{3}\right)^0\left(\frac{2}{3}\right)^2 = (1)(1)\left(\frac{2}{3}\right)^2 = .4444$$

$$p(1) = \binom{2}{1}\left(\frac{1}{3}\right)^1\left(\frac{2}{3}\right)^1 = \frac{2!}{1!1!}\left(\frac{1}{3}\right)^1\left(\frac{2}{3}\right)^1 = (2)\left(\frac{1}{3}\right)^1\left(\frac{2}{3}\right)^1 = .4444$$

$$p(2) = \binom{2}{2}\left(\frac{1}{3}\right)^2\left(\frac{2}{3}\right)^0 = \frac{2!}{2!0!}\left(\frac{1}{3}\right)^2\left(\frac{2}{3}\right)^0 = (1)\left(\frac{1}{3}\right)^2(1) = .1111$$

Summarizing in table form gives

x	$p(x)$
0	.4444
1	.4444
2	.1111

This means that about 44.4% of the time, a person who is just guessing would pick the correct shirt on neither trial, about 44.4% of the time the correct shirt would be identified on one of the two trials, and about 11.1% of the time the correct shirt would be identified on both trials.

The authors actually performed this experiment with 44 subjects. They reported that 47.7% of the subjects identified the correct shirt on neither trial, 22.7% identified the correct shirt on one trial, and 31.7% identified the correct shirt on both trials. The fact that these observed percentages differed quite a bit from what would have been expected if participants were just guessing (as specified by the binomial probabilities in the table above) was interpreted by the authors as evidence that some women could in fact identify their roommates by smell.

EXAMPLE 7.19 Computer Sales

Sixty percent of all computers sold by a large computer retailer are laptops and 40% are desktop models. The type of computer purchased by each of the next 12 customers will be noted. Define a random variable x by

x = number of computers among these 12 that are laptops

Because x counts the number of laptops, we use S to denote the sale of a laptop. Then x is a binomial random variable with $n = 12$ and $p = P(S) = .60$. The probability distribution of x is given by

$$p(x) = \frac{12!}{x!(12-x)!}(.6)^x(.4)^{n-x} \qquad x = 0, 1, 2, \ldots, 12$$

The probability that exactly four computers are laptops is

$$\begin{aligned} p(4) &= P(x = 4) \\ &= \frac{12!}{4!8!}(.6)^4(.4)^8 \\ &= (495)(.6)^4(.4)^8 \\ &= .042 \end{aligned}$$

If group after group of 12 purchases is examined, the long-run percentage of those with exactly four laptops will be 4.2%. According to this calculation, 495 of the possible outcomes have $x = 4$.

The probability that between four and seven (inclusive) are laptops is

$$P(4 \le x \le 7) = P(x = 4 \textit{ or } x = 5 \textit{ or } x = 6 \textit{ or } x = 7)$$

Since these outcomes are disjoint, this is equal to

$$\begin{aligned} P(4 \le x \le 7) &= p(4) + p(5) + p(6) + p(7) \\ &= \frac{12!}{4!8!}(.6)^4(.4)^8 + \cdots + \frac{12!}{7!5!}(.6)^7(.4)^5 \\ &= .042 + .101 + .177 + .227 \\ &= .547 \end{aligned}$$

Notice that

$$\begin{aligned} P(4 < x < 7) &= P(x = 5 \textit{ or } x = 6) \\ &= p(5) + p(6) \\ &= .278 \end{aligned}$$

so the probability depends on whether $<$ or $\le$ appears. (This is typical of *discrete* random variables.)

The binomial distribution formula can be tedious to use unless n is small. Appendix Table 9 gives binomial probabilities for selected n in combination with various values of p. Appendix Table 9 should help you practice using the binomial distribution without getting bogged down in arithmetic.

Using Appendix Table 9

To find $p(x)$ for any particular value of x,

1. Locate the part of the table corresponding to your value of n (5, 10, 15, 20, or 25).
2. Move down to the row labeled with your value of x.
3. Go across to the column headed by the specified value of p.

The desired probability is at the intersection of the designated x row and p column. For example, when $n = 20$ and $p = .8$,

$$p(15) = P(x = 15) = (\text{entry at intersection of } n = 15 \text{ row and } p = .8 \text{ column}) = .175$$

Although $p(x)$ is positive for every possible x value, many probabilities are zero to three decimal places, so they appear as .000 in the table. More extensive binomial tables are available. Alternatively, most statistics software packages and graphing calculators are programmed to calculate these probabilities.

Sampling Without Replacement Usually, sampling is carried out without replacement; that is, once an element has been selected for the sample, it is not a candidate for future selection. If sampling is done by selecting an element from the population, observing whether it is a success or a failure, and then returning it to the population before the next selection is made, the variable x = number of successes observed in the sample would fit all the requirements of a binomial random variable. When sampling is done without replacement, the trials (individual selections) are not independent. In this case, the number of successes observed in the sample does not have a binomial distribution but rather a different type of distribution called a *hypergeometric distribution.* The probability calculations for this distribution are even more tedious than for the binomial distribution. Fortunately, when the sample size n is much smaller than N, the population size, probabilities calculated using the binomial distribution and the hypergeometric distribution are very close in value. They are so close, in fact, that statisticians often ignore the difference and use the binomial probabilities in place of the hypergeometric probabilities. Most statisticians recommend the following guideline for determining whether the binomial probability distribution is appropriate when sampling without replacement.

Let x denote the number of S's in a sample of size n selected without replacement from a population consisting of N individuals or objects. If $(n/N) \leq 0.05$ (that is, at most 5% of the population is sampled), then the binomial distribution gives a good approximation to the actual (hypergeometric) probability distribution of x.*

EXAMPLE 7.20 Online Security

The 2009 National Cyber Security Alliance (NCSA) Symantec Online Safety Study found that only about 25% of adult Americans change passwords on online accounts at least quarterly as recommended by the NCSA ("New Study Shows Need for Ameri-

*In Chapter 8, we will see a different situation where a similar condition is introduced, but where the requirement is that at most 10% of the population is included in the sample, Be careful not to confuse these rules.

cans to Focus on Securing Online Accounts and Backing Up Critical Data," PRNewswire, October 29, 2009). Suppose that exactly 25% of adult Americans change passwords quarterly. Consider a random sample of $n = 20$ adult Americans (much less than 5% of the population). Then $x =$ the number in the sample who change passwords quarterly has (approximately) a binomial distribution with $n = 20$ and $p = .25$. The probability that five of those sampled change passwords quarterly is

$$\begin{aligned} P(5) &= P(x = 5) \\ &= \text{entry in } x = 5 \text{ row and } p = .25 \text{ column in Appendix Table 9 for } n = 20 \\ &= .202 \end{aligned}$$

The probability that at least half of those in the sample (that is, 10 or more) change passwords quarterly is

$$\begin{aligned} P(x \geq 10) &= P(x = 10, 11, 12, \ldots, 20) \\ &= p(10) + p(11) + \cdots + p(20) \\ &= .010 + .003 + .001 + \cdots + .000 \\ &= .014 \end{aligned}$$

If, in fact, $p = .25$, only about 1.4% of all samples of size 20 would result in at least 10 people who change passwords quarterly. Because $P(x \geq 10)$ is so small when $p = .25$, if $x \geq 10$ were actually observed, we would have to wonder whether the reported value of $p = .25$ is correct. Although it is possible that we would observe $x \geq 10$ when $p = .25$ (this would happen about 1.4% of the time in the long run), it might also be the case that p is actually greater than .25. In Chapter 10, we show how hypothesis-testing methods can be used to decide which of two contradictory claims about a population (such as $p = .25$ or $p > 25$) is more believable.

The binomial formula or tables can be used to compute each of the 21 probabilities $p(0), p(1), \ldots, p(20)$. Figure 7.16 shows the probability histogram for the binomial distribution with $n = 20$ and $p = .25$. Notice that the distribution is skewed to the right. (The binomial distribution is symmetric only when $p = .5$.)

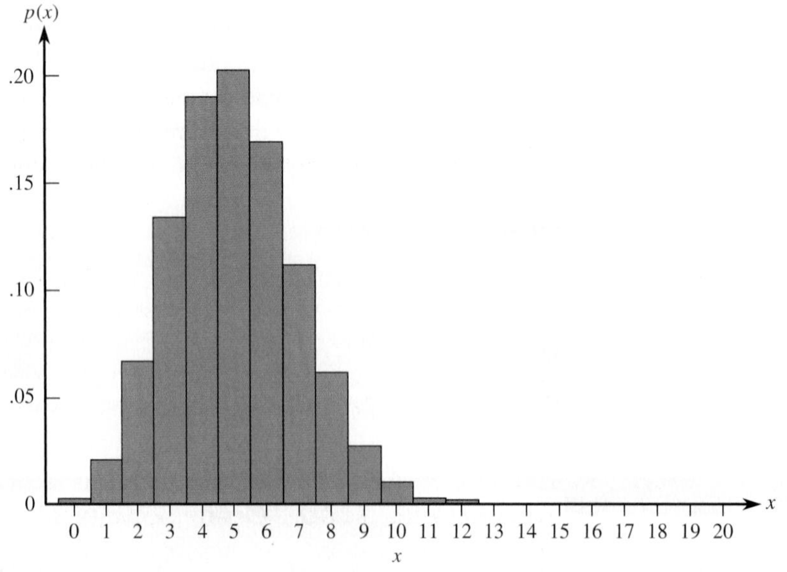

FIGURE 7.16
The binomial probability histogram when $n = 20$ and $p = .25$.

Mean and Standard Deviation of a Binomial Random Variable A binomial random variable x based on n trials has possible values $0, 1, 2, \ldots, n$, so the mean value is

$$\mu_x = \Sigma xp(x) = (0)p(0) + (1)p(1) + \cdots + (n)p(n)$$

and the variance of x is

$$\sigma_x^2 = \sum (x - \mu_x)^2 \cdot p(x)$$
$$= (0 - \mu_x)^2 p(0) + (1 - \mu_x)^2 p(1) + \cdots + (n - \mu_x)^2 p(n)$$

These expressions would be very tedious to evaluate for any particular values of n and p. Fortunately, algebraic manipulation results in simple formulas for the mean and standard deviation of a binomial random variable.

The mean value and the standard deviation of a binomial random variable are, respectively,

$$\mu_x = np \quad \text{and} \quad \sigma_x = \sqrt{np(1 - p)}$$

EXAMPLE 7.21 Credit Cards Paid in Full

The paper "Debt Literacy, Financial Experiences and Overindebtedness" (*Social Science Research Network*, Working Paper w14808, 2008) reported that 37% of credit card users pay their bills in full each month. This figure represents an average over different types of credit cards issued by many different banks. Suppose that 40% of all individuals holding Visa cards issued by a certain bank pay in full each month. A random sample of $n = 25$ cardholders is to be selected. The bank is interested in the variable x = number in the sample who pay in full each month. Even though sampling is done without replacement, the sample size $n = 25$ is most likely very small compared to the total number of credit card holders, so we can approximate the probability distribution of x using a binomial distribution with $n = 25$ and $p = .4$. We have defined "paid in full" as a success because this is the outcome counted by the random variable x. The mean value of x is then

$$\mu_x = np = 25(.40) = 10.0$$

and the standard deviation is

$$\sigma_x = \sqrt{np(1 - p)} = \sqrt{25(.40)(.60)} = \sqrt{6} = 2.45$$

The probability that x is farther than 1 standard deviation from its mean value is

$$\begin{aligned} P(x < \mu_x - \sigma_x \text{ or } x > \mu_x + \sigma_x) &= P(x < 7.55 \text{ or } x > 12.45) \\ &= P(x \le 7) + P(x \ge 13) \\ &= p(0) + \cdots + p(7) + p(13) + \cdots + p(25) \\ &= .307 \text{ (using Appendix Table 9)} \end{aligned}$$

The value of σ_x is 0 when $p = 0$ or $p = 1$. In these two cases, there is no uncertainty in x. We are sure to observe $x = 0$ when $p = 0$ and $x = n$ when $p = 1$. It is also easily verified that $p(1 - p)$ is largest when $p = .5$. Thus the binomial distribution spreads out the most when sampling from a 50–50 population. The farther p is from .5, the less spread out and the more skewed the distribution.

Geometric Distributions

A binomial random variable is defined as the number of successes in n independent trials, where each trial can result in either a success or a failure and the probability of success is the same for each trial. Suppose, however, that we are not interested in the number of successes in a fixed number of trials but rather in the number of trials that must be carried out before a success occurs. Two examples are counting the number of boxes of cereal that must be purchased before finding one with a rare toy and counting the number of games that a professional bowler must play before achieving a score over 250.

The variable

x = number of trials to first success

is called a *geometric random variable*, and the probability distribution that describes its behavior is called a *geometric probability distribution.*

Suppose an experiment consists of a sequence of trials with the following conditions:

1. The trials are independent.
2. Each trial can result in one of two possible outcomes, success and failure.
3. The probability of success is the same for all trials.

A **geometric random variable** is defined as

x = number of trials until the first success is observed (including the success trial)

The probability distribution of x is called the **geometric probability distribution.**

For example, suppose that 40% of the students who drive to campus at your university carry jumper cables. Your car has a dead battery and you don't have jumper cables, so you decide to stop students who are headed to the parking lot and ask them whether they have a pair of jumper cables. You might be interested in the number of students you would have to stop before finding one who has jumper cables. If we define success as a student with jumper cables, a trial would consist of asking an individual student for help. The random variable x = number of students who must be stopped before finding one with jumper cables is an example of a geometric random variable, because it can be viewed as the number of trials to the first success in a sequence of independent trials.

The probability distribution of a geometric random variable is easy to construct. We use p to denote the probability of success on any given trial. Possible outcomes can be denoted as follows:

Outcome	x = Number of Trials to First Success
S	1
FS	2
FFS	3
⋮	⋮
$FFFFFFS$	7
⋮	⋮

Each possible outcome consists of 0 or more failures followed by a single success. So,

$$\begin{aligned} p(x) &= P(x \text{ trials to first success}) \\ &= P(FF\ldots FS) \end{aligned}$$

$x - 1$ failures followed by a success on trial x

Because the probability of success is p for each trial, the probability of failure for each trial is $1 - p$. Because the trials are independent,

$$\begin{aligned} p(x) &= P(x \text{ trials to first success}) = P(FF\ldots FS) \\ &= P(F)P(F)\cdots P(F)P(S) \\ &= (1-p)(1-p)\cdots(1-p)p \\ &= (1-p)^{x-1}p \end{aligned}$$

This leads us to the formula for the geometric probability distribution.

Geometric Probability Distribution

If x is a geometric random variable with probability of success $= p$ for each trial, then

$$p(x) = (1-p)^{x-1}p \quad x = 1, 2, 3, \ldots$$

EXAMPLE 7.22 Jumper Cables

© Stone +/Greg Ceo/Getty Images

Consider the jumper cable problem described previously. For this problem, $p = .4$, because 40% of the students who drive to campus carry jumper cables. The probability distribution of

$x =$ number of students who must be stopped before finding a student with jumper cables

is

$$p(x) = (.6)^{x-1}(.4) \quad x = 1, 2, 3, \ldots$$

The probability distribution can now be used to compute various probabilities. For example, the probability that the first student stopped has jumper cables (that is, $x = 1$) is

$$p(1) = (.6)^{1-1}(.4) = (.6)^0(.4) = .4$$

The probability that three or fewer students must be stopped is

$$\begin{aligned} P(x \le 3) &= p(1) + p(2) + p(3) \\ &= (.6)^0(.4) + (.6)^1(.4) + (.6)^2(.4) \\ &= .4 + .24 + .144 \\ &= .784 \end{aligned}$$

EXERCISES 7.43 - 7.62

7.43 Consider two binomial experiments.

a. The first binomial experiment consists of six trials. How many outcomes have exactly one success, and what are these outcomes?

b. The second binomial experiment consists of 20 trials. How many outcomes have exactly 10 successes? exactly 15 successes? exactly five successes?

7.44 Suppose that in a certain metropolitan area, nine out of 10 households have cable TV. Let x denote the number among four randomly selected households that have cable TV, so x is a binomial random variable with $n = 4$ and $p = .9$.

a. Calculate $p(2) = P(x = 2)$, and interpret this probability.

b. Calculate $p(4)$, the probability that all four selected households have cable TV.
c. Determine $P(x \leq 3)$.

7.45 ✦ The *Los Angeles Times* (December 13, 1992) reported that what airline passengers like to do most on long flights is rest or sleep; in a survey of 3697 passengers, almost 80% did so. Suppose that for a particular route the actual percentage is exactly 80%, and consider randomly selecting six passengers. Then x, the number among the selected six who rested or slept, is a binomial random variable with $n = 6$ and $p = .8$.
a. Calculate $p(4)$, and interpret this probability.
b. Calculate $p(6)$, the probability that all six selected passengers rested or slept.
c. Determine $P(x \geq 4)$.

7.46 Refer to Exercise 7.45, and suppose that 10 rather than six passengers are selected ($n = 10$, $p = .8$), so that Appendix Table 9 can be used.
a. What is $p(8)$?
b. Calculate $P(x \leq 7)$.
c. Calculate the probability that more than half of the selected passengers rested or slept.

7.47 Twenty-five percent of the customers of a grocery store use an express checkout. Consider five randomly selected customers, and let x denote the number among the five who use the express checkout.
a. What is $p(2)$, that is, $P(x = 2)$?
b. What is $P(x \leq 1)$?
c. What is $P(2 \leq x)$? (Hint: Make use of your answer from Part (b).)
d. What is $P(x \neq 2)$?

7.48 Example 7.18 described a study in which a person was asked to determine which of three t-shirts had been worn by her roommate by smelling the shirts ("Sociochemosensory and Emotional Functions," *Psychological Science* [2009]: 1118–1123). Suppose that instead of three shirts, each participant was asked to choose among four shirts and that the process was repeated five times. Then, assuming that the participant is choosing at random, x = number of correct identifications is a binomial random variable with $n = 5$ and $p = \frac{1}{4}$.
a. What are the possible values of x?
b. For each possible value of x, find the associated probability $p(x)$ and display the possible x values and $p(x)$ values in a table.
c. Construct a probability histogram for the probability distribution of x.

7.49 In a press release dated October 2, 2008, The National Cyber Security Alliance reported that approximately 80% of adult Americans who own a computer claim to have a firewall installed on their computer to prevent hackers from stealing personal information. This estimate was based on a survey of 3000 people. It was also reported that in a study of 400 computers, only about 40% actually had a firewall installed.
a. Suppose that the true proportion of computer owners who have a firewall installed is .80. If 20 computer owners are selected at random, what is the probability that more than 15 have a firewall installed?
b. Suppose that the true proportion of computer owners who have a firewall installed is .40. If 20 computer owners are selected at random, what is the probability that more than 15 have a firewall installed?
c. Suppose that a random sample of 20 computer owners is selected and that 14 have a firewall installed. Is it more likely that the true proportion of computer owners who have a firewall installed is .40 or .80? Justify your answer based on probability calculations.

7.50 A breeder of show dogs is interested in the number of female puppies in a litter. If a birth is equally likely to result in a male or a female puppy, give the probability distribution of the variable x = number of female puppies in a litter of size 5.

7.51 The article "FBI Says Fewer than 25 Failed Polygraph Test" (*San Luis Obispo Tribune*, July 29, 2001) states that false-positives in polygraph tests (i.e., tests in which an individual fails even though he or she is telling the truth) are relatively common and occur about 15% of the time. Suppose that such a test is given to 10 trustworthy individuals.
a. What is the probability that all 10 pass?
b. What is the probability that more than two fail, even though all are trustworthy?
c. The article indicated that 500 FBI agents were required to take a polygraph test. Consider the random variable x = number of the 500 tested who fail. If all 500 agents tested are trustworthy, what are the mean and standard deviation of x?
d. The headline indicates that fewer than 25 of the 500 agents tested failed the test. Is this a surprising result if all 500 are trustworthy? Answer based on the values of the mean and standard deviation from Part (c).

7.52 Industrial quality control programs often include inspection of incoming materials from suppliers. If parts are purchased in large lots, a typical plan might be to select 20 parts at random from a lot and inspect them. A lot might be judged acceptable if one or fewer defective parts are found among those inspected. Otherwise, the lot is rejected and returned to the supplier. Use Appendix Table 9 to find the probability of accepting lots that have each of the following (Hint: Identify success with a defective part):

a. 5% defective parts
b. 10% defective parts
c. 20% defective parts

7.53 Suppose that the probability is .1 that any given citrus tree will show measurable damage when the temperature falls to 30°F. If the temperature does drop to 30°F, what is the expected number of citrus trees showing damage in orchards of 2000 trees? What is the standard deviation of the number of trees that show damage?

7.54 Thirty percent of all automobiles undergoing an emissions inspection at a certain inspection station fail the inspection.

a. Among 15 randomly selected cars, what is the probability that at most five fail the inspection?
b. Among 15 randomly selected cars, what is the probability that between five and 10 (inclusive) fail to pass inspection?
c. Among 25 randomly selected cars, what is the mean value of the number that pass inspection, and what is the standard deviation of the number that pass inspection?
d. What is the probability that among 25 randomly selected cars, the number that pass is within 1 standard deviation of the mean value?

7.55 You are to take a multiple-choice exam consisting of 100 questions with five possible responses to each question. Suppose that you have not studied and so must guess (select one of the five answers in a completely random fashion) on each question. Let x represent the number of correct responses on the test.

a. What kind of probability distribution does x have?
b. What is your expected score on the exam? (Hint: Your expected score is the mean value of the x distribution.)
c. Compute the variance and standard deviation of x.
d. Based on your answers to Parts (b) and (c), is it likely that you would score over 50 on this exam? Explain the reasoning behind your answer.

7.56 Suppose that 20% of the 10,000 signatures on a certain recall petition are invalid. Would the number of invalid signatures in a sample of 2000 of these signatures have (approximately) a binomial distribution? Explain.

7.57 A city ordinance requires that a smoke detector be installed in all residential housing. There is concern that too many residences are still without detectors, so a costly inspection program is being contemplated. Let p be the proportion of all residences that have a detector. A random sample of 25 residences is selected. If the sample strongly suggests that $p < .80$ (less than 80% have detectors), as opposed to $p \geq .80$, the program will be implemented. Let x be the number of residences among the 25 that have a detector, and consider the following decision rule: Reject the claim that $p = .8$ and implement the program if $x \leq 15$.

a. What is the probability that the program is implemented when $p = .80$?
b. What is the probability that the program is not implemented if $p = .70$? if $p = .60$?
c. How do the "error probabilities" of Parts (a) and (b) change if the value 15 in the decision rule is changed to 14?

7.58 Suppose that 90% of all registered California voters favor banning the release of information from exit polls in presidential elections until after the polls in California close. A random sample of 25 registered California voters is to be selected.

a. What is the probability that more than 20 favor the ban?
b. What is the probability that at least 20 favor the ban?
c. What are the mean value and standard deviation of the number of voters in the sample who favor the ban?
d. If fewer than 20 voters in the sample favor the ban, is this at odds with the assertion that (at least) 90% of California registered voters favors the ban? (Hint: Consider $P(x < 20)$ when $p = .9$.)

7.59 Suppose a playlist on an MP3 music player consists of 100 songs, of which eight are by a particular artist. Suppose that songs are played by selecting a song at random (with replacement) from the playlist. The random variable x represents the number of songs played until a song by this artist is played.

a. Explain why the probability distribution of x is not binomial.

b. Find the following probabilities:
i. $p(4)$
ii. $P(x \leq 4)$
iii. $P(x > 4)$
iv. $P(x \geq 4)$

c. Interpret each of the probabilities in Part (b) and explain the difference between them.

7.60 Sophie is a dog that loves to play catch. Unfortunately, she isn't very good, and the probability that she catches a ball is only .1. Let x be the number of tosses required until Sophie catches a ball.

a. Does x have a binomial or a geometric distribution?
b. What is the probability that it will take exactly two tosses for Sophie to catch a ball?
c. What is the probability that more than three tosses will be required?

7.61 Suppose that 5% of cereal boxes contain a prize and the other 95% contain the message, "Sorry, try again." Consider the random variable x, where x = number of boxes purchased until a prize is found.

a. What is the probability that at most two boxes must be purchased?
b. What is the probability that exactly four boxes must be purchased?
c. What is the probability that more than four boxes must be purchased?

7.62 ✦ The article on polygraph testing of FBI agents referenced in Exercise 7.51 indicated that the probability of a false-positive (a trustworthy person who nonetheless fails the test) is .15. Let x be the number of trustworthy FBI agents tested until someone fails the test.

a. What is the probability distribution of x?
b. What is the probability that the first false-positive will occur when the third person is tested?
c. What is the probability that fewer than four are tested before the first false-positive occurs?
d. What is the probability that more than three agents are tested before the first false-positive occurs?

Bold exercises answered in back ● Data set available online ✦ Video Solution available

7.6 Normal Distributions

Normal distributions formalize the notion of mound-shaped histograms introduced in Chapter 4. Normal distributions are widely used for two reasons. First, they provide a reasonable approximation to the distribution of many different variables. They also play a central role in many of the inferential procedures that will be discussed in later chapters.

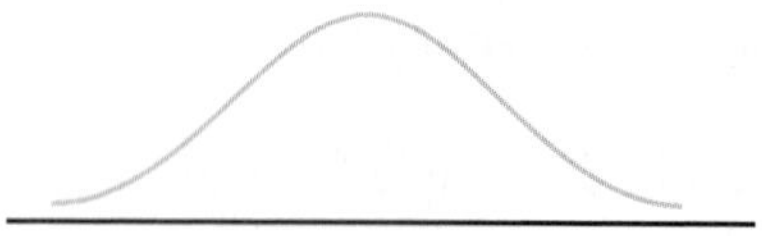

FIGURE 7.17
A normal distribution.

Normal distributions are continuous probability distributions that are bell-shaped and symmetric, as shown in Figure 7.17. Normal distributions are sometimes referred to as a *normal curves.*

There are many different normal distributions, and they are distinguished from one another by their mean μ and standard deviation σ. The mean μ of a normal distribution describes where the corresponding curve is centered, and the standard deviation σ describes how much the curve spreads out around that center. As with all continuous probability distributions, the total area under any normal curve is equal to 1.

Three normal distributions are shown in Figure 7.18. Notice that the smaller the standard deviation, the taller and narrower the corresponding curve. Remember that areas under a continuous probability distribution curve represent probabilities, so when the standard deviation is small, a larger area is concentrated near the center of the curve and the chance of observing a value near the mean is much greater (because μ is at the center).

The value of μ is the number on the measurement axis lying directly below the top of the bell. The value of σ can also be ascertained from a picture of the curve. Consider the normal curve in Figure 7.19. Starting at the top of the bell (above

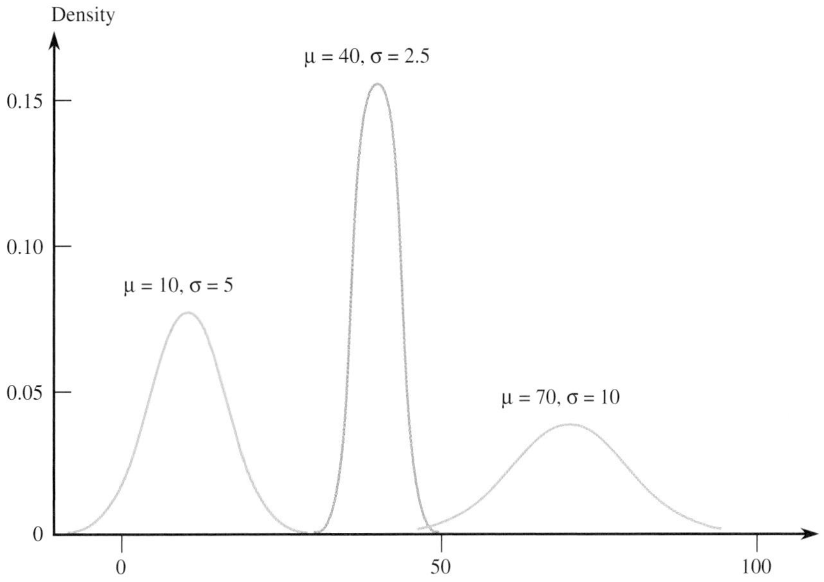

FIGURE 7.18
Three normal distributions.

$\mu = 100$) and moving to the right, the curve turns downward until it is above the value 110. After that point, it continues to decrease in height but is turning upward rather than downward. Similarly, to the left of $\mu = 100$, the curve turns downward until it reaches 90 and then begins to turn upward. The curve changes from turning downward to turning upward at a distance of 10 on either side of μ. In general, σ is the distance to either side of μ at which a normal curve changes from turning downward to turning upward, so $\sigma = 10$ for the normal curve in Figure 7.19.

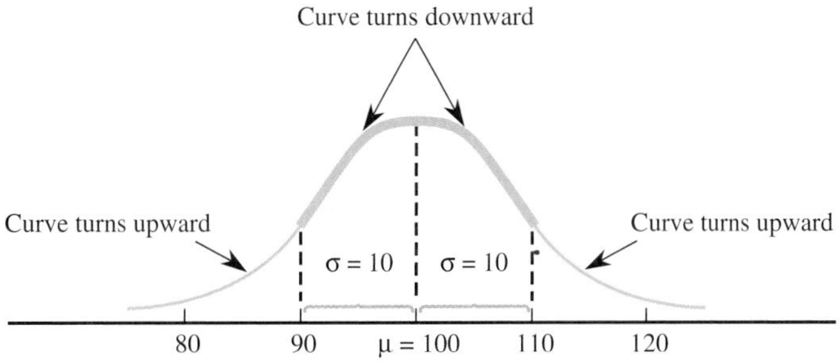

FIGURE 7.19
Mean μ and standard deviation σ for a normal curve.

If a particular normal distribution is to be used to describe the behavior of a random variable, a mean and a standard deviation must be specified. For example, a normal distribution with mean 7 and standard deviation 1 might be used as a model for the distribution of x = birth weight (in pounds). If this model is a reasonable description of the probability distribution, we could use areas under the normal curve with $\mu = 7$ and $\sigma = 1$ to approximate various probabilities related to birth weight. The probability that a birth weight is over 8 pounds (expressed symbolically as $P(x > 8)$) corresponds to the shaded area in Figure 7.20(a). The shaded area in Figure

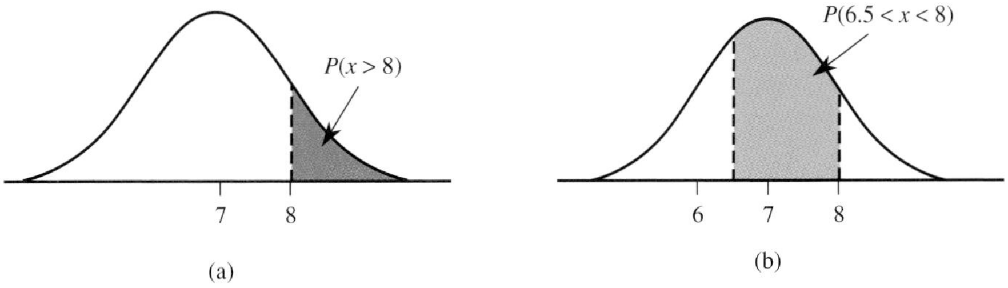

FIGURE 7.20
Normal distribution for birth weight:
(a) shaded area = $P(x > 8)$;
(b) shaded area = $P(6.5 < x < 8)$.

7.20(b) is the (approximate) probability $P(6.5 < x < 8)$ of a birth weight falling between 6.5 and 8 pounds.

Unfortunately, direct computation of such probabilities (areas under a normal curve) is not simple. To overcome this difficulty, we rely on technology or a table of areas for a reference normal distribution, called the *standard normal distribution.*

DEFINITION

The **standard normal distribution** is the normal distribution with

$$\mu = 0 \quad \text{and} \quad \sigma = 1$$

The corresponding density curve is called the *standard normal curve.* It is customary to use the letter z to represent a variable whose distribution is described by the standard normal curve. The term *z curve* is often used in place of *standard normal curve.*

Few naturally occurring variables have distributions that are well described by the standard normal distribution, but this distribution is important because it is also used in probability calculations for other normal distributions. When we are interested in finding a probability based on some other normal curve, we either rely on technology or we first translate our problem into an equivalent problem that involves finding an area under the standard normal curve. A table for the standard normal distribution is then used to find the desired area. To be able to do this, we must first learn to work with the standard normal distribution.

The Standard Normal Distribution

In working with normal distributions, we need two general skills:

1. We must be able to use the normal distribution to compute probabilities, which are areas under a normal curve and above given intervals.
2. We must be able to characterize extreme values in the distribution, such as the largest 5%, the smallest 1%, and the most extreme 5% (which would include the largest 2.5% and the smallest 2.5%).

Let's begin by looking at how to accomplish these tasks when the distribution of interest is the standard normal distribution.

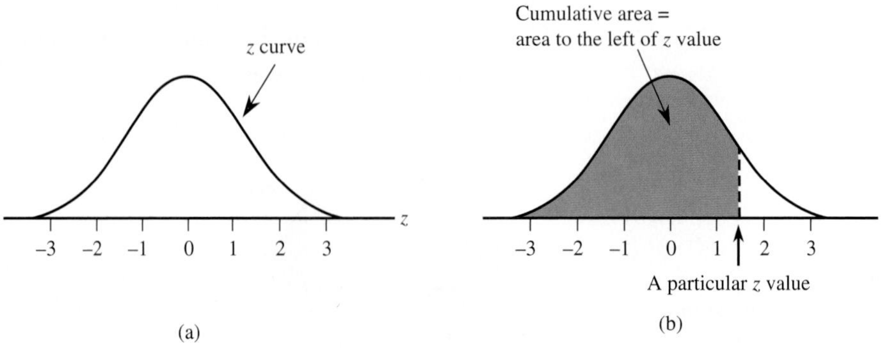

FIGURE 7.21
(a) A standard normal (z) curve;
(b) a cumulative area.

The standard normal or z curve is shown in Figure 7.21(a). It is centered at $\mu = 0$, and the standard deviation, $\sigma = 1$, is a measure of the extent to which it spreads out about its mean (in this case, 0). Note that this picture is consistent with the Empirical Rule of Chapter 4: About 95% of the area (probability) is associated with values that are within 2 standard deviations of the mean (between -2 and 2), and almost all of the area is associated with values that are within 3 standard deviations of the mean (between -3 and 3).

Appendix Table 2 tabulates cumulative z curve areas of the sort shown in Figure 7.21(b) for many different values of z. The smallest value for which the cumulative area is given is -3.89, a value far out in the lower tail of the z curve. The next smallest value for which the area appears is -3.88, then -3.87, then -3.86, and so on in increments of 0.01, terminating with the cumulative area to the left of 3.89.

Using the Table of Standard Normal Curve Areas

For any number z^* between -3.89 and 3.89 and rounded to two decimal places, Appendix Table 2 gives

$$(\text{area under } z \text{ curve to the left of } z^*) = P(z < z^*) = P(z \leq z^*)$$

where the letter z is used to represent a random variable whose distribution is the standard normal distribution.

To find this probability using the table, locate the following:

1. The row labeled with the sign of z^* and the digit to either side of the decimal point (for example, -1.7 or 0.5)
2. The column identified with the second digit to the right of the decimal point in z^* (for example, .06 if $z^* = -1.76$)

The number at the intersection of this row and column is the desired probability, $P(z < z^*)$.

A portion of the table of standard normal curve areas appears in Figure 7.22. To find the area under the z curve to the left of 1.42, look in the row labeled 1.4 and the column labeled .02 (the highlighted row and column in Figure 7.22). From the table, the corresponding cumulative area is .9222. So

$$z \text{ curve area to the left of } 1.42 = .9222$$

We can also use the table to find the area to the right of a particular value. Because the total area under the z curve is 1, it follows that

$$\begin{aligned}(z \text{ curve area to the right of } 1.42) &= 1 - (z \text{ curve area to the left of } 1.42)\\ &= 1 - .9222\\ &= .0778\end{aligned}$$

These probabilities can be interpreted to mean that in a long sequence of observations, roughly 92.22% of the observed z values will be smaller than 1.42, and 7.78% will be larger than 1.42.

z^*	.00	.01	.02	.03	.04	.05
0.0	.5000	.5040	.5080	.5120	.5160	.5199
0.1	.5398	.5438	.5478	.5517	.5557	.5596
0.2	.5793	.5832	.5871	.5910	.5948	.5987
0.3	.6179	.6217	.6255	.6293	.6331	.6368
0.4	.6554	.6591	.6628	.6664	.6700	.6736
0.5	.6915	.6950	.6985	.7019	.7054	.7088
0.6	.7257	.7291	.7324	.7357	.7389	.7422
0.7	.7580	.7611	.7642	.7673	.7704	.7734
0.8	.7881	.7910	.7939	.7967	.7995	.8023
0.9	.8159	.8186	.8212	.8238	.8264	.8289
1.0	.8413	.8438	.8461	.8485	.8508	.8531
1.1	.8643	.8665	.8686	.8708	.8729	.8749
1.2	.8849	.8869	.8888	.8907	.8925	.8944
1.3	.9032	.9049	.9066	.9082	.9099	.9115
1.4	.9192	.9207	.9222	.9236	.9251	.9265
1.5	.9332	.9345	.9357	.9370	.9382	.9394
1.6	.9452	.9463	.9474	.9484	.9495	.9505
1.7	.9554	.9564	.9573	.9582	.9591	.9599
1.8	.9641	.9649	.9656	.9664	.9671	.9678

$P(z < 1.42)$

FIGURE 7.22
Portion of the table of standard normal curve areas.

EXAMPLE 7.23 Finding Standard Normal Curve Areas

The probability $P(z < -1.76)$ is found at the intersection of the -1.7 row and the .06 column of the z table. The result is

$$P(z < -1.76) = .0392$$

as shown in the following figure:

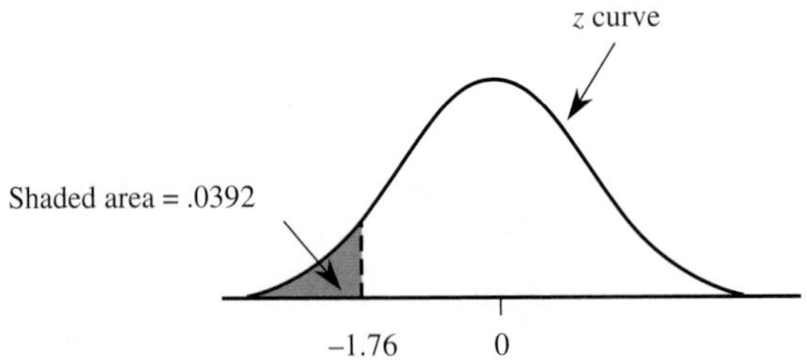

In other words, in a long sequence of observations, roughly 3.9% of the observed z values will be smaller than -1.76. Similarly,

$$P(z \leq 0.58) = \text{entry in 0.5 row and .08 column of Table 2} = .7190$$

as shown in the following figure:

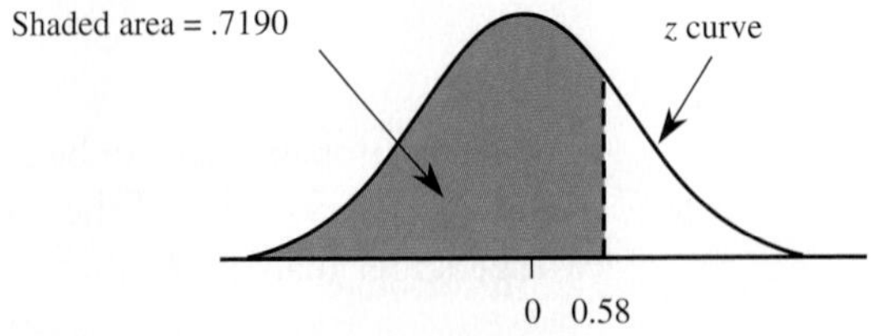

Now consider $P(z < -4.12)$. This probability does not appear in Appendix Table 2; there is no -4.1 row. However, it must be less than $P(z < -3.89)$, the smallest z value in the table, because -4.12 is farther out in the lower tail of the z curve. Since $P(z < -3.89) \approx .0000$ (that is, zero to four decimal places), it follows that

$$P(z < -4.12) \approx 0$$

Similarly,

$$P(z < 4.18) > P(z < 3.89) \approx 1.0000$$

from which we conclude that

$$P(z < 4.18) \approx 1$$

As illustrated in Example 7.23, we can use the cumulative areas tabulated in Appendix Table 2 to calculate other probabilities involving z. The probability that z is larger than a value c is

$$\text{P}(z > c) = \text{area under the } z \text{ curve to the right of } c = 1 - P(z \le c)$$

In other words, the area to the right of a value (a right-tail area) is 1 minus the corresponding cumulative area. This is illustrated in Figure 7.23.

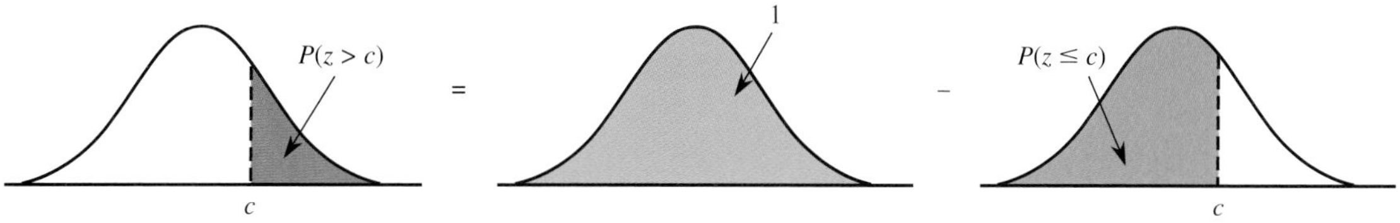

FIGURE 7.23
The relationship between an upper-tail area and a cumulative area.

Similarly, the probability that z falls in the interval between a lower limit a and an upper limit b is

$$\begin{aligned} P(a < z < b) &= \text{area under the } z \text{ curve and above the interval from } a \text{ to } b \\ &= P(z < b) - P(z < a) \end{aligned}$$

That is, $P(a < z < b)$ is the difference between two cumulative areas, as illustrated in Figure 7.24.

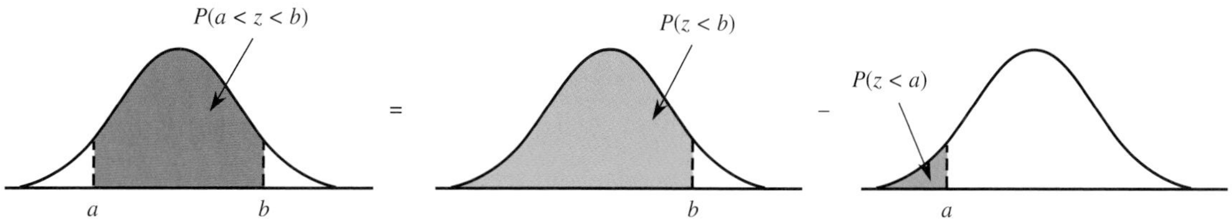

FIGURE 7.24
$P(a < z < b)$ as the difference between the two cumulative areas.

EXAMPLE 7.24 More About Standard Normal Curve Areas

The probability that z is between -1.76 and 0.58 is

$$\begin{aligned} P(-1.76 < z < 0.58) &= P(z < 0.58) - P(z < -1.76) \\ &= .7190 - .0392 \\ &= .6798 \end{aligned}$$

as shown in the following figure:

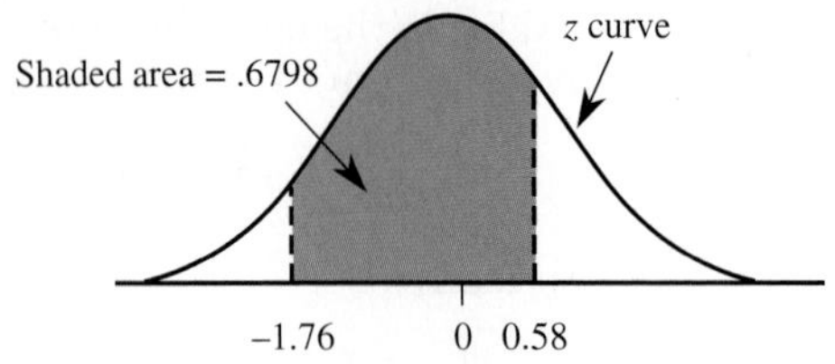

The probability that z is between -2 and $+2$ (within 2 standard deviations of its mean, since $\mu = 0$ and $\sigma = 1$) is

$$\begin{aligned} P(-2.00 < z < 2.00) &= P(z < 2.00) - P(z < -2.00) \\ &= .9772 - .0228 \\ &= .9544 \\ &\approx .95 \end{aligned}$$

as shown in the following figure:

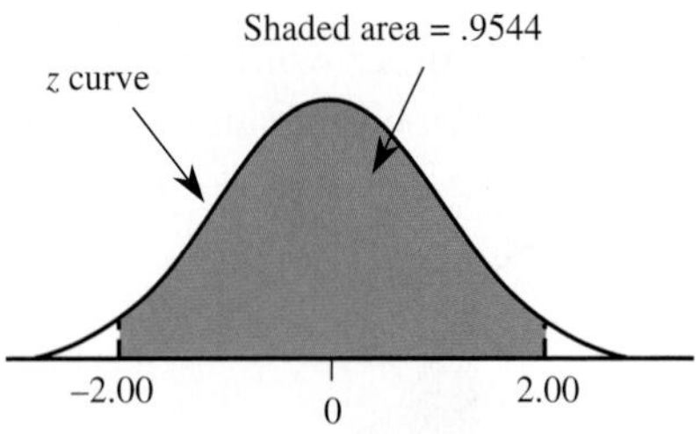

This last probability is the basis for one part of the Empirical Rule, which states that when a histogram is well approximated by a normal curve, roughly 95% of the values are within 2 standard deviations of the mean.

The probability that the value of z exceeds 1.96 is

$$\begin{aligned} P(z > 1.96) &= 1 - P(z < 1.96) \\ &= 1 - .9750 \\ &= .0250 \end{aligned}$$

as shown in the following figure:

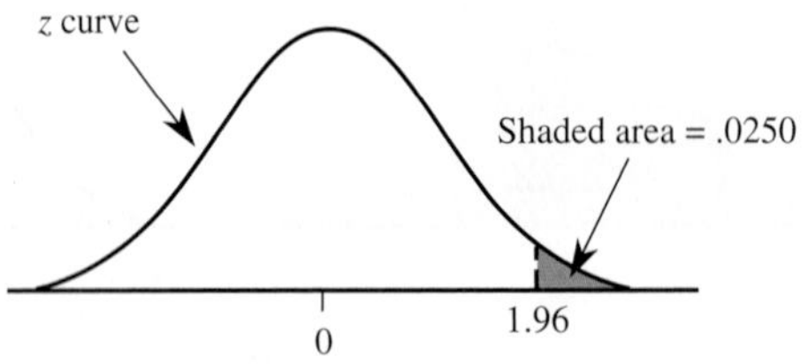

That is, 2.5% of the area under the z curve lies to the right of 1.96 in the upper tail.

Similarly,

$$\begin{aligned} P(z > -1.28) &= \text{area to the right of } -1.28 \\ &= 1 - P(z < -1.28) \\ &= 1 - .1003 \\ &= .8997 \\ &\approx .90 \end{aligned}$$

Identifying Extreme Values

Suppose that we want to describe the values included in the smallest 2% of a distribution or the values making up the most extreme 5% (which includes the largest 2.5% and the smallest 2.5%). Let's see how we can identify extreme values in the distribution by working through Examples 7.25 and 7.26.

EXAMPLE 7.25 Identifying Extreme Values

Suppose that we want to describe the values that make up the smallest 2% of the standard normal distribution. Symbolically, we are trying to find a value (call it z^*) such that

$$P(z < z^*) = .02$$

This is illustrated in Figure 7.25, which shows that the cumulative area for z^* is .02. Therefore, we look for a cumulative area of .0200 in the body of Appendix Table 2. The closest cumulative area in the table is .0202, in the -2.0 row and .05 column; we will use $z^* = -2.05$, the best approximation from the table. Variable values less than -2.05 make up the smallest 2% of the standard normal distribution.

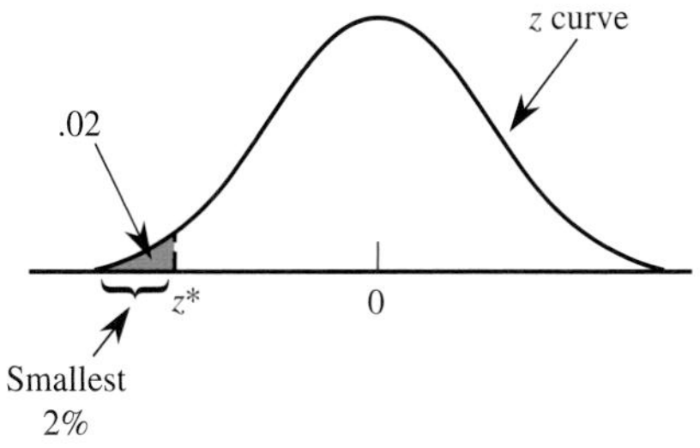

FIGURE 7.25
The smallest 2% of the standard normal distribution.

Now suppose that we had been interested in the largest 5% of all z values. We would then be trying to find a value of z^* for which

$$P(z > z^*) = .05$$

as illustrated in Figure 7.26. Because Appendix Table 2 always works with cumulative area (area to the left), the first step is to determine

$$\text{area to the left of } z^* = 1 - .05 = .95$$

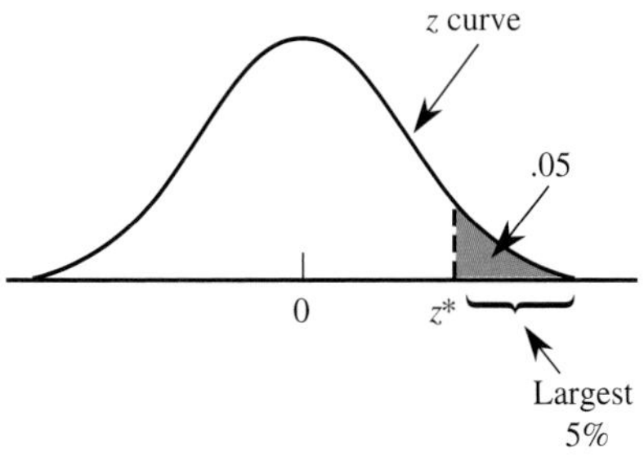

FIGURE 7.26
The largest 5% of the standard normal distribution.

Looking for the cumulative area closest to .95 in Appendix Table 2, we find that .95 falls exactly halfway between .9495 (corresponding to a z value of 1.64) and .9505 (corresponding to a z value of 1.65). Because .9500 is exactly halfway between the two areas, we use a z value that is halfway between 1.64 and 1.65. (If one value had been closer to .9500 than the other, we would just use the z value corresponding to the closest area.) This gives

$$z^* = \frac{1.64 + 1.65}{2} = 1.645$$

Values greater than 1.645 make up the largest 5% of the standard normal distribution. By symmetry, -1.645 separates the smallest 5% of all z values from the others.

EXAMPLE 7.26 More Extremes

Sometimes we are interested in identifying the most extreme (unusually large *or* small) values in a distribution. Consider describing the values that make up the most extreme 5% of the standard normal distribution. That is, we want to separate the middle 95% from the extreme 5%. This is illustrated in Figure 7.27.

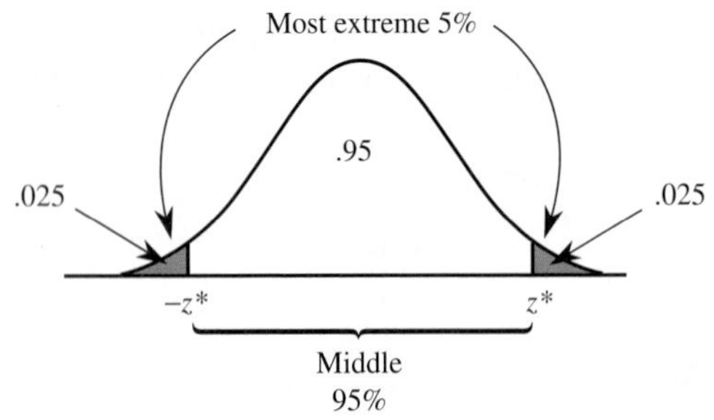

FIGURE 7.27
The most extreme 5% of the standard normal distribution.

Because the standard normal distribution is symmetric, the most extreme 5% is equally divided between the high side and the low side of the distribution, resulting in an area of .025 for each of the tails of the z curve. Symmetry about 0 implies that if z^* denotes the value that separates the largest 2.5%, the value that separates the smallest 2.5% is simply $-z^*$.

To find z^*, first determine the cumulative area for z^*, which is

area to the left of $z^* = .95 + .025 = .975$

The cumulative area .9750 appears in the 1.9 row and .06 column of Appendix Table 2, so $z^* = 1.96$. For the standard normal distribution, 95% of the variable values fall between -1.96 and 1.96; the most extreme 5% are those values that are either greater than 1.96 or less than -1.96.

Other Normal Distributions

We now show how z curve areas can be used to calculate probabilities and to describe values for any normal distribution. Remember that the letter z is reserved for those variables that have a standard normal distribution; the letter x is used more generally for any variable whose distribution is described by a normal curve with mean μ and standard deviation σ.

Suppose that we want to compute $P(a < x < b)$, the probability that the variable x lies in a particular range. This probability corresponds to an area under a normal curve and above the interval from a to b, as shown in Figure 7.28(a).

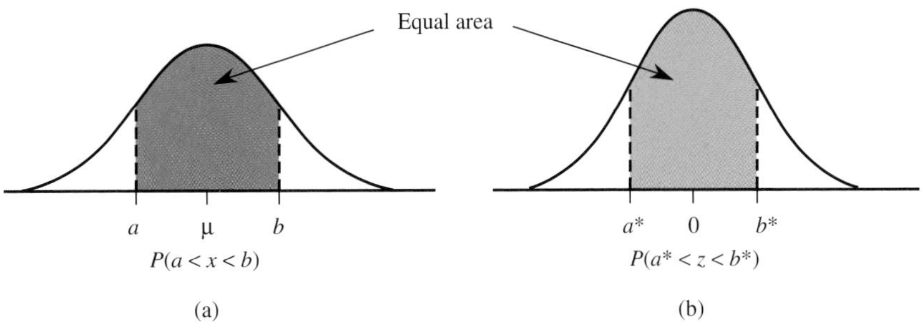

FIGURE 7.28
Equality of nonstandard and standard normal curve areas.

The strategy for obtaining this probability is to find an equivalent problem involving the standard normal distribution. Finding an equivalent problem means determining an interval (a^*, b^*) that has the same probability for z (same area under the z curve) as does the interval (a, b) in our original normal distribution (Figure 7.28(b)). The asterisk is used to distinguish a and b, the values from the original normal distribution with mean μ and standard deviation σ, from a^* and b^*, the values from the z curve. To find a^* and b^*, we simply calculate z scores for the endpoints of the interval for which a probability is desired. This process is called **standardizing** the endpoints. For example, suppose that the variable x has a normal distribution with mean $\mu = 100$ and standard deviation $\sigma = 5$. To find

$$P(98 < x < 107)$$

we first translate this problem into an equivalent problem for the standard normal distribution. Recall from Chapter 4 that a z score, or standardized score, tells how many standard deviations away from the mean a value lies. The z score is calculated by first subtracting the mean and then dividing by the standard deviation. Converting the lower endpoint $a = 98$ to a z score gives

$$a^* = \frac{98 - 100}{5} = \frac{-2}{5} = -.40$$

and converting the upper endpoint yields

$$b^* = \frac{107 - 100}{5} = \frac{7}{5} = 1.40$$

Then

$$P(98 < x < 107) = P(-.40 < z < 1.40)$$

The probability $P(-.40 < z < 1.40)$ can now be evaluated using Appendix Table 2.

Finding Probabilities

To calculate probabilities for any normal distribution, standardize the relevant values and then use the table of z curve areas. More specifically, if x is a variable whose behavior is described by a normal distribution with mean μ and standard deviation σ, then

$$P(x < b) = P(z < b^*)$$
$$P(x > a) = P(z > a^*)$$
$$P(a < x < b) = P(a^* < z < b^*)$$

(continued)

where z is a variable whose distribution is standard normal and

$$a^* = \frac{a - \mu}{\sigma} \qquad b^* = \frac{b - \mu}{\sigma}$$

EXAMPLE 7.27 Newborn Birth Weights

Data from the paper "Fetal Growth Parameters and Birth Weight: Their Relationship to Neonatal Body Composition" (*Ultrasound in Obstetrics and Gynecology* [2009]: 441–446) suggest that a normal distribution with mean $\mu = 3500$ grams and standard deviation $\sigma = 600$ grams is a reasonable model for the probability distribution of the continuous numerical variable x = birth weight of a randomly selected full-term baby. What proportion of birth weights are between 2900 and 4700 grams?

To answer this question, we must find

$$P(2900 < x < 4700)$$

First, we translate the interval endpoints to equivalent endpoints for the standard normal distribution:

$$a^* = \frac{a - \mu}{\sigma} = \frac{2900 - 3500}{600} = -1.00$$

$$b^* = \frac{b - \mu}{\sigma} = \frac{4700 - 3500}{600} = 2.00$$

Then

$$\begin{aligned} P(2900 < x < 4700) &= P(-1.00 < z < 2.00) \\ &= (z \text{ curve area to the left of } 2.00) \\ &\quad -(z \text{ curve area to the left of } -1.00) \\ &= .9772 - .1587 \\ &= .8185 \end{aligned}$$

The probabilities for x and z are shown in Figure 7.29. If birth weight were observed for many babies from this population, about 82% of them would fall between 2900 and 4700 grams.

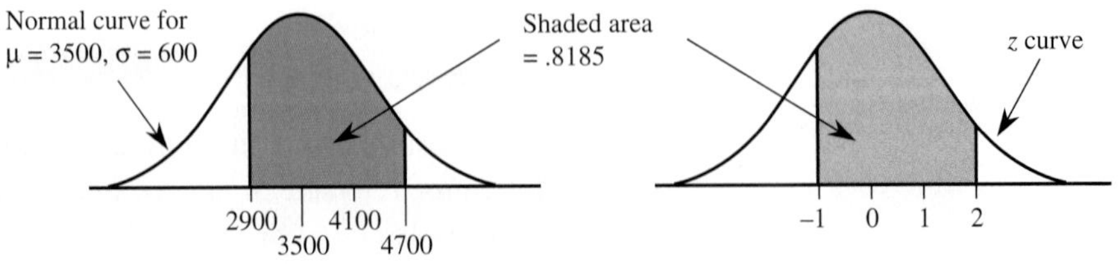

FIGURE 7.29
$P(2900 < x < 4700)$ and corresponding z curve area for the birth weight problem of Example 7.27.

What is the probability that a randomly chosen baby will have a birth weight greater than 4500? To evaluate $P(x > 4500)$, we first compute

$$a^* = \frac{a - \mu}{\sigma} = \frac{4500 - 3500}{600} = 1.67$$

Step-by-Step technology instructions available online

Then (see Figure 7.30)

$$P(x > 4500) = P(z > 1.67)$$
$$= z \text{ curve area to the right of } 1.67$$
$$= 1 - (z \text{ curve area to the left of } 1.67)$$
$$= 1 - .9525$$
$$= .0475$$

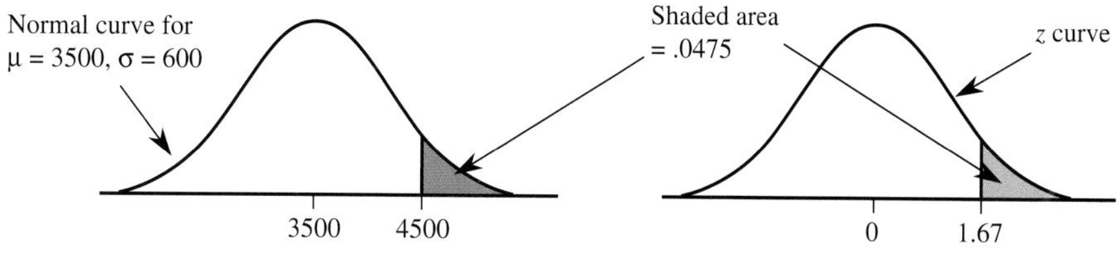

FIGURE 7.30
$P(x > 4500)$ and corresponding z curve area for the birth weight problem of Example 7.27.

EXAMPLE 7.28 IQ Scores

Although there is some controversy regarding the appropriateness of IQ scores as a measure of intelligence, IQ scores are commonly used for a variety of purposes. One commonly used IQ scale (the Stanford-Binet) has a mean of 100 and a standard deviation of 15, and IQ scores are approximately normally distributed. (IQ score is actually a discrete variable [because it is based on the number of correct responses on a test], but its population distribution closely resembles a normal curve.) If we define the random variable

x = IQ score of a randomly selected individual

then x has approximately a normal distribution with $\mu = 100$ and $\sigma = 15$.

One way to become eligible for membership in Mensa, an organization purportedly for those of high intelligence, is to have a Stanford–Binet IQ score above 130. What proportion of the population would qualify for Mensa membership? An answer to this question requires evaluating $P(x > 130)$. This probability is shown in Figure 7.31. With $a = 130$,

$$a^* = \frac{a - \mu}{\sigma} = \frac{130 - 100}{15} = 2.00$$

So (see Figure 7.32)

$$P(x > 130) = P(z > 2.00)$$
$$= z \text{ curve area to the right of } 2.00$$
$$= 1 - (z \text{ curve area to the left of } 2.00)$$
$$= 1 - .9772$$
$$= .0228$$

Only 2.28% of the population would qualify for Mensa membership.

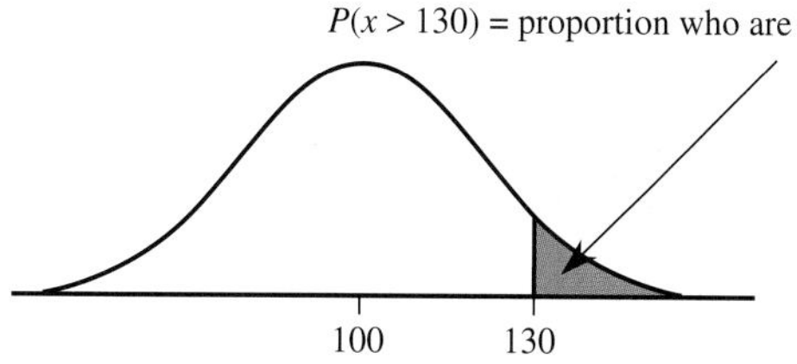

FIGURE 7.31
Normal distribution and desired proportion for Example 7.28.

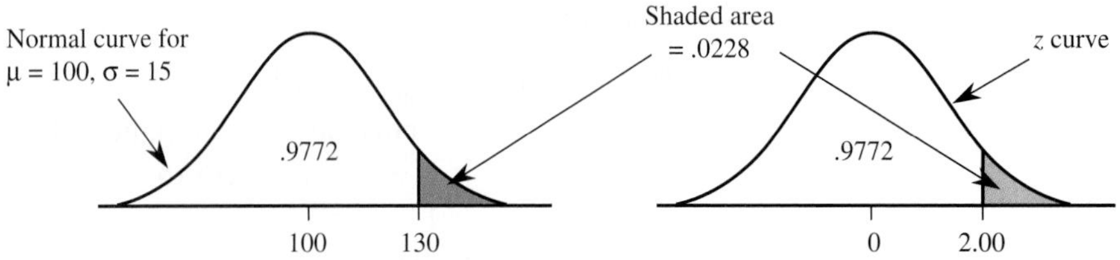

FIGURE 7.32
$P(x > 130)$ and corresponding z curve area for the IQ problem of Example 7.28.

Suppose that we are interested in the proportion of the population with IQ scores below 80—that is, $P(x < 80)$. With $b = 80$,

$$b^* = \frac{b - \mu}{\sigma} = \frac{80 - 100}{15} = -1.33$$

So

$$\begin{aligned} P(x < 80) &= P(z < -1.33) \\ &= z \text{ curve area to the left of } -1.33 \\ &= .0918 \end{aligned}$$

as shown in Figure 7.33. This probability (.0918) tells us that just a little over 9% of the population has an IQ score below 80.

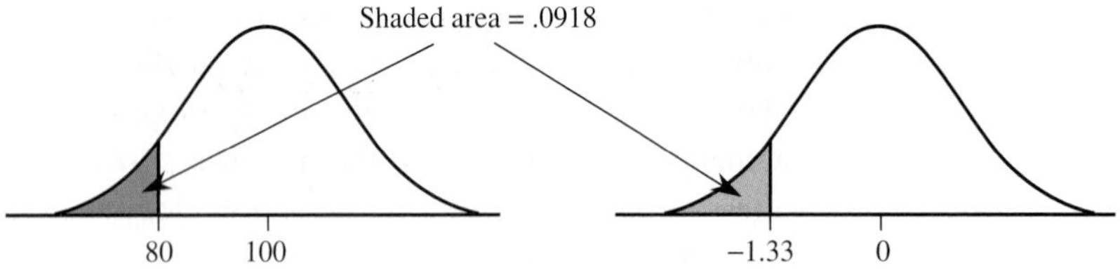

FIGURE 7.33
$P(x < 80)$ and corresponding z curve area for the IQ problem of Example 7.28.

Now consider the proportion of the population with IQs between 75 and 125. Using $a = 75$ and $b = 125$, we obtain

$$a^* = \frac{75 - 100}{15} = -1.67 \qquad b^* = \frac{125 - 100}{15} = 1.67$$

so

$$\begin{aligned} P(75 < x < 125) &= P(-1.67 < z < 1.67) \\ &= z \text{ curve area between } -1.67 \text{ and } 1.67 \\ &= (z \text{ curve area to the left of } 1.67) \\ &\quad - (z \text{ curve area to the left of } -1.67) \\ &= .9525 - .0475 \\ &= .9050 \end{aligned}$$

This is illustrated in Figure 7.34. The calculation tells us that 90.5% of the population has an IQ score between 75 and 125. Of the 9.5% whose IQ score is not between 75 and 125, half of them (4.75%) have scores over 125, and the other half have scores below 75.

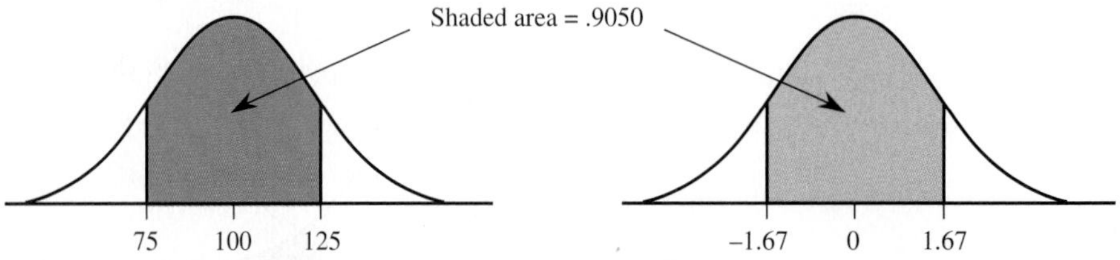

FIGURE 7.34
$P(75 < x < 125)$ and corresponding z curve area for the IQ problem of Example 7.28.

When we translate from a problem involving a normal distribution with mean μ and standard deviation σ to a problem involving the standard normal distribution, we convert to z scores:

$$z = \frac{x - \mu}{\sigma}$$

Because a z score can be interpreted as giving the distance of an x value from the mean in units of the standard deviation, a z score of 1.4 corresponds to an x value that is 1.4 standard deviations above the mean, and a z score of -2.1 corresponds to an x value that is 2.1 standard deviations below the mean.

Suppose that we are trying to evaluate $P(x < 60)$ for a variable whose distribution is normal with $\mu = 50$ and $\sigma = 5$. Converting the endpoint 60 to a z score gives

$$z = \frac{60 - 50}{5} = 2$$

which tells us that the value 60 is 2 standard deviations above the mean. We then have

$$P(x < 60) = P(z < 2)$$

where z is a standard normal variable. Notice that for the standard normal distribution, the value 2 is also 2 standard deviations above the mean, because the mean is 0 and the standard deviation is 1. The value $z = 2$ is located the same distance (measured in standard deviations) from the mean of the standard normal distribution as is the value $x = 60$ from the mean in the normal distribution with $\mu = 50$ and $\sigma = 5$. This is why the translation using z scores results in an equivalent problem involving the standard normal distribution.

Describing Extreme Values in a Normal Distribution

To describe the extreme values for a normal distribution with mean μ and standard deviation σ, we first solve the corresponding problem for the standard normal distribution and then translate our answer into one for the normal distribution of interest. This process is illustrated in Example 7.29.

EXAMPLE 7.29 Registration Times

Data on the length of time required to complete registration for classes using an online registration system suggest that the distribution of the variable

$$x = \text{time to register}$$

for students at a particular university can be well approximated by a normal distribution with mean $\mu = 12$ minutes and standard deviation $\sigma = 2$ minutes. (The normal distribution might not be an appropriate model for x = time to register at another university. Many factors influence the shape, center, and spread of such a distribution.) Because some students do not log off properly, the university would like to log off students automatically after some amount of time has elapsed. It is decided to choose this time such that only 1% of the students are logged off while they are still attempting to register. To determine the amount of time that should be allowed before disconnecting a student, we need to describe the largest 1% of the distribution

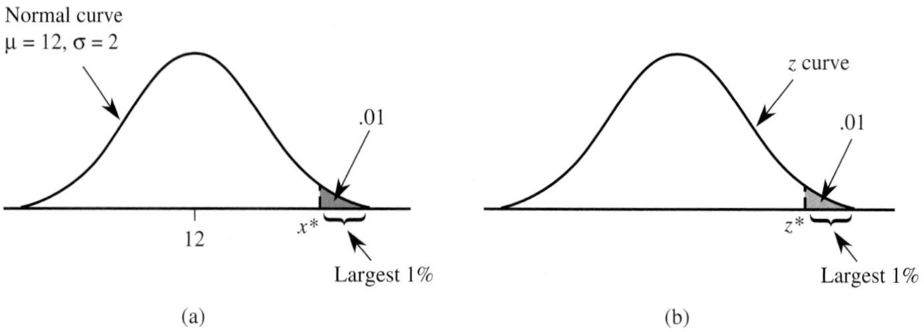

FIGURE 7.35
Capturing the largest 1% in a normal distribution for the problem in Example 7.29.

of time to register. These are the individuals who will be mistakenly disconnected. This is illustrated in Figure 7.35(a). To determine the value of x^*, we first solve the analogous problem for the standard normal distribution, as shown in Figure 7.35(b).

By looking at Appendix Table 2 for a cumulative area of .99, we find the closest entry (.9901) in the 2.3 row and the .03 column, from which $z^* = 2.33$. For the standard normal distribution, the largest 1% of the distribution is made up of those values greater than 2.33. An equivalent statement is that the largest 1% are those with z scores greater than 2.33. This implies that in the distribution of x = time to register (or any other normal distribution), the largest 1% are those values with z scores greater than 2.33 or, equivalently, those x values more than 2.33 standard deviations above the mean. Here, the standard deviation is 2, so 2.33 standard deviations is 2.33(2), and it follows that

$$x^* = 12 + 2.33(2) = 12 + 4.66 = 16.66$$

The largest 1% of the distribution for time to register is made up of values that are greater than 16.66 minutes. If the university system was set to log off students after 16.66 minutes, only 1% of the students registering would be logged off before completing their registration.

A general formula for converting a z score back to an x value results from solving $z^* = \dfrac{x^* - \mu}{\sigma}$ for x^*, as shown in the accompanying box.

To convert a z score z^* back to an x value, use

$$x = \mu + z^*\sigma$$

EXAMPLE 7.30 Garbage Truck Processing Times

Garbage trucks entering a particular waste management facility are weighed and then they offload garbage into a landfill. Data from the paper "Estimating Waste Transfer Station Delays Using GPS" (*Waste Management* [2008]: 1742–1750) suggest that a normal distribution with mean $\mu = 13$ minutes and $\sigma = 3.9$ minutes is a reasonable model for the probability distribution of the random variable x = total processing time for a garbage truck at this waste management facility (total processing time includes waiting time as well as the time required to weigh the truck and offload the garbage). Suppose that we want to describe the total processing times of the trucks making up the 10% with the longest processing times. These trucks would be the 10% with times corresponding to the shaded region in the accompanying illustration.

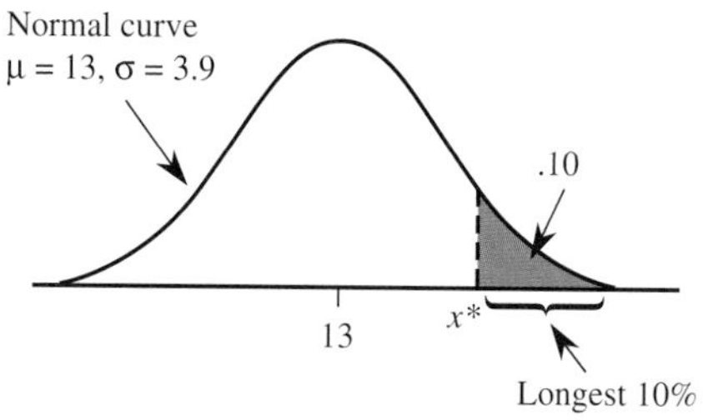

For the standard normal distribution, the largest 10% are those with z values greater than $z^* = 1.28$ (from Appendix Table 2, based on a cumulative area of .90). Then

$$\begin{aligned} x^* &= \mu + z^*\sigma \\ &= 13 + 1.28(3.9) \\ &= 13 + 4.992 \\ &= 17.992 \end{aligned}$$

About 10% of the garbage trucks using this facility would have a total processing time of more than 17.992 minutes.

The 5% with the fastest processing times would be those with z values less than $z^* = -1.645$ (from Appendix Table 2, based on a cumulative area of .05). Then

$$\begin{aligned} x^* &= \mu + z^*\sigma \\ &= 13 + (-1.645)(3.9) \\ &= 13 - 6.416 \\ &= 6.584 \end{aligned}$$

About 5% of the garbage trucks processed at this facility will have total processing times of less than 6.584 minutes.

EXERCISES 7.63 - 7.82

7.63 Determine the following standard normal (z) curve areas:

a. The area under the z curve to the left of 1.75
b. The area under the z curve to the left of -0.68
c. The area under the z curve to the right of 1.20
d. The area under the z curve to the right of -2.82
e. The area under the z curve between -2.22 and 0.53
f. The area under the z curve between -1 and 1
g. The area under the z curve between -4 and 4

7.64 Determine each of the following areas under the standard normal (z) curve:

a. To the left of -1.28
b. To the right of 1.28
c. Between -1 and 2
d. To the right of 0
e. To the right of -5
f. Between -1.6 and 2.5
g. To the left of 0.23

7.65 Let z denote a random variable that has a standard normal distribution. Determine each of the following probabilities:

a. $P(z < 2.36)$
b. $P(z \leq 2.36)$
c. $P(z < -1.23)$
d. $P(1.14 < z < 3.35)$
e. $P(-0.77 \leq z \leq -0.55)$
f. $P(z > 2)$
g. $P(z \geq -3.38)$
h. $P(z < 4.98)$

7.66 Let z denote a random variable having a normal distribution with $\mu = 0$ and $\sigma = 1$. Determine each of the following probabilities:

a. $P(z < 0.10)$
b. $P(z < -0.10)$
c. $P(0.40 < z < 0.85)$
d. $P(-0.85 < z < -0.40)$

e. $P(-0.40 < z < 0.85)$
f. $P(z > -1.25)$
g. $P(z < -1.50 \text{ or } z > 2.50)$

7.67 Let z denote a variable that has a standard normal distribution. Determine the value z^* to satisfy the following conditions:

a. $P(z < z^*) = .025$
b. $P(z < z^*) = .01$
c. $P(z < z^*) = .05$
d. $P(z > z^*) = .02$
e. $P(z > z^*) = .01$
f. $P(z > z^* \text{ or } z < -z^*) = .20$

7.68 Determine the value z^* that

a. Separates the largest 3% of all z values from the others
b. Separates the largest 1% of all z values from the others
c. Separates the smallest 4% of all z values from the others
d. Separates the smallest 10% of all z values from the others

7.69 Determine the value of z^* such that

a. $-z^*$ and z^* separate the middle 95% of all z values from the most extreme 5%
b. $-z^*$ and z^* separate the middle 90% of all z values from the most extreme 10%
c. $-z^*$ and z^* separate the middle 98% of all z values from the most extreme 2%
d. $-z^*$ and z^* separate the middle 92% of all z values from the most extreme 8%

7.70 Because $P(z < .44) = .67$, 67% of all z values are less than .44, and .44 is the 67th percentile of the standard normal distribution. Determine the value of each of the following percentiles for the standard normal distribution (Hint: If the cumulative area that you must look for does not appear in the z table, use the closest entry):

a. The 91st percentile (Hint: Look for area .9100.)
b. The 77th percentile
c. The 50th percentile
d. The 9th percentile
e. What is the relationship between the 70th z percentile and the 30th z percentile?

7.71 Consider the population of all 1-gallon cans of dusty rose paint manufactured by a particular paint company. Suppose that a normal distribution with mean $\mu =$ 5 ml and standard deviation $\sigma = 0.2$ ml is a reasonable model for the distribution of the variable $x =$ amount of red dye in the paint mixture. Use the normal distribution model to calculate the following probabilities:

a. $P(x < 5.0)$
b. $P(x < 5.4)$
c. $P(x \leq 5.4)$
d. $P(4.6 < x < 5.2)$
e. $P(x > 4.5)$
f. $P(x > 4.0)$

7.72 Consider babies born in the "normal" range of 37–43 weeks gestational age. The paper referenced in Example 7.27 ("Fetal Growth Parameters and Birth Weight: Their Relationship to Neonatal Body Composition," *Ultrasound in Obstetrics and Gynecology* [2009]: 441–446) suggests that a normal distribution with mean $\mu = 3500$ grams and standard deviation $\sigma =$ 600 grams is a reasonable model for the probability distribution of the continuous numerical variable $x =$ birth weight of a randomly selected full-term baby.

a. What is the probability that the birth weight of a randomly selected full-term baby exceeds 4000 g? is between 3000 and 4000 g?
b. What is the probability that the birth weight of a randomly selected full-term baby is either less than 2000 g or greater than 5000 g?
c. What is the probability that the birth weight of a randomly selected full-term baby exceeds 7 pounds? (Hint: 1 lb = 453.59 g.)
d. How would you characterize the most extreme 0.1% of all full-term baby birth weights?
e. If x is a random variable with a normal distribution and a is a numerical constant ($a \neq 0$), then $y = ax$ also has a normal distribution. Use this formula to determine the distribution of full-term baby birth weight expressed in pounds (shape, mean, and standard deviation), and then recalculate the probability from Part (c). How does this compare to your previous answer?

7.73 Emissions of nitrogen oxides, which are major constituents of smog, can be modeled using a normal distribution. Let x denote the amount of this pollutant emitted by a randomly selected vehicle (in parts per billion). The distribution of x can be described by a normal distribution with $\mu = 1.6$ and $\sigma = 0.4$. Suppose that the EPA wants to offer some sort of incentive to get the worst polluters off the road. What emission levels constitute the worst 10% of the vehicles?

7.74 The paper referenced in Example 7.30 ("Estimating Waste Transfer Station Delays Using GPS," *Waste Management* [2008]: 1742–1750) describing processing times for garbage trucks also provided information on processing times at a second facility. At this second facility, the mean total processing time was 9.9 minutes and the standard deviation of the processing times was 6.2 minutes. Explain why a normal distribution with mean 9.9 and standard deviation 6.2 would not be an appropriate model for the probability distribution of the variable x = total processing time of a randomly selected truck entering this facility.

7.75 The size of the left upper chamber of the heart is one measure of cardiovascular health. When the upper left chamber is enlarged, the risk of heart problems is increased. The paper "Left Atrial Size Increases with Body Mass Index in Children" (*International Journal of Cardiology* [2009]: 1–7) described a study in which the left atrial size was measured for a large number of children age 5 to 15 years. Based on this data, the authors concluded that for healthy children, left atrial diameter was approximately normally distributed with a mean of 26.4 mm and a standard deviation of 4.2 mm.

a. Approximately what proportion of healthy children has left atrial diameters less than 24 mm?
b. Approximately what proportion of healthy children has left atrial diameters greater than 32 mm?
c. Approximately what proportion of healthy children has left atrial diameters between 25 and 30 mm?
d. For healthy children, what is the value for which only about 20% have a larger left atrial diameter?

7.76 The paper referenced in the previous exercise also included data on left atrial diameter for children who were considered overweight. For these children, left atrial diameter was approximately normally distributed with a mean of 28 mm and a standard deviation of 4.7 mm.

a. Approximately what proportion of overweight children has left atrial diameters less than 25 mm?
b. Approximately what proportion of overweight children has left atrial diameters greater than 32 mm?
c. Approximately what proportion of overweight children has left atrial diameters between 25 and 30 mm?
d. What proportion of overweight children has left atrial diameters greater than the mean for healthy children?

7.77 According to the paper "Commuters' Exposure to Particulate Matter and Carbon Monoxide in Hanoi, Vietnam" (*Transportation Research* [2008]: 206–211), the carbon monoxide exposure of someone riding a motorbike for 5 km on a highway in Hanoi is approximately normally distributed with a mean of 18.6 ppm. Suppose that the standard deviation of carbon monoxide exposure is 5.7 ppm. Approximately what proportion of those who ride a motorbike for 5 km on a Hanoi highway will experience a carbon monoxide exposure of more than 20 ppm? More than 25 ppm?

7.78 A machine that cuts corks for wine bottles operates in such a way that the distribution of the diameter of the corks produced is well approximated by a normal distribution with mean 3 cm and standard deviation 0.1 cm. The specifications call for corks with diameters between 2.9 and 3.1 cm. A cork not meeting the specifications is considered defective. (A cork that is too small leaks and causes the wine to deteriorate; a cork that is too large doesn't fit in the bottle.) What proportion of corks produced by this machine are defective?

7.79 Refer to Exercise 7.78. Suppose that there are two machines available for cutting corks. The machine described in the preceding problem produces corks with diameters that are approximately normally distributed with mean 3 cm and standard deviation 0.1 cm. The second machine produces corks with diameters that are approximately normally distributed with mean 3.05 cm and standard deviation 0.01 cm. Which machine would you recommend? (Hint: Which machine would produce fewer defective corks?)

7.80 A gasoline tank for a certain car is designed to hold 15 gallons of gas. Suppose that the variable x = actual capacity of a randomly selected tank has a distribution that is well approximated by a normal curve with mean 15.0 gallons and standard deviation 0.1 gallon.

a. What is the probability that a randomly selected tank will hold at most 14.8 gallons?
b. What is the probability that a randomly selected tank will hold between 14.7 and 15.1 gallons?
c. If two such tanks are independently selected, what is the probability that both hold at most 15 gallons?

7.81 ✦ The time that it takes a randomly selected job applicant to perform a certain task has a distribution that can be approximated by a normal distribution with a mean value of 120 seconds and a standard deviation of 20 seconds. The fastest 10% are to be given advanced training. What task times qualify individuals for such training?

7.82 ✦ Suppose that the distribution of typing speed in words per minute (wpm) for experienced typists using a new type of split keyboard can be approximated by a normal curve with mean 60 wpm and standard deviation 15 wpm ("The Effects of Split Keyboard Geometry on Upper body Postures," *Ergonomics* [2009]: 104–111).

a. What is the probability that a randomly selected typist's speed is at most 60 wpm? less than 60 wpm?

b. What is the probability that a randomly selected typist's speed is between 45 and 90 wpm?
c. Would you be surprised to find a typist in this population whose speed exceeded 105 wpm?
d. Suppose that two typists are independently selected. What is the probability that both their typing speeds exceed 75 wpm?
e. Suppose that special training is to be made available to the slowest 20% of the typists. What typing speeds would qualify individuals for this training?

7.7 Checking for Normality and Normalizing Transformations

Some of the most frequently used statistical methods are valid only when a sample $x_1, x_2, \ldots, x_n$ has come from a population distribution that is at least approximately normal. One way to see whether an assumption of population normality is plausible is to construct a **normal probability plot** of the data. One version of this plot uses quantities called **normal scores.** The values of the normal scores depend on the sample size n. For example, the normal scores when $n = 10$ are as follows:

−1.539	−1.001	−.656	−.376	−.123
.123	.376	.656	1.001	1.539

To interpret these numbers, think of selecting sample after sample from a standard normal distribution, each one consisting of $n = 10$ observations. Then -1.539 is the long-run average of the smallest observation from each sample, -1.001 is the long-run average of the second smallest observation from each sample, and so on. In other words, -1.539 is the mean value of the smallest observation in a sample of size 10 from the z distribution and -1.001 is the mean value of the second smallest observation, and so on.

Tables of normal scores for many different sample sizes are available. Alternatively, many software packages (such as Minitab and SAS) and some graphing calculators can compute these scores on request and then construct a normal probability plot. Not all calculators and software packages use the same algorithm to compute normal scores. However, this does not change the overall character of a normal probability plot, so either the tabulated values or those given by the computer or calculator can be used.

After the sample observations are ordered from smallest to largest, the smallest normal score is paired with the smallest observation, the second smallest normal score with the second smallest observation, and so on. The first number in a pair is the normal score, and the second number in the pair is the observed data value. A normal probability plot is just a scatterplot of these (normal score, observed value) pairs.

If the sample has been selected from a *standard* normal distribution, the second number in each pair should be reasonably close to the first number (ordered observation ≈ corresponding mean value). Then the n plotted points will fall near a line with slope equal to 1 (a 45° line) passing through (0, 0). When the sample has been obtained from *some* normal population distribution (but not necessarily the standard normal distribution), the plotted points should be close to *some* straight line (but not necessarily one with slope 1 and intercept 0).

DEFINITION

A **normal probability plot** is a scatterplot of the (normal score, observed value) pairs. A strong linear pattern in a normal probability plot suggests that population normality is plausible. On the other hand, systematic departure from a straight-line pattern (such as curvature in the plot) indicates that it is not reasonable to assume that the population distribution is normal.

EXAMPLE 7.31 Egg Weights

The following data represent egg weights (in grams) for a sample of 10 eggs. These data are consistent with summary quantities in the paper "Evaluation of Egg Quality Traits of Chickens Reared under Backyard System in Western Uttar Pradesh" (*Indian Journal of Poultry Science*, 2009).

53.04	53.50	52.53	53.00	53.07	52.86	52.66	53.23	53.26	53.16

Arranging the sample observations in order from smallest to largest results in

52.53	52.66	52.86	53.00	53.04	53.07	53.16	53.23	53.26	53.50

Pairing these ordered observations with the normal scores for a sample of size 10 (previously given) results in the following 10 pairs that can be used to construct the normal probability plot:

(−1.539, 52.53)	(−1.001, 52.66)
(−0.656, 52.86)	(−0.376, 53.00)
(−0.123, 53.04)	(0.123, 53.07)
(0.376, 53.16)	(0.656, 53.23)
(1.001, 53.26)	(1.539, 53.50)

The normal probability plot is shown in Figure 7.36. The linear pattern in the plot supports the assumption that the egg-weight distribution from which these observations were drawn is normal.

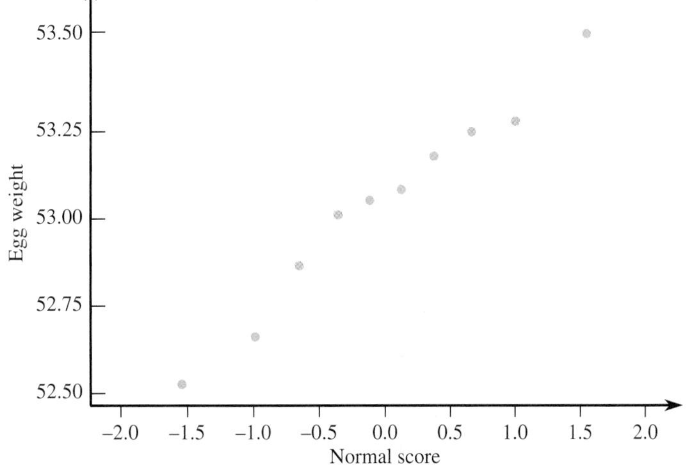

FIGURE 7.36
A normal probability plot for Example 7.31.

The decision as to whether a plot shows a strong linear pattern is somewhat subjective. Particularly when n is small, normality should not be ruled out unless the departure from linearity is clear-cut. Figure 7.37 displays several plots that suggest a nonnormal population distribution.

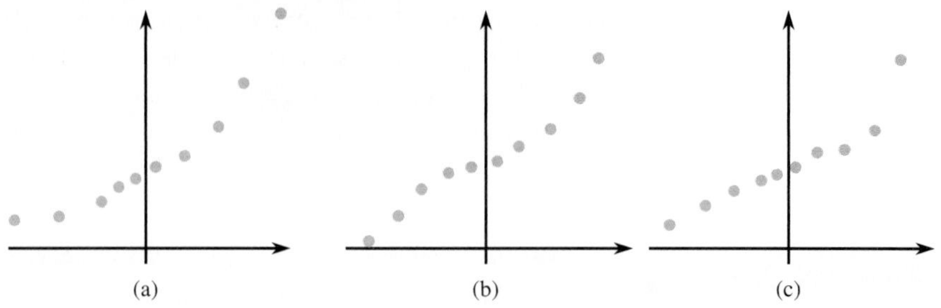

FIGURE 7.37
Plots suggesting nonnormality: (a) indication that the population distribution is skewed; (b) indication that the population distribution has heavier tails than a normal curve; (c) presence of an outlier.

Using the Correlation Coefficient to Check Normality

The correlation coefficient r was introduced in Chapter 5 as a quantitative measure of the extent to which the points in a scatterplot fall close to a straight line. Consider the n (normal score, observed value) pairs:

(smallest normal score, smallest observation)
⋮
(largest normal score, largest observation)

Then the correlation coefficient can be computed as discussed in Chapter 5. The normal probability plot always slopes upward (because it is based on values ordered from smallest to largest), so r will be a positive number. A value of r quite close to 1 indicates a very strong linear relationship in the normal probability plot. If r is too much smaller than 1, normality of the underlying distribution is questionable.

How far below 1 does r have to be before we begin to seriously doubt the plausibility of normality? The answer depends on the sample size n. If n is small, an r value somewhat below 1 is not surprising, even when the population distribution is normal, but if n is large, only an r value very close to 1 supports the assumption of normality. For selected values of n, Table 7.2 gives critical values to which r can be compared to check for normality. If your sample size is in between two tabulated values of n, use the critical value for the larger sample size. (For example, if $n = 46$, use the value .966 for sample size 50.)

TABLE 7.2 Values to Which r Can Be Compared to Check for Normality*

n	5	10	15	20	25	30	40	50	60	75
Critical r	.832	.880	.911	.929	.941	.949	.960	.966	.971	.976

*Source: *Minitab User's Manual.*

If

$r <$ critical r for corresponding n

it is probably not reasonable to assume that the population distribution is normal.

How were the critical values in Table 7.2 obtained? Consider the critical value .941 for $n = 25$. Suppose that the underlying distribution is actually normal. Consider obtaining a large number of different samples, each one consisting of 25 observations, and computing the value of r for each one. Then it can be shown that only 1% of the samples result in an r value less than the critical value .941. That is, .941 was chosen to guarantee a 1% error rate: In only 1% of all cases will we judge normality implausible when the distribution is really normal. The other critical values are also chosen to yield a 1% error rate for the corresponding sample sizes.

It might have occurred to you that another type of error is possible: obtaining a large value of r and concluding that normality is a reasonable assumption when the distribution is actually nonnormal. This type of error is more difficult to control than the type mentioned previously, but the procedure we have described generally does a good job in controlling for both types of error.

EXAMPLE 7.32 Egg Weights Continued

The sample size for the egg-weight data of Example 7.31 is $n = 10$. The critical r, from Table 7.2 is then .880. From Minitab, the correlation coefficient calculated using the (normal score, observed value) pairs is $r = .986$. Because r is larger than the critical r for a sample of size 10, it is plausible that the population distribution of egg weights from which this sample was drawn is approximately normal.

Correlations: Egg Weight, Normal Score

Pearson correlation of Egg Weight and Normal Score = 0.986

Transforming Data to Obtain a Distribution That Is Approximately Normal

Many of the most frequently used statistical methods are valid only when the sample is selected at random from a population whose distribution is at least approximately normal. When a sample histogram shows a distinctly nonnormal shape, it is common to use a transformation or reexpression of the data. By *transforming* data, we mean applying some specified mathematical function (such as the square root, logarithm, or reciprocal) to each data value to produce a set of transformed data. We can then study and summarize the distribution of these transformed values using methods that require normality. We saw in Chapter 5 that, with bivariate data, one or both of the variables can be transformed in an attempt to find two variables that are linearly related. With univariate data, a transformation is usually chosen to yield a distribution of transformed values that is more symmetric and more closely approximated by a normal curve than was the original distribution.

EXAMPLE 7.33 Rainfall Data

● Data that have been used by several investigators to introduce the concept of transformation consist of values of March precipitation for Minneapolis–St. Paul over a period of 30 years. These values are given in Table 7.3, along with the square root of each value. Histograms of both the original and the transformed data appear in Figure 7.38. The distribution of the original data is clearly skewed, with a long upper

● Data set available online

tail. The square-root transformation results in a substantially more symmetric distribution, with a typical (i.e., central) value of around 1.1.

TABLE 7.3 Original and Square-Root-Transformed Values of March Precipitation in Minneapolis–St. Paul over a 30-year Period

Year	Precipitation	$\sqrt{\text{Precipitation}}$	Year	Precipitation	$\sqrt{\text{Precipitation}}$
1	.77	.88	16	1.62	1.27
2	1.74	1.32	17	1.31	1.14
3	.81	.90	18	.32	.57
4	1.20	1.10	19	.59	.77
5	1.95	1.40	20	.81	.90
6	1.20	1.10	21	2.81	1.68
7	.47	.69	22	1.87	1.37
8	1.43	1.20	23	1.18	1.09
9	3.37	1.84	24	1.35	1.16
10	2.20	1.48	25	4.75	2.18
11	3.00	1.73	26	2.48	1.57
12	3.09	1.76	27	.96	.98
13	1.51	1.23	28	1.89	1.37
14	2.10	1.45	29	.90	.95
15	.52	.72	30	2.05	1.43

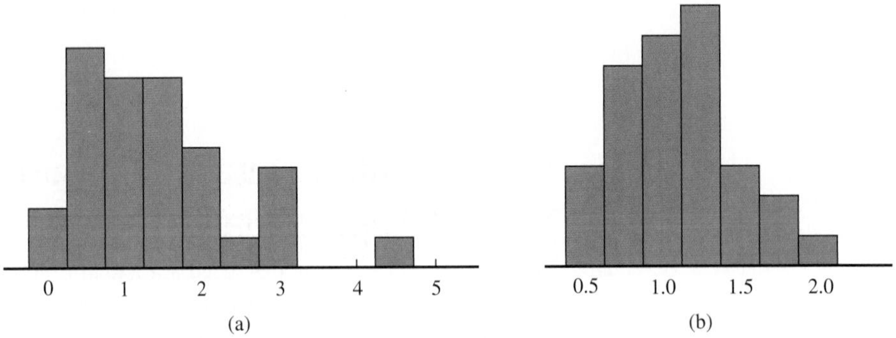

FIGURE 7.38
Histograms of the precipitation data used in Example 7.33:
(a) untransformed data;
(b) square-root transformed data.

Logarithmic transformations are also common and, as with bivariate data, either the natural logarithm or the base 10 logarithm can be used. A logarithmic transformation is usually applied to data that are positively skewed (a long upper tail). This affects values in the upper tail substantially more than values in the lower tail, yielding a more symmetric—and often more nearly normal—distribution.

EXAMPLE 7.34 Markers for Kidney Disease

Two measures of kidney function are the levels of a substance called AGT found in blood and urine. The paper "Urinary Angiotensinogen as a Potential Biomarker of Severity of Chronic Kidney Diseases" (*Journal of the American Society of Hypertension* [2008]: 349–354) describes a study in which blood plasma AGT levels and urinary AGT levels were measured for a sample of adults with chronic kidney disease. Representative data (consistent with summary quantities and descriptions given in the paper) for 40 patients are given in Table 7.4.

TABLE 7.4 Plasma and Urinary AGT Levels

Plasma AGT	Plasma AGT	Urinary AGT	Urinary AGT
21.0	16.7	56.2	41.7
36.0	20.2	288.4	29.5
22.9	24.5	45.7	208.9
8.0	18.5	426.6	229.1
27.3	40.2	190.6	186.2
32.4	18.8	616.6	29.5
17.2	28.1	97.7	229.1
30.9	26.8	66.1	13.5
27.2	24.1	2.6	407.4
30.0	14.1	74.1	1122.0
35.1	18.9	14.5	66.1
21.6	25.6	56.2	7.4
22.7	10.2	812.8	177.8
2.5	29.2	11.5	6.2
30.2	29.5	346.7	67.6
27.3	24.3	9.6	20.0
19.6	22.3	288.4	28.8
19.0	16.5	147.9	186.2
13.4	25.6	17.0	141.3
18.0	23.0	575.4	724.4

The authors of the paper stated that the distribution of plasma AGT levels was approximately normal. Minitab was used to construct the histogram and normal probability plot for the plasma AGT levels shown in Figure 7.39. The histogram is reasonably symmetric and the normal probability plot shows a strong linear pattern. This is consistent with the authors' statement about the approximate normality of the plasma AGT levels.

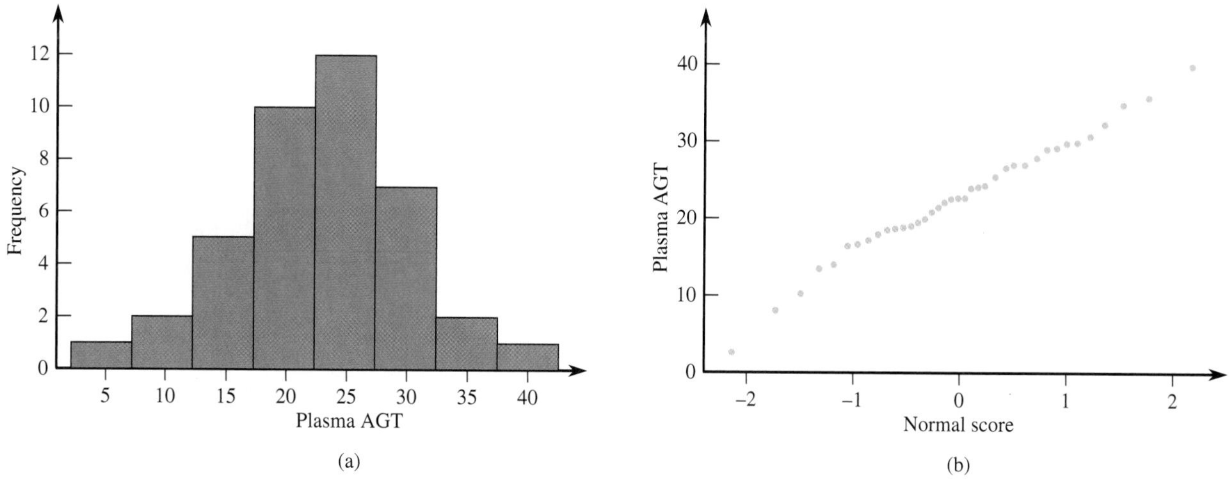

FIGURE 7.39
Graphical displays for the plasma AGT data of Example 7.34: (a) histogram; (b) normal probability plot.

When the authors considered urinary AGT levels, they found that the distribution of the sample data was skewed, and they used a log transformation in order to obtain a distribution that was more approximately normal. Table 7.5 gives the urinary AGT levels along with the log-transformed data. Figure 7.40 shows histograms of the original urinary AGT data and the transformed urinary AGT data. Notice that the histogram for the transformed data is more symmetric and more mound shaped than the histogram of the untransformed data.

TABLE 7.5 Urinary AGT Levels and Log-Transformed Levels

Urinary AGT	Log(Urinary AGT)	Urinary AGT	Log(Urinary AGT)
56.2	1.75	41.7	1.62
288.4	2.46	29.5	1.47
45.7	1.66	208.9	2.32
426.6	2.63	229.1	2.36
190.6	2.28	186.2	2.27
616.6	2.79	29.5	1.47
97.7	1.99	229.1	2.36
66.1	1.82	13.5	1.13
2.6	0.41	407.4	2.61
74.1	1.87	1122.0	3.05
14.5	1.16	66.1	1.82
56.2	1.75	7.4	0.87
812.8	2.91	177.8	2.25
11.5	1.06	6.2	0.79
346.7	2.54	67.6	1.83
9.6	0.98	20.0	1.30
288.4	2.46	28.8	1.46
147.9	2.17	186.2	2.27
17.0	1.23	141.3	2.15
575.4	2.76	724.4	2.86

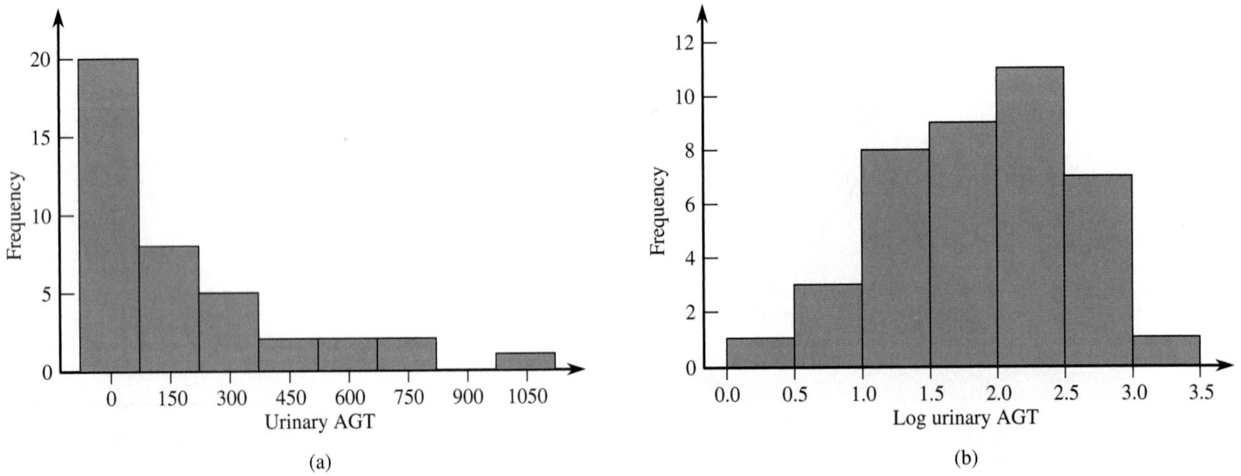

FIGURE 7.40
Histograms of urinary AGT data from Example 7.34: (a) untransformed data; (b) transformed data.

Figure 7.41 displays Minitab normal probability plots for the original data and for the transformed data. The plot for the transformed data is clearly more linear in appearance than the plot for the original data.

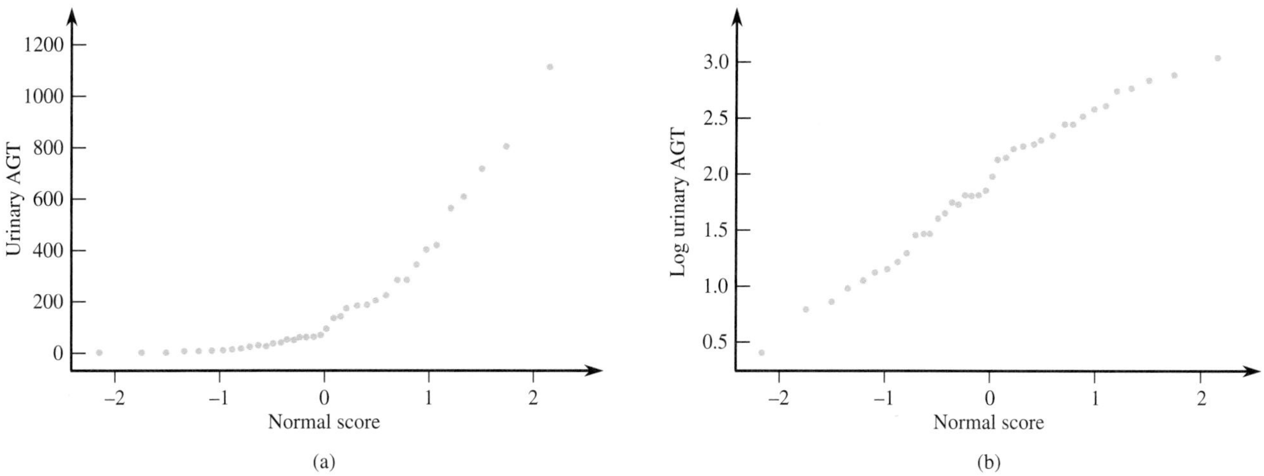

FIGURE 7.41
Minitab normal probability plots for the data of Example 7.34: (a) original data; (b) transformed data.

Minitab was also used to compute the correlation coefficient for the (data, normal score) pairs.

Correlations: Urinary AGT, Normal Score

Pearson correlation of Urinary AGT and Normal Score = 0.866

Correlations: Log(Urinary AGT), Normal Score

Pearson correlation of Log(Urinary AGT) and Normal Score = 0.990

With $n = 40$, the critical r value from Table 7.2 is $r = .960$. The correlation coefficient for the untransformed data is .866, which is less than the critical r, indicating that it is not reasonable to regard the distribution of urinary AGT values as normal. However, the correlation coefficient for the transformed data is $r = .990$, which is much larger than the critical r, supporting the authors' belief that the log-transformed data distribution is approximately normal.

Selecting a Transformation

Occasionally, a particular transformation can be dictated by some theoretical argument, but often this is not the case and you may want to try several different transformations to find one that is satisfactory. Figure 7.42, from the article "Distribution of Sperm Counts in Suspected Infertile Men" (*Journal of Reproduction and Fertility* [1983]: 91–96), shows what can result from such a search. Other investigators in this field had previously used all three of the transformations illustrated, but the log transformation shown in Figure 7.42(b) appears to be the best choice.

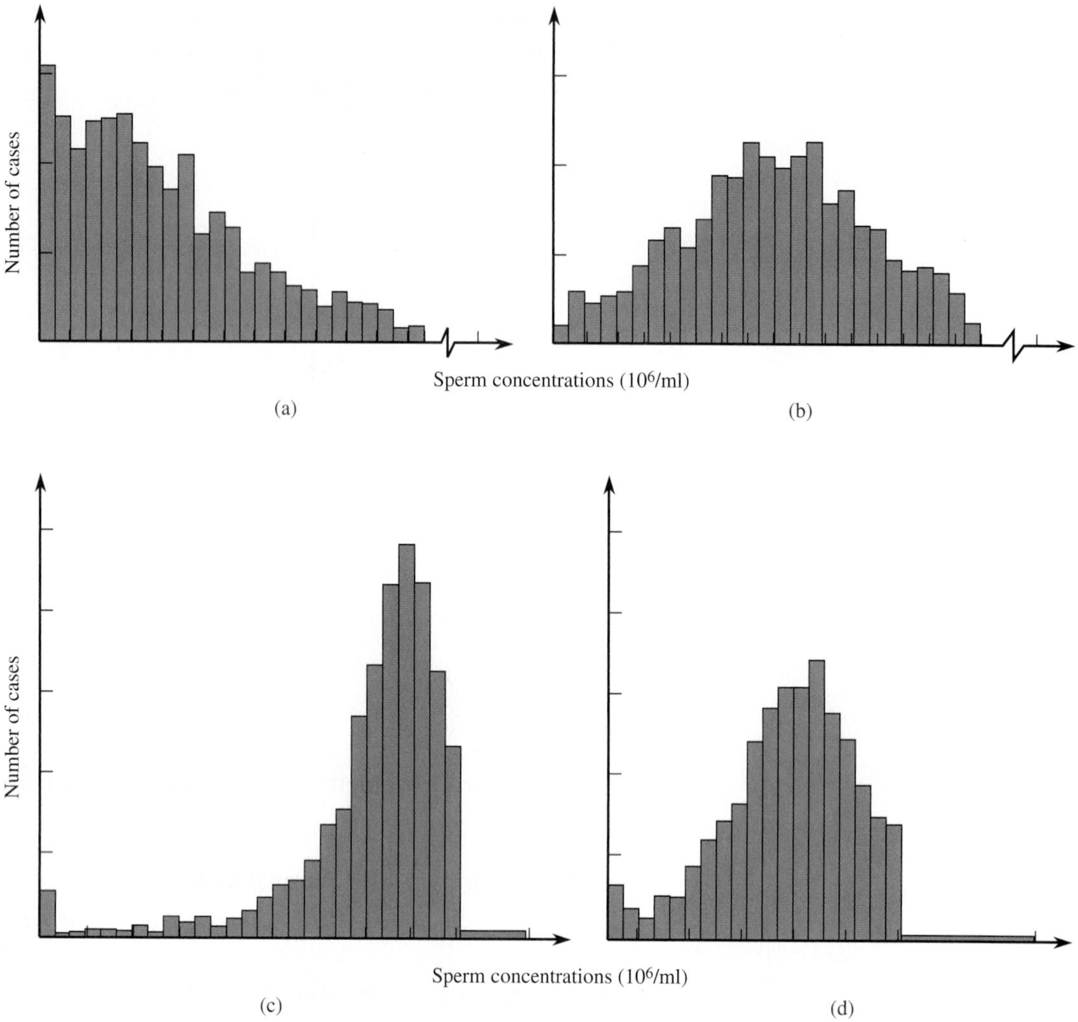

FIGURE 7.42
Histograms of sperm concentrations for 1711 suspected infertile men: (a) untransformed data (highly skewed); (b) log-transformed data (reasonably symmetric); (c) square-root-transformed data; (d) cube-root-transformed data.

EXERCISES 7.83 - 7.93

7.83 ● The authors of the paper "Development of Nutritionally At-Risk Young Children is Predicted by Malaria, Anemia, and Stunting in Pemba, Zanzibar" (*The Journal of Nutrition* [2009]:763–772) studied factors that might be related to dietary deficiencies in children. Children were observed for a length of time and the time spent in various activities was recorded. One variable of interest was the length of time (in minutes) a child spent fussing. The authors comment that the distribution of fussing times was skewed and that they used a square root transformation to create a distribution that was more approximately normal. Data consistent with summary quantities in the paper for 15 children are given in the accompanying table. Normal scores for a samples size of 15 are also given.

Fussing Time	Normal Score
0.05	−1.739
0.10	−1.245
0.15	−0.946

(continued)

Fussing Time	Normal Score
0.40	−0.714
0.70	−0.515
1.05	−0.333
1.95	−0.165
2.15	0.000
3.70	0.165
3.90	0.335
4.50	0.515
6.00	0.714
8.00	0.946
11.00	1.245
14.00	1.739

a. Construct a normal probability plot for the fussing time data. Does the plot look linear? Do you agree with the authors of the paper that the fussing time distribution is not normal?

b. Transform the data by taking the square root of each data value. Construct a normal probability plot for the square root transformed data. How does this normal probability plot compare to the one from Part (a) for the untransformed data?

7.84 ● The paper "Risk Behavior, Decision Making, and Music Genre in Adolescent Males" (Marshall University, May 2009) examined the effect of type of music playing and performance on a risky, decision-making task.

a. Participants in the study responded to a questionnaire that was used to assign a risk behavior score. Risk behavior scores (read from a graph that appeared in the paper) for 15 participants follow. Use these data to construct a normal probability plot (the normal scores for a sample of size 15 appear in the previous exercise).

102	105	113	120	125	127	134	135
139	141	144	145	149	150	160	

b. Participants also completed a positive and negative affect scale (PANAS) designed to measure emotional response to music. PANAS values (read from a graph that appeared in the paper) for 15 participants follow. Use these data to construct a normal probability plot (the normal scores for a sample of size 15 appear in the previous exercise).

36	40	45	47	48	49	50	52
53	54	56	59	61	62	70	

c. The author of the paper states that he believes that it is reasonable to consider both risk behavior scores and PANAS scores to be approximately normally distributed. Do the normal probability plots from Parts (a) and (b) support this conclusion? Explain.

7.85 ● Measures of nerve conductivity are used in the diagnosis of certain medical conditions. The paper "Effects of Age, Gender, Height, and Weight on Late Responses and Nerve Conduction Study Parameters" (*Acta Neurologica Taiwanica* [2009]: 242–249) describes a study in which the ulnar nerve was stimulated in healthy patients and the amplitude and velocity of the response was measured. Representative data (consistent with summary quantities and descriptions given in the paper) for 30 patients for the variable x = response velocity (m/s) are given in the accompanying table. Also given are values of the log and square root of x.

x	log(x)	sqrt(x)
60.1	1.78	7.75
48.7	1.69	6.98
51.7	1.71	7.19
52.9	1.72	7.27
50.5	1.70	7.11
58.5	1.77	7.65
53.6	1.73	7.32
60.3	1.78	7.77
64.5	1.81	8.03
50.4	1.70	7.10
56.5	1.75	7.52
55.5	1.74	7.45
53.0	1.72	7.28
50.5	1.70	7.11
54.0	1.73	7.35
53.6	1.73	7.32
55.2	1.74	7.43
57.9	1.76	7.61
61.5	1.79	7.84
58.0	1.76	7.62
57.6	1.76	7.59
67.1	1.83	8.19
56.2	1.75	7.50
53.8	1.73	7.33
55.7	1.75	7.46
52.9	1.72	7.27
54.0	1.73	7.35
52.6	1.72	7.25
61.8	1.79	7.86
62.8	1.80	7.92

a. Construct a histogram of the untransformed data. Does the distribution of x appear to be approximately normal? Explain.
b. Construct a histogram of the log transformed data. Is this histogram more symmetric than the histogram of the untransformed data?
c. Construct a histogram of the square root transformed data. Does either of the two transformations (square root or log) result in a histogram that is more nearly normal in shape?

7.86 ● Macular degeneration is the most common cause of blindness in people older than 60 years. One variable thought to be related to a type of inflammation associated with this disease is level of a substance called soluble Fas ligand (sFasL) in the blood. The accompanying table contains representative data on $x =$ sFasL level for 10 patients with age-related macular degeneration. These data are consistent with summary quantities and descriptions of the data given in the paper "Associations of Plasma-Soluble Fas Ligand with Aging and Age-Related Macular Degeneration" (*Investigative Ophthalmology & Visual Science* [2008]: 1345–1349). The authors of the paper noted that the distribution of sFasL level was skewed and recommended a cube-root transformation. The cube-root values and the normal scores for a sample size of 10 are also given in the accompanying table.

x	Cube Root of x	Normal Score
0.069	0.41	−1.539
0.074	0.42	−1.001
0.176	0.56	−0.656
0.185	0.57	−0.376
0.216	0.60	−0.123
0.287	0.66	0.123
0.343	0.70	0.376
0.343	0.70	0.656
0.512	0.80	1.001
0.729	0.90	1.539

a. Construct a normal probability plot using the untransformed data. Does the normal probability plot appear linear or curved?
b. Compute the correlation coefficient for the (normal score, x) pairs. Compare this value to the critical r value from Table 7.2 to determine if it is reasonable to consider the distribution of sFasL levels to be approximately normal.
c. Construct a normal probability plot using the transformed data. Does the normal probability plot appear more nearly linear than the plot for the untransformed data?
d. Compute the correlation coefficient for the (normal score, transformed x) pairs. Compare this value to the critical r value from Table 7.2 to determine if it is reasonable to consider the distribution of transformed sFasL levels to be approximately normal.

7.87 The following normal probability plot was constructed using part of the data appearing in the paper "Trace Metals in Sea Scallops" (*Environmental Concentration and Toxicology* 19: 1326–1334).

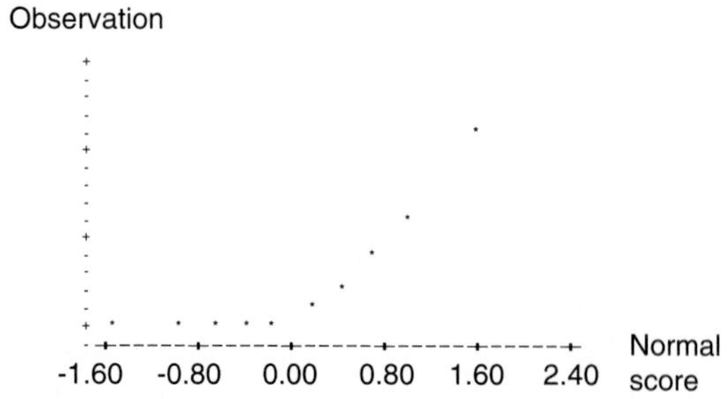

The variable under study was the amount of cadmium in North Atlantic scallops. Do the sample data suggest that the cadmium concentration distribution is not normal? Explain.

7.88 ● Consider the following 10 observations on the lifetime (in hours) for a certain type of power supply: 152.7, 172.0, 172.5, 173.3, 193.0, 204.7, 216.5, 234.9, 262.6, and 422.6. Construct a normal probability plot, and comment on the plausibility of a normal distribution as a model for power supply lifetime. (The normal scores for a sample of size 10 are −1.539, −1.001, −.656, −.376, −.123, .123, .376, .656, 1.001, and 1.539.)

7.89 ● Consider the following sample of 25 observations on the diameter x (in centimeters) of a disk used in a certain system:

16.01	16.08	16.13	15.94	16.05	16.27	15.89
15.84	15.95	16.10	15.92	16.04	15.82	16.15
16.06	15.66	15.78	15.99	16.29	16.15	16.19
16.22	16.07	16.13	16.11			

The 13 largest normal scores for a sample of size 25 are 1.965, 1.524, 1.263, 1.067, 0.905, 0.764, 0.637, 0.519, 0.409, 0.303, 0.200, 0.100, and 0. The 12 smallest scores result from placing a negative sign in front of each of the given nonzero scores. Construct a normal probability plot. Does it appear plausible that disk diameter is normally distributed? Explain.

7.90 ● Example 7.33 examined rainfall data for Minneapolis–St. Paul. The square-root transformation was used to obtain a distribution of values that was more symmetric than the distribution of the original data. Another power transformation that has been suggested by meteorologists is the cube root: transformed value = (original value)$^{1/3}$. The original values and their cube roots (the transformed values) are given in the following table:

Original	Transformed	Original	Transformed
0.32	0.68	1.51	1.15
0.47	0.78	1.62	1.17
0.52	0.80	1.74	1.20
0.59	0.84	1.87	1.23
0.77	0.92	1.89	1.24
0.81	0.93	1.95	1.25
0.81	0.93	2.05	1.27
0.90	0.97	2.10	1.28
0.96	0.99	2.20	1.30
1.18	1.06	2.48	1.35
1.20	1.06	2.81	1.41
1.20	1.06	3.00	1.44
1.31	1.09	3.09	1.46
1.35	1.11	3.37	1.50
1.43	1.13	4.75	1.68

Construct a histogram of the transformed data. Compare your histogram to those given in Figure 7.38. Which of the cube-root and square-root transformations appear to result in the more symmetric histogram?

7.91 The article "The Distribution of Buying Frequency Rates" (*Journal of Marketing Research* [1980]: 210–216) reported the results of a $3\frac{1}{2}$-year study of toothpaste purchases. The investigators conducted their research using a national sample of 2071 households and recorded the number of toothpaste purchases for each household participating in the study. The results are given in the following frequency distribution:

Number of Purchases	Number of Households (Frequency)
10 to <20	904
20 to <30	500
30 to <40	258
40 to <50	167
50 to <60	94
60 to <70	56
70 to <80	26
80 to <90	20
90 to <100	13
100 to <110	9
110 to <120	7
120 to <130	6
130 to <140	6
140 to <150	3
150 to <160	0
160 to <170	2

(continued)

a. Draw a histogram for this frequency distribution. Would you describe the histogram as positively or negatively skewed?

b. Does the square-root transformation result in a histogram that is more symmetric than that of the original data? (Be careful! This one is a bit tricky because you don't have the raw data; transforming the endpoints of the class intervals will result in class intervals that are not necessarily of equal widths, so the histogram of the transformed values will have to be drawn with this in mind.)

7.92 ● The paper "Temperature and the Northern Distributions of Wintering Birds" (*Ecology* [1991]: 2274–2285) gave the following body masses (in grams) for 50 different bird species:

7.7	10.1	21.6	8.6	12.0	11.4	16.6	9.4
11.5	9.0	8.2	20.2	48.5	21.6	26.1	6.2
19.1	21.0	28.1	10.6	31.6	6.7	5.0	68.8
23.9	19.8	20.1	6.0	99.6	19.8	16.5	9.0
448.0	21.3	17.4	36.9	34.0	41.0	15.9	12.5
10.2	31.0	21.5	11.9	32.5	9.8	93.9	10.9
19.6	14.5						

a. Construct a stem-and-leaf display in which 448.0 is listed separately beside the display as an outlier on the high side, the stem of an observation is the tens digit, the leaf is the ones digit, and the tenths digit is suppressed (e.g., 21.5 has stem 2 and leaf 1). What do you perceive as the most prominent feature of the display?

b. Draw a histogram based on class intervals 5 to <10, 10 to <15, 15 to <20, 20 to <25, 25 to <30, 30 to <40, 40 to <50, 50 to <100, and 100 to <500. Is a transformation of the data desirable? Explain.

c. Use a calculator or statistical computer package to calculate logarithms of these observations, and construct a histogram. Is the log transformation successful in producing a more symmetric distribution?

d. Consider transformed value $= \dfrac{1}{\sqrt{\text{original value}}}$ and construct a histogram of the transformed data. Does the histogram appear to resemble a normal curve?

7.93 The following figure appeared in the paper "EDTA-Extractable Copper, Zinc, and Manganese in Soils of the Canterbury Plains" (*New Zealand Journal of Agricultural Research* [1984]: 207–217). A large number of topsoil samples were analyzed for manganese (Mn), zinc (Zn), and copper (Cu), and the resulting data were summarized using histograms. The investigators transformed each data set using logarithms in an effort to obtain more symmetric distributions of values. Do you think the transformations were successful? Explain.

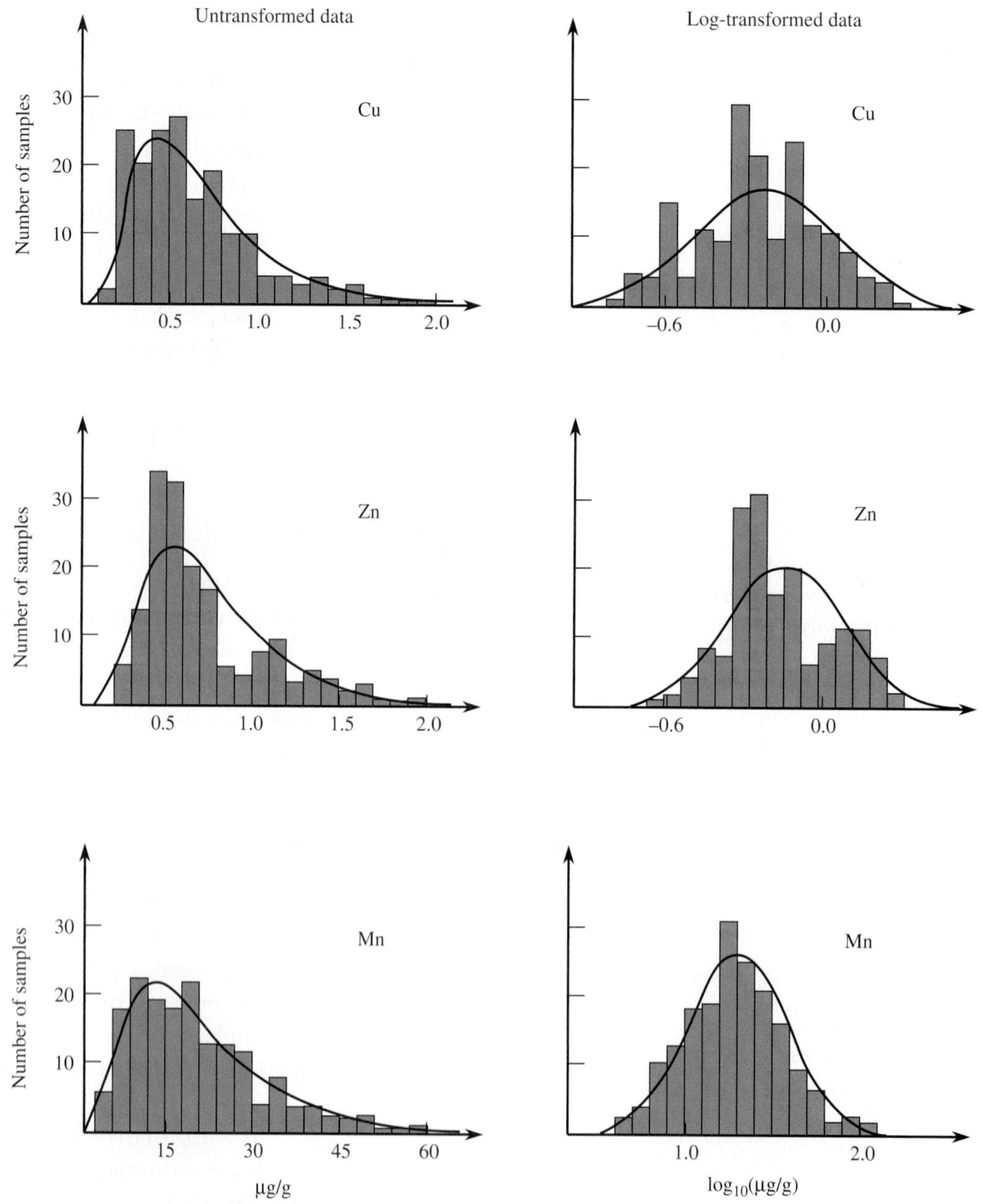

7.8 Using the Normal Distribution to Approximate a Discrete Distribution

The distributions of many random variables can be approximated by a carefully chosen normal distributions. In this section, we show how probabilities for some discrete random variables can be approximated using a normal curve. The most important case of this is the approximation of binomial probabilities.

The Normal Curve and Discrete Variables

The probability distribution of a discrete random variable x is represented graphically by a probability histogram. The probability of a particular value is the area of the rectangle centered at that value. Possible values of x are isolated points on the number line, usually whole numbers. For example, if $x =$ the IQ of a randomly selected 8-year-old child, then x is a discrete random variable, because an IQ score must be a whole number.

Often, a probability histogram can be well approximated by a normal curve, as illustrated in Figure 7.43. In such cases, it is customary to say that x has approximately a normal distribution. The normal distribution can then be used to calculate approximate probabilities of events involving x.

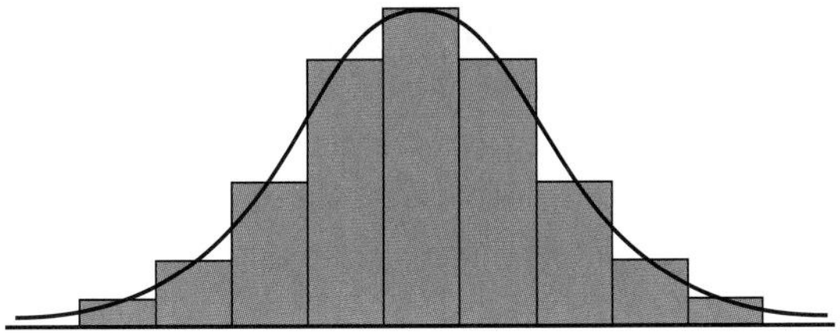

FIGURE 7.43
A normal curve approximation to a probability histogram.

EXAMPLE 7.35 Express Mail Packages

The number of express mail packages mailed at a certain post office on a randomly selected day is approximately normally distributed with mean 18 and standard deviation 6. Let's first calculate the approximate probability that $x = 20$. Figure 7.44(a) shows a portion of the probability histogram for x with the approximating normal curve superimposed. The area of the shaded rectangle is $P(x = 20)$. The left edge of this rectangle is at 19.5 on the horizontal scale, and the right edge is at 20.5. Therefore, the desired probability is approximately the area under the normal curve between 19.5 and 20.5. Standardizing these limits gives

$$\frac{20.5 - 18}{6} = .42 \qquad \frac{19.5 - 18}{6} = .25$$

from which we get

$$P(x = 20) \approx P(.25 < z < .42) = .6628 - .5987 = .0641$$

In a similar fashion, Figure 7.44(b) shows that $P(x \leq 10)$ is approximately the area under the normal curve to the left of 10.5. Then

$$P(x \leq 10) \approx P\left(z \leq \frac{10.5 - 18}{6}\right) = P(z \leq -1.25)$$
$$= .1056$$

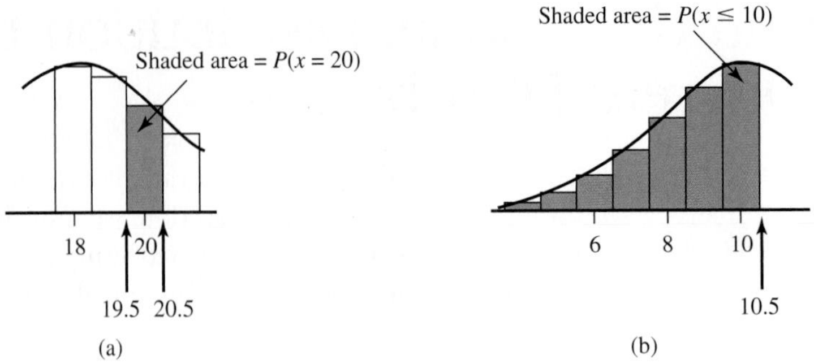

FIGURE 7.44
The normal approximation for Example 7.35.

The calculation of probabilities in Example 7.35 illustrates the use of what is known as a **continuity correction.** Because the rectangle for $x = 10$ extends to 10.5 on the right, we use the normal curve area to the left of 10.5 rather than 10. In general, if possible x values are consecutive whole numbers, then $P(a \leq x \leq b)$ will be approximately the normal curve area between limits $a - \frac{1}{2}$ and $b + \frac{1}{2}$.

Normal Approximation to a Binomial Distribution

Figure 7.45 shows the probability histograms for two binomial distributions, one with $n = 25$, $p = .4$, and the other with $n = 25$, $p = .1$. For each distribution, we computed $\mu = np$ and $\sigma = \sqrt{np(1 - p)}$ and then we superimposed a normal curve with this μ and σ on the corresponding probability histogram. A normal curve fits the probability histogram well in the first case (Figure 7.45(a)). When this happens, binomial probabilities can be accurately approximated by areas under the normal curve. Because of this, statisticians say that both x (the number of successes) and x/n (the proportion of successes) are approximately normally distributed. In the second case (Figure 7.45(b)), the normal curve does not give a good approximation because the probability histogram is skewed, whereas the normal curve is symmetric.

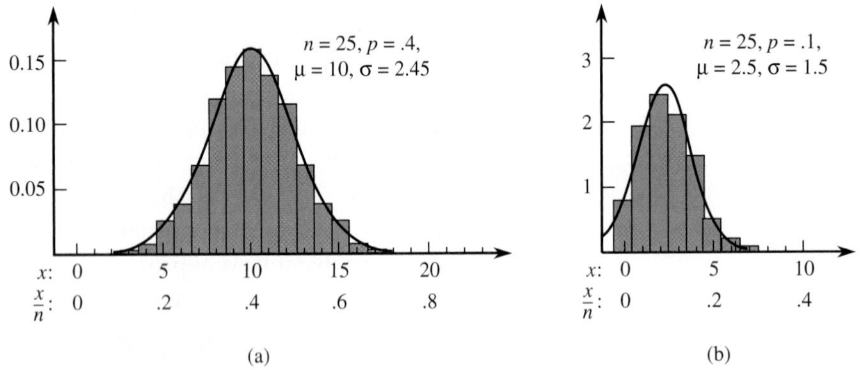

FIGURE 7.45
Normal approximations to binomial distributions.

Let x be a binomial random variable based on n trials and success probability p, so that

$$\mu = np \text{ and } \sigma = \sqrt{np(1 - p)}$$

If n and p are such that

$$np \geq 10 \text{ and } n(1 - p) \geq 10$$

Then x has approximately a normal distribution.

(continued)

Combining this result with the continuity correction implies that

$$P(a \le x \le b) = P\left(\frac{a - \frac{1}{2} - \mu}{\sigma} \le z \le \frac{b + \frac{1}{2} - \mu}{\sigma}\right)$$

That is, the probability that x is between a and b inclusive is approximately the area under the approximating normal curve between $a - \frac{1}{2}$ and $b + \frac{1}{2}$.
Similarly,

$$P(x \le b) \approx P\left(z \le \frac{b + \frac{1}{2} - \mu}{\sigma}\right) \qquad P(a \le x) \approx P\left(\frac{a - \frac{1}{2} - \mu}{\sigma} \le z\right)$$

When either $np < 10$ or $n(1 - p) < 10$, the binomial distribution is too skewed for the normal approximation to give reasonably accurate probability estimates.

EXAMPLE 7.36 Premature Babies

Premature babies are those born before 37 weeks, and those born before 34 weeks are most at risk. The paper "Some Thoughts on the True Value of Ultrasound" (*Ultrasound in Obstetrics and Gynecology* [2007]: 671–674) reported that 2% of births in the United States occur before 34 weeks. Suppose that 1000 births are randomly selected and that the number of these births that occurred prior to 34 weeks, x, is to be determined. Because

$$\begin{aligned} np &= 1000(.02) = 20 \ge 10 \\ n(1 - p) &= 1000(.98) = 980 \ge 10 \end{aligned}$$

x has approximately a normal distribution with

$$\mu = np = 1000(.02) = 20$$

$$\sigma = \sqrt{np(1 - p)} = \sqrt{1000(.02)(.98)} = \sqrt{19.60} = 4.427$$

The probability that the number of babies in a sample of 1000 born prior to 34 weeks will be between 10 and 25 (inclusive) is

$$\begin{aligned} P(10 \le x \le 25) &= P\left(\frac{9.5 - 20}{4.427} \le z \le \frac{25.5 - 20}{4.427}\right) \\ &= P(-2.37 \le z \le 1.29) \\ &= .9015 - .0089 \\ &= .8926 \end{aligned}$$

as shown in the following figure:

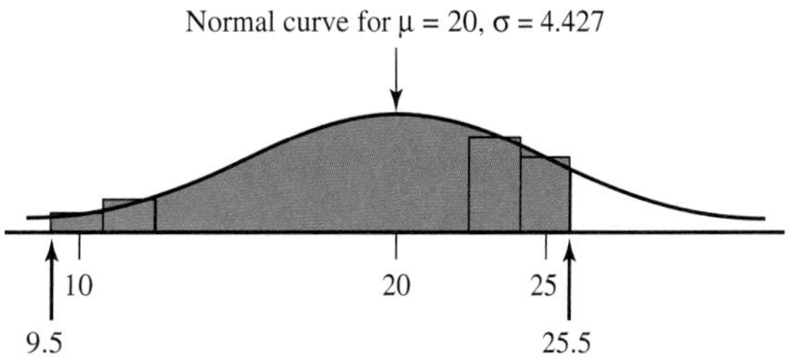

EXERCISES 7.94 - 7.104

7.94 Let x denote the IQ for an individual selected at random from a certain population. The value of x must be a whole number. Suppose that the distribution of x can be approximated by a normal distribution with mean value 100 and standard deviation 15. Approximate the following probabilities:

a. $P(x = 100)$
b. $P(x \leq 110)$
c. $P(x < 110)$ (Hint: $x < 110$ is the same as $x \leq 109$.)
d. $P(75 \leq x \leq 125)$

7.95 Suppose that the distribution of the number of items x produced by an assembly line during an 8-hour shift can be approximated by a normal distribution with mean value 150 and standard deviation 10.

a. What is the probability that the number of items produced is at most 120?
b. What is the probability that at least 125 items are produced?
c. What is the probability that between 135 and 160 (inclusive) items are produced?

7.96 The number of vehicles leaving a turnpike at a certain exit during a particular time period has approximately a normal distribution with mean value 500 and standard deviation 75. What is the probability that the number of cars exiting during this period is

a. At least 650?
b. Strictly between 400 and 550? (*Strictly* means that the values 400 and 550 are not included.)
c. Between 400 and 550 (inclusive)?

7.97 Suppose that x has a binomial distribution with $n = 50$ and $p = .6$, so that $\mu = np = 30$ and $\sigma = \sqrt{np(1 - p)} = 3.4641$. Calculate the following probabilities using the normal approximation with the continuity correction:

a. $P(x = 30)$
b. $P(x = 25)$
c. $P(x \leq 25)$
d. $P(25 \leq x \leq 40)$
e. $P(25 < x < 40)$ (Hint: $25 < x < 40$ is the same as $26 \leq x \leq 39$.)

7.98 Symptom validity tests (SVTs) are sometimes used to confirm diagnosis of psychiatric disorders. The paper "Developing a Symptom Validity Test for Post-Traumatic Stress Disorder: Application of the Binomial Distribution" (*Journal of Anxiety Disorders* [2008]: 1297–1302) investigated the use of SVTs in the diagnosis of post-traumatic stress disorder. One SVT proposed is a 60-item test (called the MENT test), where each item has only a correct or incorrect response. The MENT test is designed so that responses to the individual questions can be considered independent of one another. For this reason, the authors of the paper believe that the score on the MENT test can be viewed as a binomial random variable with $n = 60$. The MENT test is designed to help in distinguishing fictitious claims of post-traumatic stress disorder. The items on the MENT test are written so that the correct response to an item should be relatively obvious, even to people suffering from stress disorders. Researchers have found that a patient with a fictitious claim of stress disorder will try to "fake" the test, and that the probability of a correct response to an item for these patients is .7 (compared to .96 for other patients). The authors used a normal approximation to the binomial distribution with $n = 60$ and $p = .70$ to compute various probabilities of interest, where x = number of correct responses on the MENT test for a patient who is trying to fake the test.

a. Verify that it is appropriate to use a normal approximation to the binomial distribution in this situation.
b. Approximate the following probabilities:
   i. $P(x = 42)$
   ii. $P(x < 42)$
   iii. $P(x \leq 42)$
c. Explain why the probabilities computed in Part (b) are not all equal.
d. The authors computed the exact binomial probability of a score of 42 or less for someone who is not faking the test. Using $p = .96$, they found

   $p(x \leq 42) = .000000000013$

   Explain why the authors computed this probability using the binomial formula rather than using a normal approximation.
e. The authors propose that someone who scores 42 or less on the MENT exam is faking the test. Explain why this is reasonable, using some of the probabilities from Parts (b) and (d) as justification.

7.99 Studies have found that women diagnosed with cancer in one breast also sometimes have cancer in the other breast that was not initially detected by mammogram or physical examination ("MRI Evaluation of the Contralateral Breast in Women with Recently Diagnosed Breast Cancer," *The New England Journal of*

Medicine [2007]: 1295–1303). To determine if magnetic resonance imaging (MRI) could detect missed tumors in the other breast, 969 women diagnosed with cancer in one breast had an MRI exam. The MRI detected tumors in the other breast in 30 of these women.

a. Use $p = \frac{30}{969} = .031$ as an estimate of the probability that a woman diagnosed with cancer in one breast has an undetected tumor in the other breast. Consider a random sample of 500 women diagnosed with cancer in one breast. Explain why it is reasonable to think that the random variable x = number in the sample who have an undetected tumor in the other breast has a binomial distribution with $n = 500$ and $p = .031$.

b. Is it reasonable to use the normal distribution to approximate probabilities for the random variable x defined in Part (b)? Explain why or why not.

c. Approximate the following probabilities:
   i. $P(x < 10)$
   ii. $P(10 \le x \le 25)$
   iii. $P(x > 20)$

d. For each of the probabilities computed in Part (c), write a sentence interpreting the probability.

7.100 Seventy percent of the bicycles sold by a certain store are mountain bikes. Among 100 randomly selected bike purchases, what is the approximate probability that

a. At most 75 are mountain bikes?
b. Between 60 and 75 (inclusive) are mountain bikes?
c. More than 80 are mountain bikes?
d. At most 30 are not mountain bikes?

7.101 Suppose that 25% of the fire alarms in a large city are false alarms. Let x denote the number of false alarms in a random sample of 100 alarms. Give approximations to the following probabilities:

a. $P(20 \le x \le 30)$
b. $P(20 < x < 30)$
c. $P(x \ge 35)$
d. The probability that x is farther than 2 standard deviations from its mean value

7.102 Suppose that 65% of all registered voters in a certain area favor a 7-day waiting period before purchase of a handgun. Among 225 randomly selected registered voters, what is the probability that

a. At least 150 favor such a waiting period?
b. More than 150 favor such a waiting period?
c. Fewer than 125 favor such a waiting period?

7.103 Flashlight bulbs manufactured by a certain company are sometimes defective.

a. If 5% of all such bulbs are defective, could the techniques of this section be used to approximate the probability that at least five of the bulbs in a random sample of size 50 are defective? If so, calculate this probability; if not, explain why not.

b. Reconsider the question posed in Part (a) for the probability that at least 20 bulbs in a random sample of size 500 are defective.

7.104 A company that manufactures mufflers for cars offers a lifetime warranty on its products, provided that ownership of the car does not change. Suppose that only 20% of its mufflers are replaced under this warranty.

a. In a random sample of 400 purchases, what is the approximate probability that between 75 and 100 (inclusive) mufflers are replaced under warranty?
b. Among 400 randomly selected purchases, what is the probability that at most 70 mufflers are ultimately replaced under warranty?
c. If you were told that fewer than 50 among 400 randomly selected purchases were ever replaced under warranty, would you question the 20% figure? Explain.

ACTIVITY 7.1 Is It Real?

Background: Three students were asked to complete an assignment that asked them to do the following:

a. Flip a coin 30 times, and note the number of heads observed in the 30 flips.
b. Repeat Step (a) 100 times, to obtain 100 observations of the random variable x = number of heads in 30 flips.
c. Construct a dotplot of the 100 x values.

Because this was a tedious assignment, one or more of the three did not really carry out the coin flipping and just made up 100 values of x that they thought would look "real." The three dotplots produced by these students are shown below.

1. Do you think that any of the three students made up the x values shown in their dotplot? If so, which ones, and what about the dotplot makes you think the student did not actually do the coin flipping?
2. Working as a group, each student in your class should flip a coin 30 times and note the number of heads in the 30 tosses. If there are fewer than 50 students in the class, each student should repeat this process until there are a total of at least 50 observations of x = number of heads in 30 flips. Using the data from the entire class, construct a dotplot of the x values.
3. After looking at the dotplot in Step 2 that resulted from actually flipping a coin 30 times and observing number of heads, reconsider your answers in Question 1. For each of the three students, explain why you now think that he or she did or did not actually do the coin flipping.

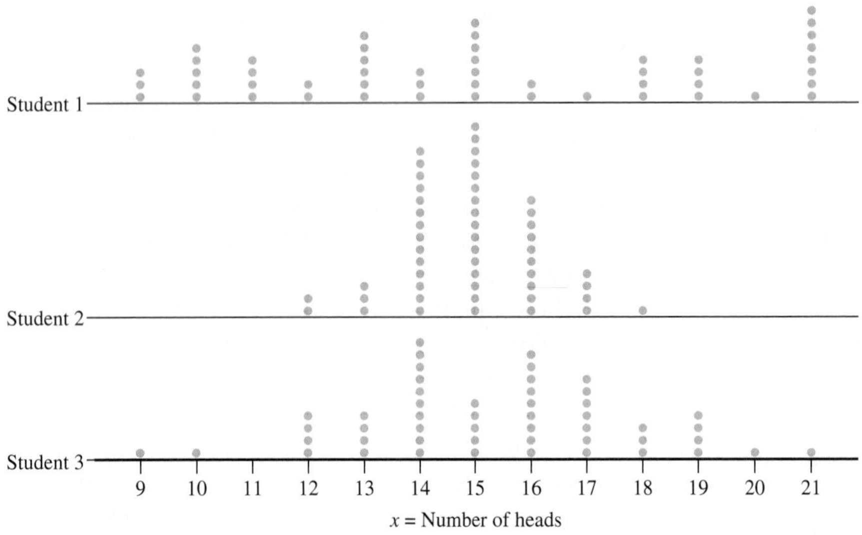

ACTIVITY 7.2 Rotten Eggs?

Background: *The Salt Lake Tribune* (October 11, 2002) printed the following account of an exchange between a restaurant manager and a health inspector:

> The recipe calls for four fresh eggs for each quiche. A Salt Lake County Health Department inspector paid a visit recently and pointed out that research by the Food and Drug Administration indicates that one in four eggs carries salmonella bacterium, so restaurants should never use more than three eggs when preparing quiche. The manager on duty wondered aloud if simply throwing out three eggs from each dozen and using the remaining nine in four-egg quiches would serve the same purpose.

1. Working in a group or as a class, discuss the folly of the above statement!
2. Suppose the following argument is made for three-egg quiches rather than four-egg quiches: Let x ≤ number of eggs that carry salmonella. Then

$$p(0) = p(x = 0) = (0.75)^3 = .422$$

for three-egg quiches and

$$p(0) = p(x = 0) = (0.75)^4 = .316$$

for four-egg quiches. What assumption must be made to justify these probability calculations? Do you think this is reasonable or not? Explain.

3. Suppose that a carton of one dozen eggs does happen to have exactly three eggs that carry salmonella and that the manager does as he proposes: selects three eggs at random and throws them out, then uses the remaining nine eggs in four-egg quiches. Let x = number of eggs that carry salmonella among four eggs selected at random from the remaining nine.

   Working with a partner, conduct a simulation to approximate the distribution of x by carrying out the following sequence of steps:
   a. Take 12 identical slips of paper and write "Good" on nine of them and "Bad" on the remaining three. Place the slips of paper in a paper bag or some other container.
   b. Mix the slips and then select three at random and remove them from the bag.
   c. Mix the remaining slips and select four "eggs" from the bags.
   d. Note the number of bad eggs among the four selected. (This is an observed x value.)
   e. Replace all slips, so that the bag now contains all 12 "eggs."
   f. Repeat Steps (b)–(d) at least 10 times, each time recording the observed x value.
4. Combine the observations from your group with those from the other groups. Use the resulting data to approximate the distribution of x. Comment on the resulting distribution in the context of the risk of salmonella exposure if the manager's proposed procedure is used.

Summary of Key Concepts and Formulas

TERM OR FORMULA	COMMENT
Random variable: discrete or continuous	A numerical variable with a value determined by the outcome of a chance experiment. A random variable is discrete if its possible values are isolated points along the number line and continuous if its possible values form an entire interval on the number line.
Probability distribution of a discrete random variable x	A formula, table, or graph that gives the probability associated with each possible x value. Conditions on $p(x)$ are (1) $p(x) \geq 0$, and (2) $\sum p(x) = 1$, where the sum is over all possible x values.
Probability distribution of a continuous random variable x	Specified by a smooth (density) curve for which the total area under the curve is 1. The probability $P(a < x < b)$ is the area under the curve and above the interval from a to b; this is also $P(a \leq x \leq b)$.
μ_x and σ_x	The mean and standard deviation, respectively, of a random variable x. These quantities describe the center and extent of spread about the center of the variable's probability distribution.
$\mu_x = \sum xp(x)$	The mean value of a discrete random variable x; it locates the center of the variable's probability distribution.
$\sigma_x^2 = \sum (x - \mu_x)^2 p(x)$ $\sigma_x = \sqrt{\sigma_x^2}$	The variance and standard deviation, respectively, of a discrete random variable; these are measures of the extent to which the variable's distribution spreads out about the mean μ_x.
Binomial probability distribution $p(x) = \frac{n!}{x!(n-x)!} p^x (1-p)^{n-x}$	This formula gives the probability of observing x successes ($x = 0, 1, \ldots, n$) among n trials of a binomial experiment.

$\mu_x = np$ $\sigma_x = \sqrt{np(1 - p)}$	The mean and standard deviation of a binomial random variable.
Normal distribution	A continuous probability distribution that has a bell-shaped density curve. A particular normal distribution is determined by specifying values of μ and σ.
Standard normal distribution	This is the normal distribution with $\mu = 0$ and $\sigma = 1$. The density curve is called the z curve, and z is the letter commonly used to denote a variable having this distribution. Areas under the z curve to the left of various values are given in Appendix Table 2.
$z = \dfrac{x - \mu}{\sigma}$	z is obtained by "standardizing": subtracting the mean and then dividing by the standard deviation. When x has a normal distribution, z has a standard normal distribution.
Normal probability plot	A graph used to judge the plausibility of the assumption that a sample has been selected from a normal population distribution. If the plot is reasonably straight, this assumption is reasonable.
Normal approximation to the binomial distribution	When both $np \geq 10$ and $n(1 - p) \geq 10$, binomial probabilities are well approximated by corresponding areas under a normal curve with $\mu = np$ and $\sigma = \sqrt{np(1 - p)}$.

Chapter Review Exercises 7.105 - 7.126

7.105 There are approximately 40,000 travel agencies in the United States, of which 11,000 are members of the American Society of Travel Agents (booking a tour through an ASTA member increases the likelihood of a refund in the event of cancellation).

a. If x is the number of ASTA members among 5000 randomly selected agencies, could you use the methods of Section 7.8 to approximate $P(1200 < x < 1400)$? Why or why not?

b. In a random sample of 100 agencies, what are the mean value and standard deviation of the number of ASTA members?

c. If the sample size in Part (b) is doubled, does the standard deviation double? Explain.

7.106 A soft-drink machine dispenses only regular Coke and Diet Coke. Sixty percent of all purchases from this machine are diet drinks. The machine currently has 10 cans of each type. If 15 customers want to purchase drinks before the machine is restocked, what is the probability that each of the 15 is able to purchase the type of drink desired? (Hint: Let x denote the number among the 15 who want a diet drink. For which possible values of x is everyone satisfied?)

7.107 A business has six customer service telephone lines. Let x denote the number of lines in use at a specified time. Suppose that the probability distribution of x is as follows:

x	0	1	2	3	4	5	6
$p(x)$	.10	.15	.20	.25	.20	.06	.04

Write each of the following events in terms of x, and then calculate the probability of each one:

a. At most three lines are in use

b. Fewer than three lines are in use

c. At least three lines are in use

d. Between two and five lines (inclusive) are in use

e. Between two and four lines (inclusive) are not in use

f. At least four lines are not in use

7.108 Refer to the probability distribution of Exercise 7.107.

a. Calculate the mean value and standard deviation of x.

b. What is the probability that the number of lines in use is farther than 3 standard deviations from the mean value?

7.109 A new battery's voltage may be acceptable (A) or unacceptable (U). A certain flashlight requires two batteries, so batteries will be independently selected and tested until two acceptable ones have been found. Suppose that 80% of all batteries have acceptable voltages, and let y denote the number of batteries that must be tested.

a. What is $p(2)$, that is, $P(y = 2)$?

b. What is $p(3)$? (Hint: There are two different outcomes that result in $y = 3$.)

c. In order to have $y = 5$, what must be true of the fifth battery selected? List the four outcomes for which $y = 5$, and then determine $p(5)$.

d. Use the pattern in your answers for Parts (a)–(c) to obtain a general formula for $p(y)$.

7.110 A pizza company advertises that it puts 0.5 pounds of real mozzarella cheese on its medium pizzas. In fact, the amount of cheese on a randomly selected medium pizza is normally distributed with a mean value of 0.5 pounds and a standard deviation of 0.025 pounds.

a. What is the probability that the amount of cheese on a medium pizza is between 0.525 and 0.550 pounds?

b. What is the probability that the amount of cheese on a medium pizza exceeds the mean value by more than 2 standard deviations?

c. What is the probability that three randomly selected medium pizzas all have at least 0.475 pounds of cheese?

7.111 Suppose that fuel efficiency for a particular model car under specified conditions is normally distributed with a mean value of 30.0 mpg and a standard deviation of 1.2 mpg.

a. What is the probability that the fuel efficiency for a randomly selected car of this type is between 29 and 31 mpg?

b. Would it surprise you to find that the efficiency of a randomly selected car of this model is less than 25 mpg?

c. If three cars of this model are randomly selected, what is the probability that all three have efficiencies exceeding 32 mpg?

d. Find a number c^* such that 95% of all cars of this model have efficiencies exceeding c^* (i.e., $P(x > c^*) = .95$).

7.112 A coin is flipped 25 times. Let x be the number of flips that result in heads (H). Consider the following rule for deciding whether or not the coin is fair:

Judge the coin fair if $8 \leq x \leq 17$.
Judge the coin biased if either $x \leq 7$ or $x \geq 18$.

a. What is the probability of judging the coin biased when it is actually fair?

b. What is the probability of judging the coin fair when $P(\text{H}) = .9$, so that there is a substantial bias? Repeat for $P(\text{H}) = .1$.

c. What is the probability of judging the coin fair when $P(\text{H}) = .6$? when $P(\text{H}) = .4$? Why are these probabilities so large compared to the probabilities in Part (b)?

d. What happens to the "error probabilities" of Parts (a) and (b) if the decision rule is changed so that the coin is judged fair if $7 \leq x \leq 18$ and unfair otherwise? Is this a better rule than the one first proposed? Explain.

7.113 The probability distribution of x, the number of defective tires on a randomly selected automobile checked at a certain inspection station, is given in the following table:

x	0	1	2	3	4
$p(x)$	.54	.16	.06	.04	.20

The mean value of x is $\mu_x = 1.2$. Calculate the values of σ_x^2 and σ_x.

7.114 The amount of time spent by a statistical consultant with a client at their first meeting is a random variable having a normal distribution with a mean value of 60 minutes and a standard deviation of 10 minutes.

a. What is the probability that more than 45 minutes is spent at the first meeting?

b. What amount of time is exceeded by only 10% of all clients at a first meeting?

c. If the consultant assesses a fixed charge of \$10 (for overhead) and then charges \$50 per hour, what is the mean revenue from a client's first meeting?

7.115 The lifetime of a certain brand of battery is normally distributed with a mean value of 6 hours and a standard deviation of 0.8 hours when it is used in a particular DVD player. Suppose that two new batteries are independently selected and put into the player. The player ceases to function as soon as one of the batteries fails.

a. What is the probability that the player functions for at least 4 hours?

b. What is the probability that the DVD player works for at most 7 hours?

c. Find a number c^* such that only 5% of all DVD players will function without battery replacement for more than c^* hours.

7.116 A machine producing vitamin E capsules operates so that the actual amount of vitamin E in each capsule is normally distributed with a mean of 5 mg and a standard deviation of 0.05 mg. What is the probability that a randomly selected capsule contains less than 4.9 mg of vitamin E? at least 5.2 mg?

7.117 The *Wall Street Journal* (February 15, 1972) reported that General Electric was sued in Texas for sex discrimination over a minimum height requirement of 5 ft. 7 in. The suit claimed that this restriction eliminated more than 94% of adult females from consideration. Let x represent the height of a randomly selected adult woman. Suppose that x is approximately normally distributed with mean 66 inches (5 ft. 6 in.) and standard deviation 2 inches.

a. Is the claim that 94% of all women are shorter than 5 ft. 7 in. correct?

b. What proportion of adult women would be excluded from employment as a result of the height restriction?

7.118 The longest "run" of S's in the sequence *SSFSSSSFFS* has length 4, corresponding to the S's on the fourth, fifth, sixth, and seventh trials. Consider a binomial experiment with $n = 4$, and let y be the length (number of trials) in the longest run of S's.

a. When $p = .5$, the 16 possible outcomes are equally likely. Determine the probability distribution of y in this case (first list all outcomes and the y value for each one). Then calculate μ_y.

b. Repeat Part (a) for the case $p = .6$.

c. Let z denote the longest run of either S's or F's. Determine the probability distribution of z when $p = .5$.

7.119 Two sisters, Allison and Teri, have agreed to meet between 1 and 6 P.M. on a particular day. In fact, Allison is equally likely to arrive at exactly 1 P.M., 2 P.M., 3 P.M., 4 P.M., 5 P.M., or 6 P.M. Teri is also equally likely to arrive at each of these six times, and Allison's and Teri's arrival times are independent of one another. Thus there are 36 equally likely (Allison, Teri) arrival-time pairs, for example, (2, 3) or (6, 1). Suppose that the first person to arrive waits until the second person arrives; let w be the amount of time the first person has to wait.

a. What is the probability distribution of w?

b. On average, how much time do you expect to elapse between the two arrivals?

7.120 Four people—a, b, c, and d—are waiting to give blood. Of these four, a and b have type AB blood, whereas c and d do not. An emergency call has just come in for some type AB blood. If blood donations are taken one by one from the four people in random order and x is the number of donations needed to obtain an AB individual (so possible x values are 1, 2, and 3), what is the probability distribution of x?

7.121 Kyle and Lygia are going to play a series of Trivial Pursuit games. The first person to win four games will be declared the winner. Suppose that outcomes of successive games are independent and that the probability of Lygia winning any particular game is .6. Define a random variable x as the number of games played in the series.

a. What is $p(4)$? (Hint: Either Kyle or Lygia could win four straight games.)

b. What is $p(5)$? (Hint: For Lygia to win in exactly five games, what has to happen in the first four games and in Game 5?)

c. Determine the probability distribution of x.

d. On average, how many games will the series last?

7.122 Refer to Exercise 7.121, and let y be the number of games won by the series loser. Determine the probability distribution of y.

7.123 Suppose that your statistics professor tells you that the scores on a midterm exam were approximately normally distributed with a mean of 78 and a standard deviation of 7. The top 15% of all scores have been designated A's. Your score is 89. Did you receive an A? Explain.

7.124 Suppose that the pH of soil samples taken from a certain geographic region is normally distributed with a mean pH of 6.00 and a standard deviation of 0.10. If the pH of a randomly selected soil sample from this region is determined, answer the following questions about it:

a. What is the probability that the resulting pH is between 5.90 and 6.15?
b. What is the probability that the resulting pH exceeds 6.10?
c. What is the probability that the resulting pH is at most 5.95?
d. What value will be exceeded by only 5% of all such pH values?

7.125 The lightbulbs used to provide exterior lighting for a large office building have an average lifetime of 700 hours. If length of life is approximately normally distributed with a standard deviation of 50 hours, how often should all the bulbs be replaced so that no more than 20% of the bulbs will have already burned out?

7.126 Let x denote the duration of a randomly selected pregnancy (the time elapsed between conception and birth). Accepted values for the mean value and standard deviation of x are 266 days and 16 days, respectively. Suppose that the probability distribution of x is (approximately) normal.
a. What is the probability that the duration of pregnancy is between 250 and 300 days?
b. What is the probability that the duration of pregnancy is at most 240 days?
c. What is the probability that the duration of pregnancy is within 16 days of the mean duration?
d. A "Dear Abby" column dated January 20, 1973, contained a letter from a woman who stated that the duration of her pregnancy was exactly 310 days. (She wrote that the last visit with her husband, who was in the Navy, occurred 310 days before birth.) What is the probability that duration of pregnancy is at least 310 days? Does this probability make you a bit skeptical of the claim?
e. Some insurance companies will pay the medical expenses associated with childbirth only if the insurance has been in effect for more than 9 months (275 days). This restriction is designed to ensure that the insurance company pays benefits for only those pregnancies for which conception occurred during coverage. Suppose that conception occurred 2 weeks after coverage began. What is the probability that the insurance company will refuse to pay benefits because of the 275-day insurance requirement?

Graphing Calculator Explorations

EXPLORATION 7.1 Discrete Probability Distributions

When used with random variables the calculator can transform minutes of mindless calculation into seconds of easy button-pushing. In our calculator presentation of random variables, we will capitalize extensively on the list capabilities of your calculator. We will demonstrate not only how to graph a discrete probability distribution, but also how to find the mean and standard deviation of a discrete random variable.

Remember that we encountered a similar problem when we considered graphing a relative frequency histogram using the frequency distribution. At that time frequencies were converted into relative frequencies for plotting; now, these relative frequencies have morphed into probabilities. We will begin by entering the possible values of the random variable in your calculator's equivalent of List1 and the corresponding probabilities of these values in List2. For our example, we will use a numerical rating of newborn children called an Apgar score. The Apgar score has 11 possible values, 0, 1, . . . , 10 based on factors such as muscle tone, skin color, etc. Suppose that the scores have the following probability distribution:

x	0	1	2	3	4	5	6	7	8	9	10
$p(x)$	.002	.001	.002	.005	.02	.04	.17	.38	.25	.12	.01

In Figure 7.46(a) a portion of the calculator screen after data entry is shown. After entering the data you can graph the probability distribution by supplying the

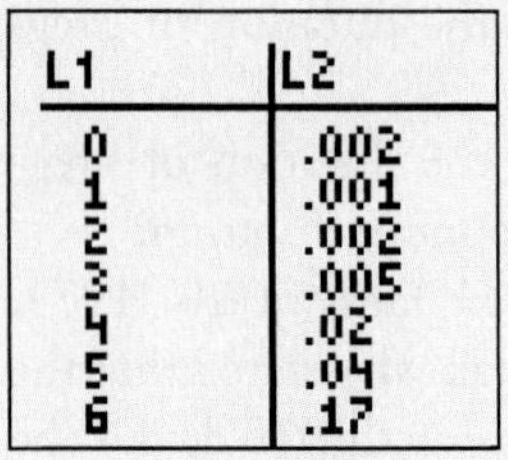

(a)

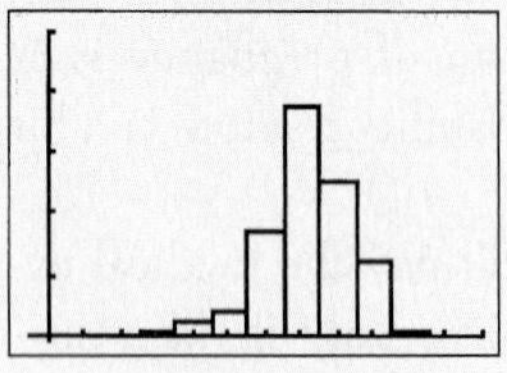

(b)

FIGURE 7.46
(a) Apgar score probability distribution; (b) probability histogram for Apgar score.

proper lists in the histogram command as was done for the relative frequency histogram. The graph for the Apgar probability distribution is shown in Figure 7.46(b). The window is set so that the horizontal and vertical axis would show in the screen to give a more informative display. The horizontal axis runs from −.5 to 12, and the vertical axis runs from −.01 to 0.5.

Now we turn our attention to calculating the mean and standard deviation of the random variable. The data are already entered and we begin by recalling the definition of the mean of a discrete random variable,

$$\mu_x = \sum_{\text{all possible } x \text{ values}} xp(x)$$

Because we have stored exactly what is needed in Lists 1 and 2, we can virtually duplicate this definition using the language of lists and list operations for the calculator:

$$\mu_x = \sum_{\text{all possible } x \text{ values}} \text{List1} * \text{List2}$$

The strategy for finding the mean of the Apgar random variable, translated from math symbols to English, is the following: calculate the products of numbers in Lists 1 and 2, store the results in List3, and then find the sum of all the numbers in List3. Multiplying to obtain the product is fairly easy as we appeal again to the language of lists:

List1 * List2 → List3

Now we need to find the sum of the numbers in List3. Exactly how this is done will vary from calculator to calculator. The most likely scenario is for you to calculate the "1-variable statistics" for List3. Calculators will usually report the sum—look for this symbol: $(\sum x)$. Be careful as you scan for the right choice in your calculator window! Don't be misled by the symbol for the *mean;* we want the *sum.* You should get the value 7.16 for the Apgar mean.

We use a similar strategy to compute the standard deviation. We will find the variance first, then take the square root. The formula for the variance,

$$\sigma_x^2 = \sum_{\text{all possible } x \text{ values}} (x - \mu_x)^2 p(x)$$

also easily translates into the language of lists:

$$\sigma_x^2 = \sum_{\text{all possible } x \text{ values}} (\text{List1} - 7.16)^2 * \text{List2}$$

The list language is only slightly more complicated than for the mean:

$(\text{List1} - 7.16)^2 * \text{List2} \rightarrow \text{List3}$

After this production the sum of the numbers in List3 is the variance of the random variable; the square root is the standard deviation. Performing these calculations, you should get a variance of 1.5684. Again, don't be misled and choose the σ_x or s_x. The standard deviation is then found by taking the square root of 1.5684, resulting in 1.2524.

EXPLORATION 7.2 Binomial Probability Calculations

Most random variable calculations are of one of three types. They are (1) the probability the variable will assume a value between two given numbers, (2) the probability the variable will assume a value less than a given number, or (3) the probability the random variable will assume a value greater than a given number. Because these procedures are so common in statistics, your calculator may have a built-in capability for finding these probabilities. In the case of a discrete random variable such as the binomial distribution, there is a special case of (1) above: the probability that the random variable will actually assume a particular value.

For the binomial distribution, we will illustrate these calculations using an example. Suppose that 60% of all computer monitors have a flat panel display and 40% have a CRT display. Suppose further that the next 12 purchases will be monitored, and the random variable is defined as the number of flat panel monitors in these 12 purchases. As an example, the probability exactly four monitors will be flat panel displays is

$$p(x) = {}_nC_x p^x(1 - p)^{n-x} = {}_{12}C_4(.6)^4(1 - .6)^{12-4} = .042$$

Even if your calculator does not have special binomial functions it is likely to have a key for the combinations, (${}_nC_r$), possibly cleverly hidden in the "math" or "probability" menu. The calculator keystrokes might look like this (don't forget that to perform the ${}_nC_r$ calculation above you will have to press n, then the ${}_nC_r$ key, and then r):

12 ${}_nC_r$ 4 * .6^4 * .4^8

If your calculator has built-in binomial capabilities, you will have fewer keystrokes. Let's consider these problems one at a time, starting with the function names. If your calculator has a built-in function for binomial calculations, it probably has two: a function for finding the probability that "x is equal to a given value" and a function for finding the probability that "x is less than or equal to a given value." The first function is known to statisticians as a "density" function and is commonly abbreviated "pdf" for "probability density function." The second is known as a "cumulative distribution function" and is commonly labeled "cdf." These two functions on your calculator will in all likelihood mirror these abbreviations.

The second problem you will face is that to find the binomial probabilities the calculator will need more than just one number, and the order you enter the numbers *does* make a difference! Look in your calculator manual for something that looks like "binomial," especially with a "pdf" somewhere. The function could be obvious, like "binompdf," or it may be a little more cryptic, like "binpdf." Your manual will be very careful to specify both what the needed function parameters are and the order you should enter them. As an example, my calculator has the following:

binompdf(*numtrials, p,* [*x*])

The manual informs that "*numtrials*" is the number of trials, "*p*" is the probability of success, and that "*x*" can be either an integer or a list of integers. This information collectively explains what is known as the "syntax" of the function. The square brackets, "[ ]," are a standard notation in the calculator world. They indicate the bracketed quantity is either optional or defaults to a preselected option if you do not enter a number in that space. For our example, the number of trials is 12, and the probability of success is 0.6. Since the probability of exactly four flat panel monitors is desired, we enter

binompdf(12, .6, 4)

Our calculator gives us 0.042042, which is the correct answer. This is a good sign! Now try this on your calculator. Remember, you must navigate to the function in the manner presented in your manual, and you have to pay attention to the syntax. While you are learning how to use this function (or any calculator function), it is a very good idea to use examples with known answers and check the results.

Now suppose you wish to find the probability of getting four *or fewer* flat panel monitors out of 12. The appropriate function here is the cumulative distribution function, or "cdf":

binomcdf(*numtrials, p,* [*x*])

Does this look disturbingly familiar? Except for the "c" instead of the "p," it looks just like the previous example. The good news is that we already understand the syntax; the bad news is that if we aren't careful we might get the wrong function in haste. Be careful! The function **binomcdf**(12, .6, 4) gives the answer .0573099213. If we are not convinced of our prowess with **binomcdf** we can use **binompdf** to check the result:

binompdf(12, .6, 0) + **binompdf**(12, .6, 1) + ⋯ + **binompdf**(12, .6, 4)
= .000016777 + .0003019898 + ⋯ + .042042
= .05731

Now let's consider another of the common calculations with random variables: What is the probability that the random variable will assume a value between 4 and 7? One common source of confusion here is that the word *between* is ambiguous. Do we mean to include 4 and 7, or do we mean only the probability of getting a 5 or 6? In this case, we wish to be inclusive. To evaluate the probability desired, we will use the cumulative distribution function for the binomial, **binomcdf.** The logic is elementary, as Sherlock Holmes would say. The probability that the binomial random variable will assume a value between 4 and 7 (inclusive) is equal to the probability of assuming a value less than or equal to 7, minus the probability of assuming a value less than or equal to 3 (*not* 4!). In symbols,

$$p(4 \le x \le 7) = p(x \le 7) - p(x \le 3)$$

which is found as follows:

binomcdf(12, .6, 7) − **binomcdf**(12, .6, 3)

gives us 0.5465545.

Our last binomial random variable calculation problem is finding the probability of a value greater than a given value. What, for instance, is the probability of more than seven monitors having flat panel displays? We know that

$$p(7 < x) + p(x \le 7) = 1$$

and so

$$p(7 < x) = 1 - p(x \le 7)$$

which we translate into:

1 − **binomcdf**(12, .6, 7)

giving us 0.438178222.

We have gone into some detail to explain how these binomial probability problems can be solved using the calculator. This detail is justified not only because of the importance of the binomial distribution, but also because these same calculator procedures will be used for finding probabilities involving the geometric and normal random variables, yet to come.

In Exploration 7.1 we discussed how to graph a discrete distribution. When we graphed the probability density function for the Apgar scores, we manually entered the outcomes and their associated probabilities. Anticipating that you may wish to consider binomial chance experiments with many trials, we will streamline the data entry process using some commands and functions we have already discussed in previous calculator explorations.

Graphing a binomial distribution will involve three steps:

1. Construct the list of possible values in List1 using the seq command (or your calculator's equivalent).
2. Construct the probabilities in List2 using the binompdf function (or your calculator's equivalent).
3. Draw the graph (in the form of a histogram) of the probability distribution.

Consider the binomial probability distribution for $n = 20$ and $p = .20$. Carrying out the steps below puts the integers 0 to 20 in List1, and $p(x)$ for x values from 0 to 20 in List2.

1. seq(x, x, 0, 20) → List1 puts a sequence of 21 integers into List1. (Remember to verify your calculator syntax and the order of the information to be entered for your calculator!)
2. binompdf(20, .2) → List2. (Remember to verify . . .)
3. Now graph the probability distribution, where List1 contains the possible data values and List2 contains the probabilities.

To check your work, partial calculator screen output for this problem is given in Figure 7.47(a), and the graph of the distribution is shown in Figure 7.47(b).

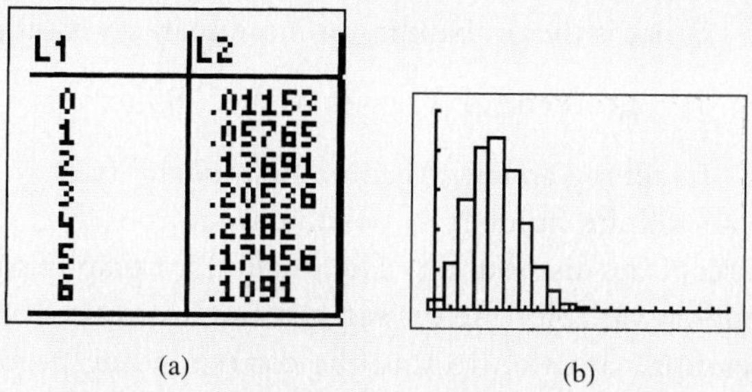

FIGURE 7.47
(a) Binomial probabilities; (b) histogram of binomial distribution.

EXPLORATION 7.3 Geometric Probability Calculations

Our calculator exploration of geometric random variables will be an echo of what was done for binomial random variables in Exploration 7.2. We again consider (1) the probability the variable will assume a value between two given numbers, (2) the probability the variable will assume a value less than a given number, and (3) the probability the random variable will assume a value greater than a given number.

Our example here will be about jumper cables. Suppose that 40% of students who drive to campus carry jumper cables. If your car has a dead battery, and you aren't one of the forward thinking 40%, how many students will you have to ask before you find one with jumper cables?

Consider the first problem: the probability of a particular number. The probability the first student stopped has jumper cables is:

$$p(1) = (1 - p)^{1-1}p = (1 - .4)^{1-1}(.4) = .4$$

The corresponding keystrokes for finding this probability will be something like

(1 − 0.4)^0*0.4.

Now let's consider problems (2) and (3). If your calculator has density and cumulative distribution functions for the geometric distribution, the functions are probably named something like geompdf and geomcdf, similar to the names for the binomial functions. The calculator syntax for the probability density function will probably look something like

geompdf(p, x)

where p is the probability of success and x is in this example the number of students you would ask until success. We want the probability of jumper cables on the very first stop. We enter **geompdf**(.4, 1), and the function returns .4.

Now suppose you wish to find the probability of jumper cables after four *or fewer* stops. Using the cumulative distribution function, **"geomcdf"** (which has the same parameters as the geompdf function), we enter **geomcdf**(.4, 4), which returns 0.8704. As with the binomial, we can check this by summing:

geompdf(.4, 1) + **geompdf**(.4, 2) + **geompdf**(.4, 4) + **geompdf**(.4, 4)
$= 0.4 + 0.24 + 0.144 + 0.0864$
$= 0.87041$

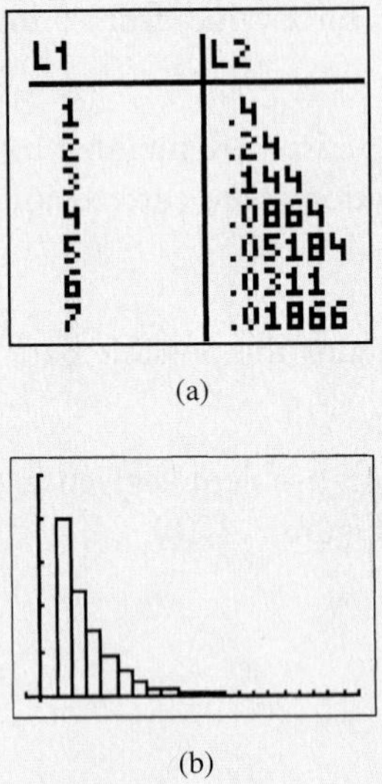

FIGURE 7.48
(a) Geometric probability distribution; (b) histogram of geometric probability distribution.

The probability that a geometric random variable will assume a value between 4 and 7 (inclusive) is equal to the probability of observing a value less than or equal to 7, minus the probability of observing a value less than or equal to 3 (*not* 4). In symbols,

$$P(4 \leq x \leq 7) = P(x \leq 7) - P(x \leq 3)$$

which is found using **geomcdf**(.4, 7) − **geomcdf**(.4, 3), giving 0.1880064.

What is the probability of more than seven stops before we get jumper cables?

1 − **geomcdf**(.4, 7) gives us 0.0279936.

Graphing an entire geometric probability distribution is not possible, since there is an infinite number of possible values—1, 2, 3, ... Nevertheless, we can graph parts of the distribution. The method for graphing is similar to that for the binomial random variable. Use the **seq** function to create a list of integers in List1; then use the **geompdf** function to find the corresponding probabilities and store them in List2; and finally plot the distribution as you would a histogram, and as we have previously done with the binomial. These steps for the geometric distribution of Example 7.22 are summarized below:

1. seq(x, x, 1, 20) → List1
2. geompdf(.4, List1) → List2
3. Graph a histogram with the domain List1, and probabilities in List2.

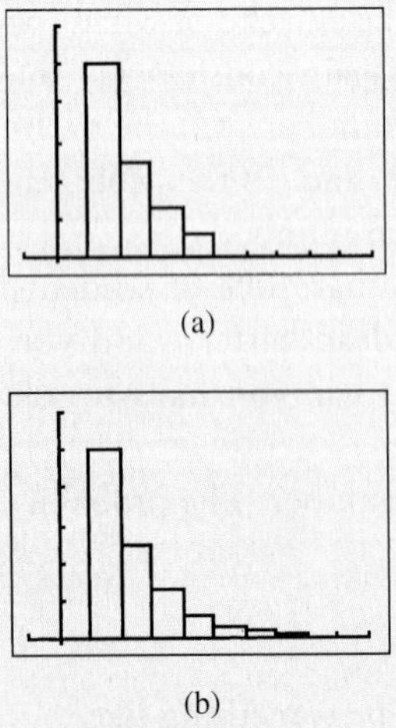

FIGURE 7.49
(a) Incorrect display; (b) correct display.

The data editing window is shown in Figure 7.48(a) and a graph of this geometric distribution appears in Figure 7.48(b).

We are really calculating probabilities for only part of the distribution, since the number of possible values is infinite. The graph should tail to the right in a gradual manner, not suddenly drop out of sight. You may notice a sudden plummeting in your graph but it could be that there are more significant probabilities to the right. As an example, suppose we consider the chance experiment of flipping a coin until a head appears. The distribution of x = number of tosses is geometric with success probability .5. If the distribution is plotted using the previous steps but only using a sequence of integers from 1 to 4, the results are shown in Figure 7.49(a). Clearly, there are values with probabilities different from zero that are not represented in the graph. The solution is to construct the sequence of integers over a larger range of values, say 1 to 16. At some point, of course, the geometric probabilities become very close to zero, as in Figure 7.49(b). If your graph looks similar to Figure 7.49(b), tailing off gradually, you can be fairly certain you have captured the essential behavior of the particular geometric distribution.

EXPLORATION 7.4 Normal Curves and the Normal Probability Distribution

The normal distribution is arguably the most famous distribution in all of statistics. As we have learned, "the" normal distribution is really a family of distributions with the same shape, but different means and standard deviations. The "standard" normal distribution is the normal probability distribution with $\mu = 0$, and $\sigma = 1.0$. From the calculator perspective, working with the normal distribution is slightly different from the binomial and geometric distributions because the normal distribution is continuous. Consequently, it will not be graphed as a histogram; normal curves are graphed just as any other function is graphed. The normal curve, however, is not particularly simple. Fortunately your calculator, if it has statistical functions, will have "normal" already in it somewhere. It might be something like this:

normalpdf(x, [μ, σ]).

If you are a glutton for punishment or your calculator does not have a built-in normalpdf function, here is the formula for a normal curve with mean μ and standard deviation σ:

$$y = \frac{1}{\sqrt{2\pi\sigma^2}}\, e^{[(x-\mu)^2/(2\sigma^2)]}$$

Here are the keystrokes for the formula:

y1 = 1/(sqr(2*$\pi\sigma$^2)*exp(−(x−μ)^2/(2*σ^2))

Assuming you are smiling because of your foresight in purchasing a calculator with a built-in normalpdf function, let's put it to good use. The syntax above for the **normalpdf** function might seem complicated but actual use is simple once you get used to it. You should check your calculator manual for two *very important* pieces of information. First, make sure you know the required order for the information you must provide. Second, look closely at the sigma, wherever it is in your calculator's syntax. Make sure you check whether you must enter σ (the standard deviation) or σ^2 (the variance). Now let's tackle the notation. First of all, if your calculator's syntax has those square brackets—[μ, σ]—remember that they indicate numbers that are optional. If you leave them out, the normalpdf function will simply default to the standard normal curve, with mean 0 and standard deviation (or variance) 1.

Let's graph three normal curves. The first has a mean and standard deviation of 10 and 5, respectively. The second has a mean and standard deviation of 40 and 2.5, and the third a mean and standard deviation of 70 and 10. Navigate your calculator's menu system to find the normal curve function, and paste this function into the function definition window where you usually define simpler functions. Using the syntax above, you should see your calculator's equivalent of the following:

y1 = **normalpdf**(x, 10, 5)
y2 = **normalpdf**(x, 40, 2.5)
y3 = **normalpdf**(x, 70, 10)

Graphing these functions using the window setting in Figure 7.50(a), we see the graphs in Figure 7.50(b).

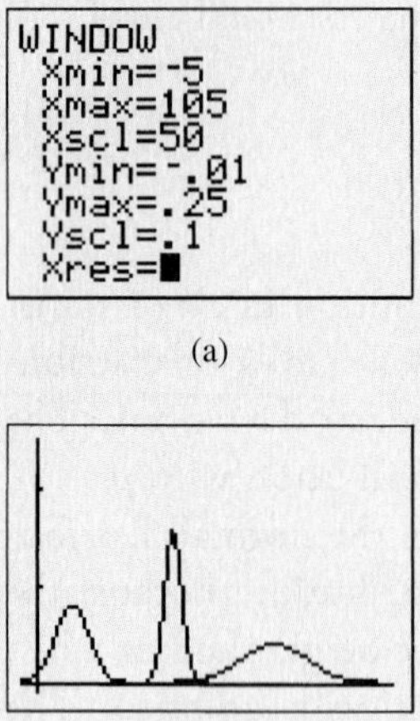

FIGURE 7.50
(a) Window settings;
(b) normal curves.

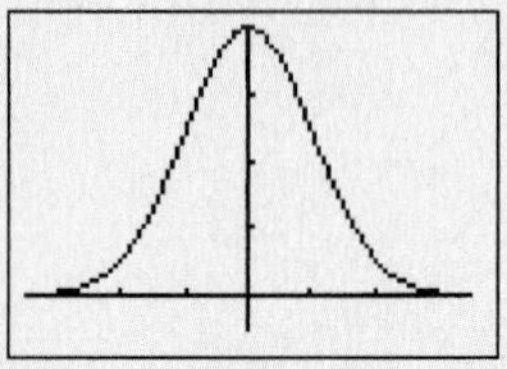

FIGURE 7.51
The standard normal distribution.

Normal C.D.
Lower :0
Upper :0
σ :0
μ :0
Execute

FIGURE 7.52
Setup for normal calculations.

Now let's graph the standard normal distribution. If your calculator syntax indicates that it defaults to a standard normal, you will only have to enter your calculator equivalent of

y1 = **normalpdf**(x).

It is also possible that your calculator does *not* default to standard normal, in which case you would have to specify the mean and standard deviation as 0 and 1, something like

y1 = **normalpdf**(x, 0, 1).

Set your graphing window with x values running from about -3.5 to 3.5 and the y values from -0.05 to 0.40. These values should be fine for the standard normal distribution. If you don't see a distribution filling the screen as in Figure 7.51, something is amiss and you need to verify your keystrokes and/or check your calculator manual.

Since the normal probability distribution is a continuous distribution, the probability that x would be equal to a specific value is, of course, 0. For continuous distributions, we are usually interested in finding (1) the area under the curve between two specific values; and (2) the area in the extremes, or "tails," of the distribution. The function that we will use to find these values will be symbolized with the notation "**normalcdf,**" which stands for the "normal cumulative distribution function." This actually is a misnomer, because the functions calling themselves "cdf" functions on many calculators actually calculate the probability that the standard normal variable is *between* two values. Calculators seem to get it right for the discrete probability density functions, but for some reason have elected to use similar names for very different kinds of calculations when they get to the continuous probability density functions—don't let this minor inconvenience confuse you!

Two strategies are used by calculator manufacturers for evaluating the probability that z is between two values, a and b. It is possible your calculator has a table for you to fill in the values as in Figure 7.52. For a calculator utilizing this strategy, you would have to fill in the lower bound, upper bound, and standard deviation (σ) and mean (μ).

Other calculators ask for the mean and standard deviation as parameters of the function. If your calculator uses this strategy, your built-in cumulative distribution function will have syntax something like this:

normalcdf(lower bound, upper bound [, μ, σ])

For a calculator using this syntax, you would fill in the lower bound and upper bound with the appropriate values for z and ignore the optional parameters, since z will have a standard normal distribution. You will specify other values for μ and σ when performing calculations that are not already in terms of z scores. After navigating your calculator's menus, you will enter something like this:

normalcdf(z-lower, z-upper).

Let's find the probability that z is between -1.76 and .58. We enter the function as **normalcdf**(-1.76, 0.58), and the calculator will return a value of 0.6798388789. We would not suggest writing all those digits; rounding off to .6798 is perfectly fine (as you may have surmised from considering Appendix Table 2).

As you might guess from its name, the **normalcdf** function can also be used for calculation of the cumulative distribution function—that is, finding the probability that z will be below a specific value. Suppose we want to find the probability that z is less than -1.76. Remembering that the set of possible values for a standard normal random variable is the entire real line, you might think to enter the following:

normalcdf($-\infty$, -1.76).

If so, your thinking is right on target, except for one thing: there is no "$-\infty$" on your calculator. Some calculators will have a special symbol for "$-\infty$", which the calculator translates internally to its equivalent of a "very small number." You should check your manual for this number and how to find it. The representation will probably be something like "-1E99" or "-1e999" which is calculator-speak for -1 times 10 raised to the highest power the calculator can handle. In the case of the standard normal curve, it may be just as easy to enter a different but still very small number in place of the "$-\infty$," perhaps **normalcdf**(-10, -1.76). On our calculator, .0392038577 is returned, which agrees with the tabled answer. (If you are squeamish about -10, use -50; using -50 we get .0392038577 also!)

Finding the probability that a z is greater than a particular value is also easy. For example, we find the area to the right of $z = 1.42$ as follows:

1 − **normalcdf**("$-\infty$", 1.42)

Using -10 for the lower bound, we get 0.0778038883.

The last type of problem examined will be the identification of extreme values. The easiest way to do this is with a built-in function, typically called "InvNormal," which stands for "inverse normal." The "InvNormal" function—or whatever it is named on your calculator—will be the reverse of finding the probability that z is less than a specified value. Earlier in our discussion, we found the probability that z is less than -1.76 to be 0.0392038577. The InvNormal function returns a z value when given the probability. Thus, InvNormal(.0392038577) equals -1.76. Except for the difference in function name, the syntax for this function should be the same as for **normalcdf**:

InvNormal(cumulative probability, [, μ, σ])

On our calculator, **InvNormal**(0.0392038577) returns -1.760000538.

EXPLORATION 7.5 The Normal Approximation to the Binomial Distribution

In an earlier Exploration, we showed you how to use your calculator to find probabilities associated with the binomial and normal distributions using built-in calculator functions. We generically used the terms *binompdf, binomcdf, normalpdf,* and *normalcdf* to refer to these functions. In this Exploration, we would like to focus on the normal approximation to the binomial distribution. Whenever a continuous distribution is used to approximate a discrete distribution, the question naturally occurs, "How good is the approximation?" The answer usually given by statistics instructors is, "it depends." In the case of the normal approximation to the binomial, the goodness of fit depends on the two quantities which define the binomial distribution: n and p. Most statisticians have a simple "rule of thumb" they apply for approximating the binomial with a normal distribution, such as:

> When either $np < 10$ or $n(1 - p) < 10$, the binomial distribution is too skewed for the normal approximation to give accurate results.

Different statisticians have different rules of thumb, some feeling comfortable with the accuracy provided by using 5 instead of 10 in the rule of thumb above. In days of yore—that is, the precalculator days—students would have to accept the rule of thumb as one of the mysteries of statistics. In more modern times, a statistics student, armed with a calculator, can not only understand what the rules of thumb are all about, but also evaluate the various rules of thumb for a particular n and p pair.

It might be argued that using the normal distribution to approximate a distribution that we can evaluate exactly seems a little foolish. There is something to this argument;

but remember: we will not always be able to find exact probabilities in other situations and must rely on approximations. Using an approximation involves a fundamental tradeoff between ease of calculation and exactness of answer. An understanding of this with the normal approximation to the binomial will give us a better understanding of the issues involved when we encounter similar tradeoffs in statistics courses yet to come. (At least you'll be more tolerant of those "rules of thumb!")

We shall reacquaint ourselves with some syntax and warm up with a distribution of the number of express mail packages mailed at a certain post office in a day. The number is approximately normally distributed with $\mu = 18$ and $\sigma = 6$. Suppose we wish to find the probability that 20 express mail packages are mailed in a given day. We calculate the probability that in a normal distribution with $\mu = 18$ and $\sigma = 6$, the event $x = 20$ would happen. Remembering the syntax from our earlier discussion,

normalcdf(lower bound, upper bound [, μ, σ])

we enter: normalcdf(19.5, 20.5, 18, 6), and our calculator returns 0.062832569.

We will now compare binomial calculations with the normal approximations. It is reported that 10% of live births in the United States are premature. Suppose we randomly select 250 live births and define the random variable x to be the number of these that are premature. We wish to calculate the probability that x is between 15 and 30 (inclusive). To find the binomial probability, we recall that we must use the built-in function we called binomcdf. This function includes the rightmost interval indicated; therefore, we subtract the probability of getting x less than or equal to 14 from the probability of getting x less than or equal to 30.

$$\begin{aligned} P(15 \le x \le 30) &= \text{binomcdf}(250, .1, 30) - \text{binomcdf}(250, .1, 14) \\ &= 0.8753286537 - 0.00931244487 \\ &= 0.8660162088. \end{aligned}$$

To estimate this probability using the normal curve approximation, we will use a normal distribution with mean $\mu = 25$ and $\sigma = 4.74341649$:

normalcdf (lower bound, upper bound [, μ, σ])
= normalcdf(14.5, 30.5 , 25, 4.74341649)
= 0.8634457937

The difference between the two probabilities is 0.0025704151. This does not seem to be a large difference, but it is a difference. According to the rule of thumb, this approximation meets the test, but the investigator in the context of his or her situation must evaluate the practical importance of the difference.

Now let's redo the calculations, not with a sample size of 250, but a sample size of only 50. Keeping the results proportionally the same by dividing by 5, we will consider approximating the probability of getting between three and six premature babies (inclusive) in a random sample of 50 babies. In this case,

$$\begin{aligned} np &= 50(.10) = 5 < 10 \\ n(1 - p) &= 50(1 - .10) = 45 \ge 10 \end{aligned}$$

Since $np < 10$, our rule of thumb would regard the binomial distribution as too skewed for the normal curve approximation to give accurate results. Let's see what happens:

$$\begin{aligned} P(3 \le \text{x} \le 6) &= \text{binomcdf}(50, .1, 6) - \text{binomcdf}(50, .1, 2) \\ &= 0.7702268435 - 0.1117287563 \\ &= 0.6584980872 \end{aligned}$$

To evaluate this probability using the normal curve approximation, we will use the normal distribution with $\mu = 50(.1) = 5$ and $\sigma = \sqrt{50(.1)(.9)} = 2.121320344$.

normalcdf(lower bound, upper bound [, μ, σ])
= normalcdf(2.5, 6.5 , 5, 2.121320344)
= 0.6409535402

The difference between the binomial and the normal approximation in this case is 0.017544547. It is interesting to note that using a rule of thumb with 5 instead of 10 would call this difference "acceptable." We do not argue with this rule of thumb in principle, but once again point out that individual judgment must be used in evaluating the goodness of the approximation.

Finally, we will superimpose the appropriate normal distribution over the binomial distribution to get a visual sense of the approximation. It is entirely possible that a given approximation will do a better job for different choices of values of the end points of the interval, and the graphs may give us an overall sense of when a normal approximation might be acceptable.

Graphing a binomial distribution and a normal distribution at the same time involves skills we have seen in previous Explorations. (You may want to refer back to the calculator explorations about the binomial and normal distributions to refresh your memory.)

We will graph the binomial and normal distributions for four distributions, each with sample size 20, but with probabilities of success of .05, .1, .25, and .5. We will change the windows to make the graphs fill the windows, but this should not affect any interpretations of the goodness of fit to the binomial by the normal distribution. As a reminder, our binomial preparations for the first graph are

1. seq(x, x, 0, 20) → List1
2. binompdf(20, .05) → List2
3. Specify that we want a histogram with the values in List1, and the corresponding binomial probabilities in List2.

For the normal curve plot, define the graphing function by supplying the mean and standard deviation of the binomial as parameters for the normalpdf function:

Y1 = normalpdf(x, 1, 0.97468)

The four plots appear in Figure 7.53.

As can be seen from a comparison of the plots, the normal approximation gets "closer and closer" to the binomial as p gets closer and closer to 0.5. For $p = .25$, the rule of thumb is satisfied for $n = 20$, and for $p = .5$, the rule of thumb is satisfied using $n = 10$. It is a bit difficult to judge whether or not the normal approximation to the binomial is "adequate" for a particular situation by just looking at the plots.

Modern technology makes it possible to do binomial calculations quickly, so the normal approximation to the binomial is not as widely used as it once was. However, there are other distributions in statistics that are "approximately" normal as long as certain conditions are satisfied. We hope that working with the approximation to the binomial has given you an appreciation for the how the normal distribution might be used to approximate these other distributions.

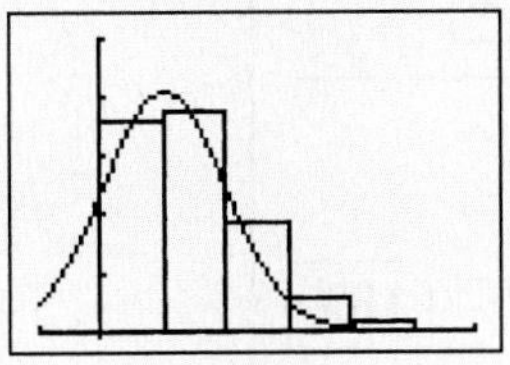

$n = 20$; $p = .05$

(a)

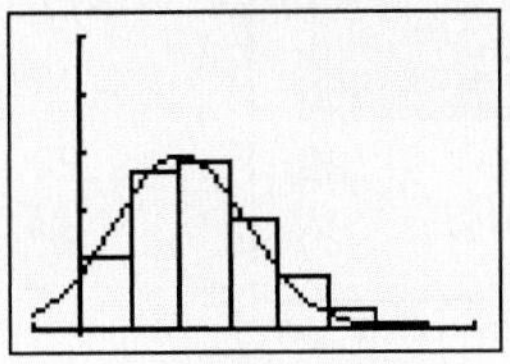

$n = 20$; $p = .10$

(b)

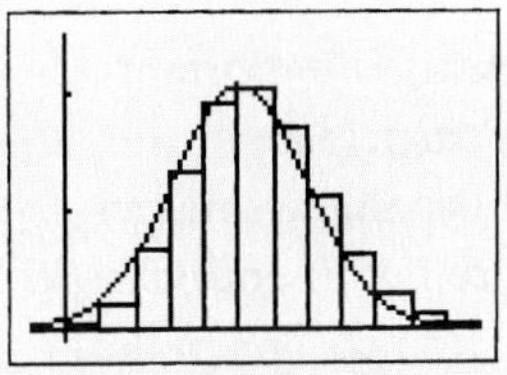

$n = 20$; $p = .25$

(c)

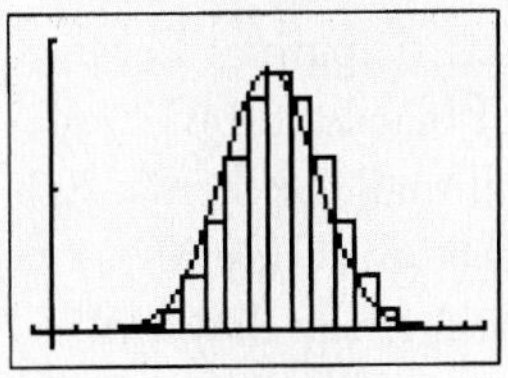

$n = 20$; $p = .50$

(d)

FIGURE 7.53
Binomial distributions: (a) $n = 20$, $p = .05$; (b) $n = 20$, $p = .10$; (c) $n = 20$, $p = .25$; (d) $n = 20$, $p = .50$.

Cumulative Review Exercises CR7.1-CR7.21

CR7.1 The paper "The Psychology of Security" (*Communications of the ACM* [2008]: 36–41) states that people are more likely to gamble for a loss than to accept a guaranteed loss. For example, the authors indicate that when presented with a scenario that allows people to choose between a guaranteed gain of \$5 and a gain of \$10 if the flip of a coin results in a head, more people will choose the guaranteed gain. However, when presented with a scenario that involves choosing between a guaranteed loss of \$5 and a loss of \$10 if the flip of a coin results in a head, more people will choose the gambling option. Describe how you would design an experiment that would allow you to test this theory.

CR7.2 ● The article "Water Consumption in the Bay Area" (*San Jose Mercury News*, January 16, 2010) reported the accompanying values for water consumption (gallons per person per day) for residential customers of 27 San Francisco Bay area water agencies:

49	52	53	59	59	61	69	70	70	73	79	80
85	87	89	90	92	93	93	95	96	97	114	149
208	318	334									

a. Use the given water consumption values to construct a boxplot. Describe any interesting features of the boxplot. Are there any outliers in the data set?
b. Compute the mean and standard deviation for this data set. If the two largest values were deleted from the data set, would the standard deviation of this new data set be larger or smaller than the standard deviation you computed for the entire data set?
c. How do the values of the mean and median of the entire data set compare? Is this consistent with the shape of the boxplot from Part (a)? Explain.

CR7.3 Red-light cameras are used in many places to deter drivers from running red lights. The following graphical display appeared in the article "Communities Put a Halt to Red-Light Cameras" (*USA Today*, January 18, 2010). Based on this graph, would it be correct to conclude that there were fewer red-light cameras in 2009 than in 2002? Explain.

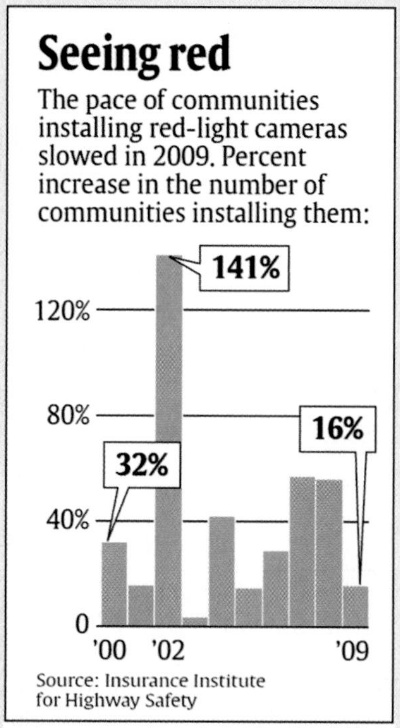

By Julie Snider, USA TODAY

CR7.4 The following quote is from *USA Today* (January 21, 2010):

> Most Americans think the Census is important, and the majority say they will participate in the count this spring—although Hispanics, younger people and the less educated are not as enthusiastic, a Pew Research Center survey found. The poll of 1504 adults found that perceptions differ: 74% of blacks and 72% of Hispanics rate the Census "very important" vs. 57% of whites. Believing it's important doesn't necessarily mean participating: Fewer than half of Hispanics, 57% of blacks and 61% of whites say they will fill out and mail the forms. Age is the greatest factor in participation: Only 36% of respondents who are 30 or younger say they will definitely participate.

Suppose that it is reasonable to regard survey participants as representative of adult Americans.

a. Suppose that an adult American is to be selected at random and consider the following events:

I = the event that the selected individual thinks that the Census is very important

W = the event that the selected individual is white

Are the events I and W independent or dependent events? Explain.

b. Give an example of two census-related events different than the ones defined in Part (a) and indicate whether they are independent or dependent events. Explain your reasoning.

CR7.5 Beverly is building a fireplace. She is using special decorative 8-inch bricks for the bottom row of the fireplace. Although the bricks are advertised as 8-inch bricks, the actual length of a brick is variable, and the brick lengths are approximately normally distributed with a mean of 8 inches and a standard deviation of 0.2 inches. Unfortunately, Beverly didn't buy enough of the 8-inch bricks, and needs to get two more bricks to try to fill the remaining 15.9 inches. The two additional bricks cannot have a combined length of more than 15.9 inches and must fit in the 15.9-inch space with no more than .1 inch of space left over. What is the probability that two randomly selected bricks will allow Beverly to complete the bottom row of the fireplace? (Hint: Define b_1 = length of the first brick and b_2 = length of the second brick. A variable that is a linear combination of independent variables that have normal distributions also has a normal distribution.)

CR7.6 ● Manatees are large marine mammals found along the coast of Florida. Data on the total number of manatee deaths per year reported by the Florida Marine Research Center is given in the accompanying table. Construct a time series plot of these data and comment on any trends over time.

Year	Number of Manatee Deaths
1974	7
1975	28
1976	58
1977	109
1978	77
1979	72
1980	56
1981	112
1982	111
1983	71
1984	119
1985	112
1986	117
1987	109
1988	127
1989	164
1990	199
1991	166
1992	156
1993	137
1994	177

CR7.7 Two shipping services offer overnight delivery of parcels, and both promise delivery before 10 A.M. A mail-order catalog company ships 30% of its overnight packages using service 1 and 70% using service 2. Service 1 fails to meet the 10 A.M. delivery promise 10% of the time, whereas Service 2 fails to deliver by 10 A.M. 8% of the time. Suppose that you made a purchase from this company and were expecting your package by 10 A.M., but it is late. Which shipping service was more likely to have been used?

CR7.8 The paper "The Effect of Temperature and Humidity on Size of Segregated Traffic Exhaust Particle Emissions" (*Atmospheric Environment* [2008]: 2369–2382) gave the following summary quantities for a measure of traffic flow (vehicles/second) during peak traffic hours at a particular location recorded daily over a long sequence of days:

Mean = 0.41 Standard Deviation = 0.26 Median = 0.45
5th percentile = 0.03 Lower quartile = 0.18
Upper quartile = 0.57 95th percentile = 0.86

Based on these summary quantities, do you think that the distribution of the measure of traffic flow could have been approximately normal? Explain your reasoning.

CR7.9 The article "Doctors Misdiagnose More Women, Blacks" (*San Luis Obispo Tribune*, April 20, 2000) gave the following information, which is based on a large study of more than 10,000 patients treated in emergency rooms in the eastern and midwestern United States:

1. Doctors misdiagnosed heart attacks in 2.1% of all patients.
2. Doctors misdiagnosed heart attacks in 4.3% of black patients.
3. Doctors misdiagnosed heart attacks in 7% of women under 55 years old.

Use the following event definitions: M = event that a heart attack is misdiagnosed, B = event that a patient is black, and W = event that a patient is a woman under

55 years old. Translate each of the three given statements into probability notation.

CR7.10 The *Cedar Rapids Gazette* (November 20, 1999) reported the following information on compliance with child restraint laws for cities in Iowa:

City	Number of Children Observed	Number Properly Restrained
Cedar Falls	210	173
Cedar Rapids	231	206
Dubuque	182	135
Iowa City (city)	175	140
Iowa City (interstate)	63	47

a. Use the information provided to estimate the following probabilities:
   i. The probability that a randomly selected child is properly restrained given that the child is observed in Dubuque.
   ii. The probability that a randomly selected child is properly restrained given that the child is observed in a city that has "Cedar" in its name.

b. Suppose that you are observing children in the Iowa City area. Use a tree diagram to illustrate the possible outcomes of an observation that considers both the location of the observation (city or interstate) and whether the child observed was properly restrained.

CR7.11 According to a study conducted by a risk assessment firm (*Associated Press*, December 8, 2005), drivers residing within 1 mile of a restaurant are 30% more likely to be in an accident in a given policy year. Consider the following two events:

A = event that a driver has an accident during a policy year

R = event that a driver lives within 1 mile of a restaurant

Which of the following four probability statements is consistent with the findings of this survey? Justify your choice.

i. $P(A|R) = .3$

ii. $P(A|R^C) = .3$

iii. $\dfrac{P(A|R)}{P(A|R^C)} = .3$

iv. $\dfrac{P(A|R) - P(A|R^C)}{P(A|R^C)} = .3$

CR7.12 The article "Men, Women at Odds on Gun Control" (*Cedar Rapids Gazette*, September 8, 1999) included the following statement: "The survey found that 56% of American adults favored stricter gun control laws. Sixty-six percent of women favored the tougher laws, compared with 45% of men." These figures are based on a large telephone survey conducted by Associated Press Polls. If an adult is selected at random, are the events *selected adult is female* and *selected adult favors stricter gun control* independent or dependent events? Explain.

CR7.13 Suppose that a new Internet company Mumble.com requires all employees to take a drug test. Mumble.com can afford only the inexpensive drug test—the one with a 5% false-positive rate and a 10% false-negative rate. (That means that 5% of those who are not using drugs will incorrectly test positive and that 10% of those who are actually using drugs will test negative.) Suppose that 10% of those who work for Mumble.com are using the drugs for which Mumble is checking. (Hint: It may be helpful to draw a tree diagram to answer the questions that follow.)

a. If one employee is chosen at random, what is the probability that the employee both uses drugs and tests positive?

b. If one employee is chosen at random, what is the probability that the employee does not use drugs but tests positive anyway?

c. If one employee is chosen at random, what is the probability that the employee tests positive?

d. If we know that a randomly chosen employee has tested positive, what is the probability that he or she uses drugs?

CR7.14 Refer to Exercise CR7.13. Suppose that because of the high rate of false-positives for the drug test, Mumble.com has instituted a mandatory independent second test for those who test positive on the first test.

a. If one employee is selected at random, what is the probability that the selected employee uses drugs and tests positive twice?

b. If one employee is selected at random, what is the probability that the employee tests positive twice?

c. If we know that the randomly chosen employee has tested positive twice, what is the probability that he or she uses drugs?

d. What is the chance that an individual who does use drugs doesn't test positive twice (either this employee tests negative on the first round and doesn't need a retest, or this employee tests positive the first time and that result is followed by a negative result on the retest)?

e. Discuss the benefits and drawbacks of using a retest scheme such as the one proposed in this question.

CR7.15 A chemical supply company currently has in stock 100 pounds of a certain chemical, which it sells to customers in 5-pound lots. Let x = the number of lots ordered by a randomly chosen customer. The probability distribution of x is as follows:

x	1	2	3	4
$p(x)$	.2	.4	.3	.1

a. Calculate the mean value of x.

b. Calculate the variance and standard deviation of x.

CR7.16 Return to Exercise CR7.15, and let y denote the amount of material (in pounds) left after the next customer's order is shipped. Find the mean and variance of y. (Hint: y is a linear function of x.)

CR7.17 An experiment was conducted to investigate whether a graphologist (a handwriting analyst) could distinguish a normal person's handwriting from that of a psychotic. A well-known expert was given 10 files, each containing handwriting samples from a normal person and from a person diagnosed as psychotic, and asked to identify the psychotic's handwriting. The graphologist made correct identifications in 6 of the 10 trials (data taken from *Statistics in the Real World*, by R. J. Larsen and D. F. Stroup [New York: Macmillan, 1976]). Does this evidence indicate that the graphologist has an ability to distinguish the handwriting of psychotics? (Hint: What is the probability of correctly guessing six or more times out of 10? Your answer should depend on whether this probability is relatively small or relatively large.)

CR7.18 A machine that produces ball bearings has initially been set so that the true average diameter of the bearings it produces is 0.500 inches. A bearing is acceptable if its diameter is within 0.004 inches of this target value. Suppose, however, that the setting has changed during the course of production, so that the distribution of the diameters produced is well approximated by a normal distribution with mean 0.499 inches and standard deviation 0.002 inches. What percentage of the bearings produced will not be acceptable?

CR7.19 Consider the variable x = time required for a college student to complete a standardized exam. Suppose that for the population of students at a particular university, the distribution of x is well approximated by a normal distribution with mean 45 minutes and standard deviation 5 minutes.

a. If 50 minutes is allowed for the exam, what proportion of students at this university would be unable to finish in the allotted time?

b. How much time should be allowed for the exam if we wanted 90% of the students taking the test to be able to finish in the allotted time?

c. How much time is required for the fastest 25% of all students to complete the exam?

CR7.20 ● The paper "The Load-Life Relationship for M50 Bearings with Silicon Nitride Ceramic Balls" (*Lubrication Engineering* [1984]: 153–159) reported the accompanying data on bearing load life (in millions of revolutions). The corresponding normal scores are also given.

x	*Normal Score*	x	Normal Score
47.1	−1.867	240.0	0.062
68.1	−1.408	240.0	0.187
68.1	−1.131	278.0	0.315
90.8	−0.921	278.0	0.448
103.6	−0.745	289.0	0.590
106.0	−0.590	289.0	0.745
115.0	−0.448	367.0	0.921
126.0	−0.315	385.9	1.131
146.6	−0.187	392.0	1.408
229.0	−0.062	395.0	1.867

Construct a normal probability plot. Is normality plausible?

CR7.21 ● The following data are a sample of survival times (days from diagnosis) for patients suffering from chronic leukemia of a certain type:

7	47	58	74	177	232	273	285
317	429	440	445	455	468	495	497
532	571	579	581	650	702	715	779
881	900	930	968	1077	1109	1314	1334
1367	1534	1712	1784	1877	1886	2045	2056
2260	2429	2509					

a. Construct a relative frequency distribution for this data set, and draw the corresponding histogram.

b. Would you describe this histogram as having a positive or a negative skew?

c. Would you recommend transforming the data? Explain.

AP* Review Questions for Chapter 7

1. The discrete random variable x = the number of 911 calls in a small town in one day.

x	1	2	3	4	5	6
$p(x)$	0.20	0.35	0.15	0.10	0.10	0.10

Which of the following could be evaluated to compute the mean of this probability distribution?

(A) $\dfrac{1 + 2 + 3 + 4 + 5 + 6}{6}$

(B) $\dfrac{0.20 + 0.35 + 0.15 + 0.10 + 0.10 + 0.10}{6}$

(C) $1(0.20) + 2(0.35) + 3(0.15) + 4(0.10) + 5(0.10) + 6(0.10)$

(D) $\dfrac{1(0.20) + 2(0.35) + 3(0.15) + 4(0.10) + 5(0.10) + 6(0.10)}{6}$

(E) $1^2(0.20) + 2^2(0.35) + 3^2(0.15) + 4^2(0.10) + 5^2(0.10) + 6^2(0.10)$

Use the following for questions 2–3

A college basketball game is made up of two 20-minute halves. Each half is 20 minutes of playing time, but the "real" time elapsed from the start of play to the end of the half is much longer. This is due to time-outs and other periods of time when the game clock is stopped. Suppose that the mean and standard deviation for the "real" time (in minutes) of each half are

	Mean	Standard Deviation
1st half	48	6
2nd half	52	8

2. What is the mean "real" time for the entire game (1st half + 2nd half)?

(A) 48
(B) 50
(C) 52
(D) 100
(E) 114

3. Under what conditions is the standard deviation of the total "real" game time (1st half + 2nd half) equal to $\sqrt{6^2 + 8^2} = 10$?

(A) No conditions are necessary—the standard deviation will be 10 minutes.
(B) The standard deviation will not be 10 minutes under any circumstances.
(C) The standard deviation will be 10 minutes only if the 1st half "real" time is shorter than the 2nd half "real" time.
(D) The standard deviation will be 10 minutes only if the "real" times in the two halves are independent.
(E) The standard deviation will be 10 minutes only if the "real" times in the two halves are mutually exclusive.

4. Ten percent of the students at a particular university smoke. Consider the chance experiment that consists of selecting a random sample of 20 students from this university. Let x = the number of students in the sample who smoke. The random variable x has which of the following probability distributions?

(A) a binomial distribution
(B) a geometric distribution
(C) a normal distribution
(D) a uniform distribution
(E) none of the above

5. Which of the following four binomial histograms, all with $n = 10$, corresponds to the distribution with the largest value of p?

(A)

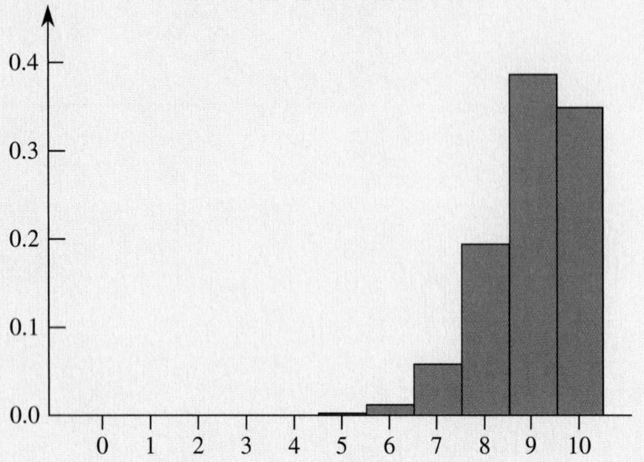

(B)

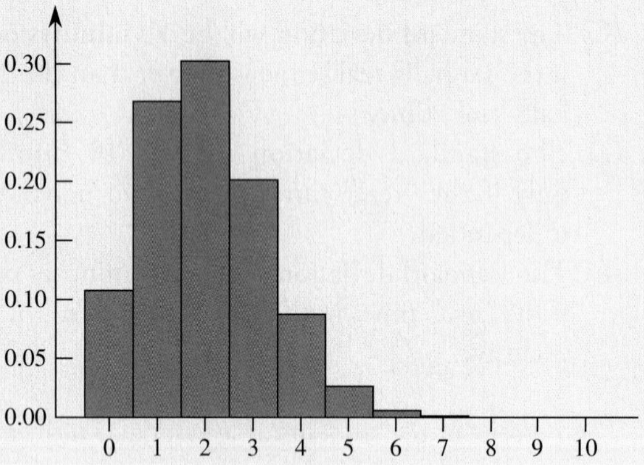

(C)

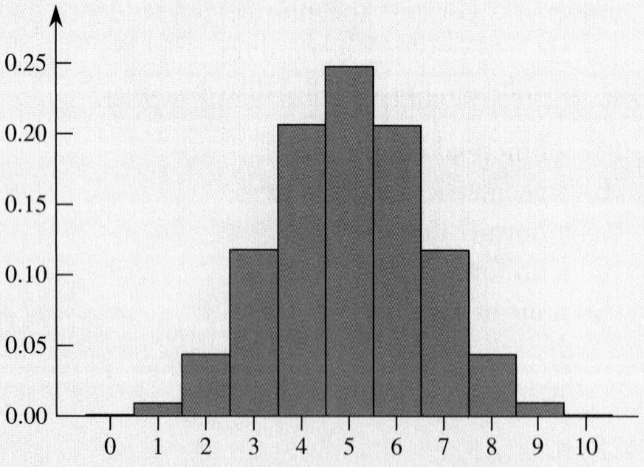

(D)

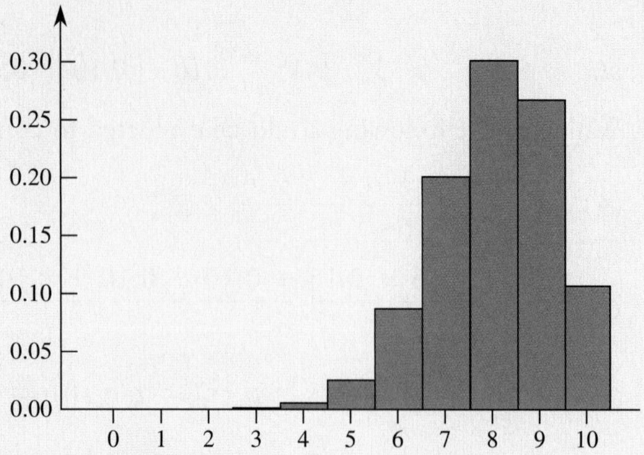

(E) Cannot be determined from the given information.

6. Let x denote the number of accidents in a given month at a certain high school parking lot. Suppose that the probability distribution of x is:

x	0	1	2	3	4	5
$p(x)$	.110	.215	.260	.214	.134	.067

If the numbers of accidents in any 2 months are independent, what is the probability that no car accidents occur in this lot for 2 consecutive months?

(A) .0121
(B) .1100
(C) .2200
(D) .8900
(E) None of the above

7. A normal probability plot suggests that a normal probability model is plausible when:

(A) No obvious patterns are present in the plot.
(B) A bell-shaped pattern is present in the plot.
(C) A substantial quadratic pattern is present in the plot.
(D) A substantial linear pattern is present in the plot.
(E) Any of the above is present in the plot.

8. For a normally distributed population with mean 0 and standard deviation 1.0, the population interquartile range is closest to which of the following values?

(A) 0.50
(B) 1.28
(C) 1.349
(D) 1.645
(E) 1.96

9. Which of the following is *not* a property of a binomial experiment?

(A) It consists of a fixed number of trials, n.
(B) Outcomes of different trials are independent.
(C) Each trial can result in one of several different outcomes.
(D) Observations consist of the number of successes for each trial of the experiment.
(E) The probability of success is constant for each trial.

10. Suppose that x has a probability distribution with density function $f(x) = \begin{cases} c, \text{ if } 6 < x < 8 \\ 0 \text{ otherwise} \end{cases}$

The value of c is:

(A) 0.5
(B) 0.6
(C) 0.7
(D) 0.8
(E) 0.9

11. The number of passengers who choose to check luggage on a flight from Los Angeles to San Francisco is a binomial random variable with n = number of passengers on the flight. If the probability that any individual passenger checks luggage is .3, what is the probability that exactly 40 of the 100 passengers on this flight on a particular day check luggage?

(A) 0
(B) 0.3
(C) $(.3)^{40}$
(D) $(.3)^{40}(.7)^{60}$
(E) $\binom{100}{40}(.3)^{40}(.7)^{60}$

12. Suppose that 65% of the students at a particular university have a Twitter account. If 100 students are selected at random from this university, what are the mean and standard deviation of the random variable x = number of selected students who have a Twitter account?

(A) mean = .65, standard deviation = .35
(B) mean = .65, standard deviation = .002
(C) mean = 65, standard deviation = 22.75
(D) mean = 65, standard deviation = .228
(E) mean = 65, standard deviation = 4.770

13. Suppose that x is a random variable that has a uniform distribution over the interval from 0 to 10. Which of the following probabilities is largest?

(A) $p(x > 8)$
(B) $p\ (x \geq 8)$
(C) $p\ (x = 10)$
(D) $p\ (3 < x < 6)$
(E) $p\ (x < 4)$

14. Suppose that 20% of cereal boxes contain a prize and the other 80% contain the message "Sorry, try again." Boxes of this cereal will be purchased and opened until a prize is found. Define the random variable x to be the number of boxes purchased. What is the probability that exactly three boxes must be purchased?

(A) $(0.20)^3$
(B) $0.8 + 0.8 + 0.2$
(C) $(0.8)^2 + (0.2)$
(D) $(0.8)^2(0.2)$
(E) $\frac{3!}{2!1!}(0.8)^2(0.2)^1$

15. For a normal distribution with mean 100 and standard deviation 10, the 95th percentile is

(A) −1.645
(B) 1.645
(C) 16.45
(D) 83.55
(E) 116.45

CHAPTER 8

Sampling Variability and Sampling Distributions

Christian Petersen/Getty Images

The inferential methods presented in Chapters 9–15 use information contained in a sample to reach conclusions about one or more characteristics of the population from which the sample was selected. For example, let μ denote the true mean fat content of quarter-pound hamburgers marketed by a national fast-food chain. To learn something about μ, we might obtain a sample of $n = 50$ hamburgers and determine the fat content for each one. The sample data might produce a mean of $\bar{x} = 28.4$ grams. How close is this sample mean to the population mean, μ? If we selected another sample of 50 quarter-pound burgers and then determine the sample mean fat content, would this second value be near 28.4, or might it be quite different? These questions can be addressed by studying what is called the *sampling distribution* of $\bar{x}$. Just as the distribution of a numerical variable describes its long-run behavior, the sampling distribution of $\bar{x}$ provides information about the long-run behavior of $\bar{x}$ when sample after sample is selected.

In this chapter, we also consider the sampling distribution of a sample proportion (the fraction of individuals or objects in a sample that have some characteristic of interest). The sampling distribution of a sample proportion, $\hat{p}$, provides information about the long-run behavior of the sample proportion that is the basis for making inferences about a population proportion.

8.1 Statistics and Sampling Variability

A quantity computed from the values in a sample is called a **statistic**. Values of statistics such as the sample mean $\bar{x}$, the sample median, the sample standard deviation s, or the proportion of individuals in a sample that possess a particular property $\hat{p}$, are our primary sources of information about various population characteristics.

The usual way to obtain information regarding the value of a population characteristic is by selecting a sample from the population. For example, to gain insight about the mean credit card balance for students at a particular university, we might select a sample of 50 students at the university. Each student would be asked about his or her credit card balance to yield a value of x = current balance. We could construct a histogram of the 50 sample x values, and we could view this histogram as a rough approximation of the population distribution of x. In a similar way, we could view the sample mean $\bar{x}$ (the mean of a sample of n values) as an approximation of μ, the mean of the population distribution. It would be nice if the value of $\bar{x}$ were equal to the value of the population mean μ, but this is not usually the case. Not only will the value of $\bar{x}$ for a particular sample from a population usually differ from μ, but the $\bar{x}$ values from different samples also usually differ from one another. (For example, two different samples of 50 student credit card balances will usually result in different $\bar{x}$ values.) This sample-to-sample variability makes it challenging to generalize from a sample to the population from which it was selected. To meet this challenge, we must understand sample-to-sample variability.

DEFINITION

Any quantity computed from values in a sample is called a **statistic.**

The observed value of a statistic depends on the particular sample selected from the population and it will vary from sample to sample. This variability is called **sampling variability.**

EXAMPLE 8.1 Exploring Sampling Variability

Consider a small population consisting of the 20 students enrolled in an upper division class. The amount of money (in dollars) each of the 20 students spent on textbooks for the current semester is shown in the following table:

Student	Amount Spent on Books	Student	Amount Spent on Books	Student	Amount Spent on Books
1	367	8	370	15	433
2	358	9	378	16	284
3	442	10	268	17	331
4	361	11	419	18	259
5	375	12	363	19	330
6	395	13	365	20	423
7	322	14	362		

For this population,

$$\mu = \frac{367 + 358 + \cdots + 423}{20} = 360.25$$

Suppose we don't know the value of the population mean, so we decide to estimate μ by taking a random sample of five students and computing the sample mean amount spent on textbooks, $\bar{x}$. Is this a reasonable thing to do? Is the estimate that results likely to be close to the value of μ, the population mean? To answer these questions, consider a simple experiment that allows us to examine the behavior of the statistic $\bar{x}$ when random samples of size 5 are repeatedly selected. (Note that this scenario is not realistic. If a population consisted of only 20 individuals, we would probably conduct a census rather than select a sample. However, this small population size is easier to work with as we develop the idea of sampling variability.)

Let's first select a random sample of size 5 from this population. This can be done by writing the numbers from 1 to 20 on otherwise identical slips of paper, mixing them well, and then selecting 5 slips without replacement. The numbers on the slips selected identify which of the 20 students will be included in our sample. Alternatively, either a table of random digits or a random number generator can be used to determine which 5 students should be selected. We used Minitab to obtain five numbers between 1 and 20, resulting in 17, 20, 7, 11, and 9, and the following sample of amounts spent on books:

331 423 322 419 378

For this sample,

$$\bar{x} = \frac{1873}{5} = 374.60$$

The sample mean is larger than the population mean of \$360.25 by about \$15. Is this difference typical, or is this particular sample mean unusually far away from μ? Taking more samples will provide some additional insight.

Four more random samples (Samples 2–5) from this same population are shown here.

SAMPLE 2		SAMPLE 3		SAMPLE 4		SAMPLE 5	
Student	x	Student	x	Student	x	Student	x
4	361	15	433	20	423	18	259
15	433	12	363	16	284	8	370
12	363	3	442	19	330	9	378
1	367	7	322	1	367	7	322
18	259	18	259	8	370	14	362
$\bar{x}$	**356.60**	$\bar{x}$	**363.80**	$\bar{x}$	**354.80**	$\bar{x}$	**338.20**

Because $\mu = 360.25$, we can see the following:

1. The value of $\bar{x}$ varies from one random sample to another (sampling variability).
2. Some samples produced $\bar{x}$ values larger than μ (Samples 1 and 3), whereas others produced values smaller than μ (Samples 2, 4, and 5).
3. Samples 2, 3, and 4 produced $\bar{x}$ values that were fairly close to the population mean, but Sample 5 resulted in a value that was \$22 below the population mean.

Continuing with the experiment, we selected 45 additional random samples (each of size $n = 5$). The resulting sample means are as follows:

Sample	$\bar{x}$	Sample	$\bar{x}$	Sample	$\bar{x}$
6	374.6	21	355.0	36	353.4
7	356.6	22	407.2	37	379.6
8	363.8	23	380.0	38	352.6
9	354.8	24	377.4	39	342.2
10	338.2	25	341.2	40	362.6
11	375.6	26	316.0	41	315.4
12	379.2	27	370.0	42	366.2
13	341.6	28	401.0	43	361.4
14	355.4	29	347.0	44	375
15	363.8	30	373.8	45	401.4
16	339.6	31	382.8	46	337
17	348.2	32	320.4	47	387.4
18	430.8	33	313.6	48	349.2
19	388.8	34	387.6	49	336.8
20	352.8	35	314.8	50	364.6

Figure 8.1, a density histogram of the 50 sample means, provides insight about the behavior of $\bar{x}$. Most samples resulted in $\bar{x}$ values that are reasonably near $\mu = 360.25$, falling between 335 and 395. A few samples, however, produced values that were far from μ. If we were to take a sample of size 5 from this population and use $\bar{x}$ as an estimate of the population mean μ, we should *not* necessarily expect $\bar{x}$ to be close to μ.

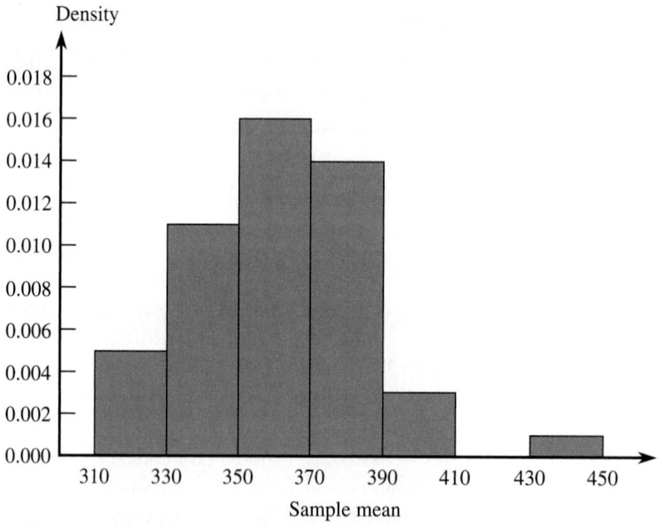

FIGURE 8.1
Density histogram of $\bar{x}$ values from the 50 random samples of Example 8.1.

The density histogram in Figure 8.1 visually conveys information about the sampling variability in the statistic $\bar{x}$. It provides an approximation to the distribution of $\bar{x}$ values that would have been observed if we had considered every different possible sample of size 5 from this population.

In the example just considered, we obtained the approximate sampling distribution of the statistic $\bar{x}$ by considering just 50 different samples. The actual sampling distribution comes from considering *all* possible samples of size n.

DEFINITION

The distribution that would be formed by considering the value of a sample statistic for every possible different sample of a given size from a population is called its **sampling distribution.**

AP* EXAM TIP

It is important to know the properties of sampling distributions of statistics like the sample mean and the sample proportion. But it is also important to understand what a sampling distribution is and what it tells us about the behavior of a sample statistic—this is a fundamental idea in statistical inference.

The sampling distribution of a statistic, such as $\bar{x}$, provides important information about variation in the values of the statistic and how this variation relates to the values of various population characteristics. The density histogram of Figure 8.1 is an *approximation* of the sampling distribution of the statistic $\bar{x}$ for samples of size 5 from the population described in Example 8.1. We could have determined the true sampling distribution of $\bar{x}$ by considering every possible different sample of size 5 from the population of 20 students, computing the mean for each sample, and then constructing a density histogram of the $\bar{x}$ values, but this would have been a lot of work—there are 15,504 different possible samples of size 5. And, for more realistic situations with larger population and sample sizes, the situation becomes even worse because there are so many possible samples that must be considered. Fortunately, as we look at a few more examples in the sections that follow, patterns emerge that enable us to describe some important aspects of the sampling distributions for some statistics without actually having to look at all possible samples.

EXERCISES 8.1 - 8.9

8.1 Explain the difference between a population characteristic and a statistic.

8.2 What is the difference between $\bar{x}$ and μ? between s and σ?

8.3 ✦ For each of the following statements, identify the number that appears in boldface type as the value of either a population characteristic or a statistic:

a. A department store reports that **84%** of all customers who use the store's credit plan pay their bills on time.

b. A sample of 100 students at a large university had a mean age of **24.1** years.

c. The Department of Motor Vehicles reports that **22%** of all vehicles registered in a particular state are imports.

d. A hospital reports that based on the 10 most recent cases, the mean length of stay for surgical patients is **6.4** days.

e. A consumer group, after testing 100 batteries of a certain brand, reported an average life of **63** hours of use.

8.4 Consider a population consisting of the following five values, which represent the number of DVD rentals during the academic year for each of five housemates:

8 14 16 10 11

a. Compute the mean of this population.

b. Select a random sample of size 2 by writing the five numbers in this population on slips of paper, mixing them, and then selecting two. Compute the mean of your sample.

c. Repeatedly select samples of size 2, and compute the $\bar{x}$ value for each sample until you have the $\bar{x}$ values for 25 samples.

d. Construct a density histogram using the 25 $\bar{x}$ values. Are most of the $\bar{x}$ values near the population mean? Do the $\bar{x}$ values differ a lot from sample to sample, or do they tend to be similar?

8.5 Select 10 additional random samples of size 5 from the population of 20 students given in Example 8.1, and compute the mean amount spent on books for each of the 10 samples. Are the $\bar{x}$ values consistent with the results of the sampling experiment summarized in Figure 8.1?

8.6 Suppose that the sampling experiment described in Example 8.1 had used samples of size 10 rather than size 5. If 50 samples of size 10 were selected, the $\bar{x}$ value for each sample computed, and a density histogram constructed, how do you think this histogram would differ from the density histogram constructed for samples of size 5 (Figure 8.1)? In what way would it be similar?

8.7 ✦ Consider the following population: {1, 2, 3, 4}. Note that the population mean is

$$\mu = \frac{1 + 2 + 3 + 4}{4} = 2.5$$

a. Suppose that a random sample of size 2 is to be selected without replacement from this population. There are 12 possible samples (provided that the order in which observations are selected is taken into account):

1, 2	1, 3	1, 4	2, 1	2, 3	2, 4
3, 1	3, 2	3, 4	4, 1	4, 2	4, 3

Compute the sample mean for each of the 12 possible samples. Use this information to construct the sampling distribution of $\bar{x}$. (Display the sampling distribution as a density histogram.)

b. Suppose that a random sample of size 2 is to be selected, but this time sampling will be done with replacement. Using a method similar to that of Part (a), construct the sampling distribution of $\bar{x}$. (Hint: There are 16 different possible samples in this case.)

c. In what ways are the two sampling distributions of Parts (a) and (b) similar? In what ways are they different?

8.8 Simulate sampling from the population of Exercise 8.7 by using four slips of paper individually marked 1, 2, 3, and 4. Select a sample of size 2 without replacement, and compute $\bar{x}$. Repeat this process 50 times, and construct a density histogram of the 50 $\bar{x}$ values. How does this sampling distribution compare to the sampling distribution of $\bar{x}$ derived in Exercise 8.7, Part (a)?

8.9 Consider the following population: {2, 3, 3, 4, 4}. The value of μ is 3.2, but suppose that this is not known to an investigator, who therefore wants to estimate μ from sample data. Three possible statistics for estimating μ are

Statistic 1: the sample mean, $\bar{x}$
Statistic 2: the sample median
Statistic 3: the average of the largest and the smallest values in the sample

A random sample of size 3 will be selected without replacement. Provided that we disregard the order in which the observations are selected, there are 10 possible samples that might result (writing 3 and 3*, 4 and 4* to distinguish the two 3's and the two 4's in the population):

2, 3, 3*	2, 3, 4	2, 3, 4*	2, 3*, 4	2, 3*, 4*
2, 4, 4*	3, 3*, 4	3, 3*, 4*	3, 4, 4*	3*, 4, 4*

For each of these 10 samples, compute Statistics 1, 2, and 3. Construct the sampling distribution of each of these statistics. Which statistic would you recommend for estimating μ and why?

8.2 The Sampling Distribution of a Sample Mean

When the objective of a statistical investigation is to make an inference about the population mean μ, it is natural to consider the sample mean $\bar{x}$ as an estimate of μ. To understand how inferential procedures based on $\bar{x}$ work, we must first study how sampling variability causes $\bar{x}$ to vary in value from one sample to another. The behavior of $\bar{x}$ is described by its sampling distribution. The sample size n and characteristics of the population—its shape, mean value μ, and standard deviation σ—are important in determining properties of the sampling distribution of $\bar{x}$.

It is helpful first to consider the results of some sampling experiments. In Examples 8.2 and 8.3, we start with a specified x population distribution, fix a sample size n, and select 500 different random samples of this size. We then compute $\bar{x}$ for each sample and construct a sample histogram of these 500 $\bar{x}$ values. Because 500 is reasonably large (a reasonably long sequence of samples), the histogram of the $\bar{x}$ values should closely resemble the true sampling distribution of $\bar{x}$ (which would be obtained from an unending sequence of $\bar{x}$ values). We repeat the experiment for several different values of n to see how the choice of sample size affects the sampling distribution. We will be able to identify some patterns that will be helpful in understanding important properties of the sampling distribution of $\bar{x}$.

EXAMPLE 8.2 Blood Platelet Volume

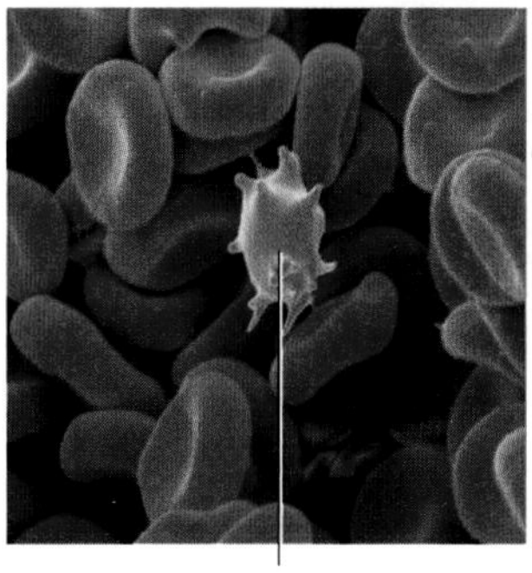

The paper "Mean Platelet Volume in Patients with Metabolic Syndrome and its Relationship with Coronary Artery Disease" (*Thrombosis Research* [2007]: 245–250) includes data that suggests that the distribution of platelet volume for patients who do not have metabolic syndrome (a combination of factors that indicates a high risk of heart disease) is approximately normal with mean $\mu = 8.25$ and standard deviation $\sigma = 0.75$.

Figure 8.2 shows a normal curve centered at 8.25, the mean value of platelet volume. The value of the population standard deviation, 0.75, determines the extent to which the x distribution spreads out about its mean value.

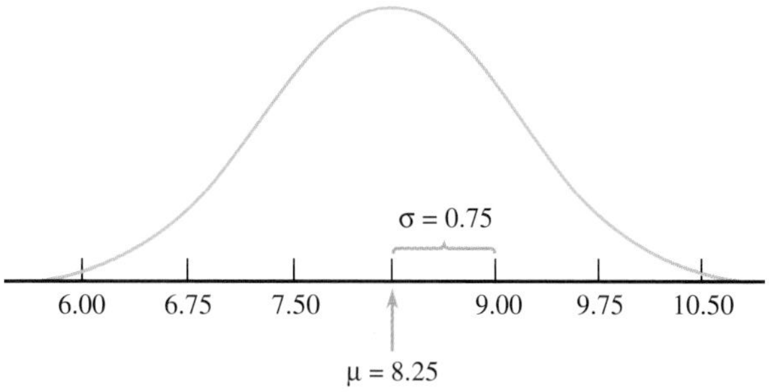

FIGURE 8.2
Normal distribution of platelet size x with $\mu = 8.25$ and $\sigma = 0.75$ for Example 8.2.

We first used Minitab to select 500 random samples from this normal distribution, with each sample consisting of $n = 5$ observations. A density histogram of the resulting 500 $\bar{x}$ values appears in Figure 8.3(a). This procedure was repeated for samples of size $n = 10$, $n = 20$, and $n = 30$. The resulting density histograms of the $\bar{x}$ values are displayed in Figure 8.3(b)–(d).

The first thing to notice about the histograms is their shape. Each of the four histograms is approximately normal in shape. The resemblance would be even more striking if each histogram had been based on many more than 500 $\bar{x}$ values. Second, notice that each histogram is centered approximately at 8.25, the mean of the population being sampled. Had the histograms been based on an unending sequence of values, their centers would have been exactly the population mean, 8.25.

The final aspect of the histograms to note is their spread relative to one another. The smaller the value of n, the greater the extent to which the sampling distribution spreads out about the population mean value. This is why the histograms for $n = 20$ and $n = 30$ are based on narrower class intervals than those for the two smaller sample sizes. For the larger sample sizes, most of the $\bar{x}$ values are quite close to 8.25. This is the effect of averaging. When n is small, a single unusual x value can result in an $\bar{x}$ value far from the center. With a larger sample size, any unusual x values, when averaged with the other sample values, still tend to yield an

$\bar{x}$ value close to μ. Combining these insights yields a result that should appeal to your intuition: *$\bar{x}$ based on a large sample size will tend to be closer to μ* than *$\bar{x}$ based on a small sample size.*

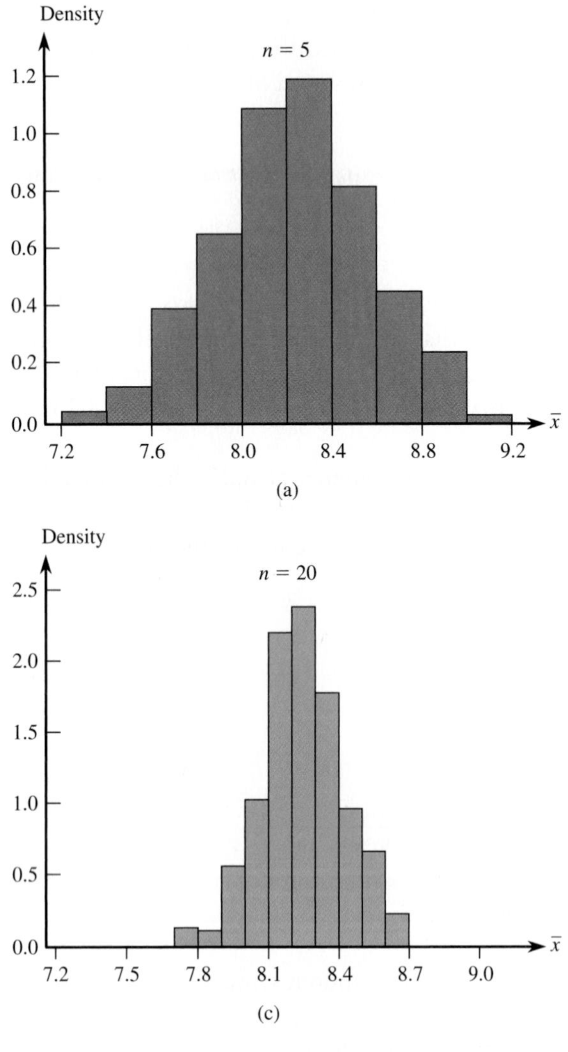

FIGURE 8.3
Density histograms for $\bar{x}$ based on 500 samples, each consisting of n observations, for Example 8.2: (a) $n = 5$; (b) $n = 10$; (c) $n = 20$; (d) $n = 30$.

EXAMPLE 8.3 Time to First Goal in Hockey

Now consider properties of the $\bar{x}$ distribution when the population is quite skewed (and thus very unlike a normal distribution). The paper "Is the Overtime Period in an NHL Game Long Enough?" (*American Statistician* [2008]: 151–154) gave data on the time (in minutes) from the start of the game to the first goal scored for the 281 regular season games from the 2005–2006 season that went into overtime. Figure 8.4 displays a density histogram of the data (read from a graph that appeared in the paper). The histogram has a long upper tail, indicating that the first goal is scored in the

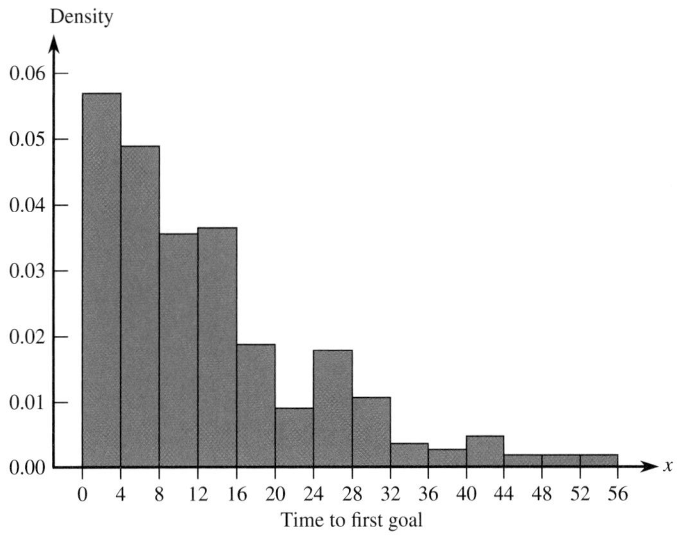

FIGURE 8.4
The population distribution for Example 8.3 ($\mu = 13$).

first 20 minutes of most games, but that for some games, the first goal is not scored until much later in the game.

If we think of the 281 values as a population, the histogram in Figure 8.4 shows the distribution of values in that population. The skewed shape makes identification of the mean value from the picture more difficult than for a normal distribution, but we computed the average of the 281 values to be $\mu = 13$ minutes. The median value for the population (10 minutes) is less than μ, a consequence of the fact that the distribution is positively skewed.

For each of the sample sizes $n = 5$, 10, 20, and 30, we selected 500 random samples of size n. This was done with replacement to approximate more nearly the usual situation, in which the sample size n is only a small fraction of the population size. We then constructed a histogram of the 500 $\bar{x}$ values for each of the four sample sizes. These histograms are displayed in Figure 8.5.

As with samples from a normal population, the averages of the 500 $\bar{x}$ values for the four different sample sizes are all close to the population mean $\mu = 13$. If each histogram had been based on an unending sequence of sample means rather than just 500 of them, each one would have been centered at exactly 13. Comparison of the four $\bar{x}$ histograms in Figure 8.5 also shows that as n increases, the histogram's spread about its center decreases. This was also true of increasing sample sizes from a normal population: $\bar{x}$ is less variable (varies less from sample to sample) for a large sample size than it is for a small sample size.

One aspect of these histograms distinguishes them from the distribution of $\bar{x}$ based on a sample from a normal population. They are skewed and differ in shape more, but they become progressively more symmetric as the sample size increases. We can also see that for $n = 30$, the histogram has a shape much like a normal curve. Again this is the effect of averaging. Even when n is large, one of the few large x values in the population doesn't appear in the sample very often. When one does appear, its contribution to $\bar{x}$ is swamped by the contributions of more typical sample values. The normal shape of the histogram for $n = 30$ is what is predicted by the Central Limit Theorem, which will be introduced shortly. According to this theorem, even if the population distribution is not well described by a normal curve, the $\bar{x}$ sampling distribution is approximately normal in shape when the sample size n is reasonably large.

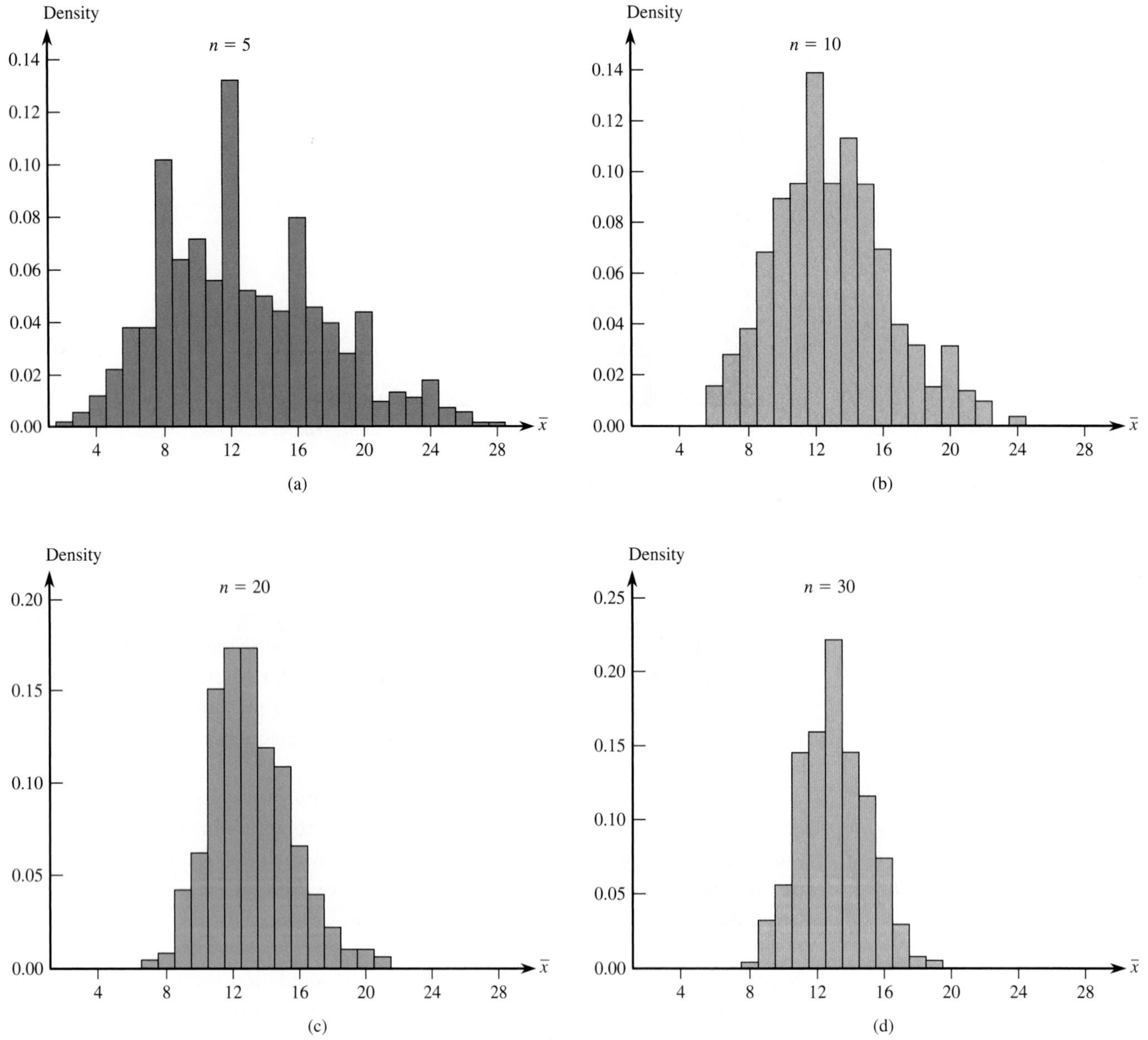

FIGURE 8.5
Four histograms of 500 $\bar{x}$ values for Example 8.3: (a) $n = 5$; (b) $n = 10$; (c) $n = 20$; (d) $n = 30$.

General Properties of the Sampling Distribution of $\bar{x}$

Examples 8.2 and 8.3 suggest that for any n, the center of the $\bar{x}$ distribution (the mean value of $\bar{x}$) coincides with the mean of the population being sampled and that the spread of the $\bar{x}$ distribution decreases as n increases, indicating that the standard deviation of $\bar{x}$ is smaller for large n than for small n. The histograms in Figures 8.3 and 8.5 also suggest that in some cases, the $\bar{x}$ distribution is approximately normal in shape. These observations are stated more formally in the following general rules.

General Properties of the Sampling Distribution of $\bar{x}$

Let $\bar{x}$ denote the mean of the observations in a random sample of size n from a population having mean μ and standard deviation σ. Denote the mean value of the $\bar{x}$ distribution by $\mu_{\bar{x}}$ and the standard deviation of the $\bar{x}$ distribution by $\sigma_{\bar{x}}$. Then the following rules hold:

Rule 1. $\mu_{\bar{x}} = \mu$.

Rule 2. $\sigma_{\bar{x}} = \dfrac{\sigma}{\sqrt{n}}$. This rule is exact if the population is infinite, and is approximately correct if the population is finite and no more than 10% of the population is included in the sample.

Rule 3. When the population distribution is normal, the sampling distribution of $\bar{x}$ is also normal for any sample size n.

Rule 4. (Central Limit Theorem) When n is sufficiently large, the sampling distribution of $\bar{x}$ is well approximated by a normal curve, even when the population distribution is not itself normal.

AP* EXAM TIP

Notice that the important characteristics of the sampling distribution are the same things that were important for data distributions: center, shape, and spread.

Rule 1, $\mu_{\bar{x}} = \mu$, states that the sampling distribution of $\bar{x}$ is always centered at the mean of the population sampled. Rule 2, $\sigma_{\bar{x}} = \dfrac{\sigma}{\sqrt{n}}$, not only states that the spread of the sampling distribution of $\bar{x}$ decreases as n increases, but also gives a precise relationship between the standard deviation of the $\bar{x}$ distribution and the population standard deviation and sample size. When $n = 4$, for example,

$$\sigma_{\bar{x}} = \frac{\sigma}{\sqrt{n}} = \frac{\sigma}{\sqrt{4}} = \frac{\sigma}{2}$$

so the $\bar{x}$ distribution has a standard deviation only half as large as the population standard deviation. Rules 3 and 4 specify circumstances under which the $\bar{x}$ distribution is normal (when the population is normal) or approximately normal (when the sample size is large). Figure 8.6 illustrates these rules by showing several $\bar{x}$ distributions superimposed over a graph of the population distribution.

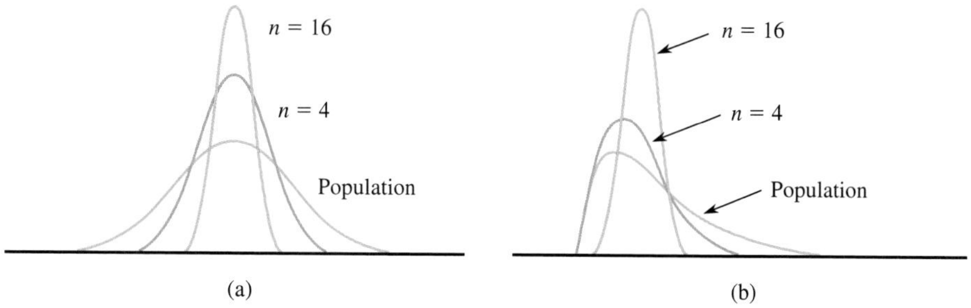

FIGURE 8.6
Population distribution and sampling distributions of $\bar{x}$: (a) symmetric population; (b) skewed population.

The Central Limit Theorem of Rule 4 states that when n is sufficiently large, the $\bar{x}$ distribution is approximately normal, no matter what the population distribution looks like. This result has enabled statisticians to develop procedures for making inferences about a population mean μ using a large sample, even when the shape of the population distribution is unknown.

Recall that a variable is standardized by subtracting the mean value and then dividing by its standard deviation. Using Rules 1 and 2 to standardize $\bar{x}$ gives an important consequence of the last two rules.

If n is large or the population distribution is normal, the standardized variable

$$z = \frac{\bar{x} - \mu_{\bar{x}}}{\sigma_{\bar{x}}} = \frac{\bar{x} - \mu}{\dfrac{\sigma}{\sqrt{n}}}$$

has (at least approximately) a standard normal (z) distribution.

Application of the Central Limit Theorem in specific situations requires a rule of thumb for deciding when n is sufficiently large. Such a rule is not as easy to come by as one might think. Look back at Figure 8.5, which shows the approximate sampling distribution of $\bar{x}$ for $n = 5$, 10, 20, and 30 when the population distribution is quite skewed. Certainly the histogram for $n = 5$ is not well described by a normal curve, and this is still true of the histogram for $n = 10$, particularly in the tails of the histogram (far away from the mean value). Among the four histograms, only the histogram for $n = 30$ has a reasonably normal shape.

On the other hand, when the population distribution is normal, the sampling distribution of $\bar{x}$ is normal for any n. If the population distribution is somewhat skewed but not to the extent of Figure 8.4, we might expect the $\bar{x}$ sampling distribution to be a bit skewed for $n = 5$ but quite well fit by a normal curve for n as small as 10 or 15. How large an n is needed for the $\bar{x}$ distribution to approximate a normal curve depends on how much the population distribution differs from a normal distribution. The closer the population distribution is to being normal, the smaller the value of n necessary for the Central Limit Theorem approximation to be accurate.

Many statisticians recommend the following conservative rule:

The Central Limit Theorem can safely be applied if n is greater than or equal to 30.

If the population distribution is believed to be reasonably close to a normal distribution, an n of 15 or 20 is often large enough for $\bar{x}$ to have approximately a normal distribution. At the other extreme, we can imagine a distribution with a much longer tail than that of Figure 8.4, in which case even $n = 40$ or 50 would not suffice for approximate normality of $\bar{x}$. In practice, however, a sample size of 30 or more is usually sufficient.

EXAMPLE 8.4 Courting Scorpion Flies

The authors of the paper "Should I Stay or Should I Go? Condition- and Status-Dependent Courtship Decisions in the Scorpion Fly *Panorpa Cognate*" (*Animal Behaviour* [2009]: 491–497) studied the courtship behavior of mating scorpion flies. One variable of interest was x = courtship time, which was defined as the time from the beginning of a female-male interaction until mating. Data from the paper suggests that it is reasonable to think that the mean and standard deviation of x are

$\mu = 117.1$ minutes and $\sigma = 109.1$ minutes. Note that the distribution of courtship times cannot be normal because for a normal distribution centered at 117.1 and with such a large standard deviation, it would not be uncommon to observe negative values, but courtship time can't have a negative value.

The sampling distribution of $\bar{x}$ = mean courtship time for a random sample of 20 scorpion fly mating pairs would have mean

$$\mu_{\bar{x}} = \mu = 117.1 \text{ minutes}$$

So the sampling distribution is centered at 117.1. The standard deviation of $\bar{x}$ is

$$\sigma_{\bar{x}} = \frac{\sigma}{\sqrt{n}} = \frac{109.1}{\sqrt{20}} = 24.40$$

which is smaller than the population standard deviation σ. Because the population distribution in not normal and because the sample size is smaller than 30, we cannot assume that the sampling distribution of $\bar{x}$ is approximately normal in shape.

EXAMPLE 8.5 Soda Volumes

A soft-drink bottler claims that, on average, cans contain 12 ounces of soda. Let x denote the actual volume of soda in a randomly selected can. Suppose that x is normally distributed with $\sigma = 0.16$ ounces. Sixteen cans are to be selected, and the soda volume will be determined for each one. Let $\bar{x}$ denote the resulting sample mean soda volume. Because the x distribution is normal, the sampling distribution of $\bar{x}$ is also normal. *If the bottler's claim is correct,* the sampling distribution of $\bar{x}$ has a mean value of $\mu_{\bar{x}} = \mu = 12$ and a standard deviation of

$$\sigma_{\bar{x}} = \frac{\sigma}{\sqrt{n}} = \frac{.16}{\sqrt{16}} = .04$$

To calculate a probability involving $\bar{x}$, we standardize by subtracting the mean value, 12, and dividing by the standard deviation (of $\bar{x}$), which is 0.04. For example, the probability that the sample mean soda volume is between 11.96 ounces and 12.08 ounces is the area between 11.96 and 12.08 under the normal curve with mean 12 and standard deviation 0.04, as shown in the following figure.

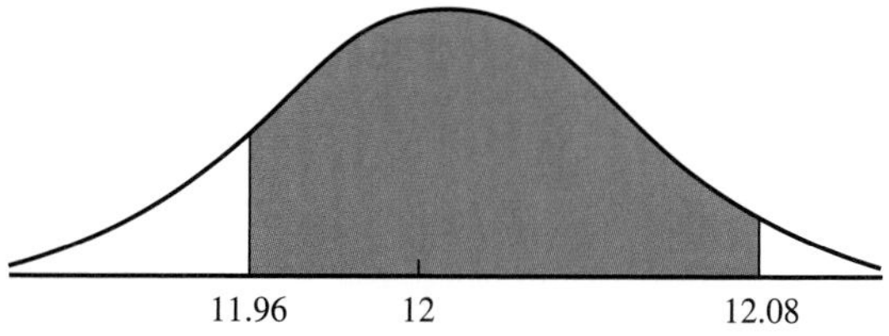

This area is calculated by first standardizing the interval limits:

$$\text{Lower limit: } a^* = \frac{11.96 - 12}{.04} = -1.0$$

$$\text{Upper limit: } b^* = \frac{12.08 - 12}{.04} = 2.0$$

Then (using Appendix Table 2)

$$\begin{aligned} P(11.96 \le \bar{x} \le 12.08) &= \text{area under the } z \text{ curve between } -1.0 \text{ and } 2.0 \\ &= (\text{area to the left of } 2.0) - (\text{area to the left of } -1.0) \\ &= .9772 - .1587 \\ &= .8185 \end{aligned}$$

The probability that the sample mean soda volume is at most 11.9 ounces is

$$\begin{aligned} P(\bar{x} \le 11.9) &= P\left(z \le \frac{11.9 - 12}{.04} = -2.5\right) \\ &= (\text{area under the } z \text{ curve to the left of } -2.5) = .0062 \end{aligned}$$

If the x distribution is as described and the bottler's claim is correct, a sample mean soda volume based on 16 observations is less than 11.9 ounces for fewer than 1% of all such samples. Thus, observation of an $\bar{x}$ value that is smaller than 11.9 ounces would cast doubt on the bottler's claim that the average soda volume is 12 ounces.

EXAMPLE 8.6 Fat Content of Hot Dogs

A hot dog manufacturer asserts that one of its brands of hot dogs has an average fat content of $\mu = 18$ grams per hot dog. Consumers of this brand would probably not be disturbed if the mean is less than 18 but would be unhappy if it exceeds 18. Let x denote the fat content of a randomly selected hot dog, and suppose that σ, the standard deviation of the x distribution, is 1.

An independent testing organization is asked to analyze a random sample of 36 hot dogs. Let $\bar{x}$ be the average fat content for this sample. The sample size, $n = 36$, is large enough to rely on the Central Limit Theorem and to regard the $\bar{x}$ distribution as approximately normal. The standard deviation of the $\bar{x}$ distribution is

$$\sigma_{\bar{x}} = \frac{\sigma}{\sqrt{n}} = \frac{1}{\sqrt{36}} = .1667$$

If the manufacturer's claim is correct, we know that $\mu_{\bar{x}} = \mu = 18$ grams. Suppose that the sample resulted in a mean of $\bar{x} = 18.4$ grams. Does this result suggest that the manufacturer's claim is incorrect?

We can answer this question by looking at the sampling distribution of $\bar{x}$. Because of sampling variability, even if $\mu = 18$, we know that $\bar{x}$ will not usually be exactly 18. But, is it likely that we would see a sample mean at least as large as 18.4 when the population mean is really 18? *If the company's claim is correct,*

$$\begin{aligned} P(\bar{x} \ge 18.4) &\approx P\left(z \ge \frac{18.4 - 18}{.1667}\right) \\ &= P(z \ge 2.4) \\ &= \text{area under the } z \text{ curve to the right of } 2.4 \\ &= 1 - .9918 = .0082 \end{aligned}$$

Values of $\bar{x}$ at least as large as 18.4 will be observed only about 0.82% of the time when a random sample of size 36 is taken from a population with mean 18 and standard deviation 1. The value $\bar{x} = 18.4$ is enough greater than 18 that we would question the manufacturer's claim.

Other Cases

We now know a great deal about the sampling distribution of $\bar{x}$ in two cases: for a normal population distribution and for a large sample size. What happens when the population distribution is not normal and n is small? Although it is still true that $\mu_{\bar{x}} = \mu$ and $\sigma_{\bar{x}} = \frac{\sigma}{\sqrt{n}}$, unfortunately there is no general result about the shape of the distribution. When the objective is to make an inference about the center of such a population, one way to proceed is to make an assumption about the shape of the distribution. Statisticians have proposed and studied a number of such models. Theoretical methods or simulation can be used to describe the $\bar{x}$ distribution corresponding to the assumed model. An alternative strategy is to use one of the transformations presented in Chapter 7 to create a data set that more closely resembles a sample from a normal population and then to base inferences on the transformed data. Yet another path is to use an inferential procedure based on a statistic other than $\bar{x}$. Consult a statistician or a more advanced text for more information.

EXERCISES 8.10 - 8.22

8.10 A random sample is selected from a population with mean $\mu = 100$ and standard deviation $\sigma = 10$. Determine the mean and standard deviation of the $\bar{x}$ sampling distribution for each of the following sample sizes:

a. $n = 9$
b. $n = 15$
c. $n = 36$
d. $n = 50$
e. $n = 100$
f. $n = 400$

8.11 For which of the sample sizes given in Exercise 8.10 would it be reasonable to think that the $\bar{x}$ sampling distribution is approximately normal in shape?

8.12 Explain the difference between σ and $\sigma_{\bar{x}}$ and between μ and $\mu_{\bar{x}}$.

8.13 ✦ Suppose that a random sample of size 64 is to be selected from a population with mean 40 and standard deviation 5.

a. What are the mean and standard deviation of the $\bar{x}$ sampling distribution? Describe the shape of the $\bar{x}$ sampling distribution.

b. What is the approximate probability that $\bar{x}$ will be within 0.5 of the population mean μ?

c. What is the approximate probability that $\bar{x}$ will differ from μ by more than 0.7?

8.14 The time that a randomly selected individual waits for an elevator in an office building has a uniform distribution over the interval from 0 to 1 minute. For this distribution $\mu = 0.5$ and $\sigma = 0.289$.

a. Let $\bar{x}$ be the sample mean waiting time for a random sample of 16 individuals. What are the mean and standard deviation of the sampling distribution of $\bar{x}$?

b. Answer Part (a) for a random sample of 50 individuals. Draw a picture of a good approximation to the sampling distribution of $\bar{x}$ when $n = 50$.

8.15 Let x denote the time (in minutes) that it takes a fifth-grade student to read a certain passage. Suppose that the mean value and standard deviation of x are $\mu =$ 2 minutes and $\sigma = 0.8$ minute, respectively.

a. If $\bar{x}$ is the sample mean time for a random sample of $n = 9$ students, where is the $\bar{x}$ distribution centered, and how much does it spread out about the center (as described by its standard deviation)?

b. Repeat Part (a) for a sample of size of $n = 20$ and again for a sample of size $n = 100$. How do the centers and spreads of the three $\bar{x}$ distributions compare to one another? Which sample size would be most likely to result in an $\bar{x}$ value close to μ, and why?

8.16 In the library on a university campus, there is a sign in the elevator that indicates a limit of 16 persons. In addition, there is a weight limit of 2500 pounds. Assume that the average weight of students, faculty, and staff on campus is 150 pounds, that the standard deviation is 27 pounds, and that the distribution of weights of individuals on campus is approximately normal. If a random sample of 16 persons from the campus is to be taken:

a. What is the expected value of the distribution of the sample mean weight?
b. What is the standard deviation of the sampling distribution of the sample mean weight?
c. What average weights for a sample of 16 people will result in the total weight exceeding the weight limit of 2500 pounds?
d. What is the chance that a random sample of 16 people will exceed the weight limit?

8.17 Suppose that the mean value of interpupillary distance (the distance between the pupils of the left and right eyes) for adult males is 65 mm and that the population standard deviation is 5 mm.

a. If the distribution of interpupillary distance is normal and a random sample of $n = 25$ adult males is to be selected, what is the probability that the sample mean distance $\bar{x}$ for these 25 will be between 64 and 67 mm? at least 68 mm?
b. Suppose that a random sample of 100 adult males is to be obtained. Without assuming that interpupillary distance is normally distributed, what is the approximate probability that the sample mean distance will be between 64 and 67 mm? at least 68 mm?

8.18 Suppose that a sample of size 100 is to be drawn from a population with standard deviation 10.

a. What is the probability that the sample mean will be within 1 of the value of μ?
b. For this example ($n = 100$, $\sigma = 10$), complete each of the following statements by computing the appropriate value:
  i. Approximately 95% of the time, $\bar{x}$ will be within _____ of μ.
  ii. Approximately 0.3% of the time, $\bar{x}$ will be farther than _____ from μ.

8.19 A manufacturing process is designed to produce bolts with a 0.5-inch diameter. Once each day, a random sample of 36 bolts is selected and the bolt diameters are recorded. If the resulting sample mean is less than 0.49 inches or greater than 0.51 inches, the process is shut down for adjustment. The standard deviation for diameter is 0.02 inches. What is the probability that the manufacturing line will be shut down unnecessarily? (Hint: Find the probability of observing an $\bar{x}$ in the shutdown range when the true process mean really is 0.5 inches.)

8.20 College students with checking accounts typically write relatively few checks in any given month, whereas nonstudent residents typically write many more checks during a month. Suppose that 50% of a bank's accounts are held by students and that 50% are held by nonstudent residents. Let x denote the number of checks written in a given month by a randomly selected bank customer.

a. Give a sketch of what the probability distribution of x might look like.
b. Suppose that the mean value of x is 22.0 and that the standard deviation is 16.5. If a random sample of $n = 100$ customers is to be selected and $\bar{x}$ denotes the sample average number of checks written during a particular month, where is the sampling distribution of $\bar{x}$ centered, and what is the standard deviation of the $\bar{x}$ distribution? Sketch a rough picture of the sampling distribution.
c. Referring to Part (b), what is the approximate probability that $\bar{x}$ is at most 20? at least 25?

8.21 ✦ An airplane with room for 100 passengers has a total baggage limit of 6000 pounds. Suppose that the total weight of the baggage checked by an individual passenger is a random variable x with a mean value of 50 pounds and a standard deviation of 20 pounds. If 100 passengers will board a flight, what is the approximate probability that the total weight of their baggage will exceed the limit? (Hint: With $n = 100$, the total weight exceeds the limit when the average weight $\bar{x}$ exceeds 6000/100.)

8.22 The thickness (in millimeters) of the coating applied to disk drives is one characteristic that determines the usefulness of the product. When no unusual circumstances are present, the thickness (x) has a normal distribution with a mean of 2 mm and a standard deviation of 0.05 mm. Suppose that the process will be monitored by selecting a random sample of 16 drives from each shift's production and determining $\bar{x}$, the mean coating thickness for the sample.

a. Describe the sampling distribution of $\bar{x}$ (for a sample of size 16).
b. When no unusual circumstances are present, we expect $\bar{x}$ to be within $3\sigma_{\bar{x}}$ of 2 mm, the desired value. An $\bar{x}$ value farther from 2 than $3\sigma_{\bar{x}}$ is interpreted as an indication of a problem that needs attention. Compute $2 \pm 3\sigma_{\bar{x}}$. (A plot over time of $\bar{x}$ values with horizontal lines drawn at the limits $\mu \pm 3\sigma_{\bar{x}}$ is called a process control chart.)
c. Referring to Part (b), what is the probability that a sample mean will be outside $2 \pm 3\sigma_{\bar{x}}$ just by chance (that is, when there are no unusual circumstances)?

d. Suppose that a machine used to apply the coating is out of adjustment, resulting in a mean coating thickness of 2.05 mm. What is the probability that a problem will be detected when the next sample is taken? (Hint: This will occur if $\bar{x} > 2 + 3\sigma_{\bar{x}}$ or $\bar{x} < 2 - 3\sigma_{\bar{x}}$ when $\mu = 2.05$.)

8.3 The Sampling Distribution of a Sample Proportion

The objective of many statistical investigations is to draw a conclusion about the proportion of individuals or objects in a population that possess a specified property—for example, cell phones that don't require service during the warranty period or coffee drinkers who regularly drink decaffeinated coffee. Traditionally, any individual or object that possesses the property of interest is labeled a success (S), and one that does not possess the property is termed a failure (F). The letter p denotes the proportion of successes in the population. The value of p is a number between 0 and 1, and $100p$ is the percentage of successes in the population. If $p = .75$, 75% of the population members are successes, and if $p = .01$, the population contains only 1% successes and 99% failures.

The value of p is usually unknown to an investigator. When a random sample of size n is selected from this type of population, some of the individuals in the sample are successes, and the rest are failures. The statistic that provides a basis for making inferences about p is $\hat{p}$, the **sample proportion of successes**:

$$\hat{p} = \frac{\text{number of S's in the sample}}{n}$$

For example, if $n = 5$ and three successes result, then $\hat{p} = 3/5 = .6$.

Just as making inferences about μ requires knowing something about the sampling distribution of the statistic $\bar{x}$, making inferences about p requires first learning about properties of the sampling distribution of the statistic $\hat{p}$. For example, when $n = 5$, the six possible values of $\hat{p}$ are 0, .2 (from 1/5), .4, .6, .8, and 1. The sampling distribution of $\hat{p}$ gives the probability of each of these six possible values, the long-run proportion of the time that each value would occur if samples with $n = 5$ were selected over and over again.

As we did for the distribution of the sample mean, we will look at some simulation experiments to develop an intuitive understanding of the distribution of the sample proportion before stating general rules. In each example, 500 random samples (each of size n) are selected from a population having a specified value of p. We compute $\hat{p}$ for each sample and then construct a histogram of the 500 values.

EXAMPLE 8.7 Gender of College Students

In the fall of 2008, there were 18,516 students enrolled at California Polytechnic State University, San Luis Obispo. Of these students, 8091 (43.7%) were female. To illustrate properties of the sampling distribution of a sample proportion, we will simulate sampling from this Cal Poly student population. With S denoting a female student and F a male student, the proportion of S's in the population is $p = .437$.

A statistical software package was used to select 500 samples of size $n = 10$, then 500 samples of size $n = 25$, then 500 samples with $n = 50$, and finally 500 samples with $n = 100$. Histograms of the 500 values of $\hat{p}$ for each of the four sample sizes are displayed in Figure 8.7.

The most noticeable feature of the histogram shapes is the progression toward the shape of a normal curve as n increases. The histogram for $n = 10$ is somewhat skewed. The histograms for $n = 25$, $n = 50$, and $n = 100$ look more symmetric and have a shape that is more like a normal curve.

All four histograms appear to be centered at roughly .437, the value of p for the population sampled. Had the histograms been based on an unending sequence of samples, each histogram would have been centered at exactly .437. Finally, as was the case with the sampling distribution of $\bar{x}$, the histograms spread out more for small sample sizes than for large sample sizes. Not surprisingly, the value of $\hat{p}$ based on a large sample size tends to be closer to p, the population proportion of successes, than does $\hat{p}$ from a small sample.

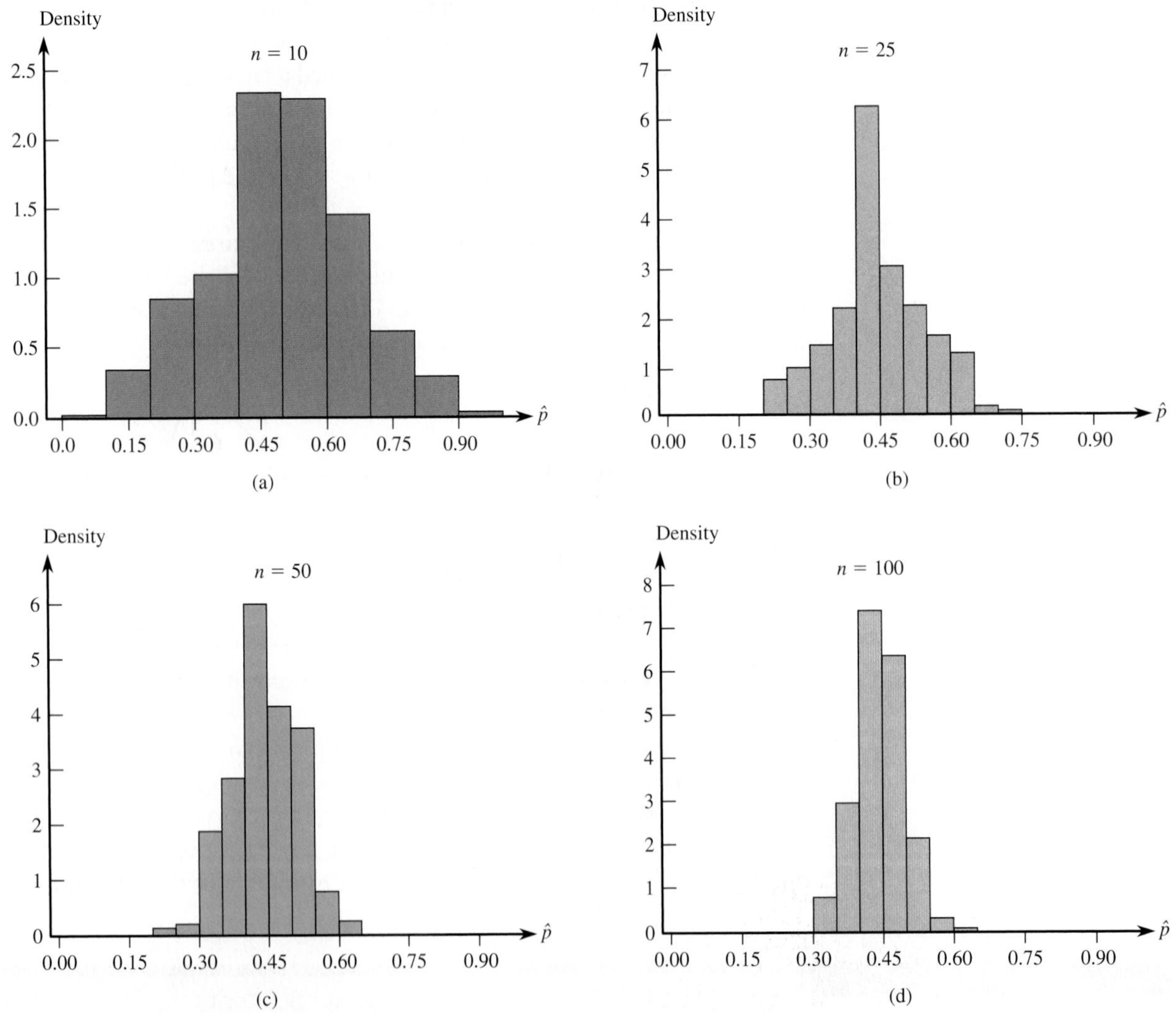

FIGURE 8.7
Histograms for 500 values of $\hat{p}$ ($p = .437$) for Example 8.7: (a) $n = 10$; (b) $n = 25$; (c) $n = 50$; (d) $n = 100$.

EXAMPLE 8.8 Contracting Hepatitis from Blood Transfusion

The development of viral hepatitis after a blood transfusion can cause serious complications for a patient. The article "Lack of Awareness Results in Poor Autologous Blood Transfusion" (*Health Care Management*, May 15, 2003) reported that hepatitis occurs in 7% of patients who receive blood transfusions during heart surgery. Here, we simulate sampling from the population of blood recipients, with S denoting a recipient who contracts hepatitis (not the sort of characteristic one usually thinks of as a success, but the S–F labeling is arbitrary), so $p = .07$. Figure 8.8 displays histograms of 500 values of $\hat{p}$ for the four sample sizes $n = 10$, 25, 50, and 100.

As was the case in Example 8.7, all four histograms are centered at approximately the value of p for the population being sampled. (The average values of $\hat{p}$ for these simulations are .0690, .0677, .0707, and .0694.) If the histograms had been based on an unending sequence of samples, they would all have been centered at exactly $p = .07$. Again, the spread of a histogram based on a large n is smaller than the spread of a histogram resulting from a small sample size. The larger the value of n, the closer the sample proportion $\hat{p}$ tends to be to the value of the population proportion p.

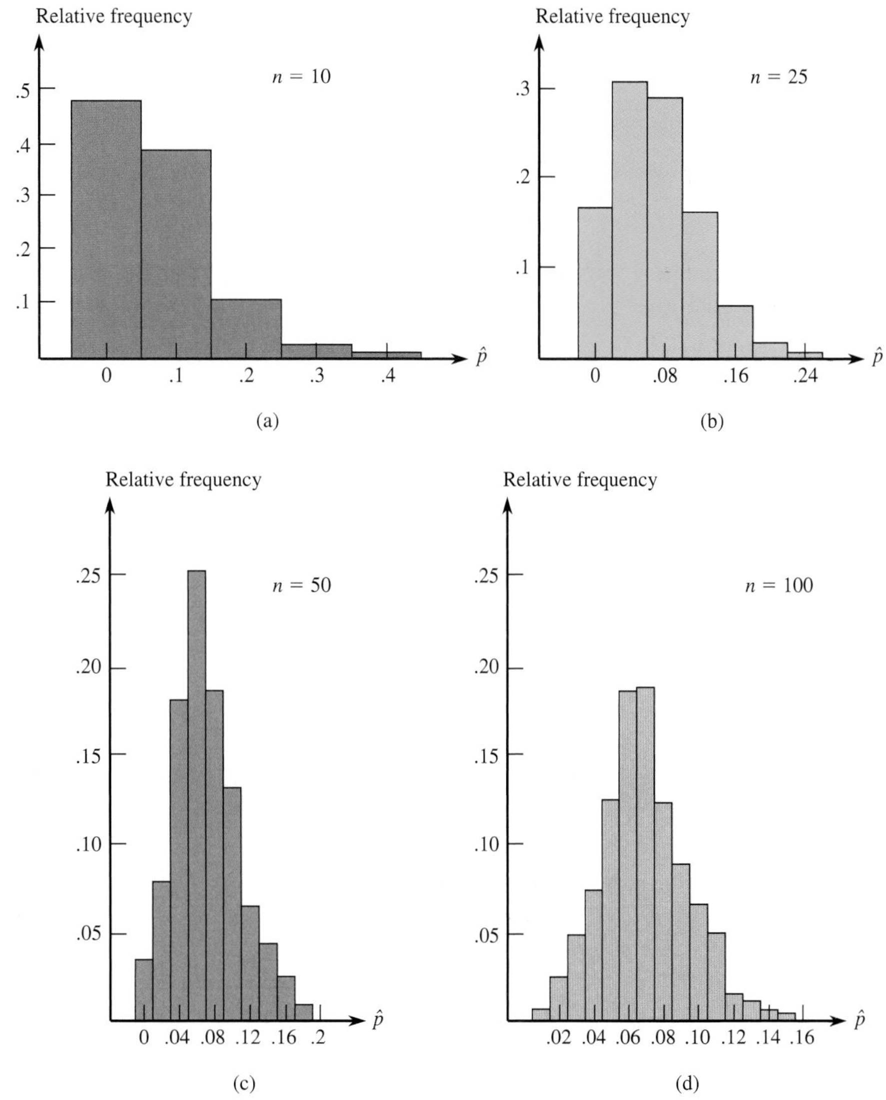

FIGURE 8.8
Histograms of 500 values of $\hat{p}$ ($p = .07$) for Example 8.8: (a) $n = 10$; (b) $n = 25$; (c) $n = 50$; (d) $n = 100$.

Furthermore, there is a progression toward the shape of a normal curve as n increases. However, the progression is much slower here than in the previous example, because the value of p is so extreme. (The same thing would happen for $p = .93$, except that the histograms would be negatively rather than positively skewed.) The histograms for $n = 10$ and $n = 25$ exhibit substantial skew, and the skew of the histogram for $n = 50$ is still moderate (compare Figure 8.8(c) with Figure 8.8(d)). Only the histogram for $n = 100$ is fit reasonably well by a normal curve. It appears that whether a normal curve provides a good approximation to the sampling distribution of $\hat{p}$ depends on the values of both n and p. Knowing only that $n = 50$ is not enough to guarantee that the shape of the histogram is approximately normal.

General Properties of the Sampling Distribution of $\hat{p}$

Examples 8.7 and 8.8 suggest that the sampling distribution of $\hat{p}$ depends on both n, the sample size, and p, the proportion of successes in the population. Key results are stated more formally in the following general rules.

General Properties of the Sampling Distribution of $\hat{p}$

Let $\hat{p}$ be the proportion of successes in a random sample of size n from a population whose proportion of S's is p. Denote the mean value of $\hat{p}$ by $\mu_{\hat{p}}$ and the standard deviation by $\sigma_{\hat{p}}$. Then the following rules hold.

Rule 1. $\mu_{\hat{p}} = p$

Rule 2. $\sigma_{\hat{p}} = \sqrt{\frac{p(1-p)}{n}}$. This rule is exact if the population is infinite, and is approximately correct if the population is finite and no more than 10% of the population is included in the sample.

Rule 3. When n is large and p is not too near 0 or 1, the sampling distribution of $\hat{p}$ is approximately normal.

AP* EXAM TIP

As the famous baseball player and philosopher, Yogi Berra, might say, "Deja-vu all over again!" The important characteristics of the sampling distribution of the sample proportion are center, shape, and spread.

The sampling distribution of $\hat{p}$ is always centered at the value of the population success proportion p, and the extent to which the distribution spreads out about p decreases as the sample size n increases.

Examples 8.7 and 8.8 indicate that both p and n must be considered in judging whether the sampling distribution of $\hat{p}$ is approximately normal.

The farther the value of p is from .5, the larger n must be for a normal approximation to the sampling distribution of $\hat{p}$ to be accurate. A conservative rule of thumb is that if both $np \geq 10$ and $n(1 - p) \geq 10$, then a normal distribution provides a reasonable approximation to the sampling distribution of $\hat{p}$.

A sample size of $n = 100$ is not by itself sufficient to justify the use of a normal approximation. If $p = .01$, the distribution of $\hat{p}$ is positively skewed even when $n = 100$, so a bell-shaped curve does not give a good approximation. Similarly, if $n = 100$ and $p = .99$ (so that $n(1 - p) = 1 < 10$), the distribution of $\hat{p}$ has a substantial negative skew. The conditions $np \geq 10$ and $n(1 - p) \geq 10$ ensure that the sampling distribution of $\hat{p}$ is not too skewed. If $p = .5$, the normal approximation can be used for n as small as 20, whereas for $p = .05$ or $.95$, n should be at least 200.

EXAMPLE 8.9 Blood Transfusions Continued

The proportion of all cardiac patients receiving blood transfusions who contract hepatitis was given as .07 in the article referenced in Example 8.8. Suppose that a new blood screening procedure is believed to reduce the incidence rate of hepatitis. Blood screened using this procedure is given to $n = 200$ blood recipients. Only 6 of the 200 patients contract hepatitis. This appears to be a favorable result, because $\hat{p} = 6/200 = .03$. The question of interest to medical researchers is, Does this result indicate that the true (long-run) proportion of patients who contract hepatitis when the new screening procedure is used is less than .07, or could this result be plausibly attributed to sampling variability (that is, to the fact that $\hat{p}$ typically differs from the population proportion, p)? *If the screening procedure is not effective and so $p = .07$,*

$$\mu_{\hat{p}} = .07$$

$$\sigma_{\hat{p}} = \sqrt{\frac{p(1-p)}{200}} = \sqrt{\frac{(.07)(.93)}{200}} = .018$$

Furthermore, because

$$np = 200(.07) = 14 \geq 10$$

and

$$n(1 - p) = 200(.93) = 186 \geq 10$$

the sampling distribution of $\hat{p}$ is approximately normal. Then, if the screening procedure is not effective,

$$P(\hat{p} \leq .03) = P\left(z \leq \frac{.03 - .07}{.018}\right) = P(z \leq -2.22) = .0132$$

This small probability tells us that it is unlikely that a sample proportion .03 or smaller would be observed if the screening procedure was ineffective. The new screening procedure appears to yield a smaller incidence rate for hepatitis.

EXERCISES 8.23 - 8.31

8.23 A random sample is to be selected from a population that has a proportion of successes $p = .65$. Determine the mean and standard deviation of the sampling distribution of $\hat{p}$ for each of the following sample sizes:

a. $n = 10$
b. $n = 20$
c. $n = 30$
d. $n = 50$
e. $n = 100$
f. $n = 200$

8.24 For which of the sample sizes given in Exercise 8.23 would the sampling distribution of $\hat{p}$ be approximately normal if $p = .65$? if $p = .2$?

8.25 ✦ The article "Unmarried Couples More Likely to Be Interracial" (*San Luis Obispo Tribune*, March 13, 2002) reported that 7% of married couples in the

United States are mixed racially or ethnically. Consider the population consisting of all married couples in the United States.

a. A random sample of $n = 100$ couples will be selected from this population and $\hat{p}$, the proportion of couples that are mixed racially or ethnically, will be computed. What are the mean and standard deviation of the sampling distribution of $\hat{p}$?

b. Is it reasonable to assume that the sampling distribution of $\hat{p}$ is approximately normal for random samples of size $n = 100$? Explain.

c. Suppose that the sample size is $n = 200$ rather than $n = 100$, as in Part (b). Does the change in sample size change the mean and standard deviation of the sampling distribution of $\hat{p}$? If so, what are the new values for the mean and standard deviation? If not, explain why not.

d. Is it reasonable to assume that the sampling distribution of $\hat{p}$ is approximately normal for random samples of size $n = 200$? Explain.

e. When $n = 200$, what is the probability that the proportion of couples in the sample who are racially or ethnically mixed will be greater than .10?

8.26 The article referenced in Exercise 8.25 reported that for unmarried couples living together, the proportion that are racially or ethnically mixed is .15. Answer the questions posed in Parts (a)–(e) of Exercise 8.25 for the population of unmarried couples living together.

8.27 ✦ A certain chromosome defect occurs in only 1 in 200 adult Caucasian males. A random sample of $n = 100$ adult Caucasian males is to be obtained.

a. What is the mean value of the sample proportion $\hat{p}$, and what is the standard deviation of the sample proportion?

b. Does $\hat{p}$ have approximately a normal distribution in this case? Explain.

c. What is the smallest value of n for which the sampling distribution of $\hat{p}$ is approximately normal?

8.28 The article "Should Pregnant Women Move? Linking Risks for Birth Defects with Proximity to Toxic Waste Sites" (*Chance* [1992]: 40–45) reported that in a large study carried out in the state of New York, approximately 30% of the study subjects lived within 1 mile of a hazardous waste site. Let p denote the proportion of all New York residents who live within 1 mile of such a site, and suppose that $p = .3$.

a. Would $\hat{p}$ based on a random sample of only 10 residents have approximately a normal distribution? Explain why or why not.

b. What are the mean value and standard deviation of $\hat{p}$ based on a random sample of size 400?

c. When $n = 400$, what is $P(.25 \le \hat{p} \le .35)$?

d. Is the probability calculated in Part (c) larger or smaller than would be the case if $n = 500$? Answer without actually calculating this probability.

8.29 The article "Thrillers" (*Newsweek*, April 22, 1985) stated, "Surveys tell us that more than half of America's college graduates are avid readers of mystery novels." Let p denote the actual proportion of college graduates who are avid readers of mystery novels. Consider a sample proportion $\hat{p}$ that is based on a random sample of 225 college graduates.

a. If $p = .5$, what are the mean value and standard deviation of $\hat{p}$? Answer this question for $p = .6$. Does $\hat{p}$ have approximately a normal distribution in both cases? Explain.

b. Calculate $P(\hat{p} \ge .6)$ for both $p = .5$ and $p = .6$.

c. Without doing any calculations, how do you think the probabilities in Part (b) would change if n were 400 rather than 225?

8.30 Suppose that a particular candidate for public office is in fact favored by 48% of all registered voters in the district. A polling organization will take a random sample of 500 voters and will use $\hat{p}$, the sample proportion, to estimate p. What is the approximate probability that $\hat{p}$ will be greater than .5, causing the polling organization to incorrectly predict the result of the upcoming election?

8.31 ✦ A manufacturer of computer printers purchases plastic ink cartridges from a vendor. When a large shipment is received, a random sample of 200 cartridges is selected, and each cartridge is inspected. If the sample proportion of defective cartridges is more than .02, the entire shipment is returned to the vendor.

a. What is the approximate probability that a shipment will be returned if the true proportion of defective cartridges in the shipment is .05?

b. What is the approximate probability that a shipment will not be returned if the true proportion of defective cartridges in the shipment is .10?

ACTIVITY 8.1 Do Students Who Take the SATs Multiple Times Have an Advantage in College Admissions?

Technology activity: Requires use of a computer or a graphing calculator.

Background: The *Chronicle of Higher Education* (January 29, 2003) summarized an article that appeared on the *American Prospect* web site titled "College Try: Why Universities Should Stop Encouraging Applicants to Take the SATs Over and Over Again." This paper argued that current college admission policies that permit applicants to take the SAT exam multiple times and then use the highest score for consideration of admission favor students from families with higher incomes (who can afford to take the exam many times). The author proposed two alternatives that he believes would be fairer than using the highest score: (1) Use the average of all test scores, or (2) use only the most recent score.

In this activity, you will investigate the differences between the three possibilities by looking at the sampling distributions of three statistics for a test taker who takes the exam twice and for a test taker who takes the exam five times. The three statistics are

Max = maximum score
Mean = average score
Recent = most recent score

An individual's score on the SAT exam fluctuates between test administrations. Suppose that a particular student's "true ability" is reflected by an SAT score of 1200 but, because of chance fluctuations, the test score on any particular administration of the exam can be considered a random variable that has a distribution that is approximately normal with mean 1200 and standard deviation 30. If we select a sample from this normal distribution, the resulting set of observations can be viewed as a collection of test scores that might have been obtained by this student.

Part 1: Begin by considering what happens if this student takes the exam twice. You will use simulation to generate samples of two test scores, Score1 and Score2, for this student. Then you will compute the values of Max, Mean, and Recent for each pair of scores. The resulting values of Max, Mean, and Recent will be used to construct approximations to the sampling distributions of the three statistics.

The instructions that follow assume the use of Minitab. If you are using a different software package or a graphing calculator, your instructor will provide alternative instructions.

a. Obtain 500 sets of two test scores by generating observations from a normal distribution with mean 1200 and standard deviation 30.

Minitab: Calc → Random Data → Normal
Enter 500 in the Generate box (to get 500 sets of scores)
Enter C1-C2 in the Store in Columns box (to get two test scores in each set)
Enter 1200 in the Mean box (because we want scores from a normal distribution with mean 1200)
Enter 30 in the Standard Deviation box (because we want scores from a normal distribution with standard deviation 30)
Click on OK

b. Looking at the Minitab worksheet, you should now see 500 rows of values in each of the first two columns. The two values in any particular row can be regarded as the test scores that might be observed when the student takes the test twice. For each pair of test scores, we now calculate the values of Max, Mean, and Recent.

i. Recent is just the last test score, so the values in C2 are the values of Recent. Name this column recent2 by typing the name into the gray box at the top of C2.

ii. Compute the maximum test score (Max) for each pair of scores, and store the values in C3, as follows:

Minitab: Calc → Row statistics
Click the button for maximum
Enter C1-C2 in the Input variables box
Enter C3 in the Store Result In box.
Click on OK

You should now see the maximum value for each pair in C3. Name this column max2.

iii. Compute the average test score (Mean) for each pair of scores, and store the values in C4, as follows:

Minitab: Calc → Row statistics
Click the button for mean
Enter C1-C2 in the Input Variables box
Enter C4 in the Store Result In box.
Click on OK

You should now see the average for each pair in C4. Name this column mean2.

c. Construct density histograms for each of the three statistics (these density histograms approximate the sampling distributions of the three statistics), as follows:

Minitab: Graph → Histogram

Enter max2, mean2, and recent2 into the first three rows of the Graph Variables box

Click on the Options button. Select Density. Click on OK. (This will produce histograms that use the density scale rather than the frequency scale.)

Click on the Frame drop-down menu, and select Multiple Graphs. Select Same X and Same Y. (This will cause Minitab to use the same scales for all three histograms, so that they can be easily compared.)

Click on OK.

Part 2: Now you will produce approximate sampling distributions for these same three statistics, but for the case of a student who takes the exam five times. Follow the same steps as in Part 1, with the following modifications:

a. Obtain 500 sets of five test scores, and store these values in columns C11– C15.

b. Recent will just be the values in C15; name this column recent5. Compute the Max and Mean values, and store them in columns C16 and C17. Name these columns max5 and mean5.

c. Construct density histograms for max5, mean5, and recent5.

Part 3: Now use the approximate sampling distributions constructed in Parts 1 and 2 to answer the following questions.

a. The statistic that is the average of the test scores is just a sample mean (for a sample of size 2 in Part 1 and for a sample of size 5 in Part 2). How do the sampling distributions of mean2 and mean5 compare to what is expected based on the general properties of the $\bar{x}$ distribution given in Section 8.2? Explain.

b. Based on the three distributions from Part 1, for a two-time test taker, describe the advantage of using the maximum score compared to using either the average score or the most recent score.

c. Now consider the approximate sampling distributions of the maximum score for two-time and for five-time test takers. How do these two distributions compare?

d. Does a student who takes the exam five times have a big advantage over a student of equal ability who takes the exam only twice if the maximum score is used for college admission decisions? Explain.

e. If you were writing admission procedures for a selective university, would you recommend using the maximum test score, the average test score, or the most recent test score in making admission decisions? Write a paragraph explaining your choice.

Summary of Key Concepts and Formulas

TERM OR FORMULA	COMMENT
Statistic	Any quantity whose value is computed from sample data.
Sampling distribution	The probability distribution of a statistic: The sampling distribution describes the long-run behavior of the statistic.
Sampling distribution of $\bar{x}$	The probability distribution of the sample mean $\bar{x}$ based on a random sample of size n. Properties of the $\bar{x}$ sampling distribution: $\mu_{\bar{x}} = \mu$ and $\sigma_{\bar{x}} = \frac{\sigma}{\sqrt{n}}$ (where μ and σ are the population mean and standard deviation, respectively). In addition, when the population distribution is normal or the sample size is large, the sampling distribution of $\bar{x}$ is (approximately) normal.
Central Limit Theorem	This important theorem states that when n is sufficiently large, the $\bar{x}$ distribution will be approximately normal. The standard rule of thumb is that the theorem can safely be applied when n is greater than 30.

TERM OR FORMULA	COMMENT
Sampling distribution of $\hat{p}$	The probability distribution of the sample proportion $\hat{p}$, based on a random sample of size n. When the sample size is sufficiently large, the sampling distribution of $\hat{p}$ is approximately normal, with $\mu_{\hat{p}} = p$ and $\sigma_{\hat{p}} = \sqrt{\frac{p(1-p)}{n}}$ where p is the value of the population proportion.

Chapter Review Exercises 8.32 - 8.37

8.32 The nicotine content in a single cigarette of a particular brand has a distribution with mean 0.8 mg and standard deviation 0.1 mg. If 100 of these cigarettes are analyzed, what is the probability that the resulting sample mean nicotine content will be less than 0.79? less than 0.77?

8.33 Let $x_1, x_2, \ldots, x_{100}$ denote the actual net weights (in pounds) of 100 randomly selected bags of fertilizer. Suppose that the weight of a randomly selected bag has a distribution with mean 50 pounds and variance 1 pound^2. Let $\bar{x}$ be the sample mean weight ($n = 100$).

a. Describe the sampling distribution of $\bar{x}$.

b. What is the probability that the sample mean is between 49.75 pounds and 50.25 pounds?

c. What is the probability that the sample mean is less than 50 pounds?

8.34 Suppose that 20% of the subscribers of a cable television company watch the shopping channel at least once a week. The cable company is trying to decide whether to replace this channel with a new local station. A survey of 100 subscribers will be undertaken. The cable company has decided to keep the shopping channel if the sample proportion is greater than .25. What is the approximate probability that the cable company will keep the shopping channel, even though the proportion of all subscribers who watch it is only .20?

8.35 Water permeability of concrete can be measured by letting water flow across the surface and determining the amount lost (in inches per hour). Suppose that the permeability index x for a randomly selected concrete specimen of a particular type is normally distributed with mean value 1000 and standard deviation 150.

a. How likely is it that a single randomly selected specimen will have a permeability index between 850 and 1300?

b. If the permeability index is to be determined for each specimen in a random sample of size 10, how likely is it that the sample mean permeability index will be between 950 and 1100? between 850 and 1300?

8.36 *Newsweek* (November 23, 1992) reported that 40% of all U.S. employees participate in "self-insurance" health plans ($p = .40$).

a. In a random sample of 100 employees, what is the approximate probability that at least half of those in the sample participate in such a plan?

b. Suppose you were told that at least 60 of the 100 employees in a sample from your state participated in such a plan. Would you think $p = .40$ for your state? Explain.

8.37 The amount of money spent by a customer at a discount store has a mean of \$100 and a standard deviation of \$30. What is the probability that a randomly selected group of 50 shoppers will spend a total of more than \$5300? (Hint: The total will be more than \$5300 when the sample mean exceeds what value?)

Graphing Calculator Explorations

EXPLORATION 8.1 Sampling Distribution of the Mean

The characteristics of the sampling distribution of a statistic are important for drawing inferences. Because the sample mean is widely used, its sampling distribution is of particular interest. The Central Limit Theorem guarantees that as long as n is large enough, the sampling distribution of the sample mean is approximately normal even though the parent population may not be normal. The graphing calculator can be used to simulate the process of sampling from a large population.

Although simulations are generally done on a very large scale, we operate on a very small scale in this calculator exploration. Our methods are suitable for performing a small number of trials of a simulation and then combining the results over a whole statistics class. To go further into simulation of sampling distributions would require programming your calculator (more on this later) or using a computer with appropriate software.

The process of selecting a random sample from a very large population is generally modeled in the following manner:

1. Construct a mathematical description—a probability distribution—of the population distribution of interest.
2. Generate a random sample from the specified distribution.
3. Calculate the statistic of interest (here, the sample mean) for the simulated random sample.
4. Repeat Steps 2 and 3 a large number of times.
5. Construct a histogram of the resulting values of the sample statistic.

We illustrate how this might be done using a graphing calculator. First, we need a population to sample from. A convenient population for our purposes here is the uniform distribution from 0 to 1. (This distribution is convenient for the calculator, as it is easy to use the *rand* function to generate the random sample.)

Now we need to sample from this population—that is, to generate random selections from a uniform population distribution. We do this by using the seq command and storing the results in a list, as discussed in Graphing Calculator Exploration 6.4. If you are following along with calculator in hand, you should note a couple of things. First, the number of random numbers you can generate depends on both your calculator's capabilities and the amount of memory your calculator has left to use. For this example we use $n = 500$. If your calculator gives you an error message, try a number smaller than 500 to check that you have the calculator syntax correct. If your calculator works for a small value of n but not a large value, the large value may exceed a maximum list size or you may have already stored many programs, pictures, and/or data in your calculator and may not have enough memory left to handle the requested computation. Second, the seq command *can* take a while to complete. Do not be worried if your calculator's attention seems to have wandered.

Here is a generic statement to generate 500 random numbers and store them in a list:

seq(*rand*, X, 1, 500) → List1

Now that we have generated a sample of size 500, let's check our results by making a histogram. We should see a distribution that mirrors the population—that is, a fairly uniform distribution of results. *It is important to check this by displaying your simulated sampling results!* Verifying these results is the equivalent of checking to see that you have a "right answer so far." Although you should expect some fluctuation

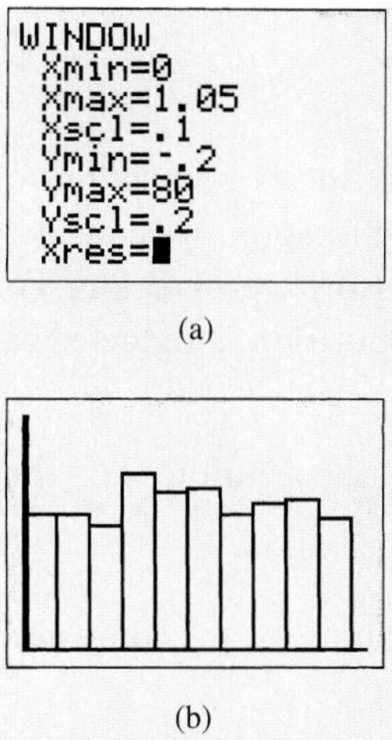

FIGURE 8.9
Displays for Exploration 8.1: (a) edit window; (b) histogram results.

from a perfect match—we are, after all, sampling—you should not get seriously distorted results with an n as large as 500. Our edit window and histogram results are displayed in Figure 8.9. Pay particular attention to the Xmin and Xscl values in Figure 8.9(a). (Recall from an earlier calculator exploration that these values determine the class size for a histogram.) We want to partition the interval from 0 to 1 into 10 equal intervals, and other choices for these values will give you a graph that is difficult to interpret. From Figure 8.9(b), the sample appears to be representative of the population from which we are sampling.

Now we calculate the sample mean of the data in List1. Our result is $\bar{x} = 0.50223$. This sample mean represents *one trial* of our simulation. To do a respectable simulation, we would have to repeat the preceding commands a large number of times. This single mean from our one trial is what we meant earlier by a very small-scale simulation. Even on this small scale, however, combining your results with similar results from your classmates can generate good simulations. Obtaining 10 trials each from 25 students is easily accomplished in a class period, and 250 trials is not to be sneezed at!

We should note that this small-scale restriction of generating sample means one at a time is easily overcome *if* you have someone in your class who knows how to do a little programming on the calculator. It is possible that if you have *no* experience programming a calculator, you could do a simulation. Having spent many frustrating hours programming, we cannot in good conscience suggest that you learn to program your calculator just for simulations. However, if you want to explore simulations on a medium-size scale and if you have someone to help you set up the accompanying program, you could be doing some simulations quickly. As written, the following program performs 500 trials of the simulation we have been discussing, using a sample size of 50. Remember, syntax will vary among calculators, but something close to this program will perform Steps 2, 3, and 4 of the simulation and store the results in List2. Consult your friendly local calculator gurus for details.

```
For (X, 1, 500)
seq(rand, X, 1, 50) → List1
mean(List1) → List2(X)
End
```

In our example, we generated random numbers from a population uniformly distributed from 0 to 1. Sampling distributions of the mean from other populations can also be considered; the populations available are limited only by your random number generation capability. Some populations might be more appropriately modeled as normal or binomial. Some calculators have built-in functions to generate the random values you would get if you were sampling from a normal or binomial population. Here are some other possible sampling simulations:

From a population of integers, 1 to 10:

seq(int(*rand* * 10) +1, X, 1, 500) → List1

or, if there is a built-in function (keystrokes denoted here by randInt):

seq(randInt, X, 1, 500) → List1

From a normal population (assuming a built-in function, keystrokes denoted by randNormal):

seq(randNormal, X, 1, 500) → List1

Your calculator may have different built-in functions or different syntax, but your exploration of the sampling distribution of the mean can begin as soon as you check that manual!

EXPLORATION 8.2 Sampling Distribution of the Sample Proportion

We saw in the previous exploration how to simulate sampling from a population to study the sampling distribution of the sample mean. In this exploration, we consider a similar process for studying the sampling distribution of the sample proportion. To review a bit, the process of random sampling from a large population is modeled as follows:

1. Construct a mathematical description—a probability distribution—of the population.
2. Generate a random sample from this population.
3. Calculate the statistic of interest (here, the sample proportion) for the simulated random sample.
4. Repeat Steps 2 and 3 a large number of times.
5. Construct a histogram of the resulting values of the sample proportion.

To model the sampling distribution of a sample proportion, we conceive of a population consisting of a set of 0's and 1's, where the proportion of 1's in the population is equal to the given population proportion p. The process of simulating a random sample consists of generating a fixed number n of 0's and 1's and finding the proportion of 1's in the sample. This value is the simulated sample proportion. For example, suppose we are simulating sampling from a population with a population proportion $p = .75$ using a sample size of $n = 12$. One simulated sample might look like this:

1 1 1 0 1 0 0 1 1 1 1 0

We note that 8 of the 12 values are 1's, giving a sample proportion of $\hat{p} = .67$. How might we accomplish this simulation on our calculator? The easiest method is to capitalize on a built-in function to generate outcomes that are from a binomial distribution. If your calculator has such a function, it is probably somewhere in a Math or Prob menu—look in your manual's index for something like RandBin or RandBinom. We use the generic name RandBin to refer to this built-in calculator function. This function needs two numbers to generate a binomial random variable: the sample size and the population proportion. For our example, you might enter RandBin(12, .75) or RandBin(.75, 12), depending on the function's syntax for your calculator.

On your calculator, find the built-in function and enter the appropriate syntax with the parameters $n = 12$ and $p = .75$. When you do this, the output might be 8.

We simulate the process of sampling and calculating a sample proportion by using the seq function, as we did earlier, but now we convert the outcomes to proportions:

seq(RandBin(12, .75)/12, X, 1, 500) $\rightarrow$ List1

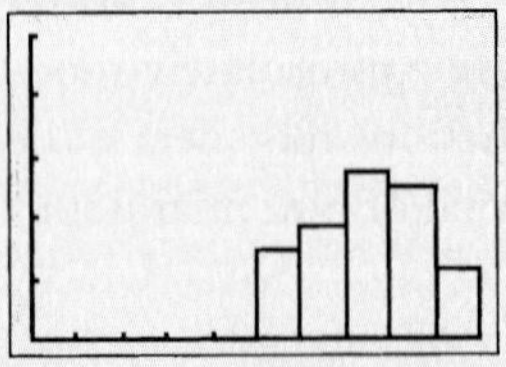

(a)

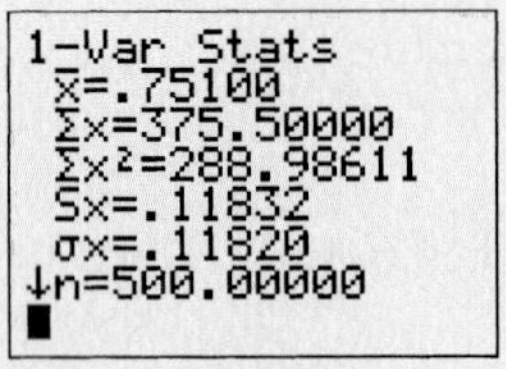

(b)

FIGURE 8.10
Displays for Exploration 8.2: (a) histogram; (b) summary values.

The distribution of our results and summary values are shown in Figure 8.10. Note that the simulated results are close to the theoretical values for the mean (0.75) and standard deviation (0.125) for the sampling distribution of $\hat{p}$.

If your calculator does not have a RandBin built-in function, you can still simulate random sampling from a population by using a slightly modified program from the one used for the sampling distribution of the mean. Be forewarned; this slight modification involves some mathematics, but it is fairly easy to implement.

The use of the same program as before capitalizes on the fact that the sample proportion is actually the mean of the 0's and 1's in the sample. The programming goal is to generate 12 random numbers between 0 and 1 and then to convert them to

12 0's and 1's before calculating the mean. That's when the "slight modification" comes in. The hitch in the plan is to find a simple (for the calculator) function that translates random numbers on the interval from 0 to 1 into 0's and 1's with the right probability. We use two common functions to make this happen: the absolute value function, usually called abs on calculators, and the greatest integer function, usually named Int or possibly Floor. The mathematical function that will perform the translation is

Y = abs(int(*rand* − *p*)), where *p* is the population proportion

For our example, this would be

Y = abs(int(*rand* − .75))

To generate a random sample, substitute the expression for *rand* appropriate to your calculator in the seq function:

```
For (X, 1, 500)
seq(abs(int(rand .75)), X, 1, 12) → List1
mean(List1) → List2(X)
End
```

Before you use the program to study the sampling distribution of the sample proportion, be sure to make a couple of trial runs and check the results with the theoretical expectations!

AP* Review Questions for Chapter 8

1. Which of the following best describes what is meant by the term *sampling variability*?

   (A) There are many different methods for selecting a sample.
   (B) Two different samples from the same population may have different values for a sample statistic.
   (C) The sample size can sometimes vary from sample to sample.
   (D) Convenience samples may not be representative of the population.
   (E) Population characteristics vary from population to population.

2. A random sample of size 2 is to be selected without replacement from the small population shown here:

   2 4 6 8

   Which of the following is the sampling distribution of the sample mean?

   (A)

$\bar{x}$	2	4	6	8
$p(\bar{x})$	.25	.25	.25	.25

   (B)

$\bar{x}$	3	4	5	6	7
$p(\bar{x})$	1/6	1/6	2/6	1/6	1/6

   (C)

$\bar{x}$	3	5	7
$p(\bar{x})$	.25	.5	.25

   (D)

$\bar{x}$	2	4	6	8
$p(\bar{x})$	.125	.375	.375	.125

   (E)

$\bar{x}$	2	4	5	6	8
$p(\bar{x})$	0	0	1	0	0

3. The histograms shown here are approximate sampling distributions of the sample mean. Each histogram is based on selecting 500 different samples, each of size n. All three histograms were constructed by sampling from the same population, but the sample sizes were different. Which histogram was based on samples with the smallest sample size, n?

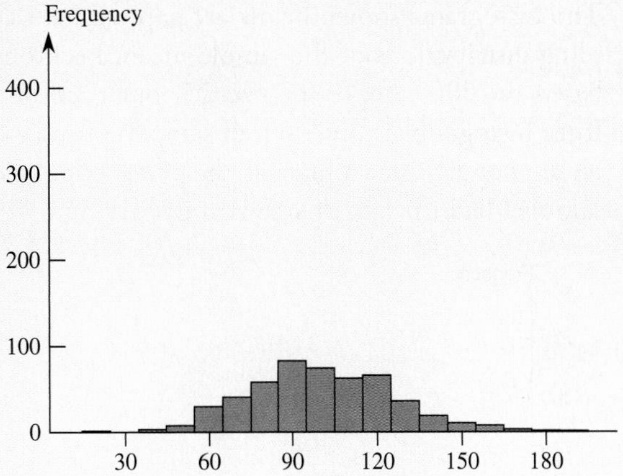

(I)

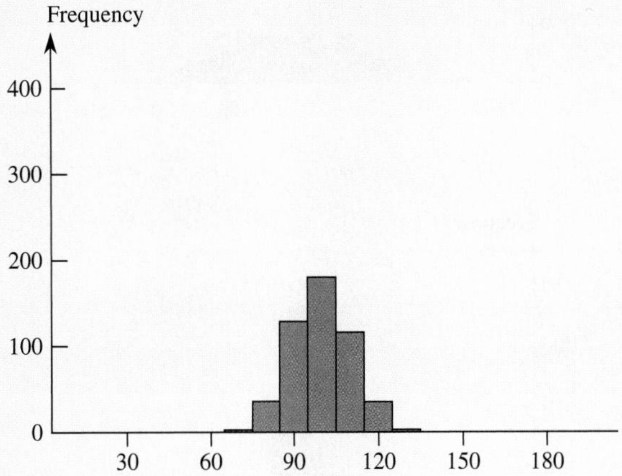

(II)

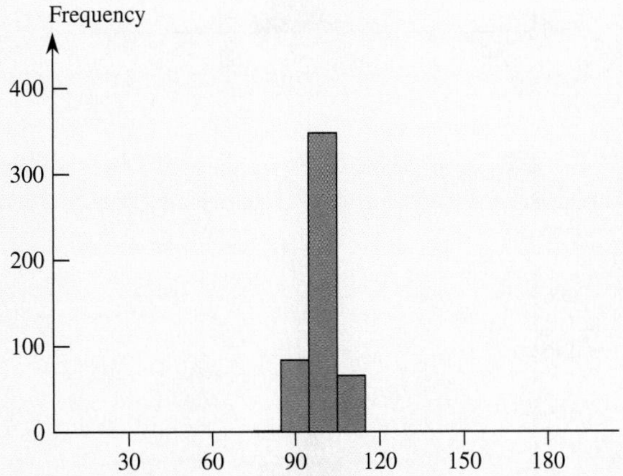

(III)

   (A) I
   (B) II
   (C) III
   (D) The same sample size was used for all three histograms.
   (E) It is not possible to tell by looking at the histograms.

*AP and the Advanced Placement Program are registered trademarks of the College Entrance Examination Board, which was not involved in the production of, and does not endorse, this product.

4. The histograms shown below are approximate sampling distributions of the sample mean. Each one is based on 500 samples of size 25, but each of the three histograms is the result of sampling from a different population. Which of the three populations sampled had the largest standard deviation?

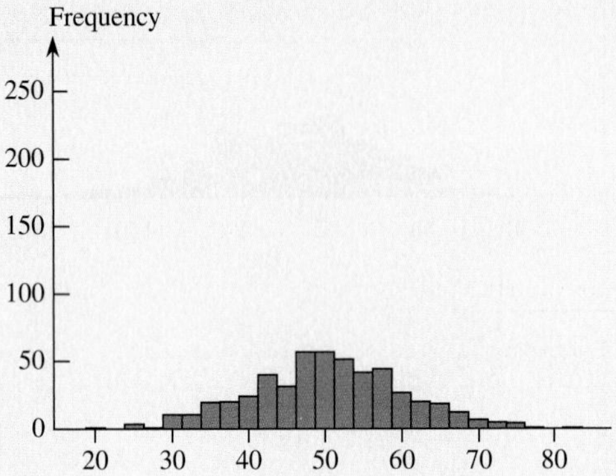

(I)

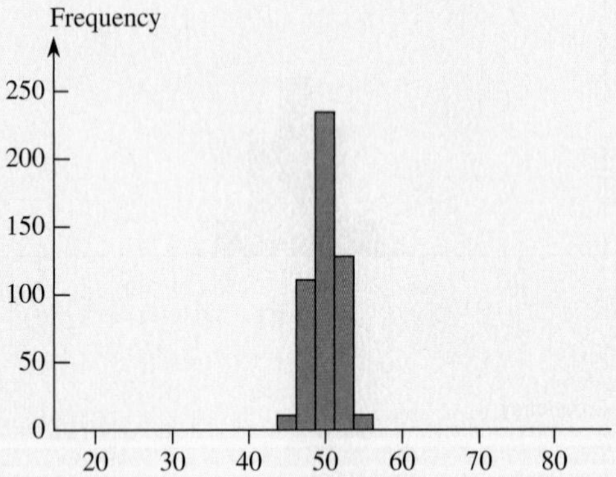

(II)

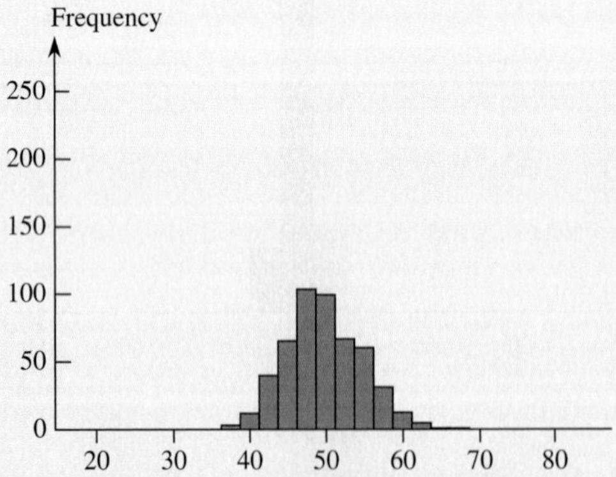

(III)

(A) I
(B) II
(C) III
(D) All three have the same standard deviation.
(E) It is not possible to tell from the histograms.

5. For a random sample from a skewed population, for which of the following sample sizes would the sampling distribution of $\bar{x}$ be closest to normal in shape?

(A) $n = 4$
(B) $n = 10$
(C) $n = 40$
(D) $n = 60$
(E) The $\bar{x}$ distribution will be normal for any sample size.

6. What is the standard deviation of $\bar{x}$ for random samples of size 100 from a population with a mean of 100 and a standard deviation of 80?

(A) .8
(B) 8
(C) 10
(D) 80
(E) 100

7. For which of the following will the sample mean tend to differ least from sample to sample?

(A) random samples of size 10
(B) random samples of size 20
(C) random samples of size 30
(D) random samples of size 50
(E) random samples of size 100

8. Commute distances for employees of a large company have a distribution that is quite skewed. Suppose the mean commute distance is 20 miles and that the standard deviation is 10 miles. What can be said about the mean commute distance for a random sample of size 4 employees from this plant?

(A) The distribution of $\bar{x}$ will be approximately normal with mean 20 and standard deviation 10.
(B) The distribution of $\bar{x}$ will be approximately normal with mean 20 and standard deviation 5.
(C) The mean and standard deviation of $\bar{x}$ will be 20 and 10, but the sampling distribution of $\bar{x}$ will not be approximately normal.
(D) The mean and standard deviation of $\bar{x}$ will be 20 and 5, but the sampling distribution of $\bar{x}$ will not be approximately normal.
(E) $\bar{x}$ will have a standard normal distribution.

9. A random sample is to be selected from a population. For which combination of n and p is it reasonable to assume that the sampling distribution of the sample proportion $\hat{p}$ will be approximately normal?

(A) $n = 10$ and $p = .4$
(B) $n = 25$ and $p = .5$
(C) $n = 30$ and $p = .2$
(D) $n = 40$ and $p = .1$
(E) $n = 100$ and $p = .05$

10. Suppose that 50% of those taking a national licensing exam pass the exam on the first attempt. A random sample of $n = 100$ people taking the exam for the first time will be selected. If $\hat{p}$ is the proportion in the sample that pass the exam on the first attempt, what are the mean and standard deviation of the sampling distribution of $\hat{p}$?

(A) The mean is .5 and the standard deviation is .25.
(B) The mean is .5 and the standard deviation is .025.
(C) The mean is .5 and the standard deviation is $\sqrt{.0025}$.
(D) The mean is .25 and the standard deviation is .25.
(E) The mean is .25 and the standard deviation is $\sqrt{.0025}$.

11. For which of the following will the sample proportion tend to differ least from sample to sample?

(A) Random samples of size 30 from a population with $p = .1$
(B) Random samples of size 40 from a population with $p = .1$
(C) Random samples of size 40 from a population with $p = .4$
(D) Random samples of size 50 from a population with $p = .5$
(E) Random samples of size 60 from a population with $p = .5$

12. Which of the following is true?

I. The sampling distribution of $\hat{p}$ has a mean equal to p.
II. The sampling distribution of $\hat{p}$ has a standard deviation equal to $\sqrt{np(1-p)}$.
III. The sampling distribution of $\hat{p}$ is always symmetric

(A) I only
(B) II only
(C) III only
(D) I and II only
(E) I and III only

13. As the sample size increases, how does the sampling distribution of $\bar{x}$ change?

(A) The mean of the sampling distribution decreases in value.
(B) The standard deviation of the sampling distribution decreases in value.
(C) The mean of the sampling distribution increases in value.
(D) The standard deviation of the sampling distribution increases in value.
(E) The mean and standard deviation of the sampling distribution do not change.

14. In order for the sampling distribution of the sample mean to be approximately normal, which of the following must be true?

I. The sample size must be large.
II. The population distribution must be normal.

(A) I only
(B) II only
(C) Either I or II
(D) Both I and II
(E) Neither I nor II is necessary

15. If a population distribution is substantially skewed and the sample size is small, which of the following is true about the sampling distribution of $\bar{x}$?

(A) $\mu_{\bar{x}} \neq \mu$ and $\sigma_{\bar{x}} \neq \frac{\sigma}{\sqrt{n}}$.
(B) $\mu_{\bar{x}} \neq \mu$ and the shape is not approximately normal.
(C) $\sigma_{\bar{x}} \neq \frac{\sigma}{\sqrt{n}}$ and the shape is not approximately normal.
(D) $\mu_{\bar{x}} = \mu$ and the shape is not approximately normal.
(E) $\sigma_{\bar{x}} \neq \frac{\sigma}{\sqrt{n}}$ and the shape is approximately normal.

CHAPTER 9

Estimation Using a Single Sample

© George Hall/Corbis

Most American college students make use of the Internet for both academic and social purposes. The authors of the paper "U.S. College Students' Internet Use: Race, Gender and Digital Divides" (*Journal of Computer-Mediated Communication* [2009]: 244–264) describe the results of a survey of 7421 students at 40 colleges and universities. The sample was selected in a way that the authors believed would result in a sample that reflected general demographics of college students in the U.S. The authors wanted to use the sample data to estimate the proportion of college students who spend more than 3 hours a day on the Internet. The methods introduced in this chapter will be used to produce the desired estimate. Because the estimate will be based only on a sample rather than on a census of all U.S. college students it is important that this estimate be constructed in a way that also conveys information about the anticipated accuracy.

The objective of inferential statistics is to use sample data to decrease our uncertainty about some characteristic of the corresponding population, such as a population mean μ or a population proportion p. One way to accomplish this uses the sample data to arrive at a single number that represents a plausible value for the characteristic of interest. Alternatively, an entire range of plausible values for the characteristic can be reported. These two estimation techniques, *point estimation* and *interval estimation*, are introduced in this chapter.

9.1 Point Estimation

The simplest approach to estimating a population characteristic involves using sample data to compute a single number that can be regarded as a plausible value of the characteristic. For example, sample data might suggest that 1000 hours is a plausible value for μ, the true mean lifetime for lightbulbs of a particular brand. In a different setting, a sample survey of students at a particular university might lead to the statement that .41 is a plausible value for p, the proportion of all students who favor a fee for recreational facilities.

DEFINITION

A **point estimate** of a population characteristic is a single number that is based on sample data and represents a plausible value of the characteristic.

In the examples just given, 1000 is a point estimate of μ and .41 is a point estimate of p. The adjective *point* reflects the fact that the estimate corresponds to a single point on the number line.

A point estimate is obtained by first selecting an appropriate statistic. The estimate is then the value of the statistic for the given sample. For example, the computed value of the sample mean is one point estimate of a population mean μ, and the sample proportion is a point estimate of a population proportion, p.

EXAMPLE 9.1 Internet Use by College Students

One of the purposes of the survey described in the chapter introduction was to estimate the proportion of college students who spend more than 3 hours a day on the Internet. Based on information given in the paper, 2998 of the 7421 students surveyed reported Internet use of more than 3 hours per day. We can use this information to estimate p, where p is the proportion of all U.S. college students who use the Internet more than 3 hours a day. With a success identified as a student who uses the Internet more than 3 hours a day, p is then the population proportion of successes. The statistic

$$\hat{p} = \frac{\text{number of successes in the sample}}{n}$$

which is the sample proportion of successes, is an obvious choice for obtaining a point estimate of p. Based on the reported information, the point estimate of p is

$$\hat{p} = \frac{2998}{7421} = .404$$

That is, based on this random sample, we estimate that 40.4% of college students in the United States spend more than 3 hours a day on the Internet.

For purposes of estimating a population proportion p, there is no obvious alternative to the statistic $\hat{p}$. In other situations, such as the one illustrated in Example 9.2, there may be several statistics that can be used to obtain an estimate.

EXAMPLE 9.2 Academic Reading

The paper "The Impact of Internet and Television Use on the Reading Habits and Practices of College Students" (*Journal of Adolescent and Adult Literacy* [2009]: 609–619) investigates the reading habits of college students. The authors distinguished between recreational reading and academic reading and asked students to keep track of time spent reading. The following observations represent the number of hours spent on academic reading in 1 week by 20 college students (these data are compatible with summary values given in the paper and have been arranged in order from smallest to largest):

1.7	3.8	4.7	9.6	11.7	12.3	12.3	12.4	12.6	13.4
14.1	14.2	15.8	15.9	18.7	19.4	21.2	21.9	23.3	28.2

A dotplot of the data is shown here:

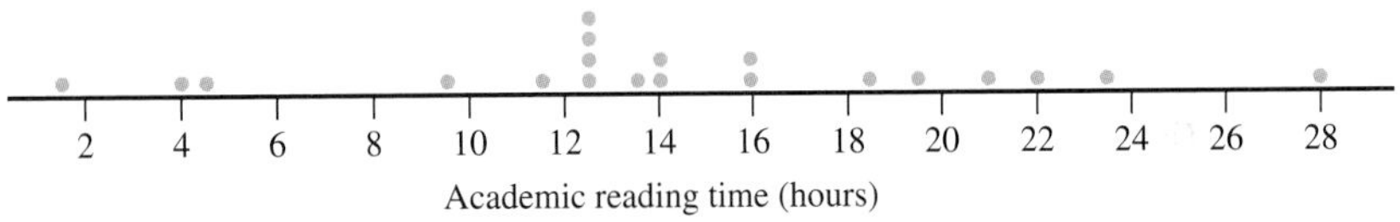

From the dotplot, we can see that the distribution of academic reading time is approximately symmetric.

If a point estimate of μ, the mean academic reading time per week for all college students, is desired, an obvious choice of a statistic for estimating μ is the sample mean, $\bar{x}$. However, there are other possibilities. We might consider using a trimmed mean or even the sample median, because the data set exhibits some symmetry. (If the corresponding population distribution is symmetric, the population mean μ and the population median are equal).

The three statistics and the resulting estimates of μ calculated from the data are

$$\text{sample mean} = \bar{x} = \frac{\sum x}{n} = \frac{287.2}{20} = 14.36$$

$$\text{sample median} = \frac{13.4 + 14.1}{2} = 13.75$$

$$10\%\text{ trimmed mean} = \left(\begin{array}{c}\text{average of middle}\\ \text{16 observations}\end{array}\right) = \frac{230.2}{16} = 14.39$$

The estimates of the mean academic reading time per week for college students differ somewhat from one another. The choice from among them should depend on which statistic tends, on average, to produce an estimate closest to the true value of μ. The following subsection discusses criteria for choosing among competing statistics.

Choosing a Statistic for Computing an Estimate

As illustrated in Example 9.2, more than one statistic may be reasonable to use to obtain a point estimate of a specified population characteristic. We would like to use a statistic that tends to produce an accurate estimate—that is, an estimate close to the value of the population characteristic. Information about the accuracy of estimation for a particular statistic is provided by the statistic's sampling distribution.

Figure 9.1 displays the sampling distributions of three different statistics. The value of the population characteristic, which is denoted by *true value* in the figure, is marked on the measurement axis. The distribution in Figure 9.1(a) is that of a statistic unlikely to yield an estimate close to the true value. The distribution is centered to the right of the true value, making it very likely that an estimate (a value of the statistic for a particular sample) will be larger than the true value. If this statistic is used to compute an estimate based on a first sample, then another estimate based on a second sample, and another estimate based on a third sample, and so on, the long-run average value of these estimates will be greater than the true value.

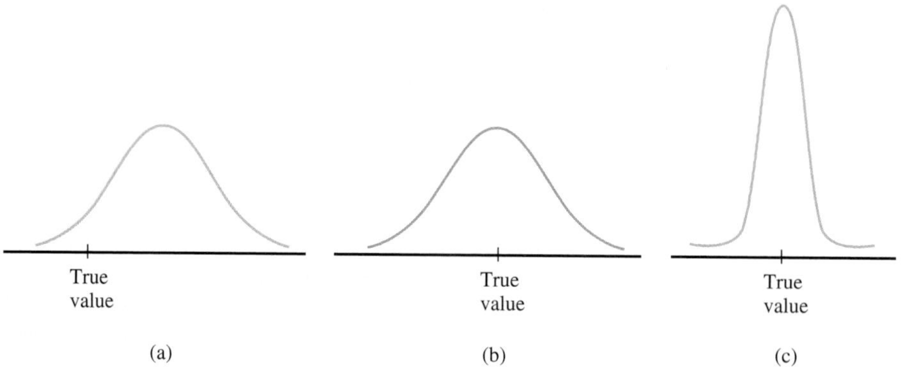

FIGURE 9.1
Sampling distributions of three different statistics for estimating a population characteristic.

The sampling distribution of Figure 9.1(b) is centered at the true value. Thus, although one estimate may be smaller than the true value and another may be larger, when this statistic is used many times over with different samples, there will be no long-run tendency to over- or underestimate the true value. Note that even though the sampling distribution is correctly centered, it spreads out quite a bit about the true value. Because of this, some estimates resulting from the use of this statistic will be far above or far below the true value, even though there is no systematic tendency to underestimate or overestimate the true value.

In contrast, the mean value of the statistic with the distribution shown in Figure 9.1(c) is equal to the true value of the population characteristic (implying no systematic error in estimation), and the statistic's standard deviation is relatively small. Estimates based on this third statistic will almost always be quite close to the true value—certainly more often than estimates resulting from the statistic with the sampling distribution shown in Figure 9.1(b).

DEFINITION

A statistic whose mean value is equal to the value of the population characteristic being estimated is said to be an **unbiased statistic**. A statistic that is not unbiased is said to be **biased**.

As an example of a statistic that is biased, consider using the sample range as an estimate of the population range. Because the range of a population is defined as the difference between the largest value in the population and the smallest value, the range for a sample tends to underestimate the population range. This is because the largest value in a sample must be less than or equal to the largest value in the population and the smallest sample value must be greater than or equal to the smallest value in the population. The sample range equals the population range *only* if the sample includes both the largest and the smallest values in the population; in all other instances, the sample range is smaller than the population range. Thus, $\mu_{\text{sample range}}$ is less than the population range, implying bias.

Let $x_1, x_2, \ldots, x_n$ represent the values in a random sample. One of the general results concerning the sampling distribution of $\bar{x}$, the sample mean, is that $\mu_{\bar{x}} = \mu$. This result says that the $\bar{x}$ values from all possible random samples of size n center around μ, the population mean. For example, if $\mu = 100$, the $\bar{x}$ distribution is centered at 100, whereas if $\mu = 5200$, then the $\bar{x}$ distribution is centered at 5200. Therefore, $\bar{x}$ is an unbiased statistic for estimating μ. Similarly, because the sampling distribution of $\hat{p}$ is centered at p, it follows that $\hat{p}$ is an unbiased statistic for estimating a population proportion.

Using an unbiased statistic that also has a small standard deviation ensures that there will be no systematic tendency to under- or overestimate the value of the population characteristic *and* that estimates will almost always be relatively close to the value of the population characteristic.

> Given several unbiased statistics that could be used for estimating a population characteristic, the best choice to use is the statistic with the smallest standard deviation.

Consider the problem of estimating a population mean, μ. The obvious choice of statistic for obtaining a point estimate of μ is the sample mean, $\bar{x}$, an unbiased statistic for this purpose. However, when the population distribution is symmetric, $\bar{x}$ is not the only choice. Other unbiased statistics for estimating μ in this case include the sample median and any trimmed mean (with the same number of observations trimmed from each end of the ordered sample). Which statistic should be used? The following facts are helpful in making a choice.

1. If the population distribution is normal, then $\bar{x}$ has a smaller standard deviation than any other unbiased statistic for estimating μ. However, in this case, a trimmed mean with a small trimming percentage (such as 10%) performs almost as well as $\bar{x}$.
2. When the population distribution is symmetric with heavy tails compared to the normal curve, a trimmed mean is a better statistic than $\bar{x}$ for estimating μ.

When the population distribution is unquestionably normal, the choice is clear: Use $\bar{x}$ to estimate μ. However, with a heavy-tailed distribution, a trimmed mean gives protection against one or two outliers in the sample that might otherwise have a large effect on the value of the estimate.

Now consider estimating another population characteristic, the population variance, σ^2. The sample variance

$$s^2 = \frac{\sum(x - \bar{x})^2}{n - 1}$$

is a good choice for obtaining a point estimate of the population variance, σ^2. It can be shown that s^2 is an unbiased statistic for estimating σ^2; that is, whatever the value of σ^2, the sampling distribution of s^2 is centered at that value. It is precisely for this reason—to obtain an unbiased statistic—that the divisor $(n - 1)$ is used. An alternative statistic is the average squared deviation

$$\frac{\sum(x - \bar{x})^2}{n}$$

which one might think has a more natural divisor than s^2. However, the average squared deviation is biased, with its values tending to be smaller, on average, than the value of σ^2.

EXAMPLE 9.3 Airborne Times for Flights from San Francisco to Washington, D.C.

The Bureau of Transportation Statistics provides data on U.S. airline flights. The airborne times (in minutes) for nonstop flights from San Francisco to Washington Dulles airport for 10 randomly selected flights in June 2009 are:

270 256 267 285 274 275 266 258 271 281

For these data $\sum x = 2703$, $\sum x^2 = 731{,}373$, $n = 10$, and

$$\begin{aligned}\sum (x - \bar{x})^2 &= \sum x^2 - \frac{(\sum x)^2}{n} \\ &= 731{,}373 - \frac{(2703)^2}{10} \\ &= 752.1\end{aligned}$$

Let σ^2 denote the true variance in airborne time for June, 2009 nonstop flights from San Francisco to Washington Dulles airport. Using the sample variance s^2 to provide a point estimate of σ^2 yields

$$s^2 = \frac{\sum (x - \bar{x})^2}{n - 1} = \frac{752.1}{9} = 83.57$$

Using the average squared deviation (with divisor $n = 10$), the resulting point estimate is

$$\frac{\sum (x - \bar{x})^2}{n} = \frac{752.1}{10} = 75.21$$

Because s^2 is an unbiased statistic for estimating σ^2, most statisticians would recommend using the point estimate 83.57.

An obvious choice of a statistic for estimating the population standard deviation σ is the sample standard deviation s. For the data given in Example 9.3,

$$s = \sqrt{83.57} = 9.14$$

Unfortunately, the fact that s^2 is an unbiased statistic for estimating σ^2 does not imply that s is an unbiased statistic for estimating σ. The sample standard deviation tends to underestimate slightly the true value of σ. However, unbiasedness is not the only criterion by which a statistic can be judged, and there are other good reasons for using s to estimate σ. In what follows, whenever we need to estimate σ based on a single random sample, we will use the statistic s to obtain a point estimate.

EXERCISES 9.1 - 9.9

9.1 ✦ Three different statistics are being considered for estimating a population characteristic. The sampling distributions of the three statistics are shown in the following illustration:

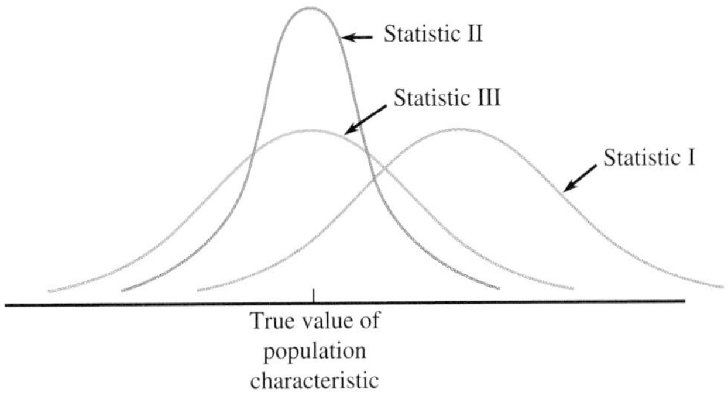

Which statistic would you recommend? Explain your choice.

9.2 Why is an unbiased statistic generally preferred over a biased statistic for estimating a population characteristic? Does unbiasedness alone guarantee that the estimate will be close to the true value? Explain. Under what circumstances might you choose a biased statistic over an unbiased statistic if two statistics are available for estimating a population characteristic?

9.3 Consumption of fast food is a topic of interest to researchers in the field of nutrition. The article "Effects of Fast-Food Consumption on Energy Intake and Diet Quality Among Children" (*Pediatrics* [2004]: 112–118) reported that 1720 of those in a random sample of 6212 U.S. children indicated that on a typical day, they ate fast food. Estimate p, the proportion of children in the United States who eat fast food on a typical day.

9.4 ● Data consistent with summary quantities in the article referenced in Exercise 9.3 on total calorie consumption on a particular day are given for a sample of children who did not eat fast food on that day and for a sample of children who did eat fast food on that day. Assume that it is reasonable to regard these samples as representative of the population of children in the United States.

No Fast Food

2331	1918	1009	1730	1469	2053	2143	1981
1852	1777	1765	1827	1648	1506	2669	

Fast Food

2523	1758	934	2328	2434	2267	2526	1195
890	1511	875	2207	1811	1250	2117	

a. Use the given information to estimate the mean calorie intake for children in the United States on a day when no fast food is consumed.
b. Use the given information to estimate the mean calorie intake for children in the United States on a day when fast food is consumed.
c. Use the given information to produce estimates of the standard deviations of calorie intake for days when no fast food is consumed and for days when fast food is consumed.

9.5 Each person in a random sample of 20 students at a particular university was asked whether he or she is registered to vote. The responses (R = registered, N = not registered) are given here:

R R N R N N R R R N R R R R R N R R R N

Use these data to estimate p, the proportion of all students at the university who are registered to vote.

9.6 Suppose that each of 935 smokers received a nicotine patch, which delivers nicotine to the bloodstream but at a much slower rate than cigarettes do. Dosage was decreased to 0 over a 12-week period. Suppose that 245 of the subjects were still not smoking 6 months after treatment. Assuming it is reasonable to regard this sample as representative of all smokers, estimate the percentage of all smokers who, when given this treatment, would refrain from smoking for at least 6 months.

9.7 ● Given below are the sodium contents (in mg) for seven brands of hot dogs rated as "very good" by *Consumer Reports* (www.consumerreports.org):

420 470 350 360 270 550 530

a. Use the given data to produce a point estimate of μ, the true mean sodium content for hot dogs.
b. Use the given data to produce a point estimate of σ^2, the variance of sodium content for hot dogs.
c. Use the given data to produce an estimate of σ, the standard deviation of sodium content. Is the statistic you used to produce your estimate unbiased?

9.8 ● A random sample of $n = 12$ four-year-old red pine trees was selected, and the diameter (in inches) of each tree's main stem was measured. The resulting observations are as follows:

11.3 10.7 12.4 15.2 10.1 12.1 16.2 10.5
11.4 11.0 10.7 12.0

a. Compute a point estimate of σ, the population standard deviation of main stem diameter. What statistic did you use to obtain your estimate?
b. Making no assumptions about the shape of the population distribution of diameters, give a point estimate for the population median diameter. What statistic did you use to obtain the estimate?
c. Suppose that the population distribution of diameter is symmetric but with heavier tails than the normal distribution. Give a point estimate of the population mean diameter based on a statistic that gives some protection against the presence of outliers in the sample. What statistic did you use?
d. Suppose that the diameter distribution is normal. Then the 90th percentile of the diameter distribution is $\mu + 1.28\sigma$ (so 90% of all trees have diameters less than this value). Compute a point estimate for this percentile. (Hint: First compute an estimate of μ in this case; then use it along with your estimate of σ from Part (a).)

9.9 ● A random sample of 10 houses heated with natural gas in a particular area, is selected, and the amount of gas (in therms) used during the month of January is determined for each house. The resulting observations are as follows:

103 156 118 89 125 147 122 109 138 99

a. Let μ_J denote the average gas usage during January by all houses in this area. Compute a point estimate of μ_J.
b. Suppose that 10,000 houses in this area use natural gas for heating. Let τ denote the total amount of gas used by all of these houses during January. Estimate τ using the given data. What statistic did you use in computing your estimate?
c. Use the data in Part (a) to estimate p, the proportion of all houses that used at least 100 therms.
d. Give a point estimate of the population median usage based on the sample of Part (a). Which statistic did you use?

9.2 Large-Sample Confidence Interval for a Population Proportion

In Section 9.1, we saw how to use a statistic to produce a point estimate of a population characteristic. The value of a point estimate depends on which sample, out of all the possible samples, happens to be selected. Different samples usually produce different estimates as a result of chance differences from one sample to another. Because of sampling variability, rarely is the point estimate from a sample exactly equal to the actual value of the population characteristic. We hope that the chosen statistic produces an estimate that is close, on average, to the true value.

Although a point estimate may represent our best single-number guess for the value of the population characteristic, it is not the only plausible value. As an alternative to a point estimate, we can use the sample data to report an interval of plausible values for the population characteristic. For example, we might be confident that for all text messages sent from cell phones, the proportion p of messages that are longer than 50 characters is in the interval from .53 to .57. The narrowness of this interval implies that we have rather precise information about the value of p. If, with the same high degree of confidence, we could only state that p was between .32 and .74, it would be clear that we had relatively imprecise knowledge of the value of p.

DEFINITION

A **confidence interval (CI)** for a population characteristic is an interval of plausible values for the characteristic. It is constructed so that, with a chosen degree of confidence, the actual value of the population characteristic will be between the lower and upper endpoints of the interval.

Associated with each confidence interval is a *confidence level*. The confidence level provides information on how much "confidence" we can have in the *method* used to construct the interval estimate (*not* our confidence in any one particular interval). Usual choices for confidence levels are 90%, 95%, and 99%, although other confidence levels are also possible. If we were to construct a 95% confidence interval using the technique to be described shortly, we would be using a method that is "successful" 95% of the time. That is, if this method was used to generate an interval estimate over and over again with different samples, in the long run 95% of the resulting intervals would include the actual value of the characteristic being estimated. Similarly, a 99% confidence interval is one that is constructed using a method that is, in the long run, successful in capturing the actual value of the population characteristic 99% of the time.

DEFINITION

The **confidence level** associated with a confidence interval estimate is the success rate of the *method* used to construct the interval.

One goal of many statistical studies is to estimate the proportion of individuals or objects in a population that possess a particular property of interest. For example, a university administrator might be interested in the proportion of students who prefer a new registration system to the previous registration method. In a different setting, a quality control engineer might be concerned about the proportion of defective parts manufactured using a particular process.

Recall that p denotes the proportion of the population that possess the property of interest. Previously, we used the sample proportion

$$\hat{p} = \frac{\text{number in the sample that possess the property of interest}}{n}$$

to calculate a point estimate of p. We can also use $\hat{p}$ to construct a confidence interval for p.

Although a small-sample confidence interval for p can be obtained, our focus is on the large-sample case. The construction of the large-sample interval is based on properties of the sampling distribution of the statistic $\hat{p}$:

1. The sampling distribution of $\hat{p}$ is centered at p; that is, $\mu_{\hat{p}} = p$. Therefore, $\hat{p}$ is an unbiased statistic for estimating p.
2. As long as the sample size is less than 10% of the population size, the standard deviation of $\hat{p}$ is well approximated by $\sigma_{\hat{p}} = \sqrt{\frac{p(1-p)}{n}}$
3. As long as n is large ($np \geq 10$ and $n(1 - p) \geq 10$) the sampling distribution of $\hat{p}$ is well approximated by a normal curve.

The accompanying box summarizes these properties.

When n is large and the sample size is less than 10% of the population size, the statistic $\hat{p}$ has a sampling distribution that is approximately

normal with mean p and standard deviation $\sqrt{\frac{p(1-p)}{n}}$.

The development of a confidence interval for p is easier to follow if we select a particular confidence level. For a confidence level of 95%, Appendix Table 2, the table of standard normal (z) curve areas, can be used to determine a value z^* such that a central area of .95 falls between $-z^*$ and z^*. In this case, the remaining area of .05 is divided equally between the two tails, as shown in Figure 9.2. The total area to the left of the desired z^* is .975 (.95 central area + .025 area below $-z^*$). By locating .9750 in the body of Appendix Table 2, we find that the corresponding z critical value is $z^* = 1.96$.

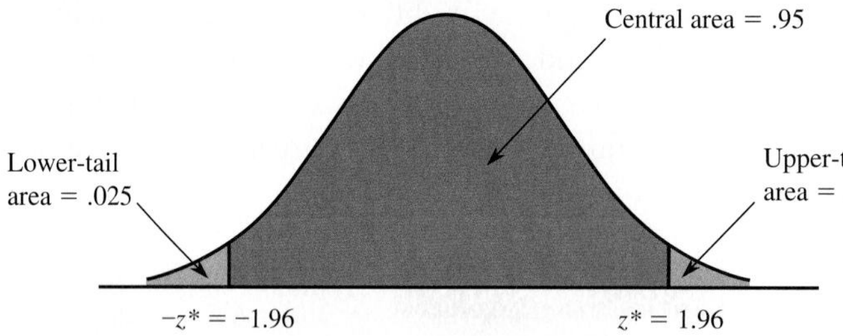

FIGURE 9.2
Capturing a central area of .95 under the z curve.

Generalizing this result to normal distributions other than the standard normal distribution tells us that for *any* normal distribution, about 95% of the values are within 1.96 standard deviations of the mean. For large random samples, the sampling distribution of $\hat{p}$ is approximately normal with mean $\mu_{\hat{p}} = p$ and standard deviation $\sigma_{\hat{p}} = \sqrt{\frac{p(1-p)}{n}}$, and we get the following result.

When n is large, approximately 95% of all samples of size n will result in a value of $\hat{p}$ that is within $1.96\sigma_{\hat{p}} = 1.96\sqrt{\frac{p(1-p)}{n}}$ of the value of the population proportion p.

If $\hat{p}$ is within $1.96\sqrt{\frac{p(1-p)}{n}}$ of p, this means the interval

$$\hat{p} - 1.96\sqrt{\frac{p(1-p)}{n}} \text{ to } \hat{p} + 1.96\sqrt{\frac{p(1-p)}{n}}$$

will capture p (and this will happen for 95% of all possible samples). However, if $\hat{p}$ is farther away from p than $1.96\sqrt{\frac{p(1-p)}{n}}$ (which will happen for about 5% of all possible samples), the interval will not include the true value of p. This is shown in Figure 9.3.

Because $\hat{p}$ is within $1.96\sigma_{\hat{p}}$ of p 95% of the time, this implies that in repeated sampling, 95% of the time the interval

$$\hat{p} - 1.96\sqrt{\frac{p(1-p)}{n}} \text{ to } \hat{p} + 1.96\sqrt{\frac{p(1-p)}{n}}$$

will contain p.

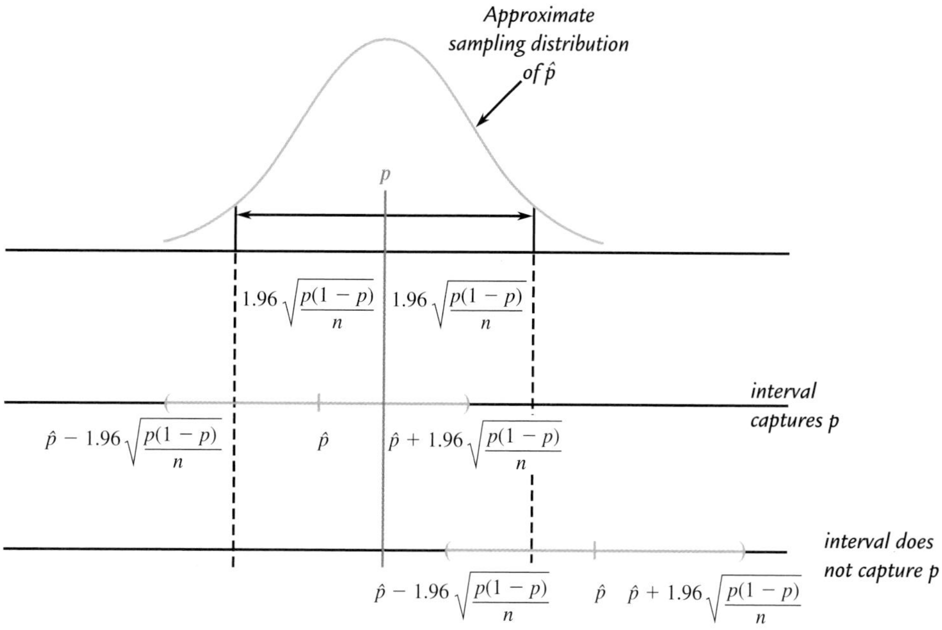

FIGURE 9.3 The population proportion p is captured in the interval from $\hat{p} - 1.96\sqrt{\frac{p(1-p)}{n}}$ to $\hat{p} + 1.96\sqrt{\frac{p(1-p)}{n}}$ when $\hat{p}$ is within $1.96\sqrt{\frac{p(1-p)}{n}}$ of p.

Since p is unknown, $\sqrt{\frac{p(1-p)}{n}}$ must be estimated. As long as the sample size is large, the value of $\sqrt{\frac{\hat{p}(1-\hat{p})}{n}}$ can be used in place of $\sqrt{\frac{p(1-p)}{n}}$.

When n is large, a 95% confidence interval for p is

$$\left(\hat{p} - 1.96\sqrt{\frac{\hat{p}(1-\hat{p})}{n}},\ \hat{p} + 1.96\sqrt{\frac{\hat{p}(1-\hat{p})}{n}}\right)$$

An abbreviated formula for the interval is

$$\hat{p} \pm 1.96\sqrt{\frac{\hat{p}(1-\hat{p})}{n}}$$

where $\hat{p} + 1.96\sqrt{\frac{\hat{p}(1-\hat{p})}{n}}$ gives the upper endpoint of the interval and $\hat{p} - 1.96\sqrt{\frac{\hat{p}(1-\hat{p})}{n}}$ gives the lower endpoint of the interval.

The interval can be used as long as

1. $n\hat{p} \geq 10$ and $n(1-\hat{p}) \geq 10$,
2. the sample size is less than 10% of the population size if sampling is without replacement, and
3. the sample can be regarded as a random sample from the population of interest.

EXAMPLE 9.4 College Education Essential for Success?

The article "How Well Are U.S. Colleges Run?" (*USA Today*, February 17, 2010) describes a survey of 1031 adult Americans. The survey was carried out by the National Center for Public Policy and the sample was selected in a way that makes it reasonable to regard the sample as representative of adult Americans. Of those surveyed, 567 indicated that they believed a college education is essential for success. With p denoting the proportion of all adult Americans who believe that a college education is essential for success, a point estimate of p is

$$\hat{p} = \frac{567}{1031} = .55$$

Before computing a confidence interval to estimate p, we should check to make sure that the three necessary conditions are met:

1. $n\hat{p} = 1031(.55) = 567$ and $n(1 - \hat{p}) = 1031(1 - .55) = 1031(.45) = 364$ are both greater than or equal to 10, so the sample size is large enough to proceed.
2. The sample size of $n = 1031$ is much smaller than 10% of the population size (the number of adult Americans).
3. The sample was selected in a way designed to produce a representative sample. So, it is reasonable to regard the sample as a random sample from the population.

Because all three conditions are met, it is appropriate to use the sample data to construct a 95% confidence interval for p.

A 95% confidence interval for p is

$$\begin{aligned}\hat{p} \pm 1.96\sqrt{\frac{\hat{p}(1-\hat{p})}{n}} &= .55 \pm 1.96\sqrt{\frac{(.55)(1-.55)}{1031}} \\ &= .55 \pm (1.96)(.015) \\ &= .55 \pm .029 \\ &= (.521, .579)\end{aligned}$$

Based on this sample, we can be 95% confident that p, the proportion of adult Americans who believe a college education is essential for success, is between .521 and .579. We used a *method* to construct this estimate that in the long run will successfully capture the actual value of p 95% of the time.

AP* EXAM TIP

You should be very careful when interpreting confidence level. It is easy to get this wrong by making a statement about probability rather than confidence. See Section 9.4 for more on correct interpretation.

The 95% confidence interval for p calculated in Example 9.4 is (.521, .579). It is tempting to say that there is a "probability" of .95 that p is between .521 and .579. *Do not yield to this temptation!* The 95% refers to the percentage of *all* possible samples resulting in an interval that includes p. In other words, if we take sample after sample from the population and use each one separately to compute a 95% confidence interval, in the long run roughly 95% of these intervals will capture p. Figure 9.4 illustrates this concept for intervals generated from 100 different random samples. In this particular set of 100 intervals, 93 include p, whereas 7 do not. Any specific interval, and our interval (.521, .579) in particular, either includes p or it does not (remember, the value of p is fixed but not known to us). We cannot make a chance (probability) statement concerning this particular interval. *The confidence level 95% refers to the method used to construct the interval rather than to any particular interval, such as the one we obtained.*

The formula given for a 95% confidence interval can easily be adapted for other confidence levels. The choice of a 95% confidence level led to the use of the z value 1.96 (chosen to capture a central area of .95 under the standard normal curve) in the formula. Any other confidence level can be obtained by using an appropriate z critical value in place of 1.96. For example, suppose that we wanted to achieve a confidence level of 99%. To obtain a central area of .99, the appropriate z critical value would

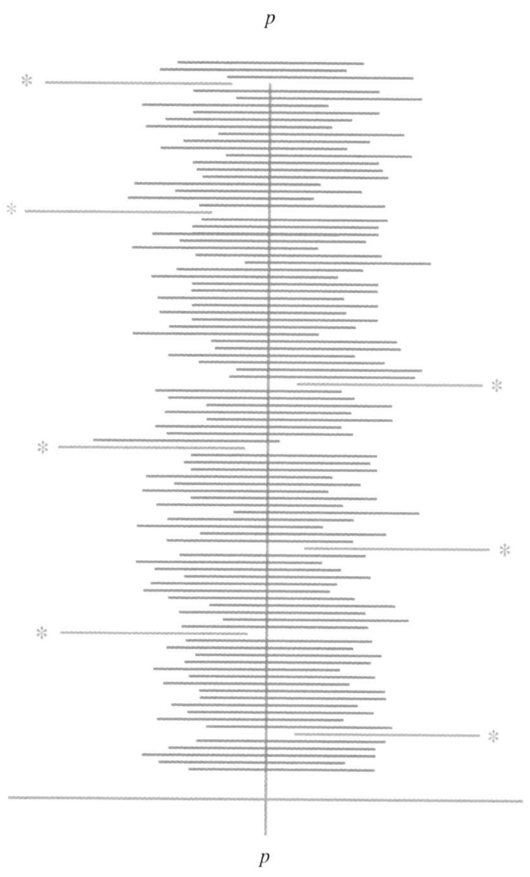

FIGURE 9.4
One hundred 95% confidence intervals for p computed from 100 different random samples (asterisks identify intervals that do not include p).

have a cumulative area (area to the left) of .995, as illustrated in Figure 9.5. From Appendix Table 2, we find that the corresponding z critical value is $z = 2.58$. A 99% confidence interval for p is then obtained by using 2.58 in place of 1.96 in the formula for the 95% confidence interval.

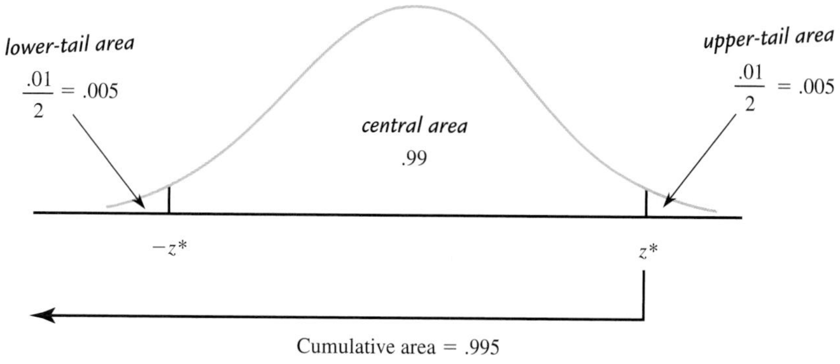

FIGURE 9.5
Finding the z critical value for a 99% confidence level.

Why settle for 95% confidence when 99% confidence is possible? Because the higher confidence level comes with a price tag. The resulting interval is wider than the 95% interval. The width of the 95% interval is $2\left(1.96\sqrt{\frac{\hat{p}(1-\hat{p})}{n}}\right)$, whereas the 99% interval has width $2\left(2.58\sqrt{\frac{\hat{p}(1-\hat{p})}{n}}\right)$. The higher *reliability* of the 99% interval (where "reliability" is specified by the confidence level) entails a loss in precision (as indicated by the wider interval). In the opinion of many investigators, a 95% confidence interval produces a reasonable compromise between reliability and precision.

The Large-Sample Confidence Interval for p

The general formula for a confidence interval for a population proportion p when

1. $\hat{p}$ is the sample proportion from a **simple random sample,**
2. the sample size n **is large** ($n\hat{p} \geq 10$ and $n(1 - \hat{p}) \geq 10$), and
3. if the sample is selected without replacement, **the sample size is small relative to the population size** (n is at most 10% of the population size)*

is

$$\hat{p} \pm (z \text{ critical value})\sqrt{\frac{\hat{p}(1 - \hat{p})}{n}}$$

The desired confidence level determines which z critical value is used. The three most commonly used confidence levels, 90%, 95%, and 99%, use z critical values 1.645, 1.96, and 2.58, respectively.

Note: This interval is not appropriate for small samples. It is possible to construct a confidence interval in the small-sample case, but this is beyond the scope of this textbook.

*In Chapter 7, we saw a different situation where a similar condition is introduced, but where the requirement was that at most 5% of the population is included in the sample. Be careful not to confuse these two rules.

EXAMPLE 9.5 Dangerous Driving

© The Image Bank/Wilfried Krecichwest/Getty Images

The article "Nine Out of Ten Drivers Admit in Survey to Having Done Something Dangerous" (*Knight Ridder Newspapers*, July 8, 2005) reported the results of a survey of 1100 drivers. Of those surveyed, 990 admitted to careless or aggressive driving during the previous 6 months. Assuming that it is reasonable to regard this sample of 1100 as representative of the population of drivers, we can use this information to construct an estimate of p, the proportion of all drivers who have engaged in careless or aggressive driving in the past 6 months.

For this sample

$$\hat{p} = \frac{990}{1100} = .900$$

Because the sample size is less than 10% of the population size and $n\hat{p} = 990$ and $n(1 - \hat{p}) = 110$ are both greater than or equal to 10, the conditions necessary for appropriate use of the formula for a large-sample confidence interval are met. A 90% confidence interval for p is then

$$\begin{aligned}\hat{p} \pm (z \text{ critical value})\sqrt{\frac{\hat{p}(1 - \hat{p})}{n}} &= .900 \pm 1.645\sqrt{\frac{(.900)(.100)}{1100}} \\ &= .900 \pm (1.645)(.009) \\ &= .900 \pm .015 \\ &= (.885, .915)\end{aligned}$$

Based on these sample data, we can be 90% confident that the proportion of all drivers who have engaged in careless or aggressive driving in the past 6 months is between .885 and .915. We have used a *method* to construct this interval estimate that has a 10% error rate.

The confidence level for the z confidence interval for a population proportion is only approximate. That is, when we report a 95% confidence interval for a population proportion, the 95% confidence level implies that we have used a method that produces an interval that includes the actual value of the population proportion 95% of the time in repeated sampling. In fact, because the normal distribution is only an approximation to the sampling distribution of $\hat{p}$, the true confidence level may differ somewhat from the reported value. If the conditions (1) $n\hat{p} \geq 10$ and $n(1 - \hat{p}) \geq 10$ and (2) n is at most 10% of the population size if sampling without replacement are met, the normal approximation is reasonable and the actual confidence level is usually not too different from the reported level; this is why it is important to check these conditions before computing and reporting a z confidence interval for a population proportion.

What should you do if these conditions are not met? If the sample size is too small to satisfy the $n\hat{p}$ and $n(1 - \hat{p})$ greater than or equal to 10 condition, an alternative procedure can be used. Consult a statistician or a more advanced textbook in this case. If the condition that the sample size is less than 10% of the population size when sampling without replacement is not satisfied, the z confidence interval tends to be conservative (that is, it tends to be wider than is necessary to achieve the desired confidence level). In this case, a finite population correction factor can be used to obtain a more precise interval. Again, it would be wise to consult a statistician or a more advanced textbook.

An Alternative to the Large-Sample z Interval

Investigators have shown that in some instances, even when the sample size conditions of the large-sample z confidence interval for a population proportion are met, the actual confidence level associated with the method may be noticeably different from the reported confidence level. A modified interval that has an actual confidence level that is closer to the reported confidence level is based on a modified sample proportion, $\hat{p}_{\text{mod}}$, the proportion of successes after adding two successes and two failures to the sample. Then $\hat{p}_{\text{mod}}$ is

$$\hat{p}_{\text{mod}} = \frac{\text{number of successes} + 2}{n + 4}$$

$\hat{p}_{\text{mod}}$ is used in place of $\hat{p}$ in the usual confidence interval formula. Properties of this modified confidence interval are investigated in Activity 9.2 at the end of the chapter.

AP* EXAM TIP

Knowing the general form of a confidence interval is helpful on the AP Statistics exam. You can use a calculator to compute the confidence interval boundaries, but there is always the possibility of a data-entry error. If you write out the formula and show what numbers you are substituting into the formula, the reader will be able to distinguish a minor data entry error from a more serious mistake.

General Form of a Confidence Interval

Many confidence intervals have the same general form as the large-sample z interval for p just considered. We started with a statistic $\hat{p}$, from which a point estimate for p was obtained. The standard deviation of this statistic is $\sqrt{p(1 - p)/n}$. This resulted in a confidence interval of the form

$$\begin{pmatrix}\text{point estimate using} \\ \text{a specified statistic}\end{pmatrix} \pm (\text{critical value})\begin{pmatrix}\text{standard deviation} \\ \text{of the statistic}\end{pmatrix}$$

Because p was unknown, we estimated the standard deviation of the statistic by $\sqrt{\hat{p}(1 - \hat{p})/n}$, which yielded the interval

$$\begin{pmatrix}\text{point estimate using} \\ \text{a specified statistic}\end{pmatrix} \pm (\text{critical value})\begin{pmatrix}\text{estimated} \\ \text{standard deviation} \\ \text{of the statistic}\end{pmatrix}$$

For a population characteristic other than p, a statistic for estimating the characteristic is selected. Then (drawing on statistical theory) a formula for the standard deviation of the statistic is given. In practice, it is almost always necessary to estimate this standard deviation (using something analogous to $\sqrt{\hat{p}(1-\hat{p})/n}$ rather than $\sqrt{p(1-p)/n}$, for example), so that the interval

$$\begin{pmatrix}\text{point estimate using}\\ \text{a specified statistic}\end{pmatrix} \pm (\text{critical value})\begin{pmatrix}\text{estimated}\\ \text{standard deviation}\\ \text{of the statistic}\end{pmatrix}$$

is the prototype confidence interval. It is common practice to refer to both the standard deviation of a statistic and the *estimated* standard deviation of a statistic as the *standard error*. In this textbook, when we use the term *standard error*, we mean the estimated standard deviation of a statistic.

DEFINITION

The **standard error** of a statistic is the estimated standard deviation of the statistic.

The 95% confidence interval for p is based on the fact that, for approximately 95% of all random samples, $\hat{p}$ is within $1.96\sqrt{\frac{p(1-p)}{n}}$ of p. The quantity $1.96\sqrt{\frac{p(1-p)}{n}}$ is sometimes called the *bound on the error of estimation* associated with a 95% confidence level—we have 95% confidence that the point estimate $\hat{p}$ is no farther than this quantity from p.

DEFINITION

If the sampling distribution of a statistic is (at least approximately) normal, the **bound on error of estimation, *B***, associated with a 95% confidence interval is (1.96) · (standard error of the statistic).

Choosing the Sample Size

Before collecting any data, an investigator may wish to determine a sample size for which a particular value of the bound on the error is achieved. For example, with p representing the actual proportion of students at a university who purchase textbooks over the Internet, the objective of an investigation may be to estimate p to within .05 with 95% confidence. The value of n necessary to achieve this is obtained by equating .05 to $1.96\sqrt{\frac{p(1-p)}{n}}$ and solving for n.

In general, suppose that we wish to estimate p to within an amount B (the specified bound on the error of estimation) with 95% confidence. Finding the necessary sample size requires solving the equation

$$B = 1.96\sqrt{\frac{p(1-p)}{n}}$$

AP* EXAM TIP

The sample size formulas are not provided on the formula sheet provided with the AP Statistics exam. Pay careful attention to the process used in this discussion so that you will still be able to solve sample size problems.

Solving this equation for n results in

$$n = p(1 - p)\left(\frac{1.96}{B}\right)^2$$

Unfortunately, the use of this formula requires the value of p, which is unknown. One possible way to proceed is to carry out a preliminary study and use the resulting data to get a rough estimate of p. In other cases, prior knowledge may suggest a reasonable estimate of p. If there is no reasonable basis for estimating p and a preliminary study is not feasible, a conservative solution follows from the observation that $p(1 - p)$ is never larger than .25 (its value when $p = .5$). Replacing $p(1 - p)$ with .25, the maximum value, yields

$$n = .25\left(\frac{1.96}{B}\right)^2$$

Using this formula to obtain n gives us a sample size for which we can be 95% confident that $\hat{p}$ will be within B of p, no matter what the value of p.

The sample size required to estimate a population proportion p to within an amount B with 95% confidence is

$$n = p(1 - p)\left(\frac{1.96}{B}\right)^2$$

The value of p may be estimated using prior information. In the absence of any such information, using $p = .5$ in this formula gives a conservatively large value for the required sample size (this value of p gives a larger n than would any other value).

EXAMPLE 9.6 Sniffing Out Cancer

Researchers have found biochemical markers of cancer in the exhaled breath of cancer patients, but chemical analysis of breath specimens has not yet proven effective in clinical diagnosis. The authors of the paper "Diagnostic Accuracy of Canine Scent Detection in Early- and Late-Stage Lung and Breast Cancers" (*Integrative Cancer Therapies* [2006]: 1–10) describe a study to investigate whether dogs can be trained to identify the presence or absence of cancer by sniffing breath specimens. Suppose we want to collect data that would allow us to estimate the long-run proportion of accurate identifications for a particular dog that has completed training. The dog has been trained to lie down when presented with a breath specimen from a cancer patient and to remain standing when presented with a specimen from a person who does not have cancer. How many different breath specimens should be used if we want to estimate the long-run proportion of correct identifications for this dog to within .05 with 95% confidence?

Using a conservative value of $p = .5$ in the formula for required sample size gives

$$n = p(1 - p)\left(\frac{1.96}{B}\right)^2 = (.5)(.5)\left(\frac{1.96}{.05}\right)^2 = 384.16$$

Thus, a sample of at least 385 breath specimens should be used. Note that in sample size calculations, we always round up.

EXERCISES 9.10 - 9.33

9.10 ✦ For each of the following choices, explain which would result in a wider large-sample confidence interval for p:

a. 90% confidence level or 95% confidence level
b. $n = 100$ or $n = 400$

9.11 The formula used to compute a large-sample confidence interval for p is

$$\hat{p} \pm (z \text{ critical value})\sqrt{\frac{\hat{p}(1-\hat{p})}{n}}$$

What is the appropriate z critical value for each of the following confidence levels?

a. 95%
b. 90%
c. 99%
d. 80%
e. 85%

9.12 The use of the interval

$$\hat{p} \pm (z \text{ critical value})\sqrt{\frac{\hat{p}(1-\hat{p})}{n}}$$

requires a large sample. For each of the following combinations of n and $\hat{p}$, indicate whether the sample size is large enough for use of this interval to be appropriate.

a. $n = 50$ and $\hat{p} = .30$
b. $n = 50$ and $\hat{p} = .05$
c. $n = 15$ and $\hat{p} = .45$
d. $n = 100$ and $\hat{p} = .01$
e. $n = 100$ and $\hat{p} = .70$
f. $n = 40$ and $\hat{p} = .25$
g. $n = 60$ and $\hat{p} = .25$
h. $n = 80$ and $\hat{p} = .10$

9.13 Discuss how each of the following factors affects the width of the confidence interval for p:

a. The confidence level
b. The sample size
c. The value of $\hat{p}$

9.14 The article "Career Expert Provides DOs and DON'Ts for Job Seekers on Social Networking" (CareerBuilder.com, August 19, 2009) included data from a survey of 2667 hiring managers and human resource professionals. The article noted that many employers are using social networks to screen job applicants and that this practice is becoming more common. Of the 2667 people who participated in the survey, 1200 indicated that they use social networking sites (such as Facebook, MySpace, and LinkedIn) to research job applicants. For the purposes of this exercise, assume that the sample is representative of hiring managers and human resource professionals. Construct and interpret a 95% confidence interval for the proportion of hiring managers and human resource professionals who use social networking sites to research job applicants.

9.15 The article "Nine Out of Ten Drivers Admit in Survey to Having Done Something Dangerous" (*Knight Ridder Newspapers*, July 8, 2005) reported the results of a survey of 1100 drivers. Of those surveyed, 990 admitted to careless or aggressive driving during the previous 6 months. Assuming that it is reasonable to regard this sample of 1100 as representative of the population of drivers, use this information to construct a 99% confidence interval to estimate p, the proportion of all drivers who have engaged in careless or aggressive driving in the previous 6 months.

9.16 In a survey on supernatural experiences, 722 of 4013 adult Americans surveyed reported that they had seen or been with a ghost ("What Supernatural Experiences We've Had," *USA Today*, February 8, 2010).

a. What assumption must be made in order for it to be appropriate to use the formula of this section to construct a confidence interval to estimate the proportion of all adult Americans who have seen or been with a ghost?
b. Construct and interpret a 90% confidence interval for the proportion of all adult Americans who have seen or been with a ghost.
c. Would a 99% confidence interval be narrower or wider than the interval computed in Part (b)? Justify your answer.

9.17 If a hurricane was headed your way, would you evacuate? The headline of a press release issued January 21, 2009 by the survey research company International Communications Research (icrsurvey.com) states, "Thirty-one Percent of People on High-Risk Coast Will Refuse Evacuation Order, Survey of Hurricane Preparedness Finds." This headline was based on a survey of 5046 adults who live within 20 miles of the coast in high hurricane risk counties of eight southern states. In selecting the sample, care was taken to ensure that the sample would be representative of the population of coastal residents in these states. Use this information to estimate the proportion of coastal residents who would evacuate using a 98% confidence interval. Write a few sentences interpreting the interval and the confidence level associated with the interval.

9.18 The study "Digital Footprints" (Pew Internet & American Life Project, www.pewinternet.org, 2007) reported that 47% of Internet users have searched for information about themselves online. The 47% figure was based on a random sample of Internet users. For purposes of this exercise, suppose that the sample size was $n = 300$ (the actual sample size was much larger). Construct and interpret a 90% confidence interval for the proportion of Internet users who have searched online for information about themselves.

9.19 The article "Kids Digital Day: Almost 8 Hours" (*USA Today*, January 20, 2010) summarized results from a national survey of 2002 Americans age 8 to 18. The sample was selected in a way that was expected to result in a sample representative of Americans in this age group.

a. Of those surveyed, 1321 reported owning a cell phone. Use this information to construct and interpret a 90% confidence interval estimate of the proportion of all Americans age 8 to 18 who own a cell phone.

b. Of those surveyed, 1522 reported owning an MP3 music player. Use this information to construct and interpret a 90% confidence interval estimate of the proportion of all Americans age 8 to 18 who own an MP3 music player.

c. Explain why the confidence interval from Part (b) is narrower than the confidence interval from Part (a) even though the confidence level and the sample size used to compute the two intervals was the same.

9.20 The article "Students Increasingly Turn to Credit Cards" (*San Luis Obispo Tribune*, July 21, 2006) reported that 37% of college freshmen and 48% of college seniors carry a credit card balance from month to month. Suppose that the reported percentages were based on random samples of 1000 college freshmen and 1000 college seniors.

a. Construct a 90% confidence interval for the proportion of college freshmen who carry a credit card balance from month to month.

b. Construct a 90% confidence interval for the proportion of college seniors who carry a credit card balance from month to month.

c. Explain why the two 90% confidence intervals from Parts (a) and (b) are not the same width.

9.21 ✦ The article "CSI Effect Has Juries Wanting More Evidence" (*USA Today*, August 5, 2004) examines how the popularity of crime-scene investigation television shows is influencing jurors' expectations of what evidence should be produced at a trial. In a survey of 500 potential jurors, one study found that 350 were regular watchers of at least one crime-scene forensics television series.

a. Assuming that it is reasonable to regard this sample of 500 potential jurors as representative of potential jurors in the United States, use the given information to construct and interpret a 95% confidence interval for the proportion of all potential jurors who regularly watch at least one crime-scene investigation series.

b. Would a 99% confidence interval be wider or narrower than the 95% confidence interval from Part (a)?

9.22 In a survey of 1000 randomly selected adults in the United States, participants were asked what their most favorite and what their least favorite subject was when they were in school (Associated Press, August 17, 2005). In what might seem like a contradiction, math was chosen more often than any other subject in both categories! Math was chosen by 230 of the 1000 as the favorite subject, and it was also chosen by 370 of the 1000 as the least favorite subject.

a. Construct a 95% confidence interval for the proportion of U.S. adults for whom math was the favorite subject in school.

b. Construct a 95% confidence interval for the proportion of U.S. adults for whom math was the least favorite subject.

9.23 The report "2005 Electronic Monitoring & Surveillance Survey: Many Companies Monitoring, Recording, Videotaping—and Firing—Employees" (American Management Association, 2005) summarized the results of a survey of 526 U.S. businesses. The report stated that 137 of the 526 businesses had fired workers for misuse of the Internet and 131 had fired workers for e-mail misuse. For purposes of this exercise, assume that it is reasonable to regard this sample as representative of businesses in the United States.

a. Construct and interpret a 95% confidence interval for the proportion of U.S. businesses that have fired workers for misuse of the Internet.

b. What are two reasons why a 90% confidence interval for the proportion of U.S. businesses that have fired workers for misuse of e-mail would be narrower than the 95% confidence interval computed in Part (a)?

9.24 In an AP-AOL sports poll (Associated Press, December 18, 2005), 394 of 1000 randomly selected U.S. adults indicated that they considered themselves to be baseball fans. Of the 394 baseball fans, 272 stated that they thought the designated hitter rule should either be expanded to both baseball leagues or eliminated.

a. Construct a 95% confidence interval for the proportion of U.S. adults who consider themselves to be baseball fans.
b. Construct a 95% confidence interval for the proportion of those who consider themselves to be baseball fans who think the designated hitter rule should be expanded to both leagues or eliminated.
c. Explain why the confidence intervals of Parts (a) and (b) are not the same width even though they both have a confidence level of 95%.

9.25 The article "Viewers Speak Out Against Reality TV" (Associated Press, September 12, 2005) included the following statement: "Few people believe there's much reality in reality TV: a total of 82% said the shows are either 'totally made up' or 'mostly distorted'." This statement was based on a survey of 1002 randomly selected adults. Compute and interpret a bound on the error of estimation for the reported percentage.

9.26 One thousand randomly selected adult Americans participated in a survey conducted by the Associated Press (June 2006). When asked "Do you think it is sometimes justified to lie or do you think lying is never justified?" 52% responded that lying was never justified. When asked about lying to avoid hurting someone's feelings, 650 responded that this was often or sometimes okay.

a. Construct a 90% confidence interval for the proportion of adult Americans who think lying is never justified.
b. Construct a 90% confidence interval for the proportion of adult American who think that it is often or sometimes okay to lie to avoid hurting someone's feelings.
c. Comment on the apparent inconsistency in the responses given by the individuals in this sample.

9.27 *USA Today* (October 14, 2002) reported that 36% of adult drivers admit that they often or sometimes talk on a cell phone when driving. This estimate was based on data from a sample of 1004 adult drivers, and a bound on the error of estimation of 3.1% was reported. Assuming a 95% confidence level, do you agree with the reported bound on the error? Explain.

9.28 The Gallup Organization conducts an annual survey on crime. It was reported that 25% of all households experienced some sort of crime during the past year. This estimate was based on a sample of 1002 randomly selected households. The report states, "One can say with 95% confidence that the margin of sampling error is ± 3 percentage points." Explain how this statement can be justified.

9.29 The article "Hospitals Dispute Medtronic Data on Wires" (*The Wall Street Journal*, February 4, 2010) describes several studies of the failure rate of defibrillators used in the treatment of heart problems. In one study conducted by the Mayo Clinic, it was reported that failures were experienced within the first 2 years by 18 of 89 patients under 50 years old and 13 of 362 patients age 50 and older who received a particular type of defibrillator. Assume it is reasonable to regard these two samples as representative of patients in the two age groups who receive this type of defibrillator.

a. Construct and interpret a 95% confidence interval for the proportion of patients under 50 years old who experience a failure within the first 2 years after receiving this type of defibrillator.
b. Construct and interpret a 99% confidence interval for the proportion of patients age 50 and older who experience a failure within the first 2 years after receiving this type of defibrillator.
c. Suppose that the researchers wanted to estimate the proportion of patients under 50 years old who experience a failure within the first 2 years after receiving this type of defibrillator to within .03 with 95% confidence. How large a sample should be used? Use the results of the study as a preliminary estimate of the population proportion.

9.30 Based on a representative sample of 511 U.S. teenagers age 12 to 17, International Communications Research estimated that the proportion of teens who support keeping the legal drinking age at 21 is $\hat{p} = 0.64$ (64%). The press release titled "Majority of Teens (Still) Favor the Legal Drinking Age" (www.icrsurvey.com, January 21, 2009) also reported a margin of error of 0.04 (4%) for this estimate. Show how the reported value for the margin of error was computed.

9.31 A discussion of digital ethics appears in the article "Academic Cheating, Aided by Cell Phones or Web, Shown to be Common" (*Los Angeles Times*, June 17, 2009). One question posed in the article is: What proportion of college students have used cell phones to cheat on an exam? Suppose you have been asked to estimate this proportion for students enrolled at a large university. How many students should you include in your sample if you want to estimate this proportion to within .02 with 95% confidence?

9.32 In spite of the potential safety hazards, some people would like to have an Internet connection in their car. A preliminary survey of adult Americans has estimated this proportion to be somewhere around .30 (*USA Today*, May 1, 2009).

a. Use the given preliminary estimate to determine the sample size required to estimate the proportion of adult Americans who would like an Internet connection in their car to within .02 with 95% confidence.
b. The formula for determining sample size given in this section corresponds to a confidence level of 95%. How would you modify this formula if a 99% confidence level was desired?
c. Use the given preliminary estimate to determine the sample size required to estimate the proportion of adult Americans who would like an Internet connection in their car to within .02 with 99% confidence.

9.33 ✦ A consumer group is interested in estimating the proportion of packages of ground beef sold at a particular store that have an actual fat content exceeding the fat content stated on the label. How many packages of ground beef should be tested to estimate this proportion to within .05 with 95% confidence?

9.3 Confidence Interval for a Population Mean

In this section, we consider how to use information from a random sample to construct a confidence interval estimate of a population mean, μ. We begin by considering the case in which (1) σ, **the population standard deviation, is known** (not realistic, but we will see shortly how to handle the more realistic situation where σ is unknown) and (2) **the sample size n is large** enough for the Central Limit Theorem to apply. In this case, the following three properties about the sampling distribution of $\bar{x}$ hold:

1. The sampling distribution of $\bar{x}$ is centered at μ, so $\bar{x}$ is an unbiased statistic for estimating μ ($\mu_{\bar{x}} = \mu$).
2. The standard deviation of $\bar{x}$ is $\sigma_{\bar{x}} = \dfrac{\sigma}{\sqrt{n}}$.
3. As long as n is large (generally $n \geq 30$), the sampling distribution of $\bar{x}$ is approximately normal, even when the population distribution itself is not normal.

The same reasoning that was used to develop the large-sample confidence interval for a population proportion p can be used to obtain a confidence interval estimate for μ.

The One-Sample z Confidence Interval for μ

The general formula for a confidence interval for a population mean μ when

1. $\bar{x}$ is the sample mean from a **simple random sample,**
2. the **sample size n is large** (generally $n \geq 30$), and
3. σ, **the population standard deviation, is known**

is

$$\bar{x} \pm (z \text{ critical value})\left(\frac{\sigma}{\sqrt{n}}\right)$$

EXAMPLE 9.7 Cosmic Radiation

Cosmic radiation levels rise with increasing altitude, prompting researchers to consider how pilots and flight crews might be affected by increased exposure to cosmic radiation. The paper "Estimated Cosmic Radiation Doses for Flight Personnel" (*Space Medicine and Medical Engineering* [2002]: 265–269) reported a mean annual cosmic radiation dose of 219 mrems for a sample of flight personnel of Xinjiang Airlines. Suppose that this mean was based on a random sample of 100 flight crew members.

Let μ denote the mean annual cosmic radiation exposure for all Xinjiang Airlines flight crew members. Although σ, the true population standard deviation, is not usually known, suppose for illustrative purposes that $\sigma = 35$ mrem is known. Because the sample size is large and σ is known, a 95% confidence interval for μ is

$$\begin{aligned}\bar{x} \pm (z \text{ critical value})\left(\frac{\sigma}{\sqrt{n}}\right) &= 219 \pm (1.96)\left(\frac{35}{\sqrt{100}}\right)\\ &= 219 \pm 6.86\\ &= (212.14, 225.86)\end{aligned}$$

Based on this sample, *plausible* values of μ, the actual mean annual cosmic radiation exposure for Xinjaing Airlines flight crew members, are between 212.14 and 225.86 mrem. A 95% confidence level is associated with the method used to produce this interval estimate.

The confidence interval just introduced is appropriate when σ is known and n is large, and it can be used regardless of the shape of the population distribution. This is because this confidence interval is based on the Central Limit Theorem, which says that when n is sufficiently large, the sampling distribution of $\bar{x}$ is approximately normal for any population distribution. When n is small, the Central Limit Theorem cannot be used to justify the normality of the $\bar{x}$ sampling distribution, so the z confidence interval can not be used. One way to proceed in the small-sample case is to make a specific assumption about the shape of the population distribution and then to use a method that is valid under this assumption.

One instance where this is easy to do is when it is reasonable to believe that the population distribution is normal in shape. Recall that for a normal population distribution the sampling distribution of $\bar{x}$ is normal even for small sample sizes. So, if n is small but the population distribution is normal, the same confidence interval formula just introduced can still be used.

If it is reasonable to believe that the distribution of values in the population is normal, a confidence interval for μ (when σ is known) is

$$\bar{x} \pm (z \text{ critical value})\left(\frac{\sigma}{\sqrt{n}}\right)$$

This interval is appropriate even when n is small, as long as it is reasonable to think that the population distribution is normal in shape.

There are several ways that sample data can be used to assess the plausibility of normality. Two common ways are to look at a normal probability plot of the sample data (looking for a plot that is reasonably straight) or to construct a boxplot of the data (looking for approximate symmetry and no outliers).

Confidence Interval for μ When σ Is Unknown

The confidence interval just developed has an obvious drawback: To compute the interval endpoints, σ must be known. Unfortunately, this is rarely the case in practice. We now turn our attention to the situation when σ is unknown. The development of the confidence interval in this instance depends on the assumption that the population distribution is normal. This assumption is not critical if the sample size is large, but it is important when the sample size is small.

To understand the derivation of this confidence interval, it is instructive to begin by taking another look at the previous 95% confidence interval. We know that $\mu_{\bar{x}} = \mu$ and $\sigma_{\bar{x}} = \frac{\sigma}{\sqrt{n}}$. Also, when the population distribution is normal, the $\bar{x}$ distribution is normal. These facts imply that the standardized variable

$$z = \frac{\bar{x} - \mu}{\frac{\sigma}{\sqrt{n}}}$$

has approximately a standard normal distribution. Because the interval from -1.96 to 1.96 captures an area of .95 under the z curve, approximately 95% of all samples result in an $\bar{x}$ value that satisfies

$$-1.96 < \frac{\bar{x} - \mu}{\frac{\sigma}{\sqrt{n}}} < 1.96$$

Manipulating these inequalities to isolate μ in the middle results in the equivalent inequalities:

$$\bar{x} - 1.96\left(\frac{\sigma}{\sqrt{n}}\right) < \mu < \bar{x} + 1.96\left(\frac{\sigma}{\sqrt{n}}\right)$$

The term $\bar{x} - 1.96\left(\frac{\sigma}{\sqrt{n}}\right)$ is the lower endpoint of the 95% large-sample confidence interval for μ, and $\bar{x} + 1.96\left(\frac{\sigma}{\sqrt{n}}\right)$ is the upper endpoint.

If σ is unknown, we must use the sample data to estimate σ. If we use the sample standard deviation as our estimate, the result is a different standardized variable denoted by t:

$$t = \frac{\bar{x} - \mu}{\frac{s}{\sqrt{n}}}$$

The value of s may not be all that close to σ, especially when n is small. As a consequence, the use of s in place of σ introduces extra variability. The value of z varies from sample to sample, because different samples generally result in different $\bar{x}$ values. There is even more variability in t, because different samples may result in different values of both $\bar{x}$ and s. Because of this, the distribution of t is more spread out than the standard normal (z) distribution.

To develop an appropriate confidence interval, we must investigate the probability distribution of the standardized variable t for a sample from a normal population. This requires that we first learn about probability distributions called *t distributions*.

t Distributions

Just as there are many different normal distributions, there are also many different *t* distributions. While normal distributions are distinguished from one another by their mean μ and standard deviation σ, *t* distributions are distinguished by a positive whole number called the number of *degrees of freedom* (df). There is a *t* distribution with 1 df, another with 2 df, and so on.

Important Properties of *t* Distributions

1. The *t* distribution corresponding to any particular number of degrees of freedom is bell shaped and centered at zero (just like the standard normal (z) distribution).
2. Each *t* distribution is more spread out than the standard normal (z) distribution.
3. As the number of degrees of freedom increases, the spread of the corresponding *t* distribution decreases.
4. As the number of degrees of freedom increases, the corresponding sequence of *t* distributions approaches the standard normal (z) distribution.

The properties discussed in the preceding box are illustrated in Figure 9.6, which shows two *t* curves along with the *z* curve.

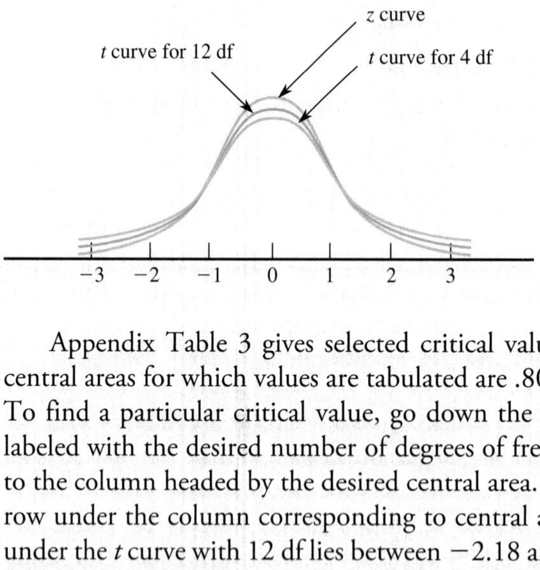

FIGURE 9.6
Comparison of the *z* curve and *t* curves for 12 df and 4 df.

Appendix Table 3 gives selected critical values for various *t* distributions. The central areas for which values are tabulated are .80, .90, .95, .98, .99, .998, and .999. To find a particular critical value, go down the left margin of the table to the row labeled with the desired number of degrees of freedom. Then move over in that row to the column headed by the desired central area. For example, the value in the 12-df row under the column corresponding to central area .95 is 2.18, so 95% of the area under the *t* curve with 12 df lies between −2.18 and 2.18. Moving over two columns, we find the critical value for central area .99 (still with 12 df) to be 3.06 (see Figure 9.7). Moving down the .99 column to the 20-df row, we see the critical value is 2.85, so the area between −2.85 and 2.85 under the *t* curve with 20 df is .99.

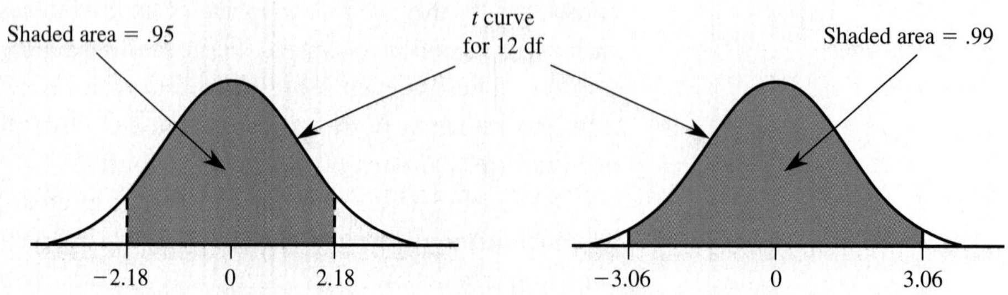

FIGURE 9.7
t critical values illustrated.

Notice that the critical values increase from left to right in each row of Appendix Table 3. This makes sense because as we move to the right, we capture larger central areas. In each column, the critical values decrease as we move downward, reflecting decreasing spread for t distributions with larger degrees of freedom.

The larger the number of degrees of freedom, the more closely the t curve resembles the z curve. To emphasize this, we have included the z critical values as the last row of the t table. Furthermore, once the number of degrees of freedom exceeds 30, the critical values change little as the number of degrees of freedom increases. For this reason, Appendix Table 3 jumps from 30 df to 40 df, then to 60 df, then to 120 df, and finally to the row of z critical values. If we need a critical value for a number of degrees of freedom between those tabulated, we just use the critical value for the closest df. For df $>$ 120, we use the z critical values. Many graphing calculators calculate t critical values for any number of degrees of freedom, so if you are using such a calculator, it is not necessary to approximate the t critical values as described.

One-Sample t Confidence Interval

The fact that the sampling distribution of $\frac{\bar{x} - \mu}{(\sigma/\sqrt{n})}$ is approximately the z (standard normal) distribution when n is large led to the z confidence interval when σ is known. In the same way, the following proposition provides the key to obtaining a confidence interval when the population distribution is normal but σ is unknown.

If $\bar{x}$ and s are the mean and standard deviation of a random sample from a normal population distribution, then the probability distribution of the standardized variable

$$t = \frac{\bar{x} - \mu}{\frac{s}{\sqrt{n}}}$$

is the t distribution with df $= n - 1$.

To see how this result leads to the desired confidence interval, consider the case $n = 25$. We use the t distribution with df $= n - 1 = 24$. From Appendix Table 3, the interval between -2.06 and 2.06 captures a central area of .95 under the t curve with 24 df. This means that 95% of all samples (with $n = 25$) from a normal population result in values of $\bar{x}$ and s for which

$$-2.06 < \frac{\bar{x} - \mu}{\frac{s}{\sqrt{n}}} < 2.06$$

Algebraically manipulating these inequalities to isolate μ yields

$$\bar{x} - 2.06\left(\frac{s}{\sqrt{25}}\right) < \mu < \bar{x} + 2.06\left(\frac{s}{\sqrt{25}}\right)$$

The 95% confidence interval for μ in this situation extends from the lower endpoint $\bar{x} - 2.06\left(\frac{s}{\sqrt{25}}\right)$ to the upper endpoint $\bar{x} + 2.06\left(\frac{s}{\sqrt{25}}\right)$. This interval can also be written

$$\bar{x} \pm 2.06\left(\frac{s}{\sqrt{25}}\right)$$

The differences between this interval and the interval when σ is known are the use of the t critical value 2.06 rather than the z critical value 1.96 and the use of the sample standard deviation as an estimate of σ. The extra uncertainty that results from estimating σ causes the t interval to be wider than the z interval.

If the sample size is something other than 25 or if the desired confidence level is something other than 95%, a different t critical value (obtained from Appendix Table 3) is used in place of 2.06.

The One-Sample t Confidence Interval for μ

The general formula for a confidence interval for a population mean μ based on a sample of size n when

1. $\bar{x}$ is the sample mean from a **simple random sample,**
2. the **population distribution is normal,** *or* **the sample size n is large** (generally $n \geq 30$), and
3. σ, **the population standard deviation, is unknown**

is

$$\bar{x} \pm (t \text{ critical value})\left(\frac{s}{\sqrt{n}}\right)$$

where the t critical value is based on df $= n - 1$. Appendix Table 3 gives critical values appropriate for each of the confidence levels 90%, 95%, and 99%, as well as several other less frequently used confidence levels.

If n is large (generally $n \geq 30$), the normality of the population distribution is not critical. *However, this confidence interval is appropriate for small n only when the population distribution is (at least approximately) normal.* If this is not the case, as might be suggested by a normal probability plot or boxplot, another estimation method should be used.

EXAMPLE 9.8 Drive-Through Medicine

During a flu outbreak, many people visit emergency rooms, where they often must wait in crowded waiting rooms where other patients may be exposed. The paper "Drive-Through Medicine: A Novel Proposal for Rapid Evaluation of Patients during an Influenza Pandemic" (*Annals of Emergency Medicine* [2010]: 268–273) describes an interesting study of the feasibility of a drive-through model where flu patients are evaluated while they remain in their cars. One of the interesting observations from this study was that not only were patients kept relatively isolated and away from other patients, but the time to process a patient was shorter because delays related to turning over examination rooms were eliminated.

In the experiment, 38 volunteers were each given a scenario from a randomly selected set of flu cases seen in the emergency room. The scenarios provided the volunteer with a medical history and a description of symptoms that would allow the volunteer to respond to questions from the examining physician. These volunteer patients were then processed using a drive-through procedure that was implemented in the parking structure of Stanford University Hospital and the time to process each case from admission to discharge was recorded.

Data read from a graph that appears in the paper was used to compute the following summary statistics for admission-to-discharge processing times (in minutes):

$$n = 38 \qquad \bar{x} = 26 \qquad s = 1.57$$

A boxplot of the 38 processing times did show a couple of outliers on the high end, corresponding to unusually long processing times, suggesting that it is probably not reasonable to think of the population distribution of drive-through processing times as being approximately normal. However, because the sample size is greater than 30 and the distribution of sample processing times was not extremely skewed, it is appropriate to consider using the t confidence interval to estimate the mean admission-to-discharge processing time for flu patients using the drive-through procedure. So, because the 38 flu scenarios were thought to be representative of the population of flu patients seen in emergency rooms and the sample size is large, we can use the formula for the t confidence interval to compute a 95% confidence interval.

Because $n = 38$, df = 37, and the appropriate t critical value is 2.02 (from the 40-df row of Appendix Table 3). The confidence interval is then

$$\bar{x} \pm (t \text{ critical value})\left(\frac{s}{\sqrt{n}}\right) = 26 \pm (2.02)\left(\frac{1.57}{\sqrt{38}}\right)$$
$$= 26 \pm .514$$
$$= (25.486, 26.514)$$

Based on the sample data, we believe that the actual mean admission-to-discharge processing time for flu patients processed using the drive-through procedure is between 25.486 minutes and 25.514 minutes. We used a method that has a 5% error rate to construct this interval. The authors of the paper indicated that the average processing time for flu patients seen in the emergency room was about 90 minutes, so it appears that the drive-through procedure has promise both in terms of keeping flu patients isolated and also in reducing processing time.

EXAMPLE 9.9 Waiting for Surgery

The Cardiac Care Network in Ontario, Canada, collected information on the time between the date a patient was recommended for heart surgery and the surgery date for cardiac patients in Ontario ("Wait Times Data Guide," Ministry of Health and Long-Term Care, Ontario, Canada, 2006). The reported mean wait times (in days) for samples of patients for two cardiac procedures are given in the accompanying table. (The standard deviations in the table were estimated from information on wait-time variability included in the report.)

Surgical Procedure	Sample Size	Mean Wait Time	Standard Deviation
Bypass	539	19	10
Angiography	847	18	9

If we had access to the raw data (the 539 + 847 = 1386 individual wait-time observations), we might begin by looking at boxplots. Data consistent with the given summary quantities were used to generate the boxplots of Figure 9.8. The boxplots for the two surgical procedures are similar. There are outliers in both data sets, which might cause us to question the normality of the two wait-time distributions, but because the sample sizes are large, it is still appropriate to use the t confidence interval.

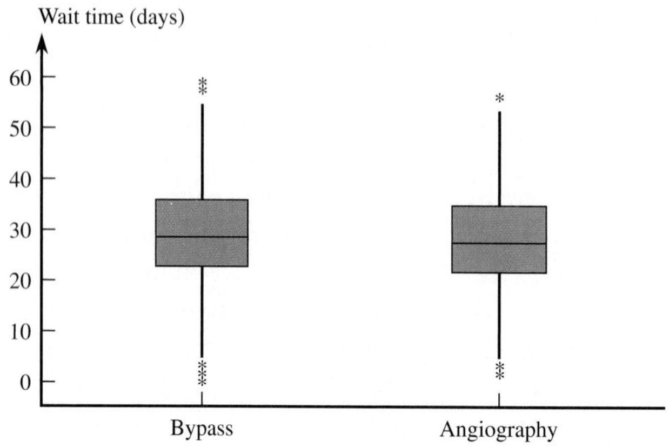

FIGURE 9.8
Boxplots for Example 9.9.

As a next step, we can use the confidence interval of this section to estimate the actual mean wait time for each of the two procedures. Let's first focus on the sample of bypass patients. For this group,

$$\begin{aligned} \text{sample size} &= n = 539 \\ \text{sample mean wait time} &= \bar{x} = 19 \\ \text{sample standard deviation} &= s = 10 \end{aligned}$$

The report referenced here indicated that it is reasonable to regard these data as representative of the Ontario population. So, with μ denoting the mean wait time for bypass surgery in Ontario, we can estimate μ using a 90% confidence interval.

From Appendix Table 3, we use t critical value $= 1.645$ (from the z critical value row because df $= n - 1 = 538 > 120$, the largest number of degrees of freedom in the table). The 90% confidence interval for μ is

$$\begin{aligned} \bar{x} \pm (t \text{ critical value})\left(\frac{s}{\sqrt{n}}\right) &= 19 \pm (1.645)\left(\frac{10}{\sqrt{539}}\right) \\ &= 19 \pm .709 \\ &= (18.291, 19.709) \end{aligned}$$

Based on this sample, we are 90% confident that μ is between 18.291 days and 19.709 days. This interval is fairly narrow, indicating that our information about the value of μ is relatively precise.

A graphing calculator or any of the commercially available statistical computing packages can produce t confidence intervals. Confidence interval output from Minitab for the angiography data is shown here.

One-Sample T

N	Mean	StDev	SE Mean	90% CI
847	18.0000	9.0000	0.3092	(17.4908, 18.5092)

The 90% confidence interval for mean wait time for angiography extends from 17.4908 days to 18.5092 days. This interval is narrower than the 90% interval for bypass surgery wait time for two reasons: the sample size is larger (847 rather than 539) and the sample standard deviation is smaller (9 rather than 10).

EXAMPLE 9.10 Selfish Chimps?

● The article "Chimps Aren't Charitable" (*Newsday*, November 2, 2005) summarized the results of a research study published in the journal *Nature*. In this study, chimpanzees learned to use an apparatus that dispensed food when either of two ropes was pulled. When one of the ropes was pulled, only the chimp controlling the apparatus received food. When the other rope was pulled, food was dispensed both to the chimp controlling the apparatus and also to a chimp in the adjoining cage. The accompanying data (approximated from a graph in the paper) represent the number of times out of 36 trials that each of seven chimps chose the option that would provide food to both chimps (the "charitable" response).

23	22	21	24	19	20	20

Figure 9.9 is a normal probability plot of these data. The plot is reasonably straight, so it seems plausible that the population distribution of number of charitable responses is approximately normal.

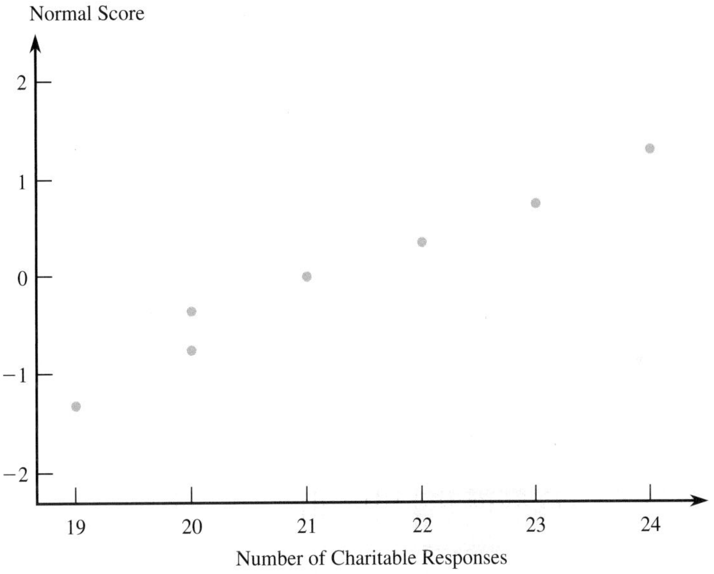

FIGURE 9.9
Normal probability plot for data of Example 9.10

For purposes of this example, let's suppose it is reasonable to regard this sample of seven chimps as representative of the population of all chimpanzees. Calculation of a confidence interval for the mean number of charitable responses for the population of all chimps requires $\bar{x}$ and s. From the given data, we compute

$$\bar{x} = 21.29 \quad s = 1.80$$

The t critical value for a 99% confidence interval based on 6 df is 3.71. The interval is

$$\begin{aligned}\bar{x} \pm (t \text{ critical value})\left(\frac{s}{\sqrt{n}}\right) &= 21.29 \pm (3.71)\left(\frac{1.80}{\sqrt{7}}\right)\\ &= 21.29 \pm 2.52\\ &= (18.77, 23.81)\end{aligned}$$

A statistical software package could also have been used to compute the 99% confidence interval. The following is output from SPSS. The slight discrepancy between

!! Step-by-Step technology instructions available online

● Data set available online

the hand-calculated interval and the one reported by SPSS occurs because SPSS uses more decimal accuracy in $\bar{x}$, s, and t critical values.

One-Sample Statistics

	N	Mean	Std. Deviation	Std. Error Mean
CharitableResponses	7	21.2857	1.79947	.68014

One-Sample

	99% Confidence Interval	
	Lower	**Upper**
CharitableResponses	18.7642	23.8073

With 99% confidence, we estimate the population mean number of charitable responses (out of 36 trials) to be between 18.77 and 23.81. Remember that the 99% confidence level implies that if the same formula is used to calculate intervals for sample after sample randomly selected from the population of chimps, in the long run 99% of these intervals will capture μ between the lower and upper confidence limits.

Notice that based on this interval, we would conclude that, on average, chimps choose the charitable option more than half the time (more than 18 out of 36 trials). The *Newsday* headline "Chimps Aren't Charitable" was based on additional data from the study indicating that chimps' charitable behavior was no different when there was another chimp in the adjacent cage than when the adjacent cage was empty. We will revisit this study in Chapter 11 to investigate this further.

Choosing the Sample Size

When estimating μ using a large sample or using a small sample from a normal population, the bound B on the error of estimation associated with a 95% confidence interval is

$$B = 1.96\left(\frac{\sigma}{\sqrt{n}}\right)$$

Before collecting any data, an investigator may wish to determine a sample size for which a particular value of the bound is achieved. For example, with μ representing the average fuel efficiency (in miles per gallon, mpg) for all cars of a certain type, the objective of an investigation may be to estimate μ to within 1 mpg with 95% confidence. The value of n necessary to achieve this is obtained by setting $B = 1$ and then solving $1 = 1.96\left(\frac{\sigma}{\sqrt{n}}\right)$ for n.

In general, suppose that we wish to estimate μ to within an amount B (the specified bound on the error of estimation) with 95% confidence. Finding the necessary sample size requires solving the equation $B = 1.96\left(\frac{\sigma}{\sqrt{n}}\right)$ for n. The result is

$$n = \left(\frac{1.96\sigma}{B}\right)^2$$

Notice that the greater the variability in the population (larger σ), the greater the required sample size will be. And, of course, the smaller the desired bound on error is, the larger the required sample size will be.

Use of the sample-size formula requires that σ be known, but this is rarely the case in practice. One possible strategy for estimating σ is to carry out a preliminary study and use the resulting sample standard deviation (or a somewhat larger value, to be conservative) to determine n for the main part of the study. Another possibility is simply to make an educated guess about the value of σ and to use that value to calculate n. For a population distribution that is not too skewed, dividing the anticipated range (the difference between the largest and the smallest values) by 4 often gives a rough idea of the value of the standard deviation.

The sample size required to estimate a population mean μ to within an amount B with 95% confidence is

$$n = \left(\frac{1.96\sigma}{B}\right)^2$$

If σ is unknown, it may be estimated based on previous information or, for a population that is not too skewed, by using (range)/4.

If the desired confidence level is something other than 95%, 1.96 is replaced by the appropriate z critical value (for example, 2.58 for 99% confidence).

EXAMPLE 9.11 Cost of Textbooks

The financial aid office wishes to estimate the mean cost of textbooks per quarter for students at a particular university. For the estimate to be useful, it should be within \$20 of the true population mean. How large a sample should be used to be 95% confident of achieving this level of accuracy?

To determine the required sample size, we must have a value for σ. The financial aid office is pretty sure that the amount spent on books varies widely, with most values between \$150 and \$550. A reasonable estimate of σ is then

$$\frac{range}{4} = \frac{550 - 150}{4} = \frac{400}{4} = 100$$

The required sample size is

$$n = \left(\frac{1.96\sigma}{B}\right)^2 = \left(\frac{(1.96)(100)}{20}\right)^2 = (9.8)^2 = 96.04$$

Rounding up, a sample size of 97 or larger is recommended.

EXERCISES 9.34 - 9.52

9.34 Given a variable that has a t distribution with the specified degrees of freedom, what percentage of the time will its value fall in the indicated region?

a. 10 df, between -1.81 and 1.81
b. 10 df, between -2.23 and 2.23
c. 24 df, between -2.06 and 2.06
d. 24 df, between -2.80 and 2.80
e. 24 df, outside the interval from -2.80 to 2.80
f. 24 df, to the right of 2.80
g. 10 df, to the left of -1.81

9.35 The formula used to compute a confidence interval for the mean of a normal population when n is small is

$$\bar{x} \pm (t \text{ critical value})\frac{s}{\sqrt{n}}$$

What is the appropriate t critical value for each of the following confidence levels and sample sizes?

a. 95% confidence, $n = 17$
b. 90% confidence, $n = 12$
c. 99% confidence, $n = 24$
d. 90% confidence, $n = 25$
e. 90% confidence, $n = 13$
f. 95% confidence, $n = 10$

9.36 The two intervals (114.4, 115.6) and (114.1, 115.9) are confidence intervals (computed using the same sample data) for μ = true average resonance frequency (in hertz) for all tennis rackets of a certain type.

a. What is the value of the sample mean resonance frequency?
b. The confidence level for one of these intervals is 90% and for the other it is 99%. Which is which, and how can you tell?

9.37 ✦ Samples of two different models of cars were selected, and the actual speed for each car was determined when the speedometer registered 50 mph. The resulting 95% confidence intervals for mean actual speed were (51.3, 52.7) and (49.4, 50.6). Assuming that the two sample standard deviations are equal, which confidence interval is based on the larger sample size? Explain your reasoning.

9.38 The authors of the paper "Deception and Design: The Impact of Communication Technology on Lying Behavior" (*Proceedings of Computer Human Interaction* [2004]) asked 30 students in an upper division communications course at a large university to keep a journal for 7 days, recording each social interaction and whether or not they told any lies during that interaction. A lie was defined as "any time you intentionally try to mislead someone." The paper reported that the mean number of lies per day for the 30 students was 1.58 and the standard deviation of number of lies per day was 1.02.

a. What assumption must be made in order for the t confidence interval of this section to be an appropriate method for estimating μ, the mean number of lies per day for all students at this university?
b. Would you recommend using the t confidence interval to construct an estimate of μ as defined in Part (a)? Explain why or why not.

9.39 In a study of academic procrastination, the authors of the paper "Correlates and Consequences of Behavioral Procrastination" (*Procrastination, Current Issues and New Directions* [2000]) reported that for a sample of 411 undergraduate students at a midsize public university preparing for a final exam in an introductory psychology course, the mean time spent studying for the exam was 7.74 hours and the standard deviation of study times was 3.40 hours. For purposes of this exercise, assume that it is reasonable to regard this sample as representative of students taking introductory psychology at this university.

a. Construct a 95% confidence interval to estimate μ, the mean time spent studying for the final exam for students taking introductory psychology at this university.
b. The paper also gave the following sample statistics for the percentage of study time that occurred in the 24 hours prior to the exam:

$$n = 411 \qquad \bar{x} = 43.18 \qquad s = 21.46$$

Construct and interpret a 90% confidence interval for the mean percentage of study time that occurs in the 24 hours prior to the exam.

9.40 How much money do people spend on graduation gifts? In 2007, the National Retail Federation (www.nrf.com) surveyed 2815 consumers who reported that they bought one or more graduation gifts that year. The sample was selected in a way designed to produce a sample representative of adult Americans who purchased graduation gifts in 2007. For this sample, the mean amount spent per gift was \$55.05. Suppose that the sample standard deviation was \$20. Construct and interpret a 98% confidence interval for the mean amount of money spent per graduation gift in 2007.

9.41 In June 2009, Harris Interactive conducted its Great Schools Survey. In this survey, the sample consisted of 1086 adults who were parents of school-aged children. The sample was selected in a way that makes it reasonable to regard it as representative of the population of parents of school-aged children. One question on the survey asked respondents how much time (in hours) per month they spent volunteering at their children's school during the previous school year. The following summary statistics for time volunteered per month were given:

$$n = 1086 \qquad \bar{x} = 5.6 \qquad \text{median} = 1$$

a. What does the fact that the mean is so much larger than the median tell you about the distribution of time spent volunteering per month?
b. Based on your answer to Part (a), explain why it is not reasonable to assume that the population distribution of time spent volunteering is approximately normal.

c. Explain why it is appropriate to use the t confidence interval to estimate the mean time spent volunteering for the population of parents of school-aged children even though the population distribution is not approximately normal.

d. Suppose that the sample standard deviation was $s = 5.2$. Compute and interpret a 98% confidence interval for μ, the mean time spent volunteering for the population of parents of school-aged children.

9.42 The authors of the paper "Driven to Distraction" (*Psychological Science* [2001]: 462–466) describe an experiment to evaluate the effect of using a cell phone on reaction time. Subjects were asked to perform a simulated driving task while talking on a cell phone. While performing this task, occasional red and green lights flashed on the computer screen. If a green light flashed, subjects were to continue driving, but if a red light flashed, subjects were to brake as quickly as possible and the reaction time (in msec) was recorded. The following summary statistics are based on a graph that appeared in the paper:

$n = 48 \qquad \bar{x} = 530 \qquad s = 70$

a. Construct and interpret a 95% confidence interval for μ, the mean time to react to a red light while talking on a cell phone. What assumption must be made in order to generalize this confidence interval to the population of all drivers?

b. Suppose that the researchers wanted to estimate the mean reaction time to within 5 msec with 95% confidence. Using the sample standard deviation from the study described as a preliminary estimate of the standard deviation of reaction times, compute the required sample size.

9.43 Suppose that a random sample of 50 bottles of a particular brand of cough medicine is selected and the alcohol content of each bottle is determined. Let μ denote the mean alcohol content (in percent) for the population of all bottles of the brand under study. Suppose that the sample of 50 results in a 95% confidence interval for μ of (7.8, 9.4).

a. Would a 90% confidence interval have been narrower or wider than the given interval? Explain your answer.

b. Consider the following statement: There is a 95% chance that μ is between 7.8 and 9.4. Is this statement correct? Why or why not?

c. Consider the following statement: If the process of selecting a sample of size 50 and then computing the corresponding 95% confidence interval is repeated 100 times, 95 of the resulting intervals will include μ. Is this statement correct? Why or why not?

9.44 ✦ Acrylic bone cement is sometimes used in hip and knee replacements to fix an artificial joint in place. The force required to break an acrylic bone cement bond was measured for six specimens under specified conditions, and the resulting mean and standard deviation were 306.09 Newtons and 41.97 Newtons, respectively. Assuming that it is reasonable to believe that breaking force under these conditions has a distribution that is approximately normal, estimate the mean breaking force for acrylic bone cement under the specified conditions using a 95% confidence interval.

9.45 The article "The Association Between Television Viewing and Irregular Sleep Schedules Among Children Less Than 3 Years of Age" (*Pediatrics* [2005]: 851–856) reported the accompanying 95% confidence intervals for average TV viewing time (in hours per day) for three different age groups.

Age Group	95% Confidence Interval
Less than 12 months	(0.8, 1.0)
12 to 23 months	(1.4, 1.8)
24 to 35 months	(2.1, 2.5)

a. Suppose that the sample sizes for each of the three age group samples were equal. Based on the given confidence intervals, which of the age group samples had the greatest variability in TV viewing time? Explain your choice.

b. Now suppose that the sample standard deviations for the three age group samples were equal, but that the three sample sizes might have been different. Which of the three age-group samples had the largest sample size? Explain your choice.

c. The interval (.768, 1.032) is either a 90% confidence interval or a 99% confidence interval for the mean TV viewing time computed using the sample data for children less than 12 months old. Is the confidence level for this interval 90% or 99%? Explain your choice.

9.46 The article "Most Canadians Plan to Buy Treats, Many Will Buy Pumpkins, Decorations and/or Costumes" (Ipsos-Reid, October 24, 2005) summarized results from a survey of 1000 randomly selected Canadian residents. Each individual in the sample was asked how much he or she anticipated spending on Halloween during 2005. The resulting sample mean and standard deviation were \$46.65 and \$83.70, respectively.

a. Explain how it could be possible for the standard deviation of the anticipated Halloween expense to be larger than the mean anticipated expense.
b. Is it reasonable to think that the distribution of the variable *anticipated Halloween expense* is approximately normal? Explain why or why not.
c. Is it appropriate to use the t confidence interval to estimate the mean anticipated Halloween expense for Canadian residents? Explain why or why not.
d. If appropriate, construct and interpret a 99% confidence interval for the mean anticipated Halloween expense for Canadian residents.

9.47 Because of safety considerations, in May 2003 the Federal Aviation Administration (FAA) changed its guidelines for how small commuter airlines must estimate passenger weights. Under the old rule, airlines used 180 pounds as a typical passenger weight (including carry-on luggage) in warm months and 185 pounds as a typical weight in cold months. The *Alaska Journal of Commerce* (May 25, 2003) reported that Frontier Airlines conducted a study to estimate average passenger plus carry-on weights. They found an average summer weight of 183 pounds and a winter average of 190 pounds. Suppose that each of these estimates was based on a random sample of 100 passengers and that the sample standard deviations were 20 pounds for the summer weights and 23 pounds for the winter weights.

a. Construct and interpret a 95% confidence interval for the mean summer weight (including carry-on luggage) of Frontier Airlines passengers.
b. Construct and interpret a 95% confidence interval for the mean winter weight (including carry-on luggage) of Frontier Airlines passengers.
c. The new FAA recommendations are 190 pounds for summer and 195 pounds for winter. Comment on these recommendations in light of the confidence interval estimates from Parts (a) and (b).

9.48 ● Example 9.3 gave the following airborne times (in minutes) for 10 randomly selected flights from San Francisco to Washington Dulles airport:

270 256 267 285 274 275 266 258 271 281

a. Compute and interpret a 90% confidence interval for the mean airborne time for flights from San Francisco to Washington Dulles.
b. Give an interpretation of the 90% confidence level associated with the interval estimate in Part (a).
c. If a flight from San Francisco to Washington Dulles is scheduled to depart at 10 A.M., what would you recommend for the published arrival time? Explain.

9.49 ● Fat content (in grams) for seven randomly selected hot dogs that were rated as very good by Consumer Reports (www.consumerreports.org) is shown below. Is it reasonable to use this data and the t confidence interval of this section to construct a confidence interval for the mean fat content of hot dogs rated as very good by Consumer Reports? Explain why or why not.

14 15 11 10 6 15 16

9.50 ● Five students visiting the student health center for a free dental examination during National Dental Hygiene Month were asked how many months had passed since their last visit to a dentist. Their responses were as follows:

6 17 11 22 29

Assuming that these five students can be considered a random sample of all students participating in the free checkup program, construct a 95% confidence interval for the mean number of months elapsed since the last visit to a dentist for the population of students participating in the program.

9.51 The Bureau of Alcohol, Tobacco, and Firearms (BATF) has been concerned about lead levels in California wines. In a previous testing of wine specimens, lead levels ranging from 50 to 700 parts per billion were recorded. How many wine specimens should be tested if the BATF wishes to estimate the true mean lead level for California wines to within 10 parts per billion with 95% confidence?

9.52 The formula described in this section for determining sample size corresponds to a confidence level of 95%. What would be the appropriate formula for determining sample size when the desired confidence level is 90%? 98%?

9.4 Interpreting and Communicating the Results of Statistical Analyses

The purpose of most surveys and many research studies is to produce estimates of population characteristics. One way of providing such an estimate is to construct and report a confidence interval for the population characteristic of interest.

Communicating the Results of Statistical Analyses

When using sample data to estimate a population characteristic, a point estimate or a confidence interval estimate might be used. Confidence intervals are generally preferred because a point estimate by itself does not convey any information about the accuracy of the estimate. For this reason, whenever you report the value of a point estimate, it is a good idea to also include an estimate of the bound on the error of estimation.

Reporting and interpreting a confidence interval estimate requires a bit of care. First, always report both the confidence interval and the confidence level associated with the method used to produce the interval. Then, remember that both the confidence interval and the confidence level should be interpreted. A good strategy is to begin with an interpretation of the confidence interval in the context of the problem and then to follow that with an interpretation of the confidence level. For example, if a 90% confidence interval for p, the proportion of students at a particular university who own a laptop computer, is (.56, .78), we might say

interpretation of interval → We can be 90% confident that between 56% and 78% of the students at this university own laptops.

explanation of "90% confidence" interpretation of confidence level → We have used a method to produce this estimate that is successful in capturing the actual population proportion 90% of the time.

When providing an interpretation of a confidence interval, remember that the interval is an estimate of a population characteristic and be careful *not* to say that the interval applies to individual values in the population or to the values of sample statistics. For example, if a 99% confidence interval for μ, the mean amount of ketchup in bottles labeled as 12 ounces, is (11.94, 11.98), this does not tell us that 99% of 12-ounce ketchup bottles contain between 11.94 and 11.98 ounces of ketchup. Nor does it tell us that 99% of samples of the same size would have sample means in this particular range. The confidence interval is an estimate of the *mean* for all bottles in the *population* of interest.

Interpreting the Results of Statistical Analyses

Unfortunately, there is no customary way of reporting the estimates of population characteristics in published sources. Possibilities include

confidence interval
estimate ± bound on error
estimate ± standard error

If the population characteristic being estimated is a population mean, then you may also see

sample mean ± sample standard deviation

If the interval reported is described as a confidence interval, a confidence level should accompany it. These intervals can be interpreted just as we have interpreted the confidence intervals in this chapter, and the confidence level specifies the long-run error rate associated with the method used to construct the interval (for example, a 95% confidence level specifies a 5% long-run error rate).

A form particularly common in news articles is estimate ± bound on error, where the bound on error is also sometimes called the **margin of error**. The bound on error reported is usually two times the standard deviation of the estimate. This method of reporting is a little less formal than a confidence interval and, if the sample size is reasonably large, is roughly equivalent to reporting a 95% confidence interval. You can interpret these intervals as you would a confidence interval with approximate confidence level of 95%.

You must use care in interpreting intervals reported in the form of an estimate ± standard error. Recall from Section 9.2 that the general form of a confidence interval is

estimate ± (critical value)(standard deviation of the estimate)

In journal articles, the estimated standard deviation of the estimate is usually referred to as the *standard error*. The critical value in the confidence interval formula was determined by the form of the sampling distribution of the estimate and by the confidence level. Note that the reported form, estimate ± standard error, is equivalent to a confidence interval with the critical value set equal to 1. For a statistic whose sampling distribution is (approximately) normal (such as the mean of a large sample or a large-sample proportion), a critical value of 1 corresponds to an approximate confidence level of about 68%. Because a confidence level of 68% is rather low, you may want to use the given information and the confidence interval formula to convert to an interval with a higher confidence level.

When researchers are trying to estimate a population mean, they sometimes report sample mean ± sample standard deviation. Be particularly careful here. To convert this information into a useful interval estimate of the population mean, you must first convert the sample standard deviation to the standard error of the sample mean (by dividing by $\sqrt{n}$) and then use the standard error and an appropriate critical value to construct a confidence interval.

For example, suppose that a random sample of size 100 is used to estimate the population mean. If the sample resulted in a sample mean of 500 and a sample standard deviation of 20, you might find the published results summarized in any of the following ways:

95% confidence interval for the population mean: (496.08, 503.92)
mean ± bound on error: 500 ± 4
mean ± standard error: 500 ± 2
mean ± standard deviation: 500 ± 20

What to Look For in Published Data

Here are some questions to ask when you encounter interval estimates in research reports.

- Is the reported interval a confidence interval, mean ± bound on error, mean ± standard error, or mean ± standard deviation? If the reported interval is not a confidence interval, you may want to construct a confidence interval from the given information.

- What confidence level is associated with the given interval? Is the choice of confidence level reasonable? What does the confidence level say about the long-run error rate of the method used to construct the interval?
- Is the reported interval relatively narrow or relatively wide? Has the population characteristic been estimated precisely?

For example, the article "Use of a Cast Compared with a Functional Ankle Brace After Operative Treatment of an Ankle Fracture" (*Journal of Bone and Joint Surgery* [2003]: 205–211) compared two different methods of immobilizing an ankle after surgery to repair damage from a fracture. The article includes the following statement:

> The mean duration (and standard deviation) between the operation and return to work was 63±13 days (median, sixty-three days; range, thirty three to ninety-eight days) for the cast group and 65±19 days (median, sixty-two days; range, eight to 131 days) for the brace group; the difference was not significant.

This is an example of a case where we must be careful—the reported intervals are of the form estimate ± standard deviation. We can use this information to construct a confidence interval for the mean time between surgery and return to work for each method of immobilization. One hundred patients participated in the study, with 50 wearing a cast after surgery and 50 wearing an ankle brace (random assignment was used to assign patients to treatment groups). Because the sample sizes are both large, we can use the t confidence interval formula

$$\text{mean} \pm (t \text{ critical value})\left(\frac{s}{\sqrt{n}}\right)$$

Each sample has df = 50 − 1 = 49. The closest df value in Appendix Table 3 is for df = 40, and the corresponding t critical value for a 95% confidence level is 2.02. The corresponding intervals are

$$\text{Cast: } 63 \pm 2.02\left(\frac{13}{\sqrt{50}}\right) = 63 \pm 3.71 = (59.29, 66.71)$$

$$\text{Brace: } 65 \pm 2.02\left(\frac{19}{\sqrt{50}}\right) = 65 \pm 5.43 = (59.57, 70.43)$$

The chosen confidence level of 95% implies that the method used to construct each of the intervals has a 5% long-run error rate. Assuming that it is reasonable to view these samples as representative of the patient population, we can interpret these intervals as follows: We can be 95% confident that the mean return-to-work time for those treated with a cast is between 59.29 and 66.71 days, and we can be 95% confident that the mean return-to-work time for those treated with an ankle brace is between 59.57 and 70.43 days. These intervals are relatively wide, indicating that the values of the treatment means have not been estimated as precisely as we might like. This is not surprising, given the sample sizes and the variability in each sample. Note that the two intervals overlap. This supports the statement that the difference between the two immobilization methods was not significant. Formal methods for directly comparing two groups, covered in Chapter 11, could be used to further investigate this issue.

A Word to the Wise: Cautions and Limitations

When working with point and confidence interval estimates, here are a few things you need to keep in mind;

1. In order for an estimate to be useful, we must know something about accuracy. You should beware of point estimates that are not accompanied by a bound on error or some other measure of accuracy.
2. A confidence interval estimate that is wide indicates that we don't have very precise information about the population characteristics being estimated. Don't be fooled by a high confidence level if the resulting interval is wide. High confidence, while desirable, is not the same thing as saying we have precise information about the value of a population characteristic.

   The width of a confidence interval is affected by the confidence level, the sample size, and the standard deviation of the statistic used (for example, $\hat{p}$ or $\bar{x}$) as the basis for constructing the interval. The best strategy for decreasing the width of a confidence interval is to take a larger sample. It is far better to think about this before collecting data and to use the required sample size formulas to determine a sample size that will result in a confidence interval estimate that is narrow enough to provide useful information.
3. The accuracy of estimates depends on the sample size, not the population size. This may be counter to intuition, but as long as the sample size is small relative to the population size (n less than 10% of the population size), the bound on error for estimating a population proportion with 95% confidence is approximately $2\sqrt{\frac{\hat{p}(1-\hat{p})}{n}}$ and for estimating a population mean with 95% confidence is approximately $2\frac{s}{\sqrt{n}}$.

   Note that each of these involves the sample size n, and both bounds decrease as the sample size increases. Neither approximate bound on error depends on the population size.

   The size of the population does need to be considered if sampling is without replacement and the sample size is more than 10% of the population size. In this case, a **finite population correction factor** $\sqrt{\frac{N-n}{N-1}}$ is used to adjust the bound on error (the given bound is multiplied by the correction factor). Since this correction factor is always less than 1, the adjusted bound on error is smaller.
4. Assumptions and "plausibility" conditions are important. The confidence interval procedures of this chapter require certain assumptions. If these assumptions are met, the confidence intervals provide us with a method for using sample data to estimate population characteristics with confidence. When the assumptions associated with a confidence interval procedure are in fact true, the confidence level specifies a correct success rate for the method. However, assumptions (such as the assumption of a normal population distribution) are rarely exactly met in practice. Fortunately, in most cases, as long as the assumptions are approximately met, the confidence interval procedures still work well.

   In general, we can only determine if assumptions are "plausible" or approximately met, and that we are in the situation where we expect the inferential procedure to work reasonably well. This is usually confirmed by knowledge of the data collection process and by using the sample data to check certain "plausibility conditions."

The formal assumptions for the z confidence interval for a population proportion are

1. The sample is a random sample from the population of interest.
2. The sample size is large enough for the sampling distribution of $\hat{p}$ to be approximately normal.
3. Sampling is without replacement.

Whether the random sample assumption is plausible will depend on how the sample was selected and the intended population. Plausibility conditions for the other two assumptions are the following:

$n\hat{p} \geq 10$ and $n(1 - \hat{p}) \geq 10$ (so the sampling distribution of $\hat{p}$ is approximately normal), and

n is less than 10% of the population size (so that the formula for the standard deviation of $\hat{p}$ provides a good approximation to the actual standard deviation).

The formal assumptions for the t confidence interval for a population mean are

1. The sample is a random sample from the population of interest.
2. The population distribution is normal, so that the distribution of

$$t = \frac{\bar{x} - \mu}{s/\sqrt{n}}$$ has a t distribution.

The plausibility of the random sample assumption, as was the case for proportions, will depend on how the sample was selected and the population of interest. The plausibility conditions for the normal population distribution assumption are the following:

A normal probability plot of the data is reasonably straight (indicating that the population distribution is approximately normal), or

The data distribution is approximately symmetric and there are no outliers. This may be confirmed by looking at a dotplot, boxplot, stem-and-leaf display, or histogram of the data.

Alternatively, if n is large ($n \geq 30$), the sampling distribution of $\bar{x}$ will be approximately normal even for nonnormal population distributions. This implies that use of the t interval is appropriate even if population normality is not plausible.

In the end, you must decide that the assumptions are met or that they are "plausible" and that the inferential method used will provide reasonable results. This is also true for the inferential methods introduced in the chapters that follow.

5. Watch out for the "±" when reading published reports. Don't fall into the trap of thinking confidence interval every time you see a ± in an expression. As was discussed earlier in this section, published reports are not consistent, and in addition to confidence intervals, it is common to see estimate ± standard error and estimate ± sample standard deviation reported.

EXERCISES 9.53 - 9.55

9.53 The following quote is from the article "Credit Card Debt Rises Faster for Seniors" (*USA Today*, July 28, 2009):

> The study, which will be released today by Demos, a liberal public policy group, shows that low- and middle-income consumers 65 and older carried \$10,235 in average credit card debt last year.

What additional information would you want in order to evaluate the accuracy of this estimate? Explain.

9.54 Authors of the news release titled "Major Gaps Still Exist Between the Perception and the Reality of Americans' Internet Security Protections, Study Finds" (The National Cyber Security Alliance) estimated the proportion of Americans who claim to have a firewall installed on their computer to protect them from computer hackers to be .80 based on a survey conducted by the Zogby market research firm. They also estimated the proportion of those who actually have a firewall installed to be .42, based on checkups performed by Norton's PC Help software. The following quote is from the news release:

> For the study, NCSA commissioned a Zogby survey of more than 3000 Americans and Symantec conducted checkups of 400 Americans' personal computers performed by PC Help by Norton (www.norton.com/tuneup). The Zogby poll has a margin of error of +/− 1.6% and the checkup has a margin of error of +/− 5%.

Explain why the margins of error for the two estimated proportions are different.

9.55 The paper "The Curious Promiscuity of Queen Honey Bees (*Apis mellifera*): Evolutionary and Behavioral Mechanisms" (*Annals of Zoology Fennici* [2001]:255–265) describes a study of the mating behavior of queen honeybees. The following quote is from the paper:

> Queens flew for an average of 24.2 ± 9.21 minutes on their mating flights, which is consistent with previous findings. On those flights, queens effectively mated with 4.6 ± 3.47 males (mean ± SD).

a. The intervals reported in the quote from the paper were based on data from the mating flights of $n = 30$ queen honeybees. One of the two intervals reported is stated to be a confidence interval for a population mean. Which interval is this? Justify your choice.

b. Use the given information to construct a 95% confidence interval for the mean number of partners on a mating flight for queen honeybees. For purposes of this exercise, assume that it is reasonable to consider these 30 queen honeybees as representative of the population of queen honeybees.

ACTIVITY 9.1 Getting a Feel for Confidence Level

Technology Activity (Applet): Open the applet (available at www.cengage.com/statistics/POD4e) called ConfidenceIntervals. You should see a screen like the one shown here.

Getting Started: If the "Method" box does not say "Means," use the drop-down menu to select Means. In the box just below, select "t' from the drop-down menu. This applet will select a random sample from a specified normal population distribution and then use the sample to construct a confidence interval for the population mean. The interval is then plotted on the display, and you can see if the resulting interval contains the actual value of the population mean.

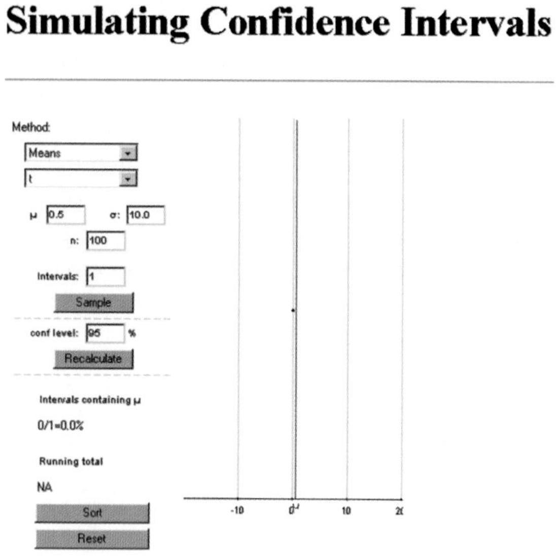

For purposes of this activity, we will sample from a normal population with mean 100 and standard deviation 5. We will begin with a sample size of $n = 10$. In the applet window, set $\mu = 100$, $\sigma = 5$, and $n = 10$. Leave the conf-level box set at 95%. Click the "Recalculate" button to rescale the picture on the right. Now click on the sample button. You should see a confidence interval appear on the display on the right-hand side. If the interval contains the actual mean of 100, the interval is drawn in green; if 100 is not in the confidence interval, the interval is shown in red. Your screen should look something like the following.

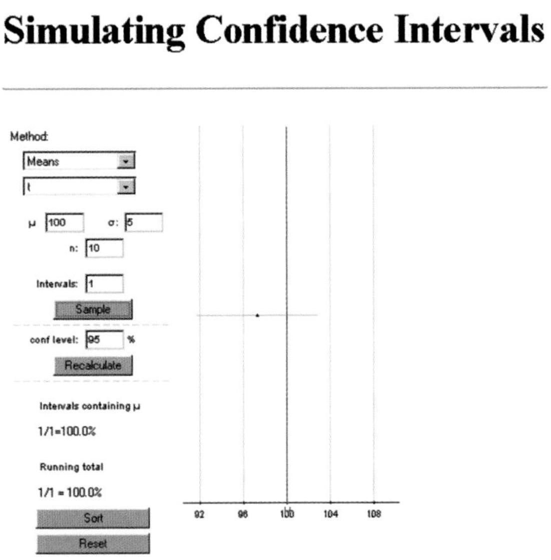

Part 1: Click on the "Sample" button several more times, and notice how the confidence interval estimate changes from sample to sample. Also notice that at the bottom of the left-hand side of the display, the applet is keeping track of the proportion of all the intervals calculated so far that include the actual value of μ. If we were to construct a large number of intervals, this proportion should closely approximate the capture rate for the confidence interval method.

To look at more than one interval at a time, change the "Intervals" box from 1 to 100, and then click the sample button. You should see a screen similar to the one at the top right of this page, with 100 intervals in the display on the right-hand side. Again, intervals containing 100 (the value of μ in this case) will be green and those that do not contain 100 will be red. Also note that the capture proportion on the left-hand side has also been updated to reflect what happened with the 100 newly generated intervals.

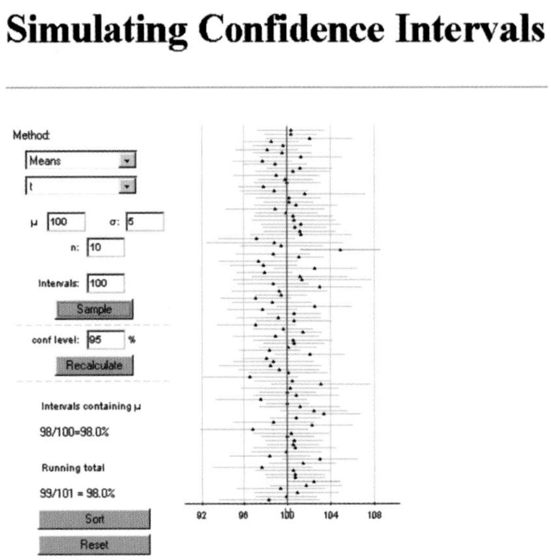

Continue generating intervals until you have seen at least 1000 intervals, and then answer the following question:

a. How does the proportion of intervals constructed that contain $\mu = 100$ compare to the stated confidence level of 95%? On how many intervals was your proportion based? (Note—if you followed the instructions, this should be at least 1000.)

Experiment with three other confidence levels of your choice, and then answer the following question:

b. In general, is the proportion of computed t confidence intervals that contain $\mu = 100$ close to the stated confidence level?

Part 2: When the population is normal but σ is unknown, we construct a confidence interval for a population mean using a t critical value rather than a z critical value. How important is this distinction?

Let's investigate. Use the drop-down menu to change the box just below the method box that's says "Means" from "t" to "z with s." The applet will now construct intervals using the sample standard deviation, but will use a z critical value rather than the t critical value.

Use the applet to construct at least 1000 95% intervals, and then answer the following question:

c. Comment on how the proportion of the computed intervals that include the actual value of the population mean compares to the stated confidence level of 95%. Is this surprising? Explain why or why not.

Now experiment with some different samples sizes. What happens when $n = 20$? $n = 50$? $n = 100$? Use what you have learned to write a paragraph explaining what these simulations tell you about the advisability of using a z critical value in the construction of a confidence interval for μ when σ is unknown.

ACTIVITY 9.2 An Alternative Confidence Interval for a Population Proportion

Technology Activity (Applet): This activity presumes that you have already worked through Activity 9.1.

Background: In Section 9.2, it was suggested that a confidence interval of the form

$$\hat{p}_{\text{mod}} \pm (z \text{ critical value})\sqrt{\frac{\hat{p}_{\text{mod}}(1 - \hat{p}_{\text{mod}})}{n}}$$

where $\hat{p}_{\text{mod}} = \dfrac{\text{successes} + 2}{n + 4}$ is an alternative to the usual large-sample z confidence interval. This alternative interval is preferred by many statisticians because, in repeated sampling, the proportion of intervals constructed that include the actual value of the population proportion, p, tends to be closer to the stated confidence level. In this activity, we will explore how the "capture rates" for the two different interval estimation methods compare.

Open the applet (available at www.cengage.com/statistics/POD4e) called ConfidenceIntervals. You should see a screen like the one shown.

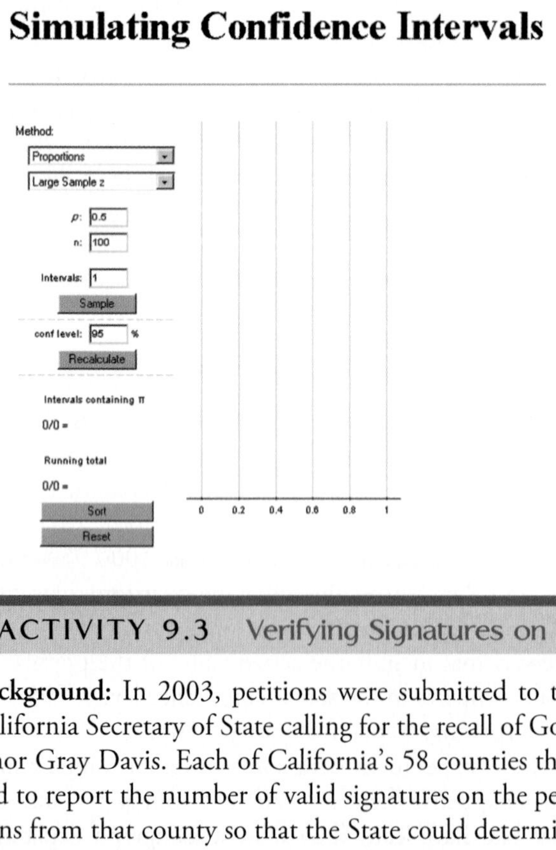

Select "Proportion" from the Method box drop-down menu, and then select "Large Sample z" from the drop-down menu of the second box. We will consider sampling from a population with $p = .3$ using a sample size of 40. In the applet window, enter $p = .3$ and $n = 40$. Note that $n = 40$ is large enough to satisfy $np \geq 10$ and $n(1 - p) \geq 10$.

Set the "Intervals" box to 100, and then use the applet to construct a large number (at least 1000) of 95% confidence intervals.

1. How does the proportion of intervals constructed that include $p = .3$, the population proportion, compare to .95? Does this surprise you? Explain.

   Now use the drop-down menu to change "Large Sample z" to "Modified." Now the applet will construct the alternative confidence interval that is based on $\hat{p}_{\text{mod}}$. Use the applet to construct a large number (at least 1000) of 95% confidence intervals.
2. How does the proportion of intervals constructed that include $p = .3$, the population proportion, compare to .95? Is this proportion closer to .95 than was the case for the large-sample z interval?
3. Experiment with different combinations of values of sample size and population proportion p. Can you find a combination for which the large sample z interval has a capture rate that is close to 95%? Can you find a combination for which it has a capture rate that is even farther from 95% than it was for $n = 40$ and $p = .3$? How does the modified interval perform in each of these cases?

ACTIVITY 9.3 Verifying Signatures on a Recall Petition

Background: In 2003, petitions were submitted to the California Secretary of State calling for the recall of Governor Gray Davis. Each of California's 58 counties then had to report the number of valid signatures on the petitions from that county so that the State could determine whether there were enough valid signatures to certify the recall and set a date for the recall election. The following paragraph appeared in the *San Luis Obispo Tribune* (July 23, 2003):

In the campaign to recall Gov. Gray Davis, the secretary of state is reporting 16,000 verified signatures from San Luis Obispo County. In all, the County Clerk's Office received 18,866 signatures on recall petitions and was instructed by the state to check a random sample of 567. Out of those, 84.48% were good. The verification process includes checking whether the signer is a registered voter and whether the address and signature on the recall petition match the voter registration.

1. Use the data from the random sample of 567 San Luis Obispo County signatures to construct a 95% confidence interval for the proportion of petition signatures that are valid.
2. How do you think that the reported figure of 16,000 verified signature for San Luis Obispo County was obtained?
3. Based on your confidence interval from Step 1, explain why you think that the reported figure of 16,000 verified signatures is or is not reasonable.

ACTIVITY 9.4 A Meaningful Paragraph

Write a meaningful paragraph that includes the following six terms: **sample, population, confidence level, estimate, mean, margin of error.**

A "meaningful paragraph" is a coherent piece writing in an appropriate context that uses all of the listed words. The paragraph should show that you understand the meanings of the terms and their relationship to one another. A sequence of sentences that just define the terms is *not* a meaningful paragraph. When choosing a context, think carefully about the terms you need to use. Choosing a good context will make writing a meaningful paragraph easier.

Summary of Key Concepts and Formulas

TERM OR FORMULA	COMMENT
Point estimate	A single number, based on sample data, that represents a plausible value of a population characteristic.
Unbiased statistic	A statistic that has a sampling distribution with a mean equal to the value of the population characteristic to be estimated.
Confidence interval	An interval that is computed from sample data and provides a range of plausible values for a population characteristic.
Confidence level	A number that provides information on how much "confidence" we can have in the method used to construct a confidence interval estimate. The confidence level specifies the percentage of all possible samples that will produce an interval containing the value of the population characteristic.
$\hat{p} \pm (z \text{ critical value})\sqrt{\frac{\hat{p}(1-\hat{p})}{n}}$	A formula used to construct a confidence interval for p when the sample size is large.
$n = p(1-p)\left(\frac{1.96}{B}\right)^2$	A formula used to compute the sample size necessary for estimating p to within an amount B with 95% confidence. (For other confidence levels, replace 1.96 with an appropriate z critical value.)
$\bar{x} \pm (z \text{ critical value})\frac{\sigma}{\sqrt{n}}$	A formula used to construct a confidence interval for μ when σ is known and either the sample size is large or the population distribution is normal.
$\bar{x} \pm (t \text{ critical value})\frac{s}{\sqrt{n}}$	A formula used to construct a confidence interval for μ when σ is unknown and either the sample size is large or the population distribution is normal.

$n = \left(\frac{1.96\sigma}{B}\right)^2$ — A formula used to compute the sample size necessary for estimating μ to within an amount B with 95% confidence. (For other confidence levels, replace 1.96 with an appropriate z critical value.)

Chapter Review Exercises 9.56 - 9.73

9.56 According to an AP-Ipsos poll (June 15, 2005), 42% of 1001 randomly selected adult Americans made plans in May 2005 based on a weather report that turned out to be wrong.

a. Construct and interpret a 99% confidence interval for the proportion of Americans who made plans in May 2005 based on an incorrect weather report.
b. Do you think it is reasonable to generalize this estimate to other months of the year? Explain.

9.57 ✦ "Tongue Piercing May Speed Tooth Loss, Researchers Say" is the headline of an article that appeared in the *San Luis Obispo Tribune* (June 5, 2002). The article describes a study of 52 young adults with pierced tongues. The researchers found receding gums, which can lead to tooth loss, in 18 of the participants. Construct a 95% confidence interval for the proportion of young adults with pierced tongues who have receding gums. What assumptions must be made for use of the z confidence interval to be appropriate?

9.58 In a study of 1710 schoolchildren in Australia (*Herald Sun*, October 27, 1994), 1060 children indicated that they normally watch TV before school in the morning. (Interestingly, only 35% of the parents said their children watched TV before school!) Construct a 95% confidence interval for the true proportion of Australian children who say they watch TV before school. What assumption about the sample must be true for the method used to construct the interval to be valid?

9.59 The authors of the paper "Short-Term Health and Economic Benefits of Smoking Cessation: Low Birth Weight" (*Pediatrics* [1999]: 1312–1320) investigated the medical cost associated with babies born to mothers who smoke. The paper included estimates of mean medical cost for low-birth-weight babies for different ethnic groups. For a sample of 654 Hispanic low-birth-weight babies, the mean medical cost was $55,007 and the standard error ($s/\sqrt{n}$) was $3011. For a sample of 13 Native American low-birth-weight babies, the mean and standard error were $73,418 and $29,577, respectively. Explain why the two standard errors are so different.

9.60 The article "Consumers Show Increased Liking for Diesel Autos" (*USA Today*, January 29, 2003) reported that 27% of U.S. consumers would opt for a diesel car if it ran as cleanly and performed as well as a car with a gas engine. Suppose that you suspect that the proportion might be different in your area and that you want to conduct a survey to estimate this proportion for the adult residents of your city. What is the required sample size if you want to estimate this proportion to within .05 with 95% confidence? Compute the required sample size first using .27 as a preliminary estimate of p and then using the conservative value of .5. How do the two sample sizes compare? What sample size would you recommend for this study?

9.61 In the article "Fluoridation Brushed Off by Utah" (Associated Press, August 24, 1998), it was reported that a small but vocal minority in Utah has been successful in keeping fluoride out of Utah water supplies despite evidence that fluoridation reduces tooth decay and despite the fact that a clear majority of Utah residents favor fluoridation. To support this statement, the article included the result of a survey of Utah residents that found 65% to be in favor of fluoridation. Suppose that this result was based on a random sample of 150 Utah residents. Construct and interpret a 90% confidence interval for p, the true proportion of Utah residents who favor fluoridation. Is this interval consistent with the statement that fluoridation is favored by a clear majority of residents?

9.62 Seventy-seven students at the University of Virginia were asked to keep a diary of conversations with their mothers, recording any lies they told during these conversations (*San Luis Obispo Telegram-Tribune*, August 16, 1995). It was reported that the mean number of lies per conversation was 0.5. Suppose that the standard deviation (which was not reported) was 0.4.

a. Suppose that this group of 77 is a random sample from the population of students at this university. Construct a 95% confidence interval for the mean number of lies per conversation for this population.
b. The interval in Part (a) does not include 0. Does this imply that all students lie to their mothers? Explain.

9.63 An Associated Press article on potential violent behavior reported the results of a survey of 750 workers who were employed full time (*San Luis Obispo Tribune*, September 7, 1999). Of those surveyed, 125 indicated that they were so angered by a coworker during the past year that they felt like hitting the coworker (but didn't). Assuming that it is reasonable to regard this sample of 750 as a random sample from the population of full-time workers, use this information to construct and interpret a 90% confidence interval estimate of p, the true proportion of full-time workers so angered in the last year that they wanted to hit a colleague.

9.64 The 1991 publication of the book *Final Exit*, which includes chapters on doctor-assisted suicide, caused a great deal of controversy in the medical community. The Society for the Right to Die and the American Medical Association quoted very different figures regarding the proportion of primary-care physicians who have participated in some form of doctor-assisted suicide for terminally ill patients (*USA Today*, July 1991). Suppose that a survey of physicians is to be designed to estimate this proportion to within .05 with 95% confidence. How many primary-care physicians should be included in the random sample?

9.65 A manufacturer of small appliances purchases plastic handles for coffeepots from an outside vendor. If a handle is cracked, it is considered defective and must be discarded. A large shipment of plastic handles is received. The proportion of defective handles p is of interest. How many handles from the shipment should be inspected to estimate p to within 0.1 with 95% confidence?

9.66 An article in the *Chicago Tribune* (August 29, 1999) reported that in a poll of residents of the Chicago suburbs, 43% felt that their financial situation had improved during the past year. The following statement is from the article: "The findings of this Tribune poll are based on interviews with 930 randomly selected suburban residents. The sample included suburban Cook County plus DuPage, Kane, Lake, McHenry, and Will Counties. In a sample of this size, one can say with 95% certainty that results will differ by no more than 3%t from results obtained if all residents had been included in the poll."

Comment on this statement. Give a statistical argument to justify the claim that the estimate of 43% is within 3% of the true proportion of residents who feel that their financial situation has improved.

9.67 A manufacturer of college textbooks is interested in estimating the strength of the bindings produced by a particular binding machine. Strength can be measured by recording the force required to pull the pages from the binding. If this force is measured in pounds, how many books should be tested to estimate the mean force required to break the binding to within 0.1 pounds with 95% conficence? Assume that σ is known to be 0.8 pound.

9.68 Recent high-profile legal cases have many people reevaluating the jury system. Many believe that juries in criminal trials should be able to convict on less than a unanimous vote. To assess support for this idea, investigators asked each individual in a random sample of Californians whether they favored allowing conviction by a 10–2 verdict in criminal cases not involving the death penalty. The Associated Press (*San Luis Obispo Telegram-Tribune*, September 13, 1995) reported that 71% supported the 10–2 verdict. Suppose that the sample size for this survey was $n = 900$. Compute and interpret a 99% confidence interval for the proportion of Californians who favor the 10–2 verdict.

9.69 The confidence intervals presented in this chapter give both lower and upper bounds on plausible values for the population characteristic being estimated. In some instances, only an upper bound or only a lower bound is appropriate. Using the same reasoning that gave the large sample interval in Section 9.3, we can say that when n is large, 99% of all samples have

$$\mu < \bar{x} + 2.33\frac{s}{\sqrt{n}}$$

(because the area under the z curve to the left of 2.33 is .99). Thus, $\bar{x} + 2.33\frac{s}{\sqrt{n}}$ is a 99% upper confidence bound for μ. Use the data of Example 9.9 to calculate the 99% upper confidence bound for the true mean wait time for bypass patients in Ontario.

9.70 The Associated Press (December 16, 1991) reported that in a random sample of 507 people, only 142 correctly described the Bill of Rights as the first 10 amendments to the U.S. Constitution. Calculate a 95% confidence interval for the proportion of the entire population that could give a correct description.

9.71 When n is large, the statistic s is approximately unbiased for estimating σ and has approximately a normal distribution. The standard deviation of this statistic when the population distribution is normal is $\sigma_s \approx \frac{\sigma}{\sqrt{2n}}$ which can be estimated by $\frac{s}{\sqrt{2n}}$. A large-sample confidence interval for the population standard deviation σ is then

$$s \pm (z \text{ critical value})\frac{s}{\sqrt{2n}}$$

Use the data of Example 9.9 to obtain a 95% confidence interval for the true standard deviation of waiting time for angiography.

9.72 The interval from -2.33 to 1.75 captures an area of .95 under the z curve. This implies that another large-sample 95% confidence interval for μ has lower limit $\bar{x} - 2.33\frac{\sigma}{\sqrt{n}}$ and upper limit $\bar{x} + 1.75\frac{\sigma}{\sqrt{n}}$. Would you recommend using this 95% interval over the 95% interval $\bar{x} \pm 1.96\frac{\sigma}{\sqrt{n}}$ discussed in the text? Explain. (Hint: Look at the width of each interval.)

9.73 The eating habits of 12 bats were examined in the article "Foraging Behavior of the Indian False Vampire Bat" (*Biotropica* [1991]: 63–67). These bats consume insects and frogs. For these 12 bats, the mean time to consume a frog was $\bar{x} = 21.9$ minutes. Suppose that the standard deviation was $s = 7.7$ minutes. Construct and interpret a 90% confidence interval for the mean suppertime of a vampire bat whose meal consists of a frog. What assumptions must be reasonable for the one-sample t interval to be appropriate?

Graphing Calculator Explorations

EXPLORATION 9.1 The Confidence Interval for a Population Proportion

Because confidence intervals are widely used, it will come as no surprise to you that your calculator may have a built-in capability to determine a confidence interval for a population proportion. Once again, you will need to navigate your calculator's menu system, looking for key words such as INTR for "interval," or possibly TESTS. (Confidence intervals are frequently associated with "hypothesis tests," a topic to come later in Chapter 10.) Once you find the right menu, look for words like "1" and "prop" and "z"—together these key words should indicate a one-sample z confidence interval for a proportion.

Once you select the correct choice, you will be presented with a screen for providing the information needed to calculate a confidence interval: the number of successes, the sample size, and the confidence level. Two representative screens are given in Figure 9.10.

```
1-Prop Zinterval
C-Level  :
x   :
n   :
Execute
```

```
1-PropZInt
C-Level  :
x :
n :
C-Level:
Calculate
```

FIGURE 9.10
Common screen presentations for confidence interval data entry.

From Example 9.4, supply the following information: $x = 567$, $n = 1031$, and the C-Level = .95. Move your cursor down to Execute or Calculate, and press the Enter, Execute, or Calculate button, depending on your calculator. The confidence interval should appear immediately. Again, two representative screens are given in Figure 9.11.

1-Prop Zinterval
Left =0.51958
Right=.58032
p̂=0.55
n=1031

1-Prop Zinterval
(.51958, .58032)
p̂=.549952
n=1031

FIGURE 9.11
Calculator screens for confidence intervals.

Notice that the formatting in these screens is slightly different. Which of these is the "right" format? Probably neither one! Recall a previous graphing calculator exploration in Chapter 3, where we discussed the differences between a calculator's presentation of information and the appropriate way to communicate this information. *Check with your instructor to determine her or his preferences about what format information is required.*

EXPLORATION 9.2 A Confidence Interval for a Population Mean

Finding the confidence interval for a single mean on your calculator will require you to navigate the menu system much as you did to find the confidence interval for a proportion. The confidence interval for the mean will have some added challenges, however:

1. You will need to decide whether to base the interval on the z or t distribution, and
2. You may use previous calculations of the sample mean and standard deviation, or the calculator will evaluate these statistics from data contained in a List.

We will use the data from Example 9.10 to construct a 99% confidence interval. We have entered the data in List1 and are ready to proceed. Since the population standard deviation is not known, we will use the t confidence interval. For the t confidence interval, the normality of the population becomes an issue. The original data are at hand, and we can assess the plausibility of a normal population via a normal probability plot. Figure 9.12 shows the normal probability plot.

After verifying the plausibility of the normality of the population, we can now construct the confidence interval. In this case, we have a choice of entering the sample calculations or letting the calculator evaluate the sample mean and standard deviation. Based on that choice, we see one of the screens shown in Figure 9.13.

Figure 9.14 shows one calculator's version of the confidence interval.

(a)

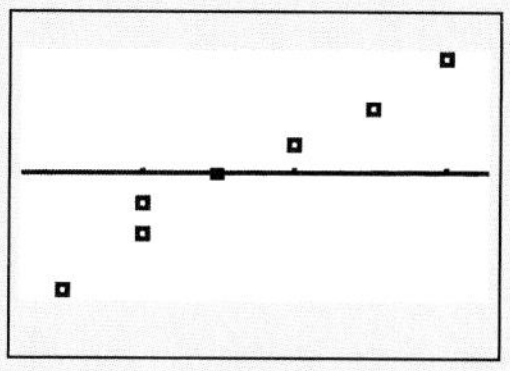

(b)

FIGURE 9.12
(a) Edit window for normal probability plot; (b) normal probability plot.

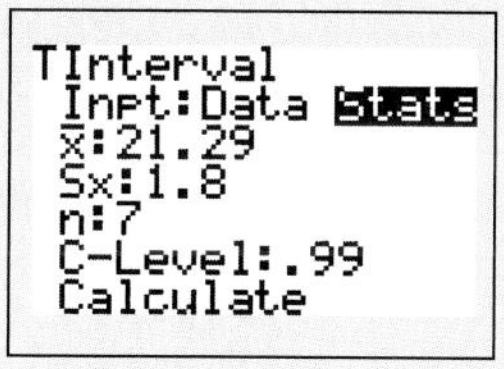

(a)

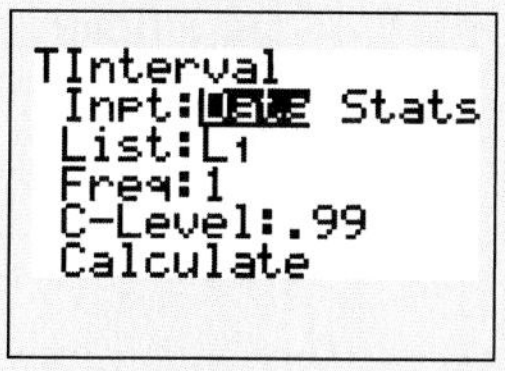

(b)

FIGURE 9.13
(a) Confidence interval input screen for raw data; (b) confidence interval input screen for summary statistics.

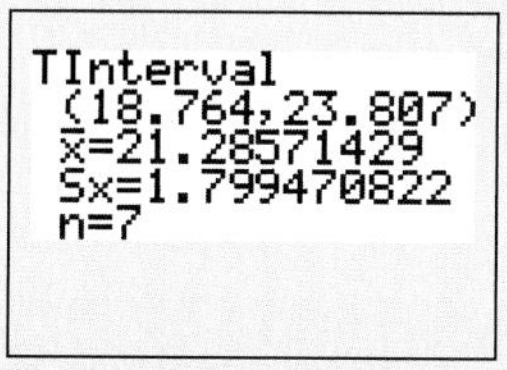

FIGURE 9.14
Calculated confidence interval.

AP* Review Questions for Chapter 9

1. Each figure below displays the sampling distribution of a statistic used to estimate a parameter. The true value of the population parameter is marked on each sampling distribution. Which is the sampling distribution of a statistic that is an unbiased estimator of the parameter of interest?

Statistic I

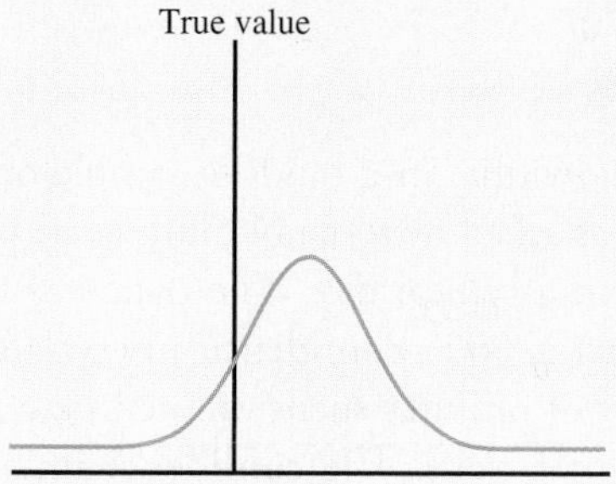

Statistic II

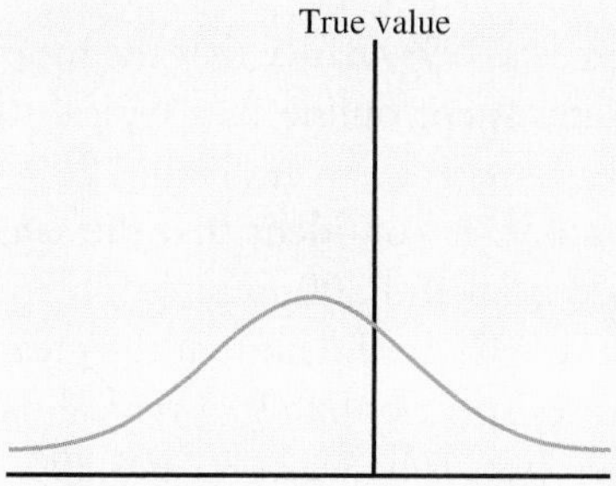

Statistic III

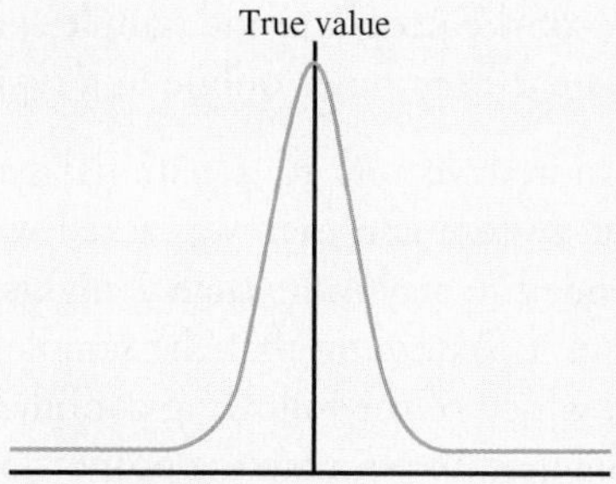

(A) Statistic I only
(B) Statistic II only
(C) Statistic III only
(D) Both Statistic I and Statistic II are unbiased.
(E) None of the three statistics is unbiased.

2. Four different statistics are being considered for estimating a population characteristic. The sampling distributions of the four statistics are shown here. Which statistic is most likely to result in an estimate that is close to the true value of the population characteristic?

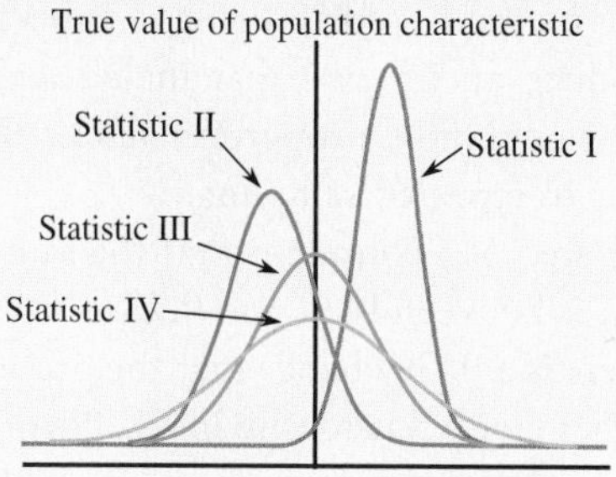

(A) Statistic I
(B) Statistic II
(C) Statistic III
(D) Statistic IV
(E) Statistics III and IV are equally likely to result in an estimate that is close to the true value.

3. Given a choice of unbiased statistics, the best statistic would be the one with a sampling distribution that

(A) is most closely approximated by a normal curve.
(B) has the smallest variance.
(C) has the largest standard error.
(D) is most nearly symmetric.
(E) is most closely approximated by a *t*distribution.

4. To estimate the proportion of faculty at a state university who own a home, a random sample of faculty is selected. For which of the following combinations of n and $\hat{p}$ would it be appropriate to use the confidence interval $\hat{p} \pm (z \text{ critical value})\sqrt{\frac{\hat{p}(1-\hat{p})}{n}}$?

(A) $n = 20$ and $\hat{p} = 0.40$
(B) $n = 40$ and $\hat{p} = 0.20$
(C) $n = 100$ and $\hat{p} = 0.05$
(D) $n = 150$ and $\hat{p} = 0.45$
(E) $n = 200$ and $\hat{p} = 0.02$

5. Suppose that a random sample of 100 high school classrooms in the state of California is selected and a 95% confidence interval for the proportion that has Internet access is (0.62, 0.78). Which of the following is a correct interpretation of the 95% confidence level?

(A) The method used to construct the interval will produce an interval that includes the value of the population proportion about 95% of the time in repeated sampling.
(B) We are 95% confident that the sample proportion is between 0.62 and 0.78.
(C) There is a 95% chance that the proportion of all high school classrooms in California that have Internet access is between 0.62 and 0.78.
(D) We are 95% confident that the proportion of all high school classrooms in California that have Internet access is between 0.62 and 0.78.
(E) None of the above is a correct interpretation of the confidence level.

6. Which of the following must be true of a sample in order for it to be appropriate to use a z confidence interval to estimate the population proportion?

(A) The sample is a random sample from the population of interest.
(B) $n\hat{p} \geq 10$ and $n(1 - \hat{p}) \geq 10$
(C) The population distribution is normal.
(D) All of (A), (B), and (C) are required for appropriate use of the z confidence interval to estimate the population proportion.
(E) Only (A) and (B) are required for appropriate use of the z confidence interval to estimate the population proportion.

7. Which of the following would tend to decrease the width of a confidence interval?

I. Increasing the sample size
II. Using a higher confidence level
III. Using a lower confidence level

(A) I only
(B) II only
(C) III only
(D) I and II only
(E) I and III only

8. Each individual in a random sample of 60 college students was asked how much money he or she spent on food in a typical month. The data was then used to construct a 99% confidence interval for the actual mean amount spent on food for all students at the college in a typical month. The confidence interval was (240, 380). Which of the following is closest to the 95% confidence interval constructed using the same sample data?

(A) (240, 380)
(B) (250, 370)
(C) (260, 360)
(D) (270, 350)
(E) (280, 340)

9. Each individual in a random sample of 50 Internet users was asked how many minutes he or she spends online in a typical day. The data was then used to construct a 99% confidence interval for the mean number of minutes spent online in a typical day for all Internet users. The confidence interval was (80, 200) minutes per day. Which of the following is a correct interpretation of the confidence interval?

(A) There is a 99% chance that the mean number of minutes spent online in a typical day of all Internet users is between 80 and 200.
(B) We are 99% confident that the sample mean is between 80 and 200 minutes.
(C) We are 99% confident that the mean number of minutes spent online in a typical day for all Internet users is between 80 and 200.
(D) 99% of all Internet users will spend between 80 and 200 minutes online in a typical day.
(E) 99% of the people in the sample spent between 80 and 200 minutes online in a typical day.

10. Two hundred visitors to a national park were selected at random and each was asked whether he or she intended to stay more than 2 nights in the park on that visit. Assuming that the sample size is large enough, which of the following confidence intervals should be used to estimate the proportion of all visitors to this national park who will stay more than 2 nights on their visit?

(A) $\bar{x} \pm (t \text{ critical value})\dfrac{s}{\sqrt{n}}$

(B) $\hat{p} \pm (t \text{ critical value})\dfrac{s}{\sqrt{n}}$

(C) $\hat{p} \pm (z \text{ critical value})\dfrac{s}{\sqrt{n}}$

(D) $\bar{x} \pm (z \text{ critical value})\dfrac{\sigma}{\sqrt{n}}$

(E) $\hat{p} \pm (z \text{ critical value})\sqrt{\dfrac{\hat{p}(1 - \hat{p})}{n}}$

11. Two-hundred visitors to a national park were selected at random and each was asked how far he or she had traveled to get to the park on that visit. Which of the following confidence intervals should be used to estimate the mean number of miles traveled by all visitors to the park?

(A) $\bar{x} \pm (t \text{ critical value})\frac{s}{\sqrt{n}}$

(B) $\mu \pm (t \text{ critical value})\frac{s}{\sqrt{n}}$

(C) $\mu \pm (z \text{ critical value})\frac{\sigma}{\sqrt{n}}$

(D) $\bar{x} \pm (z \text{ critical value})\frac{\sigma}{\sqrt{n}}$

(E) $\hat{p} \pm (z \text{ critical value})\sqrt{\frac{\hat{p}(1-\hat{p})}{n}}$

12. Suppose you take a random sample from a population known to be normally distributed, but the value of σ is unknown. Your sample size is $n = 10$. Which formula below should be used to find the 90% confidence interval for the mean?

(A) $\bar{x} \pm 1.645\frac{s}{\sqrt{10}}$

(B) $\bar{x} \pm 1.645\frac{\sigma}{\sqrt{10}}$

(C) $\bar{x} \pm 1.833\frac{s}{\sqrt{10}}$

(D) $\bar{x} \pm 1.812\frac{\sigma}{\sqrt{10}}$

(E) $\bar{x} \pm 1.833\frac{\sigma}{\sqrt{10}}$

13. A large sample ($n = 250$) was used to compute $\bar{x} \pm \frac{s}{\sqrt{n}}$. This interval is equivalent to an approximate

(A) 50% confidence interval
(B) 68% confidence interval
(C) 84% confidence interval
(D) 90% confidence interval
(E) 95% confidence interval

14. Which of the following is certain to reduce the width of a confidence interval?

(A) Larger sample size and higher confidence level
(B) Larger sample size and lower confidence level
(C) Smaller sample size and higher confidence level
(D) Smaller sample size and lower confidence level
(E) None of the above

15. Suppose that two different random samples are to be selected from a population and that each sample will be used to compute a 95% confidence interval for the population mean, μ. What is the probability that both of the intervals will capture the population mean?

(A) $(0.95)^2$
(B) $1 - (0.95)^2$
(C) $\frac{0.95 + 0.95}{2}$
(D) $(0.95)(0.05) + (0.05)(0.95)$
(E) $0.95 + 0.95 + (0.95)^2$

CHAPTER 10

Hypothesis Testing Using a Single Sample

PictureNet/Corbis Yellow/Corbis

In Chapter 9, we considered situations in which the primary goal was to estimate the unknown value of some population characteristic. Sample data can also be used to decide whether some claim or *hypothesis* about a population characteristic is plausible.

For example, sharing of prescription drugs is a practice that has many associated risks. Is this a common practice among teens? Is there evidence that more than 10% of teens have shared prescription medications with a friend? The article "Many Teens Share Prescription Drugs" (*Calgary Herald*, August 3, 2009) summarized the results of a survey of a representative sample of 592 U.S. teens age 12 to 17 and reported that 118 of those surveyed admitted to having shared a prescription drug with a friend. With p representing the proportion of all U.S. teens age 12 to 17, we can use the hypothesis testing methods of this chapter to decide whether the sample data provide convincing evidence that p is greater than .10.

As another example, a report released by the National Association of Colleges and Employers stated that the average starting salary for students graduating with a bachelor's

Make the most of your study time by accessing everything you need to succeed online with CourseMate.
Visit http://www.cengagebrain.com where you will find:

- An interactive eBook, which allows you to take notes, highlight, bookmark, search the text, and use in-context glossary definitions
- Step-by-step instructions for Minitab, Excel, TI-83/84, SPSS, and JMP
- Video solutions to selected exercises
- Data sets available for selected examples and exercises
- Online quizzes
- Flashcards
- Videos

degree in 2010 is \$48,351 ("Winter 2010 Salary Survey," www.naceweb.org). Suppose that you are interested in investigating whether the mean starting salary for students graduating from your university this year is greater than the 2010 average of \$48,351. You select a random sample of $n = 40$ graduates from the current graduating class of your university and determine the starting salary of each one. If this sample produced a mean starting salary of \$49,958 and a standard deviation of \$1214, is it reasonable to conclude that μ, the mean starting salary for all graduates in the current graduating class at your university, is greater than \$48,351? We will see in this chapter how the sample data can be analyzed to decide whether $\mu > 48{,}351$ is a reasonable conclusion.

10.1 Hypotheses and Test Procedures

A hypothesis is a claim or statement about the value of a single population characteristic or the values of several population characteristics. The following are examples of legitimate hypotheses:

$\mu = 1000$, where μ is the mean number of characters in an e-mail message
$p < .01$, where p is the proportion of e-mail messages that are undeliverable

In contrast, the statements $\bar{x} = 1000$ and $\hat{p} = .01$ are *not* hypotheses, because $\bar{x}$ and $\hat{p}$ are *sample* characteristics.

AP* EXAM TIP

The logic of testing hypotheses about population parameters is the same for all of the tests we will consider. If you focus on the concepts in the first few sections of this chapter, you will be able to apply them to the different hypothesis tests that you will see in the following chapters.

A **test of hypotheses** or **test procedure** is a method that uses sample data to decide between two competing claims (hypotheses) about a population characteristic. One hypothesis might be $\mu = 1000$ and the other $\mu \neq 1000$ or one hypothesis might be $p = .01$ and the other $p < .01$. If it were possible to carry out a census of the entire population, we would know which of the two hypotheses is correct, but usually we must decide between them using information from a sample.

A criminal trial is a familiar situation in which a choice between two contradictory claims must be made. The person accused of the crime must be judged either guilty or not guilty. Under the U.S. system of justice, the individual on trial is initially presumed not guilty. Only strong evidence to the contrary causes the not guilty claim to be rejected in favor of a guilty verdict. The burden is thus put on the prosecution to prove the guilty claim. The French perspective in criminal proceedings is the opposite. Once enough evidence has been presented to justify bringing an individual to trial, the initial assumption is that the accused is guilty. The burden of proof then falls on the accused to establish otherwise.

As in a judicial proceeding, we initially assume that a particular hypothesis, called the *null hypothesis,* is the correct one. We then consider the evidence (the sample data) and reject the null hypothesis in favor of the competing hypothesis, called the *alternative hypothesis,* only if there is *convincing* evidence against the null hypothesis.

DEFINITION

The **null hypothesis**, denoted by H_0, is a claim about a population characteristic that is initially assumed to be true.

The **alternative hypothesis**, denoted by H_a, is the competing claim.

In carrying out a test of H_0 versus H_a, the null hypothesis H_0 will be rejected in favor of H_a only if sample evidence strongly suggests that H_0 is false. If the sample does not provide such evidence, H_0 will not be rejected. The two possible conclusions are then *reject* H_0 or *fail to reject* H_0.

EXAMPLE 10.1 Tennis Ball Diameters

Because of variation in the manufacturing process, tennis balls produced by a particular machine do not have identical diameters. Let μ denote the mean diameter for all tennis balls currently being produced. Suppose that the machine was initially calibrated to achieve the design specification $\mu = 3$ inches. However, the manufacturer is now concerned that the diameters no longer conform to this specification. That is, $\mu \neq 3$ inches must now be considered a possibility. If sample evidence suggests that $\mu \neq 3$ inches, the production process will have to be halted while the machine is recalibrated. Because stopping production is costly, the manufacturer wants to be quite sure that $\mu \neq 3$ inches before undertaking recalibration. Under these circumstances, a sensible choice of hypotheses is

H_0: $\mu = 3$ (the specification is being met, so recalibration is unnecessary)
H_a: $\mu \neq 3$ (the specification is not being met, so recalibration is necessary)

H_0 would be rejected in favor of H_a only if the sample provides compelling evidence against the null hypothesis.

EXAMPLE 10.2 Compact Florescent Lightbulb Lifetimes

Compact florescent (cfl) lightbulbs are much more energy efficient than standard incandescent light bulbs. Ecobulb brand 60-watt cfl lightbulbs state on the package "Average life 8,000 hours." Let μ denote the true mean life of Ecobulb 60-watt cfl lightbulbs. Then the advertised claim is $\mu = 8000$ hours. People who purchase this brand would be unhappy if μ is actually less than the advertised value. Suppose that a sample of Ecobulb cfl lightbulbs is selected and tested. The lifetime for each bulb in the sample is recorded. The sample results can then be used to test the hypothesis $\mu = 8000$ hours against the hypothesis $\mu < 8000$ hours. The accusation that the company is overstating the mean lifetime is a serious one, and it is reasonable to require compelling evidence before concluding that $\mu < 8000$. This suggests that the claim $\mu = 8000$ should be selected as the null hypothesis and that $\mu < 8000$ should be selected as the alternative hypothesis. Then

H_0: $\mu = 8000$

would be rejected in favor of

H_a: $\mu < 8000$

only if sample evidence strongly suggests that the initial assumption, $\mu = 8000$ hours, is not plausible.

Because the alternative hypothesis in Example 10.2 asserted that $\mu < 8000$ (true average lifetime is less than the advertised value), it might have seemed sensible to state H_0 as the inequality $\mu \geq 8000$. The assertion $\mu \geq 8000$ is in fact the *implicit* null hypothesis, but we will state H_0 explicitly as a claim of equality. There are several reasons for this. First of all, the development of a decision rule is most easily understood if there is only a single hypothesized value of μ (or p or whatever other population characteristic is under consideration). Second, suppose that the sample data provided compelling evidence that H_0: $\mu = 8000$ should be rejected in favor of H_a: $\mu < 8000$.

This means that we were convinced by the sample data that the true mean was smaller than 8000. It follows that we would have also been convinced that the true mean could not have been 8001 or 8010 or any other value that was larger than 8000. As a consequence, the conclusion when testing H_0: $\mu = 8000$ versus H_a: $\mu < 8000$ is always the same as the conclusion for a test where the null hypothesis is H_0: $\mu \geq 8000$. For these reasons, it is customary to state the null hypothesis H_0 as a claim of equality.

The form of a null hypothesis is

H_0: population characteristic = hypothesized value

where the hypothesized value is a specific number determined by the problem context.

The alternative hypothesis will have one of the following three forms:

H_a: population characteristic > hypothesized value
H_a: population characteristic < hypothesized value
H_a: population characteristic ≠ hypothesized value

Thus, we might test H_0: $p = .1$ versus H_a: $p < .1$; but we won't test H_0: $\mu = 50$ versus H_a: $\mu > 100$. The number appearing in the alternative hypothesis must be identical to the hypothesized value in H_0.

Example 10.3 illustrates how the selection of H_0 (the claim initially assumed to be true) and H_a depends on the objectives of a study.

EXAMPLE 10.3 Evaluating a New Medical Treatment

A medical research team has been given the task of evaluating a new laser treatment for certain types of tumors. Consider the following two scenarios:

Scenario 1: The current standard treatment is considered reasonable and safe by the medical community, has no major side effects, and has a known success rate of 0.85 (85%).

Scenario 2: The current standard treatment sometimes has serious side effects, is costly, and has a known success rate of 0.30 (30%).

In the first scenario, research efforts would probably be directed toward determining whether the new treatment has a higher success rate than the standard treatment. Unless convincing evidence of this is presented, it is unlikely that current medical practice would be changed. With p representing the true proportion of successes for the laser treatment, the following hypotheses would be tested:

H_0: $p = .85$ versus H_a: $p > .85$

In this case, rejection of the null hypothesis indicates compelling evidence that the success rate is higher for the new treatment.

In the second scenario, the current standard treatment does not have much to recommend it. The new laser treatment may be considered preferable because of cost or because it has fewer or less serious side effects, as long as the success rate for the new procedure is no worse than that of the standard treatment. Here, researchers might decide to test the hypothesis

H_0: $p = .30$ versus H_a: $p < .30$

If the null hypothesis is rejected, the new treatment will not be put forward as an alternative to the standard treatment, because there is strong evidence that the laser method has a lower success rate.

If the null hypothesis is not rejected, we are able to conclude only that there is not convincing evidence that the success rate for the laser treatment is lower than that for the standard. This is *not* the same as saying that we have evidence that the laser treatment is as good as the standard treatment. If medical practice were to embrace the new procedure, it would not be because it has a higher success rate but rather because it costs less or has fewer side effects, and there is not strong evidence that it has a lower success rate than the standard treatment.

You should be careful in setting up the hypotheses for a test. *A statistical hypothesis test is only capable of demonstrating strong support for the alternative hypothesis (by rejection of the null hypothesis). When the null hypothesis is not rejected, it does not mean strong support for H_0—only lack of strong evidence against it.* In the lightbulb scenario of Example 10.2, if H_0: $\mu = 8000$ is rejected in favor of H_a: $\mu < 8000$, it is because we have strong evidence for believing that actual mean lifetime is less than the advertised value. However, nonrejection of H_0 does not necessarily provide strong support for the advertised claim. If the objective is to demonstrate that the average lifetime is greater than 8000 hours, the hypotheses that would be tested are H_0: $\mu = 8000$ versus H_a: $\mu > 8000$. Now rejection of H_0 indicates strong evidence that $\mu > 8000$. When deciding which alternative hypothesis to use, *keep the research objectives in mind.*

EXERCISES 10.1 - 10.11

10.1 Explain why the statement $\bar{x} = 50$ is not a legitimate hypothesis.

10.2 For the following pairs, indicate which do not comply with the rules for setting up hypotheses, and explain why:

a. H_0: $\mu = 15$, H_a: $\mu = 15$
b. H_0: $p = .4$, H_a: $p > .6$
c. H_0: $\mu = 123$, H_a: $\mu < 123$
d. H_0: $\mu = 123$, H_a: $\mu = 125$
e. H_0: $\hat{p} = .1$, H_a: $\hat{p} \neq .1$

10.3 To determine whether the pipe welds in a nuclear power plant meet specifications, a random sample of welds is selected and tests are conducted on each weld in the sample. Weld strength is measured as the force required to break the weld. Suppose that the specifications state that the mean strength of welds should exceed 100 lb/in^2. The inspection team decides to test H_0: $\mu = 100$ versus H_a: $\mu > 100$. Explain why this alternative hypothesis was chosen rather than $\mu < 100$.

10.4 Do state laws that allow private citizens to carry concealed weapons result in a reduced crime rate? The author of a study carried out by the Brookings Institution is reported as saying, "The strongest thing I could say is that I don't see any strong evidence that they are reducing crime" (*San Luis Obispo Tribune*, January 23, 2003).

a. Is this conclusion consistent with testing

H_0: concealed weapons laws reduce crime

versus

H_a: concealed weapons laws do not reduce crime

or with testing

H_0: concealed weapons laws do not reduce crime

versus

H_a: concealed weapons laws reduce crime

Explain.

b. Does the stated conclusion indicate that the null hypothesis was rejected or not rejected? Explain.

10.5 Consider the following quote from the article "Review Finds No Link Between Vaccine and Autism" (*San Luis Obispo Tribune*, October 19, 2005): "'We found no evidence that giving MMR causes Crohn's disease and/or autism in the children that get the MMR,' said Tom Jefferson, one of the authors of *The Cochrane Review*. 'That does not mean it doesn't cause it. It means we could find no evidence of it.'" (MMR is a measles-mumps-rubella vaccine.) In the context of a hypothesis test with the null hypothesis being that MMR does not cause autism, explain why the author could not conclude that the MMR vaccine does not cause autism.

10.6 A certain university has decided to introduce the use of plus and minus with letter grades, as long as there is evidence that more than 60% of the faculty favor the change. A random sample of faculty will be selected, and the resulting data will be used to test the relevant hypotheses. If p represents the proportion of all faculty that favor a change to plus–minus grading, which of the following pair of hypotheses should the administration test:

H_0: $p = .6$ versus H_a: $p < .6$

or

H_0: $p = .6$ versus H_a: $p > .6$

Explain your choice.

10.7 ✦ A certain television station has been providing live coverage of a particularly sensational criminal trial. The station's program director wishes to know whether more than half the potential viewers prefer a return to regular daytime programming. A survey of randomly selected viewers is conducted. Let p represent the proportion of all viewers who prefer regular daytime programming. What hypotheses should the program director test to answer the question of interest?

10.8 A researcher speculates that because of differences in diet, Japanese children may have a lower mean blood cholesterol level than U.S. children do. Suppose that the mean level for U.S. children is known to be 170. Let μ represent the mean blood cholesterol level for all Japanese children. What hypotheses should the researcher test?

10.9 A county commissioner must vote on a resolution that would commit substantial resources to the construction of a sewer in an outlying residential area. Her fiscal decisions have been criticized in the past, so she decides to take a survey of constituents to find out whether they favor spending money for a sewer system. She will vote to appropriate funds only if she can be reasonably sure that a majority of the people in her district favor the measure. What hypotheses should she test?

10.10 The mean length of long-distance telephone calls placed with a particular phone company was known to be 7.3 minutes under an old rate structure. In an attempt to be more competitive with other long-distance carriers, the phone company lowered long-distance rates, thinking that its customers would be encouraged to make longer calls and thus that there would not be a big loss in revenue. Let μ denote the mean length of long-distance calls after the rate reduction. What hypotheses should the phone company test to determine whether the mean length of long-distance calls increased with the lower rates?

10.11 ✦ Many older homes have electrical systems that use fuses rather than circuit breakers. A manufacturer of 40-amp fuses wants to make sure that the mean amperage at which its fuses burn out is in fact 40. If the mean amperage is lower than 40, customers will complain because the fuses require replacement too often. If the mean amperage is higher than 40, the manufacturer might be liable for damage to an electrical system as a result of fuse malfunction. To verify the mean amperage of the fuses, a sample of fuses is selected and tested. If a hypothesis test is performed using the resulting data, what null and alternative hypotheses would be of interest to the manufacturer?

10.2 Errors in Hypothesis Testing

Once hypotheses have been formulated, a **test procedure** uses sample data to determine whether H_0 should be rejected. Just as a jury may reach the wrong verdict in a trial, there is some chance that using a test procedure with sample data may lead us to the wrong conclusion about a population characteristic. In this section, we discuss the kinds of errors that can occur and consider how the choice of a test procedure influences the chances of these errors.

One erroneous conclusion in a criminal trial is for a jury to convict an innocent person, and another is for a guilty person to be set free. Similarly, there are two different types of errors that might be made when making a decision in a hypothesis testing problem. One type of error involves rejecting H_0 even though the null hypothesis is true. The second type of error results from failing to reject H_0 when it is false. These errors are known as Type I and Type II errors, respectively.

AP* EXAM TIP

It is sometimes difficult to remember which of the two possible errors is labeled as Type I and which is labeled as Type II. On the AP exam, unless a definition is specifically requested, it is acceptable to substitute the concept for the name of the error. For example, if your memory fails, you could write "the error of rejecting a true null hypothesis" in place of "Type I error."

DEFINITION

Type I error: the error of rejecting H_0 when H_0 is true
Type II error: the error of failing to reject H_0 when H_0 is false

The only way to guarantee that neither type of error occurs is to base the decision on a census of the entire population. Risk of error is the price researchers pay for basing the decision on sample data.

EXAMPLE 10.4 On-Time Arrivals

The U.S. Bureau of Transportation Statistics reports that for 2009, 72% of all domestic passenger flights arrived on time (meaning within 15 minutes of the scheduled arrival). Suppose that an airline with a poor on-time record decides to offer its employees a bonus if, in an upcoming month, the airline's proportion of on-time flights exceeds the overall 2009 industry rate of .72. Let p be the actual proportion of the airline's flights that are on time during the month of interest. A random sample of flights might be selected and used as a basis for choosing between

H_0: $p = .72$ and H_a: $p > .72$

In this context, a Type I error (rejecting a true H_0) results in the airline rewarding its employees when in fact the actual proportion of on-time flights did not exceed .72. A Type II error (not rejecting a false H_0) results in the airline employees *not* receiving a reward that they deserved.

EXAMPLE 10.5 Slowing the Growth of Tumors

In 2004, Vertex Pharmaceuticals, a biotechnology company, issued a press release announcing that it had filed an application with the Food and Drug Administration to begin clinical trials of an experimental drug VX-680 that had been found to reduce the growth rate of pancreatic and colon cancer tumors in animal studies (*New York Times*, February 24, 2004).

Let μ denote the true mean growth rate of tumors for patients receiving the experimental drug. Data resulting from the planned clinical trials can be used to test

H_0: μ = mean growth rate of tumors for patients not taking the experimental drug

versus

H_a: μ < mean growth rate of tumors for patients not taking the experimental drug

The null hypothesis states that the experimental drug is not effective—that the mean growth rate of tumors for patients receiving the experimental drug is the same as for patients who do not take the experimental drug. The alternative hypothesis states that the experimental drug is effective in reducing the mean growth rate of tumors. In this context, a Type I error consists of incorrectly concluding that the experimental drug is effective in slowing the growth rate of tumors. A potential consequence of making a Type I error would be that the company would continue to devote resources to the development of the drug when it really is not effective. A Type II error consists of concluding that the experimental drug is ineffective when in fact the mean growth rate of tumors is reduced. A potential consequence of making a Type II error is that the company might abandon development of a drug that was effective.

Examples 10.4 and 10.5 illustrate the two different types of error that might occur when testing hypotheses. Type I and Type II errors—and the associated consequences of making such errors—are quite different. The accompanying box introduces the terminology and notation used to describe error probabilities.

DEFINITION

The **probability of a Type I error** is denoted by α and is called the **significance level** of the test. For example, a test with $\alpha = .01$ is said to have a significance level of .01.

The **probability of a Type II error** is denoted by β.

EXAMPLE 10.6 Blood Test for Ovarian Cancer

Women with ovarian cancer usually are not diagnosed until the disease is in an advanced stage, when it is most difficult to treat. The paper "Diagnostic Markers for Early Detection of Ovarian Cancer" (*Clinical Cancer Research* [2008]: 1065–1072) describes a new approach to diagnosing ovarian cancer that is based on using six different blood biomarkers (a blood biomarker is a biochemical characteristic that is measured in laboratory testing). The authors report the following results using the six biomarkers:

- For 156 women known to have ovarian cancer, the biomarkers correctly identified 151 as having ovarian cancer.
- For 362 women known not to have ovarian cancer, the biomarkers correctly identified 360 of them as being ovarian cancer free.

We can think of using this blood test to choose between two hypotheses:

H_0: woman has ovarian cancer
H_a: woman does not have ovarian cancer

Note that although these are not "statistical hypotheses" (statements about a population characteristic), the possible decision errors are analogous to Type I and Type II errors.

In this situation, believing that a woman with ovarian cancer is cancer free would be a Type I error—rejecting the hypothesis of ovarian cancer when it is in fact true. Believing that a woman who is actually cancer free does have ovarian cancer is a Type II error—not rejecting the null hypothesis when it is in fact false. Based on the study results, we can estimate the error probabilities. The probability of a Type I error, α, is approximately $5/156 = .032$. The probability of a Type II error, β, is approximately $2/363 = .006$.

The ideal test procedure would result in both $\alpha = 0$ and $\beta = 0$. However, if we must base our decision on incomplete information—a sample rather than a census—it is impossible to achieve this ideal. The standard test procedures allow us to control α, but they provide no direct control over β. Because α represents the probability of rejecting a true null hypothesis, selecting a significance level $\alpha = .05$ results in a test procedure that, used over and over with different samples, rejects a *true* H_0 about 5 times in 100. Selecting $\alpha = .01$ results in a test procedure with a Type I error rate of 1% in long-term repeated use. Choosing a small value for α implies that the user wants a procedure for which the risk of a Type I error is quite small.

One question arises naturally at this point: If we can select α, the probability of making a Type I error, why would we ever select $\alpha = .05$ rather than $\alpha = .01$? Why not always select a very small value for α? To achieve a small probability of making a Type I error, we would need the corresponding test procedure to require the evidence against H_0 to be very strong before the null hypothesis can be rejected. Although this makes a Type I error unlikely, it increases the risk of a Type II error (*not* rejecting H_0 when it should have been rejected). Frequently the investigator must balance the consequences of Type I and Type II errors. If a Type II error has serious consequences, it may be a good idea to select a somewhat larger value for α.

In general, there is a compromise between small α and small β, leading to the following widely accepted principle for specifying a test procedure.

After assessing the consequences of Type I and Type II errors, identify the largest α that is tolerable for the problem. Then employ a test procedure that uses this maximum acceptable value—rather than anything smaller—as the level of significance (because using a smaller α increases β). In other words, don't choose α to be smaller than it needs to be.

EXAMPLE 10.7 Lead in Tap Water

The Environmental Protection Agency (EPA) has adopted what is known as the Lead and Copper Rule, which defines drinking water as unsafe if the concentration of lead is 15 parts per billion (ppb) or greater or if the concentration of copper is 1.3 parts per million (ppm) or greater. With μ denoting the mean concentration of lead, the manager of a community water system might use lead level measurements from a sample of water specimens to test

$$H_0: \mu = 15 \text{ versus } H_a: \mu > 15$$

The null hypothesis (which also implicitly includes the $\mu > 15$ case) states that the mean lead concentration is excessive by EPA standards. The alternative hypothesis states that the mean lead concentration is at an acceptable level and that the water system meets EPA standards for lead.

In this context, a Type I error leads to the conclusion that a water source meets EPA standards for lead when in fact it does not. Possible consequences of this type of error include health risks associated with excessive lead consumption (for example, increased blood pressure, hearing loss, and, in severe cases, anemia and kidney damage). A Type II error is to conclude that the water does not meet EPA standards for lead when in fact it actually does. Possible consequences of a Type II error include elimination of a community water source. Because a Type I error might result in

AP* EXAM TIP

In discussing errors, be sure to distinguish between the error itself and the possible consequences of the error.

potentially serious public health risks, a small value of α (Type I error probability), such as $\alpha = .01$, could be selected. Of course, selecting a small value for α increases the risk of a Type II error. If the community has only one water source, a Type II error could also have very serious consequences for the community, and we might want to rethink the choice of α.

EXERCISES 10.12 - 10.22

10.12 Researchers at the University of Washington and Harvard University analyzed records of breast cancer screening and diagnostic evaluations ("Mammogram Cancer Scares More Frequent than Thought," *USA Today*, April 16, 1998). Discussing the benefits and downsides of the screening process, the article states that, although the rate of false-positives is higher than previously thought, if radiologists were less aggressive in following up on suspicious tests, the rate of false-positives would fall but the rate of missed cancers would rise. Suppose that such a screening test is used to decide between a null hypothesis of H_0: no cancer is present and an alternative hypothesis of H_a: cancer is present. (Although these are not hypotheses about a population characteristic, this exercise illustrates the definitions of Type I and Type II errors.)

a. Would a false-positive (thinking that cancer is present when in fact it is not) be a Type I error or a Type II error?
b. Describe a Type I error in the context of this problem, and discuss the consequences of making a Type I error.
c. Describe a Type II error in the context of this problem, and discuss the consequences of making a Type II error.
d. What aspect of the relationship between the probability of Type I and Type II errors is being described by the statement in the article that if radiologists were less aggressive in following up on suspicious tests, the rate of false-positives would fall but the rate of missed cancers would rise?

10.13 The paper "MRI Evaluation of the Contralateral Breast in Women with Recently Diagnosed Breast Cancer" (*New England Journal of Medicine* [2007]: 1295–1303) describes a study of the use of MRI (Magnetic Resonance Imaging) exams in the diagnosis of breast cancer. The purpose of the study was to determine if MRI exams do a better job than mammograms of determining if women who have recently been diagnosed with cancer in one breast have cancer in the other breast. The study participants were 969 women who had been diagnosed with cancer in one breast and for whom a mammogram did not detect cancer in the other breast. These women had an MRI exam of the other breast, and 121 of those exams indicated possible cancer. After undergoing biopsies, it was determined that 30 of the 121 did in fact have cancer in the other breast, whereas 91 did not. The women were all followed for one year, and three of the women for whom the MRI exam did not indicate cancer in the other breast were subsequently diagnosed with cancer that the MRI did not detect. The accompanying table summarizes this information.

	Cancer Present	Cancer Not Present	Total
MRI Positive for Cancer	30	91	**121**
MRI Negative for Cancer	3	845	**848**
Total	**33**	**936**	**969**

Suppose that for women recently diagnosed with cancer in only one breast, the MRI is used to decide between the two "hypotheses"

H_0: woman has cancer in the other breast
H_a: woman does not have cancer in the other breast

(Although these are not hypotheses about a population characteristic, this exercise illustrates the definitions of Type I and Type II errors.)

a. One possible error would be deciding that a woman who does have cancer in the other breast is cancer-free. Is this a Type I or a Type II error? Use the information in the table to approximate the probability of this type of error.
b. There is a second type of error that is possible in this setting. Describe this error and use the information in the given table to approximate the probability of this type of error.

10.14 Medical personnel are required to report suspected cases of child abuse. Because some diseases have symptoms that mimic those of child abuse, doctors who see a child with these symptoms must decide between two competing hypotheses:

H_0: symptoms are due to child abuse
H_a: symptoms are due to disease

(Although these are not hypotheses about a population characteristic, this exercise illustrates the definitions of Type I and Type II errors.) The article "Blurred Line Between Illness, Abuse Creates Problem for Authorities" (*Macon Telegraph*, February 28, 2000) included the following quote from a doctor in Atlanta regarding the consequences of making an incorrect decision: "If it's disease, the worst you have is an angry family. If it is abuse, the other kids (in the family) are in deadly danger."

a. For the given hypotheses, describe Type I and Type II errors.
b. Based on the quote regarding consequences of the two kinds of error, which type of error does the doctor quoted consider more serious? Explain.

10.15 Ann Landers, in her advice column of October 24, 1994 (*San Luis Obispo Telegram-Tribune*), described the reliability of DNA paternity testing as follows: "To get a completely accurate result, you would have to be tested, and so would (the man) and your mother. The test is 100% accurate if the man is *not* the father and 99.9% accurate if he is."

a. Consider using the results of DNA paternity testing to decide between the following two hypotheses:

H_0: a particular man is the father
H_a: a particular man is not the father

In the context of this problem, describe Type I and Type II errors. (Although these are not hypotheses about a population characteristic, this exercise illustrates the definitions of Type I and Type II errors.)

b. Based on the information given, what are the values of α, the probability of a Type I error, and β, the probability of a Type II error?

c. Ann Landers also stated, "If the mother is not tested, there is a 0.8% chance of a false positive." For the hypotheses given in Part (a), what is the value of β if the decision is based on DNA testing in which the mother is not tested?

10.16 A television manufacturer claims that (at least) 90% of its TV sets will need no service during the first 3 years of operation. A consumer agency wishes to check this claim, so it obtains a random sample of $n = 100$ purchasers and asks each whether the set purchased needed repair during the first 3 years after purchase. Let $\hat{p}$ be the sample proportion of responses indicating no repair (so that no repair is identified with a success). Let p denote the actual proportion of successes for all sets made by this manufacturer. The agency does not want to claim false advertising unless sample evidence strongly suggests that $p < .9$. The appropriate hypotheses are then H_0: $p = .9$ versus H_a: $p < .9$.

a. In the context of this problem, describe Type I and Type II errors, and discuss the possible consequences of each.
b. Would you recommend a test procedure that uses $\alpha = .10$ or one that uses $\alpha = .01$? Explain.

10.17 A manufacturer of hand-held calculators receives large shipments of printed circuits from a supplier. It is too costly and time-consuming to inspect all incoming circuits, so when each shipment arrives, a sample is selected for inspection. Information from the sample is then used to test H_0: $p = .01$ versus H_a: $p > .01$, where p is the actual proportion of defective circuits in the shipment. If the null hypothesis is not rejected, the shipment is accepted, and the circuits are used in the production of calculators. If the null hypothesis is rejected, the entire shipment is returned to the supplier because of inferior quality. (A shipment is defined to be of inferior quality if it contains more than 1% defective circuits.)

a. In this context, define Type I and Type II errors.
b. From the calculator manufacturer's point of view, which type of error is considered more serious?
c. From the printed circuit supplier's point of view, which type of error is considered more serious?

10.18 Water samples are taken from water used for cooling as it is being discharged from a power plant into a river. It has been determined that as long as the mean temperature of the discharged water is at most 150°F, there will be no negative effects on the river's ecosystem. To investigate whether the plant is in compliance with regulations that prohibit a mean discharge water temperature above 150°F, researchers will take 50 water samples at randomly selected times and record the temperature of each sample. The resulting data will be used to test the hypotheses H_0: $\mu = 150°F$ versus H_a: $\mu > 150°F$. In the context of this example, describe Type I and Type II errors. Which type of error would you consider more serious? Explain.

10.19 ✦ Occasionally, warning flares of the type contained in most automobile emergency kits fail to ignite. A consumer advocacy group wants to investigate a claim against a manufacturer of flares brought by a person who claims that the proportion of defective flares is much higher than the value of .1 claimed by the manufacturer. A large number of flares will be tested, and the results will be used to decide between H_0: $p = .1$ and H_a: $p > .1$, where p represents the proportion of defective flares made by this manufacturer. If H_0 is rejected, charges of false advertising will be filed against the manufacturer.

a. Explain why the alternative hypothesis was chosen to be H_a: $p > .1$.

b. In this context, describe Type I and Type II errors, and discuss the consequences of each.

10.20 Suppose that you are an inspector for the Fish and Game Department and that you are given the task of determining whether to prohibit fishing along part of the Oregon coast. You will close an area to fishing if it is determined that fish in that region have an unacceptably high mercury content.

a. Assuming that a mercury concentration of 5 ppm is considered the maximum safe concentration, which of the following pairs of hypotheses would you test:

H_0: $\mu = 5$ versus H_a: $\mu > 5$

or

H_0: $\mu = 5$ versus H_a: $\mu < 5$

Give the reasons for your choice.

b. Would you prefer a significance level of .1 or .01 for your test? Explain.

10.21 The National Cancer Institute conducted a 2-year study to determine whether cancer death rates for areas near nuclear power plants are higher than for areas without nuclear facilities (*San Luis Obispo Telegram-Tribune*, September 17, 1990). A spokesperson for the Cancer Institute said, "From the data at hand, there was no convincing evidence of any increased risk of death from any of the cancers surveyed due to living near nuclear facilities. However, no study can prove the absence of an effect."

a. Let p denote the proportion of the population in areas near nuclear power plants who die of cancer during a given year. The researchers at the Cancer Institute might have considered the two rival hypotheses of the form

H_0: $p =$ value for areas without nuclear facilities
H_a: $p >$ value for areas without nuclear facilities

Did the researchers reject H_0 or fail to reject H_0?

b. If the Cancer Institute researchers were incorrect in their conclusion that there is no increased cancer risk associated with living near a nuclear power plant, are they making a Type I or a Type II error? Explain.

c. Comment on the spokesperson's last statement that no study can *prove* the absence of an effect. Do you agree with this statement?

10.22 An automobile manufacturer is considering using robots for part of its assembly process. Converting to robots is an expensive process, so it will be undertaken only if there is strong evidence that the proportion of defective installations is lower for the robots than for human assemblers. Let p denote the proportion of defective installations for the robots. It is known that human assemblers have a defect proportion of .02.

a. Which of the following pairs of hypotheses should the manufacturer test:

H_0: $p = .02$ versus H_a: $p < .02$

or

H_0: $p = .02$ versus H_a: $p > .02$

Explain your answer.

b. In the context of this exercise, describe Type I and Type II errors.

c. Would you prefer a test with $\alpha = .01$ or $\alpha = .1$? Explain your reasoning.

10.3 Large-Sample Hypothesis Tests for a Population Proportion

Now that the basic concepts of hypothesis testing have been introduced, we are ready to turn our attention to the development of procedures for using sample information to decide between a null and an alternative hypothesis. There are two possible conclusions: We either reject H_0 or we fail to reject H_0. The fundamental idea behind hypothesis-testing procedures is this: *We reject the null hypothesis if the observed sample is very unlikely to have occurred when H_0 is true.*

In this section, we consider testing hypotheses about a population proportion when the sample size n is large. Let p denote the proportion of individuals or objects in a specified population that possess a certain property. A random sample of n individuals or objects is selected from the population. The sample proportion

$$\hat{p} = \frac{\text{number in the sample that possess the property}}{n}$$

is the natural statistic for making inferences about p.

The large-sample test procedure is based on the same properties of the sampling distribution of $\hat{p}$ that were used previously to obtain a confidence interval for p, namely:

1. $\mu_{\hat{p}} = p$
2. $\sigma_{\hat{p}} = \sqrt{\dfrac{p(1-p)}{n}}$
3. When n is large, the sampling distribution of $\hat{p}$ is approximately normal.

These three results imply that the standardized variable

$$z = \frac{\hat{p} - p}{\sqrt{\dfrac{p(1-p)}{n}}}$$

has approximately a standard normal distribution when n is large. Example 10.8 shows how this information allows us to make a decision.

EXAMPLE 10.8 Impact of Food Labels

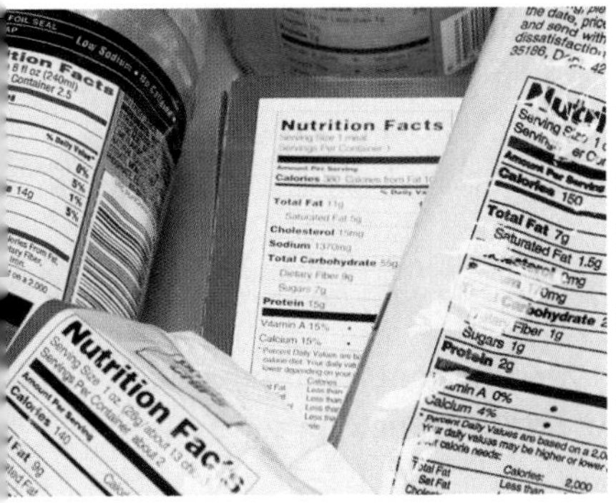

C. Sherburne/PhotoDisc/Getty Images

In June 2006, an Associated Press survey was conducted to investigate how people use the nutritional information provided on food package labels. Interviews were conducted with 1003 randomly selected adult Americans, and each participant was asked a series of questions, including the following two:

Question 1: When purchasing packaged food, how often do you check the nutrition labeling on the package?

Question 2: How often do you purchase foods that are bad for you, even after you've checked the nutrition labels?

It was reported that 582 responded "frequently" to the question about checking labels and 441 responded very often or somewhat often to the question about purchasing "bad" foods even after checking the label.

Let's start by looking at the responses to the first question. Based on these data, is it reasonable to conclude that a majority of adult Americans frequently check the nutritional labels when purchasing packaged foods? We can answer this question by testing hypotheses, where

p = true proportion of adult Americans who frequently check nutritional labels

H_0: $p = .5$
H_a: $p > .5$ (The proportion of adult Americans who frequently check nutritional labels is greater than .5. That is, more than half (a majority) frequently check nutritional labels.)

Recall that in a hypothesis test, the null hypothesis is rejected only if there is convincing evidence against it—in this case, convincing evidence that $p > .5$. If H_0 is rejected, there is strong support for the claim that a majority of adult Americans frequently check nutritional labels when purchasing packaged foods.

For this sample,

$$\hat{p} = \frac{582}{1003} = .58$$

The observed sample proportion is certainly greater than .5, but this could just be due to sampling variability. That is, when $p = .5$ (meaning H_0 is true), the sample proportion $\hat{p}$ usually differs somewhat from .5 simply because of chance variation from one sample to another. Is it plausible that a sample proportion of $\hat{p} = .58$ occurred as a result of this chance variation, or is it unusual to observe a sample proportion this large when $p = .5$?

To answer this question, we form a *test statistic,* the quantity used as a basis for making a decision between H_0 and H_a. Creating a test statistic involves replacing p with the hypothesized value in the z variable $z = \dfrac{\hat{p} - p}{\sqrt{p(1-p)/n}}$ to obtain

$$z = \frac{\hat{p} - .5}{\sqrt{\dfrac{(.5)(.5)}{n}}}$$

If the null hypothesis is true, this statistic should have approximately a standard normal distribution, because when the sample size is large and H_0 is true,

1. $\mu_{\hat{p}} = .5$
2. $\sigma_{\hat{p}} = \sqrt{\dfrac{(.5)(.5)}{n}}$
3. $\hat{p}$ has approximately a normal distribution.

The calculated value of z expresses the distance between $\hat{p}$ and the hypothesized value as a number of standard deviations. If, for example, $z = 3$, then the value of $\hat{p}$ that came from the sample is 3 standard deviations (of $\hat{p}$) greater than what we would have expected if the null hypothesis were true. How likely is it that a z value at least this inconsistent with H_0 would be observed if in fact H_0 is true? The test statistic z is constructed using the hypothesized value from the null hypothesis; if H_0 is true, the test statistic has (approximately) a standard normal distribution. Therefore,

$$P(z \geq 3 \text{ when } H_0 \text{ is true}) = \text{area under the } z \text{ curve to the right of } 3.00 = .0013$$

That is, if H_0 is true, very few samples (much less than 1% of all samples) produce a value of z at least as inconsistent with H_0 as $z = 3$. Because this z value is in the most extreme 1% of the z distribution, it is sensible to reject H_0.

For our data,

$$z = \frac{\hat{p} - .5}{\sqrt{\dfrac{(.5)(.5)}{n}}} = \frac{.58 - .5}{\sqrt{\dfrac{(.5)(.5)}{1003}}} = \frac{.08}{.016} = 5.00$$

That is, $\hat{p} = .58$ is 5 standard deviations greater than what we would expect it to be if the null hypothesis H_0: $p = .5$ was true. The sample data appear to be much more consistent with the alternative hypothesis, H_a: $p > .5$. In particular,

$$\begin{aligned} &P(\text{value of } z \text{ is at least as contradictory to } H_0 \text{ as } 5.00 \text{ when } H_0 \text{ is true}) \\ &\quad = P(z \geq 5.00 \text{ when } H_0 \text{ is true}) \\ &\quad = \text{area under the } z \text{ curve to the right of } 5.00 \\ &\quad \approx 0 \end{aligned}$$

There is virtually no chance of seeing a sample proportion and corresponding z value this extreme as a result of chance variation alone when H_0 is true. If $\hat{p}$ is 5 standard deviations or more away from .5, how can we believe that $p = .5$? The evidence for rejecting H_0 in favor of H_a is very compelling.

Interestingly, in spite of the fact that there is strong evidence that a majority of adult Americans frequently check nutritional labels, the data on responses to the second question suggest that the percentage of people who then ignore the information on the label and purchase "bad" foods anyway is not small—the sample proportion who responded very often or somewhat often was .44.

The preceding example illustrates the reasoning behind large-sample procedures for testing hypotheses about p (and other test procedures as well). We begin by assuming that the null hypothesis is correct. The sample is then examined in light of this assumption. If the observed sample proportion would not be unusual when H_0 is true, then chance variability from one sample to another is a plausible explanation for what has been observed, and H_0 should not be rejected. On the other hand, if the observed sample proportion would have been quite unlikely when H_0 is true, then we would take the sample as convincing evidence against the null hypothesis and we should reject H_0. We base a decision to reject or to fail to reject the null hypothesis on an assessment of how extreme or unlikely the observed sample is if H_0 is true.

The assessment of how inconsistent the observed data are with H_0 is based on first computing the value of the test statistic

$$z = \frac{\hat{p} - \text{hypothesized value}}{\sqrt{\dfrac{(\text{hypothesized value})(1 - \text{hypothesized value})}{n}}}$$

We then calculate the *P-value,* the probability, assuming that H_0 is true, of obtaining a z value at least as inconsistent with H_0 as what was actually observed.

DEFINITION

A **test statistic** is computed using sample data and is the value used to reach a conclusion to reject or fail to reject H_0.

The ***P*-value** (also sometimes called the **observed significance level**) is a measure of inconsistency between the hypothesized value for a population characteristic and the observed sample. It is the probability, assuming that H_0 is true, of obtaining a test statistic value at least as inconsistent with H_0 as what was observed.

EXAMPLE 10.9 Detecting Plagiarism

Plagiarism is a growing concern among college and university faculty members, and many universities are now using software tools to detect student work that is not original.

Researchers at an Australian university that introduced the use of plagiarism detection software in a number of courses surveyed 171 students enrolled in those courses ("Student and Staff Perceptions of the Effectiveness of Plagiarism Detection Software," *Australian Journal of Educational Technology* [2008]: 222–240). In the survey, 58 of the 171 students indicated that they believed that the use of plagiarism-detection software unfairly targeted students.

Assuming it is reasonable to regard the sample as representative of students at this university, does the sample provide convincing evidence that more than one-third of the students at the university believe that the use of plagiarism-detection software unfairly targets students?

With

p = proportion of all students at the university who believe that the use of plagiarism-detection software unfairly targets students

the relevant hypotheses are

$$H_0: p = \frac{1}{3} = .33$$

$$H_a: p > .33$$

The sample proportion is $\hat{p} = \frac{58}{171} = .34.$

Does the value of $\hat{p}$ exceed one-third by enough to cast substantial doubt on H_0?

Because the sample size is large, the statistic

$$z = \frac{\hat{p} - .33}{\sqrt{\frac{(.33)(1 - .33)}{n}}}$$

has approximately a standard normal distribution when H_0 is true. The calculated value of the test statistic is

$$z = \frac{.34 - .33}{\sqrt{\frac{(.33)(1 - .33)}{171}}} = \frac{.01}{.036} = 0.28$$

The probability that a z value at least this inconsistent with H_0 would be observed if in fact H_0 is true is

$$\begin{aligned} P\text{-value} &= P(z \geq 0.28 \text{ when } H_0 \text{ is true}) \\ &= \text{area under the } z \text{ curve to the right of } 0.28 \\ &= 1 - .6103 \\ &= .3897 \end{aligned}$$

This probability indicates that when $p = .33$, it would not be unusual to observe a sample proportion as large as .34. When H_0 is true, roughly 40% of all samples would have a sample proportion as large as or larger than .34, so a sample proportion of .34 is reasonably consistent with the null hypothesis. Although .34 is larger than the hypothesized value of $p = .33$, chance variation from sample to sample is a plausible explanation for what was observed. There is not strong evidence that the proportion of students who believe that the use of plagiarism detection software unfairly targets students is greater than one-third.

As illustrated by Examples 10.8 and 10.9, small P-values indicate that sample results are inconsistent with H_0, whereas larger P-values are interpreted as meaning that the data are consistent with H_0 and that sampling variability alone is a plausible explanation for what was observed in the sample. As you probably noticed, the two cases examined (P-value ≈ 0 and P-value $= .3897$) were such that a decision between rejecting or not rejecting H_0 was clear-cut. A decision in other cases might not be so obvious. For example, what if the sample had resulted in a P-value of .04? Is this unusual enough to warrant rejection of H_0? How small must the P-value be before H_0 should be rejected?

The answer depends on the significance level, α (the probability of a Type I error), selected for the test. For example, suppose that we set $\alpha = .05$. This implies that the probability of rejecting a true null hypothesis is .05. To obtain a test procedure with this probability of Type I error, we would reject the null hypothesis if the sample result is among the most unusual 5% of all samples when H_0 is true. That is, H_0 is rejected if the computed P-value $\leq .05$. If we had selected $\alpha = .01$, H_0 would be rejected only if we observed a sample result so extreme that it would be among the most unusual 1% if H_0 is true (which occurs when P-value $\leq .01$).

A decision about whether to reject or to fail to reject H_0 results from comparing the P-value to the chosen α:

H_0 should be rejected if P-value $\leq \alpha$.
H_0 should not be rejected if P-value $> \alpha$.

Suppose, for example, that the P-value $= .0352$ and that a significance level of .05 is chosen. Then, because

$$P\text{-value} = .0352 \leq .05 = \alpha$$

H_0 would be rejected. This would not be the case, though, for $\alpha = .01$, because then P-value $> \alpha$.

Computing a *P*-Value for a Large-Sample Test Concerning *p*

The computation of the P-value depends on the form of the inequality in the alternative hypothesis, H_a. Suppose, for example, that we wish to test

$$H_0\text{: } p = .6 \qquad \text{versus} \qquad H_a\text{: } p > .6$$

based on a large sample. The appropriate test statistic is

$$z = \frac{\hat{p} - .6}{\sqrt{\frac{(.6)(1 - .6)}{n}}}$$

Values of $\hat{p}$ inconsistent with H_0 and much more consistent with H_a are those much *larger* than .6 (because $p = .6$ when H_0 is true and $p > .6$ when H_0 is false and H_a is true). Such values of $\hat{p}$ correspond to z values considerably greater than 0. If $n = 400$ and $\hat{p} = .679$, then

$$z = \frac{.679 - .6}{\sqrt{\frac{(.6)(1 - .6)}{400}}} = \frac{.079}{.025} = 3.16$$

The value $\hat{p} = .679$ is more than 3 standard deviations larger than what we would have expected if H_0 were true. Then,

$$\begin{aligned} P\text{-value} &= P(z \text{ at least as inconsistent with } H_0 \text{ as } 3.16 \text{ when } H_0 \text{ is true}) \\ &= P(z \geq 3.16 \text{ when } H_0 \text{ is true}) \\ &= \text{area under the } z \text{ curve to the right of } 3.16 \\ &= 1 - .9992 \\ &= .0008 \end{aligned}$$

This P-value is illustrated in Figure 10.1. If H_0 is true, in the long run, only 8 out of 10,000 samples would result in a z value as or more extreme than what actually resulted. Most people would consider such a z quite unusual. Using a significance level of .01, we reject the null hypothesis because $P\text{-value} = .0008 \leq .01 = \alpha$.

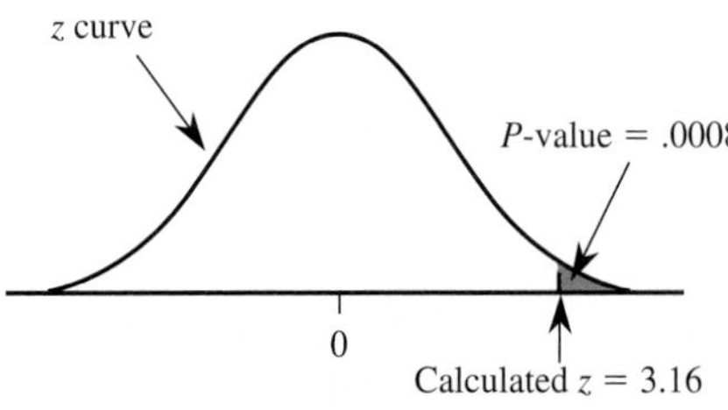

FIGURE 10.1
Calculating a P-value.

Now consider testing H_0: $p = .3$ versus H_a: $p \neq .3$. A value of $\hat{p}$ *either* much greater than .3 *or* much less than .3 is inconsistent with H_0 and provides support for H_a. Such a $\hat{p}$ corresponds to a z value far out in *either* tail of the z curve. If

$$z = \frac{\hat{p} - .3}{\sqrt{\dfrac{(.3)(1 - .3)}{n}}} = 1.75$$

then (as shown in Figure 10.2)

$$\begin{aligned} P\text{-value} &= P(z \text{ value at least as inconsistent with } H_0 \text{ as } 1.75 \text{ when } H_0 \text{ is true}) \\ &= P(z \geq 1.75 \text{ or } z \leq -1.75 \text{ when } H_0 \text{ is true}) \\ &= (z \text{ curve area to the right of } 1.75) + (z \text{ curve area to the left of } -1.75) \\ &= (1 - .9599) + .0401 \\ &= .0802 \end{aligned}$$

If $z = -1.75$, the P-value in this situation is also .0802 because 1.75 and -1.75 are equally inconsistent with H_0.

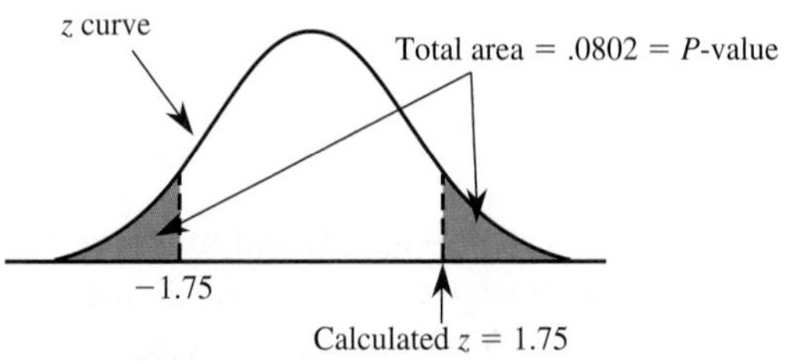

FIGURE 10.2
P-value as the sum of two tail areas.

The symmetry of the z curve implies that when the test is two-tailed (the "not equal" alternative), it is not necessary to add two curve areas. Instead,

If z is positive, $P\text{-value} = 2(\text{area to the right of } z)$.
If z is negative, $P\text{-value} = 2(\text{area to the left of } z)$.

Determination of the *P*-Value When the Test Statistic Is *z*

1. **Upper-tailed test:**

   H_a: $p >$ hypothesized value

   P-value computed as illustrated:

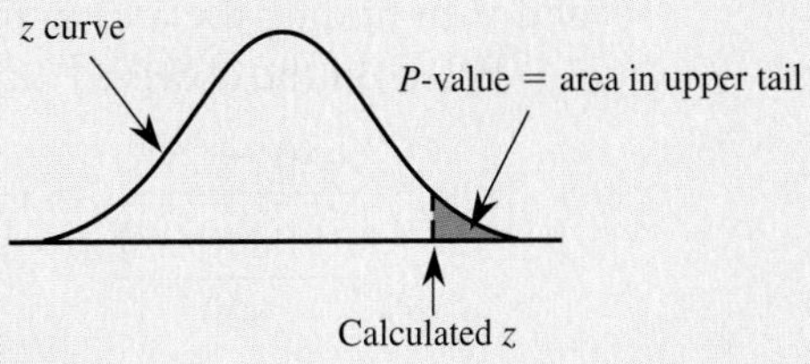

2. **Lower-tailed test:**

   H_a: $p <$ hypothesized value

   P-value computed as illustrated:

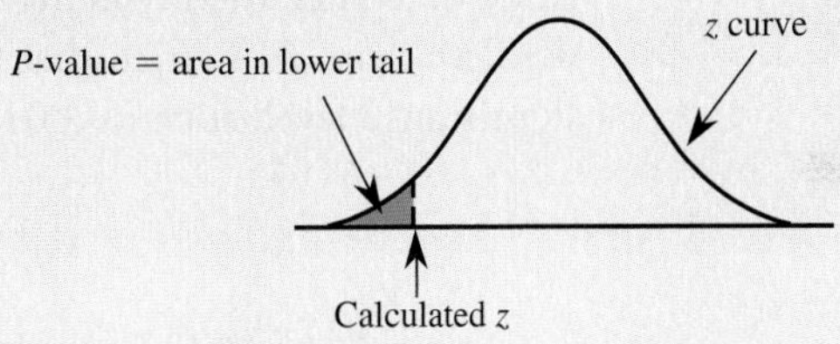

3. **Two-tailed test:**

   H_a: $p \neq$ hypothesized value

   P-value computed as illustrated:

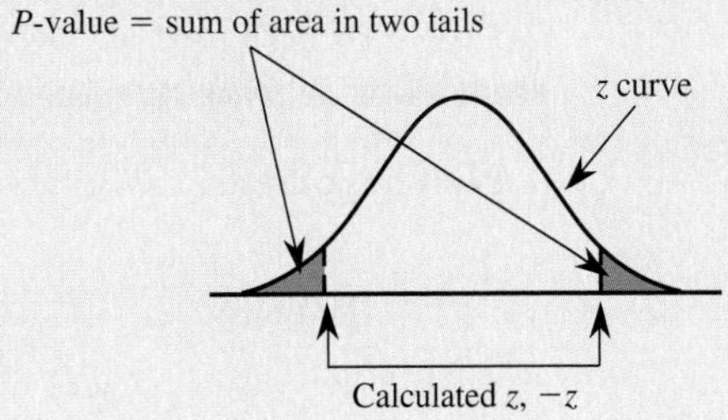

EXAMPLE 10.10 Water Conservation

In December 2009, a county-wide water conservation campaign was conducted in a particular county. In January 2010, a random sample of 500 homes was selected, and water usage was recorded for each home in the sample. The county supervisors wanted to know whether their data supported the claim that fewer than half the households in the county reduced water consumption. The relevant hypotheses are

$$H_0\text{: } p = .5 \qquad \text{versus} \qquad H_a\text{: } p < .5$$

where p is the proportion of all households in the county with reduced water usage.

Suppose that the sample results were $n = 500$ and $\hat{p} = .440$. Because the sample size is large and this is a lower-tailed test, we can compute the P-value by first calculating the value of the z test statistic

$$z = \frac{\hat{p} - .5}{\sqrt{\frac{(.5)(1 - .5)}{n}}}$$

and then finding the area under the z curve to the left of this z.

Based on the observed sample data,

$$z = \frac{.440 - .5}{\sqrt{\frac{(.5)(1 - .5)}{500}}} = \frac{-.060}{.0224} = -2.68$$

The P-value is then equal to the area under the z curve and to the left of -2.68. From the entry in the -2.6 row and .08 column of Appendix Table 2, we find that

$$P\text{-value} = .0037$$

Using a .01 significance level, we reject H_0 (because $.0037 \le .01$), leading us to conclude that there is convincing evidence that the proportion with reduced water usage was less than .5. Notice that rejection of H_0 would not be justified if a *very* small significance level, such as .001, had been selected.

Example 10.10 illustrates the calculation of a P-value for a lower-tailed test. The use of P-values in upper-tailed and two-tailed tests is illustrated in Examples 10.11 and 10.12. But first we summarize large-sample tests of hypotheses about a population proportion and introduce a step-by-step procedure for carrying out a hypothesis test.

Summary of Large-Sample z Test for p

Null hypothesis: H_0: $p =$ hypothesized value

Test statistic: $$z = \frac{\hat{p} - \text{hypothesized value}}{\sqrt{\frac{(\text{hypothesized value})(1 - \text{hypothesized value})}{n}}}$$

Alternative Hypothesis:	***P*-Value:**
H_a: $p >$ hypothesized value	Area under z curve to right of calculated z
H_a: $p <$ hypothesized value	Area under z curve to left of calculated z
H_a: $p \neq$ hypothesized value	(1) 2(area to right of z) if z is positive, or (2) 2(area to left of z) if z is negative

Assumptions:
1. $\hat{p}$ is the sample proportion from a *random sample.*
2. The *sample size is large.* This test can be used if n satisfies both n(hypothesized value) ≥ 10 and $n(1 -$ hypothesized value$) \ge 10$.
3. If sampling is without replacement, the sample size is no more than 10% of the population size.

We recommend that the following sequence of steps be used when carrying out a hypothesis test.

Steps in a Hypothesis-Test

1. Describe the population characteristic about which hypotheses are to be tested.
2. State the null hypothesis H_0.
3. State the alternative hypothesis H_a.
4. Select the significance level α for the test.
5. Display the test statistic to be used, with substitution of the hypothesized value identified in Step 2 but without any computation at this point.
6. Check to make sure that any assumptions required for the test are reasonable.
7. Compute all quantities appearing in the test statistic and then the value of the test statistic itself.
8. Determine the P-value associated with the observed value of the test statistic.
9. State the conclusion (which is to reject H_0 if P-value $\leq \alpha$ and not to reject H_0 otherwise). The conclusion should then be stated in the context of the problem, and the level of significance should be included.

Steps 1–4 constitute a statement of the problem, Steps 5–8 give the analysis that leads to a decision, and Step 9 provides the conclusion.

EXAMPLE 10.11 Unfit Teens

The article "7 Million U.S. Teens Would Flunk Treadmill Tests" (Associated Press, December 11, 2005) summarized the results of a study in which 2205 adolescents age 12 to 19 took a cardiovascular treadmill test. The researchers conducting the study indicated that the sample was selected in such a way that it could be regarded as representative of adolescents nationwide. Of the 2205 adolescents tested, 750 showed a poor level of cardiovascular fitness. Does this sample provide support for the claim that more than 30% of adolescents have a low level of cardiovascular fitness? We answer this question by following the nine steps for carrying out a hypothesis test. We will use a .05 significance level for this example.

1. Population characteristic of interest:

   p = proportion of all adolescents who have a low level of cardiovascular fitness

2. Null hypothesis: H_0: $p = .3$
3. Alternative hypothesis: H_a: $p > .3$ (the percentage of adolescents with a low fitness level is greater than 30%)
4. Significance level: $\alpha = .05$
5. Test statistic:

$$z = \frac{\hat{p} - \text{hypothesized value}}{\sqrt{\frac{(\text{hypothesized value})(1 - \text{hypothesized value})}{n}}} = \frac{\hat{p} - .3}{\sqrt{\frac{(.3)(1 - .3)}{n}}}$$

Step-by-Step technology instructions available online

6. Assumptions: This test requires a random sample and a large sample size. The given sample was considered to be representative of adolescents nationwide, and if this is the case, it is reasonable to regard the sample as if it were a random sample. The sample size was $n = 2205$. Since $2205(.3) \geq 10$ and $2205(1 - .3) \geq 10$, the large-sample test is appropriate. The population is all adolescents age 12 to 19, so the sample size is small compared to the population size.
7. Computations: $n = 2205$ and $\hat{p} = 750/2205 = .34$, so

$$z = \frac{.34 - .3}{\sqrt{\frac{(.3)(1 - .3)}{2205}}} = \frac{.04}{.010} = 4.00$$

8. *P*-value: This is an upper-tailed test (the inequality in H_a is >), so the *P*-value is the area to the right of the computed z value. Since $z = 4.00$ is so far out in the upper tail of the standard normal distribution, the area to its right is negligible, and

$$P\text{-value} \approx 0$$

9. Conclusion: Since $P\text{-value} \leq \alpha$ $(0 \leq .05)$, H_0 is rejected at the .05 level of significance. We conclude that the proportion of adolescents who have a low level of cardiovascular fitness is greater than .3. That is, the sample provides convincing evidence in support of the claim that more than 30% of adolescents have a low fitness level.

EXAMPLE 10.12 College Attendance

The report "California's Education Skills Gap: Modest Improvements Could Yield Big Gains" (Public Policy Institute of California, April 16, 2008, www.ppic.org) states that nationwide, 61% of high school graduates go on to attend a two-year or four-year college the year after graduation. The college-going rate for high school graduates in California was estimated to be 55%. Suppose that the estimate of 55% was based on a random sample of 1500 California high school graduates in 2009. Can we reasonably conclude that the proportion of California high school graduates in 2009 who attended college the year after graduation is different from the national figure? We will use the nine-step hypothesis testing procedure and a significance level of $\alpha = .01$ to answer this question.

1. p = proportion of all 2009 high school graduates who attended college the year after graduation
2. H_0: $p = .61$
3. H_a: $p \neq .61$ (differs from the national proportion)
4. Significance level: $\alpha = .01$
5. Test statistic:

$$z = \frac{\hat{p} - \text{hypothesized value}}{\sqrt{\frac{(\text{hypothesized value})(1 - \text{hypothesized value})}{n}}} = \frac{\hat{p} - .61}{\sqrt{\frac{(.61)(.39)}{n}}}$$

6. Assumptions: This test requires a random sample and a large sample size. The given sample was a random sample, the population size is much larger than the sample size, and the sample size was $n = 1500$. Because $1500(.61) \geq 10$ and $1500(.39) \geq 10$, the large-sample test is appropriate.

7. Computations: $\hat{p} = .55$, so

$$z = \frac{.55 - .61}{\sqrt{\frac{(.61)(.39)}{1500}}} = \frac{-.06}{.013} = -4.62$$

8. *P*-value: The area under the z curve to the left of -4.62 is approximately 0, so *P*-value $\approx 2(0) = 0$.
9. Conclusion: At significance level .01, we reject H_0 because *P*-value $\approx 0 < .01 = \alpha$. The data provide convincing evidence that the proportion of 2009 California high school graduates who attended college during the year after graduation differs from the nationwide proportion.

Most statistical computer packages and graphing calculators can calculate and report *P*-values for a variety of hypothesis-testing situations, including the large sample test for a proportion. Minitab was used to carry out the test of Example 10.10, and the resulting computer output follows:

Test and Confidence Interval for One Proportion

Test of p = 0.5 vs p < 0.5

Sample	X	N	Sample p	95.0 % CI	Z-Value	P-Value
1	220	500	0.440000	(0.396491, 0.483509)	−2.68	0.004

From the Minitab output, $z = -2.68$, and the associated *P*-value is .004. The small difference between the *P*-value here and the one computed in Example 10.10 (.0037) is the result of rounding.

It is also possible to compute the value of the z test statistic and then use a statistical computer package or graphing calculator to determine the corresponding *P*-value as an area under the standard normal curve. For example, the user can specify a value and Minitab will determine the area to the left of this value for any particular normal distribution. Because of this, the computer can be used in place of Appendix Table 2. In Example 10.10, the computed z was -2.68. Using Minitab gives the following output:

Normal with mean = 0 and standard deviation = 1.00000

x	P(X ≤ x)
−2.6800	0.0037

From the output, we learn that the area to the left of $-2.68 = .0037$, which agrees with the value obtained by using the tables.

EXERCISES 10.23 - 10.41

10.23 Use the definition of the *P*-value to explain the following:

a. Why H_0 would be rejected if *P*-value = .0003

b. Why H_0 would not be rejected if *P*-value = .350

10.24 For which of the following *P*-values will the null hypothesis be rejected when performing a test with a significance level of .05:

a. .001
b. .021
c. .078
d. .047
e. .148

10.25 Pairs of P-values and significance levels, α, are given. For each pair, state whether the observed P-value leads to rejection of H_0 at the given significance level.

a. P-value $= .084$, $\alpha = .05$
b. P-value $= .003$, $\alpha = .001$
c. P-value $= .498$, $\alpha = .05$
d. P-value $= .084$, $\alpha = .10$
e. P-value $= .039$, $\alpha = .01$
f. P-value $= .218$, $\alpha = .10$

10.26 Let p denote the proportion of grocery store customers who use the store's club card. For a large-sample z test of H_0: $p = .5$ versus H_a: $p > .5$, find the P-value associated with each of the given values of the test statistic:

a. 1.40
b. 0.93
c. 1.96
d. 2.45
e. -0.17

10.27 Assuming a random sample from a large population, for which of the following null hypotheses and sample sizes n is the large-sample z test appropriate:

a. H_0: $p = .2$, $n = 25$
b. H_0: $p = .6$, $n = 210$
c. H_0: $p = .9$, $n = 100$
d. H_0: $p = .05$, $n = 75$

10.28 In a survey conducted by CareerBuilder.com, employers were asked if they had ever sent an employee home because they were dressed inappropriately (June 17, 2008, www.careerbuilder.com). A total of 2765 employers responded to the survey, with 968 saying that they had sent an employee home for inappropriate attire. In a press release, CareerBuilder makes the claim that more than one-third of employers have sent an employee home to change clothes. Do the sample data provide convincing evidence in support of this claim? Test the relevant hypotheses using $\alpha = .05$. For purposes of this exercise, assume that it is reasonable to regard the sample as representative of employers in the United States.

10.29 In a survey of 1000 women age 22 to 35 who work full time, 540 indicated that they would be willing to give up some personal time in order to make more money (*USA Today*, March 4, 2010). The sample was selected in a way that was designed to produce a sample that was representative of women in the targeted age group.

a. Do the sample data provide convincing evidence that the majority of women age 22 to 35 who work full-time would be willing to give up some personal time for more money? Test the relevant hypotheses using $\alpha = .01$.
b. Would it be reasonable to generalize the conclusion from Part (a) to all working women? Explain why or why not.

10.30 The paper "Debt Literacy, Financial Experiences and Over-Indebtedness" (*Social Science Research Network*, Working paper W14808, 2008) included analysis of data from a national sample of 1000 Americans. One question on the survey was:

> "You owe \$3000 on your credit card. You pay a minimum payment of \$30 each month. At an Annual Percentage Rate of 12% (or 1% per month), how many years would it take to eliminate your credit card debt if you made no additional charges?"

Answer options for this question were: (a) less than 5 years; (b) between 5 and 10 years; (c) between 10 and 15 years; (d) never—you will continue to be in debt; (e) don't know; and (f) prefer not to answer.

a. Only 354 of the 1000 respondents chose the correct answer of never. For purposes of this exercise, you can assume that the sample is representative of adult Americans. Is there convincing evidence that the proportion of adult Americans who can answer this question correctly is less than .40 (40%)? Use $\alpha = .05$ to test the appropriate hypotheses.
b. The paper also reported that 37.8% of those in the sample chose one of the wrong answers (a, b, and c) as their response to this question. Is it reasonable to conclude that more than one-third of adult Americans would select a wrong answer to this question? Use $\alpha = .05$.

10.31 "Most Like it Hot" is the title of a press release issued by the Pew Research Center (March 18, 2009, www.pewsocialtrends.org). The press release states that "by an overwhelming margin, Americans want to live in a sunny place." This statement is based on data from a nationally representative sample of 2260 adult Americans. Of those surveyed, 1288 indicated that they would prefer to live in a hot climate rather than a cold climate. Do the sample data provide convincing evidence that a majority of all adult Americans prefer a hot climate over a cold climate? Use the nine-step hypothesis testing process with $\alpha = .01$ to answer this question.

10.32 In a survey of 1005 adult Americans, 46% indicated that they were somewhat interested or very interested in having web access in their cars (*USA Today*, May 1, 2009). Suppose that the marketing manager of a car manufacturer claims that the 46% is based only on a sample and that 46% is close to half, so there is no reason to believe that the proportion of all adult Americans who want car web access is less than .50. Is the marketing manager correct in his claim? Provide statistical evidence to support your answer. For purposes of this exercise, assume that the sample can be considered as representative of adult Americans.

10.33 The article "Poll Finds Most Oppose Return to Draft, Wouldn't Encourage Children to Enlist" (Associated Press, December 18, 2005) reports that in a random sample of 1000 American adults, 700 indicated that they oppose the reinstatement of a military draft. Is there convincing evidence that the proportion of American adults who oppose reinstatement of the draft is greater than two-thirds? Use a significance level of .05.

10.34 The poll referenced in the previous exercise ("Military Draft Study," AP-Ipsos, June 2005) also included the following question: "If the military draft were reinstated, would you favor or oppose drafting women as well as men?" Forty-three percent of the 1000 people responding said that they would favor drafting women if the draft were reinstated. Using a .05 significance level, carry out a test to determine if there is convincing evidence that fewer than half of adult Americans would favor the drafting of women.

10.35 The article "Irritated by Spam? Get Ready for Spit" (*USA Today*, November 10, 2004) predicts that "spit," spam that is delivered via Internet phone lines and cell phones, will be a growing problem as more people turn to web-based phone services. In a 2004 poll of 5500 cell phone users conducted by the Yankee Group, 20% indicated that they had received commercial messages or ads on their cell phones. Is there sufficient evidence to conclude that the proportion of cell phone users who have received commercial messages or ads in 2004 was greater than the proportion of .13 reported for the previous year?

10.36 According to a *Washington Post-ABC News* poll, 331 of 502 randomly selected U.S. adults interviewed said they would not be bothered if the National Security Agency collected records of personal telephone calls they had made. Is there sufficient evidence to conclude that a majority of U.S. adults feel this way? Test the appropriate hypotheses using a .01 significance level.

10.37 According to a survey of 1000 adult Americans conducted by Opinion Research Corporation, 210 of those surveyed said playing the lottery would be the most practical way for them to accumulate $200,000 in net wealth in their lifetime ("One in Five Believe Path to Riches Is the Lottery," *San Luis Obispo Tribune*, January 11, 2006). Although the article does not describe how the sample was selected, for purposes of this exercise, assume that the sample can be regarded as a random sample of adult Americans. Is there convincing evidence that more than 20% of adult Americans believe that playing the lottery is the best strategy for accumulating $200,000 in net wealth?

10.38 The article "Theaters Losing Out to Living Rooms" (*San Luis Obispo Tribune*, June 17, 2005) states that movie attendance declined in 2005. The Associated Press found that 730 of 1000 randomly selected adult Americans preferred to watch movies at home rather than at a movie theater. Is there convincing evidence that the majority of adult Americans prefer to watch movies at home? Test the relevant hypotheses using a .05 significance level.

10.39 The article referenced in the previous exercise also reported that 470 of 1000 randomly selected adult Americans thought that the quality of movies being produced was getting worse.

a. Is there convincing evidence that fewer than half of adult Americans believe that movie quality is getting worse? Use a significance level of .05.

b. Suppose that the sample size had been 100 instead of 1000, and that 47 thought that the movie quality was getting worse (so that the sample proportion is still .47). Based on this sample of 100, is there convincing evidence that fewer than half of adult Americans believe that movie quality is getting worse? Use a significance level of .05.

c. Write a few sentences explaining why different conclusions were reached in the hypothesis tests of Parts (a) and (b).

10.40 The report "2007 Electronic Monitoring & Surveillance Survey: Many Companies Monitoring, Recording, Videotaping—and Firing—Employees" (American Management Association, 2007) summarized the results of a survey of 304 U.S. businesses. Of these companies, 201 indicated that they monitor employees' web site visits. For purposes of this exercise, assume that it is reasonable to regard this sample as representative of businesses in the United States.

a. Is there sufficient evidence to conclude that more than 60% of U.S. businesses monitor employees' web site visits? Test the appropriate hypotheses using a significance level of .01.

b. Is there sufficient evidence to conclude that a majority of U.S. businesses monitor employees' web site visits? Test the appropriate hypotheses using a significance level of .01.

10.41 The article "Fewer Parolees Land Back Behind Bars" (*Associated Press*, April 11, 2006) includes the following statement: "Just over 38% of all felons who were released from prison in 2003 landed back behind bars by the end of the following year, the lowest rate since 1979." Explain why it would not be necessary to carry out a hypothesis test to determine if the proportion of felons released in 2003 was less than .40.

10.4 Hypothesis Tests for a Population Mean

We now turn our attention to developing a method for testing hypotheses about a population mean. The test procedures in this case are based on the same two results that led to the z and t confidence intervals in Chapter 9:

1. When either n is large or the population distribution is approximately normal, then

$$z = \frac{\bar{x} - \mu}{\frac{\sigma}{\sqrt{n}}}$$

has approximately a standard normal distribution.

2. When either n is large or the population distribution is approximately normal, then

$$t = \frac{\bar{x} - \mu}{\frac{s}{\sqrt{n}}}$$

has approximately a t distribution with df $= n - 1$.

A consequence of these two results is that if we are interested in testing a null hypothesis of the form

H_0: μ = hypothesized value

then, depending on whether σ is known or unknown, we can use (as long as n is large or the population distribution is approximately normal) either the following z or t test statistic:

Case 1: σ known

Test statistic: $z = \dfrac{\bar{x} - \text{hypothesized value}}{\frac{\sigma}{\sqrt{n}}}$

P-value: Computed as an area under the z curve

Case 2: σ unknown

Test statistic: $t = \dfrac{\bar{x} - \text{hypothesized value}}{\frac{s}{\sqrt{n}}}$

P-value: Computed as an area under the t curve with df $= n - 1$

Because it is rarely the case that σ, the population standard deviation, is known, we focus our attention on the test procedure for the case in which σ is unknown.

When testing a hypothesis about a population mean, the null hypothesis specifies a particular hypothesized value for μ, specifically, H_0: μ = hypothesized value. The alternative hypothesis has one of the following three forms, depending on the research question being addressed:

H_a: $\mu >$ hypothesized value
H_a: $\mu <$ hypothesized value
H_a: $\mu \neq$ hypothesized value

If n is large or if the population distribution is approximately normal, the test statistic

$$t = \frac{\bar{x} - \text{hypothesized value}}{\frac{s}{\sqrt{n}}}$$

can be used. For example, if the null hypothesis to be tested is H_0: $\mu = 100$, the test statistic becomes

$$t = \frac{\bar{x} - 100}{\frac{s}{\sqrt{n}}}$$

Consider the alternative hypothesis H_a: $\mu > 100$, and suppose that a sample of size $n = 24$ gives $\bar{x} = 104.20$ and $s = 8.23$. The resulting test statistic value is

$$t = \frac{104.20 - 100}{\frac{8.23}{\sqrt{24}}} = \frac{4.20}{1.6799} = 2.50$$

Because this is an upper-tailed test, if the test statistic had been z rather than t, the P-value would be the area under the z curve to the right of 2.50. With a t statistic, the P-value is the area under an appropriate t curve (here with df $= 24 - 1 = 23$) to the right of 2.50. Appendix Table 4 is a tabulation of t curve tail areas. Each column of the table is for a different number of degrees of freedom: 1, 2, 3, . . . , 30, 35, 40, 60, 120, and a last column for df $= \infty$, which is the same as for the z curve. The table gives the area under each t curve to the right of values ranging from 0.0 to 4.0 in increments of 0.1. Part of this table appears in Figure 10.3. For example,

area under the 23-df t curve to the right of 2.5 = .010
= P-value for an upper-tailed t test

Suppose that $t = -2.7$ for a lower-tailed test based on 23 df. Then, because each t curve is symmetric about 0,

P-value = area to the left of -2.7 = area to the right of 2.7 = .006

As is the case for z tests, we double the tail area to obtain the P-value for two-tailed t tests. Thus, if $t = 2.6$ or if $t = -2.6$ for a two-tailed t test with 23 df, then

P-value = 2(.008) = .016

Once past 30 df, the tail areas change very little, so the last column (∞) in Appendix Table 4 provides a good approximation.

The following two boxes show how the P-value is obtained as a t curve area and give a general description of the test procedure.

t \ df	1	2	...	22	23	24	...	60	120
0.0									
0.1									
⋮				⋮	⋮	⋮			
2.5			...	.010	.010	.010	...		
2.6			...	.008	.008	.008	...		
2.7			...	.007	.006	.006	...		
2.8			...	.005	.005	.005	...		
⋮				⋮	⋮	⋮			
4.0									

Area under 23-df t curve to right of 2.7

FIGURE 10.3
Part of Appendix Table 4: t curve tail areas.

Finding P-Values for a t Test

1. **Upper-tailed test:**

   H_a: $\mu >$ hypothesized value

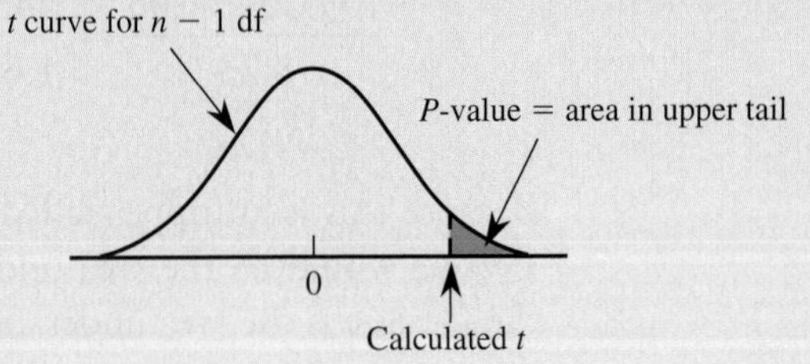

2. **Lower-tailed test:**

   H_a: $\mu <$ hypothesized value

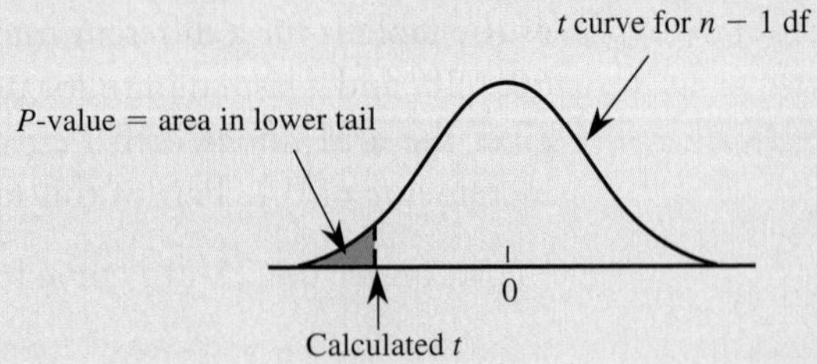

3. **Two-tailed test:**

   H_a: $\mu \neq$ hypothesized value

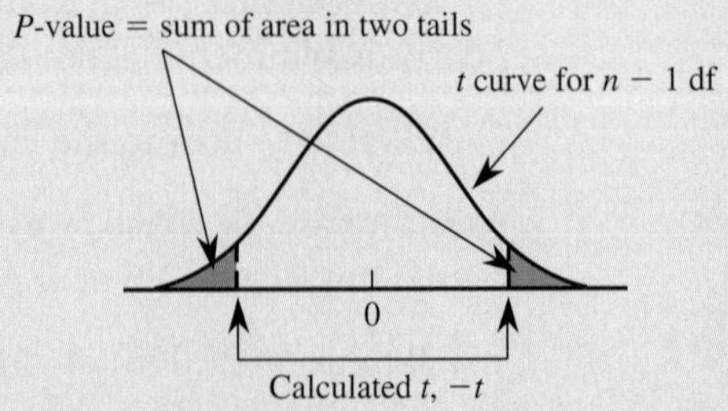

Appendix Table 4 gives upper-tail t curve areas to the right of values 0.0, 0.1, . . . , 4.0. These areas are P-values for upper-tailed tests and, by symmetry, also for lower-tailed tests. Doubling an area gives the P-value for a two-tailed test.

The One-Sample t Test for a Population Mean

Null hypothesis: H_0: μ = hypothesized value

Test statistic: $t = \dfrac{\bar{x} - \text{hypothesized value}}{\dfrac{s}{\sqrt{n}}}$

Alternative Hypothesis:	***P*-Value:**
H_a: $\mu >$ hypothesized value	Area to the right of calculated t under t curve with df $= n - 1$
H_a: $\mu <$ hypothesized value	Area to the left of calculated t under t curve with df $= n - 1$
H_a: $\mu \neq$ hypothesized value	(1) 2(area to the right of t) if t is positive, or (2) 2(area to the left of t) if t is negative

Assumptions: 1. $\bar{x}$ and s are the sample mean and sample standard deviation from a *random sample.*
2. The *sample size is large* (generally $n \geq 30$) or *the population distribution is at least approximately normal.*

EXAMPLE 10.13 Time Stands Still (or So It Seems)

● A study conducted by researchers at Pennsylvania State University investigated whether time perception, an indication of a person's ability to concentrate, is impaired during nicotine withdrawal. The study results were presented in the paper "Smoking Abstinence Impairs Time Estimation Accuracy in Cigarette Smokers" (*Psychopharmacology Bulletin* [2003]: 90–95). After a 24-hour smoking abstinence, 20 smokers were asked to estimate how much time had passed during a 45-second period. Suppose the resulting data on perceived elapsed time (in seconds) were as follows (these data are artificial but are consistent with summary quantities given in the paper):

69	65	72	73	59	55	39	52	67	57
56	50	70	47	56	45	70	64	67	53

From these data, we obtain

$$n = 20 \qquad \bar{x} = 59.30 \qquad s = 9.84$$

The researchers wanted to determine whether smoking abstinence had a negative impact on time perception, causing elapsed time to be overestimated. With μ representing the mean perceived elapsed time for smokers who have abstained from smoking for 24 hours, we can answer this question by testing

H_0: $\mu = 45$ (no consistent tendency to overestimate the time elapsed)

versus

H_a: $\mu > 45$ (tendency for elapsed time to be overestimated)

The null hypothesis is rejected only if there is convincing evidence that $\mu > 45$. The observed value, 59.30, is certainly larger than 45, but can a sample mean as large as this be plausibly explained by chance variation from one sample to another when $\mu = 45$? To answer this question, we carry out a hypothesis test with a significance level of .05 using the nine-step procedure described in Section 10.3.

1. Population characteristic of interest:

   μ = mean perceived elapsed time for smokers who have abstained from smoking for 24 hours

● Data set available online

2. Null hypothesis: H_0: $\mu = 45$
3. Alternative hypothesis: H_a: $\mu > 45$
4. Significance level: $\alpha = .05$
5. Test statistic: $t = \dfrac{\bar{x} - \text{hypothesized value}}{\dfrac{s}{\sqrt{n}}} = \dfrac{\bar{x} - 45}{\dfrac{s}{\sqrt{n}}}$
6. Assumptions: This test requires a random sample and either a large sample size or a normal population distribution. The authors of the paper believed that it was reasonable to consider this sample as representative of smokers in general, and if this is the case, it is reasonable to regard it as if it were a random sample. Because the sample size is only 20, for the t test to be appropriate, we must be willing to assume that the population distribution of perceived elapsed times is at least approximately normal. Is this reasonable? The following graph gives a boxplot of the data:

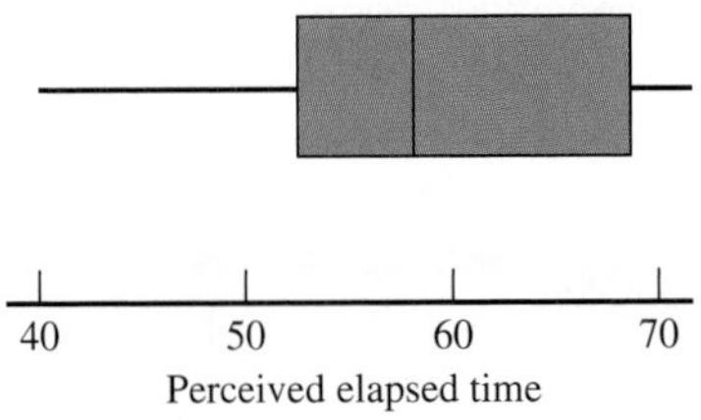

Although the boxplot is not perfectly symmetric, it does not appear to be too skewed and there are no outliers, so we judge the use of the t test to be reasonable.

7. Computations: $n = 20$, $\bar{x} = 59.30$, and $s = 9.84$, so

$$t = \frac{59.30 - 45}{\dfrac{9.84}{\sqrt{20}}} = \frac{14.30}{2.20} = 6.50$$

8. P-value: This is an upper-tailed test (the inequality in H_a is "greater than"), so the P-value is the area to the right of the computed t value. Because df $= 20 - 1 = 19$, we can use the df $= 19$ column of Appendix Table 4 to find the P-value. With $t = 6.50$, we obtain P-value $=$ area to the right of $6.50 \approx 0$ (because 6.50 is greater than 4.0, the largest tabulated value).
9. Conclusion: Because P-value $\leq \alpha$, we reject H_0 at the .05 level of significance. There is virtually no chance of seeing a sample mean (and hence a t value) this extreme as a result of just chance variation when H_0 is true. There is convincing evidence that the mean perceived time elapsed is greater than the actual time elapsed of 45 seconds.

This paper also looked at perception of elapsed time for a sample of nonsmokers and for a sample of smokers who had not abstained from smoking. The investigators found that the null hypothesis of $\mu = 45$ could not be rejected for either of these groups.

EXAMPLE 10.14 Goofing Off at Work

Step-by-Step technology instructions available online

Data set available online

● A growing concern of employers is time spent in activities like surfing the Internet and e-mailing friends during work hours. The *San Luis Obispo Tribune* summarized the findings from a survey of a large sample of workers in an article that ran under the headline "Who Goofs Off 2 Hours a Day? Most Workers, Survey Says" (August 3,

2006). Suppose that the CEO of a large company wants to determine whether the average amount of wasted time during an 8-hour work day for employees of her company is less than the reported 120 minutes. Each person in a random sample of 10 employees was contacted and asked about daily wasted time at work. (Participants would probably have to be guaranteed anonymity to obtain truthful responses!) The resulting data are the following:

108 112 117 130 111 131 113 113 105 128

Summary quantities are $n = 10$, $\bar{x} = 116.80$, and $s = 9.45$.

Do these data provide evidence that the mean wasted time for this company is less than 120 minutes? To answer this question, let's carry out a hypothesis test with $\alpha = .05$.

1. μ = mean daily wasted time for employees of this company
2. H_0: $\mu = 120$
3. H_a: $\mu < 120$
4. $\alpha = .05$
5. $t = \dfrac{\bar{x} - \text{hypothesized value}}{\dfrac{s}{\sqrt{n}}} = \dfrac{\bar{x} - 120}{\dfrac{s}{\sqrt{n}}}$
6. This test requires a random sample and either a large sample or a normal population distribution. The given sample was a random sample of employees. Because the sample size is small, we must be willing to assume that the population distribution of times is at least approximately normal. The accompanying normal probability plot appears to be reasonably straight, and although the normal probability plot and the boxplot reveal some skewness in the sample, there are no outliers.

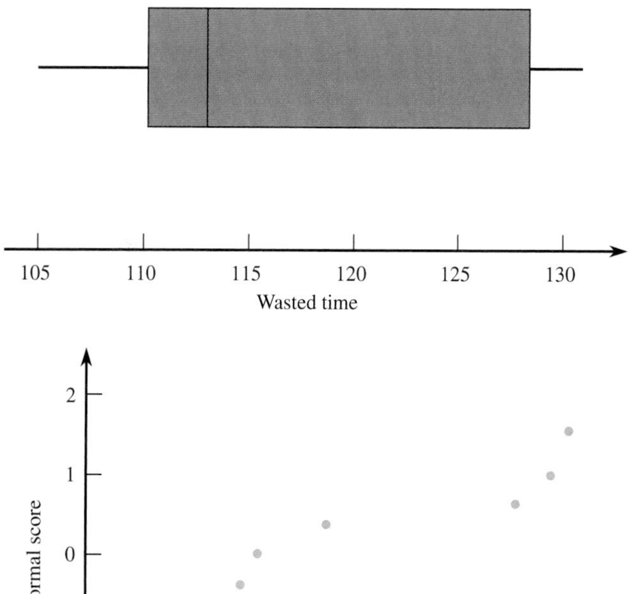

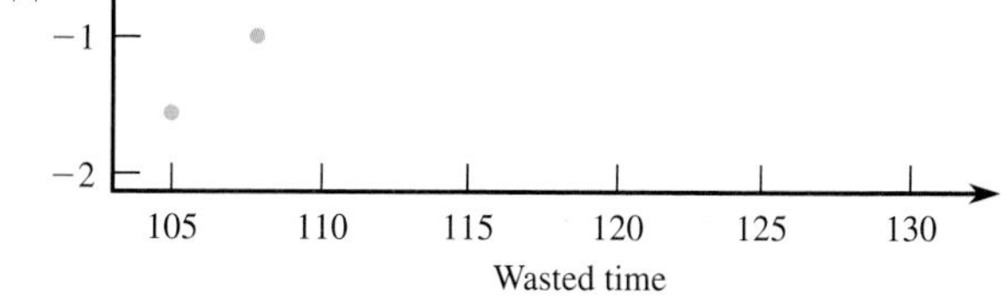

Correlations (Pearson)

Correlation of Time and Normal Score = 0.943

Also, the correlation between the expected normal scores and the observed data for this sample is .943, which is well above the critical r value for $n = 10$ of .880 (see Chapter 5 for critical r values). Based on these observations, it is plausible that the population distribution is approximately normal, so we proceed with the t test.

7. Test statistic: $t = \dfrac{116.80 - 120}{\dfrac{9.45}{\sqrt{10}}} = -1.07$

8. From the df = 9 column of Appendix Table 4 and by rounding the test statistic value to -1.1, we get

   P-value = area to the left of -1.1 = area to the right of $1.1 = .150$

as shown:

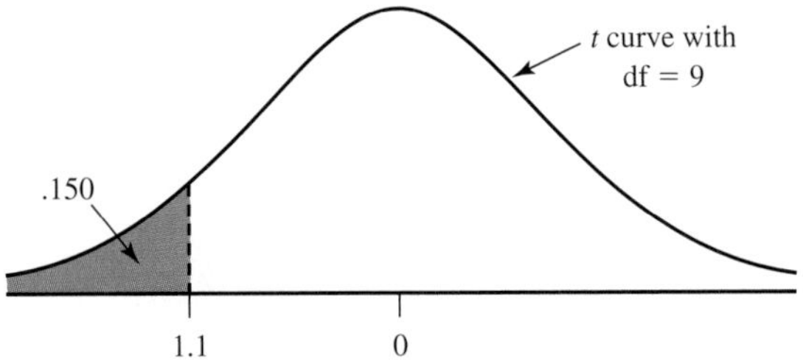

9. Because the P-value $> \alpha$, we fail to reject H_0. There is not sufficient evidence to conclude that the mean wasted time per 8-hour work day for employees at this company is less than 120 minutes.

Minitab could also have been used to carry out the test, as shown in the output below.

One-Sample T: Wasted Time
Test of mu = 120 vs < 120

Variable	N	Mean	StDev	SE Mean	95% Upper Bound	T	P
Wasted Time	10	116.800	9.449	2.988	122.278	–1.07	0.156

Although we had to round the computed t value to -1.1 to use Appendix Table 4, Minitab was able to compute the P-value corresponding to the actual value of the test statistic, which was P-value = 0.156.

EXAMPLE 10.15 Cricket Love

© Dynamic Graphics/Creatas/Alamy

The article "Well-Fed Crickets Bowl Maidens Over" (*Nature Science Update*, February 11, 1999) reported that female field crickets are attracted to males that have high chirp rates and hypothesized that chirp rate is related to nutritional status. The usual chirp rate for male field crickets was reported to vary around a mean of 60 chirps per second. To investigate whether chirp rate was related to nutritional status, investigators fed male crickets a high protein diet for 8 days, after which chirp rate was measured. The mean chirp rate for the crickets on the high protein diet was reported to be 109 chirps per second. Is this convincing evidence that the mean chirp rate for crickets on a high protein diet is greater than 60 (which would then imply an advantage in attracting the ladies)? Suppose that the sample size and sample standard deviation are $n = 32$ and $s = 40$. Let's test the relevant hypotheses with $\alpha = .01$.

1. μ = mean chirp rate for crickets on a high protein diet
2. H_0: $\mu = 60$
3. H_a: $\mu > 60$
4. $\alpha = .01$
5. $t = \dfrac{\bar{x} - \text{hypothesized value}}{\frac{s}{\sqrt{n}}} = \dfrac{\bar{x} - 60}{\frac{s}{\sqrt{n}}}$
6. This test requires a random sample and either a large sample or a normal population distribution. Because the sample size is large ($n = 32$), it is reasonable to proceed with the t test as long as we are willing to consider the 32 male field crickets in this study as if they were a random sample from the population of male field crickets.
7. Test statistic: $t = \dfrac{109 - 60}{\frac{40}{\sqrt{32}}} = \dfrac{49}{7.07} = 6.93$
8. This is an upper-tailed test, so the P-value is the area under the t curve with df = 31 and to the right of 6.93. From Appendix Table 4, P-value ≈ 0.
9. Because P-value ≈ 0, which is less than the significance level, α, we reject H_0. There is convincing evidence that the mean chirp rate is higher for male field crickets that eat a high protein diet.

Statistical Versus Practical Significance

Carrying out a hypothesis test amounts to deciding whether the value obtained for the test statistic could plausibly have resulted when H_0 is true. When the value of the test statistic leads to rejection of H_0, it is customary to say that the result is **statistically significant** at the chosen significance level α. The finding of statistical significance means that, in the investigator's opinion, the observed deviation from what was expected under H_0 cannot reasonably be attributed to only chance variation. However, statistical significance is not the same as concluding that the true situation differs from what the null hypothesis states in any practical sense. That is, even after H_0 has been rejected, the data may suggest that there is no *practical* difference between the actual value of the population characteristic and what the null hypothesis states that value to be. This is illustrated in Example 10.16.

EXAMPLE 10.16 "Significant" but Unimpressive Test Score Improvement

Let μ denote the average score on a standardized test for all children in a certain region of the United States. The average score for all children in the United States is 100. Regional education authorities are interested in testing H_0: $\mu = 100$ versus H_a: $\mu > 100$ using a significance level of .001. A sample of 2500 children resulted in the values $n = 2500$, $\bar{x} = 101.0$, and $s = 15.0$. Then

$$t = \frac{101.0 - 100}{\frac{15}{\sqrt{2500}}} = 3.3$$

This is an upper-tailed test, so (using the z column of Appendix Table 4 because df = 2499) P-value = area to the right of $3.33 \approx .000$. Because P-value $< .001$, we reject H_0. There is evidence that the mean score for this region is greater than 100.

However, with $n = 2500$, the point estimate $\bar{x} = 101.0$ is almost surely very close to the true value of μ. Therefore, it looks as though H_0 was rejected because $\mu \approx 101$ rather than 100. And, from a practical point of view, a 1-point difference is most likely of no practical importance.

EXERCISES 10.42 - 10.58

10.42 Give as much information as you can about the P-value of a t test in each of the following situations:

a. Upper-tailed test, df = 8, $t = 2.0$
b. Upper-tailed test, $n = 14$, $t = 3.2$
c. Lower-tailed test, df = 10, $t = -2.4$
d. Lower-tailed test, $n = 22$, $t = -4.2$
e. Two-tailed test, df = 15, $t = -1.6$
f. Two-tailed test, $n = 16$, $t = 1.6$
g. Two-tailed test, $n = 16$, $t = 6.3$

10.43 Give as much information as you can about the P-value of a t test in each of the following situations:

a. Two-tailed test, df = 9, $t = 0.73$
b. Upper-tailed test, df = 10, $t = -0.5$
c. Lower-tailed test, $n = 20$, $t = -2.1$
d. Lower-tailed test, $n = 20$, $t = -5.1$
e. Two-tailed test, $n = 40$, $t = 1.7$

10.44 Paint used to paint lines on roads must reflect enough light to be clearly visible at night. Let μ denote the mean reflectometer reading for a new type of paint under consideration. A test of H_0: $\mu = 20$ versus H_a: $\mu > 20$ based on a sample of 15 observations gave $t = 3.2$. What conclusion is appropriate at each of the following significance levels?

a. $\alpha = .05$
b. $\alpha = .01$
c. $\alpha = .001$

10.45 A certain pen has been designed so that true average writing lifetime under controlled conditions (involving the use of a writing machine) is at least 10 hours. A random sample of 18 pens is selected, the writing lifetime of each is determined, and a normal probability plot of the resulting data supports the use of a one-sample t test. The relevant hypotheses are H_0: $\mu = 10$ versus H_a: $\mu < 10$.

a. If $t = -2.3$ and $\alpha = .05$ is selected, what conclusion is appropriate?
b. If $t = -1.83$ and $\alpha = .01$ is selected, what conclusion is appropriate?
c. If $t = 0.47$, what conclusion is appropriate?

10.46 The true average diameter of ball bearings of a certain type is supposed to be 0.5 inch. What conclusion is appropriate when testing H_0: $\mu = 0.5$ versus H_a: $\mu \neq 0.5$ inch each of the following situations:

a. $n = 13$, $t = 1.6$, $\alpha = .05$
b. $n = 13$, $t = -1.6$, $\alpha = .05$
c. $n = 25$, $t = -2.6$, $\alpha = .01$
d. $n = 25$, $t = -3.6$

10.47 The paper "Playing Active Video Games Increases Energy Expenditure in Children" (*Pediatrics* [2009]: 534–539) describes an interesting investigation of the possible cardiovascular benefits of active video games. Mean heart rate for healthy boys age 10 to 13 after walking on a treadmill at 2.6 km/hour for 6 minutes is 98 beats per minute (bpm). For each of 14 boys, heart rate was measured after 15 minutes of playing Wii Bowling. The resulting sample mean and standard deviation were 101 bpm and 15 bpm, respectively. For purposes of this exercise, assume that it is reasonable to regard the sample of boys as representative of boys age 10 to 13 and that the distribution of heart rates after 15 minutes of Wii Bowling is approximately normal.

a. Does the sample provide convincing evidence that the mean heart rate after 15 minutes of Wii Bowling is different from the known mean heart rate after 6 minutes walking on the treadmill? Carry out a hypothesis test using $\alpha = .01$.
b. The known resting mean heart rate for boys in this age group is 66 bpm. Is there convincing evidence that the mean heart rate after Wii Bowling for 15 minutes is higher than the known mean resting heart rate for boys of this age? Use $\alpha = .01$.

c. Based on the outcomes of the tests in Parts (a) and (b), write a paragraph comparing the benefits of treadmill walking and Wii Bowling in terms of raising heart rate over the resting heart rate.

10.48 A study of fast-food intake is described in the paper "What People Buy From Fast-Food Restaurants" (*Obesity* [2009]: 1369–1374). Adult customers at three hamburger chains (McDonald's, Burger King, and Wendy's) at lunchtime in New York City were approached as they entered the restaurant and asked to provide their receipt when exiting. The receipts were then used to determine what was purchased and the number of calories consumed was determined. In all, 3857 people participated in the study. The sample mean number of calories consumed was 857 and the sample standard deviation was 677.

a. The sample standard deviation is quite large. What does this tell you about number of calories consumed in a hamburger-chain lunchtime fast-food purchase in New York City?
b. Given the values of the sample mean and standard deviation and the fact that the number of calories consumed can't be negative, explain why it is *not* reasonable to assume that the distribution of calories consumed is normal.
c. Based on a recommended daily intake of 2000 calories, the online Healthy Dining Finder (www.healthydiningfinder.com) recommends a target of 750 calories for lunch. Assuming that it is reasonable to regard the sample of 3857 fast-food purchases as representative of all hamburger-chain lunchtime purchases in New York City, carry out a hypothesis test to determine if the sample provides convincing evidence that the mean number of calories in a New York City hamburger-chain lunchtime purchase is greater than the lunch recommendation of 750 calories. Use $\alpha = .01$.
d. Would it be reasonable to generalize the conclusion of the test in Part (c) to the lunchtime fast-food purchases of all adult Americans? Explain why or why not.
e. Explain why it is better to use the customer receipt to determine what was ordered rather than just asking a customer leaving the restaurant what he or she purchased.
f. Do you think that asking a customer to provide his or her receipt before they ordered could have introduced a potential bias? Explain.

10.49 The report "Highest Paying Jobs for 2009–10 Bachelor's Degree Graduates" (National Association of Colleges and Employers, February 2010) states that the mean yearly salary offer for students graduating with a degree in accounting in 2010 is \$48,722. Suppose that a random sample of 50 accounting graduates at a large university who received job offers resulted in a mean offer of \$49,850 and a standard deviation of \$3300. Do the sample data provide strong support for the claim that the mean salary offer for accounting graduates of this university is higher than the 2010 national average of \$48,722? Test the relevant hypotheses using $\alpha = .05$.

10.50 ● *The Economist* collects data each year on the price of a Big Mac in various countries around the world. The price of a Big Mac for a sample of McDonald's restaurants in Europe in May 2009 resulted in the following Big Mac prices (after conversion to U.S. dollars):

3.80 5.89 4.92 3.88 2.65 5.57 6.39 3.24

The mean price of a Big Mac in the U.S. in May 2009 was \$3.57. For purposes of this exercise, assume it is reasonable to regard the sample as representative of European McDonald's restaurants. Does the sample provide convincing evidence that the mean May 2009 price of a Big Mac in Europe is greater than the reported U.S. price? Test the relevant hypotheses using $\alpha = .05$.

10.51 A credit bureau analysis of undergraduate students credit records found that the average number of credit cards in an undergraduate's wallet was 4.09 ("Undergraduate Students and Credit Cards in 2004," Nellie Mae, May 2005). It was also reported that in a random sample of 132 undergraduates, the sample mean number of credit cards that the students said they carried was 2.6. The sample standard deviation was not reported, but for purposes of this exercise, suppose that it was 1.2. Is there convincing evidence that the mean number of credit cards that undergraduates report carrying is less than the credit bureau's figure of 4.09?

10.52 ● Medical research has shown that repeated wrist extension beyond 20 degrees increases the risk of wrist and hand injuries. Each of 24 students at Cornell University used a proposed new computer mouse design, and while using the mouse, each student's wrist extension was recorded. Data consistent with summary values given in the paper "Comparative Study of Two Computer Mouse Designs" (Cornell Human Factors Laboratory Technical Report RP7992) are given. Use these data to test the hypothesis that the mean wrist extension for people using this new mouse design is greater than 20 degrees. Are any assumptions required in order for it to be appropriate to generalize the results of your test to the population of Cornell students? To the population of all university students?

27	28	24	26	27	25	25	24	24	24	25	28
22	25	24	28	27	26	31	25	28	27	27	25

10.53 The international polling organization Ipsos reported data from a survey of 2000 randomly selected Canadians who carry debit cards (Canadian Account Habits Survey, July 24, 2006). Participants in this survey were asked what they considered the minimum purchase amount for which it would be acceptable to use a debit card. Suppose that the sample mean and standard deviation were \$9.15 and \$7.60, respectively. (These values are consistent with a histogram of the sample data that appears in the report.) Do these data provide convincing evidence that the mean minimum purchase amount for which Canadians consider the use of a debit card to be appropriate is less than \$10? Carry out a hypothesis test with a significance level of .01.

10.54 A comprehensive study conducted by the National Institute of Child Health and Human Development tracked more than 1000 children from an early age through elementary school (*New York Times*, November 1, 2005). The study concluded that children who spent more than 30 hours a week in child care before entering school tended to score higher in math and reading when they were in the third grade. The researchers cautioned that the findings should not be a cause for alarm because the effects of child care were found to be small. Explain how the difference between the sample mean math score for third graders who spent long hours in child care and the known overall mean for third graders could be small but the researchers could still reach the conclusion that the mean for the child care group is significantly higher than the overall mean for third graders.

10.55 In a study of computer use, 1000 randomly selected Canadian Internet users were asked how much time they spend using the Internet in a typical week (Ipsos Reid, August 9, 2005). The mean of the sample observations was 12.7 hours.

a. The sample standard deviation was not reported, but suppose that it was 5 hours. Carry out a hypothesis test with a significance level of .05 to decide if there is convincing evidence that the mean time spent using the Internet by Canadians is greater than 12.5 hours.

b. Now suppose that the sample standard deviation was 2 hours. Carry out a hypothesis test with a significance level of .05 to decide if there is convincing evidence that the mean time spent using the Internet by Canadians is greater than 12.5 hours.

c. Explain why the null hypothesis was rejected in the test of Part (b) but not in the test of Part (a).

10.56 The paper titled "Music for Pain Relief" (*The Cochrane Database of Systematic Reviews*, April 19, 2006) concluded, based on a review of 51 studies of the effect of music on pain intensity, that "Listening to music reduces pain intensity levels . . . However, the magnitude of these positive effects is small, the clinical relevance of music for pain relief in clinical practice is unclear." Are the authors of this paper claiming that the pain reduction attributable to listening to music is not statistically significant, not practically significant, or neither statistically nor practically significant? Explain.

10.57 ● ✦ Many consumers pay careful attention to stated nutritional contents on packaged foods when making purchases. It is therefore important that the information on packages be accurate. A random sample of $n = 12$ frozen dinners of a certain type was selected from production during a particular period, and the calorie content of each one was determined. (This determination entails destroying the product, so a census would certainly not be desirable!) Here are the resulting observations, along with a boxplot and normal probability plot:

255	244	239	242	265	245	259	248
225	226	251	233				

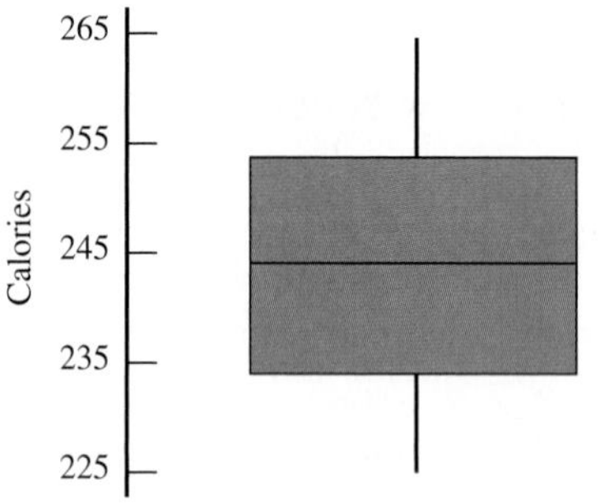

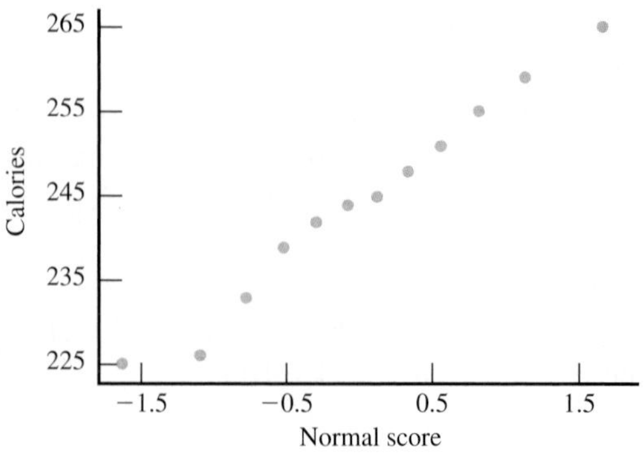

a. Is it reasonable to test hypotheses about mean calorie content μ by using a t test? Explain why or why not.
b. The stated calorie content is 240. Does the boxplot suggest that true average content differs from the stated value? Explain your reasoning.
c. Carry out a formal test of the hypotheses suggested in Part (b).

10.58 ● Much concern has been expressed regarding the practice of using nitrates as meat preservatives. In one study involving possible effects of these chemicals, bacteria cultures were grown in a medium containing nitrates. The rate of uptake of radio-labeled amino acid (in dpm, disintegrations per minute) was then determined for each culture, yielding the following observations:

7251	6871	9632	6866	9094	5849	8957	7978
7064	7494	7883	8178	7523	8724	7468	

Suppose that it is known that the mean rate of uptake for cultures without nitrates is 8000. Do the data suggest that the addition of nitrates results in a decrease in the mean rate of uptake? Test the appropriate hypotheses using a significance level of .10.

10.5 Power and Probability of Type II Error

In this chapter, we have introduced test procedures for testing hypotheses about population characteristics, such as μ and p. What characterizes a "good" test procedure? It makes sense to think that a good test procedure is one that has both a small probability of rejecting H_0 when it is true (a Type I error) and a high probability of rejecting H_0 when it is false. The test procedures presented in this chapter allow us to directly control the probability of rejecting a true H_0 by our choice of the significance level α. But what about the probability of rejecting H_0 when it is false? As we will see, several factors influence this probability. Let's begin by considering an example.

Suppose that the student body president at a university is interested in studying the amount of money that students spend on textbooks each semester. The director of the financial aid office believes that the average amount spent on books is \$500 per semester and uses this figure to determine the amount of financial aid for which a student is eligible. The student body president plans to ask each individual in a random sample of students how much he or she spent on books this semester and has decided to use the resulting data to test

$$H_0\text{: } \mu = 500 \quad \text{versus} \quad H_a\text{: } \mu > 500$$

using a significance level of .05. If the true mean is 500 (or less than 500), the correct decision is to fail to reject the null hypothesis. Incorrectly rejecting the null hypothesis is a Type I error. On the other hand, if the true mean is 525 or 505 or even 501, the correct decision is to reject the null hypothesis. Not rejecting the null hypothesis is a Type II error. How likely is it that the null hypothesis will in fact be rejected?

If the true mean is 501, the probability that we reject H_0: $\mu = 500$ is not very great. This is because when we carry out the test, we are essentially looking at the sample mean and asking, Does this look like what we would expect to see if the population mean were 500? As illustrated in Figure 10.4, if the true mean is greater than but very close to 500, chances are that the sample mean will look pretty much like what we would expect to see if the population mean were 500, and we will be unconvinced that the null hypothesis should be rejected. If the true mean is 525, it is less likely that the sample will be mistaken for a sample from a population with mean 500; sample means will tend to cluster around 525, and so it is more likely that we will correctly reject H_0. If the true mean is 550, rejection of H_0 is even more likely.

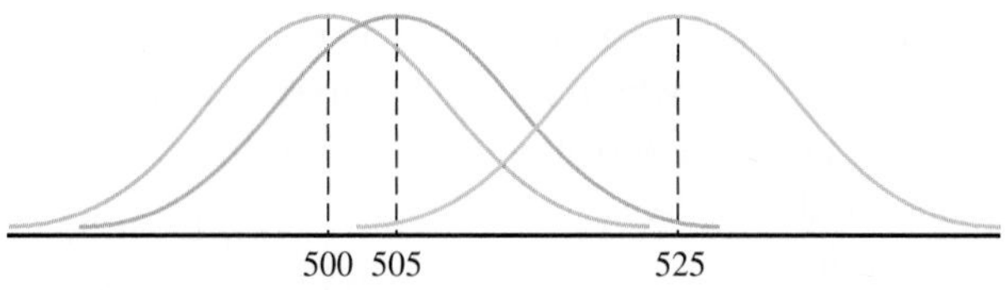

FIGURE 10.4
Sampling distribution of $\bar{x}$ when $\mu = 500, 505, 525$.

When we consider the probability of rejecting the null hypothesis, we are looking at what statisticians refer to as the **power** of the test.

The **power of a test** is the probability of rejecting the null hypothesis.

From the previous discussion, it should be apparent that when a hypothesis about a population mean is being tested, the power of the test depends on the true value of the population mean, μ. Because the actual value of μ is unknown (if we knew the value of μ we wouldn't be doing the hypothesis test!), we cannot know what the power is for the actual value of μ. It is possible, however, to gain some insight into the power of a test by looking at a number of "what if" scenarios. For example, we might ask, What is the power if the actual mean is 525? or What is the power if the actual mean is 505? and so on. That is, we can determine the power at $\mu = 525$, the power at $\mu = 505$, and the power at any other value of interest. Although it is technically possible to consider power when the null hypothesis is true, an investigator is usually concerned about the power only at values for which the null hypothesis is false.

In general, when testing a hypothesis about a population characteristic, there are three factors that influence the power of the test:

1. The size of the difference between the actual value of the population characteristic and the hypothesized value (the value that appears in the null hypothesis);
2. The choice of significance level, α, for the test; and
3. The sample size.

Effect of Various Factors on the Power of a Test

1. The larger the size of the discrepancy between the hypothesized value and the actual value of the population characteristic, the higher the power.
2. The larger the significance level, α, the higher the power of the test.
3. The larger the sample size, the higher the power of the test.

Let's consider each of the statements in the box above. The first statement has already been discussed in the context of the textbook example. Because power is the probability of rejecting the null hypothesis, it makes sense that the power will be higher when the actual value of a population characteristic is quite different from the hypothesized value than when it is close to that value.

The effect of significance level on power is not quite as obvious. To understand the relationship between power and significance level, it helps to see the relationship between power and β, the probability of a Type II error.

When H_0 is false, power $= 1 - \beta$.

This relationship follows from the definitions of power and Type II error. A Type II error results from *not* rejecting a false H_0. Because power is the probability of rejecting H_0, it follows that *when H_0 is false*

$$\begin{aligned} \text{power} &= \text{probability of rejecting a false } H_0 \\ &= 1 - \text{probability of not rejecting a false } H_0 \\ &= 1 - \beta \end{aligned}$$

AP* EXAM TIP

Because the computation of power is complicated, the AP exam does not include power calculations. However, you do need to know how power is related to sample size, significance level, and the actual value of the population characteristic.

Recall from Section 10.2 that the choice of α, the Type I error probability, affects the value of β, the Type II error probability. Choosing a larger value for α results in a smaller value for β (and therefore a larger value for $1 - \beta$). In terms of power, this means that choosing a larger value for α results in a larger value for the power of the test. That is, the larger the Type I error probability we are willing to tolerate, the more likely it is that the test will be able to detect any particular departure from H_0.

The third factor that affects the power of a test is the sample size. When H_0 is false, the power of a test is the probability that we will in fact "detect" that H_0 is false and, based on the observed sample, reject H_0. Intuition suggests that we will be more likely to detect a departure from H_0 with a large sample than with a small sample. This is in fact the case—the larger the sample size, the higher the power.

Consider testing the hypotheses presented previously:

H_0: $\mu = 500$ versus H_a: $\mu > 500$

The observations about power imply the following, for example:

1. For any value of μ exceeding 500, the power of a test based on a sample of size 100 is higher than the power of a test based on a sample of size 75 (assuming the same significance level).
2. For any value of μ exceeding 500, the power of a test using a significance level of .05 is higher than the power of a test using a significance level of .01 (assuming the same sample size).
3. For any value of μ exceeding 500, the power of the test is greater if the actual mean is 550 than if the actual mean is 525 (assuming the same sample size and significance level).

As was mentioned previously in this section, it is impossible to calculate the *exact* power of a test because in practice we do not know the values of population characteristics. However, we can evaluate the power at a selected alternative value which would tell us whether the power would be high or low if this alternative value is the actual value.

The following optional subsection shows how Type II error probabilities and power can be evaluated for selected tests.

Calculating Power and Type II Error Probabilities for Selected Tests (Optional)

The test procedures presented in this chapter are designed to control the probability of a Type I error (rejecting H_0 when H_0 is true) at the desired significance level α. However, little has been said so far about calculating the value of β, the probability of a Type II error (not rejecting H_0 when H_0 is false). Here, we consider the determination of β and power for the hypothesis tests previously introduced.

When we carry out a hypothesis test, we specify the desired value of α, the probability of a Type I error. The probability of a Type II error, β, is the probability of not rejecting H_0 even though it is false. Suppose that we are testing

H_0: $\mu = 1.5$ versus H_a: $\mu > 1.5$

Because we do not know the actual value of μ, we cannot calculate the value of β. However, the vulnerability of the test to Type II error can be investigated by calculating β for several different potential values of μ, such as $\mu = 1.55$, $\mu = 1.6$, and $\mu = 1.7$. Once the value of β has been determined, the power of the test at the corresponding alternative value is just $1 - \beta$.

EXAMPLE 10.17 Calculating Power

An airline claims that the mean time on hold for callers to its customer service phone line is 1.5 minutes. We might investigate this claim by testing

$$H_0\text{: } \mu = 1.5 \text{ versus } H_a\text{: } \mu > 1.5$$

where μ is the actual mean customer hold time. A random sample of $n = 36$ calls is to be selected, and the resulting data will be used to reach a conclusion. Suppose that the standard deviation of hold time (σ) is known to be 0.20 minutes and that a significance level of .01 is to be used. Our test statistic (because $\sigma = 0.20$) is

$$z = \frac{\bar{x} - 1.5}{\frac{.20}{\sqrt{n}}} = \frac{\bar{x} - 1.5}{\frac{.20}{\sqrt{36}}} = \frac{\bar{x} - 1.5}{.0333}$$

The inequality in H_a implies that

$$P\text{-value} = \text{area under } z \text{ curve to the right of calculated } z$$

From Appendix Table 2, it is easily verified that the z critical value 2.33 captures an upper-tail z curve area of .01. Thus, P-value $\leq .01$ only when $z \geq 2.33$. This is equivalent to the decision rule

$$\text{reject } H_0 \text{ if calculated } z \geq 2.33$$

which becomes

$$\text{reject } H_0 \text{ if } \frac{\bar{x} - 1.5}{.0333} \geq 2.33$$

Solving this inequality for $\bar{x}$ we get

$$\bar{x} \geq 1.5 + 2.33(.0333)$$

or

$$\bar{x} \geq 1.578$$

So if $\bar{x} \geq 1.578$, we will reject H_0, and if $\bar{x} < 1.578$, we will fail to reject H_0. This decision rule corresponds to $\alpha = .01$.

Suppose now that $\mu = 1.6$ (so that H_0 is false). A Type II error will then occur if $\bar{x} < 1.578$. What is the probability that this occurs? If $\mu = 1.6$, the sampling distribution of $\bar{x}$ is approximately normal, centered at 1.6, and has a standard deviation of .0333. The probability of observing an $\bar{x}$ value less than 1.578 can then be determined by finding an area under a normal curve with mean 1.6 and standard deviation .0333, as illustrated in Figure 10.5.

Because the curve in Figure 10.5 is not the standard normal (z) curve, we must first convert to a z score before using Appendix Table 2 to find the area. Here,

$$z \text{ score for } 1.578 = \frac{1.578 - \mu_{\bar{x}}}{\sigma_{\bar{x}}} = \frac{1.578 - 1.6}{.0333} = -.66$$

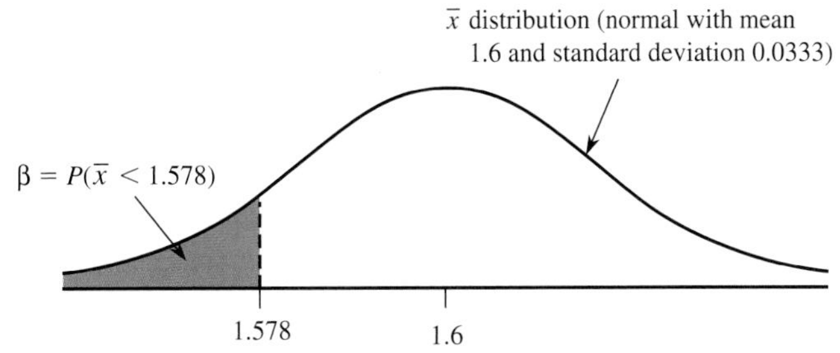

FIGURE 10.5
β when $\mu = 1.6$ in Example 10.17.

and

$$\text{area under } z \text{ curve to left of } -0.66 = .2546$$

So, if $\mu = 1.6$, $\beta = .2546$. This means that if μ is 1.6, about 25% of all samples would still result in $\bar{x}$ values less than 1.578 and failure to reject H_0.

The power of the test at $\mu = 1.6$ is then

$$\begin{aligned}(\text{power at } \mu = 1.6) &= 1 - (\beta \text{ when } \mu \text{ is } 1.6)\\ &= 1 - .2546\\ &= .7454\end{aligned}$$

This means that if the actual mean is 1.6, the probability of rejecting H_0: $\mu = 1.5$ in favor of H_a: $\mu > 1.5$ is .7454. That is, if μ is 1.6 and the test is used repeatedly with random samples selected from the population, in the long run about 75% of the samples will result in the correct conclusion to reject H_0.

Now consider β and power when $\mu = 1.65$. The normal curve in Figure 10.5 would then be centered at 1.65. Because β is the area to the left of 1.578 and the curve has shifted to the right, β decreases. Converting 1.578 to a z score and using Appendix Table 2 gives $\beta = .0154$. Also,

$$(\text{power at } \mu = 1.65) = 1 - .0154 = .9846$$

As expected, the power at $\mu = 1.65$ is higher than the power at $\mu = 1.6$ because 1.65 is farther from the hypothesized value of 1.5.

Statistical software and graphing calcultors can calculate the power for specified values of σ, α, n, and the difference between the actual and hypothesized values of μ. The following Minitab output shows power calculations corresponding to those in Example 10.17:

```
1-Sample Z Test
Testing mean = null (versus > null)
Alpha = 0.01    Sigma = 0.2    Sample Size = 36
Difference    Power
0.10          0.7497
0.15          0.9851
```

The slight differences between the power values computed by Minitab and those previously obtained are due to rounding in Example 10.17.

The probability of a Type II error and the power for z tests concerning a population proportion are calculated in an analogous manner.

EXAMPLE 10.18 Power for Testing Hypotheses About Proportions

A package delivery service advertises that at least 90% of all packages brought to its office by 9 A.M. for delivery in the same city are delivered by noon that day. Let p denote the proportion of all such packages actually delivered by noon. The hypotheses of interest are

$$H_0\colon p = .9 \quad \text{versus} \quad H_a\colon p < .9$$

where the alternative hypothesis states that the company's claim is untrue. The value $p = .8$ represents a substantial departure from the company's claim. If the hypotheses are tested at level .01 using a sample of $n = 225$ packages, what is the probability that the departure from H_0 represented by this alternative value will go undetected?

At significance level .01, H_0 is rejected if P-value $\leq .01$. For the case of a lower-tailed test, this is the same as rejecting H_0 if

$$z = \frac{\hat{p} - \mu_{\hat{p}}}{\sigma_{\hat{p}}} = \frac{\hat{p} - .9}{\sqrt{\dfrac{(.9)(.1)}{225}}} = \frac{\hat{p} - .9}{.02} \leq -2.33$$

(Because -2.33 captures a lower-tail z curve area of .01, the smallest 1% of all z values satisfy $z \leq -2.33$.) This inequality is equivalent to $\hat{p} \leq .853$, so H_0 is *not* rejected if $\hat{p} > .853$. When $p = .8$, $\hat{p}$ has approximately a normal distribution with

$$\mu_{\hat{p}} = .8$$

$$\sigma_{\hat{p}} = \sqrt{\frac{(.8)(.2)}{225}} = .0267$$

Then β is the probability of obtaining a sample proportion greater than .853, as illustrated in Figure 10.6.

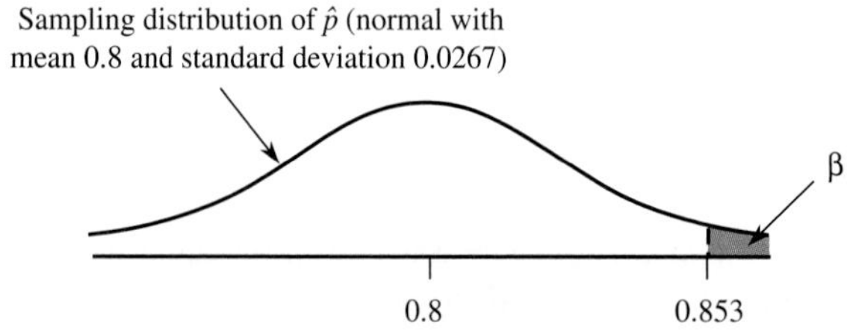

FIGURE 10.6
β when $p = .8$ in Example 10.18.

Converting to a z score results in

$$z = \frac{.853 - .8}{.0267} = 1.99$$

and Appendix Table 2 gives

$$\beta = 1 - .9767 = .0233$$

When $p = .8$ and a level .01 test is used, less than 3% of all samples of size $n = 225$ will result in a Type II error. The power of the test at $p = .8$ is $1 - .0233 = .9767$. This means that the probability of rejecting $H_0\colon p = .9$ in favor of $H_a\colon p < .9$ when p is really .8 is .9767, which is quite high.

β and Power for the t Test (Optional)

The power and β values for t tests can be determined by using a set of curves specially constructed for this purpose or by using appropriate software. As with the z test, the value of β depends not only on the actual value of μ but also on the selected significance level α; β increases as α is made smaller. In addition, β depends on the number of degrees of freedom, $n - 1$. For any fixed significance level α, it should be easier for the test to detect a specific departure from H_0 when n is large than when n is small. This is indeed the case; for a fixed alternative value, β decreases as $n - 1$ increases.

Unfortunately, there is one other quantity on which β depends: the population standard deviation σ. As σ increases, so does $\sigma_{\bar{x}}$. This in turn makes it more likely that an $\bar{x}$ value far from μ will be observed just by chance, resulting in an incorrect conclusion. Once α is specified and n is fixed, the determination of β at a particular alternative value of μ requires that a value of σ be chosen, because each different value of σ yields a different value of β. (This did not present a problem with the z test because when using a z test, the value of σ is known.) If the investigator can specify a range of plausible values for σ, then using the largest such value will give a pessimistic β (one on the high side) and a pessimistic value of power (one on the low side).

Figure 10.7 shows three different β curves for a one-tailed t test (appropriate for H_a: $\mu >$ hypothesized value or for H_a: $\mu <$ hypothesized value). A more complete set of curves for both one- and two-tailed tests when $\alpha = .05$ and when $\alpha = .01$ appears in Appendix Table 5. To determine β, first compute the quantity

$$d = \frac{|\text{alternative value} - \text{hypothesized value}|}{\sigma}$$

Then locate d on the horizontal axis, move directly up to the curve for $n - 1$ df, and move over to the vertical axis to find β.

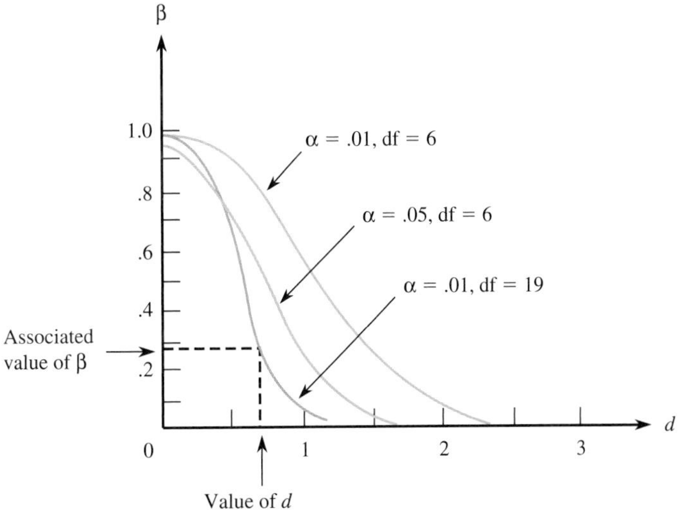

FIGURE 10.7
β curves for the one-tailed t test.

EXAMPLE 10.19 β and Power for t Tests

Consider testing

$$H_0: \mu = 100 \text{ versus } H_a: \mu > 100$$

and focus on the alternative value $\mu = 110$. Suppose that $\sigma = 10$, the sample size is $n = 7$, and a significance level of .01 has been selected. For $\sigma = 10$,

$$d = \frac{|110 - 100|}{10} = \frac{10}{10} = 1$$

Figure 10.7 (using df $= 7 - 1 = 6$) gives $\beta \approx .6$. The interpretation is that if $\sigma = 10$ and a level .01 test based on $n = 7$ is used when $\mu = 110$ (and thus H_0 is false), roughly 60% of all samples result in an incorrect decision to not reject H_0! Equivalently, the power of the test at $\mu = 110$ is only $1 - .6 = .4$. The probability of rejecting H_0 when $\mu = 110$ is not very large. If a .05 significance level is used instead, then $\beta \approx .3$, which is still rather large. Using a .01 significance level with $n = 20$ (df = 19) yields, from Figure 10.7, $\beta \approx .05$. At the alternative value $\mu = 110$, for $\sigma = 10$ the level .01 test based on $n = 20$ has smaller β than the level .05 test with $n = 7$. Substantially increasing n counterbalances using the smaller α.

Now consider the alternative $\mu = 105$, again with $\sigma = 10$, so that

$$d = \frac{|105 - 100|}{10} = \frac{5}{10} = .5$$

Then, from Figure 10.7, $\beta = .95$ when $\alpha = .01$, $n = 7$; $\beta = .7$ when $\alpha = .05$, $n = 7$; and $\beta = .65$ when $\alpha = .01$, $n = 20$. These values of β are all quite large; with $\sigma = 10$, $\mu = 105$ is too close to the hypothesized value of 100 for any of these three tests to have a good chance of detecting such a departure from H_0. A substantial decrease in β would require using a much larger sample size. For example, from Appendix Table 5, $\beta = .08$ when $\alpha = .05$ and $n = 40$.

The curves in Figure 10.7 also give β when testing H_0: $\mu = 100$ versus H_a: $\mu < 100$. If the alternative value $\mu = 90$ is of interest and $\sigma = 10$,

$$d = \frac{|90 - 100|}{10} = \frac{10}{10} = 1$$

and values of β are the same as those given in the first paragraph of this example.

Because curves for only selected degrees of freedom appear in Appendix Table 5, other degrees of freedom require a visual approximation. For example, the 27-df curve (for $n = 28$) lies between the 19-df and 29-df curves, which do appear, and it is closer to the 29-df curve. This type of approximation is adequate because it is the general magnitude of β—large, small, or moderate—that is of primary concern.

Minitab can also evaluate power for the t test. For example, the following output shows Minitab calculations for power at $\mu = 110$ for samples of size 7 and 20 when $\alpha = .01$. The corresponding approximate values from Appendix Table 5 found in Example 10.19 are fairly close to the Minitab values.

```
1-Sample t Test
Testing mean = null (versus > null)
Calculating power for mean = null + 10
Alpha = 0.01    Sigma = 10
Sample Size     Power
          7     0.3968
         20     0.9653
```

The β curves in Appendix Table 5 are those for t tests. When the alternative value in H_a corresponds to a value of d relatively close to 0, β for a t test may be rather large. One might wonder whether there is another type of test that has the same level of significance α as does the t test and smaller values of β. The following result provides the answer to this question.

When the population distribution is normal, the t test for testing hypotheses about μ has smaller β than does any other test procedure that has the same level of significance α.

Stated another way, among all tests with level of significance α, the t test makes β as small as it can possibly be when the population distribution is normal. In this sense, the t test is a best test. Statisticians have also shown that when the population distribution is not too far from a normal distribution, no test procedure can improve on the t test by very much (i.e., no test procedure can have the same α and substantially smaller β). However, when the population distribution is believed to be strongly nonnormal (heavy-tailed, highly skewed, or multimodal), the t test should not be used. Then it's time to consult your friendly neighborhood statistician, who can provide you with alternative methods of analysis.

EXERCISES 10.59 - 10.65

10.59 The power of a test is influenced by the sample size and the choice of significance level.

a. Explain how increasing the sample size affects the power (when significance level is held fixed).

b. Explain how increasing the significance level affects the power (when sample size is held fixed).

10.60 Water samples are taken from water used for cooling as it is being discharged from a power plant into a river. It has been determined that as long as the mean temperature of the discharged water is at most 150°F, there will be no negative effects on the river's ecosystem. To investigate whether the plant is in compliance with regulations that prohibit a mean discharge water temperature above 150°F, a scientist will take 50 water samples at randomly selected times and will record the water temperature of each sample. She will then use a z statistic

$$z = \frac{\bar{x} - 150}{\frac{\sigma}{\sqrt{n}}}$$

to decide between the hypotheses H_0: $\mu = 150$ and H_a: $\mu > 150$, where μ is the mean temperature of discharged water. Assume that σ is known to be 10.

a. Explain why use of the z statistic is appropriate in this setting.

b. Describe Type I and Type II errors in this context.

c. The rejection of H_0 when $z \geq 1.8$ corresponds to what value of α? (That is, what is the area under the z curve to the right of 1.8?)

d. Suppose that the actual value for μ is 153 and that H_0 is to be rejected if $z \geq 1.8$. Draw a sketch (similar to that of Figure 10.5) of the sampling distribution of $\bar{x}$, and shade the region that would represent β, the probability of making a Type II error.

e. For the hypotheses and test procedure described, compute the value of β when $\mu = 153$.

f. For the hypotheses and test procedure described, what is the value of β if $\mu = 160$?

g. What would be the conclusion of the test if H_0 is rejected when $z \geq 1.8$ and $\bar{x} = 152.4$? What type of error might have been made in reaching this conclusion?

10.61 ✦ Let μ denote the true average lifetime (in hours) for a certain type of battery under controlled laboratory conditions. A test of H_0: $\mu = 10$ versus H_a: $\mu < 10$ will be based on a sample of size 36. Suppose that σ is known to be 0.6, from which $\sigma_{\bar{x}} = .1$. The appropriate test statistic is then

$$z = \frac{\bar{x} - 10}{0.1}$$

a. What is α for the test procedure that rejects H_0 if $z \leq -1.28$?

b. If the test procedure of Part (a) is used, calculate β when $\mu = 9.8$, and interpret this error probability.

c. Without doing any calculation, explain how β when $\mu = 9.5$ compares to β when $\mu = 9.8$. Then check your assertion by computing β when $\mu = 9.5$.

d. What is the power of the test when $\mu = 9.8$? when $\mu = 9.5$?

10.62 The city council in a large city has become concerned about the trend toward exclusion of renters with children in apartments within the city. The housing coordinator has decided to select a random sample of 125 apartments and determine for each whether children are permitted. Let p be the proportion of all apartments that prohibit children. If the city council is convinced that p is greater than 0.75, it will consider appropriate legislation.

a. If 102 of the 125 sampled apartments exclude renters with children, would a level .05 test lead you to the conclusion that more than 75% of all apartments exclude children?

b. What is the power of the test when $p = .8$ and $\alpha = .05$?

10.63 The amount of shaft wear after a fixed mileage was determined for each of seven randomly selected internal combustion engines, resulting in a mean of 0.0372 inch and a standard deviation of 0.0125 inch.

a. Assuming that the distribution of shaft wear is normal, test at level .05 the hypotheses H_0: $\mu = .035$ versus H_a: $\mu > .035$.

b. Using $\sigma = 0.0125$, $\alpha = .05$, and Appendix Table 5, what is the approximate value of β, the probability of a Type II error, when $\mu = .04$?

c. What is the approximate power of the test when $\mu = .04$ and $\alpha = .05$?

10.64 Optical fibers are used in telecommunications to transmit light. Suppose current technology allows production of fibers that transmit light about 50 km. Researchers are trying to develop a new type of glass fiber that will increase this distance. In evaluating a new fiber, it is of interest to test H_0: $\mu = 50$ versus H_a: $\mu > 50$, with μ denoting the mean transmission distance for the new optical fiber.

a. Assuming $\sigma = 10$ and $n = 10$, use Appendix Table 5 to find β, the probability of a Type II error, for each of the given alternative values of μ when a test with significance level .05 is employed:
i. 52 ii. 55 iii. 60 iv. 70

b. What happens to β in each of the cases in Part (a) if σ is actually larger than 10? Explain your reasoning.

10.65 Let μ denote the mean diameter for bearings of a certain type. A test of H_0: $\mu = 0.5$ versus H_a: $\mu \neq 0.5$ will be based on a sample of n bearings. The diameter distribution is believed to be normal. Determine the value of β in each of the following cases:

a. $n = 15$, $\alpha = .05$, $\sigma = 0.02$, $\mu = 0.52$

b. $n = 15$, $\alpha = .05$, $\sigma = 0.02$, $\mu = 0.48$

c. $n = 15$, $\alpha = .01$, $\sigma = 0.02$, $\mu = 0.52$

d. $n = 15$, $\alpha = .05$, $\sigma = 0.02$, $\mu = 0.54$

e. $n = 15$, $\alpha = .05$, $\sigma = 0.04$, $\mu = 0.54$

f. $n = 20$, $\alpha = .05$, $\sigma = 0.04$, $\mu = 0.54$

g. Is the way in which β changes as n, α, σ, and μ vary consistent with your intuition? Explain.

10.6 Interpreting and Communicating the Results of Statistical Analyses

The nine-step procedure that we have proposed for testing hypotheses provides a systematic approach for carrying out a complete test. However, you rarely see the results of a hypothesis test reported in publications in such a complete way.

Communicating the Results of Statistical Analyses

When summarizing the results of a hypothesis test, it is important that you include several things in the summary in order to provide all the relevant information. These are:

1. *Hypotheses.* Whether specified in symbols or described in words, it is important that both the null and the alternative hypotheses be clearly stated. If you are using symbols to define the hypotheses, be sure to describe them in the context of the problem at hand (for example, μ = population mean calorie intake).
2. *Test procedure.* You should be clear about what test procedure was used (for example, large-sample z test for proportions) and why you think it was reasonable to use this procedure. The plausibility of any required assumptions should be satisfactorily addressed.
3. *Test statistic.* Be sure to include the value of the test statistic and the P-value. Including the P-value allows a reader who may have chosen a different significance level to see whether she would have reached the same or a different conclusion.
4. *Conclusion in context.* Never end the report of a hypothesis test with the statement "I rejected (or did not reject) H_0." Always provide a conclusion that is in the context of the problem and that answers the original research question which the hypothesis test was designed to answer. Be sure also to indicate the level of significance used as a basis for the decision.

AP* EXAM TIP

The hypothesis testing procedure described in the text consists of nine steps. These nine steps are grouped here into four key things that need to be communicated when you carry out a hypothesis test. All of these are required in order for a response on a hypothesis testing problem to be considered as complete on the AP exam.

Interpreting the Results of Statistical Analyses

When the results of a hypothesis test are reported in a journal article or other published source, it is common to find only the value of the test statistic and the associated P-value accompanying the discussion of conclusions drawn from the data. Often, especially in newspaper articles, only sample summary statistics are given, with the conclusion immediately following. You may have to fill in some of the intermediate steps for yourself to see whether or not the conclusion is justified.

For example, the article "Physicians' Knowledge of Herbal Toxicities and Adverse Herb-Drug Interactions" (*European Journal of Emergency Medicine*, August 2004) summarizes the results of a study to assess doctors' familiarity with adverse effects of herbal remedies as follows: "A total of 142 surveys and quizzes were completed by 59 attending physicians, 57 resident physicians, and 26 medical students. The mean subject score on the quiz was only slightly higher than would have occurred from random guessing." The quiz consisted of 16 multiple-choice questions. If each question had four possible choices, the statement that the mean quiz score was only slightly higher than would have occurred from random guessing suggests that the researchers considered the hypotheses H_0: $\mu = 4$ and H_a: $\mu > 4$, where μ represents the mean score for the population of all physicians and medical students and the null hypothesis corresponds to the expected number of correct choices for someone who is guessing. Assuming that it is reasonable to regard this sample as representative of the population of interest, the data from the sample could be used to carry out a test of these hypotheses.

What to Look For in Published Data

Here are some questions to consider when you are reading a report that contains the results of a hypothesis test:

- What hypotheses are being tested? Are the hypotheses about a population mean, a population proportion, or some other population characteristic?
- Was the appropriate test used? Does the validity of the test depend on any assumptions about the sample or about the population from which the sample was selected? If so, are the assumptions reasonable?
- What is the *P*-value associated with the test? Was a significance level reported (as opposed to simply reporting the *P*-value)? Is the chosen significance level reasonable?
- Are the conclusions drawn consistent with the results of the hypothesis test?

For example, consider the following statement from the paper "Didgeridoo Playing as Alternative Treatment for Obstructive Sleep Apnoea Syndrome" (*British Medical Journal* [2006]: 266–270): "We found that four months of training of the upper airways by didgeridoo playing reduces daytime sleepiness in people with snoring and obstructive apnoea syndrome." This statement was supported by data on a measure of daytime sleepiness called the Epworth scale. For the 14 participants in the study, the mean improvement in Epworth scale was 4.4 and the standard deviation was 3.7. The paper does not indicate what test was performed or what the value of the test statistic was. It appears that the hypotheses of interest are H_0: $\mu = 0$ (no improvement) versus H_a: $\mu > 0$, where μ represents the mean improvement in Epworth score after four months of didgeridoo playing for all people with snoring and obstructive sleep apnoea. Because the sample size is not large, the one-sample t test would be appropriate if the sample can be considered a random sample and the distribution of Epworth scale improvement scores is approximately normal. If these assumptions are reasonable (something that was not addressed in the paper), the t test results in $t = 4.45$ and an associated *P*-value of .000. Because the reported *P*-value is so small H_0 would be rejected, supporting the conclusion in the paper that didgeridoo playing is an effective treatment. (In case you are wondering, a didgeridoo is an Australian Aboriginal woodwind instrument.)

A Word to the Wise: Cautions and Limitations

There are several things you should watch for when conducting a hypothesis test or when evaluating a written summary of a hypothesis test.

1. The result of a hypothesis test can never show strong support for the null hypothesis. Make sure that you don't confuse "There is no reason to believe the null hypothesis is not true" with the statement "There is convincing evidence that the null hypothesis is true." These are very different statements!
2. If you have complete information for the population, don't carry out a hypothesis test! It should be obvious that no test is needed to answer questions about a population if you have complete information and don't need to generalize from a sample, but people sometimes forget this fact. For example, in an article on growth in the number of prisoners by state, the *San Luis Obispo Tribune* (August 13, 2001) reported "California's numbers showed a statistically insignificant change, with 66 fewer prisoners at the end of 2000." The use of the term "statistically insignificant" implies some sort of statistical inference, which is not appropriate when a complete accounting of the entire prison population is known. Perhaps the author confused statistical and practical significance. Which brings us to . . .
3. Don't confuse statistical significance with practical significance. When statistical significance has been declared, be sure to step back and evaluate the result in light of its practical importance. For example, we may be convinced that the propor-

tion who respond favorably to a proposed medical treatment is greater than .4, the known proportion that responds favorably for the currently recommended treatments. But if our estimate of this proportion for the proposed treatment is .405, is this of any practical interest? It might be if the proposed treatment is less costly or has fewer side effects, but in other cases it may not be of any real interest. Results must always be interpreted in context.

EXERCISES 10.66 - 10.67

10.66 In 2006, Boston Scientific sought approval for a new heart stent (a medical device used to open clogged arteries) called the Liberte. This stent was being proposed as an alternative to a stent called the Express that was already on the market. The following excerpt is from an article that appeared in *The Wall Street Journal* (August 14, 2008):

> Boston Scientific wasn't required to prove that the Liberte was 'superior' than a previous treatment, the agency decided—only that it wasn't 'inferior' to Express. Boston Scientific proposed—and the FDA okayed—a benchmark in which Liberte could be up to three percentage points worse than Express—meaning that if 6% of Express patients' arteries reclog, Boston Scientific would have to prove that Liberte's rate of reclogging was less than 9%. Anything more would be considered 'inferior.' . . . In the end, after nine months, the Atlas study found that 85 of the patients suffered reclogging. In comparison, historical data on 991 patients implanted with the Express stent show a 7% rate. Boston Scientific then had to answer this question: Could the study have gotten such results if the Liberte were truly inferior to Express?"

Assume a 7% reclogging rate for the Express stent. Explain why it would be appropriate for Boston Scientific to carry out a hypothesis test using the following hypotheses:

H_0: $p = .10$
H_a: $p < .10$

where p is the proportion of patients receiving Liberte stents that suffer reclogging. Be sure to address both the choice of the hypothesized value and the form of the alternative hypothesis in your explanation.

10.67 The article "Boy or Girl: Which Gender Baby Would You Pick?" (*LiveScience*, March 23, 2005, www.livescience.com) summarized the findings of a study that was published in *Fertility and Sterility*. The *LiveScience* article makes the following statements: "When given the opportunity to choose the sex of their baby, women are just as likely to choose pink socks as blue, a new study shows" and "Of the 561 women who participated in the study, 229 said they would like to choose the sex of a future child. Among these 229, there was no greater demand for boys or girls." These statements are equivalent to the claim that for women who would like to choose the baby's sex, the proportion who would choose a girl is 0.50 or 50%.

a. The journal article on which the *LiveScience* summary was based ("Preimplantation Sex-Selection Demand and Preferences in an Infertility Population," *Fertility and Sterility* [2005]: 649–658) states that of the 229 women who wanted to select the baby's sex, 89 wanted a boy and 140 wanted a girl. Does this provide convincing evidence against the statement of no preference in the *LiveScience* summary? Test the relevant hypotheses using $\alpha = .05$. Be sure to state any assumptions you must make about the way the sample was selected in order for your test to be appropriate.

b. The journal article also provided the following information about the study:
- A survey with 19 questions was mailed to 1385 women who had visited the Center for Reproductive Medicine at Brigham and Women's Hospital.
- 561 women returned the survey.

Do you think it is reasonable to generalize the results from this survey to a larger population? Do you have any concerns about the way the sample was selected or about potential sources of bias? Explain.

ACTIVITY 10.1 Comparing the t and z Distributions

Technology Activity: Requires use of a computer or a graphing calculator.

The instructions that follow assume the use of Minitab. If you are using a different software package or a graphing calculator, your instructor will provide alternative instructions.

Background: Suppose a random sample will be selected from a population that is known to have a normal distribution. Then the statistic

$$z = \frac{\bar{x} - \mu}{\frac{\sigma}{\sqrt{n}}}$$

has a standard normal (z) distribution. Since it is rarely the case that σ is known, inferences for population means are usually based on the statistic $t = \frac{\bar{x} - \mu}{(s/\sqrt{n})}$, which has a t distribution rather than a z distribution. The informal justification for this was that the use of s to estimate σ introduces additional variability, resulting in a statistic whose distribution is more spread out than is the z distribution.

In this activity, you will use simulation to sample from a known normal population and then investigate how the behavior of $t = \frac{\bar{x} - \mu}{s/\sqrt{n}}$ compares with the behavior of $z = \frac{\bar{x} - \mu}{\sigma/(\sqrt{n})}$.

1. Generate 200 random samples of size 5 from a normal population with mean 100 and standard deviation 10.

   Using Minitab, go to the Calc Menu. Then

   Calc→ Random Data → Normal
   In the "Generate" box, enter 200
   In the "Store in columns" box, enter c1-c5
   In the mean box, enter 100
   In the standard deviation box, enter 10
   Click on OK

   You should now see 200 rows of data in each of the first 5 columns of the Minitab worksheet.

2. Each row contains five values that have been randomly selected from a normal population with mean 100 and standard deviation 10. Viewing each row as a sample of size 5 from this population, calculate the mean and standard deviation for each of the 200 samples (the 200 rows) by using Minitab's row statistics functions, which can also be found under the Calc menu:

   Calc→ Row statistics
   Choose the "Mean" button
   In the "Input Variables" box, enter c1-c5
   In the "Store result in" box, enter c7
   Click on OK

   You should now see the 200 sample means in column 7 of the Minitab worksheet. Name this column "x-bar" by typing the name in the gray box at the top of c7.

   Now follow a similar process to compute the 200 sample standard deviations, and store them in c8. Name c8 "s."

3. Next, calculate the value of the z statistic for each of the 200 samples. We can calculate z in this example because we know that the samples were selected from a population for which $\sigma = 10$. Use the calculator function of Minitab to compute $z = \frac{\bar{x} - \mu}{(\sigma/\sqrt{n})} = \frac{\bar{x} - 100}{(10/\sqrt{5})}$ as follows:

   Calc → Calculator
   In the "Store results in" box, enter c10
   In the "Expression box" type in the following: (c7-100)/(10/sqrt(5))
   Click on OK

   You should now see the z values for the 200 samples in c11. Name c11 "z."

4. Now calculate the value of the t statistic for each of the 200 samples. Use the calculator function of Minitab to compute $t = \frac{\bar{x} - \mu}{(s/\sqrt{n})} = \frac{\bar{x} - 100}{(s/\sqrt{5})}$ as follows:

   Calc → Calculator
   In the "Store results in" box, enter c11
   In the "Expression box" type in the following: (c7-100)/(c8/sqrt(5))
   Click on OK

   You should now see the t values for the 200 samples in c10. Name c10 "t."

5. Graphs, at last! Now construct histograms of the 200 z values and the 200 t values. These two graphical displays will provide insight about how each of these two statistics behaves in repeated sampling. Use the same scale for the two histograms so that it will be easier to compare the two distributions.

   Graph → Histogram
   In the "Graph variables" box, enter c10 for graph 1 and c11 for graph 2
   Click the Frame dropdown menu and select multiple graphs.
   Then under the scale choices, select "Same X and same Y."

6. Now use the histograms from Step 5 to answer the following questions:
   a. Write a brief description of the shape, center, and spread for the histogram of the z values. Is what you see in the histogram consistent with what you would have expected to see? Explain. (Hint: In theory, what is the distribution of the z statistic?)
   b. How does the histogram of the t values compare to the z histogram? Be sure to comment on center, shape, and spread.
   c. Is your answer to Part (b) consistent with what would be expected for a statistic that has a t distribution? Explain.
   d. The z and t histograms are based on only 200 samples, and they only approximate the corresponding sampling distributions. The 5th percentile for the standard normal distribution is -1.645 and the 95th percentile is $+1.645$. For a t distribution with df $= 5 - 1 = 4$, the 5th and 95th percentiles are -2.13 and $+2.13$, respectively. How do these percentiles compare to those of the distributions displayed in the histograms? (Hint: Sort the 200 z values—in Minitab, choose "Sort" from the Manip menu. Once the values are sorted, percentiles from the histogram can be found by counting in 10 [which is 5% of 200] values from either end of the sorted list. Then repeat this with the t values.)
   e. Are the results of your simulation and analysis consistent with the statement that the statistic $z = \dfrac{\bar{x} - \mu}{(\sigma/\sqrt{n})}$ has a standard normal (z) distribution and the statistic $t = \dfrac{\bar{x} - \mu}{(s/\sqrt{n})}$ has a t distribution? Explain.

ACTIVITY 10.2 A Meaningful Paragraph

Write a meaningful paragraph that includes the following six terms: **hypotheses, *P*-value, reject H_0, Type I error, statistical significance, practical significance.**

A "meaningful paragraph" is a coherent piece of writing in an appropriate context that uses all of the listed words. The paragraph should show that you understand the meaning of the terms and their relationship to one another. A sequence of sentences that just define the terms is *not* a meaningful paragraph. When choosing a context, think carefully about the terms you need to use. Choosing a good context will make writing a meaningful paragraph easier.

Summary of Key Concepts and Formulas

TERM OR FORMULA	COMMENT
Hypothesis	A claim about the value of a population characteristic.
Null hypothesis, H_0	The hypothesis initially assumed to be true. It has the form H_0: population characteristic = hypothesized value.
Alternative hypothesis, H_a	A hypothesis that specifies a claim that is contradictory to H_0 and is judged the more plausible claim when H_0 is rejected.
Type I error	Rejecting H_0 when H_0 is true; the probability of a Type I error is denoted by α and is referred to as the significance level for the test.
Type II error	Not rejecting H_0 when H_0 is false; the probability of a Type II error is denoted by β.
Test statistic	A value computed from sample data that is then used as the basis for making a decision between H_0 and H_a.

TERM OR FORMULA	COMMENT
P-value	The probability, computed assuming H_0 to be true, of obtaining a value of the test statistic at least as contradictory to H_0 as what actually resulted. H_0 is rejected if *P*-value $\leq \alpha$ and not rejected if *P*-value $> \alpha$, where α is the chosen significance level.
$z = \dfrac{\hat{p} - \text{hypothesized value}}{\sqrt{\dfrac{(\text{hyp. val})(1 - \text{hyp. val})}{n}}}$	A test statistic for testing H_0: p = hypothesized value when the sample size is large. The *P*-value is determined as an area under the z curve.
$z = \dfrac{\bar{x} - \text{hypothesized value}}{\dfrac{\sigma}{\sqrt{n}}}$	A test statistic for testing H_0: μ = hypothesized value when σ is known and either the population distribution is normal or the sample size is large. The *P*-value is determined as an area under the z curve.
$t = \dfrac{\bar{x} - \text{hypothesized value}}{\dfrac{s}{\sqrt{n}}}$	A test statistic for testing H_0: μ = hypothesized value when σ is unknown and either the population distribution is normal or the sample size is large. The *P*-value is determined from the t curve with df $= n - 1$.
Power	The power of a test is the probability of rejecting the null hypothesis. Power is affected by the size of the difference between the hypothesized value and the actual value, the sample size, and the significance level.

Chapter Review Exercises 10.68 - 10.82

10.68 In a representative sample of 1000 adult Americans, only 430 could name at least one justice who is currently serving on the U.S. Supreme Court (Ipsos, January 10, 2006). Using a significance level of .01, carry out a hypothesis test to determine if there is convincing evidence to support the claim that fewer than half of adult Americans can name at least one justice currently serving on the Supreme Court.

10.69 ✦ In a national survey of 2013 adults, 1590 responded that lack of respect and courtesy in American society is a serious problem, and 1283 indicated that they believe that rudeness is a more serious problem than in past years (Associated Press, April 3, 2002). Is there convincing evidence that less than three-quarters of U.S. adults believe that rudeness is a worsening problem? Test the relevant hypotheses using a significance level of .05.

10.70 Students at the Akademia Podlaka conducted an experiment to determine whether the Belgium-minted Euro coin was equally likely to land heads up or tails up. Coins were spun on a smooth surface, and in 250 spins, 140 landed with the heads side up (*New Scientist*, January 4, 2002). Should the students interpret this result as convincing evidence that the proportion of the time the coin would land heads up is not .5? Test the relevant hypotheses using $\alpha = .01$. Would your conclusion be different if a significance level of .05 had been used? Explain.

10.71 An article titled "Teen Boys Forget Whatever It Was" appeared in the Australian newspaper *The Mercury* (April 21, 1997). It described a study of academic performance and attention span and reported that the mean time to distraction for teenage boys working on an independent task was 4 minutes. Although the sample size was not given in the article, suppose that this mean was based on a random sample of 50 teenage Australian boys and that the sample standard deviation was 1.4 minutes. Is there convincing evidence that the average attention span for teenage boys is less than 5 minutes? Test the relevant hypotheses using $\alpha = .01$.

10.72 The authors of the article "Perceived Risks of Heart Disease and Cancer Among Cigarette Smokers" (*Journal of the American Medical Association* [1999]: 1019–1021) expressed the concern that a majority of smokers do not view themselves as being at increased risk of heart disease or cancer. A study of 737 current smokers selected at random from U.S. households with telephones found that of the 737 smokers surveyed, 295 indicated that they believed they have a higher than average risk of cancer. Do these data suggest that p, the true proportion of smokers who view themselves as being at increased risk of cancer is in fact less than .5, as claimed by the authors of the paper? Test the relevant hypotheses using $\alpha = .05$.

10.73 A number of initiatives on the topic of legalized gambling have appeared on state ballots. Suppose that a political candidate has decided to support legalization of casino gambling if he is convinced that more than two-thirds of U.S. adults approve of casino gambling. Suppose that 1523 adults (selected at random from households with telephones) were asked whether they approved of casino gambling. The number in the sample who approved was 1035. Does the sample provide convincing evidence that more than two-thirds approve?

10.74 Although arsenic is known to be a poison, it also has some beneficial medicinal uses. In one study of the use of arsenic to treat acute promyelocytic leukemia (APL), a rare type of blood cell cancer, APL patients were given an arsenic compound as part of their treatment. Of those receiving arsenic, 42% were in remission and showed no signs of leukemia in a subsequent examination (*Washington Post*, November 5, 1998). It is known that 15% of APL patients go into remission after the conventional treatment. Suppose that the study had included 100 randomly selected patients (the actual number in the study was much smaller). Is there sufficient evidence to conclude that the proportion in remission for the arsenic treatment is greater than .15, the remission proportion for the conventional treatment? Test the relevant hypotheses using a .01 significance level.

10.75 Many people have misconceptions about how profitable small, consistent investments can be. In a survey of 1010 randomly selected U.S. adults (Associated Press, October 29, 1999), only 374 responded that they thought that an investment of \$25 per week over 40 years with a 7% annual return would result in a sum of over \$100,000 (the correct amount is \$286,640). Is there sufficient evidence to conclude that less than 40% of U.S. adults are aware that such an investment would result in a sum of over \$100,000? Test the relevant hypotheses using $\alpha = .05$.

10.76 The same survey described in the previous exercise also asked the individuals in the sample what they thought was their best chance to obtain more than \$500,000 in their lifetime. Twenty-eight percent responded "win a lottery or sweepstakes." Does this provide convincing evidence that more than one-fourth of U.S. adults see a lottery or sweepstakes win as their best chance of accumulating \$500,000? Carry out a test using a significance level of .01.

10.77 Speed, size, and strength are thought to be important factors in football performance. The article "Physical and Performance Characteristics of NCAA Division I Football Players" (*Research Quarterly for Exercise and Sport* [1990]: 395–401) reported on physical characteristics of Division I starting football players in the 1988 football season. Information for teams ranked in the top 20 was easily obtained, and it was reported that the mean weight of starters on top-20 teams was 105 kg. A random sample of 33 starting players (various positions were represented) from Division I teams that were not ranked in the top 20 resulted in a sample mean weight of 103.3 kg and a sample standard deviation of 16.3 kg. Is there sufficient evidence to conclude that the mean weight for non-top-20 starters is less than 105, the known value for top-20 teams?

10.78 Duck hunting in populated areas faces opposition on the basis of safety and environmental issues. In a survey to assess public opinion regarding duck hunting on Morro Bay (located along the central coast of California), a random sample of 750 local residents included 560 who strongly opposed hunting on the bay. Does this sample provide sufficient evidence to conclude that the majority of local residents oppose hunting on Morro Bay? Test the relevant hypotheses using $\alpha = .01$.

10.79 Past experience has indicated that the true response rate is 40% when individuals are approached with a request to fill out and return a particular questionnaire in a stamped and addressed envelope. An investigator believes that if the person distributing the questionnaire is stigmatized in some obvious way, potential respondents would feel sorry for the distributor and thus tend to respond at a rate higher than 40%. To investigate this theory, a distributor is fitted with an eye patch. Of the 200 questionnaires distributed by this individual, 109 were returned. Does this strongly suggest that the response rate in this situation exceeds the rate in the past? State and test the appropriate hypotheses at significance level .05.

10.80 ● An automobile manufacturer who wishes to advertise that one of its models achieves 30 mpg (miles per gallon) decides to carry out a fuel efficiency test. Six nonprofessional drivers are selected, and each one drives a car from Phoenix to Los Angeles. The resulting fuel efficiencies (in miles per gallon) are:

27.2	29.3	31.2	28.4	30.3	29.6

Assuming that fuel efficiency is normally distributed under these circumstances, do the data contradict the claim that true average fuel efficiency is (at least) 30 mpg?

10.81 A student organization uses the proceeds from a particular soft-drink dispensing machine to finance its activities. The price per can had been $0.75 for a long time, and the average daily revenue during that period had been $75.00. The price was recently increased to $1.00 per can. A random sample of $n = 20$ days after the price increase yielded a sample mean daily revenue and sample standard deviation of $70.00 and $4.20, respectively. Does this information suggest that the true average daily revenue has decreased from its value before the price increase? Test the appropriate hypotheses using $\alpha = .05$.

10.82 A hot tub manufacturer advertises that with its heating equipment, a temperature of 100°F can be achieved on average in 15 minutes or less. A random sample of 25 tubs is selected, and the time necessary to achieve a 100°F temperature is determined for each tub. The sample mean time and sample standard deviation are 17.5 minutes and 2.2 minutes, respectively. Does this information cast doubt on the company's claim? Carry out a test of hypotheses using significance level .05.

Bold exercises answered in back ● Data set available online ✦ Video Solution available

Graphing Calculator Explorations

EXPLORATION 10.1 Hypothesis Test for a Population Proportion

Using your calculator's hypothesis-testing capability begins, as usual, with navigating your calculator's menu system. This time we are looking for key words such as "hypothesis" and "tests." As before with confidence intervals, look for words such as "1" and "prop" and "z."

Once you select the correct choice, you will be presented with a screen for providing information. This information is exactly what you would need to test the hypotheses on paper: the sample number of successes, the sample size, the level of significance, and so on. Figure 10.8 shows two representative screens, with information filled in from Example 10.10 in the text (the screen in Figure 10.8(b) has the "less than" alternative hypothesis selected by shading, although the shading doesn't show up in the figure).

Move your cursor down to Execute or Calculate, and press the Enter, Execute, or Calculate button, depending on your calculator. The results should appear immediately. Again, we show two representative screens in Figure 10.9.

(a)

1-Prop ZTest
Prop : $<p_0$
p_0 :.5
x :220
n :500
Execute

(b)

1-Prop ZTest
p_0:.5
x:220
n:500
Prop $<$: p_0 $<p_0$ $<p_0$
Calculate Draw

FIGURE 10.8
Representative calculator screens for a one-proportion hypothesis test.

(a)

1-Prop ZTest
Prop<0.5
$Z = -2.683281573$
$p = .003645226$
$\hat{p} = .44$
$n = 500$

(b)

1-Prop ZInt
prop<0.5
z = −2.683281573
p = .003645226
$\hat{p} = .44$
n = 500

FIGURE 10.9
Representative output for a one-proportion hypothesis test.

Notice there is a slight difference between the text and calculator answers that results from rounding in the hand calculations.

The calculator does the work for only a few of the steps in a hypothesis test. Remember, there are still some communication steps for you to do in order to complete the analysis.

EXPLORATION 10.2 Hypothesis Test for a Population Mean

Testing a hypothesis for a single mean on your calculator requires you to navigate the menu system once again. As was true with the confidence interval for the mean,

1. you must decide whether to base the test on the *z* or a *t* distribution, and
2. you can use previous calculations of the sample mean and standard deviation, or the calculator will evaluate these statistics from data contained in a list.

We follow Example 10.14 and use the *t* test after entering the data in List1. The normality of the population must be assessed as before. A calculator boxplot and normal probability plot are shown in Figure 10.10.

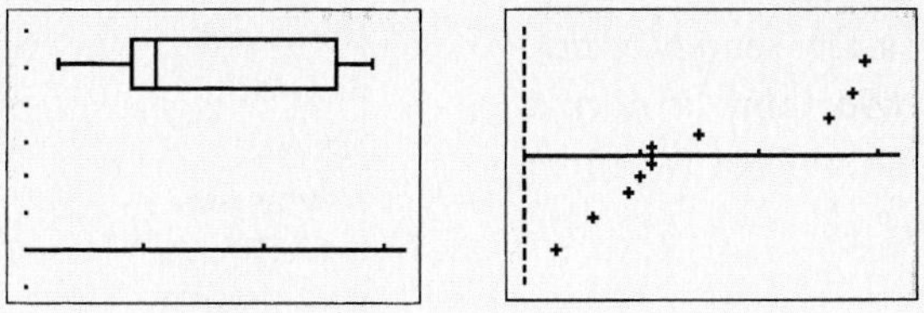

(a) (b)

FIGURE 10.10
Plots for data of Example 10.14: (a) boxpolt; (b) normal probability plot.

After assessing the plausibility of the normality of the population, we test the hypotheses. Again, we have the choice of entering the sample calculations or providing data in a list and letting the calculator evaluate the sample mean and standard deviation. Based on that choice, we see one of the screens shown in Figure 10.11.

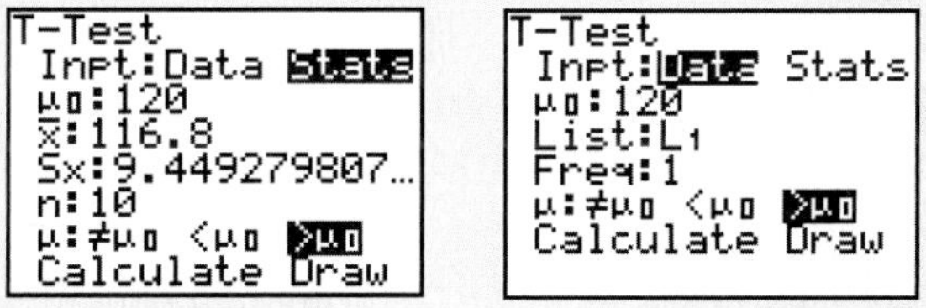

(a) (b)

FIGURE 10.11
Representative calculator screens for a one-sample *t* test.

Figure 10.12 shows calculator output for the hypothesis test. Remember, just writing the calculator output is *not* a complete response to a hypothesis-testing task—there is necessary communication in the hypothesis-testing procedure that you must write yourself.

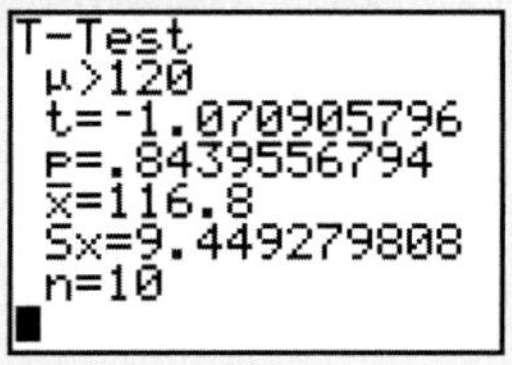

FIGURE 10.12
Calculator output for the one-sample *t* test.

Cumulative Review Exercises CR10.1 - CR10.16

CR10.1 The *AARP Bulletin* (March 2010) included the following short news brief: "Older adults who did 1 hour of tai chi twice weekly cut their pain from knee osteoarthritis considerably in a 12-week study conducted at Tufts University School of Medicine." Suppose you were asked to design a study to investigate this claim. Describe an experiment that would allow comparison of the reduction in knee pain for those who did 1 hour of tai chi twice weekly to the reduction in knee pain for those who did not do tai chi. Include a discussion of how study participants would be selected, how pain reduction would be measured, and how participants would be assigned to experimental groups.

CR10.2 The following graphical display appeared in *USA Today* (June 3, 2009). Write a few sentences critiquing this graphical display. Do you think it does a good job of creating a visual representation of the three percentages in the display?

USA TODAY Snapshots®

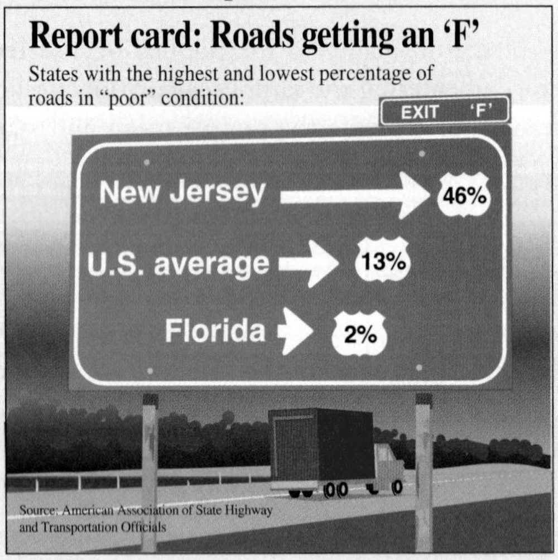

By Anne R. Carey and Dave Merrill, USA TODAY

USA TODAY. June 3, 2009. Reprinted with permission.

CR10.3 ● The article "Flyers Trapped on Tarmac Push for Rules on Release" (*USA Today*, July 28, 2009) included the accompanying data on the number of flights with a tarmac delay of more than 3 hours between October 2008 and May 2009 for U.S. airlines.

Airline	Number of Flights	Rate per 100,000 Flights
AirTran	7	0.4
Alaska	0	0.0
American	48	1.3
American Eagle	44	1.6
Atlantic Southeast	11	0.6
Comair	29	2.7
Continental	72	4.1
Delta	81	2.8
ExpressJet	93	4.9
Frontier	5	0.9
Hawaiian	0	0.0
JetBlue	18	1.4
Mesa	17	1.1
Northwest	24	1.2
Pinnacle	13	0.7
SkyWest	29	0.8
Southwest	11	0.1
United	29	1.1
US Airways	46	1.6

a. Construct a dotplot of the data on number of flights delayed for more than 3 hours. Are there any unusual observations that stand out in the dot plot? What airlines appear to be the worst in terms of number of flights delayed on the tarmac for more than 3 hours?

b. Construct a dotplot of the data on rate per 100,000 flights. Write a few sentences describing the interesting features of this plot.

c. If you wanted to compare airlines on the basis of tarmac delays, would you recommend using the data on number of flights delayed or on rate per 100,000 flights? Explain the reason for your choice.

CR10.4 ● The article "Wait Times on Rise to See Doctor" (*USA Today*, June 4, 2009) gave the accompanying data on average wait times in days to get an appointment with a medical specialist in 15 U.S. cities. Construct a boxplot of the average wait-time data. Are there any outliers in the data set?

City	Average Appointment Wait Time
Atlanta	11.2
Boston	49.6

Continued

City	Average Appointment Wait Time
Dallas	19.2
Denver	15.4
Detroit	12.0
Houston	23.4
Los Angeles	24.2
Miami	15.4
Minneapolis	19.8
New York	19.2
Philadelphia	27.0
Portland	14.4
San Diego	20.2
Seattle	14.2
Washington, D.C.	22.6

CR10.5 The report "New Study Shows Need for Americans to Focus on Securing Online Accounts and Backing up Critical Data" (PRNewswire, October 29, 2009) reported that only 25% of Americans change computer passwords quarterly, in spite of a recommendation from the National Cyber Security Alliance that passwords be changed at least once every 90 days. For purposes of this exercise, assume that the 25% figure is correct for the population of adult Americans.

a. If a random sample of 20 adult Americans is selected, what is the probability that exactly 3 of them change passwords quarterly?

b. What is the probability that more than 8 people in a random sample of 20 adult Americans change passwords quarterly?

c. What is the mean and standard deviation of the variable x = number of people in a random sample of 100 adult Americans who change passwords quarterly?

d. Find the approximate probability that the number of people who change passwords quarterly in a random sample of 100 adult Americans is less than 20.

CR10.6 The article "Should Canada Allow Direct-to-Consumer Advertising of Prescription Drugs?" (*Canadian Family Physician* [2009]: 130–131) calls for the legalization of advertising of prescription drugs in Canada. Suppose you wanted to conduct a survey to estimate the proportion of Canadians who would support allowing this type of advertising. How large a random sample would be required to estimate this proportion to within .02 with 95% confidence?

CR10.7 The National Association of Colleges and Employers carries out a student survey each year. A summary of data from the 2009 survey included the following information:

- 26% of students graduating in 2009 intended to go on to graduate or professional school.
- Only 40% of those who graduated in 2009 received at least one job offer prior to graduation.
- Of those who received a job offer, only 45% had accepted an offer by the time they graduated.

Consider the following events:

O = event that a randomly selected 2009 graduate received at least one job offer

A = event that a randomly selected 2009 graduate accepted a job offer prior to graduation

G = event that a randomly selected 2009 graduate plans to attend graduate or professional school

Compute the following probabilities.

a. $P(O)$

b. $P(A)$

c. $P(G)$

d. $P(A|O)$

e. $P(O|A)$

f. $P(A \cap O)$

CR10.8 It probably wouldn't surprise you to know that Valentine's Day means big business for florists, jewelry stores, and restaurants. But would it surprise you to know that it is also a big day for pet stores? In January 2010, the National Retail Federation conducted a survey of consumers who they believed were selected in a way that would produce a sample representative of the population of adults in the United States ("This Valentine's Day, Couples Cut Back on Gifts to Each Other, According to NRF Survey," www.nrf.com). One of the questions in the survey asked if the respondent planned to spend money on a Valentine's Day gift for his or her pet this year.

a. The proportion who responded that they did plan to purchase a gift for their pet was .173. Suppose that the sample size for this survey was n = 200. Construct and interpret a 95% confidence interval for the proportion of all U.S. adults who planned to purchase a Valentine's Day gift for their pet in 2010.

b. The actual sample size for the survey was much larger than 200. Would a 95% confidence interval computed using the actual sample size have been narrower or wider than the confidence interval computed in Part (a)?

c. Still assuming a sample size of $n = 200$, carry out a hypothesis test to determine if the data provides convincing evidence that the proportion who planned to buy a Valentine's Day gift for their pet in 2010 was greater than .15. Use a significance level of .05.

CR10.9 The article "Doctors Cite Burnout in Mistakes" (*San Luis Obispo Tribune*, March 5, 2002) reported that many doctors who are completing their residency have financial struggles that could interfere with training. In a sample of 115 residents, 38 reported that they worked moonlighting jobs and 22 reported a credit card debt of more than \$3000. Suppose that it is reasonable to consider this sample of 115 as a random sample of all medical residents in the United States.

a. Construct and interpret a 95% confidence interval for the proportion of U.S. medical residents who work moonlighting jobs.

b. Construct and interpret a 90% confidence interval for the proportion of U.S. medical residents who have a credit card debt of more than \$3000.

c. Give two reasons why the confidence interval in Part (a) is wider than the confidence interval in Part (b).

CR10.10 The National Geographic Society conducted a study that included 3000 respondents, age 18 to 24, in nine different countries (*San Luis Obispo Tribune*, November 21, 2002). The society found that 10% of the participants could not identify their own country on a blank world map.

a. Construct a 90% confidence interval for the proportion who can identify their own country on a blank world map.

b. What assumptions are necessary for the confidence interval in Part (a) to be valid?

c. To what population would it be reasonable to generalize the confidence interval estimate from Part (a)?

CR10.11 "Heinz Plays Catch-up After Under-Filling Ketchup Containers" is the headline of an article that appeared on CNN.com (November 30, 2000). The article stated that Heinz had agreed to put an extra 1% of ketchup into each ketchup container sold in California for a 1-year period. Suppose that you want to make sure that Heinz is in fact fulfilling its end of the agreement. You plan to take a sample of 20-oz bottles shipped to California, measure the amount of ketchup in each bottle, and then use the resulting data to estimate the mean amount of ketchup in each bottle. A small pilot study showed that the amount of ketchup in 20-oz bottles varied from 19.9 to 20.3 oz. How many bottles should be included in the sample if you want to estimate the true mean amount of ketchup to within 0.1 oz with 95% confidence?

CR10.12 In a survey conducted by Yahoo Small Business, 1432 of 1813 adults surveyed said that they would alter their shopping habits if gas prices remain high (Associated Press, November 30, 2005). The article did not say how the sample was selected, but for purposes of this exercise, assume that it is reasonable to regard this sample as representative of adult Americans. Based on these survey data, is it reasonable to conclude that more than three-quarters of adult Americans plan to alter their shopping habits if gas prices remain high?

CR10.13 In an AP-AOL sports poll (Associated Press, December 18, 2005), 272 of 394 randomly selected baseball fans stated that they thought the designated hitter rule should either be expanded to both baseball leagues or eliminated. Based on the given information, is there sufficient evidence to conclude that a majority of baseball fans feel this way?

CR10.14 ✦ The article "Americans Seek Spiritual Guidance on Web" (*San Luis Obispo Tribune*, October 12, 2002) reported that 68% of the general population belong to a religious community. In a survey on Internet use, 84% of "religion surfers" (defined as those who seek spiritual help online or who have used the web to search for prayer and devotional resources) belong to a religious community. Suppose that this result was based on a sample of 512 religion surfers. Is there convincing evidence that the proportion of religion surfers who belong to a religious community is different from .68, the proportion for the general population? Use $\alpha = .05$.

CR10.15 A survey of teenagers and parents in Canada conducted by the polling organization Ipsos ("Untangling the Web: The Facts About Kids and the Internet," January 25, 2006) included questions about Internet use. It was reported that for a sample of 534 randomly selected teens, the mean number of hours per week spent online was 14.6 and the standard deviation was 11.6.

a. What does the large standard deviation, 11.6 hours, tell you about the distribution of online times for this sample of teens?

b. Do the sample data provide convincing evidence that the mean number of hours that teens spend online is greater than 10 hours per week?

CR10.16 The same survey referenced in the previous exercise reported that for a random sample of 676 parents of Canadian teens, the mean number of hours parents thought their teens spent online was 6.5 and the sample standard deviation was 8.6.

a. Do the sample data provide convincing evidence that the mean number of hours that parents think their teens spend online is less than 10 hours per week?

b. Write a few sentences commenting on the results of the test in Part (a) and of the test in Part (b) of the previous exercise.

AP* Review Questions for Chapter 10

1. A university administrator in charge of computing facilities will close a computer lab if there is convincing evidence that the proportion of students at the university who have access to a computer at home is greater than .6. What hypotheses should the administrator test?

   (A) H_0: $\mu < .6$ versus H_a: $\mu = .6$
   (B) H_0: $\mu = .6$ versus H_a: $\mu > .6$
   (C) H_0: $p = .6$ versus H_a: $p > .6$
   (D) H_0: $p > .6$ versus H_a: $p = .6$
   (E) H_0: $p > .6$ versus H_a: $p < .6$

2. The manager of a large hotel must decide whether to hire additional front desk staff. He has decided to hire more staff if there is evidence that the average time customers must wait in line before being assisted with check-in is greater than 3 minutes. He decides to test H_0: $\mu = 3$ versus H_a: $\mu > 3$. Which of the following would be a consequence of making a Type II error?

   (A) Deciding not to hire additional staff when the wait time really is greater than 3 minutes.
   (B) Deciding not to hire additional staff when the wait time really is not greater than 3 minutes.
   (C) Deciding to hire additional staff when the wait time really is greater than 3 minutes.
   (D) Deciding to hire additional staff when the wait time really is not greater than 3 minutes.
   (E) Deciding that a wait time of greater than 3 minutes is acceptable.

3. The principal at a large high school will implement a proposed after-school tutoring program if there is evidence that the proportion of students at the school who would take advantage of such a program is greater than .10. She decides to collect data in order to test H_0: $p = .1$ versus H_a: $p > .1$. In this setting, which of the following would be a consequence of making a Type I error?

   (A) Implementing the program when the proportion of students who would take advantage of the program is greater than .10.
   (B) Not implementing the program when the proportion of students who would take advantage of the program is greater than .10.
   (C) Implementing the program when the proportion of students who would take advantage of the program is not greater than .10.
   (D) Not implementing the program when the proportion of students who would take advantage of the program is not greater than .10.
   (E) Deciding that it is acceptable to implement the program as long as 5% of the students would participate.

4. The marketing department of a national department store chain designs its advertising to target 18- to 24-year-olds. The marketing manager worries that the average age of the chain's customers is greater than 24, in which case the marketing plan should be reconsidered. He decides to survey a random sample of 100 customers and will use the resulting data to test H_0: $\mu = 24$ versus H_a: $\mu > 24$, where μ is the mean customer age. Suppose that the *P*-value from this test was .03. Which of the following is a correct interpretation of this *P*-value?

   (A) The probability that the null hypothesis is true is .03.
   (B) The probability that the null hypothesis is false is .03.
   (C) When the null hypothesis is true, the probability of seeing results as or more extreme than what was observed in the sample is .03.
   (D) When the null hypothesis is false, the probability of seeing results as extreme as what was observed in the sample is .03.
   (E) Approximately 3% of the chain's customers are older than 24.

5. In a random sample of 200 subscribers of a cooking magazine, 30 reported that they had logged on to the magazine website to download a recipe within the last month. These data were used to test the hypothesis

H_0: $p = .25$ versus H_a: $p < .25$

where p is the proportion of all subscribers who have downloaded recipes in the last month. The P-value for this test was .001. Which of the following is a correct conclusion if a significance level of .01 is used?

(A) There is convincing evidence that the proportion of subscribers who have downloaded a recipe during the last month is .25.
(B) There is convincing evidence that the proportion of subscribers who have downloaded a recipe during the last month is less than .25.
(C) There is not convincing evidence that the proportion of subscribers who have downloaded a recipe during the last month is less than .25.
(D) Because the P-value is so small, it is not possible to reach a conclusion.
(E) Because the significance level of .01 is smaller than the hypothesized value of .25, the null hypothesis is not rejected.

6. In a study of student backpack weights, a researcher at a large university selected 50 students at random. Backpacks belonging to the selected students were weighed. The researcher is interested in using these data to determine if there is evidence that the mean backpack weight for students at the university is greater than 20 pounds. Which of the following test statistics is appropriate?

(A)

$$z = \frac{\hat{p} - \text{hypothesized value}}{\sqrt{\frac{(\text{hypothesized value})(1 - \text{hypothesized value})}{n}}}$$

(B)

$$t = \frac{\hat{p} - \text{hypothesized value}}{\sqrt{\frac{(\text{hypothesized value})(1 - \text{hypothesized value})}{n}}}$$

(C) $z = \dfrac{\bar{x} - \text{hypothesized value}}{\dfrac{\sigma}{\sqrt{n}}}$

(D) $t = \dfrac{\bar{x} - \text{hypothesized value}}{\dfrac{s}{\sqrt{n}}}$

(E) None of the above is appropriate.

7. In 2005, California instituted a campaign to increase enforcement of seat belt laws. Suppose that prior to this campaign, the proportion of traffic citations that were for failure to wear a seat belt was .07. A random sample of traffic citations will be selected from those issued in 2005 in order to test H_0: $p = .07$ versus H_a: $p < .07$, where p is the proportion of 2005 traffic citations that are for failure to wear a seat belt. Of those listed below, what is the smallest sample size for which it would be appropriate to use the large sample z test to test these hypotheses?

(A) 30
(B) 100
(C) 200
(D) 500
(E) 1000

8. In order to test a claim that more than half of all calls to the emergency 911 phone number in a particular county are actually not for emergency situations, 100 recordings of 911 calls are selected at random from those received in the past year, and each call is classified as either emergency on non-emergency. Which of the following test statistics is appropriate for testing the hypothesis of interest?

(A)

$$z = \frac{\hat{p} - \text{hypothesized value}}{\sqrt{\frac{(\text{hypothesized value})(1 - \text{hypothesized value})}{n}}}$$

(B)

$$t = \frac{\hat{p} - \text{hypothesized value}}{\sqrt{\frac{(\text{hypothesized value})(1 - \text{hypothesized value})}{n}}}$$

(C) $z = \dfrac{\bar{x} - \text{hypothesized value}}{\dfrac{\sigma}{\sqrt{n}}}$

(D) $t = \dfrac{\bar{x} - \text{hypothesized value}}{\dfrac{s}{\sqrt{n}}}$

(E) None of the above is appropriate.

9. Which of the following affects the power of a test?

I. The sample size
II. The significance level of the test
III. The size of the discrepancy between the actual value and the hypothesized value of the population characteristic

(A) I only
(B) II only
(C) III only
(D) I and II only
(E) I, II, and III

10. Assuming the same significance level is used, how does increasing the sample size from 50 to 100 affect the power of a test?

(A) The power decreases.
(B) The power increases.
(C) The power does not change.
(D) The power does change, but it might either decrease or increase.
(E) It is not possible to predict whether the power will increase, decrease, or remain the unchanged.

11. Assuming the same sample size is used, how does changing the significance level from .05 to .01 affect the power of a test?

(A) The power decreases.
(B) The power increases.
(C) The power does not change.
(D) The power does change, but it might either decrease or increase.
(E) It is not possible to predict whether the power will increase, decrease, or remain the unchanged.

12. In a test of H_0: $\mu = 100$ versus H_a: $\mu > 100$, the power of the test will be lowest when the actual value of the population mean is

(A) 101
(B) 110
(C) 120
(D) 200
(E) The power will be the same for any value greater than 100.

13. Which of the calculated values of a test statistic would have the smallest *P*-value for a test where the alternative hypothesis is H_a: $\mu > 50$?

(A) $z = 3.05$
(B) $t = 3.05$ with 10 degrees of freedom
(C) $t = 3.05$ with 15 degrees of freedom
(D) $t = 3.05$ with 30 degrees of freedom
(E) $t = 3.05$ with 35 degrees of freedom

14. The value of the test statistic in a one-sample *z* test is $z = -2.36$. What is the *P*-value for this test if the alternative hypothesis is H_a: $\mu < 50$?

(A) $P(z > -2.36)$
(B) $P(z < -2.36)$
(C) $2P(z > -2.36)$
(D) $2P(z < -2.36)$
(E) $P(z < -2.36) + P(z > 2.36)$

15. For which sample size and choice of significance level will the power of a test be greatest?

(A) $n = 10, \alpha = .1$
(B) $n = 10, \alpha = .01$
(C) $n = 100, \alpha = .1$
(D) $n = 100, \alpha = .05$
(E) $n = 100, \alpha = .01$

CHAPTER 11

Comparing Two Populations or Treatments

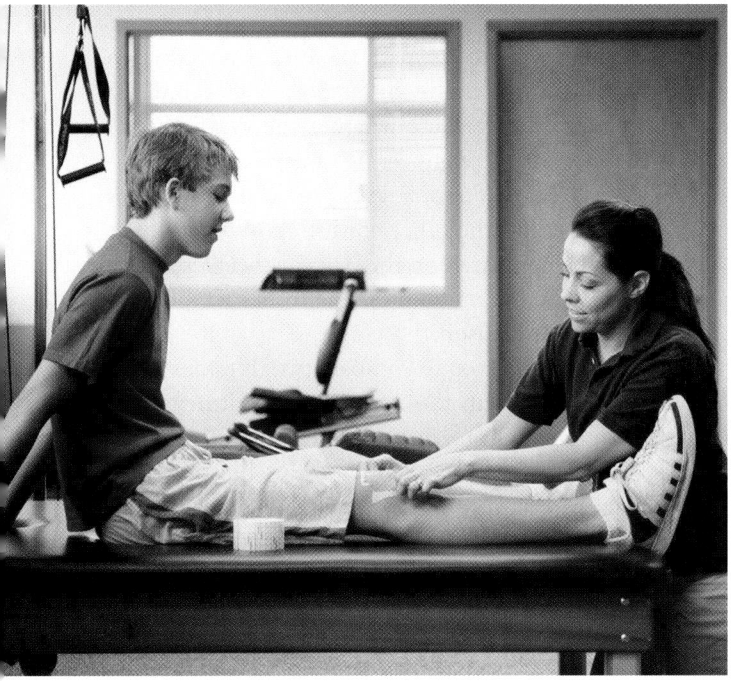

Andersen Ross/Digital Vision/Jupiter Images

Many investigations are carried out for the purpose of comparing two populations or treatments. For example, the article "What Do Happy People Do?" (*Social Indicators Research* [2008]: 565–571) investigates differences in the way happy people and unhappy people spend their time. By comparing data from a large national sample of people who described themselves as very happy to data from a large national sample of people who described themselves as not happy, the authors were able to investigate whether the mean amount of time spent in various activities was higher for one group than for the other. Using hypothesis tests to be introduced in this chapter, the authors were able to conclude that there was no significant difference in the mean number of hours per day spent on the Internet for happy and unhappy people but that the mean number of hours per day spent watching TV was significantly higher for unhappy people. In this chapter, we will see hypothesis tests and confidence intervals that can be used to compare two populations or treatments.

Make the most of your study time by accessing everything you need to succeed online with CourseMate.
Visit http://www.cengagebrain.com where you will find:

- An interactive eBook, which allows you to take notes, highlight, bookmark, search the text, and use in-context glossary definitions
- Step-by-step instructions for Minitab, Excel, TI-83/84, SPSS, and JMP
- Video solutions to selected exercises
- Data sets available for selected examples and exercises
- Online quizzes
- Flashcards
- Videos

11.1 Inferences Concerning the Difference Between Two Population or Treatment Means Using Independent Samples

In this section, we consider using sample data to compare two population means or two treatment means. An investigator may wish to estimate the difference between two population means or to test hypotheses about this difference. For example, a university financial aid director may want to determine whether the mean cost of textbooks is different for students enrolled in the engineering college than for students enrolled in the liberal arts college. Here, two populations (one consisting of all students enrolled in the engineering college and the other consisting of all students enrolled in the liberal arts college) are to be compared on the basis of their respective mean textbook costs. Information from two random samples, one from each population, could be the basis for making such a comparison.

In other cases, an experiment might be carried out to compare two different treatments or to compare the effect of a treatment with the effect of no treatment. For example, an agricultural experimenter might wish to compare weight gains for animals placed on two different diets (each diet is a treatment), or an educational researcher might wish to compare online instruction to traditional classroom instruction by studying the difference in mean scores on a common final exam (each type of instruction is a treatment).

In previous chapters, the symbol μ was used to denote the mean of a single population under study. When comparing two populations or treatments, we must use notation that distinguishes between the characteristics of the first and those of the second. This is accomplished by using subscripts, as shown in the accompanying box.

Notation

	Mean	Variance	Standard Deviation
Population or Treatment 1	μ_1	σ_1^2	σ_1
Population or Treatment 2	μ_2	σ_2^2	σ_2

	Sample Size	Mean	Variance	Standard Deviation
Sample from Population or Treatment 1	n_1	$\bar{x}_1$	s_1^2	s_1
Sample from Population or Treatment 2	n_2	$\bar{x}_2$	s_2^2	s_2

A comparison of means focuses on the difference, $\mu_1 - \mu_2$. When $\mu_1 - \mu_2 = 0$, the two population or treatment means are identical. That is,

$$\mu_1 - \mu_2 = 0 \text{ is equivalent to } \mu_1 = \mu_2$$

Similarly,

$$\mu_1 - \mu_2 > 0 \text{ is equivalent to } \mu_1 > \mu_2$$

and

$$\mu_1 - \mu_2 < 0 \text{ is equivalent to } \mu_1 < \mu_2$$

Before developing inferential procedures concerning $\mu_1 - \mu_2$, we must consider how the two samples, one from each population, are selected. Two samples are said to be **independent** samples if the selection of the individuals or objects that make up one sample does not influence the selection of individuals or objects in the other sample. However, when observations from the first sample are paired in some meaningful way with observations in the second sample, the samples are said to be **paired**. For example, to study the effectiveness of a speed-reading course, the reading speed of subjects could be measured before they take the class and again after they complete the course. This gives rise to two related samples—one from the population of individuals who have not taken this particular course (the "before" measurements) and one from the population of individuals who have had such a course (the "after" measurements). These samples are paired. The two samples are not independently chosen, because the selection of individuals from the first (before) population completely determines which individuals make up the sample from the second (after) population. In this section, we consider procedures based on independent samples. Methods for analyzing data resulting from paired samples are presented in Section 11.2.

Because $\bar{x}_1$ provides an estimate of μ_1 and $\bar{x}_2$ gives an estimate of μ_2, it is natural to use $\bar{x}_1 - \bar{x}_2$ as a point estimate of $\mu_1 - \mu_2$. The value of $\bar{x}_1$ varies from sample to sample (it is a *statistic*), as does the value of $\bar{x}_2$. Since the difference $\bar{x}_1 - \bar{x}_2$ is calculated from sample values, it is also a statistic and, therefore, has a sampling distribution.

Properties of the Sampling Distribution of $\bar{x}_1 - \bar{x}_2$

If the random samples on which $\bar{x}_1$ and $\bar{x}_2$ are based are selected independently of one another, then

1. $$\mu_{\bar{x}_1-\bar{x}_2} = \begin{pmatrix}\text{mean value}\\ \text{of } \bar{x}_1 - \bar{x}_2\end{pmatrix} = \mu_{\bar{x}_1} - \mu_{\bar{x}_2} = \mu_1 - \mu_2$$

   The sampling distribution of $\bar{x}_1 - \bar{x}_2$ is always centered at the value of $\mu_1 - \mu_2$, so $\bar{x}_1 - \bar{x}_2$ is an unbiased statistic for estimating $\mu_1 - \mu_2$.

2. $$\sigma^2_{\bar{x}_1-\bar{x}_2} = \begin{pmatrix}\text{variance of}\\ \bar{x}_1 - \bar{x}_2\end{pmatrix} = \sigma^2_{\bar{x}_1} + \sigma^2_{\bar{x}_2} = \frac{\sigma_1^2}{n_1} + \frac{\sigma_2^2}{n_2}$$

   and

   $$\sigma_{\bar{x}_1-\bar{x}_2} = \begin{pmatrix}\text{standard deviation}\\ \text{of } \bar{x}_1 - \bar{x}_2\end{pmatrix} = \sqrt{\frac{\sigma_1^2}{n_1} + \frac{\sigma_2^2}{n_2}}$$

3. If n_1 and n_2 are both large or the population distributions are (at least approximately) normal, $\bar{x}_1$ and $\bar{x}_2$ each have (at least approximately) a normal distribution. This implies that the sampling distribution of $\bar{x}_1 - \bar{x}_2$ is also normal or approximately normal.

Properties 1 and 2 follow from the following general results:

1. The mean value of a difference in means is the difference of the two individual mean values.
2. The variance of a difference of *independent* quantities is the *sum* of the two individual variances.

When the sample sizes are large or when the population distributions are approximately normal, the properties of the sampling distribution of $\bar{x}_1 - \bar{x}_2$ imply that

$\bar{x}_1 - \bar{x}_2$ can be standardized to obtain a variable with a sampling distribution that is approximately the standard normal (z) distribution. This leads to the following result.

When two random samples are independently selected and when n_1 and n_2 are both large or the population distributions are (at least approximately) normal, the distribution of

$$z = \frac{\bar{x}_1 - \bar{x}_2 - (\mu_1 - \mu_2)}{\sqrt{\frac{\sigma_1^2}{n_1} + \frac{\sigma_2^2}{n_2}}}$$

is described (at least approximately) by the standard normal (z) distribution.

Although it is possible to base a test procedure and confidence interval on this result, the values of σ_1^2 and σ_2^2 are rarely known. As a result, the z statistic is rarely used. When σ_1^2 and σ_2^2 are unknown, we must estimate them using the corresponding sample variances, s_1^2 and s_2^2. The result on which both a test procedure and confidence interval are based is given in the accompanying box.

AP* EXAM TIP

This formula for df is not on the formula sheet for the AP exam. Fortunately, most graphing calculators will compute df, so you won't need to memorize this formula. When you report the df in an exam response, you should note that you used your calculator to compute df.

When two random samples are independently selected and when n_1 and n_2 are both large or when the population distributions are normal, the standardized variable

$$t = \frac{\bar{x}_1 - \bar{x}_2 - (\mu_1 - \mu_2)}{\sqrt{\frac{s_1^2}{n_1} + \frac{s_2^2}{n_2}}}$$

has approximately a t distribution with

$$\text{df} = \frac{(V_1 + V_2)^2}{\frac{V_1^2}{n_1 - 1} + \frac{V_2^2}{n_2 - 1}} \quad \text{where } V_1 = \frac{s_1^2}{n_1} \text{ and } V_2 = \frac{s_2^2}{n_2}$$

The computed value of df should be truncated (rounded down) to obtain an integer value of df.

If one or both sample sizes are small, we must consider the shape of the population distributions. We can use normal probability plots or boxplots to evaluate whether it is reasonable to consider the population distributions to be approximately normal.

Test Procedures

In a test designed to compare two population means, the null hypothesis is of the form

$$H_0\text{: } \mu_1 - \mu_2 = \text{hypothesized value}$$

Often the hypothesized value is 0, indicating that there is no difference between the population means. The alternative hypothesis involves the same hypothesized value but uses one of three inequalities (less than, greater than, or not equal to), depending on the research question of interest. As an example, let μ_1 and μ_2 denote the average fuel efficiencies (in miles per gallon, mpg) for two models of a certain type of car equipped with 4-cylinder and 6-cylinder engines, respectively. The hypotheses under consideration might be

$$H_0\colon \mu_1 - \mu_2 = 5 \quad \text{versus} \quad H_a\colon \mu_1 - \mu_2 > 5$$

The null hypothesis is equivalent to the claim that the mean fuel efficiency for the 4-cylinder engine exceeds the mean fuel efficiency for the 6-cylinder engine by 5 mpg. The alternative hypothesis states that the difference between the mean fuel efficiencies is more than 5 mpg.

A test statistic is obtained by replacing $\mu_1 - \mu_2$ in the standardized t variable (given in the previous box) with the hypothesized value that appears in H_0. Thus, the t statistic for testing $H_0\colon \mu_1 - \mu_2 = 5$ is

$$t = \frac{\bar{x}_1 - \bar{x}_2 - 5}{\sqrt{\dfrac{s_1^2}{n_1} + \dfrac{s_2^2}{n_2}}}$$

When the sample sizes are large or when the population distributions are normal, the sampling distribution of the test statistic is approximately a t distribution when H_0 is true. The P-value for the test is obtained by first computing the appropriate number of degrees of freedom and then using Appendix Table 4, a graphing calculator, or a statistical software package. The following box gives a general description of the test procedure.

Summary of the Two-Sample *t* Test for Comparing Two Populations

Null hypothesis: $H_0\colon \mu_1 - \mu_2 =$ hypothesized value

Test statistic: $t = \dfrac{\bar{x}_1 - \bar{x}_2 - \text{hypothesized value}}{\sqrt{\dfrac{s_1^2}{n_1} + \dfrac{s_2^2}{n_2}}}$

The appropriate df for the two-sample t test is

$$\text{df} = \frac{(V_1 + V_2)^2}{\dfrac{V_1^2}{n_1 - 1} + \dfrac{V_2^2}{n_2 - 1}} \quad \text{where } V_1 = \frac{s_1^2}{n_1} \text{ and } V_2 = \frac{s_2^2}{n_2}$$

The computed number of degrees of freedom should be truncated (rounded down) to an integer.

Alternative hypothesis:	***P*-value:**
$H_a\colon \mu_1 - \mu_2 >$ hypothesized value	Area under appropriate t curve to the right of the computed t
$H_a\colon \mu_1 - \mu_2 <$ hypothesized value	Area under appropriate t curve to the left of the computed t
$H_a\colon \mu_1 - \mu_2 \neq$ hypothesized value	(1) 2(area to the right of the computed t) if t is positive or (2) 2(area to the left of the computed t) if t is negative

Assumptions: 1. The two samples are *independently selected random samples* from the populations of interest.
2. The *sample sizes are large* (generally 30 or larger) or *the population distributions are (at least approximately) normal.*

EXAMPLE 11.1 Brain Size

Do children diagnosed with attention deficit/hyperactivity disorder (ADHD) have smaller brains than children without this condition? This question was the topic of a research study described in the paper "Developmental Trajectories of Brain Volume Abnormalities in Children and Adolescents with Attention Deficit/Hyperactivity Disorder" (*Journal of the American Medical Association* [2002]: 1740–1747). Brain scans were completed for 152 children with ADHD and 139 children of similar age without ADHD. Summary values for total cerebral volume (in milliliters) are given in the following table:

	n	$\bar{x}$	s
Children with ADHD	152	1059.4	117.5
Children without ADHD	139	1104.5	111.3

Do these data provide evidence that the mean brain volume of children with ADHD is smaller than the mean for children without ADHD? Let's test the relevant hypotheses using a .05 level of significance.

1. μ_1 = true mean brain volume for children with ADHD
   μ_2 = true mean brain volume for children without ADHD
   $\mu_1 - \mu_2$ = difference in mean brain volume
2. H_0: $\mu_1 - \mu_2 = 0$ (no difference in mean brain volume)
3. H_a: $\mu_1 - \mu_2 < 0$ (mean brain volume is smaller for children with ADHD)
4. Significance level: $\alpha = .05$
5. Test statistic: $t = \dfrac{\bar{x}_1 - \bar{x}_2 - \text{hypothesized value}}{\sqrt{\dfrac{s_1^2}{n_1} + \dfrac{s_2^2}{n_2}}} = \dfrac{\bar{x}_1 - \bar{x}_2 - 0}{\sqrt{\dfrac{s_1^2}{n_1} + \dfrac{s_2^2}{n_2}}}$
6. Assumptions: The paper states that the study controlled for age and that the participants were "recruited from the local community." This is not equivalent to random sampling, but the authors of the paper (five of whom were doctors at well-known medical institutions) believed that it was reasonable to regard these samples as representative of the two groups under study. Both sample sizes are large, so it is reasonable to proceed with the two-sample t test.
7. Calculation:

$$t = \frac{(1059.4 - 1104.5) - 0}{\sqrt{\dfrac{(117.5)^2}{152} + \dfrac{(111.3)^2}{139}}} = \frac{-45.10}{\sqrt{90.831 + 89.120}} = \frac{-45.10}{13.415} = -3.36$$

8. P-value: We first compute the df for the two-sample t test:

$$V_1 = \frac{s_1^2}{n_1} = 90.831 \quad V_2 = \frac{s_2^2}{n_2} = 89.120$$

$$\text{df} = \frac{(V_1 + V_2)^2}{\dfrac{V_1^2}{n_1 - 1} + \dfrac{V_2^2}{n_2 - 1}} = \frac{(90.831 + 89.120)^2}{\dfrac{(90.831)^2}{151} + \dfrac{(89.120)^2}{138}} = \frac{32{,}382.362}{112.191} = 288.636$$

We truncate the number of degrees of freedom to 288. Appendix Table 4 shows that the area under the t curve with 288 df (using the z critical value column because 288 is larger than 120 df) to the left of -3.36 is approximately 0. Therefore,

P-value ≈ 0

9. Conclusion: Because P-value $\approx 0 \leq .05$, we reject H_0. There is convincing evidence that the mean brain volume for children with ADHD is smaller than the mean for children without ADHD.

EXAMPLE 11.2 Sex and Salary

● Are women still paid less than men for comparable work? The authors of the paper "Sex and Salary: A Survey of Purchasing and Supply Professionals" (*Journal of Purchasing and Supply Management* [2008]: 112–124) carried out a study in which salary data was collected from a random sample of men and a random sample of women who worked as purchasing managers and who were subscribers to *Purchasing* magazine. Salary data consistent with summary quantities given in the paper appear below (the actual sample sizes for the study were much larger):

Annual Salary (in thousands of dollars)

Men	81	69	81	76	76	74	69	76	79	65
Women	78	60	67	61	62	73	71	58	68	48

Even though the samples were selected from subscribers of a particular magazine, the authors of the paper believed that it was reasonable to view the samples in the study as representative of the two populations of interest—male purchasing managers and female purchasing managers. For purposes of this example, we will assume that it is also reasonable to consider the two samples given here as representative of the populations. We will use the given data and a significance level of .05 to determine if there is convincing evidence that the mean annual salary for male purchasing managers is greater than the mean annual salary for female purchasing managers.

1. μ_1 = mean annual salary for male purchasing managers
   μ_2 = mean annual salary for female purchasing managers
   $\mu_1 - \mu_2$ = difference in mean annual salary
2. H_0: $\mu_1 - \mu_2 = 0$
3. H_a: $\mu_1 - \mu_2 > 0$
4. Significance level: $\alpha = .05$
5. Test statistic: $t = \dfrac{\bar{x}_1 - \bar{x}_2 - \text{hypothesized value}}{\sqrt{\dfrac{s_1^2}{n_1} + \dfrac{s_2^2}{n_2}}} = \dfrac{\bar{x}_1 - \bar{x}_2 - 0}{\sqrt{\dfrac{s_1^2}{n_1} + \dfrac{s_2^2}{n_2}}}$
6. Assumptions: For the two-sample t test to be appropriate, we must be willing to assume that the two samples can be viewed as independently selected random samples from the two populations of interest. As previously noted, we assume that this is reasonable. Because both of the sample sizes are small, it is also necessary to

● Data set available online

assume that the salary distribution is approximately normal for each of these two populations. Boxplots constructed using the sample data are shown here:

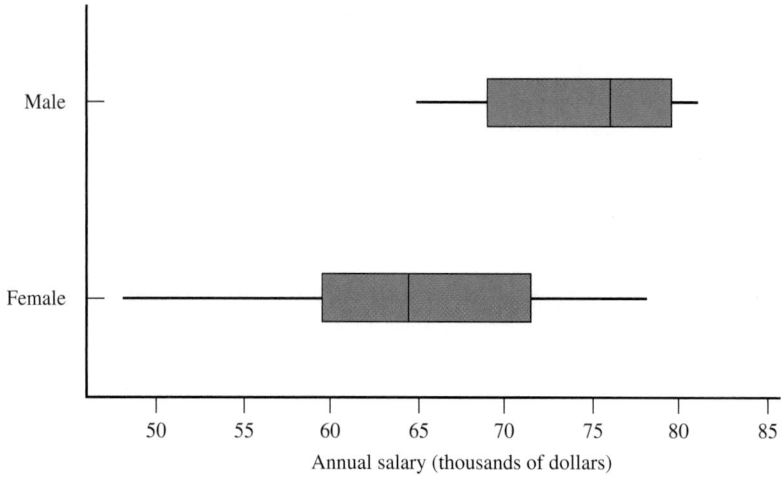

Because the boxplots are reasonably symmetric and because there are no outliers, it is reasonable to proceed with the two-sample t-test.

7. Calculation: For the given data:

$$\bar{x} = 74.6 \; s_1 = 5.4 \; \bar{x}_2 = 64.6 \; s_2 = 8.6, \text{ and}$$

$$t = \frac{(74.6 - 64.6) - 0}{\sqrt{\frac{(5.4)^2}{10} + \frac{(8.6)^2}{10}}} = \frac{10}{\sqrt{2.916 + 7.396}} = \frac{10}{3.211} = 3.11$$

8. P-value: We first compute the df for the two-sample t test:

$$V_1 = \frac{s_1^2}{n_1} = 2.916 \quad V_2 = \frac{s_2^2}{n_2} = 7.396$$

$$\text{df} = \frac{(V_1 + V_2)^2}{\frac{V_1^2}{n_1 - 1} + \frac{V_2^2}{n_2 - 1}} = \frac{(2.916 + 7.396)^2}{\frac{(2.916)^2}{9} + \frac{(7.396)^2}{9}} = \frac{106.337}{7.023} = 15.14$$

We truncate df to 15. Appendix Table 4 shows that the area under the t curve with 15 df to the right of 3.1 is .004, so P-value = .004.

9. Conclusion: Because the P-value of .004 is less than .05, we reject H_0. There is convincing evidence to support the claim that mean annual salary for male purchasing managers is higher than mean annual salary for female purchasing managers.

Suppose the computed value of the test statistic in Step 7 had been 1.13 rather than 3.11. Then the P-value would have been .143 (the area to the right of 1.1 under the t curve with 15 df) and the decision would have been to not reject the null hypothesis. We then would have concluded that there was not convincing evidence that the mean annual salary was higher for males than for females. Notice that when we fail to reject the null hypothesis of no difference between the population means, we are not saying that there is convincing evidence that the means are equal—we can only say that we were not convinced that they were different.

Many statistical computer packages can perform the calculations for the two-sample t test. The accompanying partial SPSS output shows summary statistics for the two groups of Example 11.2. The second part of the output gives the number of degrees of freedom, the test-statistic value, and a two-sided P-value. Since the test in Example 11.2 is a one-sided test, we need to divide the two-sided P-value in half to obtain the correct value for our test, which is $\frac{.0072}{2} = .0036$. This P-value differs from the value in

Example 11.2 because Appendix Table 4 gives only tail areas for t values to one decimal place and so we rounded the test statistic to 3.1. As a consequence, the P-value given in the example is only approximate; the P-value from SPSS is more accurate.

GROUP STATISTICS

	Sex	N	Mean	Std. Deviation	Std. Error Mean
Salary	**male**	10	74.60	5.40	1.71
	female	10	64.60	8.62	2.73

						95% CONFIDENCE INTERVAL OF THE DIFFERENCE	
	t	df	Sig. (2-tailed)	Mean Difference	Std. Error Difference	Lower	Upper
Equal Variances Not Assumed	3.11	15.14	.0072	10.000	3.211	3.1454	16.8546

Comparing Treatments

When an experiment is carried out to compare two treatments (or to compare a single treatment with a control), the investigator is interested in the effect of the treatments on some response variable. The treatments are "applied" to individuals (as in an experiment to compare two different medications for decreasing blood pressure) or objects (as in an experiment to compare two different baking temperatures on the density of bread), and the value of some response variable (for example, blood pressure, density) is recorded. Based on the resulting data, the investigator might wish to determine whether there is a difference in the mean response for the two treatments.

In many actual experimental situations, the individuals or objects to which the treatments will be applied are not selected at random from some larger population. A consequence of this is that it is not possible to generalize the results of the experiment to some larger population. However, *if the experimental design provides for random assignment of the individuals or objects used in the experiment to treatments (or for random assignment of treatments to the individuals or objects), it is possible to test hypotheses about treatment differences.*

It is common practice to use the two-sample t test statistic previously described if the experiment employs random assignment and if either the sample sizes are large or it is reasonable to think that the treatment response distributions (the distributions of response values that would result if the treatments were applied to a *very* large number of individuals or objects) are approximately normal.

Two-Sample *t* Test for Comparing Two Treatments

When

1. *individuals or objects are randomly assigned* to treatments (or vice versa; that is, treatments are randomly assigned to individuals or objects), and
2. the *sample sizes are large* (generally 30 or larger) or the *treatment response distributions are approximately normal,*

the two-sample t test can be used to test H_0: $\mu_1 - \mu_2 =$ *hypothesized value,* where μ_1 and μ_2 represent the mean response for treatments 1 and 2, respectively.

In this case, these two conditions replace the assumptions previously stated for comparing two population means. Whether the assumption of normality of the treatment response distributions is reasonable can be assessed by constructing normal probability plots or boxplots of the response values in each sample.

When the two-sample t test is used to compare two treatments when the individuals or objects used in the experiment are not randomly selected from some population, it is only an approximate test (the reported P-values are only approximate). However, this is still the most common way to analyze such data.

EXAMPLE 11.3 Reading Emotions

Pierre Bourrier/Iconica/Getty Images

The paper "How Happy Was I, Anyway? A Retrospective Impact Bias" (*Social Cognition* [2003]: 421–446) reported on an experiment designed to assess the extent to which people rationalize poor performance. In this study, 246 college undergraduates were assigned at random to one of two groups—a negative feedback group or a positive feedback group. Each participant took a test in which they were asked to guess the emotions displayed in photographs of faces. At the end of the test, those in the negative feedback group were told that they had correctly answered 21 of the 40 items and were assigned a "grade" of D. Those in the positive feedback group were told that they had answered 35 of 40 correctly and were assigned an A grade. After a brief time, participants were asked to answer two sets of questions. One set of questions asked about the validity of the test and the other set of questions asked about the importance of being able to read faces. The researchers hypothesized that those in the negative feedback group would tend to rationalize their poor performance by rating both the validity of the test and the importance of being a good face reader lower than those in the positive feedback group. Do the data from this experiment support the researchers' hypotheses?

		TEST VALIDITY RATING		FACE READING IMPORTANCE RATING	
Group	Sample Size	Mean	Standard Deviation	Mean	Standard Deviation
Negative feedback	123	5.51	.79	5.36	1.00
Positive feedback	123	6.95	1.09	6.62	1.19

We will test the relevant hypotheses using a significance level of .01, beginning with the hypotheses about the test validity rating.

1. Let μ_1 denote the mean test validity score for the negative feedback group and define μ_2 analogously for the positive feedback group. Then $\mu_1 - \mu_2$ is the difference between the mean test validity scores for the two treatment groups.
2. H_0: $\mu_1 - \mu_2 = 0$
3. H_a: $\mu_1 - \mu_2 < 0$
4. Significance level: $\alpha = .01$
5. Test statistic: $t = \dfrac{\bar{x}_1 - \bar{x}_2 - \text{hypothesized value}}{\sqrt{\dfrac{s_1^2}{n_1} + \dfrac{s_2^2}{n_2}}} = \dfrac{\bar{x}_1 - \bar{x}_2 - 0}{\sqrt{\dfrac{s_1^2}{n_1} + \dfrac{s_2^2}{n_2}}}$
6. Assumptions: Subjects were randomly assigned to the treatment groups, and both sample sizes are large, so use of the two-sample t test is reasonable.
7. Calculation: $t = \dfrac{(5.51 - 6.95) - 0}{\sqrt{\dfrac{(.79)^2}{123} + \dfrac{(1.09)^2}{123}}} = \dfrac{-1.44}{0.1214} = -11.86$
8. P-value: We first compute the df for the two-sample t test:

   $$V_1 = \frac{s_1^2}{n_1} = .0051 \quad V_2 = \frac{s_2^2}{n_2} = .0097$$

   $$\text{df} = \frac{(V_1 + V_2)^2}{\dfrac{V_1^2}{n_1 - 1} + \dfrac{V_2^2}{n_2 - 1}} = \frac{(.0051 + .0097)^2}{\dfrac{(.0051)^2}{122} + \dfrac{(.0097)^2}{122}} = \frac{.000219}{.000001} = 219$$

   This is a lower-tailed test, so the P-value is the area under the t curve with df = 219 and to the left of -11.86. Since -11.86 is so far out in the lower tail of this t curve, P-value ≈ 0.
9. Conclusion: Since P-value $\le \alpha$, H_0 is rejected. There is evidence that the mean validity rating score for the positive feedback group is higher. The data support the conclusion that those who received negative feedback did not rate the validity of the test, on average, as highly as those who thought they had done well on the test.

We will use Minitab to test the researchers' hypothesis that those in the negative feedback group would also not rate the importance of being able to read faces as highly as those in the positive group.

1. Let μ_1 denote the mean face reading importance rating for the negative feedback group and define μ_2 analogously for the positive feedback group. Then $\mu_1 - \mu_2$ is the difference between the mean face reading ratings for the two treatment groups.
2. H_0: $\mu_1 - \mu_2 = 0$
3. H_a: $\mu_1 - \mu_2 < 0$
4. Significance level: $\alpha = .01$
5. Test statistic: $t = \dfrac{\bar{x}_1 - \bar{x}_2 - \text{hypothesized value}}{\sqrt{\dfrac{s_1^2}{n_1} + \dfrac{s_2^2}{n_2}}} = \dfrac{\bar{x}_1 - \bar{x}_2 - 0}{\sqrt{\dfrac{s_1^2}{n_1} + \dfrac{s_2^2}{n_2}}}$
6. Assumptions: Subjects were randomly assigned to the treatment groups, and both sample sizes are large, so use of the two-sample t test is reasonable.

7. Calculation: Minitab output is shown here. From the output, $t = -8.99$.

Two-Sample T-Test and CI

Sample	N	Mean	StDev	SE Mean
1	123	5.36	1.00	0.090
2	123	6.62	1.19	0.11

Difference = mu (1) – mu (2)
Estimate for difference: –1.26000
95% upper bound for difference: –1.02856
T-Test of difference = 0 (vs <): T-Value = –8.99 P-Value = 0.000 DF = 236

8. *P*-value: From the Minitab output, *P*-value $= 0.000$.
9. Conclusion: Since *P*-value $\leq \alpha$, H_0 is rejected. There is evidence that the mean face reading importance rating for the positive feedback group is higher.

AP* EXAM TIP

The AP exam assumes that you are using a calculator capable of computing df for the two-sample t test. If your calculator does not have this capability, this simple conservative rule can be used.

You have probably noticed that evaluating the formula for number of degrees of freedom for the two-sample t test involves quite a bit of arithmetic. An alternative approach is to compute a conservative estimate of the *P*-value—one that is close to but larger than the actual *P*-value. If H_0 is rejected using this conservative estimate, then it will also be rejected if the actual *P*-value is used. *A conservative estimate of the P-value for the two-sample t test can be found by using the t curve with the number of degrees of freedom equal to the smaller of* $(n_1 - 1)$ *and* $(n_2 - 1)$.

The Pooled *t* Test

The two-sample t test procedure just described is appropriate when it is reasonable to assume that the population distributions are approximately normal. If it is also known that the variances of the two populations are equal $(\sigma_1^2 = \sigma_2^2)$, an alternative procedure known as the *pooled t test* can be used. This test procedure combines information from both samples to obtain a "pooled" estimate of the common variance and then uses this pooled estimate of the variance in place of s_1^2 and s_2^2 in the t test statistic. This test procedure was widely used in the past, but it has fallen into some disfavor because it is quite sensitive to departures from the assumption of equal population variances. If the population variances are equal, the pooled t procedure has a slightly better chance of detecting departures from H_0 than does the two-sample t test of this section. However, *P*-values based on the pooled t procedure can be seriously in error if the population variances are not equal, so, in general, the two-sample t procedure is a better choice than the pooled t test.

Comparisons and Causation

If the assignment of treatments to the individuals or objects used in a comparison of treatments is not made by the investigators, the study is observational. As an example, the article "Lead and Cadmium Absorption Among Children near a Nonferrous Metal Plant" (*Environmental Research* [1978]: 290–308) reported data on blood lead concentrations for two different samples of children. The first sample was drawn from a population residing within 1 km of a lead smelter, whereas those in the second sample were selected from a rural area much farther from the smelter. It was the parents of the children, rather than the investigators, who determined whether the children would be in the close-to-smelter group or the far-from-smelter group. As a second example, a letter in the *Journal of the American Medical Association* (May 19, 1978) reported on a comparison of doctors' longevity after medical school graduation for those with an academic affiliation and those in private practice. (The letter writer's stated objective was to see whether "publish or perish" really meant "publish *and* perish.") Here again, an investigator did not start out with a group of doctors, assigning some to academic and others to nonacademic careers. The doctors themselves selected their groups.

The difficulty with drawing conclusions based on an observational study is that a statistically significant difference may be due to some underlying factors that have not been controlled rather than to conditions that define the groups. Does the type of medical practice itself have an effect on longevity, or is the observed difference in lifetimes caused by other factors, which themselves led graduates to choose academic or nonacademic careers? Similarly, is the observed difference in blood lead concentration levels due to proximity to the smelter? Perhaps other physical and socioeconomic factors are related both to choice of living area and to concentration.

In general, rejection of H_0: $\mu_1 - \mu_2 = 0$ in favor of H_a: $\mu_1 - \mu_2 > 0$ suggests that, on average, higher values of the variable are *associated* with individuals in the first population or receiving the first treatment than with those in the second population or receiving the second treatment. But *association does not imply causation.* Strong statistical evidence for a causal relationship can be built up over time through many different comparative studies that point to the same conclusions (as in the many investigations linking smoking to lung cancer). A **randomized controlled experiment,** in which investigators assign subjects at random to the treatments or conditions being compared, is particularly effective in suggesting causality. With such random assignment, the investigator and other interested parties can have more confidence in the conclusion that an observed difference is caused by the difference in treatments or conditions.

A Confidence Interval

A confidence interval for $\mu_1 - \mu_2$ is easily obtained from the basic t variable of this section. Both the derivation of and the formula for the interval are similar to those of the one-sample t interval discussed in Chapter 9.

The Two-Sample t Confidence Interval for the Difference Between Two Population or Treatment Means

The general formula for a confidence interval for $\mu_1 - \mu_2$ when

1. the two samples are *independently chosen random samples,* and
2. the *sample sizes are both large* (generally $n_1 \geq 30$ and $n_2 \geq 30$
   or
   the *population distributions are approximately normal*

is

$$(\bar{x}_1 - \bar{x}_2) \pm (t \text{ critical value})\sqrt{\frac{s_1^2}{n_1} + \frac{s_2^2}{n_2}}$$

The t critical value is based on

$$\text{df} = \frac{(V_1 + V_2)^2}{\dfrac{V_1^2}{n_1 - 1} + \dfrac{V_2^2}{n_2 - 1}} \quad \text{where } V_1 = \frac{s_1^2}{n_1} \text{ and } V_2 = \frac{s_2^2}{n_2}$$

(continued)

df should be truncated (rounded down) to an integer. The t critical values for the usual confidence levels are given in Appendix Table 3.

For a comparison of two treatments, when

1. *individuals or objects are randomly assigned* to treatments (or vice versa), and
2. the *sample sizes are large* (generally 30 or larger)
   or
   the *treatment response distributions are approximately normal,*

the two-sample t confidence interval formula can be used to estimate $\mu_1 - \mu_2$.

EXAMPLE 11.4 Effect of Talking on Blood Pressure

● Does talking elevate blood pressure, contributing to the tendency for blood pressure to be higher when measured in a doctor's office than when measured in a less stressful environment? (This well-documented effect is called the "white coat effect.") The article "The Talking Effect and 'White Coat' Effect in Hypertensive Patients: Physical Effort or Emotional Content" (*Behavioral Medicine* [2001]: 149–157) described a study in which patients with high blood pressure were randomly assigned to one of two groups. Those in the first group (the talking group) were asked questions about their medical history and about the sources of stress in their lives in the minutes before their blood pressure was measured. Those in the second group (the counting group) were asked to count aloud from 1 to 100 four times before their blood pressure was measured. The following data values for diastolic blood pressure (in millimeters of Hg) are consistent with summary quantities appearing in the paper:

Talking	104	110	107	112	108	103	108	118
		$n_1 = 8$		$\bar{x}_1 = 108.75$		$s_1 = 4.74$		
Counting	110	96	103	98	100	109	97	105
		$n_2 = 8$		$\bar{x}_2 = 102.25$		$s_2 = 5.39$		

Subjects were randomly assigned to the two treatments. Because both sample sizes are small, we must first investigate whether it is reasonable to assume that the diastolic blood pressure distributions are approximately normal for the two treatments. There are no outliers in either sample, and the boxplots are reasonably symmetric, suggesting that the assumption of approximate normality is reasonable.

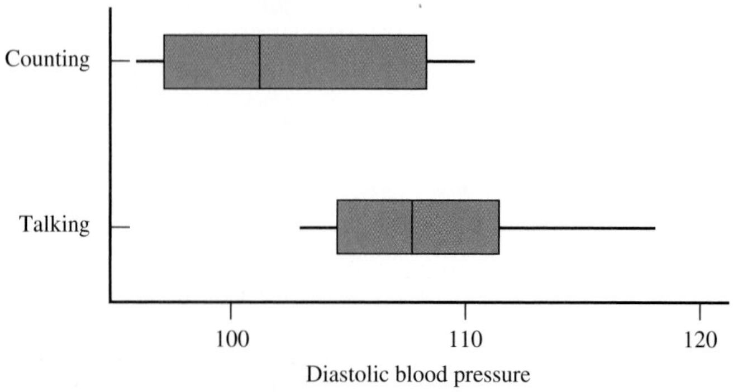

!! Step-by-Step technology instructions available online

● Data set available online

To estimate $\mu_1 - \mu_2$, the difference in mean diastolic blood pressure for the two treatments, we will calculate a 95% confidence interval.

$$V_1 = \frac{s_1^2}{n_1} = \frac{(4.74)^2}{8} = 2.81 \quad V_2 = \frac{s_2^2}{n_2} = \frac{(5.39)^2}{8} = 3.63$$

$$\text{df} = \frac{(V_1 + V_2)^2}{\frac{V_1^2}{n_1 - 1} + \frac{V_2^2}{n_2 - 1}} = \frac{(2.81 + 3.63)^2}{\frac{(2.81)^2}{7} + \frac{(3.63)^2}{7}} = \frac{41.47}{3.01} = 13.78$$

Truncating to an integer gives df = 13. In the 13-df row of Appendix Table 3, the t critical value for a 95% confidence level is 2.16. The interval is then

$$(\bar{x}_1 - \bar{x}_2) \pm (t \text{ critical value})\sqrt{\frac{s_1^2}{n_1} + \frac{s_2^2}{n_2}}$$
$$= (108.75 - 102.25) \pm (2.16)\sqrt{\frac{(4.74)^2}{8} + \frac{(5.39)^2}{8}}$$
$$= 6.5 \pm (2.16)(2.54)$$
$$= 6.5 \pm 5.49$$
$$= (1.01, 11.99)$$

This interval is rather wide, because the two sample variances are large and the sample sizes are small. Notice that the interval does not include 0, so 0 is not one of the plausible values for $\mu_1 - \mu_2$. Based on this computed interval, we estimate that the mean diastolic blood pressure when talking is higher than the mean when counting by somewhere between 1.01 and 11.99 mm Hg. This result supports the existence of a talking effect over and above the "white coat" effect. The 95% confidence level means that we used a method to produce this estimate that correctly captures the true value of $\mu_1 - \mu_2$ 95% of the time in repeated sampling.

Most statistical computer packages can compute the two-sample t confidence interval. Minitab was used to construct a 95% confidence interval using the data of this example; the resulting output is shown here:

Two-Sample T-Test and CI: Talking, Counting

Two-sample T for Talking vs Counting

	N	Mean	StDev	SE Mean
Talking	8	108.75	4.74	1.7
Counting	8	102.25	5.39	1.9

95% CI for difference: (1.01, 11.99)

EXERCISES 11.1 - 11.21

11.1 Consider two populations for which $\mu_1 = 30$, $\sigma_1 = 2$, $\mu_2 = 25$, and $\sigma_2 = 3$. Suppose that two independent random samples of sizes $n_1 = 40$ and $n_2 = 50$ are selected. Describe the approximate sampling distribution of $\bar{x}_1 - \bar{x}_2$ (center, spread, and shape).

11.2 An individual can take either a scenic route to work or a nonscenic route. She decides that use of the nonscenic route can be justified only if it reduces the mean travel time by more than 10 minutes.

a. If μ_1 is the mean for the scenic route and μ_2 for the nonscenic route, what hypotheses should be tested?

b. If μ_1 is the mean for the nonscenic route and μ_2 for the scenic route, what hypotheses should be tested?

11.3 ✦ Reduced heart rate variability (HRV) is known to be a predictor of mortality after a heart attack. One measure of HRV is the average of normal-to-normal beat interval (in milliseconds) for a 24-hour time period. Twenty-two heart attack patients who were dog owners and 80 heart attack patients who did not own a dog participated in a study of the effect of pet ownership on HRV, resulting in the summary statistics shown in the accompanying table ("Relationship Between Pet Ownership and Heart Rate Variability in Patients with Healed Myocardial Infarcts," *The American Journal of Cardiology* [2003]: 718–721).

	Measure of HRV (average normal-to-normal beat interval)	
	Mean	Standard Deviation
Owns Dog	873	136
Does Not Own Dog	800	134

a. The authors of this paper used a two-sample t test to test H_0: $\mu_1 - \mu_2 = 0$ versus H_a: $\mu_1 - \mu_2 \neq 0$. What assumptions must be reasonable in order for this to be an appropriate method of analysis?

b. The paper indicates that the null hypothesis from Part (a) was rejected and reports that the P-value is less than .05. Carry out a two-sample t test. Is your conclusion consistent with that of the paper?

11.4 In the paper "Happiness for Sale: Do Experiential Purchases Make Consumers Happier than Material Purchases?" (*Journal of Consumer Research* [2009]: 188–197), the authors distinguish between spending money on experiences (such as travel) and spending money on material possessions (such as a car). In an experiment to determine if the type of purchase affects how happy people are with the purchase after it has been made, 185 college students were randomly assigned to one of two groups. The students in the "experiential" group were asked to recall a time when they spent about \$300 on an experience, and then they rated this purchase on three different happiness scales that were then combined into an overall measure of happiness. The students assigned to the "material" group were asked to recall a time that they spent about \$300 on an object. The mean happiness score was 5.75 for the experiential group and 5.27 for the material group. Standard deviations and sample sizes were not given in the paper, but for purposes of this exercise, suppose that they were as follows:

Experiential	Material
$n_1 = 92$	$n_2 = 93$
$s_1 = 1.2$	$s_2 = 1.5$

Use the following Minitab output to carry out a hypothesis test to determine if the data supports the authors' conclusion that "experiential purchases induced more reported happiness." Use $\alpha = .05$.

```
Two-Sample T-Test and CI
Sample    N    Mean    StDev    SE Mean
1         92   5.75    1.20     0.13
2         93   5.27    1.50     0.16
Difference = mu (1) - mu (2)
Estimate for difference: 0.480000
95% lower bound for difference: 0.149917
T-Test of difference = 0 (vs >): T-Value = 2.40 P-Value =
0.009 DF = 175
```

11.5 ● The article "Plugged In, but Tuned Out" (*USA Today*, January 20, 2010) summarizes data from two surveys of kids age 8 to 18. One survey was conducted in 1999 and the other was conducted in 2009. Data on number of hours per day spent using electronic media that are consistent with summary quantities given in the article are given below (the actual sample sizes for the two surveys were much larger). For purposes of this exercise, assume that it is reasonable to regard the two samples as representative of kids age 8 to 18 in each of the 2 years that the surveys were conducted.

2009	5	9	5	8	7	6	7	9	7	9	6	9	10	9	8
1999	4	5	7	7	5	7	5	6	5	6	7	8	5	6	6

a. Because the given sample sizes are small, in order for the two-sample t test to be appropriate, what assumption must be made about the distribution of electronic media use times? Use the given data to construct graphical displays that would be useful in determining whether this assumption is reasonable. Do you think it is reasonable to use these data to carry out a two-sample t test?

b. Do the given data provide convincing evidence that the mean number of hours per day spent using electronic media was greater in 2009 than in 1999? Test the relevant hypotheses using a significance level of .01.

c. Construct and interpret a 98% confidence interval estimate of the difference between the mean number of hours per day spent using electronic media in 2009 and 1999.

11.6 Can moving their hands help children learn math? This question was investigated in the paper "Gesturing Gives Children New Ideas about Math" (*Psychological Science* [2009]: 267–272). Eighty-five children in the third and fourth grades who did not answer any questions correctly on a test with six problems of the form $3 + 2 + 8 = \_\_ + 8$ were participants in an experiment. The children were randomly assigned to either a no-gesture group or a gesture group. All the children were given a lesson on how to solve problems of this form using the strategy of trying to make both sides of the equation equal. Children in the gesture group were also taught to point to the first two numbers on the left side of the equation with the index and middle finger of one hand and then to point at the blank on the right side of the equation. This gesture was supposed to emphasize that grouping is involved in solving the problem. The children then practiced additional problems of this type. All children were then given a test with six problems to solve, and the number of correct answers was recorded for each child. Summary statistics read from a graph in the paper are given below.

	n	$\bar{x}$	s
No gesture	42	1.3	0.3
Gesture	43	2.2	0.4

Is there evidence to support the theory that learning the gesturing approach to solving problems of this type results in a higher mean number of correct responses? Test the relevant hypotheses using $\alpha = .01$.

11.7 ● The accompanying data on food intake (in Kcal) for 15 men on the day following two nights of only 4 hours of sleep each night and for 15 men on the day following two nights of 8 hours of sleep each night is consistent with summary quantities in the paper "Short-Term Sleep Loss Decreases Physical Activity under Free-Living Conditions But Does Not Increase Food Intake under Time Deprived Laboratory Conditions in Healthy Men" (*American Journal of Clinical Nutrition* [2009]: 1476–1482). The men participating in this experiment were randomly assigned to one of the two sleep conditions.

4-hour sleep group:	3585	4470	3068	5338	2221
	4791	4435	3099	3187	3901
	3868	3869	4878	3632	4518
8-hour sleep group:	4965	3918	1987	4993	5220
	3653	3510	3338	4100	5792
	4547	3319	3336	4304	4057

If appropriate, carry out a two-sample t test with $\alpha = .05$ to determine if there is a significant difference in mean food intake for the two different sleep conditions.

11.8 The paper "If It's Hard to Read, It's Hard to Do" (*Psychological Science* [2008]: 986–988) described an interesting study of how people perceive the effort required to do certain tasks. Each of 20 students was randomly assigned to one of two groups. One group was given instructions for an exercise routine that were printed in an easy-to-read font (Arial). The other group received the same set of instructions, but printed in a font that is considered difficult to read (Brush). After reading the instructions, subjects estimated the time (in minutes) they thought it would take to complete the exercise routine. Summary statistics are given below.

	Easy font	Difficult font
n	10	10
$\bar{x}$	8.23	15.10
s	5.61	9.28

The authors of the paper used these data to carry out a two-sample t test, and concluded that at the .10 significance level, there was convincing evidence that the mean estimated time to complete the exercise routine was less when the instructions were printed in an easy-to-read font than when printed in a difficult-to-read font. Discuss the appropriateness of using a two-sample t test in this situation.

11.9 Is injecting medical cement effective in reducing pain for people who have suffered fractured vertebrae? The paper "A Randomized Trial of Vertebroplasty for Osteoporotic Spinal Fractures" (*New England Journal of Medicine* [2009]: 569–578) describes an experiment to compare patients who underwent vertebroplasty (the injection of cement) to patients in a placebo group who underwent a fake procedure in which no cement was actually injected. Because the placebo procedure was similar to the vertebroplasty procedure except for the actual injection of cement, patients participating in the experiment were not aware of which treatment they received. All patients were asked to rate their pain at three different times—3 days, 14 days, and 1 month after the procedure. Summary statistics are given in the accompanying table.

	Pain Intensity			
	Vertebroplasty Group		Placebo Group	
	$n = 68$		$n = 63$	
	mean	sd	mean	sd
3 days	4.2	2.8	3.9	2.9
14 days	4.3	2.9	4.5	2.8
1 month	3.9	2.9	4.6	3.0

a. Briefly explain why the researchers may have chosen to include a placebo group that underwent a fake procedure rather than just comparing the vertebroplasty group to a group of patients who did not receive any treatment.

b. Construct and interpret a 95% confidence interval for the difference in mean pain intensity 3 days after treatment for the vertebroplasty treatment and the fake treatment.

c. Construct and interpret 95% confidence intervals for the difference in mean pain intensity at 14 days and at 1 month after treatment.

d. Based on the confidence intervals from Parts (b) and (c), comment on the effectiveness of injecting cement as a way of reducing pain for those with fractured vertebrae.

11.10 Each person in a random sample of 228 male teenagers and a random sample of 306 female teenagers was asked how many hours he or she spent online in a typical week (Ipsos, January 25, 2006). The sample mean and standard deviation were 15.1 hours and 11.4 hours for males and 14.1 and 11.8 for females.

a. The standard deviation for each of the samples is large, indicating a lot of variability in the responses to the question. Explain why it is not reasonable to think that the distribution of responses would be approximately normal for either the population of male teenagers or the population of female teenagers. *Hint:* The number of hours spent online in a typical week cannot be negative.

b. Given your response to Part (a), would it be appropriate to use the two-sample t test to test the null hypothesis that there is no difference in the mean number of hours spent online in a typical week for male teenagers and female teenagers? Explain why or why not.

c. If appropriate, carry out a test to determine if there is convincing evidence that the mean number of hours spent online in a typical week is greater for male teenagers than for female teenagers. Use a .05 significance level.

11.11 Each person in random samples of 247 male and 253 female working adults living in Calgary, Canada, was asked how long, in minutes, his or her typical daily commute was ("Calgary Herald Traffic Study," Ipsos, September 17, 2005). Use the accompanying summary statistics and an appropriate hypothesis test to determine if there is convincing evidence that the mean commute times for male and female working Calgary residents differ. Use a significance level of .05.

Males			Females		
Sample Size	$\bar{x}$	s	Sample Size	$\bar{x}$	s
247	29.6	24.3	253	27.3	24.0

11.12 The paper "Effects of Fast-Food Consumption on Energy Intake and Diet Quality Among Children in a National Household Survey" (*Pediatrics* [2004]: 112–118) investigated the effect of fast-food consumption on other dietary variables. For a sample of 663 teens who reported that they did not eat fast food during a typical day, the mean daily calorie intake was 2258 and the sample standard deviation was 1519. For a sample of 413 teens who reported that they did eat fast food on a typical day, the mean calorie intake was 2637 and the standard deviation was 1138.

a. What assumptions about the two samples must be reasonable in order for the use of the two-sample t confidence interval to be appropriate?

b. Use the given information to estimate the difference in mean daily calorie intake for teens who do eat fast food on a typical day and those who do not.

11.13 In a study of malpractice claims where a settlement had been reached, two random samples were selected: a random sample of 515 closed malpractice claims that were found not to involve medical errors and a random sample of 889 claims that were found to involve errors (*New England Journal of Medicine* [2006]: 2024–2033). The following statement appeared in the referenced paper: "When claims not involving errors were compensated, payments were significantly lower on average than were payments for claims involving errors ($313,205 vs. $521,560, $P = 0.004$)."

a. What hypotheses must the researchers have tested in order to reach the stated conclusion?

b. Which of the following could have been the value of the test statistic for the hypothesis test? Explain your reasoning.
i. $t = 5.00$ ii. $t = 2.65$ iii. $t = 2.33$ iv. $t = 1.47$

11.14 In a study of the effect of college student employment on academic performance, the following summary statistics for GPA were reported for a sample of students who worked and for a sample of students who did not work (*University of Central Florida Undergraduate Research Journal*, Spring 2005):

	Sample Size	Mean GPA	Standard Deviation
Students Who Are Employed	184	3.12	.485
Students Who Are Not Employed	114	3.23	.524

The samples were selected at random from working and nonworking students at the University of Central Florida. Does this information support the hypothesis that for students at this university, those who are not employed have a higher mean GPA than those who are employed?

11.15 ● ✦ Acrylic bone cement is commonly used in total joint replacement to secure the artificial joint. Data on the force (measured in Newtons, N) required to break a cement bond under two different temperature conditions and in two different mediums appear in the accompanying table. (These data are consistent with summary quantities appearing in the paper "Validation of the Small-Punch Test as a Technique for Characterizing the Mechanical Properties of Acrylic Bone Cement" (*Journal of Engineering in Medicine* [2006]: 11–21).)

Temperature	Medium	Data on Breaking Force
22 degrees	Dry	100.8, 141.9, 194.8, 118.4, 176.1, 213.1
37 degrees	Dry	302.1, 339.2, 288.8, 306.8, 305.2, 327.5
22 degrees	Wet	385.3, 368.3, 322.6, 307.4, 357.9, 321.4
37 degrees	Wet	363.5, 377.7, 327.7, 331.9, 338.1, 394.6

a. Estimate the difference between the mean breaking force in a dry medium at 37 degrees and the mean breaking force at the same temperature in a wet medium using a 90% confidence interval.

b. Is there sufficient evidence to conclude that the mean breaking force in a dry medium at the higher temperature is greater than the mean breaking force at the lower temperature by more than 100 N? Test the relevant hypotheses using a significance level of .10.

11.16 ● The article "Genetic Tweak Turns Promiscuous Animals Into Loyal Mates" (*Los Angeles Times*, June 17, 2004) summarizes the results of a research study that appeared in the June 2004 issue of *Nature*. In this study, 11 male meadow voles who had a single gene introduced into a specific part of the brain were compared to 20 male meadow voles who did not undergo this genetic manipulation. All of the voles were paired with a receptive female partner for 24 hours. At the end of the 24-hour period, the male was placed in a situation where he could choose either the partner from the previous 24 hours or a different female. The percentage of the time during a 3-hour trial that the male spent with his previous partner was recorded. The accompanying data are approximate values read from a graph that appeared in the *Nature* article. Do these data support the researchers' hypothesis that the mean percentage of the time spent with the previous partner is significantly greater for genetically altered voles than for voles that did not have the gene introduced? Test the relevant hypotheses using $\alpha = .05$.

	Percent of Time Spent with Previous Partner							
Genetically Altered	59	62	73	80	84	85	89	92
	92	93	100					
Not Genetically Altered	2	5	13	28	34	40	48	50
	51	54	60	67	70	76	81	84
	85	92	97	99				

11.17 A newspaper story headline reads "Gender Plays Part in Monkeys' Toy Choices, Research Finds—Like Humans, Male Monkeys Choose Balls and Cars, While Females Prefer Dolls and Pots" (*Knight Ridder Newspapers*, December 8, 2005). The article goes on to summarize findings published in the paper "Sex Differences in Response to Children's Toys in Nonhuman Primates" (*Evolution and Human Behavior* [2002]: 467–479). Forty-four male monkeys and 44 female monkeys were each given a variety of toys, and the time spent playing with each toy was recorded. The table at

Table for Exercise 11.17

		Percent of Time					
		Female Monkeys			Male Monkeys		
		n	Sample Mean	Sample Standard Deviation	n	Sample Mean	Sample Standard Deviation
Toy	Police Car	44	8	4	44	18	5
	Doll	44	20	4	44	9	2
	Furry Dog	44	20	5	44	25	5

the top of this page gives means and standard deviations (approximate values read from graphs in the paper) for the percentage of the time that a monkey spent playing with a particular toy. Assume that it is reasonable to regard these two samples of 44 monkeys as representative of the populations of male monkeys and female monkeys. Use a .05 significance level for any hypothesis tests that you carry out when answering the various parts of this exercise.

a. The police car was considered a "masculine toy." Do these data provide convincing evidence that the mean percentage of the time spent playing with the police car is greater for male monkeys than for female monkeys?

b. The doll was considered a "feminine toy." Do these data provide convincing evidence that the mean percentage of the time spent playing with the doll is greater for female monkeys than for male monkeys?

c. The furry dog was considered a "neutral toy." Do these data provide convincing evidence that the mean percentage of the time spent playing with the furry dog is not the same for male and female monkeys?

d. Based on the conclusions from the hypothesis tests of Parts (a)–(c), is the quoted newspaper story headline a reasonable summary of the findings? Explain.

e. Explain why it would be inappropriate to use the two-sample t test to decide if there was evidence that the mean percentage of the time spent playing with the police car and the mean percentage of the time spent playing with the doll is not the same for female monkeys.

11.18 ● The paper "The Observed Effects of Teenage Passengers on the Risky Driving Behavior of Teenage Drivers" (*Accident Analysis and Prevention* [2005]: 973–982) investigated the driving behavior of teenagers by observing their vehicles as they left a high school parking lot and then again at a site approximately $\frac{1}{2}$ mile from the school. Assume that it is reasonable to regard the teen drivers in this study as representative of the population of teen drivers. Use a .01 level of significance for any hypothesis tests.

a. Data consistent with summary quantities appearing in the paper are given in the accompanying table. The measurements represent the difference between the observed vehicle speed and the posted speed limit (in miles per hour) for a sample of male teenage drivers and a sample of female teenage drivers. Do these data provide convincing support for the claim that, on average, male teenage drivers exceed the speed limit by more than do female teenage drivers?

Amount by Which Speed Limit Was Exceeded

Male Driver	Female Driver
1.3	−0.2
1.3	0.5
0.9	1.1
2.1	0.7
0.7	1.1
1.3	1.2
3	0.1
1.3	0.9
0.6	0.5
2.1	0.5

b. Consider the average miles per hour over the speed limit for teenage drivers with passengers shown in the table at the top of the following page. For purposes of this exercise, suppose that each driver-passenger combination mean is based on a sample of size $n = 40$ and that all sample standard deviations are equal to .8.

	Male Passenger	Female Passenger
Male Driver	5.2	.3
Female Driver	2.3	.6

i. Is there sufficient evidence to conclude that the average number of miles per hour over the speed limit is greater for male drivers with male passengers than it is for male drivers with female passengers?
ii. Is there sufficient evidence to conclude that the average number of miles per hour over the speed limit is greater for female drivers with male passengers than it is for female drivers with female passengers?
iii. Is there sufficient evidence to conclude that the average number of miles per hour over the speed limit is smaller for male drivers with female passengers than it is for female drivers with male passengers?

c. Write a few sentences commenting on the effects of gender on teenagers driving with passengers.

11.19 Fumonisins are environmental toxins produced by a type of mold and have been found in corn and in products made from raw corn. The Center for Food Safety and Applied Nutrition provided recommendations on allowable fumonisin levels in human food and in animal feed based on a study of corn meal. The study compared corn meal made from partially degermed corn (corn that has had the germ, the part of the kernel located at the bottom center of the kernel that is used to produce corn oil, partially removed) and corn meal made from corn that has not been degermed. Specimens of corn meal were analyzed and the total fumonisin level (ppm) was determined for each specimen. Summary statistics for total fumonisin level from the U.S. Food and Drug Administration's web site are given here.

	$\bar{x}$	s
Partially Degermed	.59	1.01
Not Degermed	1.21	1.71

a. If the given means and standard deviations had been based on a random sample of 10 partially degermed specimens and a random sample of 10 specimens made from corn that was not degermed, explain why it would not be appropriate to carry out a two-sample t test to determine if there is a significant difference in the mean fumonisin level for the two types of corn meal.

b. Suppose instead that each of the random samples had included 50 corn meal specimens. Explain why it would now be reasonable to carry out a two-sample t test.

c. Assuming that each random sample size was 50, carry out a test to determine if there is a significant difference in mean fumonisin level for the two types of corn meal. Use a significance level of .01.

11.20 A researcher at the Medical College of Virginia conducted a study of 60 randomly selected male soccer players and concluded that frequently "heading" the ball in soccer lowers players' IQs (*USA Today*, August 14, 1995). The soccer players were divided into two groups, based on whether they averaged 10 or more headers per game. Mean IQs were reported in the article, but the sample sizes and standard deviations were not given. Suppose that these values were as given in the accompanying table.

	n	Sample Mean	Sample sd
Fewer Than 10 Headers	35	112	10
10 or More Headers	25	103	8

Do these data support the researcher's conclusion? Test the relevant hypotheses using $\alpha = .05$. Can you conclude that heading the ball *causes* lower IQ?

11.21 Do certain behaviors result in a severe drain on energy resources because a great deal of energy is expended in comparison to energy intake? The article "The Energetic Cost of Courtship and Aggression in a Plethodontid Salamander" (*Ecology* [1983]: 979–983) reported on one of the few studies concerned with behavior and energy expenditure. The accompanying table gives oxygen consumption (mL/g/hr) for male-female salamander pairs. (The determination of consumption values is rather complicated. It is partly for this reason that so few studies of this type have been carried out.)

Behavior	Sample Size	Sample Mean	Sample sd
Noncourting	11	.072	.0066
Courting	15	.099	.0071

a. The pooled t test is a test procedure for testing H_0: $\mu_1 - \mu_2 =$ *hypothesized value* when it is reasonable to assume that the two population distributions are normal with equal standard deviations ($\sigma_1 = \sigma_2$). The test statistic for the pooled t test is obtained by replacing both s_1 and s_2 in the two-sample t test statistic with s_p *where*

$$s_p = \sqrt{\frac{(n_1 - 1)s_1^2 + (n_2 - 1)s_2^2}{n_1 + n_2 - 2}}$$

When the population distributions are normal with equal standard deviations and H_0 is true, the resulting pooled t statistic has a t distribution with df $= n_1 + n_2 - 2$. For the reported data, the two sample standard deviations are similar. Use the pooled t test with $\alpha = .05$ to determine whether the mean oxygen consumption for courting pairs is higher than the mean oxygen consumption for noncourting pairs.

b. Would the conclusion in Part (a) have been different if the two-sample t test had been used rather than the pooled t test?

11.2 Inferences Concerning the Difference Between Two Population or Treatment Means Using Paired Samples

Two samples are said to be *independent* if the selection of the individuals or objects that make up one of the samples has no bearing on the selection of individuals or objects in the other sample. In some situations, a study with independent samples is not the best way to obtain information about a possible difference between two populations. For example, suppose that an investigator wants to determine whether regular aerobic exercise affects blood pressure. A random sample of people who jog regularly and a second random sample of people who do not exercise regularly are selected independently of one another. The researcher then uses the two-sample t test to conclude that a significant difference exists between the mean blood pressures for joggers and nonjoggers. But is it reasonable to think that the difference in mean blood pressure is attributable to jogging? It is known that blood pressure is related to both diet and body weight. Might it not be the case that joggers in the sample tend to be leaner and adhere to a healthier diet than the nonjoggers and that *this* might account for the observed difference? On the basis of this study, the researcher would not be able to rule out the possibility that the observed difference in blood pressure is explained by weight differences between the people in the two samples and that aerobic exercise itself has no effect.

AP* EXAM TIP

As the number of statistical inference procedures increases, it is important to be able to decide which one to use in a given problem. The answer will depend on the type of data gathered and on how the data were collected. For questions about the difference in means, a key question is: "Are the data paired?" You need to answer this question before deciding on an appropriate method.

One way to avoid this difficulty is to match subjects by weight. The researcher would find pairs of subjects so that the jogger and nonjogger in each pair were similar in weight (although weights for different pairs might vary widely). The factor *weight* could then be ruled out as a possible explanation for an observed difference in mean blood pressure between the two groups. Matching the subjects by weight results in two samples for which each observation in the first sample is paired in a meaningful way with a particular observation in the second sample. Such samples are said to be **paired.**

Studies can be designed to yield paired data in a number of different ways. Some studies involve using the same group of individuals with measurements recorded both before and after some intervening treatment. Others might use naturally occurring pairs, such as twins or husbands and wives, and some investigations construct pairs by matching on factors with effects that might otherwise obscure differences (or the lack of them) between the two populations of interest (as might weight in the jogging example). Paired samples often provide more information than independent samples.

EXAMPLE 11.5 Benefits of Ultrasound

● Ultrasound is often used in the treatment of soft tissue injuries. In an experiment to investigate the effect of an ultrasound and stretch therapy on knee extension, range of motion was measured both before and after treatment for a sample of physical therapy patients. A subset of the data appearing in the paper "Location of Ultrasound Does Not Enhance Range of Motion Benefits of Ultrasound and Stretch Treatment" (University of Virginia Thesis, Trae Tashiro, 2003) is given in the accompanying table.

	Range of Motion						
Subject	1	2	3	4	5	6	7
Pre-treatment	31	53	45	57	50	43	32
Post-treatment	32	59	46	64	49	45	40

We can regard the data as consisting of two samples—a sample of knee range of motion measurements for physical therapy patients prior to treatment and a sample of physical therapy patients after ultrasound and stretch treatment. The samples are paired rather than independent because both samples are composed of observations on the same seven patients.

Is there evidence that the ultrasound and stretch treatment increases range of motion? Let μ_1 denote the mean range of motion for the population of all physical therapy patients prior to treatment. Similarly, let μ_2 denote the mean range of motion for physical therapy patients after ultrasound and stretch treatment. Hypotheses of interest might be

$$H_0\text{: } \mu_1 - \mu_2 = 0 \qquad \text{versus} \qquad \text{H}_a\text{: } \mu_1 - \mu_2 < 0$$

with the null hypothesis indicating that the mean range of motion before treatment and the mean after treatment are equal and the alternative hypothesis stating that the mean range of motion after treatment is greater than the mean before treatment. Notice that in six of the seven data pairs, the range of motion measurement is higher after treatment than before treatment. Intuitively, this suggests that the population means may not be equal.

Disregarding the paired nature of the samples results in a loss of information. Both the pre-treatment and post-treatment range of motion measurements vary from one patient to another. It is this variability that may obscure the difference when the two-sample t test is used. If we were to (incorrectly) use the two-sample t test for independent samples on the given data, the resulting t test statistic value would be -0.61. This value would not lead to rejection of the null hypothesis even at level of significance .10. This result might surprise you at first, but remember that this test procedure ignores the information about how the samples are paired. Two plots of the data are given in Figure 11.1. The first plot (Figure 11.1(a)) ignores the pairing, and the two samples look quite similar. The plot in which pairs are identified (Figure 11.1(b)) does suggest a difference, because for six of the seven pairs the actual post-treatment observation is greater than the pre-treatment observation.

● Data set available online

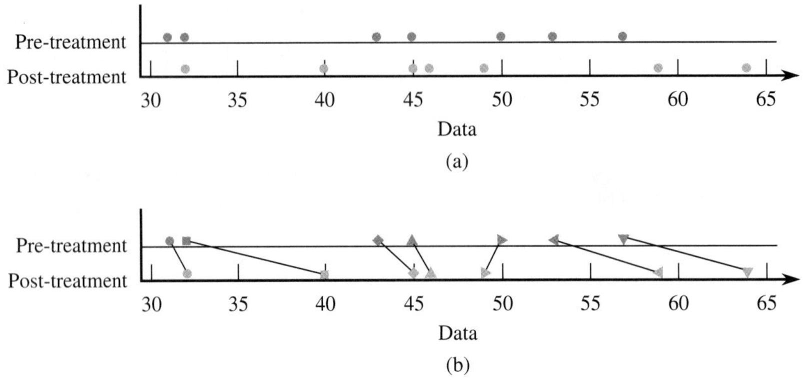

FIGURE 11.1
Two plots of the paired data from Example 11.5: (a) pairing ignored; (b) pairs identified.

Example 11.5 suggests that the methods of inference developed for independent samples are not adequate for dealing with paired samples. When sample observations from the first population are paired in some meaningful way with sample observations from the second population, inferences can be based on the differences between the two observations within each sample pair. The n sample differences can then be regarded as having been selected from a large population of differences. For example, in Example 11.5, we can think of the seven (pre-treatment $-$ post-treatment) differences as having been selected from an entire population of differences.

Let

$$\mu_d = \text{mean value of the difference population}$$

and

$$\sigma_d = \text{standard deviation of the difference population}$$

The relationship between the two individual population means and the mean difference is

$$\mu_d = \mu_1 - \mu_2$$

Therefore, when the samples are paired, inferences about $\mu_1 - \mu_2$ are equivalent to inferences about μ_d. Since inferences about μ_d can be based on the n observed sample differences, the original two-sample problem becomes a familiar one-sample problem.

Paired *t* Test

To compare two population or treatment means when the samples are paired, we first translate the hypotheses of interest from ones about the value of $\mu_1 - \mu_2$ to equivalent hypotheses involving μ_d:

Hypothesis	**Equivalent Hypothesis When Samples Are Paired**
H_0: $\mu_1 - \mu_2 =$ hypothesized value	H_0: $\mu_d =$ hypothesized value
H_a: $\mu_1 - \mu_2 >$ hypothesized value	H_a: $\mu_d >$ hypothesized value
H_a: $\mu_1 - \mu_2 <$ hypothesized value	H_a: $\mu_d <$ hypothesized value
H_a: $\mu_1 - \mu_2 \neq$ hypothesized value	H_a: $\mu_d \neq$ hypothesized value

Sample differences (Sample 1 value $-$ Sample 2 value) are then computed and used as the basis for testing hypotheses about μ_d. When the number of differences is large or when it is reasonable to assume that the population of differences is approximately normal, the one-sample t test based on the differences is the recommended test procedure. In general, if each of the two individual populations is normal, the population of differences is also normal. A normal probability plot or boxplot of the differences can be used to decide if the assumption of normality is reasonable.

Summary of the Paired t Test for Comparing Two Population or Treatment Means

Null hypothesis: H_0: μ_d = hypothesized value

Test statistic: $t = \dfrac{\bar{x}_d - \text{hypothesized value}}{\dfrac{s_d}{\sqrt{n}}}$

where n is the number of sample differences and $\bar{x}_d$ and s_d are the mean and standard deviation of the sample differences. This test is based on df = $n - 1$.

Alternative hypothesis:	***P*-value:**
H_a: $\mu_d >$ hypothesized value	Area under the appropriate t curve to the right of the calculated t
H_a: $\mu_d <$ hypothesized value	Area under the appropriate t curve to the left of the calculated t
H_a: $\mu_d \neq$ hypothesized value	(1) 2(area to the right of t) if t is positive, or (2) 2(area to the left of t) if t is negative

Assumptions:
1. The samples are *paired.*
2. The n sample differences can be viewed as a *random sample* from a population of differences.
3. The *number of sample differences is large* (generally at least 30) or the *population distribution of differences is approximately normal.*

EXAMPLE 11.6 Improve Memory by Playing Chess?

Ryan McVay/PhotoDisc/Getty Images

● Can taking chess lessons and playing chess daily improve memory? The online article "The USA Junior Chess Olympics Research: Developing Memory and Verbal Reasoning" (*New Horizons for Learning*, April 2001; available at www.newhorizons.org) described a study in which sixth-grade students who had not previously played chess participated in a program in which they took chess lessons and played chess daily for 9 months. Each student took a memory test (the Test of Cognitive Skills) before starting the chess program and again at the end of the 9-month period. Data (read from a graph in the article) and computed differences are given in the accompanying table.

The author of the article proposed using these data to test the theory that students who participated in the chess program tend to achieve higher memory scores after completion of the program. We can consider the pre-test scores as a sample of scores from the population of sixth-grade students who have not participated in the chess program and the post-test scores as a sample of scores from the population of sixth-grade students who have completed the chess training program. The samples were not independently chosen, because each sample is composed of the same 12 students.

● Data set available online

	Memory Test Score		
Student	Pre-test	Post-test	Difference
1	510	850	−340
2	610	790	−180
3	640	850	−210
4	675	775	−100
5	600	700	−100
6	550	775	−225
7	610	700	−90
8	625	850	−225
9	450	690	−240
10	720	775	−55
11	575	540	35
12	675	680	−5

Let

μ_1 = mean memory score for sixth-graders with no chess training
μ_2 = mean memory score for sixth-graders after chess training

and

$\mu_d = \mu_1 - \mu_2$ = mean memory score difference between students with no chess training and students who have completed chess training

The question of interest can be answered by testing the hypothesis

H_0: $\mu_d = 0$ versus H_a: $\mu_d < 0$

Using the 12 differences, we compute

$$\sum diff = -1735 \quad \sum (diff)^2 = 383{,}325$$

$$\bar{x}_d = \frac{\sum diff}{n} = \frac{-1735}{12} = -144.58$$

$$s_d^2 = \frac{\sum (diff)^2 - \frac{(\sum diff)^2}{n}}{n-1} = \frac{383{,}325 - \frac{(-1735)^2}{12}}{11} = 12{,}042.99$$

$$s_d = \sqrt{s_d^2} = 109.74$$

We now use the paired t test with a significance level of .05 to carry out the hypothesis test.

1. μ_d = mean memory score difference between students with no chess training and students with chess training
2. H_0: $\mu_d = 0$
3. H_a: $\mu_d < 0$
4. Significance level: $\alpha = .05$
5. Test statistic: $t = \dfrac{\bar{x}_d - \text{hypothesized value}}{\frac{s_d}{\sqrt{n}}}$
6. Assumptions: Although the sample of 12 sixth-graders was not a random sample, the author believed that it was reasonable to view the 12 sample differences

as a random sample of all such differences. A boxplot of the differences is approximately symmetric and does not show any outliers, so the assumption of normality is not unreasonable and we will proceed with the paired t test.

7. Calculation: $t = \dfrac{-144.6 - 0}{\dfrac{109.74}{\sqrt{12}}} = -4.56$

8. P-value: This is a lower-tailed test, so the P-value is the area to the left of the computed t value. The appropriate df for this test is df $= 12 - 1 = 11$. From the 11-df column of Appendix Table 4, we find that P-value $< .001$ because the area to the left of -4.0 is .001 and the test statistic (-4.56) is even farther out in the lower tail.
9. Conclusion: Because P-value $\leq \alpha$, we reject H_0. The data support the theory that the mean memory score is higher for sixth-graders after completion of the chess training than the mean score before training.

Using the two-sample t test (for independent samples) for the data in Example 11.6 would have been incorrect, because the samples are not independent. Inappropriate use of the two-sample t test would have resulted in a computed test statistic value of -4.25. The conclusion would still be to reject the hypothesis of equal mean memory scores in this particular example, but this is not always the case.

EXAMPLE 11.7 Charitable Chimps

● The authors of the paper "Chimpanzees Are Indifferent to the Welfare of Unrelated Group Members" (*Nature* [2005]: 1357–1359) concluded that "chimpanzees do not take advantage of opportunities to deliver benefits to individuals at no cost to themselves." This conclusion was based on data from an experiment in which a sample of chimpanzees was trained to use an apparatus that would deliver food just to the subject chimpanzee when one lever was pushed and would deliver food to both the subject chimpanzee and another chimpanzee in an adjoining cage when another lever was pushed. After training, the chimps were observed when there was no chimp in the adjoining cage and when there was another chimp in the adjoining cage.

The researchers hypothesized that if chimpanzees were motivated by the welfare of others, they would choose the option that provided food to both chimpanzees more often when there was a chimpanzee in the adjoining cage. Data on the number of times the "feed both" option was chosen out of 36 opportunities (approximate values read from a graph in the paper) are given in the accompanying table.

	NUMBER OF TIMES "FEED BOTH" OPTION WAS CHOSEN	
Chimp	No Chimp in Adjoining Cage	Chimp in Adjoining Cage
1	21	23
2	22	22
3	23	21
4	21	23
5	18	19
6	16	19
7	19	19

● Data set available online

Most statistical software packages will perform a paired t test, and we will use Minitab to carry out a test to determine if there is convincing evidence that the mean number of times the "feed both" option is selected is higher when another chimpanzee is present in the adjoining cage than when the subject chimpanzee is alone.

1. μ_d = difference between mean number of "feed both" selections for chimpanzees who are alone and for chimpanzees who have company in the adjoining cage
2. H_0: $\mu_d = 0$
3. H_a: $\mu_d < 0$
4. Significance level: $\alpha = .05$
5. Test statistic: $t = \dfrac{\bar{x}_d - \text{hypothesized value}}{\dfrac{s_d}{\sqrt{n}}}$
6. Assumptions: Although the chimpanzees in this study were not randomly selected, the authors considered them to be representative of the population of chimpanzees. A boxplot of the differences is approximately symmetric and does not show any outliers, so the assumption of normality is not unreasonable and we will proceed with the paired t test.
7. Calculation: From the given Minitab output, $t = -1.35$.

Paired T-Test and CI: Alone, Companion

Paired T for Alone - Companion

	N	Mean	StDev	SE Mean
Alone	7	20.0000	2.4495	0.9258
Companion	7	20.8571	1.8645	0.7047
Difference	7	–0.857143	1.676163	0.633530

95% CI for mean difference: (–2.407335, 0.693050)

T-Test of mean difference = 0 (vs not = 0): T-Value = –1.35 P-Value = 0.225

8. P-value: From the Minitab output, P-value $= .225$.
9. Conclusion: Since P-value $> \alpha$, H_0 is not rejected. The data do not provide evidence that the mean number of times that the "feed both" option is chosen is greater when there is a chimpanzee in the adjoining cage. This is the basis for the statement quoted at the beginning of this example.

Notice that the numerators $\bar{x}_d$ and $\bar{x}_1 - \bar{x}_2$ of the paired t and the two-sample t test statistics are always equal. The difference lies in the denominator. The variability in differences is usually smaller than the variability in each sample separately (because measurements in a pair tend to be similar). As a result, the value of the paired t statistic is usually larger in magnitude than the value of the two-sample t statistic. Pairing typically reduces variability that might otherwise obscure small but nevertheless significant differences.

A Confidence Interval

The one-sample t confidence interval for μ given in Chapter 9 is easily adapted to obtain an interval estimate for μ_d.

Paired t Confidence Interval for μ_d

When

1. the samples are *paired*,
2. the n sample differences can be viewed as a *random sample* from a population of differences, and
3. the *number of sample differences is large* (generally at least 30) or the *population distribution of differences is approximately normal,*

the paired t confidence interval for μ_d is

$$\bar{x}_d \pm (t \text{ critical value}) \cdot \frac{s_d}{\sqrt{n}}$$

For a specified confidence level, the $(n - 1)$ df row of Appendix Table 3 gives the appropriate t critical values.

EXAMPLE 11.8 Benefits of Ultrasound Revisited

● Let's use the data from Example 11.5 to estimate the difference in mean range of motion prior to treatment and the mean range of motion after ultrasound and stretch treatment for physical therapy patients. The data and the computed differences are shown in the accompanying table.

	Range of Motion						
Subject	1	2	3	4	5	6	7
Pre-treatment	31	53	45	57	50	43	32
Post-treatment	32	59	46	64	49	45	40
Difference	**−1**	**−6**	**−1**	**−7**	**1**	**−2**	**−8**

We will use these data to estimate the mean change in range of motion using a 95% confidence interval, assuming that the seven patients participating in this study can be considered as representative of physical therapy patients. The accompanying boxplot of the seven sample differences is not inconsistent with a difference population that is approximately normal, so the paired t confidence interval is appropriate.

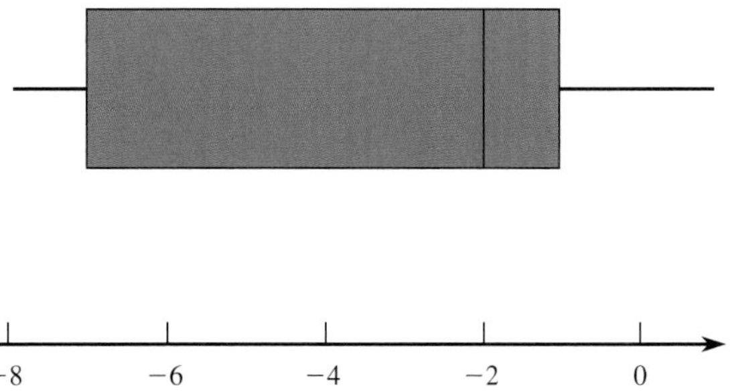

Step-by-Step technology instructions available online

● Data set available online

The mean and standard deviation computed using the seven sample differences are −3.43 and 3.51, respectively. The t critical value for df = 6 and a 95% confidence level is 2.45, and so the confidence interval is

$$\bar{x}_d \pm (t \text{ critical value}) \cdot \frac{s_d}{\sqrt{n}} = -3.43 \pm (2.45) \cdot \frac{3.51}{\sqrt{7}}$$
$$= -3.43 \pm 3.25$$
$$= (-6.68, -0.18)$$

Based on the sample data, we can be 95% confident that the difference in mean range of motion is between −6.68 and −0.18. That is, we are 95% confident that the mean increase in range of motion after ultrasound and stretch therapy is somewhere between 0.18 and 6.68.

Minitab output is also shown. Minitab carries a bit more decimal accuracy, and reports a 95% confidence interval of (−6.67025, −0.18690).

Paired T-Test and CI: Pre, Post

Paired T for Pre – Post

	N	Mean	StDev	SE Mean
Pre	7	44.4286	9.9976	3.7787
Post	7	47.8571	10.8847	4.1140
Difference	7	–3.42857	3.50510	1.32480

95% CI for mean difference: (–6.67025, –0.18690)

T-Test of mean difference = 0 (vs not = 0): T-Value = –2.59 P-Value = 0.041

When two populations must be compared to draw a conclusion on the basis of sample data, a researcher might choose to use independent samples or paired samples. In many situations, paired data provide a more effective comparison by screening out the effects of extraneous variables that might obscure differences between the two populations or that might suggest a difference when none exists.

EXERCISES 11.22 - 11.36

11.22 Suppose that you were interested in investigating the effect of a drug that is to be used in the treatment of patients who have glaucoma in both eyes. A comparison between the mean reduction in eye pressure for this drug and for a standard treatment is desired. Both treatments are applied directly to the eye.

a. Describe how you would go about collecting data for your investigation.
b. Does your method result in paired data?
c. Can you think of a reasonable method of collecting data that would not result in paired samples? Would such an experiment be as informative as a paired experiment? Comment.

11.23 Two different underground pipe coatings for preventing corrosion are to be compared. The effect of a coating (as measured by maximum depth of corrosion penetration on a piece of pipe) may vary with depth, orientation, soil type, pipe composition, etc. Describe how an experiment that filters out the effects of these extraneous factors could be carried out.

11.24 ● ✦ To determine if chocolate milk was as effective as other carbohydrate replacement drinks, nine male cyclists performed an intense workout followed by a drink and a rest period. At the end of the rest period, each cyclist performed an endurance trial in which he exercised until exhausted and time to exhaustion was measured. Each cyclist completed the entire regimen on two different days. On one day the drink provided was chocolate milk and on the other day the drink provided was a carbohydrate replacement drink. Data consistent with sum-

Table for Exercise 11.24

Cyclist	Time to Exhaustion (minutes)								
	1	2	3	4	5	6	7	8	9
Chocolate Milk	24.85	50.09	38.30	26.11	36.54	26.14	36.13	47.35	35.08
Carbohydrate Replacement	10.02	29.96	37.40	15.52	9.11	21.58	31.23	22.04	17.02

mary quantities appearing in the paper "The Efficacy of Chocolate Milk as a Recovery Aid" (*Medicine and Science in Sports and Exercise* [2004]: S126) appear in the table at the top of the page. Is there evidence that the mean time to exhaustion is greater after chocolate milk than after carbohydrate replacement drink? Use a significance level of .05.

11.25 ● The humorous paper "Will Humans Swim Faster or Slower in Syrup?" (*American Institute of Chemical Engineers Journal* [2004]: 2646–2647) investigates the fluid mechanics of swimming. Twenty swimmers each swam a specified distance in a water-filled pool and in a pool in which the water was thickened with food grade guar gum to create a syrup-like consistency. Velocity, in meters per second, was recorded. Values estimated from a graph that appeared in the paper are given. The authors of the paper concluded that swimming in guar syrup does not change swimming speed. Are the given data consistent with this conclusion? Carry out a hypothesis test using a .01 significance level.

Swimmer	Velocity (m/s) Water	Velocity (m/s) Guar Syrup
1	0.90	0.92
2	0.92	0.96
3	1.00	0.95
4	1.10	1.13
5	1.20	1.22
6	1.25	1.20
7	1.25	1.26
8	1.30	1.30
9	1.35	1.34
10	1.40	1.41
11	1.40	1.44
12	1.50	1.52
13	1.65	1.58
14	1.70	1.70
15	1.75	1.80
16	1.80	1.76
17	1.80	1.84
18	1.85	1.89
19	1.90	1.88
20	1.95	1.95

(continued)

11.26 ● The study described in the paper "Marketing Actions Can Modulate Neural Representation of Experienced Pleasantness" (*Proceedings of the National Academy of Science* [2008]: 1050–1054) investigated whether price affects people's judgment. Twenty people each tasted six cabernet sauvignon wines and rated how they liked them on a scale of 1 to 6. Prior to tasting each wine, participants were told the price of the wine. Of the six wines tasted, two were actually the same wine, but for one tasting the participant was told that the wine cost \$10 per bottle and for the other tasting the participant was told that the wine cost \$90 per bottle. The participants were randomly assigned either to taste the \$90 wine first and the \$10 wine second, or the \$10 wine first and the \$90 wine second. Differences (computed by subtracting the rating for the tasting in which the participant thought the wine cost \$10 from the rating for the tasting in which the participant thought the wine cost \$90) were computed. The differences that follow are consistent with summary quantities given in the paper.

Difference (\$90 − \$10)
2 4 1 2 1 0 0 3 0 2 1 3 3 1 4 1 2 2 1 −1

Carry out a hypothesis test to determine if the mean rating assigned to the wine when the cost is described as \$90 is greater than the mean rating assigned to the wine when the cost is described as \$10. Use $\alpha = .01$.

11.27 ● In the experiment described in the paper "Exposure to Diesel Exhaust Induces Changes in EEG in Human Volunteers" (*Particle and Fibre Toxicology* [2007]), 10 healthy men were exposed to diesel exhaust for 1 hour. A measure of brain activity (called median power frequency, or MPF) was recorded at two different locations in the brain both before and after the diesel exhaust exposure. The resulting data are given in the accompanying table. For purposes of this example, assume that it is reasonable to regard the sample of 10 men as representative of healthy adult males.

MPF (in Hz)

Subject	Location 1 Before	Location 1 After	Location 2 Before	Location 2 After
1	6.4	8.0	6.9	9.4
2	8.7	12.6	9.5	11.2
3	7.4	8.4	6.7	10.2
4	8.7	9.0	9.0	9.6
5	9.8	8.4	9.7	9.2
6	8.9	11.0	9.0	11.9
7	9.3	14.4	7.9	9.1
8	7.4	11.3	8.3	9.3
9	6.6	7.1	7.2	8.0
10	8.9	11.2	7.4	9.1

a. Do the data provide convincing evidence that the mean MPF at brain location 1 is higher after diesel exposure? Test the relevant hypotheses using a significance level of .05.

b. Construct and interpret a 90% confidence interval estimate for the difference in mean MPF at brain location 2 before and after exposure to diesel exhaust.

11.28 The paper "Less Air Pollution Leads to Rapid Reduction of Airway Inflammation and Improved Airway Function in Asthmatic Children" (*Pediatrics* [2009]: 1051–1058) describes a study in which children with mild asthma who live in a polluted urban environment were relocated to a less polluted rural environment for 7 days. Various measures of respiratory function were recorded first in the urban environment and then again after 7 days in the rural environment. The accompanying graphs show the urban and rural values for three of these measures: nasal eosinophils, exhaled FE_{NO} concentration, and peak expiratory flow (PEF). Urban and rural values for the same child are connected by a line. The authors of the paper used paired t tests to determine that there was a significant difference in the urban and rural means for each of these three measures. One of these tests resulted in a P-value less than .001, one resulted in a P-value between .001 and .01, and one resulted in a P-value between .01 and .05.

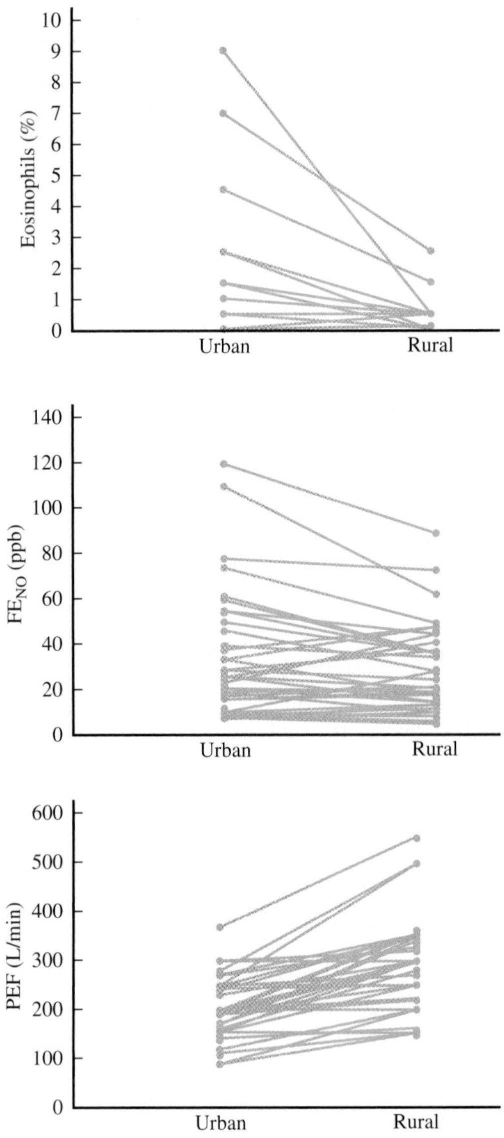

a. Which measure (Eosinophils, FE_{NO}, or PEF) do you think resulted in a test with the P-value that was less than .001? Explain your reasoning.

b. Which measure (Eosinophils, FE_{NO}, or PEF) do you think resulted in the test with the largest P-value? Explain your reasoning.

11.29 The paper "The Truth About Lying in Online Dating Profiles" (*Proceedings, Computer-Human Interactions* [2007]: 1–4) describes an investigation in which 40 men and 40 women with online dating profiles agreed to participate in a study. Each participant's height (in inches) was measured and the actual height was compared to the height given in that person's online profile. The differences between the online profile height and the actual height (profile − actual) were used to compute the values in the accompanying table.

Men	Women
$\bar{x}_d = 0.57$	$\bar{x}_d = 0.03$
$s_d = 0.81$	$s_d = 0.75$
$n = 40$	$n = 40$

For purposes of this exercise, assume it is reasonable to regard the two samples in this study as being representative of male online daters and female online daters. (Although the authors of the paper believed that their samples were representative of these populations, participants were volunteers recruited through newspaper advertisements, so we should be a bit hesitant to generalize results to all online daters!)

a. Use the paired t test to determine if there is convincing evidence that, on average, male online daters overstate their height in online dating profiles. Use $\alpha = .05$.

b. Construct and interpret a 95% confidence interval for the difference between the mean online dating profile height and mean actual height for female online daters.

c. Use the two-sample t test of Section 11.1 to test H_0: $\mu_m - \mu_f = 0$ versus H_a: $\mu_m - \mu_f > 0$, where μ_m is the mean height difference (profile – actual) for male online daters and μ_f is the mean height difference (profile – actual) for female online daters.

d. Explain why a paired t test was used in Part (a) but a two-sample t test was used in Part (c).

11.30 The press release titled "Keeping Score When It counts: Graduation Rates and Academic Progress Rates" (The Institute for Diversity and Ethics in Sport, March 16, 2009) gave the 2009 graduation rates for African-American basketball players and for white basketball players at every NCAA Division I university with a basketball program. Explain why it is not necessary to use a paired t test to determine if the mean graduation rate for African-American basketball players differs from the mean graduation rate for white basketball players for Division I schools.

11.31 ● Breast feeding sometimes results in a temporary loss of bone mass as calcium is depleted in the mother's body to provide for milk production. The paper "Bone Mass Is Recovered from Lactation to Postweaning in Adolescent Mothers with Low Calcium Intakes" (*American Journal of Clinical Nutrition* [2004]: 1322–1326) gave the accompanying data on total body bone mineral content (g) for a sample of mothers both during breast feeding (B) and in the postweaning period (P). Do the data suggest that true average total body bone mineral content during postweaning is greater than that during breast feeding by more than 25 g? State and test the appropriate hypotheses using a significance level of .05.

Subject	1	2	3	4	5	6
B	1928	2549	2825	1924	1628	2175
P	2126	2885	2895	1942	1750	2184
Subject	7	8	9	10		
B	2114	2621	1843	2541		
P	2164	2626	2006	2627		

11.32 ● The paper "Quantitative Assessment of Glenohumeral Translation in Baseball Players" (*The American Journal of Sports Medicine* [2004]: 1711–1715) considered various aspects of shoulder motion for a sample of pitchers and another sample of position players. The authors kindly supplied the data on the following page on anteroposterior translation (mm), a measure of the extent of anterior and posterior motion, both for the dominant arm and the nondominant arm.

a. Estimate the true average difference in translation between dominant and nondominant arms for pitchers using a 95% confidence interval.

b. Estimate the true average difference in translation between dominant and nondominant arms for position players using a 95% confidence interval.

c. The authors asserted that pitchers have greater difference in mean anteroposterior translation of their shoulders than do position players. Do you agree? Explain.

11.33 Two proposed computer mouse designs were compared by recording wrist extension in degrees for 24 people who each used both mouse types ("Comparative Study of Two Computer Mouse Designs," Cornell Human Factors Laboratory Technical Report RP7992). The difference in wrist extension was computed by subtracting extension for mouse type B from the wrist extension for mouse type A for each student. The mean difference was reported to be 8.82 degrees. Assume that it is reasonable to regard this sample of 24 people as representative of the population of computer users.

a. Suppose that the standard deviation of the differences was 10 degrees. Is there convincing evidence that the mean wrist extension for mouse type A is greater than for mouse type B? Use a .05 significance level.

Data for Exercise 11.32

Player	Position Player Dominant Arm	Position Player Nondominant Arm	Pitcher	Pitcher Dominant Arm	Pitcher Nondominant Arm
1	30.31	32.54	1	27.63	24.33
2	44.86	40.95	2	30.57	26.36
3	22.09	23.48	3	32.62	30.62
4	31.26	31.11	4	39.79	33.74
5	28.07	28.75	5	28.50	29.84
6	31.93	29.32	6	26.70	26.71
7	34.68	34.79	7	30.34	26.45
8	29.10	28.87	8	28.69	21.49
9	25.51	27.59	9	31.19	20.82
10	22.49	21.01	10	36.00	21.75
11	28.74	30.31	11	31.58	28.32
12	27.89	27.92	12	32.55	27.22
13	28.48	27.85	13	29.56	28.86
14	25.60	24.95	14	28.64	28.58
15	20.21	21.59	15	28.58	27.15
16	33.77	32.48	16	31.99	29.46
17	32.59	32.48	17	27.16	21.26
18	32.60	31.61			
19	29.30	27.46			

b. Suppose that the standard deviation of the differences was 26 degrees. Is there convincing evidence that the mean wrist extension for mouse type A is greater than for mouse type B? Use a .05 significance level.

c. Briefly explain why a different conclusion was reached in the hypothesis tests of Parts (a) and (b).

11.34 ● The article "More Students Taking AP Tests" (*San Luis Obispo Tribune,* January 10, 2003) provided the following information on the percentage of students in grades 11 and 12 taking one or more AP exams and the percentage of exams that earned credit in 1997 and 2002 for seven high schools on the central coast of California.

School	Percentage of Students Taking One or More AP Exams 1997	2002	Percentage of Exams That Earned College Credit 1997	2002
1	13.6	18.4	61.4	52.8
2	20.7	25.9	65.3	74.5
3	8.9	13.7	65.1	72.4
4	17.2	22.4	65.9	61.9
5	18.3	43.5	42.3	62.7
6	9.8	11.4	60.4	53.5
7	15.7	17.2	42.9	62.2

a. Assuming it is reasonable to regard these seven schools as a random sample of high schools located on the central coast of California, carry out an appropriate test to determine if there is convincing evidence that the mean percentages of exams earning college credit at central coast high schools for 1997 and 2002 were different.

b. Do you think it is reasonable to generalize the conclusion of the test in Part (a) to all California high schools? Explain.

c. Would it be reasonable to use the paired *t* test with the data on percentage of students taking one or more AP classes? Explain.

11.35 Babies born extremely prematurely run the risk of various neurological problems and tend to have lower IQ and verbal ability scores than babies that are not premature. The article "Premature Babies May Recover Intelligence, Study Says" (*San Luis Obispo Tribune,* February 12, 2003) summarized the results of medical research that suggests that the deficit observed at an early age may decrease as children age. Children who were born prematurely were given a test of verbal ability at age 3 and again at age 8. The test is scaled so that a score of 100 would be average for a normal-birth-weight child. Data that are consistent with summary quantities given in the paper for 50 children who were born prematurely were used to generate the accompanying Minitab output, where Age3 represents the verbal ability score at age 3 and Age8 represents the verbal ability score at age 8. Use the Minitab output to carry out a test to determine if there is evidence that the mean verbal ability score for children born prematurely increases between age 3 and age 8. You may assume that it is reasonable to regard the sample of 50 children as a random sample from the population of all children born prematurely.

Paired T-Test and CI: Age8, Age3

Paired T for Age8 – Age3

	N	Mean	StDev	SE Mean
Age8	50	97.21	16.97	2.40
Age3	50	87.30	13.84	1.96
Difference	50	9.91	22.11	3.13

T-Test of mean difference = 0 (vs > 0): T-Value = 3.17 P-Value = 0.001

11.36 Do girls think they don't need to take as many science classes as boys? The article "Intentions of Young Students to Enroll in Science Courses in the Future: An Examination of Gender Differences" (*Science Education* [1999]: 55–76) gives information from a survey of children in grades 4, 5, and 6. The 224 girls participating in the survey each indicated the number of science courses they intended to take in the future, and they also indicated the number of science courses they thought boys their age should take in the future. For each girl, the authors calculated the difference between the number of science classes she intends to take and the number she thinks boys should take.

a. Explain why these data are paired.

b. The mean of the differences was −.83 (indicating girls intended, on average, to take fewer classes than they thought boys should take), and the standard deviation was 1.51. Construct and interpret a 95% confidence interval for the mean difference.

11.3 Large-Sample Inferences Concerning the Difference Between Two Population or Treatment Proportions

Large-sample methods for estimating and testing hypotheses about a single population proportion were presented in Chapters 9 and 10. The symbol p was used to represent the proportion of individuals in the population who possess some characteristic (the successes). Inferences about the value of p were based on $\hat{p}$, the corresponding sample proportion of successes.

Many investigations are carried out to compare the proportion of successes in one population (or resulting from one treatment) to the proportion of successes in a second population (or from a second treatment). As was the case for means, we use the subscripts 1 and 2 to distinguish between the two population proportions, sample sizes, and sample proportions.

Notation

Population or Treatment 1: Proportion of "successes" $= p_1$
Population or Treatment 2: Proportion of "successes" $= p_2$

	Sample Size	Proportion of Successes
Sample from Population or Treatment 1	n_1	$\hat{p}_1$
Sample from Population or Treatment 2	n_2	$\hat{p}_2$

When comparing two populations or treatments on the basis of "success" proportions, it is common to focus on the quantity $p_1 - p_2$, the difference between the two proportions. Because $\hat{p}_1$ provides an estimate of p_1 and $\hat{p}_2$ provides an estimate of p_2, the obvious choice for an estimate of $p_1 - p_2$ is $\hat{p}_1 - \hat{p}_2$.

Because $\hat{p}_1$ and $\hat{p}_2$ each vary in value from sample to sample, so will the difference $\hat{p}_1 - \hat{p}_2$. For example, a first sample from each of two populations might yield

$$\hat{p}_1 = .69 \qquad \hat{p}_2 = .70 \qquad \hat{p}_1 - \hat{p}_2 = .01$$

A second sample from each might result in

$$\hat{p}_1 = .79 \qquad \hat{p}_2 = .67 \qquad \hat{p}_1 - \hat{p}_2 = .12$$

and so on. Because the statistic $\hat{p}_1 - \hat{p}_2$ is the basis for drawing inferences about $p_1 - p_2$, we need to know something about its behavior.

Properties of the Sampling Distribution of $\hat{p}_1 - \hat{p}_2$

If two random samples are selected independently of one another, the following properties hold:

1. $\mu_{\hat{p}_1 - \hat{p}_2} = p_1 - p_2$
   This says that the sampling distribution of $\hat{p}_1 - \hat{p}_2$ is centered at $p_1 - p_2$, so $\hat{p}_1 - \hat{p}_2$ is an unbiased statistic for estimating $p_1 - p_2$.
2. $\sigma^2_{\hat{p}_1 - \hat{p}_2} = \sigma^2_{\hat{p}_1} + \sigma^2_{\hat{p}_2} = \frac{p_1(1 - p_1)}{n_1} + \frac{p_2(1 - p_2)}{n_2}$

   and

   $$\sigma_{\hat{p}_1 - \hat{p}_2} = \sqrt{\frac{p_1(1 - p_1)}{n_1} + \frac{p_2(1 - p_2)}{n_2}}$$
3. If both n_1 and n_2 are large (that is, if $n_1p_1 \geq 10$, $n_1(1 - p_1) \geq 10$, $n_2p_2 \geq 10$, and $n_2(1 - p_2) \geq 10$), then $\hat{p}_1$ and $\hat{p}_2$ each have a sampling distribution that is approximately normal, and their difference $\hat{p}_1 - \hat{p}_2$ also has a sampling distribution that is approximately normal.

The properties in the box imply that when the samples are independently selected and when both sample sizes are large, the distribution of the standardized variable

$$z = \frac{\hat{p}_1 - \hat{p}_2 - (p_1 - p_2)}{\sqrt{\frac{p_1(1 - p_1)}{n_1} + \frac{p_2(1 - p_2)}{n_2}}}$$

is described approximately by the standard normal (z) curve.

A Large-Sample Test Procedure

Comparisons of p_1 and p_2 are often based on large, independently selected samples, and we restrict ourselves to this case. The most general null hypothesis of interest has the form

$$H_0\text{: } p_1 - p_2 = \text{hypothesized value}$$

However, when the hypothesized value is something other than 0, the appropriate test statistic differs somewhat from the test statistic used for H_0: $p_1 - p_2 = 0$. Because this H_0 is almost always the relevant one in applied problems, we focus exclusively on it.

Our basic testing principle has been to use a procedure that controls the probability of a Type I error at the desired level α. This requires using a test statistic with a sampling distribution that is known when H_0 is true. That is, the test statistic should be developed under the assumption that $p_1 = p_2$ (as specified by the null hypothesis $p_1 - p_2 = 0$). In this case, p is used to denote the common value of the two population proportions. The z variable obtained by standardizing $\hat{p}_1 - \hat{p}_2$ then simplifies to

$$z = \frac{\hat{p}_1 - \hat{p}_2}{\sqrt{\dfrac{p(1-p)}{n_1} + \dfrac{p(1-p)}{n_2}}}$$

Unfortunately, this cannot serve as a test statistic, because the denominator cannot be computed. H_0 says that there is a common value p, but it does not specify what that value is. A test statistic can be obtained, though, by first *estimating p* from the sample data and then using this estimate in the denominator of z.

When $p_1 = p_2$, both $\hat{p}_1$ and $\hat{p}_2$ are estimates of the common proportion p. However, a better estimate than either $\hat{p}_1$ or $\hat{p}_2$ is a weighted average of the two, in which more weight is given to the sample proportion based on the larger sample.

DEFINITION

The **combined estimate of the common population proportion** is

$$\hat{p}_c = \frac{n_1\hat{p}_1 + n_2\hat{p}_2}{n_1 + n_2} = \frac{\text{total number of } S\text{'s in the two samples}}{\text{total of the two sample sizes}}$$

The test statistic for testing H_0: $p_1 - p_2 = 0$ results from using $\hat{p}_c$, the combined estimate, in place of p in the standardized variable z given previously. This z statistic has approximately a standard normal distribution when H_0 is true, so a test that has the desired significance level α can be obtained by calculating a P-value using the z table.

Summary of Large-Sample z Tests for $p_1 - p_2 = 0$

Null hypothesis: H_0: $p_1 - p_2 = 0$

Test statistic: $$z = \frac{\hat{p}_1 - \hat{p}_2}{\sqrt{\dfrac{\hat{p}_c(1-\hat{p}_c)}{n_1} + \dfrac{\hat{p}_c(1-\hat{p}_c)}{n_2}}}$$

Alternative hypothesis:	***P*-value:**
H_a: $p_1 - p_2 > 0$	Area under the z curve to the right of the computed z
H_a: $p_1 - p_2 < 0$	Area under the z curve to the left of the computed z
H_a: $p_1 - p_2 \neq 0$	(1) 2(area to the right of z) if z is positive or (2) 2(area to the left of z) if z is negative

(continued)

Assumptions: 1. The samples are *independently chosen random samples,* or *treatments were assigned at random to individuals or objects* (or subjects were assigned at random to treatments).
2. Both *sample sizes are large:*

$$n_1\hat{p}_1 \geq 10 \quad n_1(1 - \hat{p}_1) \geq 10 \quad n_2\hat{p}_2 \geq 10 \quad n_2(1 - \hat{p}_2) \geq 10$$

EXAMPLE 11.9 Duct Tape to Remove Warts?

Some people seem to believe that you can fix anything with duct tape. Even so, many were skeptical when researchers announced that duct tape may be a more effective and less painful alternative to liquid nitrogen, which doctors routinely use to freeze warts. The article "What a Fix-It: Duct Tape Can Remove Warts" (*San Luis Obispo Tribune*, October 15, 2002) described a study conducted at Madigan Army Medical Center. Patients with warts were randomly assigned to either the duct tape treatment or the more traditional freezing treatment. Those in the duct tape group wore duct tape over the wart for 6 days, then removed the tape, soaked the area in water, and used an emery board to scrape the area. This process was repeated for a maximum of 2 months or until the wart was gone. Data consistent with values in the article are summarized in the following table:

Treatment	*n*	Number with Wart Successfully Removed
Liquid nitrogen freezing	100	60
Duct tape	104	88

Do these data suggest that freezing is less successful than duct tape in removing warts? Let p_1 represent the true proportion of warts that would be successfully removed by freezing, and let p_2 represent the true proportion of warts that would be successfully removed with the duct tape treatment. We test the relevant hypotheses

$$H_0\colon p_1 - p_2 = 0 \quad \text{versus} \quad H_a\colon p_1 - p_2 < 0$$

using $\alpha = .01$. For these data,

$$\hat{p}_1 = \frac{60}{100} = .60$$

$$\hat{p}_2 = \frac{88}{104} = .85$$

Suppose that $p_1 = p_2$ and let p denote the common value. Then $\hat{p}_c$, the combined estimate of p, is

$$\hat{p}_c = \frac{n_1\hat{p}_1 + n_2\hat{p}_2}{n_1 + n_2} = \frac{100(.60) + 104(.85)}{100 + 104} = .73$$

The nine-step procedure can now be used to perform the hypothesis test:

1. $p_1 - p_2$ is the difference between the true proportions of warts removed by freezing and by the duct tape treatment.
2. $H_0\colon p_1 - p_2 = 0 \quad (p_1 = p_2)$

3. H_a: $p_1 - p_2 < 0$ ($p_1 < p_2$, in which case the proportion of warts removed by freezing is lower than the proportion by duct tape.)
4. Significance level: $\alpha = .01$
5. Test statistic: $z = \dfrac{\hat{p}_1 - \hat{p}_2}{\sqrt{\dfrac{\hat{p}_c(1-\hat{p}_c)}{n_1} + \dfrac{\hat{p}_c(1-\hat{p}_c)}{n_2}}}$
6. Assumptions: The subjects were assigned randomly to the two treatments. Checking to make sure that the sample sizes are large enough, we have

$$\begin{aligned} n_1\hat{p}_1 &= 100(.60) = 60 \geq 10 \\ n_1(1-\hat{p}_1) &= 100(.40) = 40 \geq 10 \\ n_2\hat{p}_2 &= 104(.85) = 88.4 \geq 10 \\ n_2(1-\hat{p}_2) &= 104(.15) = 15.6 \geq 10 \end{aligned}$$

7. Calculations:

$n_1 = 100$ $n_2 = 104$ $\hat{p}_1 = .60$ $\hat{p}_2 = .85$ $\hat{p}_c = .73$

and so

$$z = \frac{.60 - .85}{\sqrt{\dfrac{(.73)(.27)}{100} + \dfrac{(.73)(.27)}{104}}} = \frac{-.25}{.062} = -4.03$$

8. *P*-value: This is a lower-tailed test, so the *P*-value is the area under the z curve and to the left of the computed $z = -4.03$. From Appendix Table 2, *P*-value ≈ 0.
9. Conclusion: Since *P*-value $\leq \alpha$, the null hypothesis is rejected at significance level .01. There is convincing evidence that the proportion of warts successfully removed is lower for freezing than for the duct tape treatment.

Minitab can also be used to carry out a two-sample z test to compare two population proportions, as illustrated in the following example.

EXAMPLE 11.10 Not Enough Sleep?

Do people who work long hours have more trouble sleeping? This question was examined in the paper "Long Working Hours and Sleep Disturbances: The Whitehall II Prospective Cohort Study" (*Sleep* [2009]: 737–745). The data in the accompanying table are from two independently selected samples of British civil service workers, all of whom were employed full-time and worked at least 35 hours per week. The authors of the paper believed that these samples were representative of full-time British civil service workers who work 35 to 40 hours per week and of British civil service workers who work more than 40 hours per week.

	n	Number who usually get less than 7 hours of sleep a night
Work over 40 hours per week	1501	750
Work 35–40 hours per week	958	407

Do these data support the theory that the proportion that usually get less than 7 hours of sleep a night is higher for those who work more than 40 hours per week than for those who work between 35 and 40 hours per week? Let's carry out a hypothesis test with $\alpha = .01$. For these samples

Over 40 hours per week	$n_1 = 1501$	$\hat{p}_1 = \frac{750}{1501} = .500$
Between 35 and 40 hours per week	$n_2 = 958$	$\hat{p}_2 = \frac{407}{958} = .425$

1. p_1 = proportion of those who work more than 40 hours per week who get less than 7 hours of sleep
   p_2 = proportion of those who work between 35 and 40 hours per week who get less than 7 hours of sleep
2. H_0: $p_1 - p_2 = 0$
3. H_a: $p_1 - p_2 > 0$
4. Significance level: $\alpha = .01$
5. Test statistic: $z = \dfrac{\hat{p}_1 - \hat{p}_2}{\sqrt{\dfrac{\hat{p}_c(1 - \hat{p}_c)}{n_1} + \dfrac{\hat{p}_c(1 - \hat{p}_c)}{n_2}}}$
6. Assumptions: The two samples were independently selected. It is reasonable to regard the samples as representative of the two populations of interest. Checking to make sure that the sample sizes are large enough by using $n_1 = 1501$, $\hat{p}_1 = .500$, $n_2 = 958$, and $\hat{p}_2 = .425$, we have

$$\begin{aligned} n_1\hat{p}_1 &= 750.50 \geq 10 \\ n_1(1 - \hat{p}_1) &= 750.50 \geq 10 \\ n_2\hat{p}_2 &= 407.15 \geq 10 \\ n_2(1 - \hat{p}_2) &= 550.85 \geq 10 \end{aligned}$$

7. Calculations: Minitab output is shown below. From the output, $z = 3.64$.

Test for Two Proportions

Sample	X	N	Sample p
1	750	1501	0.499667
2	407	958	0.424843

Difference = p (1) − p (2)
Estimate for difference: 0.0748235
Test for difference = 0 (vs > 0): Z = 3.64 P-Value = 0.000

8. *P*-value: From the computer output, *P*-value = 0.000
9. Conclusion: Because *P*-value $\leq \alpha$, the null hypothesis is rejected at significance level .01.

There is strong evidence that the proportion that gets less than 7 hours of sleep a night is higher for British civil service workers who work more than 40 hours per week than it is for those who work between 35 and 40 hours per week. Note that because the data were from an observational study, we are not able to conclude that there is a cause and effect relationship between work hours and sleep. Although we can conclude that a higher proportion of those who work long hours get less than 7 hours of sleep a night, we can't conclude that working long hours is the cause of shorter sleep. We should also note that the sample was selected from British civil service workers, so it would not be a good idea to generalize this conclusion to all workers.

A Confidence Interval

A large-sample confidence interval for $p_1 - p_2$ is a special case of the general z interval formula

point estimate $\pm$ (z critical value)(estimated standard deviation)

The statistic $\hat{p}_1 - \hat{p}_2$ gives a point estimate of $p_1 - p_2$, and the standard deviation of this statistic is

$$\sigma_{\hat{p}_1 - \hat{p}_2} = \sqrt{\frac{p_1(1 - p_1)}{n_1} + \frac{p_2(1 - p_2)}{n_2}}$$

An estimated standard deviation is obtained by using the sample proportions $\hat{p}_1$ and $\hat{p}_2$ in place of p_1 and p_2, respectively, under the square-root symbol. Notice that this estimated standard deviation differs from the one used previously in the test statistic. When constructing a confidence interval, there isn't a null hypothesis that claims $p_1 = p_2$, so there is no assumed common value of p to estimate.

AP* EXAM TIP

In the hypothesis test where the null hypothesis specified that two population or treatment proportions were equal, a pooled estimate of the common proportion was used. When computing a confidence interval estimate of the difference in two proportions, we don't assume equal proportions, and a pooled estimate is not used.

A Large-Sample Confidence Interval for $p_1 - p_2$

When

1. the samples are *independently selected random samples* or *treatments were assigned at random to individuals or objects* (or vice versa), and
2. both *sample sizes are large*:

   $n_1\hat{p}_1 \geq 10 \quad n_1(1 - \hat{p}_1) \geq 10 \quad n_2\hat{p}_2 \geq 10 \quad n_2(1 - \hat{p}_2) \geq 10$

   a large-sample confidence interval for $p_1 - p_2$ is

$$(\hat{p}_1 - \hat{p}_2) \pm (z \text{ critical value})\sqrt{\frac{\hat{p}_1(1 - \hat{p}_1)}{n_1} + \frac{\hat{p}_2(1 - \hat{p}_2)}{n_2}}$$

EXAMPLE 11.11 Opinions on Freedom of Speech

The article "Freedom of What?" (*Associated Press*, February 1, 2005) described a study in which high school students and high school teachers were asked whether they agreed with the following statement: "Students should be allowed to report controversial issues in their student newspapers without the approval of school authorities." It was reported that 58% of the students surveyed and 39% of the teachers surveyed agreed with the statement. The two samples—10,000 high school students and 8000 high school teachers—were selected from 544 different schools across the country.

We will use the given information to estimate the difference between the proportion of high school students who agree that students should be allowed to report controversial issues in their student newspapers without the approval of school authorities, p_1, and the proportion of high school teachers who agree with the statement, p_2.

The sample sizes are large enough for the large-sample interval to be valid ($n_1\hat{p}_1 = 10{,}000(.58) \geq 10$, $n_1(1 - \hat{p}_1) = 10{,}000(.42) \geq 10$, etc.). A 90% confidence interval for $p_1 - p_2$ is

$$(\hat{p}_1 - \hat{p}_2) \pm (z \text{ critical value})\sqrt{\frac{\hat{p}_1(1 - \hat{p}_1)}{n_1} + \frac{\hat{p}_2(1 - \hat{p}_2)}{n_2}}$$

$$= (.58 - .39) \pm (1.645)\sqrt{\frac{(.58)(.42)}{10{,}000} + \frac{(.39)(.61)}{8000}}$$

$$= .19 \pm (1.645)(.0074)$$

$$= .19 \pm .012$$

$$(.178, .202)$$

Statistical software or a graphing calculator could also have been used to compute the endpoints of the confidence interval. Minitab output is shown here.

Test and CI for Two Proportions

Sample	X	N	Sample p
1	5800	10000	0.580000
2	3120	8000	0.390000

Difference = p (1) – p (2)
Estimate for difference: 0.19
90% CI for difference: (0.177902, 0.202098)
Test for difference = 0 (vs not = 0): Z = 25.33 P-Value = 0.000

Assuming that it is reasonable to regard these two samples as being independently selected and also that they are representative of the two populations of interest, we can say that we believe that the proportion of high school students who agree that students should be allowed to report controversial issues in their student newspapers without the approval of school authorities exceeds that for teachers by somewhere between .178 and .202. We used a method to construct this estimate that captures the true difference in proportions 90% of the time in repeated sampling.

EXERCISES 11.37 - 11.57

11.37 A hotel chain is interested in evaluating reservation processes. Guests can reserve a room by using either a telephone system or an online system that is accessed through the hotel's web site. Independent random samples of 80 guests who reserved a room by phone and 60 guests who reserved a room online were selected. Of those who reserved by phone, 57 reported that they were satisfied with the reservation process. Of those who reserved online, 50 reported that they were satisfied. Based on these data, is it reasonable to conclude that the proportion who are satisfied is higher for those who reserve a room online? Test the appropriate hypotheses using $\alpha = .05$.

11.38 The authors of the paper "Adolescents and MP3 Players: Too Many Risks, Too Few Precautions" (*Pediatrics* [2009]: e953–e958) concluded that more boys than girls listen to music at high volumes. This conclusion was based on data from independent random samples of 764 Dutch boys and 748 Dutch girls age 12 to 19. Of the boys, 397 reported that they almost always listen to music at a high volume setting. Of the girls, 331 reported listening to music at a high volume setting. Do the sample data support the authors' conclusion that the proportion of Dutch boys who listen to music at high volume is greater than this proportion for Dutch girls? Test the relevant hypotheses using a .01 significance level.

11.39 After the 2010 earthquake in Haiti, many charitable organizations conducted fundraising campaigns to raise money for emergency relief. Some of these campaigns allowed people to donate by sending a text message using a cell phone to have the donated amount added to their cell-phone bill. The report "Early Signals on Mobile Philanthropy: Is Haiti the Tipping Point?" (Edge Research, 2010) describes the results of a national survey of 1526 people that investigated the ways in which people made donations to the Haiti relief effort. The report states that 17% of Gen Y respondents (those born between 1980 and 1988) and 14% of Gen X respondents (those born between 1968 and 1979) said that they had made a donation to the Haiti relief effort via text message. The percentage making a donation via text message was much lower for older respondents. The report did not say how many respondents were in the Gen Y and Gen X samples, but for purposes of this exercise, suppose that both sample sizes were 400 and that it is reasonable to regard the samples as representative of the Gen Y and Gen X populations.

a. Is there convincing evidence that the proportion of those in Gen Y who donated to Haiti relief via text message is greater than the proportion for Gen X? Use $\alpha = .01$.

b. Estimate the difference between the proportion of Gen Y and the proportion of Gen X that made a donation via text message using a 99% confidence interval. Provide an interpretation of both the interval and the associated confidence level.

11.40 Common Sense Media surveyed 1000 teens and 1000 parents of teens to learn about how teens are using social networking sites such as Facebook and MySpace ("Teens Show, Tell Too Much Online," *San Francisco Chronicle*, August 10, 2009). The two samples were independently selected and were chosen in a way that makes it reasonable to regard them as representative of American teens and parents of American teens.

a. When asked if they check their online social networking sites more than 10 times a day, 220 of the teens surveyed said yes. When parents of teens were asked if their teen checked his or her site more than 10 times a day, 40 said yes. Use a significance level of .01 to carry out a hypothesis test to determine if there is convincing evidence that the proportion of all parents who think their teen checks a social networking site more than 10 times a day is less than the proportion of all teens who report that they check more than 10 times a day.

b. The article also reported that 390 of the teens surveyed said they had posted something on their networking site that they later regretted. Would you use the two-sample z test of this section to test the hypothesis that more than one-third of all teens have posted something on a social networking site that they later regretted? Explain why or why not.

c. Using an appropriate test procedure, carry out a test of the hypothesis given in Part (b). Use $\alpha = .05$ for this test.

11.41 The report "Audience Insights: Communicating to Teens (Aged 12–17)" (www.cdc.gov, 2009) described teens' attitudes about traditional media, such as TV, movies, and newspapers. In a representative sample of American teenage girls, 41% said newspapers were boring. In a representative sample of American teenage boys, 44% said newspapers were boring. Sample sizes were not given in the report.

a. Suppose that the percentages reported had been based on a sample of 58 girls and 41 boys. Is there convincing evidence that the proportion of those who think that newspapers are boring is different for teenage girls and boys? Carry out a hypothesis test using $\alpha = .05$.

b. Suppose that the percentages reported had been based on a sample of 2000 girls and 2500 boys. Is there convincing evidence that the proportion of those who think that newspapers are boring is different for teenage girls and boys? Carry out a hypothesis test using $\alpha = .05$.

c. Explain why the hypothesis tests in Parts (a) and (b) resulted in different conclusions.

11.42 The director of the Kaiser Family Foundation's Program for the Study of Entertainment Media and Health said, "It's not just teenagers who are wired up and tuned in, its babies in diapers as well." A study by Kaiser Foundation provided one of the first looks at media use among the very youngest children—those from 6 months to 6 years of age (Kaiser Family Foundation, 2003, www.kff.org). Because previous research indicated that children who have a TV in their bedroom spend less time reading than other children, the authors of the Foundation study were interested in learning about the proportion of kids who have a TV in their bedroom. They collected data from two independent random samples of parents. One sample consisted of parents of children age 6 months to 3 years old. The second sample consisted of parents of children age 3 to 6 years old. They found that the proportion of children who had a TV in their bedroom was .30 for the sample of children age 6 months to 3 years and .43 for the sample of children age 3 to 6 years old. Suppose that the two sample sizes were each 100.

a. Construct and interpret a 95% confidence interval for the proportion of children age 6 months to 3 years who have a TV in their bedroom. *Hint:* This is a one-sample confidence interval.
b. Construct and interpret a 95% confidence interval for the proportion of children age 3 to 6 years who have a TV in their bedroom.
c. Do the confidence intervals from Parts (a) and (b) overlap? What does this suggest about the two population proportions?
d. Construct and interpret a 95% confidence interval for the difference in the proportion that have TVs in the bedroom for children age 6 months to 3 years and for children age 3 to 6 years.
e. Is the interval in Part (d) consistent with your answer in Part (c)? Explain.

11.43 The Insurance Institute for Highway Safety issued a press release titled "Teen Drivers Often Ignoring Bans on Using Cell Phones" (June 9, 2008). The following quote is from the press release:

> Just 1–2 months prior to the ban's Dec. 1, 2006 start, 11 percent of teen drivers were observed using cell phones as they left school in the afternoon. About 5 months after the ban took effect, 12% of teen drivers were observed using cell phones.

Suppose that the two samples of teen drivers (before the ban, after the ban) can be regarded as representative of these populations of teen drivers. Suppose also that 200 teen drivers were observed before the ban (so $n_1 = 200$ and $\hat{p}_1 = .11$) and 150 teen drivers were observed after the ban.

a. Construct and interpret a 95% confidence interval for the difference in the proportion using a cell phone while driving before the ban and the proportion after the ban.
b. Is zero included in the confidence interval of Part (c)? What does this imply about the difference in the population proportions?

11.44 The press release referenced in the previous exercise also included data from independent surveys of teenage drivers and parents of teenage drivers. In response to a question asking if they approved of laws banning the use of cell phones and texting while driving, 74% of the teens surveyed and 95% of the parents surveyed said they approved. The sample sizes were not given in the press release, but for purposes of this exercise, suppose that 600 teens and 400 parents of teens responded to the surveys and that it is reasonable to regard these samples as representative of the two populations. Do the data provide convincing evidence that the proportion of teens that approve of cell-phone and texting bans while driving is less than the proportion of parents of teens who approve? Test the relevant hypotheses using a significance level of .05.

11.45 The article "Fish Oil Staves Off Schizophrenia" (*USA Today*, February 2, 2010) describes a study in which 81 patients age 13 to 25 who were considered at-risk for mental illness were randomly assigned to one of two groups. Those in one group took four fish oil capsules daily. The other group took a placebo. After 1 year, 5% of those in the fish oil group and 28% of those in the placebo group had become psychotic. Is it appropriate to use the two-sample z test of this section to test hypotheses about the difference in the proportions of patients receiving the fish oil and the placebo treatments who became psychotic? Explain why or why not.

11.46 The report "Young People Living on the Edge" (Greenberg Quinlan Rosner Research, 2008) summarizes a survey of people in two independent random samples. One sample consisted of 600 young adults (age 19 to 35) and the other sample consisted of 300 parents of children age 19 to 35. The young adults were presented with a variety of situations (such as getting married or buying a house) and were asked if they thought that their parents were likely to provide financial support in that situation. The parents of young adults were presented with the same situations and asked if they would be likely to provide financial support to their child in that situation.

a. When asked about getting married, 41% of the young adults said they thought parents would provide financial support and 43% of the parents said they would provide support. Carry out a hypothesis test to determine if there is convincing evidence that the proportion of young adults who think parents would provide financial support and the proportion of parents who say they would provide support are different.
b. The report stated that the proportion of young adults who thought parents would help with buying a house or apartment was .37. For the sample of parents, the proportion who said they would help with buying a house or an apartment was .27. Based on these data, can you conclude that the proportion

of parents who say they would help with buying a house or an apartment is significantly less than the proportion of young adults who think that their parents would help?

11.47 Some commercial airplanes recirculate approximately 50% of the cabin air in order to increase fuel efficiency. The authors of the paper "Aircraft Cabin Air Recirculation and Symptoms of the Common Cold" (*Journal of the American Medical Association* [2002]: 483–486) studied 1100 airline passengers who flew from San Francisco to Denver between January and April 1999. Some passengers traveled on airplanes that recirculated air and others traveled on planes that did not recirculate air. Of the 517 passengers who flew on planes that did not recirculate air, 108 reported post-flight respiratory symptoms, while 111 of the 583 passengers on planes that did recirculate air reported such symptoms. Is there sufficient evidence to conclude that the proportion of passengers with post-flight respiratory symptoms differs for planes that do and do not recirculate air? Test the appropriate hypotheses using $\alpha = .05$. You may assume that it is reasonable to regard these two samples as being independently selected and as representative of the two populations of interest.

11.48 "Doctors Praise Device That Aids Ailing Hearts" (*Associated Press*, November 9, 2004) is the headline of an article that describes the results of a study of the effectiveness of a fabric device that acts like a support stocking for a weak or damaged heart. In the study, 107 people who consented to treatment were assigned at random to either a standard treatment consisting of drugs or the experimental treatment that consisted of drugs plus surgery to install the stocking. After two years, 38% of the 57 patients receiving the stocking had improved and 27% of the patients receiving the standard treatment had improved. Do these data provide convincing evidence that the proportion of patients who improve is higher for the experimental treatment than for the standard treatment? Test the relevant hypotheses using a significance level of .05.

11.49 The article "Portable MP3 Player Ownership Reaches New High" (*Ipsos Insight*, June 29, 2006) reported that in 2006, 20% of those in a random sample of 1112 Americans age 12 and older indicated that they owned an MP3 player. In a similar survey conducted in 2005, only 15% reported owning an MP3 player. Suppose that the 2005 figure was also based on a random sample of size 1112. Estimate the difference in the proportion of Americans age 12 and older who owned an MP3 player in 2006 and the corresponding proportion for 2005 using a 95% confidence interval. Is zero included in the interval? What does this tell you about the change in this proportion from 2005 to 2006?

11.50 The article referenced in the previous exercise also reported that 24% of the males and 16% of the females in the 2006 sample reported owning an MP3 player. Suppose that there were the same number of males and females in the sample of 1112. Do these data provide convincing evidence that the proportion of females that owned an MP3 player in 2006 is smaller than the corresponding proportion of males? Carry out a test using a significance level of .01.

11.51 Public Agenda conducted a survey of 1379 parents and 1342 students in grades 6–12 regarding the importance of science and mathematics in the school curriculum (Associated Press, February 15, 2006). It was reported that 50% of students thought that understanding science and having strong math skills are essential for them to succeed in life after school, whereas 62% of the parents thought it was crucial for today's students to learn science and higher-level math. The two samples—parents and students—were selected independently of one another. Is there sufficient evidence to conclude that the proportion of parents who regard science and mathematics as crucial is different than the corresponding proportion for students in grades 6–12? Test the relevant hypotheses using a significance level of .05.

11.52 The article "Spray Flu Vaccine May Work Better Than Injections for Tots" (*San Luis Obispo Tribune*, May 2, 2006) described a study that compared flu vaccine administered by injection and flu vaccine administered as a nasal spray. Each of the 8000 children under the age of 5 who participated in the study received both a nasal spray and an injection, but only one was the real vaccine and the other was salt water. At the end of the flu season, it was determined that 3.9% of the 4000 children receiving the real vaccine by nasal spray got sick with the flu and 8.6% of the 4000 receiving the real vaccine by injection got sick with the flu.

a. Why would the researchers give every child both a nasal spray and an injection?
b. Use the given data to estimate the difference in the proportion of children who get sick with the flu after being vaccinated with an injection and the proportion of children who get sick with the flu after being vaccinated with the nasal spray using a 99% confi-

dence interval. Based on the confidence interval, would you conclude that the proportion of children who get the flu is different for the two vaccination methods?

11.53 "Smartest People Often Dumbest About Sunburns" is the headline of an article that appeared in the *San Luis Obispo Tribune* (July 19, 2006). The article states that "those with a college degree reported a higher incidence of sunburn that those without a high school degree—43% versus 25%." For purposes of this exercise, suppose that these percentages were based on random samples of size 200 from each of the two groups of interest (college graduates and those without a high school degree). Is there convincing evidence that the proportion experiencing a sunburn is higher for college graduates than it is for those without a high school degree? Answer based on a test with a .05 significance level.

11.54 The following quote is from the article "Canadians Are Healthier Than We Are" (*Associated Press*, May 31, 2006): "The Americans also reported more heart disease and major depression, but those differences were too small to be statistically significant." This statement was based on the responses of a sample of 5183 Americans and a sample of 3505 Canadians. The proportion of Canadians who reported major depression was given as .082.

a. Assuming that the researchers used a one-sided test with a significance level of .05, could the sample proportion of Americans reporting major depression have been as large as .09? Explain why or why not.
b. Assuming that the researchers used a significance level of .05, could the sample proportion of Americans reporting major depression have been as large as .10? Explain why or why not.

11.55 "Mountain Biking May Reduce Fertility in Men, Study Says" was the headline of an article appearing in the *San Luis Obispo Tribune* (December 3, 2002). This conclusion was based on an Austrian study that compared sperm counts of avid mountain bikers (those who ride at least 12 hours per week) and nonbikers. Ninety percent of the avid mountain bikers studied had low sperm counts, as compared to 26% of the nonbikers. Suppose that these percentages were based on independent samples of 100 avid mountain bikers and 100 nonbikers and that it is reasonable to view these samples as representative of Austrian avid mountain bikers and nonbikers.

a. Do these data provide convincing evidence that the proportion of Austrian avid mountain bikers with low sperm count is higher than the proportion of Austrian nonbikers?
b. Based on the outcome of the test in Part (a), is it reasonable to conclude that mountain biking 12 hours per week or more causes low sperm count? Explain.

11.56 Women diagnosed with breast cancer whose tumors have not spread may be faced with a decision between two surgical treatments—mastectomy (removal of the breast) or lumpectomy (only the tumor is removed). In a long-term study of the effectiveness of these two treatments, 701 women with breast cancer were randomly assigned to one of two treatment groups. One group received mastectomies and the other group received lumpectomies and radiation. Both groups were followed for 20 years after surgery. It was reported that there was no statistically significant difference in the proportion surviving for 20 years for the two treatments (*Associated Press*, October 17, 2002). What hypotheses do you think the researchers tested in order to reach the given conclusion? Did the researchers reject or fail to reject the null hypothesis?

11.57 In December 2001, the Department of Veterans Affairs announced that it would begin paying benefits to soldiers suffering from Lou Gehrig's disease who had served in the Gulf War (*The New York Times*, December 11, 2001). This decision was based on an analysis in which the Lou Gehrig's disease incidence rate (the proportion developing the disease) for the approximately 700,000 soldiers sent to the Gulf between August 1990 and July 1991 was compared to the incidence rate for the approximately 1.8 million other soldiers who were not in the Gulf during this time period. Based on these data, explain why it is not appropriate to perform a formal inference procedure (such as the two-sample z test) and yet it is still reasonable to conclude that the incidence rate is higher for Gulf War veterans than for those who did not serve in the Gulf War.

11.4 Interpreting and Communicating the Results of Statistical Analyses

Many different types of research involve comparing two populations or treatments. It is easy to find examples of the two-sample hypothesis tests introduced in this chapter in published sources in a wide variety of disciplines.

Communicating the Results of Statistical Analyses

As was the case with one-sample hypothesis tests, it is important to include a description of the hypotheses, the test procedure used, the value of the test statistic and the *P*-value, and a conclusion in context when summarizing the results of a two-sample test.

Correctly interpreting confidence intervals in the two-sample case is more difficult than in the one-sample case, so take particular care when providing a two-sample confidence interval interpretation. Because the two-sample confidence intervals of this chapter estimate a difference ($\mu_1 - \mu_2$ or $p_1 - p_2$), the most important thing to note is whether or not the interval includes 0. If both endpoints of the interval are positive, then it is correct to say that, based on the interval, you believe that μ_1 is greater than μ_2 (or that p_1 is greater than p_2 if you are working with proportions) and then the interval provides an estimate of how much greater. Similarly, if both interval endpoints are negative, you would say that μ_1 is less than μ_2 (or that p_1 is less than p_2), with the interval providing an estimate of the size of the difference. If 0 is included in the interval, it is plausible that μ_1 and μ_2 (or p_1 and p_2) are equal.

Interpreting the Results of Statistical Analyses

As with one-sample tests, it is common to find only the value of the test statistic and the associated *P*-value (or sometimes only the *P*-value) in published reports. You may have to think carefully about the missing steps to determine whether or not the conclusions are justified.

What to Look For in Published Data

Here are some questions to consider when you are reading a report that contains the result of a two-sample hypothesis test or confidence interval:

- Are only two groups being compared? If more than two groups are being compared two at a time, then a different type of analysis is preferable (see Chapter 15).
- Were the samples selected independently, or were the samples paired? If the samples were paired, was the analysis that was performed appropriate for paired samples?
- If a confidence interval is reported, is it correctly interpreted as an estimate of a population or treatment difference in means or proportions?
- What hypotheses are being tested? Is the test one- or two-tailed?
- Does the validity of the test performed depend on any assumptions about the sampled populations (such as normality)? If so, do the assumptions appear to be reasonable?
- What is the *P*-value associated with the test? Does the *P*-value lead to rejection of the null hypothesis?
- Are the conclusions consistent with the results of the hypothesis test? In particular, if H_0 was rejected, does this indicate practical significance or only statistical significance?

For example, the paper "Ginkgo for Memory Enhancement" (*Journal of the American Medical Association* [2003]: 835–840) included the following statement in the summary of conclusions from an experiment where participants were randomly assigned to receive ginkgo or a placebo:

> Figure 2 shows the 95% confidence intervals (CIs) for differences (treatment group minus control) for performance on each test in the modified intent-to-treat analysis. Each interval contains a zero, indicating that none of the differences are statistically significant.

Because participants were assigned at random to the two treatments and the sample sizes were large (115 in each sample), use of the two-sample t confidence interval was appropriate. The 95% confidence intervals included in the paper (for example, $(-1.71, 0.65)$ and $(-2.25, 0.20)$ for two different measures of logical memory) did all include 0 and were interpreted correctly in the quoted conclusion.

As another example, we consider a study reported in the article "The Relationship Between Distress and Delight in Males' and Females' Reactions to Frightening Films" (*Human Communication Research* [1991]: 625–637).The investigators measured emotional responses of 50 males and 60 females after the subjects viewed a segment from a horror film. The article included the following statement: "Females were much more likely to express distress than were males. While males did express higher levels of delight than females, the difference was not statistically significant." The following summary information was also contained in the article:

Gender	Distress Index Mean	Delight Index Mean
Males	31.2	12.02
Females	40.4	9.09
	P-value $< .001$	Not significant (P-value $> .05$)

The P-values are the only evidence of the hypothesis tests that support the given conclusions. The P-value $< .001$ for the distress index means that the hypothesis H_0: $\mu_F - \mu_M = 0$ was rejected in favor of H_a: $\mu_F - \mu_M > 0$, where μ_F and μ_M are the mean distress indexes for females and males, respectively.

The nonsignificant P-value (P-value $> .05$) reported for the delight index means that the hypothesis H_0: $\mu_F - \mu_M = 0$ (where μ_F and μ_M now refer to mean delight index for females and males, respectively) could not be rejected. Chance sample-to-sample variability is a plausible explanation for the observed difference in sample means. We would want to be cautious about the author's statement that males express higher levels of delight than females, because it is based only on the fact that $12.02 > 9.09$, which could plausibly be due entirely to sampling variability.

The article describes the samples as consisting of undergraduates selected from the student body of a large Midwestern university. The authors extrapolate their results to American men and women in general. If this type of generalization is considered unreasonable, we could be more conservative and view the sampled populations as male and female university students or male and female Midwestern university students or even male and female students at this particular university.

The comparison of males and females was based on two independently selected groups (not paired). Because the sample sizes were large, the two-sample t test for means could reasonably have been used, and this would have required no specific assumptions about the two underlying populations.

In a newspaper article, you may find even less information than in a journal article. For example, the article "Prayer Is Little Help to Some Heart Patients, Study Shows" (*Chicago Tribune*, March 31, 2006) included the following paragraphs:

> Bypass patients who consented to take part in the experiment were divided randomly into three groups. Some patients received prayers but were not informed of that. In the second group the patients got no prayers, and also were not informed one way or the other. The third group got prayers and were told so.
>
> There was virtually no difference in complication rates between the patients in the first two groups. But the third group, in which patients knew they were receiving prayers, had a complication rate of 59 percent—significantly more than the rate of 52 percent in the no-prayer group.

Earlier in the article, the total number of participants in the experiment was given as 1800. The author of this article has done a good job of describing the important aspects of the experiment. The final comparison in the quoted paragraph was probably based on a two-sample z test for proportions, comparing the sample proportion with complications for the 600 patients in the no-prayer group with the sample proportion with complications for the 600 participants who knew that someone was praying for them. For the reported sample sizes and sample proportions, the test statistic for testing H_0: $p_1 - p_2 = 0$ versus H_a: $p_1 - p_2 < 0$ (where p_1 represents the complication proportion for patients who did not receive prayers and p_2 represents the complication proportion for patients who knew they were receiving prayers) is $z = -2.10$. The associated P-value is .036, supporting the conclusion stated in the article.

A Word to the Wise: Cautions and Limitations

The three cautions that appeared at the end of Chapter 10 apply here as well. They were (see Chapter 10 for more detail):

1. Remember that the result of a hypothesis test can never show strong support for the null hypothesis. In two-sample situations, this means that we shouldn't be *convinced* that there is no difference between population means or proportions based on the outcome of a hypothesis test.
2. If you have complete information (a census) of both populations, there is no need to carry out a hypothesis test or to construct a confidence interval—in fact, it would be inappropriate to do so.
3. Don't confuse statistical significance and practical significance. In the two-sample setting, it is possible to be convinced that two population means or proportions are not equal even in situations where the actual difference between them is small enough that it is of no practical interest. After rejecting a null hypothesis of no difference (statistical significance), it is useful to look at a confidence interval estimate of the difference to get a sense of practical significance.

And here's one new caution to keep in mind for two-sample tests:

4. Be sure to think carefully about how the data were collected, and make sure that an appropriate test procedure or confidence interval is used. A common mistake is to overlook pairing and to analyze paired samples as if they were independent. The question, Are the samples paired? is usually easy to answer—you just have to remember to ask!

EXERCISES 11.58 - 11.60

11.58 The paper "The Psychological Consequences of Money" (*Science* [2006]: 1154–1156) describes several experiments designed to investigate the way in which money can change behavior. In one experiment, participants completed one of two versions of a task in which they were given lists of five words and were asked to rearrange four of the words to create a sensible phrase. For one group, half of the 30 unscrambled phrases related to money, whereas the other half were phrases that were unrelated to money. For the second group (the control group), none of the 30 unscrambled phrases related to money. Participants were 44 students at Florida State University. Participants received course credit and $2 for their participation. The following description of the experiment is from the paper:

> Participants were randomly assigned to one of two conditions, in which they descrambled phrases that primed money or neutral concepts. Then participants completed some filler questionnaires, after which the experimenter told them that the experiment was finished and gave them a false debriefing. This step was done so that participants would not connect the donation opportunity to the experiment. As the experimenter exited the room, she mentioned that the lab was taking donations for the University Student Fund and that there was a box by the door if the participant wished to donate. Amount of money donated was the measure of helping. We found that participants primed with money donated significantly less money to the student fund than participants not primed with money [$t(38) = 2.13$, $P < 0.05$].

The paper also gave the following information on amount donated for the two experimental groups.

Group	Mean	Standard Deviation
Money primed	$0.77	$0.74
Control	$1.34	$1.02

a. Explain why the random assignment of participants to experimental groups is important in this experiment.
b. Use the given information to verify the values of the test statistic and degrees of freedom (38, given in parentheses just after the t in the quote from the paper) and the statement about the P-value. Assume that both sample sizes are 22.
c. Do you think that use of the two-sample t test was appropriate in this situation? *Hint:* Are the assumptions required for the two-sample t test reasonable?

11.59 An experiment to determine if an online intervention can reduce references to sex and substance abuse on social networking web sites of adolescents is described in the paper "Reducing At-Risk Adolescents' Display of Risk Behavior on a Social Networking Web Site" (*Archives of Pediatrics and Adolescent Medicine* [2009]: 35–41). Researchers selected public MySpace profiles of people who described themselves as between 18 and 20 years old and who referenced sex or substance use (alcohol or drugs) in their profiles. The selected subjects were assigned at random to an intervention group or a control group. Those in the intervention group were sent an e-mail from a physician about the risks associated with having a public profile and of referencing sex or substance use in their profile. Three months later, networking sites were revisited to see if any changes had been made. The following excerpt is from the paper:

> At baseline, 54.2% of subjects referenced sex and 85.3% referenced substance use on their social networking site profiles. The proportion of profiles in which references decreased to 0 was 13.7% in the intervention group vs. 5.3% in the control group for sex ($P = .05$) and 26% vs. 22% for substance use ($P = .61$). The proportion of profiles set to "private" at follow-up was 10.5% in the intervention group and 7.4% in the control group ($P = .45$). The proportion of profiles in which any of these three protective changes were made was 42.1% in the intervention group and 29.5% in the control group ($P = .07$).

a. The quote from the paper references four hypothesis tests. For each test, indicate what hypotheses you think were tested and whether or not the null hypothesis was rejected.
b. Based on the information provided by the hypothesis tests, what conclusions can be drawn about the effectiveness of the e-mail intervention?

11.60 The paper "Ready or Not? Criteria for Marriage Readiness among Emerging Adults" (*Journal of Adolescent Research* [2009]: 349–375) surveyed emerging adults (defined as age 18 to 25) from five different colleges in the United States. Several questions on the survey were used to construct a scale designed to measure endorsement of cohabitation. The paper states that "on average, emerging adult men (M = 3.75, SD = 1.21) reported higher levels of cohabitation endorsement than emerging adult women (M = 3.39, SD = 1.17)." The sample sizes were 481 for women and 307 for men.

a. Carry out a hypothesis test to determine if the reported difference in sample means provides convincing evidence that the mean cohabitation endorsement for emerging adult women is significantly less than the mean for emerging adult men for students at these five colleges.
b. What additional information would you want in order to determine whether it is reasonable to generalize the conclusion of the hypothesis test from Part (a) to all college students?

ACTIVITY 11.1 Helium-Filled Footballs?

Technology activity: Requires Internet access.

Background: Do you think that a football filled with helium will travel farther than a football filled with air? Two researchers at the Ohio State University investigated this question by performing an experiment in which 39 people each kicked a helium-filled football and an air-filled football. Half were assigned to kick the air-filled football first and then the helium-filled ball, whereas the other half kicked the helium-filled ball first followed by the air-filled ball. Distance (in yards) was measured for each kick.

In this activity, you will use the Internet to obtain the data from this experiment and then carry out a hypothesis test to determine whether the mean distance is greater for helium-filled footballs than for air-filled footballs.

1. Do you think that helium-filled balls will tend to travel farther than air-filled balls when kicked? Before looking at the data, write a few sentences indicating what you think the outcome of this experiment was and describing the reasoning that supports your prediction.
2. The data from this experiment can be found in the Data and Story Library at the following web site:

   http://lib.stat.cmu.edu/DASL/Datafiles/heliumfootball.html

   Go to this web site and print out the data for the 39 trials.
3. There are two samples in this data set. One consists of distances traveled for the 39 kicks of the air-filled football, and the other consists of the 39 distances for the helium-filled football. Are these samples independent or paired? Explain.
4. Carry out an appropriate hypothesis test to determine whether there is convincing evidence that the mean distance traveled is greater for a helium-filled football than for an air-filled football.
5. Is the conclusion in the test of Step 4 consistent with your initial prediction of the outcome of this experiment? Explain.
6. Write a paragraph for the sports section of your school newspaper describing this experiment and the conclusions that can be drawn from it.

ACTIVITY 11.2 Thinking About Data Collection

Background: In this activity you will design two experiments that would allow you to investigate whether people tend to have quicker reflexes when reacting with their dominant hand than with their nondominant hand.

1. Working in a group, design an experiment to investigate the given research question that would result in independent samples. Be sure to describe how you plan to measure quickness of reflexes, what extraneous variables will be directly controlled, and the role that randomization plays in your design.
2. How would you modify the design from Step 1 so that the resulting data are paired? Is the way in which randomization is incorporated into the new design different from the way it is incorporated in the design from Step 1? Explain.

3. Which of the two proposed designs would you recommend, and why?
4. If assigned to do so by your instructor, carry out one of your experiments and analyze the resulting data. Write a brief report that describes the experimental design, includes both graphical and numerical summaries of the resulting data, and communicates the conclusions that follow from your data analysis.

ACTIVITY 11.3 A Meaningful Paragraph

Write a meaningful paragraph that includes the following six terms: **paired samples, significantly different, *P*-value, sample, population, alternative hypothesis.**

A "meaningful paragraph" is a coherent piece of writing in an appropriate context that uses all of the listed words. The paragraph should show that you understand the meaning of the terms and their relationship to one another. A sequence of sentences that just define the terms is *not* a meaningful paragraph. When choosing a context, think carefully about the terms you need to use. Choosing a good context will make writing a meaningful paragraph easier.

Summary of Key Concepts and Formulas

TERM OR FORMULA	COMMENT
Independent samples	Two samples where the individuals or objects in the first sample are selected independently from those in the second sample.
Paired samples	Two samples for which each observation in one sample is paired in a meaningful way with a particular observation in a second sample.
$t = \dfrac{(\bar{x}_1 - \bar{x}_2) - \text{hypothesized value}}{\sqrt{\dfrac{s_1^2}{n_1} + \dfrac{s_2^2}{n_2}}}$	The test statistic for testing H_0: $\mu_1 - \mu_2 =$ hypothesized value when the samples are independently selected and the sample sizes are large or it is reasonable to assume that both population distributions are normal.
$(\bar{x}_1 - \bar{x}_2) \pm (t \text{ critical value})\sqrt{\dfrac{s_1^2}{n_1} + \dfrac{s_2^2}{n_2}}$	A formula for constructing a confidence interval for $\mu_1 - \mu_2$ when the samples are independently selected and the sample sizes are large or it is reasonable to assume that the population distributions are normal.
$\text{df} = \dfrac{(V_1 + V_2)^2}{\dfrac{V_1^2}{n_1 - 1} + \dfrac{V_2^2}{n_2 - 1}}$ where $V_1 = \dfrac{s_1^2}{n_1}$ and $V_2 = \dfrac{s_2^2}{n_2}$	The formula for determining df for the two-sample t test and confidence interval.
$\bar{x}_d$	The sample mean difference.
s_d	The standard deviation of the sample differences.
μ_d	The mean value for the population of differences.
σ_d	The standard deviation for the population of differences.
$t = \dfrac{\bar{x}_d - \text{hypothesized value}}{\dfrac{s_d}{\sqrt{n}}}$	The paired t test statistic for testing H_0: $\mu_d =$ hypothesized value.
$\bar{x}_d \pm (t \text{ critical value})\dfrac{s_d}{\sqrt{n}}$	The paired t confidence interval formula.

$$\hat{p}_c = \frac{n_1\hat{p}_1 + n_2\hat{p}_2}{n_1 + n_2}$$

$\hat{p}_c$ is the statistic for estimating the common population proportion when $p_1 = p_2$.

$$z = \frac{\hat{p}_1 - \hat{p}_2}{\sqrt{\frac{\hat{p}_c(1-\hat{p}_c)}{n_1} + \frac{\hat{p}_c(1-\hat{p}_c)}{n_2}}}$$

The test statistic for testing
H_0: $p_1 - p_2 = 0$
when the samples are independently selected and both sample sizes are large.

$$(\hat{p}_1 - \hat{p}_2) \pm (z \text{ critical value})\sqrt{\frac{\hat{p}_1(1-\hat{p}_1)}{n_1} + \frac{\hat{p}_2(1-\hat{p}_2)}{n_2}}$$

A formula for constructing a confidence interval for $p_1 - p_2$ when both sample sizes are large.

Chapter Review Exercises 11.61 - 11.82

11.61 Do faculty and students have similar perceptions of what types of behavior are inappropriate in the classroom? This question was examined by the author of the article "Faculty and Student Perceptions of Classroom Etiquette" (*Journal of College Student Development* (1998): 515–516). Each individual in a random sample of 173 students in general education classes at a large public university was asked to judge various behaviors on a scale from 1 (totally inappropriate) to 5 (totally appropriate). Individuals in a random sample of 98 faculty members also rated the same behaviors. The mean rating for three of the behaviors studied are shown here (the means are consistent with data provided by the author of the article). The sample standard deviations were not given, but for purposes of this exercise, assume that they are all equal to 1.0.

Student Behavior	Student Mean Rating	Faculty Mean Rating
Wearing hats in the classroom	2.80	3.63
Addressing instructor by first name	2.90	2.11
Talking on a cell phone	1.11	1.10

a. Is there sufficient evidence to conclude that the mean "appropriateness" score assigned to wearing a hat in class differs for students and faculty?

b. Is there sufficient evidence to conclude that the mean "appropriateness" score assigned to addressing an instructor by his or her first name is higher for students than for faculty?

c. Is there sufficient evidence to conclude that the mean "appropriateness" score assigned to talking on a cell phone differs for students and faculty? Does the result of your test imply that students and faculty consider it acceptable to talk on a cell phone during class?

11.62 Are girls less inclined to enroll in science courses than boys? One study ("Intentions of Young Students to Enroll in Science Courses in the Future: An Examination of Gender Differences," *Science Education* [1999]: 55–76) asked randomly selected fourth-, fifth-, and sixth-graders how many science courses they intend to take. The following data were obtained:

	n	Mean	Standard Deviation
Males	203	3.42	1.49
Females	224	2.42	1.35

Calculate a 99% confidence interval for the difference between males and females in mean number of science courses planned. Interpret your interval. Based on your interval, how would you answer the question posed at the beginning of the exercise?

11.63 ● A deficiency of the trace element selenium in the diet can negatively impact growth, immunity, muscle and neuromuscular function, and fertility. The introduction of selenium supplements to dairy cows is justified when pastures have low selenium levels. Authors of the paper "Effects of Short-Term Supplementation with Selenised Yeast on Milk Production and Composition of Lactating Cows" (*Australian Journal of Dairy Technology*, [2004]: 199–203) supplied the following data on milk selenium concentration (mg/L) for a sample of cows given a selenium supplement (the treatment group) and a control sample given no supplement, both initially and after a 9-day period.

Initial Measurement		After 9 Days	
Treatment	Control	Treatment	Control
11.4	9.1	138.3	9.3
9.6	8.7	104.0	8.8
10.1	9.7	96.4	8.8
8.5	10.8	89.0	10.1
10.3	10.9	88.0	9.6
10.6	10.6	103.8	8.6
11.8	10.1	147.3	10.4
9.8	12.3	97.1	12.4
10.9	8.8	172.6	9.3
10.3	10.4	146.3	9.5
10.2	10.9	99.0	8.4
11.4	10.4	122.3	8.7
9.2	11.6	103.0	12.5
10.6	10.9	117.8	9.1
10.8		121.5	
8.2		93.0	

a. Use the given data for the treatment group to determine if there is sufficient evidence to conclude that the mean selenium concentration is greater after 9 days of the selenium supplement.

b. Are the data for the cows in the control group (no selenium supplement) consistent with the hypothesis of no significant change in mean selenium concentration over the 9-day period?

c. Would you use the paired *t* test to determine if there was a significant difference in the initial mean selenium concentration for the control group and the treatment group? Explain why or why not.

11.64 ● The Oregon Department of Health web site provides information on the cost-to-charge ratio (the percentage of billed charges that are actual costs to the hospital). The cost-to-charge ratios for both inpatient and outpatient care in 2002 for a sample of six hospitals in Oregon follow.

Hospital	2002 Inpatient Ratio	2002 Outpatient Ratio
1	68	54
2	100	75
3	71	53
4	74	56
5	100	74
6	83	71

Is there evidence that the mean cost-to-charge ratio for Oregon hospitals is lower for outpatient care than for inpatient care? Use a significance level of .05.

11.65 The article "A 'White' Name Found to Help in Job Search" (*Associated Press,* January 15, 2003) described an experiment to investigate if it helps to have a "white-sounding" first name when looking for a job. Researchers sent 5000 resumes in response to ads that appeared in the *Boston Globe* and *Chicago Tribune.* The resumes were identical except that 2500 of them had "white-sounding" first names, such as Brett and Emily, whereas the other 2500 had "black-sounding" names such as Tamika and Rasheed. Resumes of the first type elicited 250 responses and resumes of the second type only 167 responses. Do these data support the theory that the proportion receiving responses is higher for those resumes with "white-sounding first" names?

11.66 In a study of a proposed approach for diabetes prevention, 339 people under the age of 20 who were thought to be at high risk of developing type I diabetes were assigned at random to two groups. One group received twice-daily injections of a low dose of insulin. The other group (the control) did not receive any insulin, but was closely monitored. Summary data (from the article "Diabetes Theory Fails Test," *USA Today,* June 25, 2001) follow.

Group	*n*	Number Developing Diabetes
Insulin	169	25
Control	170	24

a. Use the given data to construct a 90% confidence interval for the difference in the proportion that develop diabetes for the control group and the insulin group.

b. Give an interpretation of the confidence interval and the associated confidence level.
c. Based on your interval from Part (a), write a few sentences commenting on the effectiveness of the proposed prevention treatment.

11.67 When a surgeon repairs injuries, sutures (stitched knots) are used to hold together and stabilize the injured area. If these knots elongate and loosen through use, the injury may not heal properly because the tissues would not be optimally positioned. Researchers at the University of California, San Francisco, tied a series of different types of knots with two types of suture material, Maxon and Ticron. Suppose that 112 tissue specimens were available and that for each specimen the type of knot and suture material were randomly assigned. The investigators tested the knots to see how much the loops elongated; the elongations (in mm) were measured and the resulting data are summarized here. For purposes of this exercise, assume it is reasonable to regard the elongation distributions as approximately normal.

	Maxon		
Types of knot	n	$\bar{x}$	sd
Square (control)	10	10.0	.1
Duncan Loop	15	11.0	.3
Overhand	15	11.0	.9
Roeder	10	13.5	.1
Snyder	10	13.5	2.0

	Ticron		
Types of knot	n	$\bar{x}$	sd
Square (control)	10	2.5	.06
Duncan Loop	11	10.9	.40
Overhand	11	8.1	1.00
Roeder	10	5.0	.04
Snyder	10	8.1	.06

a. Is there a significant difference in mean elongation between the square knot and the Duncan loop for Maxon thread?
b. Is there a significant difference in mean elongation between the square knot and the Duncan loop for Ticron thread?
c. For the Duncan loop knot, is there a significant difference in mean elongation between the Maxon and Ticron threads?

11.68 The article "Trial Lawyers and Testosterone: Blue-Collar Talent in a White-Collar World" (*Journal of Applied Social Psychology* [1998]: 84–94) compared trial lawyers and nontrial lawyers on the basis of mean testosterone level. Random samples of 35 male trial lawyers, 31 male nontrial lawyers, 13 female trial lawyers, and 18 female nontrial lawyers were selected for study. The article includes the following statement: "Trial lawyers had higher testosterone levels than did nontrial lawyers. This was true for men, $t(64) = 3.75, p < .001$, and for women, $t(29) = 2.26, p < .05$."
a. Based on the information given, is the mean testosterone level for male trial lawyers significantly higher than for male nontrial lawyers?
b. Based on the information given, is the mean testosterone level for female trial lawyers significantly higher than for female nontrial lawyers?
c. Do you have enough information to carry out a test to determine whether there is a significant difference in the mean testosterone levels of male and female trial lawyers? If so, carry out such a test. If not, what additional information would you need to be able to conduct the test?

11.69 In a study of memory recall, eight students from a large psychology class were selected at random and given 10 minutes to memorize a list of 20 nonsense words. Each was asked to list as many of the words as he or she could remember both 1 hour and 24 hours later. The data are as shown in the accompanying table. Is there evidence to suggest that the mean number of words recalled after 1 hour exceeds the mean recall after 24 hours by more than 3? Use a level .01 test.

Subject	1	2	3	4	5	6	7	8
1 hour later	14	12	18	7	11	9	16	15
24 hour later	10	4	14	6	9	6	12	12

11.70 As part of a study to determine the effects of allowing the use of credit cards for alcohol purchases in Canada (see "Changes in Alcohol Consumption Patterns Following the Introduction of Credit Cards in Ontario Liquor Stores," *Journal of Studies on Alcohol* [1999]: 378–382), randomly selected individuals were given a questionnaire asking them (among other things) how many drinks they had consumed during the previous week. A year later (after liquor stores started accepting credit cards for purchases), these same individuals were again asked how many drinks they had consumed in the previous week. The data shown are consistent with summary statistics presented in the article.

	n	1994 Mean	1995 Mean	$\bar{x}_d$	s_d
Credit-Card Shoppers	96	6.72	6.34	.38	5.52
Non-Credit-Card Shoppers	850	4.09	3.97	.12	4.58

a. The standard deviations of the differences were quite large. Explain how this could be the case.
b. Calculate a 95% confidence interval for the mean difference in drink consumption for credit-card shoppers between 1994 and 1995. Is there evidence that the mean number of drinks decreased?
c. Test the hypothesis that there was no change in the mean number of drinks between 1994 and 1995 for the non-credit-card shoppers. Be sure to calculate and interpret the P-value for this test.

11.71 ● Several methods of estimating the number of seeds in soil samples have been developed by ecologists. An article in the *Journal of Ecology* ("A Comparison of Methods for Estimating Seed Numbers in the Soil" [1990]: 1079–1093) considered three such methods. The accompanying data give number of seeds detected by the direct method and by the stratified method for 27 soil specimens.

Specimen	Direct	Stratified	Specimen	Direct	Stratified
1	24	8	**2**	32	36
3	0	8	**4**	60	56
5	20	52	**6**	64	64
7	40	28	**8**	8	8
9	12	8	**10**	92	100
11	4	0	**12**	68	56
13	76	68	**14**	24	52
15	32	28	**16**	0	0
17	36	36	**18**	16	12
19	92	92	**20**	4	12
21	40	48	**22**	24	24
23	0	0	**24**	8	12
25	12	40	**26**	16	12
27	40	76			

Do the data provide sufficient evidence to conclude that the mean number of seeds detected differs for the two methods? Test the relevant hypotheses using α =.05.

11.72 Are college students who take a freshman orientation course more or less likely to stay in college than those who do not take such a course? The article "A Longitudinal Study of the Retention and Academic Performance of Participants in Freshmen Orientation Courses" (*Journal of College Student Development* [1994]: 444–449) reported that 50 of 94 randomly selected students who did not participate in an orientation course returned for a second year. Of 94 randomly selected students who did take the orientation course, 56 returned for a second year. Construct a 95% confidence interval for $p_1 - p_2$, the difference in the proportion returning for students who do not take an orientation course and those who do. Give an interpretation of this interval.

11.73 The article "Truth and DARE: Tracking Drug Education to Graduation" (*Social Problems* [1994]: 448–456) compared the drug use of 288 randomly selected high school seniors exposed to a drug education program (DARE) and 335 randomly selected high school seniors who were not exposed to such a program. Data for marijuana use are given in the accompanying table. Is there evidence that the proportion using marijuana is lower for students exposed to the DARE program? Use α = .05.

	n	Number Who Use Marijuana
Exposed to DARE	288	141
Not Exposed to DARE	335	181

11.74 The article "Softball Sliding Injuries" (*American Journal of Diseases of Children* [1988]: 715–716) provided a comparison of breakaway bases (designed to reduce injuries) and stationary bases. Consider the accompanying data (which agree with summary values given in the paper).

	Number of Games Played	Number of Games Where a Player Suffered a Sliding Injury
Stationary Bases	1250	90
Breakaway Bases	1250	20

Is the proportion of games with a player suffering a sliding injury significantly lower for games using breakaway bases? Answer by performing a level .01 test. What did you have to assume in order for your conclusion to be valid? Do you think it is likely that this assumption was satisfied in this study?

11.75 The positive effect of water fluoridation on dental health is well documented. One study that validates this is described in the article "Impact of Water Fluoridation on Children's Dental Health: A Controlled Study of Two Pennsylvania Communities" (*American Statistical Association Proceedings of the Social Statistics Section* [1981]: 262–265). Two communities were compared. One had adopted fluoridation in 1966, whereas the other had no such program. Of 143 randomly selected children from the town without fluoridated water, 106 had decayed teeth, and 67 of 119 randomly selected children from the town with fluoridated water had decayed teeth. Let p_1 denote proportion of all children in the community with fluoridated water who have decayed teeth, and let p_2 denote the analogous proportion for children in the community with unfluoridated water. Estimate $p_1 - p_2$ using a 90% confidence interval. Does the interval contain 0? Interpret the interval.

11.76 Wayne Gretzky was one of ice hockey's most prolific scorers when he played for the Edmonton Oilers. During his last season with the Oilers, Gretzky played in 41 games and missed 17 games due to injury. The article "The Great Gretzky" (*Chance* [1991]: 16–21) looked at the number of goals scored by the Oilers in games with and without Gretzky, as shown in the accompanying table. If we view the 41 games with Gretzky as a random sample of all Oiler games in which Gretzky played and the 17 games without Gretzky as a random sample of all Oiler games in which Gretzky did not play, is there evidence that the mean number of goals scored by the Oilers is higher for games in which Gretzky played? Use $\alpha = .01$.

	n	Sample Mean	Sample sd
Games with Gretzky	41	4.73	1.29
Games without Gretzky	17	3.88	1.18

11.77 Here's one to sink your teeth into: The authors of the article "Analysis of Food Crushing Sounds During Mastication: Total Sound Level Studies" (*Journal of Texture Studies* [1990]: 165–178) studied the nature of sounds generated during eating. Peak loudness (in decibels at 20 cm away) was measured for both open-mouth and closed-mouth chewing of potato chips and of tortilla chips. Forty subjects participated, with ten assigned at random to each combination of conditions (such as closed-mouth potato chip, and so on). We are not making this up! Summary values taken from plots given in the article appear in the accompanying table. For purposes of this exercise, suppose that it is reasonable to regard the peak loudness distributions as approximately normal.

	n	$\bar{x}$	s
Potato Chip			
Open mouth	10	63	13
Closed mouth	10	54	16
Tortilla Chip			
Open mouth	10	60	15
Closed mouth	10	53	16

a. Construct a 95% confidence interval for the difference in mean peak loudness between open-mouth and closed-mouth chewing of potato chips. Interpret the resulting interval.

b. For closed-mouth chewing (the recommended method!), is there sufficient evidence to indicate that there is a difference between potato chips and tortilla chips with respect to mean peak loudness? Test the relevant hypotheses using $\alpha = .01$.

c. The means and standard deviations given here were actually for stale chips. When ten measurements of peak loudness were recorded for closed-mouth chewing of fresh tortilla chips, the resulting mean and standard deviation were 56 and 14, respectively. Is there sufficient evidence to conclude that fresh tortilla chips are louder than stale chips? Use $\alpha = .05$.

11.78 Are very young infants more likely to imitate actions that are modeled by a person or simulated by an object? This question was the basis of a research study summarized in the article "The Role of Person and Object in Eliciting Early Imitation" (*Journal of Experimental Child Psychology* [1991]: 423–433). One action examined was mouth opening. This action was modeled repeatedly by either a person or a doll, and the number of times that the infant imitated the behavior was recorded. Twenty-seven infants participated, with 12 exposed to a human model and 15 exposed to the doll. Summary values are at the top of the following page. Is there sufficient evidence to conclude that the mean number of imitations is higher for infants who watch a human model than for infants who watch a doll? Test the relevant hypotheses using a .01 significance level.

	Person Model	Doll Model
$\bar{x}$	5.14	3.46
s	1.60	1.30

11.79 Dentists make many people nervous (even more so than statisticians!). To see whether such nervousness elevates blood pressure, the blood pressure and pulse rates of 60 subjects were measured in a dental setting and in a medical setting ("The Effect of the Dental Setting on Blood Pressure Measurement," *American Journal of Public Health* [1983]: 1210–1214). For each subject, the difference (dental-setting blood pressure minus medical-setting blood pressure) was calculated. The analogous differences were also calculated for pulse rates. Summary data follows.

	Mean Difference	Standard Deviation of Differences
Systolic Blood Pressure	4.47	8.77
Pulse (beats/min)	−1.33	8.84

a. Do the data strongly suggest that true mean blood pressure is higher in a dental setting than in a medical setting? Use a level .01 test.

b. Is there sufficient evidence to indicate that true mean pulse rate in a dental setting differs from the true mean pulse rate in a medical setting? Use a significance level of .05.

11.80 Key terms in survey questions too often are not well understood, and such ambiguity can affect responses. As an example, the article "How Unclear Terms Affect Survey Data" (*Public Opinion Quarterly* [1992]: 218–231) described a survey in which each individual in a sample was asked, "Do you exercise or play sports regularly?" But what constitutes exercise? The following revised question was then asked of each individual in the same sample: "Do you do any sports or hobbies involving physical activities, or any exercise, including walking, on a regular basis?" The resulting data are shown in the accompanying table.

	Yes	No
Initial Question	48	52
Revised Question	60	40

Is there any difference between the true proportions of yes responses to these questions? Can a procedure from this chapter be used to answer the question posed? If yes, use it; if not, explain why not.

11.81 An electronic implant that stimulates the auditory nerve has been used to restore partial hearing to a number of deaf people. In a study of implant acceptability (*Los Angeles Times*, January 29, 1985), 250 adults born deaf and 250 adults who went deaf after learning to speak were followed for a period of time after receiving an implant. Of those deaf from birth, 75 had removed the implant, whereas only 25 of those who went deaf after learning to speak had done so. Does this suggest that the true proportion who remove the implants differs for those who were born deaf and those who went deaf after learning to speak? Test the relevant hypotheses using a .01 significance level.

11.82 ● Samples of both surface soil and subsoil were taken from eight randomly selected agricultural locations in a particular county. The soil samples were analyzed to determine both surface pH and subsoil pH, with the results shown in the accompanying table.

Location	1	2	3	4	5	6	7	8
Surface pH	6.55	5.98	5.59	6.17	5.92	6.18	6.43	5.68
Subsoil pH	6.78	6.14	5.80	5.91	6.10	6.01	6.18	5.88

a. Compute a 90% confidence interval for the mean difference between surface and subsoil pH for agricultural land in this county.

b. What assumptions are necessary for the interval in Part (a) to be valid?

Graphing Calculator Explorations

EXPLORATION 11.1 Inference about Differences in Means

Using your calculator to construct confidence intervals and test hypotheses about differences between two population means involves actions similar to working with a single mean. You must navigate the menu system of your calculator to the point at which these procedures can be selected. Of course, by now you are an old hand at such navigation! We will use Example 11.2 to illustrate a two-sample t test of equal population means.

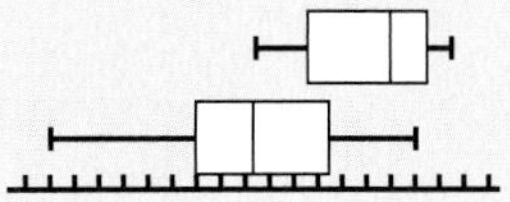

FIGURE 11.2
Boxplots of the two samples.

Testing Hypotheses Enter the data in your calculator, using the lists of your choice. (We will use List1 and List2.) We will check the assumption of approximate normality of the populations by displaying boxplots of the two data sets, as shown in Figure 11.2. (Be sure to choose the modified boxplot option!)

After verifying the plausibility of the normality of the populations, navigate your calculator's menu system to choose a procedure. For the two-sample t test, the common calculator screens are not large enough to show all relevant data, so in Figure 11.3 we again show "larger-than-life" representations rather than capture the actual screens.

2-Sample t Test	2-SampTTest
Data: List	Inpt: Data Stats
$\mu1$: $>\mu2$	List1: L1
List1: List1	List2: L2
List2: List2	Freq1: 1
Freq1: 1	Freq2: 1
Freq2: 1	$\mu1$: $\neq\mu2$ $<\mu2$ $>\mu2$
Pooled: Off	Pooled: No Yes
Execute	Calculate Draw

FIGURE 11.3
Windows from two different calculators for the two-sample t test.

2-Sample t Test	2-SampTTest
$\mu1 > \mu2$	$\mu1 > \mu2$
t = 3.109517945	t = 3.109517945
p = .0035597268	p = .0035597268
df = 15.12279179	df = 15.12279179
$\bar{x}_1$ = 74.6	$\bar{x}_1$ = 74.6
$\bar{x}_2$ = 64.6	$\bar{x}_2$ = 64.6
$x1\sigma n - 1$ = 5.39958846	Sx1 = 5.39958846
$x2\sigma n - 1$ = 8.61781101	Sx2 = 8.61781101
n1 = 10	n1 = 10
n2 = 10	n2 = 10

FIGURE 11.4
Output from two different calculators for the two-sample t test.

Notice from Figure 11.3 that you have choices similar to the hypothesis testing for a single population mean, with one exception: pooling. Pooling with two samples has fallen into disfavor among statisticians, so your choice here should be "Off" or "No." The subsequent output also requires more than one calculator screen, and we therefore show a "big screen" representation in Figure 11.4.

Once again, we will remind you that although this information is "all there" in the sense that the results of the hypothesis test are completely displayed, it is *not* in a form that should be used for communicating your results to others. You should still complete and report all of the appropriate steps for a hypothesis test.

Confidence Intervals We will now turn our attention to confidence intervals for the difference between two population means, using data from Example 11.4.

Enter the data in your calculator, using the lists of your choice. (We again use List1 and List2.) After verifying the plausibility of the normality of the populations, navigate the calculator's menu system to choose a procedure. For the two-sample t confidence interval, the data entry will be the same as for a hypothesis test, and there should be an additional piece of information needed: the confidence level. Two potential displays are shown in Figure 11.5. Remember, your calculator may display only some of this information, and you will thus have to scroll to see it all.

2-Sample t Interval	2-SampTInt
Data: List	Inpt: Data Stats
C-Level: .95	List1: L1
List1: List1	List2: L2
List2: List2	Freq1: 1
Freq1: 1	Freq2: 1
Freq2: 1	C-Level: .95
Pooled: Off	Pooled: No Yes
Execute	Calculate

FIGURE 11.5
Windows from two different calculators for the two-sample t confidence interval.

We can see from the screen representations in Figure 11.5 that the data are contained in lists and that the confidence level is 95%. Once again, choose *not* to pool. The results from the calculations are displayed in Figure 11.6. These boxes represent two common displays calculators use to report confidence intervals.

2-Sample tInterval	2-SampTInt
Left = 1.0461	(1.0461, 11.954)
Right = 11.954	df = 13.77631629
df = 13.7763	$\bar{x}_1$ = 108.75
$\bar{x}_1$ = 108.75	$\bar{x}_2$ = 102.25
$\bar{x}_2$ = 102.25	Sx1 = 4.74341649
$x1\sigma n - 1$ = 4.7434	Sx2 = 5.3917927
$x2\sigma n - 1$ = 5.3918	n1 = 8
n1 = 8	n2 = 8
n2 = 8	

FIGURE 11.6
Output from two different calculators for the two-sample t confidence interval.

EXPLORATION 11.2 Inferences About Differences in Means Using Paired Samples

Procedures for making inferences about the difference between two population means using paired samples is similar to inference using a single sample. To test hypotheses or to construct confidence intervals using these differences, you must enter the observations in your calculator, and create the differences by subtraction. We will use Example 11.6 to illustrate how this is done on the calculator. Recall that the data are from the study of memory improvement from taking chess lessons and playing daily.

If you are following along with your calculator, enter the pre-test data into List1 and the post-test data into List2. After entering the data, use list commands to subtract the post-test scores from the pre-test scores (pre-test minus post-test) and store the result in List3:

List1 − List2 → List3

L1	L2	L3 1
510	850	-340
610	790	-180
640	850	-210
675	775	-100
600	700	-100
550	775	-225
610	700	-90
L1(1) = 510		

FIGURE 11.7
Edit data screen.

At this point, you should see something like Figure 11.7 in your data edit screen. The list of interest for our paired *t* procedures is List3. We proceed from here as we did with inference for a single sample. Because the sample size in this example is small, the approximate normality of the differences is an important consideration—we must assess the plausibility of a normal population *of differences*.

The boxplot for the differences (List3) shown in Figure 11.8 does not indicate any difficulties with the assumption of approximate normality, so we proceed to the hypothesis test and construction of a confidence interval as discussed in Graphing Calculator Exploration 11.1. The results are shown in Figure 11.9. The alternative hypothesis is that the mean difference would be less than 0, a one-tailed test. In the case of the confidence interval, we used a 95% confidence level. You should compare the results shown in Figure 11.9 with your calculator results to check that you have correctly implemented the paired *t* calculator process. Remember, the calculator will typically give answers with more decimal accuracy than is shown in the text, so slight differences should not be cause for worry.

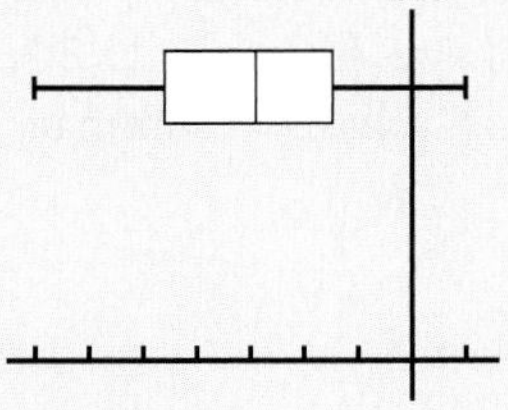

FIGURE 11.8
Boxplot of differences.

T-Test
$\mu < 0$
t = −4.563958109
p = 4.0568244E-4
$\bar{x}_2$ = −144.5833333
Sx = 109.7405687
n = 12

Tinterval
(−214.3, −74.86)
$\bar{x}$ = −144.5833333
Sx = 109.7405687
n = 12

FIGURE 11.9
Calculator output for the *t* test and confidence interval windows.

EXPLORATION 11.3 Inference about Differences in Proportions

Using your calculator for making inferences about the difference in population proportions is similar to the procedure for making inferences about the difference in population means using independent samples. Once again, navigate your calculator's menu system, this time looking for something like hypothesis tests and confidence intervals for "2 sample proportions."

Testing Hypotheses Data entry for a test of the null hypothesis of equal population proportions is very simple. Once you correctly identify the number of "successes" in the problem at hand, the most difficult part is remembering to check the large sample assumptions! We will use Example 11.9 for illustrative purposes. Recall that this example considered the efficacy of duct tape in removing warts. The data on successful wart removal are summarized in the accompanying table.

	Liquid Nitrogen Treatment	Duct Tape Treatment
Sample Size	$n_1 = 100$	$n_2 = 104$
Number of Successes	60	88
Sample Proportion	$\hat{p}_1 = 60/100 = .6$	$\hat{p}_2 = 88/104 = .846$

2-PropZTest
x1: 60
n1: 100
x2: 88
n2: 104
p1: $\neq p2 < p2 > p2$
Calculate Draw

FIGURE 11.10
Setup window for a two-proportion z test.

After transferring this data to the calculator screen, you should have something similar to the Figure 11.10.

Notice that you must choose your alternative hypothesis from among the three listed—in Example 11.9, the alternative hypothesis is H_a: $p_1 - p_2 < 0$, equivalent to

```
2-PropZTest
p1 < p2
z = −3.938342737
p = 4.1040568E-5
p̂1 = .6
p̂2 = .8461538462
p̂ = .7254901961
n1 = 100
n2 = 104
```

FIGURE 11.11
Output screen for a two-proportion z test.

$p_1 < p_2$. (On this calculator, the corresponding alternative hypothesis would be selected by moving the cursor to "<p2" and pressing Enter.)

When Enter is pressed, we are again presented with more information than will fit on one screen, so Figure 11.11 is another "larger than life" screen. This calculator screen presents enough information to reconstruct the hypothesis test of the example.

Confidence Intervals We now turn our attention to confidence intervals for the difference between two population proportions, using data from Example 11.11. Recall that this example looked at opinions on freedom of speech. Here is a summary of the data:

Group	Sample Size	Number in Agreement	*P*
Students	10,000	5,800	.58
Teachers	8,000	3,120	.39

```
2-PropZInt
x1:5800
n1:10000
x2:3120
n2:8000
C-Level: .90
Calculate
```

FIGURE 11.12
Setup window for a two-proportion z interval.

After navigating your calculator's menu system, you should find a screen for data entry. The entry of the data is similar to that for the hypothesis test, but here you must specify the confidence level, which was unnecessary for the hypothesis test. Figure 11.12 shows a representative screen.

After entering the appropriate values and pressing Enter, you should see something like Figure 11.13.

```
2-PropZInt
(.1779, .2021)
p̂1 .5800
p̂2 .3900
n1=10000.0000
n2=8000.0000
```

FIGURE 11.13
Output screen for a two-proportion z interval.

Notice that there is no actual point estimate of the difference in population proportions on this screen. If you want to express your confidence interval in point estimate ± error bound form, you must find the point estimate by subtracting the sample proportions. The values to add and subtract from the point estimate can be found by computing one-half the interval length given in the screen. These calculations are illustrated here:

$$\text{point estimate} = .5800 - .3900 = .1900$$
$$\text{error bound} = (.2021 - .1779)/2 = .0121.$$

The 90% confidence interval is then $.1900 \pm .0121$. Except for the effects of rounding, these values are in agreement with Example 11.11.

AP* Review Questions for Chapter 11

1. A study was carried out to determine if pulse rates are significantly higher after listening to rock music than after listening to classical music. Participants were randomly assigned to listen to either rock music or classical music. The heart rate of each participant was recorded after 30 minutes of listening to the assigned music. Let μ_1 represent the mean heart rate after listening to rock music, and let μ_2 represents the mean heart rate after listening to classical music. Which of the following hypotheses should be tested to determine if the mean heart rate after listening to rock music is significantly higher than the mean heart rate after listening to classical music?

   (A) H_0: $\mu_1 - \mu_2 = 0$ vs. H_a: $\mu_1 - \mu_2 < 0$
   (B) H_0: $\mu_1 - \mu_2 = 0$ vs. H_a: $\mu_1 - \mu_2 \neq 0$
   (C) H_0: $\mu_1 - \mu_2 = 0$ vs. H_a: $\mu_1 - \mu_2 > 0$
   (D) H_0: $\mu_1 - \mu_2 < 0$ vs. H_a: $\mu_1 - \mu_2 = 0$
   (E) H_0: $\mu_1 - \mu_2 > 0$ vs. H_a: $\mu_1 - \mu_2 = 0$

2. A medical researcher suspects that left-handed people have shorter right arms than left arms. To study this, he randomly selects 60 left-handed people and measures both the right and left arms of each. Let μ_{Right} be the average length (in inches) of the right arm of all left-handed people. Let μ_{Left} be the average length (in inches) of the left arm of all left-handed people. Let μ_d be the average difference (right – left) of the right arm and left arm of all left-handed people. Which of the following is the *best* pair of hypotheses for this study?

   (A) H_0: $\mu_{Right} - \mu_{Left} = 0$ vs. H_a: $\mu_{Right} - \mu_{Left} > 0$
   (B) H_0: $\mu_{Right} - \mu_{Left} > 0$ vs. H_a: $\mu_{Right} - \mu_{Left} < 0$
   (C) H_0: $\mu_d = 0$ vs. H_a: $\mu_d > 0$
   (D) H_0: $\mu_d = 0$ vs. H_a: $\mu_d < 0$
   (E) H_0: $\mu_d = 0$ vs. H_a: $\mu_d \neq 0$

3. Each person in a random sample of 200 students and a random sample of 186 faculty at a large university was asked "Do you take public transportation to campus?" Fifty-six percent of the students and 40% of the faculty responded "Yes." This data was used to carry out a test of the hypotheses H_0: $p_{Students} - p_{Faculty} = 0$ vs. H_a: $p_{Students} - p_{Faculty} \neq 0$. The value of the test statistic was $z = 3.14$. For a significance level of 0.01, which of the following is correct?

   (A) H_0 should be rejected; there is convincing evidence that the proportion of people who take public transportation to campus is different for students and faculty.
   (B) H_0 should be rejected; there is convincing evidence that the proportion of people who take public transportation to campus is the same for students and faculty.
   (C) H_0 should not be rejected; there is not convincing evidence that the proportion of people who take public transportation to campus is different for students and faculty.
   (D) H_0 should not be rejected; there is not convincing evidence that the proportion of people who take public transportation to campus is the same for students and faculty.
   (E) There is not enough information provided to be able to decide whether H_0 should be rejected or not.

4. Margie conducted a two-sample t-test of the hypotheses H_0: $\mu_1 - \mu_2 = 0$ versus H_a: $\mu_1 - \mu_2 > 0$, where μ_1 represents the mean dexterity score for female students and μ_2 represents the mean dexterity score for male students. After checking to make sure that the necessary assumptions were reasonable, she computed the P-value for her test to be .067. Jose used the same data to carry out a test to determine if there is evidence that the mean dexterity score for males is smaller than the mean for females, but he defined μ_1 as the mean for males and μ_2 as the mean for females. Which of the following statements is correct?

(A) Jose would have obtained a P-value of .933 when he conducted his test.
(B) Jose would have obtained a P-value of .467 when he conducted his test.
(C) Jose would have obtained a P-value of .134 when he conducted his test.
(D) Jose would have obtained a P-value of .067 when he conducted his test.
(E) Jose would have obtained a P-value of .032 when he conducted his test.

5. An investigator conducted a two-sample t-test of the hypotheses H_0: $\mu_1 - \mu_2 = 0$ versus H_a: $\mu_1 - \mu_2 > 0$, where μ_1 represents the mean dexterity score for female students and μ_2 represents the mean dexterity score for male students. After checking to make sure that the necessary assumptions were reasonable, she computed the P-value for her test to be .067. If she has selected a significance level of .05 for the test, what conclusion will she reach?

(A) She will fail to reject H_0 and conclude that there is not convincing evidence that the mean dexterity score is lower for males.
(B) She will fail to reject H_0 and conclude that there is convincing evidence that the mean dexterity score is the same for males and females.
(C) She will reject H_0 and conclude that there is convincing evidence that the mean dexterity score is lower for males.
(D) She will reject H_0 and conclude that there is not convincing evidence that the mean dexterity score is the same for males and females.
(E) Because .067 is greater that .05, it is not possible to make a decision about whether the null hypothesis should be rejected.

6. In a study to determine if a keyboarding class is effective in increasing typing speed, 40 of the students enrolling in the course have been randomly selected for testing, resulting in a "first day" sample and a "last day" sample. Because the samples are paired, the differences (last day − first day) will be used to carry out a paired t-test to decide if there is convincing evidence that mean typing speed of students who take this course is greater at the end of the course than on the first day. What are the appropriate null and alternative hypotheses?

(A) H_0: $\mu_d = 0$ versus H_a: $\mu_d < 0$
(B) H_0: $\mu_d = 0$ versus H_a: $\mu_d \neq 0$
(C) H_0: $\mu_d = 0$ versus H_a: $\mu_d > 0$
(D) H_0: $\mu_d < 0$ versus H_a: $\mu_d = 0$
(E) H_0: $\mu_d > 0$ versus H_a: $\mu_d = 0$

7. Some scientists believe that environmental factors affect population density. Spiders are very important species in terrestrial communities, and their survival is ecologically important. To better understand the relation between food level and spider survival, an experiment was conducted by supplementing the food supply of immature spiders in an area of low population density. In a control group of immature spiders, 83 out of 112 survived to the end of the experiment; in the food-supplemented experimental group, 86 out of 97 survived. The 90% confidence interval for the difference in population proportions is:

(A) -0.146 ± 0.103
(B) -0.146 ± 0.086
(C) -0.146 ± 0.052
(D) -0.146 ± 0.005
(E) -0.146 ± 0.003

8. One of the t-procedures for making inferences about the difference in two population means requires that the samples are independent. Of the following, which would guarantee independent samples?

(A) Each sample is a simple random sample from the corresponding population.
(B) The sample sizes are at least 30 for each of the populations.
(C) The populations are normally distributed.
(D) The population variances are equal.
(E) The sample sizes are equal.

9. For independent random samples, the sampling distribution of $\bar{x}_1 - \bar{x}_2$ is approximately normal if

(A) either one of the sample sizes is at least 30.
(B) at least one of the sample sizes is at least 30.
(C) both of the sample sizes are at least 30.
(D) the total number sampled is at least 30.
(E) the total number sampled at least 60.

10. For two independent random samples, the estimated standard deviation of $\bar{x}_1 - \bar{x}_2$ is

(A) $\sqrt{\frac{\sigma_1^2}{n_1} - \frac{\sigma_2^2}{n_2}}$
(B) $\sqrt{\frac{\sigma_1^2}{n_1} + \frac{\sigma_2^2}{n_2}}$
(C) $\sqrt{\frac{s_1^2}{n_1} - \frac{s_2^2}{n_2}}$
(D) $\sqrt{\frac{s_1^2}{n_1} + \frac{s_2^2}{n_2}}$
(E) None of the above.

11. For independent random samples, the sampling distribution of $\hat{p}_1 - \hat{p}_2$ is approximately normal for:

(A) $n_1 = n_2 = 50$, $p_1 = .05$, and $p_2 = .10$
(B) $n_1 = n_2 = 20$, $p_1 = .50$, and $p_2 = .40$
(C) $n_1 = n_2 = 100$, $p_1 = .02$, and $p_2 = .10$
(D) $n_1 = n_2 = 100$, $p_1 = .06$, and $p_2 = .10$
(E) $n_1 = n_2 = 100$, $p_1 = .15$, and $p_2 = .10$

12. Researchers conducted a two-sample t test of the hypotheses H_0: $\mu_A - \mu_B = 0$ vs. H_a: $\mu_A - \mu_B < 0$,where μ_A represents the mean number of text messages sent per month by people with cell phone service A and μ_B represents the mean number of text messages sent per month by people with cell phone service B. After checking to make sure that the necessary assumptions were reasonable, the *P*-value was found to be 0.079. At a significance level of $\alpha = 0.01$ the researchers should decide to ________ H_0, and at a significance level of $\alpha = 0.05$ they should decide to ________ H_0.

(A) reject; reject
(B) fail to reject; reject
(C) fail to reject; fail to reject
(D) reject; fail to reject
(E) The conclusion would be the same for both significance levels, but it is not possible to determine whether the conclusion would be to reject or fail to reject.

13. Each person in a sample of 200 students and a sample of 100 faculty members at a large university was asked "Do you exercise regularly?" The resulting data were used to carry out a test of the hypotheses H_0: $p_{\text{Students}} - p_{\text{Faculty}} = 0$ vs. H_a: $p_{\text{Students}} - p_{\text{Faculty}} > 0$. The value of the test statistic was $z = 3.46$. Which of the following could be the 95% confidence interval for $p_{\text{Students}} - p_{\text{Faculty}}$ computed from this same data?

(A) (−0.26, −0.06)
(B) (−0.26, 0.06)
(C) (−0.06, 0.26)
(D) (0.06, 0.26)
(E) (6, 26)

14. An experiment was carried out to investigate whether lighting affects the quality of work produced by machine operators at a factory. Forty machine operators volunteered to participate as subjects in the experiment. The subjects were assigned at random to one of two experimental groups. Subjects in Group 1 worked for two days in bright light and subjects in Group 2 worked for 2 days in dim light. The number of defective items produced during the two days was recorded for each subject. It was determined that the mean number of defective items produced was significantly higher for Group 2 than for Group 1. Which of the following is the most appropriate conclusion that can be drawn from this experiment?

(A) The observed difference in mean number of defective items is likely to be due to chance and so lighting has no effect on number of defective items produced.
(B) It is not possible to draw any conclusions from this experiment because volunteers were used.
(C) It is possible to conclude that the observed difference in mean number of defective items produced is attributable to differences in lighting, but it is not reasonable to generalize this result to all machine operators at this factory.
(D) It is not possible to conclude that the observed difference in mean number of defective items produced is attributable to differences in lighting, but it is reasonable to generalize this result to all machine operators at this factory.
(E) It is possible to conclude that the observed difference in mean number of defective items produced is attributable to differences in lighting, and it is reasonable to generalize this result to all machine operators at this factory.

15. A study was conducted to investigate whether teenagers who play online games for more than 1 hour in a typical day have quicker reaction times than those who do not play online games more than 1 hour in a typical day. Because mean reaction time might be different for boys and girls, only boys were studied. Two hundred boys were randomly selected from the students attending a large high school, and they were divided into groups based on whether or not they played online games for more than 1 hour in a typical day. Time to react to a visual stimulus was recorded for each boy. The mean reaction time for those who reported playing online games more than 1 hour a day was significantly lower than the mean reaction time for those who did not play more than 1 hour a day. Which of the following conclusions is reasonable based on this study?

(A) Playing online games for more than 1 hour a day decreases reaction time.
(B) Playing online games for more than 1 hour a day decreases the reaction time of boys.
(C) Playing online games for more than 1 hour a day decreased the reaction time of boys in at this school.
(D) Boys at this school who play online games for more than 1 hour a day have a lower mean reaction time than boys at this school who do not play online games for more than 1 hour a day.
(E) Teenagers who play online games for more than 1 hour a day have quicker reaction times, on average, than teenagers who do not play online games for more than 1 hour a day.

CHAPTER 12

The Analysis of Categorical Data and Goodness-of-Fit Tests

Greg Flume/NewSport/Corbis

It is often the case that information is collected on categorical variables, such as political affiliation, gender, or college major. As with numerical data, categorical data sets can be univariate (consisting of observations on a single categorical variable), bivariate (observations on two categorical variables), or even multivariate. In this chapter, we will first consider inferential methods for analyzing univariate categorical data sets and then turn to techniques appropriate for use with bivariate categorical data.

Make the most of your study time by accessing everything you need to succeed online with CourseMate.
Visit http://www.cengagebrain.com where you will find:

- An interactive eBook, which allows you to take notes, highlight, bookmark, search the text, and use in-context glossary definitions
- Step-by-step instructions for Minitab, Excel, TI-83/84, SPSS, and JMP
- Video solutions to selected exercises
- Data sets available for selected examples and exercises
- Online quizzes
- Flashcards
- Videos

12.1 Chi-Square Tests for Univariate Data

Univariate categorical data sets arise in a variety of settings. If each student in a sample of 100 is classified according to whether he or she is enrolled full-time or part-time, data on a categorical variable with two categories result. Each airline passenger in a sample of 50 might be classified into one of three categories based on type of ticket—coach, business class, or first class. Each registered voter in a sample of 100 selected from those registered in a particular city might be asked which of the five city council members he or she favors for mayor. This would yield observations on a categorical variable with five categories.

AP* EXAM TIP

In this chapter we will consider three different chi-square tests. If you have an older graphing calculator or an older operating system on your calculator, you may not have all three of these tests built in. Check to see if you have these tests; if not, go online and download the latest operating system and chi-square programs.

Univariate categorical data are most conveniently summarized in a **one-way frequency table.** For example, the article "Fees Keeping American Taxpayers From Using Credit Cards to Make Tax Payments" (*IPSOS Insight*, March 24, 2006) surveyed American taxpayers regarding their intent to pay taxes with a credit card. Suppose that 100 randomly selected taxpayers participated in such a survey, with possible responses being definitely will use a credit card to pay taxes next year, probably will use a credit card, probably won't use a credit card, and definitely won't use a credit card. The first few observations might be

Probably will	Definitely will not	Probably will not
Probably will not	Definitely will	Definitely will not

Counting the number of observations of each type might then result in the following one-way table:

	Outcome			
	Definitely Will	Probably Will	Probably Will Not	Definitely Will Not
Frequency	14	12	24	50

For a categorical variable with k possible values (k different levels or categories), sample data are summarized in a one-way frequency table consisting of k cells, which may be displayed either horizontally or vertically.

In this section, we consider testing hypotheses about the proportion of the population that falls into each of the possible categories. For example, the manager of a tax preparation company might be interested in determining whether the four possible responses to the tax credit card question occur equally often. If this is indeed the case, the long-run proportion of responses falling into each of the four categories is 1/4, or .25. The test procedure to be presented shortly would allow the manager to decide whether the hypothesis that all four category proportions are equal to .25 is plausible.

Notation

k = number of categories of a categorical variable
p_1 = true proportion for Category 1
p_2 = true proportion for Category 2
⋮
p_k = true proportion for Category k
(Note: $p_1 + p_2 + \cdots + p_k = 1$)

(continued)

The hypotheses to be tested have the form

H_0: p_1 = hypothesized proportion for Category 1
p_2 = hypothesized proportion for Category 2
⋮
p_k = hypothesized proportion for Category k

H_a: H_0 is not true, so at least one of the true category proportions differs from the corresponding hypothesized value.

For the example involving responses to the tax survey, let

p_1 = the proportion of all taxpayers who will definitely pay by credit card
p_2 = the proportion of all taxpayers who will probably pay by credit card
p_3 = the proportion of all taxpayers who will probably not pay by credit card

and

p_4 = the proportion of all taxpayers who will definitely not pay by credit card

The null hypothesis of interest is then

$$H_0\text{: } p_1 = .25, p_2 = .25, p_3 = .25, p_4 = .25$$

A null hypothesis of the type just described can be tested by first selecting a random sample of size n and then classifying each sample response into one of the k possible categories. To decide whether the sample data are compatible with the null hypothesis, we compare the observed cell counts (frequencies) to the cell counts that would have been expected when the null hypothesis is true. The expected cell counts are

Expected cell count for Category 1 = np_1
Expected cell count for Category 2 = np_2

and so on. The expected cell counts when H_0 is true result from substituting the corresponding hypothesized proportion for each p_i.

EXAMPLE 12.1 Births and the Lunar Cycle

Anthony Ise/PhotoDisc/Getty Images//Cengage Learning/Getty Images

● A common urban legend is that more babies than expected are born during certain phases of the lunar cycle, especially near the full moon. The paper "The Effect of the Lunar Cycle on Frequency of Births and Birth Complications" (*American Journal of Obstetrics and Gynecology* [2005]: 1462–1464) classified births according to the lunar cycle. Data for a sample of randomly selected births occurring during 24 lunar

Lunar Phase	Number of Days	Number of Births
New moon	24	7,680
Waxing crescent	152	48,442
First quarter	24	7,579
Waxing gibbous	149	47,814
Full moon	24	7,711
Waning gibbous	150	47,595
Last quarter	24	7,733
Waning crescent	152	48,230

● Data set available online

cycles consistent with summary quantities appearing in the paper are given in the accompanying table.

Let's define lunar phase category proportions as follows:

AP* EXAM TIP

If there are a lot of categories, defining all of the category proportions can take a bit of time. On the AP exam, the number of categories will usually be small, which should make it possible for you to carefully define the category proportions.

p_1 = proportion of births that occur during the new moon
p_2 = proportion of births that occur during the waxing crescent moon
p_3 = proportion of births that occur during the first quarter moon
p_4 = proportion of births that occur during the waxing gibbous moon
p_5 = proportion of births that occur during the full moon
p_6 = proportion of births that occur during the waning gibbous moon
p_7 = proportion of births that occur during the last quarter moon
p_8 = proportion of births that occur during the waning crescent moon

If there is no relationship between number of births and the lunar cycle, then the number of births in each lunar cycle category should be proportional to the number of days included in that category. Since there are a total of 699 days in the 24 lunar cycles considered and 24 of those days are in the new moon category, if there is no relationship between number of births and lunar cycle,

$$p_1 = \frac{24}{699} = .0343$$

Similarly, in the absence of any relationship,

$$p_2 = \frac{152}{699} = .2175 \qquad p_3 = \frac{24}{699} = .0343$$

$$p_4 = \frac{149}{699} = .2132 \qquad p_5 = \frac{24}{699} = .0343$$

$$p_6 = \frac{150}{699} = .2146 \qquad p_7 = \frac{24}{699} = .0343$$

$$p_8 = \frac{152}{699} = .2175$$

The hypotheses of interest are then

H_0: $p_1 = .0343, p_2 = .2175, p_3 = .0343, p_4 = .2132, p_5 = .0343, p_6 = .2146,$
$p_7 = .0343, p_8 = .2175$
H_a: H_0 is not true.

There were a total of 222,784 births in the sample, so if H_0 is true, the expected counts for the first two categories are

$$\begin{pmatrix}\text{expected count}\\ \text{for new moon}\end{pmatrix} = n\begin{pmatrix}\text{hypothesized proportion}\\ \text{for new moon}\end{pmatrix}$$
$$= 222{,}784(.0343) = 7641.49$$

$$\begin{pmatrix}\text{expected count}\\ \text{for waxing crescent}\end{pmatrix} = n\begin{pmatrix}\text{hypothesized proportion}\\ \text{for waxing crescent}\end{pmatrix}$$
$$= 222{,}784(.2175) = 48{,}455.52$$

Expected counts for the other six categories are computed in a similar fashion, and observed and expected cell counts are given in the following table.

Lunar Phase	Observed Number of Births	Expected Number of Births
New moon	7,680	7,641.49
Waxing crescent	48,442	48,455.52
First quarter	7,579	7,641.49
Waxing gibbous	47,814	47,497.55
Full moon	7,711	7,641.49
Waning gibbous	47,595	47,809.45
Last quarter	7,733	7,641.49
Waning crescent	48,230	48,455.52

Because the observed counts are based on a *sample* of births, it would be somewhat surprising to see *exactly* 3.43% of the sample falling in the first category, exactly 21.75% in the second, and so on, even when H_0 is true. If the differences between the observed and expected cell counts can reasonably be attributed to sampling variation, the data are considered compatible with H_0. On the other hand, if the discrepancy between the observed and the expected cell counts is too large to be attributed solely to chance differences from one sample to another, H_0 should be rejected in favor of H_a. To make a decision, we need an assessment of how different the observed and expected counts are.

The goodness-of-fit statistic, denoted by X^2, is a quantitative measure of the extent to which the observed counts differ from those expected when H_0 is true. (The Greek letter χ is often used in place of X. The symbol X^2 is referred to as the chi-square [χ^2] statistic. In using X^2 rather than χ^2, we are adhering to the convention of denoting sample quantities by Roman letters.)

The **goodness-of-fit statistic**, X^2, results from first computing the quantity

$$\frac{(\text{observed cell count} - \text{expected cell count})^2}{\text{expected cell count}}$$

for each cell, where, for a sample of size n,

$$\begin{pmatrix}\text{expected cell}\\ \text{count}\end{pmatrix} = n\begin{pmatrix}\text{hypothesized value of corresponding}\\ \text{population proportion}\end{pmatrix}$$

The X^2 statistic is the sum of these quantities for all k cells:

$$X^2 = \sum_{\text{all cells}} \frac{(\text{observed cell count} - \text{expected cell count})^2}{\text{expected cell count}}$$

The value of the X^2 statistic reflects the magnitude of the discrepancies between observed and expected cell counts. When the differences are sizable, the value of X^2 tends to be large. Therefore, large values of X^2 suggest rejection of H_0. A small value of X^2 (it can never be negative) occurs when the observed cell counts are quite similar to those expected when H_0 is true and so would be consistent with H_0.

As with previous test procedures, a conclusion is reached by comparing a *P*-value to the significance level for the test. The *P*-value is computed as the probability of observing a value of X^2 at least as large as the observed value when H_0 is true. This requires information about the sampling distribution of X^2 when H_0 is true.

When the null hypothesis is correct and the sample size is sufficiently large, the behavior of X^2 is described approximately by a **chi-square distribution**. A chi-square curve has no area associated with negative values and is asymmetric, with a longer tail on the right. There are actually many chi-square distributions, each one identified with a different number of degrees of freedom. Curves corresponding to several chi-square distributions are shown in Figure 12.1.

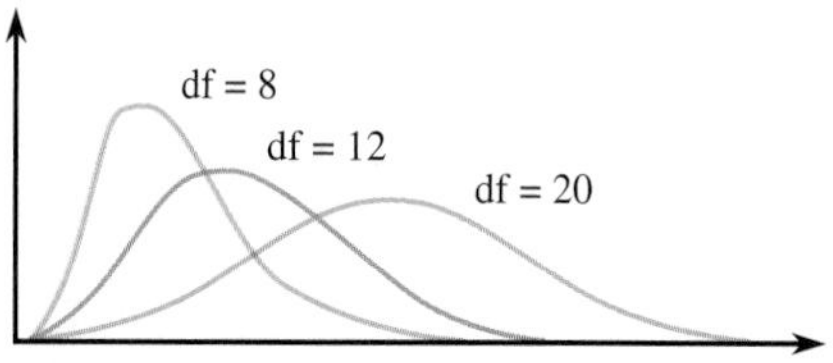

FIGURE 12.1
Chi-square curves.

For a test procedure based on the X^2 statistic, the associated *P*-value is the area under the appropriate chi-square curve and to the right of the computed X^2 value. Appendix Table 8 gives upper-tail areas for chi-square distributions with up to 20 df. Our chi-square table has a different appearance from the *t* table used in previous chapters. In the *t* table, there is a single "value" column on the far left and then a column of *P*-values (tail areas) for each different number of degrees of freedom. A single column of *t* values works for the *t* table because all *t* curves are centered at 0, and the *t* curves approach the *z* curve as the number of degrees of freedom increases. However, because the chi-square curves move farther and farther to the right and spread out more as the number of degrees of freedom increases, a single "value" column is impractical in this situation.

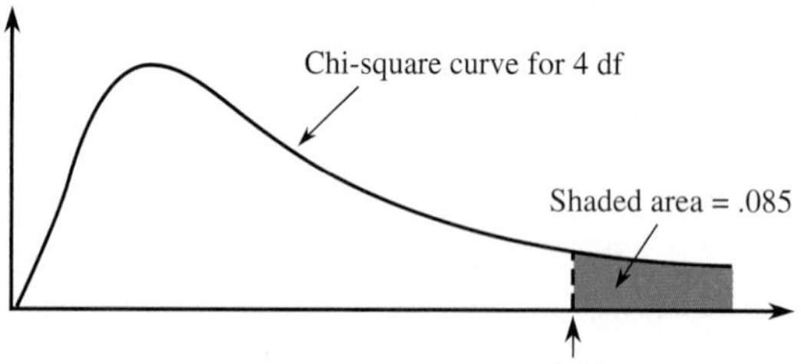

FIGURE 12.2
A chi-square upper-tail area.

To find the area to the right of a particular X^2 value, locate the appropriate df column in Appendix Table 8. Determine which listed value is closest to the X^2 value of interest, and read the right-tail area corresponding to this value from the left-hand column of the table. For example, for a chi-square distribution with df = 4, the area to the right of $X^2 = 8.18$ is .085, as shown in Figure 12.2. For this same chi-square distribution (df = 4), the area to the right of 9.70 is approximately .045 (the area to the right of 9.74, the closest entry in the table for df = 4).

It is also possible to use computer software or a graphing calculator to compute areas under a chi-square curve. This provides more accurate values for the area.

Goodness-of-Fit Tests

When H_0 is true, the X^2 goodness-of-fit statistic has approximately a chi-square distribution with df = $(k - 1)$, as long as none of the expected cell counts are too small. When expected counts are small, and especially when an expected count is less than 1, the value of $\frac{(\text{observed cell count} - \text{expected cell count})^2}{\text{expected cell count}}$ can be inflated because it involves dividing by a small number. *It is generally agreed that use of the chi-square distribution is appropriate when the sample size is large enough for every expected cell count to be at least 5.* If any of the expected cell frequencies are less than 5, categories can be combined in a sensible way to create acceptable expected cell counts. Just remember to compute the number of degrees of freedom based on the reduced number of categories.

Goodness-of-Fit Test Procedure

Hypotheses: H_0: p_1 = hypothesized proportion for Category 1

$\vdots$

p_k = hypothesized proportion for Category k

H_a: H_0 is not true

Test statistic:
$$X^2 = \sum_{\text{all cells}} \frac{(\text{observed cell count} - \text{expected cell count})^2}{\text{expected cell count}}$$

***P*-values:** When H_0 is true and all expected counts are at least 5, X^2 has approximately a chi-square distribution with df $= k - 1$. Therefore, the P-value associated with the computed test statistic value is the area to the right of X^2 under the df $= k - 1$ chi-square curve. Upper-tail areas for chi-square distributions are found in Appendix Table 8.

Assumptions:
1. Observed cell counts are based on a *random sample.*
2. The *sample size is large.* The sample size is large enough for the chi-square test to be appropriate as long as every expected cell count is at least 5.

EXAMPLE 12.2 Births and the Lunar Cycle Revisited

We use the births data of Example 12.1 to test the hypothesis that number of births is unrelated to lunar cycle. Let's use a .05 level of significance and the nine-step hypothesis-testing procedure illustrated in previous chapters.

1. Let $p_1, p_2, p_3, p_4, p_5, p_6, p_7$, and p_8 denote the proportions of all births falling in the eight lunar cycle categories as defined in Example 12.1.
2. H_0: $p_1 = .0343$, $p_2 = .2175$, $p_3 = .0343$, $p_4 = .2132$, $p_5 = .0343$, $p_6 = .2146$, $p_7 = .0343$, $p_8 = .2175$
3. H_a: H_0 is not true.
4. Significance level: $\alpha = .05$.
5. Test statistic: $X^2 = \sum_{\text{all cells}} \frac{(\text{observed cell count} - \text{expected cell count})^2}{\text{expected cell count}}$
6. Assumptions: The expected cell counts (from Example 12.1) are all greater than 5. The births represent a random sample of births occurring during the lunar cycles considered.
7. Calculation:

$$X^2 = \frac{(7680 - 7641.49)^2}{7641.49} + \frac{(48442 - 48455.52)^2}{48455.52} + \cdots + \frac{(48230 - 48455.52)^2}{48455.52}$$
$$= .194 + .004 + .511 + 2.108 + .632 + .962 + 1.096 + 1.050$$
$$= 6.557$$

8. P-value: The P-value is based on a chi-square distribution with df = 8 − 1 = 7. The computed value of X^2 is smaller than 12.01 (the smallest entry in the df = 7 column of Appendix Table 8), so P-value > .10.
9. Conclusion: Because P-value > α, H_0 cannot be rejected. There is not sufficient evidence to conclude that number of births and lunar cycle are related. This is consistent with the conclusion in the paper: "We found no statistical evidence that deliveries occurred in a predictable pattern across the phases of the lunar cycle."

Statistical software can be used to perform a chi-square goodness-of-fit test. Minitab output for the data and hypothesized proportions of this example is shown here.

Chi-Square Goodness-of-Fit Test for Observed Counts in Variable: Number of Births
Using category names in Lunar Phase

Category	Observed	Test Proportion	Expected	Contribution to Chi-Sq
First Quarter	7579	0.0343	7641.5	0.51105
Full Moon	7711	0.0343	7641.5	0.63227
Last Quarter	7733	0.0343	7641.5	1.09584
New Moon	7680	0.0343	7641.5	0.19406
Waning Crescent	48230	0.2175	48455.5	1.04961
Waning Gibbous	47595	0.2146	47809.4	0.96189
Waxing Crescent	48442	0.2175	48455.5	0.00377
Waxing Gibbous	47814	0.2132	47497.5	2.10835

N	DF	Chi-Sq	P-Value
222784	7	6.55683	0.476

Note that Minitab has reordered the categories from smallest to largest based on the observed count. Minitab also carried a bit more decimal accuracy in the computation of the chi-square statistic, reporting $X^2 = 6.55683$ and an associated P-value of .476. The computed P-value = .476 is consistent with the statement P-value > .10 from Step 8 of the hypothesis test.

EXAMPLE 12.3 Hybrid Car Purchases

● *USA Today* ("Hybrid Car Sales Rose 81% Last Year," April 25, 2005) reported the top five states for sales of hybrid cars in 2004 as California, Virginia, Washington, Florida, and Maryland. Suppose that each car in a sample of 2004 hybrid car sales is classified by state where the sale took place. Sales from states other than the top five were excluded from the sample, resulting in the accompanying table.

State	Observed Frequency
California	250
Virginia	56
Washington	34
Florida	33
Maryland	33
Total	**406**

(The given observed counts are artificial, but they are consistent with hybrid sales figures given in the article.)

● Data set available online

We will use the X^2 goodness-of-fit test and a significance level of $\alpha = .01$ to test the hypothesis that hybrid sales for these five states are proportional to the 2004 population for these states. 2004 population estimates from the Census Bureau web site are given in the following table. The population proportion for each state was computed by dividing each state population by the total population for all five states.

State	2004 Population	Population Proportion
California	35,842,038	0.495
Virginia	7,481,332	0.103
Washington	6,207,046	0.085
Florida	17,385,430	0.240
Maryland	5,561,332	0.077
Total	**72,477,178**	

If these same population proportions hold for hybrid car sales, the expected counts are

$$\begin{aligned}
\text{Expected count for California} &= 406(.495) = 200.970\\
\text{Expected count for Virginia} &= 406(.103) = 41.818\\
\text{Expected count for Washington} &= 406(.085) = 34.510\\
\text{Expected count for Florida} &= 406(.240) = 97.440\\
\text{Expected count for Maryland} &= 406(.077) = 31.362
\end{aligned}$$

These expected counts have been entered in Table 12.1.

TABLE 12.1 Observed and Expected Counts for Example 12.3

State	Observed Counts	Expected Counts
California	250	200.970
Virginia	56	41.818
Washington	34	34.510
Florida	33	97.440
Maryland	33	31.262

1. Let $p_1, p_2, \ldots, p_5$ denote the actual proportion of hybrid car sales for the five states in the following order: California, Virginia, Washington, Florida, and Maryland.
2. H_0: $p_1 = .495, p_2 = .103, p_3 = .085, p_4 = .240, p_5 = .077$
3. H_a: H_0 is not true.
4. Significance level: $\alpha = .01$
5. Test statistic: $X^2 = \sum_{\text{all cells}} \frac{(\text{observed cell count} - \text{expected cell count})^2}{\text{expected cell count}}$
6. Assumptions: The sample was a random sample of hybrid car sales. All expected counts are greater than 5, so the sample size is large enough to use the chi-square test.

7. Calculation: From Minitab

Chi-Square Goodness-of-Fit Test for Observed Counts in Variable: Hybrid Sales

Using category names in State

Category	Observed	Test Proportion	Expected	Contribution to Chi-Sq
California	250	0.495	200.970	11.9617
Florida	33	0.240	97.440	42.6161
Maryland	33	0.077	31.262	0.0966
Virginia	56	0.103	41.818	4.8096
Washington	34	0.085	34.510	0.0075

N	DF	Chi-Sq	P-Value
406	4	59.4916	0.000

8. *P*-value: All expected counts exceed 5, so the *P*-value can be based on a chi-square distribution with df $= 5 - 1 = 4$. From Minitab, the *P*-value is 0.000.
9. Conclusion: Since *P*-value $\leq \alpha$, H_0 is rejected. There is convincing evidence that hybrid sales are not proportional to population size for at least one of the five states.

Based on the hybrid sales data, we have determined that there is convincing evidence that at least one of these five states has hybrid sales that are not proportional to population size. Looking back at the Minitab output, notice that there is a column labeled "Contribution to Chi-Sq." This column shows the individual values of $\frac{(\text{observed cell count} - \text{expected cell count})^2}{\text{expected cell count}}$, which are summed to produce the value of the chi-square statistic. Notice that the two states with the largest contribution to the chi-square statistic are Florida and California. For Florida, observed hybrid sales were smaller than expected (observed = 33, expected = 97.44), whereas for California observed sales were higher than expected (observed = 250, expected = 200.970).

EXERCISES 12.1 - 12.13

12.1 From the given information in each case below, state what you know about the *P*-value for a chi-square test and give the conclusion for a significance level of $\alpha = .01$.

a. $X^2 = 7.5$, df $= 2$
b. $X^2 = 13.0$, df $= 6$
c. $X^2 = 18.0$, df $= 9$
d. $X^2 = 21.3$, df $= 4$
e. $X^2 = 5.0$, df $= 3$

12.2 A particular paperback book is published in a choice of four different covers. A certain bookstore keeps copies of each cover on its racks. To test the hypothesis that sales are equally divided among the four choices, a random sample of 100 purchases is identified.

a. If the resulting X^2 value were 6.4, what conclusion would you reach when using a test with significance level .05?
b. What conclusion would be appropriate at significance level .01 if $X^2 = 15.3$?
c. If there were six different covers rather than just four, what would you conclude if $X^2 = 13.7$ and a test with $\alpha = .05$ was used?

12.3 Packages of mixed nuts made by a certain company contain four types of nuts. The percentages of nuts of Types 1, 2, 3, and 4 are supposed to be 40%, 30%, 20%, and 10%, respectively. A random sample of nuts is selected, and each one is categorized by type.

a. If the sample size is 200 and the resulting test statistic value is $X^2 = 19.0$, what conclusion would be appropriate for a significance level of .001?

b. If the random sample had consisted of only 40 nuts, would you use the chi-square test here? Explain your reasoning.

12.4 ● The article "In Bronx, Hitting Home Runs Is A Breeze" (*USA Today*, June 2, 2009) included a classification of 87 home runs hit at the new Yankee Stadium according to direction that the ball was hit, resulting in the accompanying data.

Direction	Left Field	Left Center	Center	Right Center	Right Field
Number of Home Runs	18	10	7	18	34

a. Assuming that it is reasonable to regard this sample of 87 home runs as representative of home runs hit at Yankee Stadium, carry out a hypothesis test to determine if there is convincing evidence that the proportion of home runs hit is not the same for all five directions.

b. Write a few sentences describing how the observed counts for the five directions differ from what would have been expected if the proportion of home runs is the same for all five directions.

12.5 ● The authors of the paper "Racial Stereotypes in Children's Television Commercials" (*Journal of Advertising Research* [2008]: 80–93) counted the number of times that characters of different ethnicities appeared in commercials aired on Philadelphia television stations, resulting in the data in the accompanying table.

Ethnicity	African-American	Asian	Caucasian	Hispanic
Observed Frequency	57	11	330	6

Based on the 2000 Census, the proportion of the U.S. population falling into each of these four ethnic groups are .177 for African-American, .032 for Asian, .734 for Caucasian, and .057 for Hispanic. Do the data provide sufficient evidence to conclude that the proportions appearing in commercials are not the same as the census proportions? Test the relevant hypotheses using a significance level of .01.

12.6 The paper "Sociochemosensory and Emotional Functions" (*Psychological Science* [2009]: 1118–1124) describes an interesting experiment to determine if college students can identify their roommates by smell. Forty-four female college students participated as subjects in the experiment. Each subject was presented with a set of three t-shirts that were identical in appearance. Each of the three t-shirts had been slept in for at least 7 hours by a person who had not used any scented products (like scented deodorant, soap, or shampoo) for at least 48 hours prior to sleeping in the shirt. One of the three shirts had been worn by the subject's roommate. The subject was asked to identify the shirt worn by her roommate. This process was then repeated with another three shirts, and the number of times out of the two trials that the subject correctly identified the shirt worn by her roommate was recorded. The resulting data is given in the accompanying table.

Number of Correct Identifications	0	1	2
Observed Count	21	10	13

a. Can a person identify her roommate by smell? If not, the data from the experiment should be consistent with what we would have expected to see if subjects were just guessing on each trial. That is, we would expect that the probability of selecting the correct shirt would be 1/3 on each of the two trials. It would then be reasonable to regard the number of correct identifications as a binomial variable with $n = 2$ and $p = 1/3$. Use this binomial distribution to compute the proportions of the time we would expect to see 0, 1, and 2 correct identifications if subjects are just guessing.

b. Use the three proportions computed in Part (a) to carry out a test to determine if the numbers of correct identifications by the students in this study are significantly different than what would have been expected by guessing. Use $\alpha = .05$. (Note: One of the expected counts is just a bit less than 5. For purposes of this exercise, assume that it is OK to proceed with a goodness-of-fit test.)

12.7 ● The paper "Cigarette Tar Yields in Relation to Mortality from Lung Cancer in the Cancer Prevention Study II Prospective Cohort" (*British Medical Journal* [2004]: 72–79) included the accompanying data on the tar level of cigarettes smoked for a sample of male smokers who subsequently died of lung cancer.

Tar Level	Frequency
0–7 mg	103
8–14 mg	378
15–21 mg	563
≥22 mg	150

Assume it is reasonable to regard the sample as representative of male smokers who die of lung cancer. Is there convincing evidence that the proportion of male smoker lung cancer deaths is not the same for the four given tar level categories?

12.8 ● The paper referenced in the previous exercise also gave the accompanying data on the age at which smoking started for a sample of 1031 men who smoked low-tar cigarettes.

Age	Frequency
<16	237
16–17	258
18–20	320
≥21	216

a. Use a chi-square goodness-of-fit test to test the null hypothesis H_0: $p_1 = .25, p_2 = .2, p_3 = .3, p_4 = .25$, where p_1 = proportion of male low-tar cigarette smokers who started smoking before age 16, and p_2, p_3, and p_4 are defined in a similar way for the other three age groups.

b. The null hypothesis from Part (a) specifies that half of male smokers of low-tar cigarettes began smoking between the ages of 16 and 20. Explain why $p_2 = .2$ and $p_3 = .3$ is consistent with the ages between 16 and 20 being equally likely to be when smoking started.

12.9 ● The report "Fatality Facts 2004: Bicycles" (Insurance Institute, 2004) included the following table classifying 715 fatal bicycle accidents according to time of day the accident occurred.

Time of Day	Number of Accidents
Midnight to 3 A.M.	38
3 A.M. to 6 A.M.	29
6 A.M. to 9 A.M.	66
9 A.M. to Noon	77
Noon to 3 P.M.	99
3 P.M. to 6 P.M.	127
6 P.M. to 9 P.M.	166
9 P.M. to Midnight	113

a. Assume it is reasonable to regard the 715 bicycle accidents summarized in the table as a random sample of fatal bicycle accidents in 2004. Do these data support the hypothesis that fatal bicycle accidents are not equally likely to occur in each of the 3-hour time periods used to construct the table? Test the relevant hypotheses using a significance level of .05.

b. Suppose a safety office proposes that bicycle fatalities are twice as likely to occur between noon and midnight as during midnight to noon and suggests the following hypothesis: H_0: $p_1 = 1/3, p_2 = 2/3$, where p_1 is the proportion of accidents occurring between midnight and noon and p_2 is the proportion occurring between noon and midnight. Do the given data provide evidence against this hypothesis, or are the data consistent with it? Justify your answer with an appropriate test. (Hint: Use the data to construct a one-way table with just two time categories.)

12.10 ● The report referenced in the previous exercise ("Fatality Facts 2004: Bicycles") also classified 719 fatal bicycle accidents according to the month in which the accident occurred, resulting in the accompanying table.

Month	Number of Accidents
January	38
February	32
March	43
April	59
May	78
June	74
July	98
August	85
September	64
October	66
November	42
December	40

a. Use the given data to test the null hypothesis H_0: $p_1 = 1/12, p_2 = 1/12, \ldots, p_{12} = 1/12$, where p_1 is the proportion of fatal bicycle accidents that occur in January, p_2 is the proportion for February, and so on. Use a significance level of .01.

b. The null hypothesis in Part (a) specifies that fatal accidents were equally likely to occur in any of the 12 months. But not all months have the same number of days. What null and alternative hypotheses would you test to determine if some months are riskier than others if you wanted to take differing month lengths into account? (Hint: 2004 was a leap year, with 366 days.)

c. Test the hypotheses proposed in Part (b) using a .05 significance level.

12.11 An article about the California lottery that appeared in the *San Luis Obispo Tribune* (December 15, 1999) gave the following information on the age distribution of adults in California: 35% are between 18 and 34 years old, 51% are between 35 and 64 years old, and 14% are 65 years old or older. The article also gave information on the age distribution of those who purchase lottery tickets. The following table is consistent with the values given in the article:

Age of Purchaser	Frequency
18–34	36
35–64	130
65 and over	34

Suppose that the data resulted from a random sample of 200 lottery ticket purchasers. Based on these sample data, is it reasonable to conclude that one or more of these three age groups buys a disproportionate share of lottery tickets? Use a chi-square goodness-of-fit test with $\alpha = .05$.

12.12 A certain genetic characteristic of a particular plant can appear in one of three forms (phenotypes). A researcher has developed a theory, according to which the hypothesized proportions are $p_1 = .25$, $p_2 = .50$, and $p_3 = .25$. A random sample of 200 plants yields $X^2 = 4.63$.

a. Carry out a test of the null hypothesis that the theory is correct, using level of significance $\alpha = .05$.
b. Suppose that a random sample of 300 plants had resulted in the same value of X^2. How would your analysis and conclusion differ from those in Part (a)?

12.13 ✦ The article "Linkage Studies of the Tomato" (*Transactions of the Royal Canadian Institute* [1931]: 1–19) reported the accompanying data on phenotypes resulting from crossing tall cut-leaf tomatoes with dwarf potato-leaf tomatoes. There are four possible phenotypes: (1) tall cut-leaf, (2) tall potato-leaf, (3) dwarf cut-leaf, and (4) dwarf potato-leaf.

	Phenotype			
	1	2	3	4
Frequency	926	288	293	104

Mendel's laws of inheritance imply that $p_1 = 9/16$, $p_2 = 3/16$, $p_3 = 3/16$, and $p_4 = 1/16$. Are the data from this experiment consistent with Mendel's laws? Use a .01 significance level.

12.2 Tests for Homogeneity and Independence in a Two-way Table

Data resulting from observations made on two different categorical variables can also be summarized using a tabular format. As an example, suppose that residents of a particular city can watch national news on affiliate stations of ABC, CBS, NBC, or PBS. A researcher wishes to know whether there is any relationship between political philosophy (liberal, moderate, or conservative) and preferred news program among those residents who regularly watch the national news. Let x denote the variable *political philosophy* and y the variable *preferred network*. A random sample of 300 regular watchers is selected, and each individual is asked for his or her x and y values. The data set is bivariate and might initially be displayed as follows:

Observation	x Value	y Value
1	Liberal	CBS
2	Conservative	ABC
3	Conservative	PBS
⋮	⋮	⋮
299	Moderate	NBC
300	Liberal	PBS

Bivariate categorical data of this sort can most easily be summarized by constructing a **two-way frequency table**, or **contingency table**. This is a rectangular table that consists of a row for each possible value of x (each category specified by this variable) and a column for each possible value of y. There is then a cell in the table for each possible (x, y) combination. Once such a table has been constructed, the number of times each particular (x, y) combination occurs in the data set is determined, and these numbers (frequencies) are entered in the corresponding cells of the table. The resulting numbers are called **observed cell counts**. The table for the example relating political philosophy to preferred network contains 3 rows and 4 columns (because x and y have 3 and 4 possible values, respectively). Table 12.2 is one possible table.

TABLE 12.2 An Example of a 3 $\times$ 4 Frequency Table

	ABC	CBS	NBC	PBS	Row Marginal Total
Liberal	20	20	25	15	**80**
Moderate	45	35	50	20	**150**
Conservative	15	40	10	5	**70**
Column Marginal Total	**80**	**95**	**85**	**40**	**300**

Marginal totals are obtained by adding the observed cell counts in each row and also in each column of the table. The row and column marginal totals, along with the total of all observed cell counts in the table—the **grand total**—have been included in Table 12.2. The marginal totals provide information on the distribution of observed values for each variable separately. In this example, the row marginal totals reveal that the sample consisted of 80 liberals, 150 moderates, and 70 conservatives. Similarly, column marginal totals indicate how often each of the preferred program categories occurred: 80 preferred ABC news, 95 preferred CBS, and so on. The grand total, 300, is the number of observations in the bivariate data set.

Two-way frequency tables are often characterized by the number of rows and columns in the table (specified in that order: rows first, then columns). Table 12.2 is called a 3 $\times$ 4 table. The smallest two-way frequency table is a 2 $\times$ 2 table, which has only two rows and two columns, resulting in four cells.

Two-way tables arise naturally in two different types of investigations. A researcher may be interested in comparing two or more populations or treatments on the basis of a single categorical variable and so may obtain independent samples from each population or treatment. For example, data could be collected at a university to compare students, faculty, and staff on the basis of primary mode of transportation to campus (car, bicycle, motorcycle, bus, or by foot). One random sample of 200 students, another of 100 faculty members, and a third of 150 staff members might be chosen, and the selected individuals could be interviewed to obtain the necessary transportation information. Data from such a study could be summarized in a 3 $\times$ 5 two-way frequency table with row categories of student, faculty, and staff and column categories corresponding to the five possible modes of transportation. The observed cell counts could then be used to gain insight into differences and similarities among the three groups with respect to mode of transportation. This type of bivariate categorical data set is characterized by having one set of marginal totals predetermined (the sample sizes for the different groups). In the 3 $\times$ 5 situation just discussed, the row totals would be fixed at 200, 100, and 150.

A two-way table also arises when the values of two different categorical variables are observed for all individuals or items in a single sample. For example, a sample of 500 registered voters might be selected. Each voter could then be asked both if he or she favored a particular property tax initiative and if he or she was a registered Democrat, Republican, or Independent. This would result in a bivariate data set with x representing the variable *political affiliation* (with categories Democrat, Republican, and Independent) and y representing the variable *response* (favors initiative or opposes initiative). The corresponding 3×2 frequency table could then be used to investigate any association between position on the tax initiative and political affiliation. This type of bivariate categorical data set is characterized by having only the grand total predetermined (by the sample size).

Comparing Two or More Populations or Treatments: A Test of Homogeneity

When the value of a categorical variable is recorded for members of independent random samples obtained from each population or treatment under study, the question of interest is whether the category proportions are the same for all the populations or treatments. As in Section 12.1, the test procedure uses a chi-square statistic that compares the observed counts to those that would be expected if there were no differences.

EXAMPLE 12.4 Risky Soccer?

● The paper "No Evidence of Impaired Neurocognitive Performance in Collegiate Soccer Players" (*American Journal of Sports Medicine* [2002]:157–162) compared collegiate soccer players, athletes in sports other than soccer, and a group of students who were not involved in collegiate sports with respect to history of head injuries. Table 12.3, a 3×4 two-way frequency table, is the result of classifying each student in independently selected random samples of 91 soccer players, 96 non-soccer athletes, and 53 non-athletes according to the number of previous concussions the student reported on a medical history questionnaire.

TABLE 12.3 Observed Counts for Example 12.4

	Number of Concussions				
	0 Concussions	1 Concussion	2 Concussions	3 or More Concussions	Row Marginal Total
Soccer Players	45	25	11	10	**91**
Non-Soccer Athletes	68	15	8	5	**96**
Non-Athletes	45	5	3	0	**53**
Column Marginal Total	**158**	**45**	**22**	**15**	**240**

Mike Powell/Allsport Concepts/Getty Images

Estimates of expected cell counts can be thought of in the following manner: There were 240 responses on number of concussions, of which 158 were "0 concussions." The proportion of the total responding "0 concussions" is then

$$\frac{158}{240} = .658$$

If there were no difference in response for the different groups, we would then expect about 65.8% of the soccer players to have responded "0 concussions," 65.8% of the non-soccer athletes to have responded "0 concussions," and so on. Therefore the estimated expected cell counts for the three cells in the "0 concussions" column are

$$\text{Expected count for soccer player } \textit{and} \text{ 0 concussions cell} = .658(91) = 59.9$$
$$\text{Expected count for non–soccer athlete } \textit{and} \text{ 0 concussions cell} = .658(96) = 63.2$$
$$\text{Expected count for non–athlete } \textit{and} \text{ 0 concussions cell} = .658(53) = 34.9$$

● Data set available online

Note that the expected cell counts need not be whole numbers. The expected cell counts for the remaining cells can be computed in a similar manner. For example,

$$\frac{45}{240} = .188$$

of all responses were in the "1 concussion" category, so

$$\begin{aligned} \text{Expected count for soccer player } \textit{and } 1 \text{ concussion cell} &= .188(91) = 17.1 \\ \text{Expected count for non–soccer athlete } \textit{and } 1 \text{ concussion cell} &= .188(96) = 18.0 \\ \text{Expected count for non–athlete } \textit{and } 1 \text{ concussion cell} &= .188(53) = 10.0 \end{aligned}$$

It is common practice to display the observed cell counts and the corresponding expected cell counts in the same table, with the expected cell counts enclosed in parentheses. Expected cell counts for the remaining cells have been computed and entered into Table 12.4. Except for small differences resulting from rounding, each marginal total for the expected cell counts is identical to that of the corresponding observed counts.

TABLE 12.4 Observed and Expected Counts for Example 12.4

	Number of Concussions				
	0 Concussions	1 Concussion	2 Concussions	3 or More Concussions	Row Marginal Total
Soccer Players	45 (59.9)	25 (17.1)	11 (8.3)	10 (5.7)	**91**
Non-Soccer Athletes	68 (63.2)	15 (18.0)	8 (8.8)	5 (6.0)	**96**
Non-Athletes	45 (34.9)	5 (10.0)	3 (4.9)	0 (3.3)	**53**
Column Marginal Total	**158**	**45**	**22**	**15**	**240**

A quick comparison of the observed and expected cell counts in Table 12.4 reveals some large discrepancies, suggesting that the proportions falling into the concussion categories may not be the same for all three groups. This will be explored further in Example 12.5.

In Example 12.4, the expected count for a cell corresponding to a particular group–response combination was computed in two steps. First, the response *marginal proportion* was computed (e.g., 158/240 for the "0 concussions" response). Then this proportion was multiplied by a marginal group total (for example, 91(158/240) for the soccer player group). Algebraically, this is equivalent to first multiplying the row and column marginal totals and then dividing by the grand total:

$$\frac{(91)(158)}{240}$$

To compare two or more populations or treatments on the basis of a categorical variable, calculate an **expected cell count** for each cell by selecting the corresponding row and column marginal totals and then computing

$$\text{expected cell count} = \frac{(\text{row marginal total})(\text{column marginal total})}{\text{grand total}}$$

These quantities represent what would be expected when there is no difference between the groups under study.

The X^2 statistic, introduced in Section 12.1, can now be used to compare the observed cell counts to the expected cell counts. A large value of X^2 results when there are large discrepancies between the observed and expected counts and suggests that the hypothesis of no differences between the populations should be rejected. A formal test procedure is described in the accompanying box.

X^2 Test for Homogeneity

Null hypothesis: H_0: The true category proportions are the same for all the populations or treatments (homogeneity of populations or treatments).

Alternative hypothesis: H_a: The true category proportions are not all the same for all of the populations or treatments.

Test statistic: $$X^2 = \sum_{\text{all cells}} \frac{(\text{observed cell count} - \text{expected cell count})^2}{\text{expected cell count}}$$

The expected cell counts are estimated from the sample data (assuming that H_0 is true) using the formula

$$\text{expected cell count} = \frac{(\text{row marginal total})(\text{column marginal total})}{\text{grand total}}$$

***P*-values:** When H_0 is true and the assumptions of the X^2 test are satisfied, X^2 has approximately a chi-square distribution with df = (number of rows − 1)(number of columns − 1). The *P*-value associated with the computed test statistic value is the area to the right of X^2 under the chi-square curve with the appropriate df. Upper-tail areas for chi-square distributions are found in Appendix Table 8.

Assumptions: 1. The data are from *independently chosen random samples or from subjects who were assigned at random to treatment groups.*
2. *The sample size is large*: all expected counts are at least 5. If some expected counts are less than 5, rows or columns of the table may be combined to achieve a table with satisfactory expected counts.

EXAMPLE 12.5 Risky Soccer Revisited

The following table of observed and expected cell counts appeared in Example 12.4:

	Number of Concussions				
	0 Concussions	1 Concussion	2 Concussions	3 or More Concussions	Row Marginal Total
Soccer Players	45 (59.9)	25 (17.1)	11 (8.3)	10 (5.7)	**91**
Non-Soccer Athletes	68 (63.2)	15 (18.0)	8 (8.8)	5 (6.0)	**96**
Non-Athletes	45 (34.9)	5 (10.0)	3 (4.9)	0 (3.3)	**53**
Column Marginal Total	**158**	**45**	**22**	**15**	**240**

Hypotheses: H_0: Proportions in each response (number of concussions) category are the same for all three groups

H_a: The category proportions are not all the same for all three groups.

Significance level: A significance level of $\alpha = .05$ will be used.

Test statistic: $X^2 = \sum_{\text{all cells}} \frac{(\text{observed cell count} - \text{expected cell count})^2}{\text{expected cell count}}$

Assumptions: The random samples were independently chosen, so use of the test is appropriate if the sample size is large enough. One of the expected cell counts (in the 3 or more concussions column) is less than 5, so we will combine the last two columns of the table prior to carrying out the chi-square test. The table we will work with is then

	NUMBER OF CONCUSSIONS			
	0 Concussions	1 Concussion	2 or More Concussions	Row Marginal Total
Soccer Players	45 (59.9)	25 (17.1)	21 (14.0)	**91**
Non-Soccer Athletes	68 (63.2)	15 (18.0)	13 (14.8)	**96**
Non-Athletes	45 (34.9)	5 (10.0)	3 (8.2)	**53**
Column Marginal Total	**158**	**45**	**22**	**240**

Calculation:

$$X^2 = \frac{(45 - 59.9)^2}{59.9} + \cdots + \frac{(3 - 8.2)^2}{8.2} = 20.6$$

P-value: The two-way table for this example has 3 rows and 3 columns, so the appropriate df is $(3 - 1)(3 - 1) = 4$. Since 20.6 is greater than 18.46, the largest entry in the 4-df column of Appendix Table 8,

$P\text{-value} < .001$

Conclusion: $P\text{-value} \le \alpha$, so H_0 is rejected. There is strong evidence to support the claim that the proportions in the number of concussions categories are not the same for the three groups compared. The largest differences between the observed frequencies and those that would be expected if there were no group differences occur in the response categories for soccer players and for non-athletes, with soccer players having higher than expected proportions in the 1 and 2 or more concussion categories and non-athletes having a higher than expected proportion in the 0 concussion category.

Most statistical computer packages can calculate expected cell counts, the value of the X^2 statistic, and the associated *P*-value. This is illustrated in the following example.

EXAMPLE 12.6 Keeping the Weight Off

● The article "Daily Weigh-ins Can Help You Keep Off Lost Pounds, Experts Say" (*Associated Press,* October 17, 2005) describes an experiment in which 291 people who had lost at least 10% of their body weight in a medical weight loss program were assigned at random to one of three groups for follow-up. One group met monthly in

● Data set available online

person, one group "met" online monthly in a chat room, and one group received a monthly newsletter by mail. After 18 months, participants in each group were classified according to whether or not they had regained more than 5 pounds, resulting in the data given in Table 12.5.

TABLE 12.5 Observed and Expected Counts for Example 12.6

	AMOUNT OF WEIGHT GAINED		
	Regained 5 Lb or Less	Regained More Than 5 Lb	Row Marginal Total
In-Person	52 (41.0)	45 (56.0)	**97**
Online	44 (41.0)	53 (56.0)	**97**
Newsletter	27 (41.0)	70 (56.0)	**97**

Does there appear to be a difference in the weight regained proportions for the three follow-up methods? The relevant hypotheses are

H_0: The proportions for the two weight-regained categories are the same for the three follow-up methods.

H_a: The weight-regained category proportions are not the same for all three follow-up methods.

Significance level: $\alpha = .01$

Test statistic: $X^2 = \sum_{\text{all cells}} \frac{(\text{observed cell count} - \text{expected cell count})^2}{\text{expected cell count}}$

Assumptions: Table 12.5 contains the computed expected counts, all of which are greater than 5. The subjects in this experiment were assigned at random to the treatment groups.

Calculation: Minitab output follows. For each cell, the Minitab output includes the observed cell count, the expected cell count, and the value of $\frac{(\text{observed cell count} - \text{expected cell count})^2}{\text{expected cell count}}$ for that cell (this is the contribution to the X^2 statistic for this cell). From the output, $X^2 = 13.773$.

```
Chi-Square Test
Expected counts are printed below observed counts
Chi-Square contributions are printed below expected counts

               <=5      >5    Total
In-person       52      45       97
             41.00   56.00
             2.951   2.161
Online          44      53       97
             41.00   56.00
             0.220   0.161
Newsletter      27      70       97
             41.00   56.00
             4.780   3.500
Total          123     168      291
Chi-Sq = 13.773,   DF = 2,   P-Value = 0.001
```

P-value: From the Minitab output, *P*-value = .001.

Conclusion: Since *P*-value $\leq \alpha$, H_0 is rejected. The data indicate that the proportions who have regained more than five pounds are not the same for the three follow-up methods. Comparing the observed and expected cell counts, we can see that the observed number in the newsletter group who had regained more than 5 pounds was higher than would have been expected and the observed number in the in-person group who had regained 5 or more pounds was lower than would have been expected if there were no difference in the three follow-up methods.

Testing for Independence of Two Categorical Variables

The X^2 test statistic and test procedure can also be used to investigate association between two categorical variables in a single population. As an example, television viewers in a particular city might be categorized with respect to both preferred network (ABC, CBS, NBC, or PBS) and favorite type of programming (comedy, drama, or information and news). The question of interest is often whether knowledge of one variable's value provides any information about the value of the other variable—that is, are the two variables independent?

Continuing the example, suppose that those who favor ABC prefer the three types of programming in proportions .4, .5, and .1 and that these proportions are also correct for individuals favoring any of the other three networks. Then, learning an individual's preferred network provides no added information about that individual's favorite type of programming. The categorical variables *preferred network* and *favorite program type* would be independent.

To see how expected counts are obtained in this situation, recall from Chapter 6 that if two outcomes A and B are independent, then

$$\text{P}(A \text{ and } B) = P(A)P(B)$$

so the proportion of time that the two outcomes occur together in the long run is the product of the two individual long-run relative frequencies. Similarly, two categorical variables are independent in a population if, for each particular category of the first variable and each particular category of the second variable,

$$\begin{pmatrix}\text{proportion of individuals}\\ \text{in a particular category}\\ \text{combination}\end{pmatrix} = \begin{pmatrix}\text{proportion in}\\ \text{specified category}\\ \text{of first variable}\end{pmatrix} \cdot \begin{pmatrix}\text{proportion in}\\ \text{specified category}\\ \text{of second variable}\end{pmatrix}$$

Thus, if 30% of all viewers prefer ABC and the proportions of program type preferences are as previously given, then, assuming that the two variables are independent, the proportion of individuals who both favor ABC and prefer comedy is (.3)(.4) = .12 (or 12%).

Multiplying the right-hand side of the expression above by the sample size gives us the expected number of individuals in the sample who are in both specified categories of the two variables when the variables are independent. However, these expected counts cannot be calculated, because the individual population proportions are not known. The solution is to estimate each population proportion using the corresponding sample proportion:

$$\begin{pmatrix}\text{estimated expected number}\\ \text{in specified categories}\\ \text{of the two varibales}\end{pmatrix} = (\text{sample size}) \cdot \frac{\begin{pmatrix}\text{observed number}\\ \text{in category of}\\ \text{first variable}\end{pmatrix}}{\text{sample size}} \cdot \frac{\begin{pmatrix}\text{observed number}\\ \text{in category of}\\ \text{second variable}\end{pmatrix}}{\text{sample size}}$$

$$= \frac{\begin{pmatrix}\text{observed number in}\\ \text{category of first variable}\end{pmatrix} \cdot \begin{pmatrix}\text{observed number in}\\ \text{category of second variable}\end{pmatrix}}{\text{sample size}}$$

Suppose that the observed counts are displayed in a rectangular table in which rows correspond to the categories of the first variable and columns to the categories of the second variable. Then, the numerator in the preceding expression for expected counts is just the product of the row and column marginal totals. This is exactly how expected counts were computed in the test for homogeneity of several populations, even though the reasoning used to arrive at the formula is different.

X^2 Test for Independence

Null hypothesis: H_0: The two variables are independent.

Alternative hypothesis: H_a: The two variables are not independent.

Test statistic: $$X^2 = \sum_{\text{all cells}} \frac{(\text{observed cell count} - \text{expected cell count})^2}{\text{expected cell count}}$$

The expected cell counts are estimated (assuming H_0 is true) by the formula

$$\text{expected cell count} = \frac{(\text{row marginal total})(\text{column marginal total})}{\text{grand total}}$$

***P*-values:** When H_0 is true and the assumptions of the X^2 test are satisfied, X^2 has approximately a chi-square distribution with

$$\text{df} = (\text{number of rows} - 1)(\text{number of columns} - 1)$$

The *P*-value associated with the computed test statistic value is the area to the right of X^2 under the chi-square curve with the appropriate df. Upper-tail areas for chi-square distributions are found in Appendix Table 8.

Assumptions:
1. The observed counts are based on data from a *random sample*.
2. The *sample size is large*: All expected counts are at least 5. If some expected counts are less than 5, rows or columns of the table should be combined to achieve a table with satisfactory expected counts.

EXAMPLE 12.7 A Pained Expression

● The paper "Facial Expression of Pain in Elderly Adults with Dementia" (*Journal of Undergraduate Research* [2006]) examined the relationship between a nurse's assessment of a patient's facial expression and his or her self-reported level of pain. Data for 89 patients are summarized in Table 12.6.

Step-by-Step technology instructions available online

● Data set available online

TABLE 12.6 Observed Counts for Example 12.7

	SELF-REPORT	
Facial Expression	No Pain	Pain
No Pain	17	40
Pain	3	29

The authors were interested in determining if there is evidence of a relationship between a facial expression that reflects pain and self-reported pain because patients with dementia do not always give a verbal indication that they are in pain.

Using a .05 significance level, we will test

H_0: Facial expression and self-reported pain are independent.
H_a: Facial expression and self-reported pain are not independent.

Significance level: $\alpha = .05$

Test statistic: $X^2 = \sum_{\text{all cells}} \frac{(\text{observed cell count} - \text{expected cell count})^2}{\text{expected cell count}}$

Assumptions: Before we can check the assumptions we must first compute the expected cell counts.

CELL		
Row	Column	Expected Cell Count
1	1	$\frac{(57)(20)}{89} = 12.81$
1	2	$\frac{(57)(69)}{89} = 44.19$
2	1	$\frac{(32)(20)}{89} = 7.19$
2	2	$\frac{(32)(69)}{89} = 24.81$

All expected cell counts are greater than 5. Although the participants in the study were not randomly selected, they were thought to be representative of the population of nursing home patients with dementia. The observed and expected counts are given together in Table 12.7.

TABLE 12.7 Observed and Expected Counts for Example 12.7

	SELF-REPORT	
Facial Expression	No Pain	Pain
No Pain	17 (12.81)	40 (44.19)
Pain	3 (7.19)	29 (24.81)

Calculation: $X^2 = \frac{(17 - 12.81)^2}{12.81} + \cdots + \frac{(29 - 24.81)^2}{24.81} = 4.92$

P-value: The table has 2 rows and 2 columns, so df = (2 − 1)(2 − 1) = 1. The entry closest to 4.92 in the 1-df column of Appendix Table 8 is 5.02, so the approximate *P*-value for this test is

$P\text{-value} \approx .025$

Conclusion: Since $P\text{-value} \leq \alpha$, we reject H_0 and conclude that there is convincing evidence of an association between a nurse's assessment of facial expression and self-reported pain.

EXAMPLE 12.8 Stroke Mortality and Education

● Table 12.8 was constructed using data from the article "Influence of Socioeconomic Status on Mortality After Stroke" (*Stroke* [2005]: 310–314). One of the questions of interest to the author was whether there was an association between survival after a stroke and level of education. Medical records for a sample of 2333 residents of Vienna, Austria, who had suffered a stroke were used to classify each individual according to two variables—survival (survived, died) and level of education (no basic education, secondary school graduation, technical training/apprenticed, higher secondary school degree, university graduate). Expected cell counts (computed under the assumption of no association between survival and level of education) appear in parentheses in the table.

TABLE 12.8 Observed and Expected Counts for Example 12.8

	No Basic Education	Secondary School Graduation	Technical Training/ Apprenticed	Higher Secondary School Degree	University Graduate
Died	13 (17.40)	91 (77.18)	196 (182.68)	33 (41.91)	36 (49.82)
Survived	97 (92.60)	397 (410.82)	959 (972.32)	232 (223.09)	279 (265.18)

The X^2 test with a significance level of .01 will be used to test the relevant hypotheses:

H_0: Survival and level of education are independent.
H_a: Survival and level of education are not independent.

Significance level: $\alpha = .01$

Test statistic: $X^2 = \sum_{\text{all cells}} \frac{(\text{observed cell count} - \text{expected cell count})^2}{\text{expected cell count}}$

Assumptions: All expected cell counts are at least 5. Assuming that the data can be viewed as representative of adults who suffer strokes, the X^2 test can be used.

● Data set available online

Calculation: Minitab output is shown. From the Minitab output, $X^2 = 12.219$.

Chi-Square Test

Expected counts are printed below observed counts

Chi-Square contributions are printed below expected counts

	1	2	3	4	5	Total
1	13	91	196	33	36	369
	17.40	77.18	182.68	41.91	49.82	
	1.112	2.473	0.971	1.896	3.835	
2	97	397	959	232	279	1964
	92.60	410.82	972.32	223.09	265.18	
	0.209	0.465	0.182	0.356	0.720	
Total	110	488	1155	265	315	2333

Chi-Sq = 12.219, DF = 4, P-Value = 0.016

P-value: From the Minitab output, *P*-value = .016.

Conclusion: Since *P*-value $> \alpha$, H_0 is not rejected. There is not sufficient evidence to conclude that an association exists between level of education and survival.

In some investigations, values of more than two categorical variables are recorded for each individual in the sample. For example, in addition to the variable *survival* and *level of education*, the researchers in the study referenced in Example 12.8 also collected information on occupation. A number of interesting questions could then be explored: Are all three variables independent of one another? Is it possible that occupation and survival are dependent but that the relationship between them does not depend on level of education? For a particular education level group, is there an association between survival and occupation? The X^2 test procedure described in this section for analysis of bivariate categorical data can be extended for use with *multivariate categorical data*. Appropriate hypothesis tests can then be used to provide insight into the relationships between variables. However, the computations required to calculate expected cell counts and to compute the value of X^2 are quite tedious, so they are seldom done without the aid of a computer. Most statistical computer packages can perform this type of analysis. Consult the references by Agresti and Findlay, Everitt, or Mosteller and Rourke listed in the back of the book for further information on the analysis of categorical data.

EXERCISES 12.14 - 12.31

12.14 A particular state university system has six campuses. On each campus, a random sample of students will be selected, and each student will be categorized with respect to political philosophy as liberal, moderate, or conservative. The null hypothesis of interest is that the proportion of students falling in these three categories is the same at all six campuses.

a. On how many degrees of freedom will the resulting X^2 test be based?

b. How does your answer in Part (a) change if there are seven campuses rather than six?

c. How does your answer in Part (a) change if there are four rather than three categories for political philosophy?

12.15 A random sample of 1000 registered voters in a certain county is selected, and each voter is categorized with respect to both educational level (four categories) and preferred candidate in an upcoming election for county supervisor (five possibilities). The hypothesis of interest is that educational level and preferred candidate are independent.

a. If $X^2 = 7.2$, what would you conclude at significance level .10?

b. If there were only four candidates running for election, what would you conclude if $X^2 = 14.5$ and $\alpha = .05$?

12.16 ● ✦ The polling organization Ipsos conducted telephone surveys in March of 2004, 2005, and 2006. In each year, 1001 people age 18 or older were asked about whether they planned to use a credit card to pay federal income taxes that year. The data given in the accompanying table are from the report "Fees Keeping Taxpayers from Using Credit Cards to Make Tax Payments" (*IPSOS Insight*, March 24, 2006). Is there evidence that the proportion falling in the three credit card response categories is not the same for all three years? Test the relevant hypotheses using a .05 significance level.

	2004	2005	2006
Definitely/Probably Will	40	50	40
Might/Might Not/Probably Not	180	190	160
Definitely Will Not	781	761	801

12.17 ● The paper "Contemporary College Students and Body Piercing" (*Journal of Adolescent Health* [2004]: 58–61) described a survey of 450 undergraduate students at a state university in the southwestern region of the United States. Each student in the sample was classified according to class standing (freshman, sophomore, junior, or senior) and body art category (body piercings only, tattoos only, both tattoos and body piercings, no body art). Use the data in the accompanying table to determine if there is evidence that there is an association between class standing and response to the body art question. Assume that it is reasonable to regard the sample of students as representative of the students at this university. Use $\alpha = .01$.

	Body Piercings Only	Tattoos Only	Both Body Piercing and Tattoos	No Body Art
Freshman	61	7	14	86
Sophomore	43	11	10	64
Junior	20	9	7	43
Senior	21	17	23	54

12.18 ● The accompanying data on degree of spirituality for a sample of natural scientists and a sample of social scientists working at research universities appeared in the paper "Conflict Between Religion and Science among Academic Scientists" (*Journal for the Scientific Study of Religion* [2009]: 276–292). Assume that it is reasonable to regard these two samples as representative of natural and social scientists at research universities. Is there evidence that the spirituality category proportions are not the same for natural and social scientists? Test the relevant hypotheses using a significance level of .01.

	Degree of Spirituality			
	Very	Moderate	Slightly	Not at All
Natural Scientists	56	162	198	211
Social Scientists	56	223	243	239

12.19 ● The authors of the paper "The Relationship of Field of Study to Current Smoking Status Among College Students" (*College Student Journal* [2009]: 744–754) carried out a study to investigate if smoking rates were different for college students in different majors. Each student in a large random sample of students at the University of Minnesota was classified according to field of study and whether or not they had smoked in the past 30 days. The data are given in the accompanying table.

Field of Study	Smoked in the Last 30 Days	Did Not Smoke in Last 30 Days
1. Undeclared	176	489
2. Art, design, performing arts	149	336
3. Humanities	197	454
4. Communication, languages, cultural studies	233	389
5. Education	56	170
6. Health sciences	227	717
7. Mathematics, engineering, sciences	245	924
8. Social science, human services	306	593
9. Individualized course of study	134	260

a. Is there evidence that field of study and smoking status are not independent? Use the Minitab output on the next page to test the relevant hypotheses using $\alpha = .01$.

Chi-Square Test: Smoked, Did Not Smoke
Expected counts are printed below observed counts
Chi-Square contributions are printed below expected counts

	Smoked	Did Not Smoke	Total
1	176	489	665
	189.23	425.77	
	0.925	0.368	
2	149	336	485
	138.01	346.99	
	0.875	0.348	
3	197	454	651
	185.25	465.75	
	0.746	0.297	
4	233	389	622
	177.00	445.00	
	17.721	7.048	
5	56	170	226
	64.31	161.69	
	1.074	0.427	
6	227	717	944
	268.62	675.38	
	6.449	2.565	
7	245	924	1169
	332.65	836.35	
	23.094	9.185	
8	306	593	899
	255.82	643.18	
	9.844	3.915	
9	134	260	394
	112.12	281.88	
	4.272	1.699	
Total	1723	4332	6055

Chi-Sq = 90.853, DF = 8, P-Value = 0.000

b. Write a few sentences describing how the smoking status categories are related to field of study. (Hint: Focus on cells that have large values of

$$\frac{(\text{observed cell count} - \text{expected cell count})^2}{\text{expected cell count}}.$$

12.20 ● The authors of the paper "Movie Character Smoking and Adolescent Smoking: Who Matters More, Good Guys or Bad Guys?" (*Pediatrics* [2009]: 135–141) classified characters who were depicted smoking in movies released between 2000 and 2005. The smoking characters were classified according to sex and whether the character type was positive, negative or neutral. The resulting data is given in the accompanying table. Assume that it is reasonable to consider this sample of smoking movie characters as representative of smoking movie characters. Do the data provide evidence of an association between sex and character type for movie characters who smoke? Use $\alpha = .05$.

	Character Type		
Sex	Positive	Negative	Neutral
Male	255	106	130
Female	85	12	49

12.21 ● The data in the accompanying table is from the paper "Gender Differences in Food Selections of Students at a Historically Black College and University" (*College Student Journal* [2009]: 800–806). Suppose that the data resulted from classifying each person in a random sample of 48 male students and each person in a random sample of 91 female students at a particular college according to their response to a question about whether they usually eat three meals a day or rarely eat three meals a day.

	Usually Eat 3 Meals a Day	Rarely Eat 3 Meals a Day
Male	26	22
Female	37	54

a. Is there evidence that the proportions falling into each of the two response categories are not the same for males and females? Use the X^2 statistic to test the relevant hypotheses with a significance level of .05.

b. Are your calculations and conclusions from Part (a) consistent with the accompanying Minitab output?

Expected counts are printed below observed counts
Chi-Square contributions are printed below expected counts

	Usually	Rarely	Total
Male	26	22	48
	21.76	26.24	
	0.828	0.686	
Female	37	54	91
	41.24	49.76	
	0.437	0.362	
Total	63	76	139

Chi-Sq = 2.314, DF = 1, P-Value = 0.128

c. Because the response variable in this exercise has only two categories (usually and rarely), we could have also answered the question posed in Part (a) by carrying out a two-sample z test of H_0: $p_1 - p_2 = 0$ versus H_a: $p_1 - p_2 \neq 0$, where p_1 is the proportion who usually eat three meals a day for males and p_2 is the proportion who usually eat three meals a day for females. Minitab output from the two-sample z test is shown on the next page. Using a significance level of .05, does the two-sample z test lead to the same conclusion as in Part (a)?

Test for Two Proportions

Sample	X	N	Sample p
Male	26	48	0.541667
Female	37	91	0.406593

Difference = p (1) - p (2)
Test for difference = 0 (vs not = 0): Z = 1.53 P-Value = 0.127

d. How do the *P*-values from the tests in Parts (a) and (c) compare? Does this surprise you? Explain?

12.22 ● In a study of high-achieving high school graduates, the authors of the report "High-Achieving Seniors and the College Decision" (Lipman Hearne, October 2009) surveyed 828 high school graduates who were considered "academic superstars" and 433 graduates who were considered "solid performers." One question on the survey asked the distance from their home to the college they attended. Assuming it is reasonable to regard these two samples as random samples of academic superstars and solid performers nationwide, use the accompanying data to determine if it is reasonable to conclude that the distribution of responses over the distance from home categories is not the same for academic superstars and solid performers. Use $\alpha = .05$.

	Distance of College from Home (in miles)				
Student Group	Less than 40	40 to 99	100 to 199	200 to 399	400 or More
Academic Superstars	157	157	141	149	224
Solid Performers	104	95	82	65	87

12.23 ● Does including a gift with a request for a donation affect the proportion who will make a donation? This question was investigated in a study described in the report "Gift-Exchange in the Field" (Institute for the Study of Labor, 2007). In this study, letters were sent to a large number of potential donors in Germany. The letter requested a donation for funding schools in Bangladesh. Those who were to receive the letter were assigned at random to one of three groups. Those in the first group received the letter with no gift. Those in the second group received a letter that included a small gift (a postcard), and those in the third group received a letter with a larger gift (four postcards). The response of interest was whether or not a letter resulted in a donation.

	Donation	No Donation
No Gift	397	2865
Small Gift	465	2772
Large Gift	691	2656

a. Carry out a hypothesis test to determine if there is convincing evidence that the proportions in the two donation categories are not the same for all three types of requests. Use a significance level of .01.

b. Based on your analysis in Part (a) and a comparison of observed and expected cell counts, write a brief description of how the proportion making a donation varies for the three types of request.

12.24 ● The paper "Credit Card Misuse, Money Attitudes, and Compulsive Buying Behavior: Comparison of Internal and External Locus of Control Consumers" (*College Student Journal* [2009]: 268–275) describes a study that surveyed a sample of college students at two midwestern public universities. Based on the survey responses, students were classified into two "locus of control" groups (internal and external) based on the extent to which they believe that they control what happens to them. Those in the internal locus of control group believe that they are usually in control of what happens to them, whereas those in the external locus of control group believe that it is usually factors outside their control that determines what happens to them. Each student was also classified according to a measure of compulsive buying. The resulting data are summarized in the accompanying table. Can the researchers conclude that there are an association between locus of control and compulsive buying behavior? Carry out a X^2 test using $\alpha = .01$. Assume it is reasonable to regard the sample as representative of college students at midwestern public universities.

		Locus of Control	
		Internal	External
Compulsive Buyer?	**Yes**	3	14
	No	52	57

12.25 ● Each person in a large sample of German adolescents was asked to indicate which of 50 popular movies they had seen in the past year. Based on the response, the amount of time (in minutes) of alcohol use contained in the movies the person had watched was estimated. Each person was then classified into one of four groups based on the amount of movie alcohol exposure (groups 1, 2, 3, and 4, with 1 being the lowest exposure and 4 being the highest exposure). Each person was also classified according to school performance. The resulting data is given in the accompanying table (from "Longitudinal Study of Exposure to Entertainment Media and Alcohol Use among German Adolescents," *Pediatrics* [2009]: 989–995). Assume it is reasonable to regard this sample as a random sample of German adolescents. Is there evidence that there is an association between school performance and movie exposure to alcohol? Carry out a hypothesis test using $\alpha = .05$.

		Alcohol Exposure Group			
		1	2	3	4
School Performance	**Excellent**	110	93	49	65
	Good	328	325	316	295
	Average/Poor	239	259	312	317

12.26 ● In a study to determine if hormone therapy increases risk of venous thrombosis in menopausal women, each person in a sample of 579 women who had been diagnosed with venous thrombosis was classified according to hormone use. Each woman in a sample of 2243 women who had not been diagnosed with venous thrombosis was also classified according to hormone use. Data from the study are given in the accompanying table (*Journal of the American Medical Association* [2004]: 1581–1587). The women in each of the two samples were selected at random from patients at a large HMO in the state of Washington.

a. Is there convincing evidence that the proportions falling into each of the hormone use categories is not the same for women who have been diagnosed with venous thrombosis and those who have not?

b. To what populations would it be reasonable to generalize the conclusions of Part (a)? Explain.

	Current Hormone Use		
	None	Esterified Estrogen	Conjugated Equine Estrogen
Venous Thrombosis	372	86	121
No Venous Thrombosis	1439	515	289

12.27 ● The paper "Overweight Among Low-Income Preschool Children Associated with the Consumption of Sweet Drinks" (*Pediatrics* [2005]: 223–229) described a study of children who were underweight or normal weight at age 2. Children in the sample were classified according to the number of sweet drinks consumed per day and whether or not the child was overweight one year after the study began. Is there evidence of an association between whether or not children are overweight after one year and the number of sweet drinks consumed? Assume that it is reasonable to regard the sample of children in this study as representative of 2- to 3-year-old children and then test the appropriate hypotheses using a .05 significance level.

Number of Sweet Drinks Consumed per Day	Overweight? Yes	No
0	22	930
1	73	2074
2	56	1681
3 or More	102	3390

12.28 ● The 2006 Expedia Vacation Deprivation Survey (*Ipsos Insight*, May 18, 2006) described the results of a poll of working adults in Canada. Each person in a random sample was classified according to gender and the number of vacation days he or she usually took each year. The resulting data are summarized in the given table. Is it reasonable to conclude that there is an association between gender and the number of vacation days taken? To what population would it be reasonable to generalize this conclusion?

	Gender	
Days of Vacation	Male	Female
None	51	42
1–5	21	25
6–10	67	79
11–15	111	94
16–20	71	70
21–25	82	58
More than 25	118	79

12.29 ● A survey was conducted in the San Francisco Bay area in which each participating individual was classified according to the type of vehicle used most often and city of residence. A subset of the resulting data are given in the accompanying table (*The Relationship of Vehicle Type Choice to Personality, Lifestyle, Attitudi-*

nal and Demographic Variables, Technical Report UCD-ITS-RR02-06, DaimlerCrysler Corp., 2002).

Vehicle Type	City: Concord	Pleasant Hills	North San Francisco
Small	68	83	221
Compact	63	68	106
Midsize	88	123	142
Large	24	18	11

Do the data provide convincing evidence of an association between city of residence and vehicle type? Use a significance level of .05. You may assume that it is reasonable to regard the sample as a random sample of Bay area residents.

12.30 ● A story describing a date rape was read by 352 high school students. To investigate the effect of the victim's clothing on subject's judgment of the situation described, the story was accompanied by either a photograph of the victim dressed provocatively, a photo of the victim dressed conservatively, or no picture. Each student was asked whether the situation described in the story was one of rape. Data from the article "The Influence of Victim's Attire on Adolescent Judgments of Date Rape" (*Adolescence* [1995]: 319–323) are given in the accompanying table. Is there evidence that the proportion who believe that the story described a rape differs for the three different photo groups? Test the relevant hypotheses using $\alpha = .01$.

Response	Picture: Provocative	Conservative	No Picture
Rape	80	104	92
Not Rape	47	12	17

12.31 ● Can people tell the difference between a female nose and a male nose? This important (?) research question was examined in the article "You Can Tell by the Nose: Judging Sex from an Isolated Facial Feature" (*Perception* [1995]: 969–973). Eight Caucasian males and eight Caucasian females posed for nose photos. The article states that none of the volunteers wore nose studs or had prominent nasal hair. Each person placed a black Lycra tube over his or her head in such a way that only the nose protruded through a hole in the material. Photos were then taken from three different angles: front view, three-quarter view, and profile. These photos were shown to a sample of undergraduate students. Each student in the sample was shown one of the nose photos and asked whether it was a photo of a male or a female; and the response was classified as either correct or incorrect. The accompanying table was constructed using summary values reported in the article. Is there evidence that the proportion of correct sex identifications differs for the three different nose views?

Sex ID	View: Front	Profile	Three-Quarter
Correct	23	26	29
Incorrect	17	14	11

12.3 Interpreting and Communicating the Results of Statistical Analyses

Many studies, particularly those in the social sciences, result in categorical data. The questions of interest in such studies often lead to an analysis that involves using a chi-square test.

AP* EXAM TIP

An effective way to communicate which test is being used is to include a careful statement of the null hypothesis.

Communicating the Results of Statistical Analyses

Three different chi-square tests were introduced in this chapter—the goodness-of-fit test, the test for homogeneity, and the test for independence. They are used in different settings and to answer different questions. When summarizing the results of a chi-square test, be sure to indicate which chi-square test was performed. One way to do this is to be clear about how the data were collected and the nature of the hypotheses being tested.

It is also a good idea to include a table of observed and expected counts in addition to reporting the computed value of the test statistic and the *P*-value. And finally, make sure to give a conclusion in context, and make sure that the conclusion is worded appropriately for the type of test conducted. For example, don't use terms such as *independence* and *association* to describe the conclusion if the test performed was a test for homogeneity.

Interpreting the Results of Statistical Analyses

As with the other hypothesis tests considered, it is common to find the result of a chi-square test summarized by giving the value of the chi-square test statistic and an associated *P*-value. Because categorical data can be summarized compactly in frequency tables, the data often are given in the article (unlike data for numerical variables, which are rarely given).

What to Look For in Published Data

Here are some questions to consider when you are reading an article that contains the results of a chi-square test:

- Are the variables of interest categorical rather than numerical?
- Are the data given in the article in the form of a frequency table?
- If a two-way frequency table is involved, is the question of interest one of homogeneity or one of independence?
- What null hypothesis is being tested? Are the results of the analysis reported in the correct context (homogeneity, etc.)?
- Is the sample size large enough to make use of a chi-square test reasonable? (Are all expected counts at least 5?)
- What is the value of the test statistic? Is the associated *P*-value given? Should the null hypothesis be rejected?
- Are the conclusions drawn by the authors consistent with the results of the test?
- How different are the observed and expected counts? Does the result have practical significance as well as statistical significance?

The authors of the article "Predicting Professional Sports Game Outcomes from Intermediate Game Scores" (*Chance* [1992]: 18–22) used a chi-square test to determine whether there was any merit to the idea that basketball games are not settled until the last quarter, whereas baseball games are over by the seventh inning. They also considered football and hockey. Data were collected for 189 basketball games, 92 baseball games, 80 hockey games, and 93 football games. The analyzed games were sampled randomly from all games played during the 1990 season for baseball and football and for the 1990–1991 season for basketball and hockey. For each game, the late-game leader was determined, and then it was noted whether the late-game leader actually ended up winning the game. The resulting data are summarized in the following table:

Sport	Late-Game Leader Wins	Late-Game Leader Loses
Basketball	150	39
Baseball	86	6
Hockey	65	15
Football	72	21

The authors stated that the "*late-game leader* is defined as the team that is ahead after three quarters in basketball and football, two periods in hockey, and seven innings in baseball. The chi-square value (with three degrees of freedom) is 10.52 ($P < .015$)." They also concluded that "the sports of basketball, hockey, and football have remarkably similar percentages of late-game reversals, ranging from 18.8% to 22.6%. The sport that is an anomaly is baseball. Only 6.5% of baseball games resulted in late reversals. . . . [The chi-square test] is statistically significant due almost entirely to baseball."

In this particular analysis, the authors are comparing four populations (games from each of the four sports) on the basis of a categorical variable with two categories (late-game leader wins and late-game leader loses). The appropriate null hypothesis is then

H_0: The population proportion in each category (leader wins, leader loses) is the same for all four sports.

Based on the reported value of the chi-square statistic and the associated P-value, this null hypothesis is rejected, leading to the conclusion that the category proportions are not the same for all four sports.

The validity of the chi-square test requires that the sample sizes be large enough so that no expected counts are less than 5. Is this reasonable here? The following Minitab output shows the expected cell counts and the computation of the X^2 statistic:

Chi-Square Test

Expected counts are printed below observed counts

	Leader W	Leader L	Total
1	150	39	189
	155.28	33.72	
2	86	6	92
	75.59	16.41	
3	65	15	80
	65.73	14.27	
4	72	21	93
	76.41	16.59	
Total	373	81	454

```
Chi-Sq =  0.180 +  0.827 +
          1.435 +  6.607 +
          0.008 +  0.037 +
          0.254 +  1.171 = 10.518
DF = 3,  P-Value = 0.015
```

The smallest expected count is 14.27, so the sample sizes are large enough to justify the use of the X^2 test. Note also that the two cells in the table that correspond to baseball contribute a total of $1.435 + 6.607 = 8.042$ to the value of the X^2 statistic of 10.518. This is due to the large discrepancies between the observed and expected counts for these two cells. There is reasonable agreement between the observed and the expected counts in the other cells. This is probably the basis for the authors' conclusion that baseball is the anomaly and that the other sports were similar.

A Word to the Wise: Cautions and Limitations

Be sure to keep the following in mind when analyzing categorical data using one of the chi-square tests presented in this chapter:

1. Don't confuse tests for homogeneity with tests for independence. The hypotheses and conclusions are different for the two types of test. Tests for homogeneity

are used when the individuals in each of two or more independent samples are classified according to a single categorical variable. Tests for independence are used when individuals in a *single* sample are classified according to two categorical variables.

2. As was the case for the hypothesis tests of earlier chapters, remember that we can never say we have strong support for the null hypothesis. For example, if we do not reject the null hypothesis in a chi-square test for independence, we cannot conclude that there is convincing evidence that the variables are independent. We can only say that we were not convinced that there is an association between the variables.
3. Be sure that the assumptions for the chi-square test are reasonable. *P*-values based on the chi-square distribution are only approximate, and if the large sample conditions are not met, the true *P*-value may be quite different from the approximate one based on the chi-square distribution. This can sometimes lead to erroneous conclusions. Also, for the chi-square test of homogeneity, the assumption of *independent* samples is particularly important.
4. Don't jump to conclusions about causation. Just as a strong correlation between two numerical variables does not mean that there is a cause-and-effect relationship between them, an association between two categorical variables does not imply a causal relationship.

EXERCISES 12.32 - 12.34

12.32 The following passage is from the paper "Gender Differences in Food Selections of Students at a Historically Black College and University" (*College Student Journal* [2009]: 800–806):

> Also significant was the proportion of males and their water consumption (8 oz. servings) compared to females ($X^2 = 8.166$, $P = .086$). Males came closest to meeting recommended daily water intake (64 oz. or more) than females (29.8% vs. 20.9%).

This statement was based on carrying out a X^2 test of independence using data in a two-way table where rows corresponded to gender (male, female) and columns corresponded to number of servings of water consumed per day, with categories none, one, two to three, four to five, and six or more.

a. What hypotheses did the researchers test? What is the number of degrees of freedom associated with the report value of the X^2 statistic?
b. The researchers based their statement that the proportions falling in the water consumption categories were not all the same for males and females on a test with a significance level of .10. Would they have reached the same conclusion if a significance level of .05 had been used? Explain.
c. The paper also included the accompanying data on how often students said they had consumed fried potatoes (fries or potato chips) in the past week.

		Number of times consumed fried potatoes in the past week					
		0	1 to 3	4 to 6	7 to 13	14 to 20	21 or more
Gender	**Male**	2	10	15	12	6	3
	Female	15	15	10	20	19	12

Use the Minitab output on the next page to carry out a X^2 test of independence. Do you agree with the authors' conclusion that there was a significant association between gender and consumption of fried potatoes?

```
Expected counts are printed below observed counts
Chi-Square contributions are printed below expected counts

          0     1-3    4-6   7-13  14-20  21 or more  Total
M         2      10     15     12      6           3     48
       5.87    8.63   8.63  11.05   8.63        5.18
      2.552   0.216  4.696  0.082  0.803       0.917
F        15      15     10     20     19          12     91
      11.13   16.37  16.37  20.95  16.37        9.82
      1.346   0.114  2.477  0.043  0.424       0.484
Total    17      25     25     32     25          15    139
Chi-Sq = 14.153, DF = 5, P-Value = 0.015
```

12.33 The press release titled "Nap Time" (pewresearch.org, July 2009) described results from a nationally representative survey of 1488 adult Americans. The survey asked several demographic questions (such as gender, age, and income) and also included a question asking respondents if they had taken a nap in the past 24 hours. The press release stated that 38% of the men surveyed and 31% of the women surveyed reported that they had napped in the past 24 hours. For purposes of this exercise, suppose that men and women were equally represented in the sample.

a. Use the given information to fill in observed cell counts for the following table:

	Napped	Did Not Nap	Row Total
Men			744
Women			744

b. Use the data in the table from Part (a) to carry out a hypothesis test to determine if there is an association between gender and napping.

c. The press release states that more men than women nap. Although this is true for the people in the sample, based on the result of your test in Part (b), is it reasonable to conclude that this holds for adult Americans in general? Explain.

12.34 Using data from a national survey, the authors of the paper "What Do Happy People Do?" (*Social Indicators Research* [2008]: 565–571) concluded that there was convincing evidence of an association between amount of time spent watching television and whether or not a person reported that they were happy. They observed that unhappy people tended to watch more television. The authors write:

This could lead us to two possible interpretations:

1. Television viewing is a pleasurable enough activity with no lasting benefit, and it pushes aside time spent in other activities—ones that might be less immediately pleasurable, but that would provide long-term benefits in one's condition. In other words, television does cause people to be less happy.
2. Television is a refuge for people who are already unhappy. TV is not judgmental nor difficult, so people with few social skills or resources for other activities can engage in it. Furthermore, chronic unhappiness can be socially and personally debilitating and can interfere with work and most social and personal activities, but even the unhappiest people can click a remote and be passively entertained by a TV. In other words, the causal order is reversed for people who watch television; unhappiness leads to television viewing.

Using only data from this study, do you think it is possible to determine which of these two conclusions is correct? If so, which conclusion do you think is correct and why? If not, explain why it is not possible to decide which conclusion is correct based on the study data.

ACTIVITY 12.1 Pick a Number, Any Number ...

Background: There is evidence to suggest that human beings are not very good random number generators. In this activity, you will investigate this phenomenon by collecting and analyzing a set of human-generated "random" digits.

For this activity, work in a group with four or five other students.

1. Each member of the group should complete this step individually. Ask 25 different people to pick a digit from 0 to 9 at random. Record the responses.
2. Combine the responses you collected with those of the other members of your group to form a single sample. Summarize the resulting data in a one-way frequency table.

3. If people are adept at picking digits at random, what would you expect for the proportion of the responses in the sample that were 0? that were 1?
4. State a null hypothesis and an alternative hypothesis that could be tested to determine whether there is evidence that the 10 digits from 0 to 9 are not selected an equal proportion of the time when people are asked to pick a digit at random.
5. Carry out the appropriate hypothesis test, and write a few sentences indicating whether or not the data support the theory that people are not good random number generators.

ACTIVITY 12.2 Color and Perceived Taste

Background: Does the color of a food or beverage affect the way people perceive its taste? In this activity you will conduct an experiment to investigate this question and analyze the resulting data using a chi-square test.

You will need to recruit at least 30 subjects for this experiment, so it is advisable to work in a large group (perhaps even the entire class) to complete this activity.

Subjects for the experiment will be assigned at random to one of two groups. Each subject will be asked to taste a sample of gelatin (for example, Jell-O) and rate the taste as not very good, acceptable, or very good. Subjects assigned to the first group will be asked to taste and rate a cube of lemon-flavored gelatin. Subjects in the second group will be asked to taste and rate a cube of lemon-flavored gelatin that has been colored an unappealing color by adding food coloring to the gelatin mix before the gelatin sets.

Note: You may choose to use something other than gelatin, such as lemonade. Any food or beverage whose color can be altered using food coloring can be used. You can experiment with the food colors to obtain a color that you think is particularly unappealing!

1. As a class, develop a plan for collecting the data. How will subjects be recruited? How will they be assigned to one of the two treatment groups (unaltered color, altered color)? What extraneous variables will be directly controlled, and how will you control them?
2. After the class is satisfied with the data collection plan, assign members of the class to prepare the gelatin to be used in the experiment.
3. Carry out the experiment, and summarize the resulting data in a two-way table like the one shown:

	Taste Rating		
Treatment	Not Very Good	Acceptable	Very Good
Unaltered Color			
Altered Color			

4. The two-way table summarizes data from two independent samples (as long as subjects were assigned *at random* to the two treatments, the samples are independent). Carry out an appropriate test to determine whether the proportion for each of the three taste rating categories is the same when the color is altered as for when the color is not altered.

Summary of Key Concepts and Formulas

TERM OR FORMULA	COMMENT
One-way frequency table	A compact way of summarizing data on a categorical variable; it gives the number of times each of the possible categories in the data set occurs (the frequencies).
$X^2 = \sum_{\text{all cells}} \frac{(\text{observed cell count} - \text{expected cell count})^2}{\text{expected cell count}}$	A statistic used to provide a comparison between observed counts and those expected when a given hypothesis is true. When none of the expected counts are too small, X^2 has approximately a chi-square distribution.
X^2 goodness-of-fit test	A hypothesis test performed to determine whether the population category proportions are different from those specified by a given null hypothesis.

TERM OR FORMULA	COMMENT
Two-way frequency table (contingency table)	A rectangular table used to summarize a categorical data set; two-way tables are used to compare several populations on the basis of a categorical variable or to determine if an association exists between two categorical variables.
X^2 test for homogeneity	The hypothesis test performed to determine whether category proportions are the same for two or more populations or treatments.
X^2 test for independence	The hypothesis test performed to determine whether an association exists between two categorical variables.

Chapter Review Exercises 12.35 - 12.45

12.35 ● Each observation in a random sample of 100 bicycle accidents resulting in death was classified according to the day of the week on which the accident occurred. Data consistent with information given on the web site www.highwaysafety.com are given in the following table

Day of Week	Frequency
Sunday	14
Monday	13
Tuesday	12
Wednesday	15
Thursday	14
Friday	17
Saturday	15

Based on these data, is it reasonable to conclude that the proportion of accidents is not the same for all days of the week? Use $\alpha = .05$.

12.36 ●✦ The color vision of birds plays a role in their foraging behavior: Birds use color to select and avoid certain types of food. The authors of the article "Colour Avoidance in Northern Bobwhites: Effects of Age, Sex, and Previous Experience" (*Animal Behaviour* [1995]: 519–526) studied the pecking behavior of 1-day-old bobwhites. In an area painted white, they inserted four pins with different colored heads. The color of the pin chosen on the bird's first peck was noted for each of 33 bobwhites, resulting in the accompanying table.

Color	First Peck Frequency
Blue	16
Green	8
Yellow	6
Red	3

Do the data provide evidence of a color preference? Test using $\alpha = .01$.

12.37 ● In November 2005, an international study to assess public opinion on the treatment of suspected terrorists was conducted ("Most in U.S., Britain, S. Korea and France Say Torture Is OK in at Least Rare Instances," *Associated Press*, December 7, 2005). Each individual in random samples of 1000 adults from each of nine different countries was asked the following question: "Do you feel the use of torture against suspected terrorists to obtain information about terrorism activities is justified?" Responses consistent with percentages given in the article for the samples from Italy, Spain, France, the United States, and South Korea are summarized in the table at the top of the next page. Based on these data, is it reasonable to conclude that the response proportions are not the same for all five countries? Use a .01 significance level to test the appropriate hypotheses.

	Response				
Country	Never	Rarely	Some-times	Often	Not Sure
Italy	600	140	140	90	30
Spain	540	160	140	70	90
France	400	250	200	120	30
United States	360	230	270	110	30
South Korea	100	330	470	60	40

12.38 ● According to Census Bureau data, in 1998 the California population consisted of 50.7% whites, 6.6% blacks, 30.6% Hispanics, 10.8% Asians, and 1.3% other ethnic groups. Suppose that a random sample of 1000 students graduating from California colleges and universities in 1998 resulted in the accompanying data on ethnic group. These data are consistent with summary statistics contained in the article titled "Crumbling Public School System a Threat to California's Future (*Investor's Business Daily*, November 12, 1999).

Ethnic Group	Number in Sample
White	679
Black	51
Hispanic	77
Asian	190
Other	3

Do the data provide evidence that the proportion of students graduating from colleges and universities in California for these ethnic group categories differs from the respective proportions in the population for California? Test the appropriate hypotheses using $\alpha = .01$.

12.39 Criminologists have long debated whether there is a relationship between weather and violent crime. The author of the article "Is There a Season for Homicide?" (*Criminology* [1988]: 287–296) classified 1361 homicides according to season, resulting in the accompanying data. Do these data support the theory that the homicide rate is not the same over the four seasons? Test the relevant hypotheses using a significance level of .05.

Season			
Winter	Spring	Summer	Fall
328	334	372	327

12.40 ● Each boy in a sample of Mexican American males, age 10 to 18, was classified according to smoking status and response to a question asking whether he likes to do risky things. The following table is based on data given in the article "The Association Between Smoking and Unhealthy Behaviors Among a National Sample of Mexican-American Adolescents" (*Journal of School Health* [1998]: 376–379):

	Smoking Status	
	Smoker	Nonsmoker
Likes Risky Things	45	46
Doesn't Like Risky Things	36	153

Assume that it is reasonable to regard the sample as a random sample of Mexican-American male adolescents.

a. Is there sufficient evidence to conclude that there is an association between smoking status and desire to do risky things? Test the relevant hypotheses using $\alpha = .05$.
b. Based on your conclusion in Part (a), is it reasonable to conclude that smoking *causes* an increase in the desire to do risky things? Explain.

12.41 ● The article "Cooperative Hunting in Lions: The Role of the Individual" (*Behavioral Ecology and Sociobiology* [1992]: 445–454) discusses the different roles taken by lionesses as they attack and capture prey. The authors were interested in the effect of the position in line as stalking occurs; an individual lioness may be in the center of the line or on the wing (end of the line) as they advance toward their prey. In addition to position, the role of the lioness was also considered. A lioness could initiate a chase (be the first one to charge the prey), or she could participate and join the chase after it has been initiated. Data from the article are summarized in the accompanying table.

	Role	
Position	Initiate Chase	Participate in Chase
Center	28	48
Wing	66	41

Is there evidence of an association between position and role? Test the relevant hypotheses using $\alpha = .01$. What assumptions about how the data were collected must be true for the chi-square test to be an appropriate way to analyze these data?

12.42 ● The authors of the article "A Survey of Parent Attitudes and Practices Regarding Underage Drinking" (*Journal of Youth and Adolescence* [1995]: 315–334) conducted a telephone survey of parents with preteen and teenage children. One of the questions asked was "How effective do you think you are in talking to your children about drinking?" Responses are summarized in the accompanying 3 × 2 table. Using a significance level of .05, carry out a test to determine whether there is an association between age of children and parental response.

	Age of Children	
Response	Preteen	Teen
Very Effective	126	149
Somewhat Effective	44	41
Not at All Effective or Don't Know	51	26

12.43 ● The article "Regional Differences in Attitudes Toward Corporal Punishment" (*Journal of Marriage and Family* [1994]: 314–324) presents data resulting from a random sample of 978 adults. Each individual in the sample was asked whether he or she agreed with the following statement: "Sometimes it is necessary to discipline a child with a good, hard spanking." Respondents were also classified according to the region of the United States in which they lived. The resulting data are summarized in the accompanying table. Is there an association between response (agree, disagree) and region of residence? Use $\alpha = .01$.

	Response	
Region	Agree	Disagree
Northeast	130	59
West	146	42
Midwest	211	52
South	291	47

12.44 ● Jail inmates can be classified into one of the following four categories according to the type of crime committed: violent crime, crime against property, drug offenses, and public-order offenses. Suppose that random samples of 500 male inmates and 500 female inmates are selected, and each inmate is classified according to type of offense. The data in the accompanying table are based on summary values given in the article "Profile of Jail Inmates" (*USA Today*, April 25, 1991). We would like to know whether male and female inmates differ with respect to type of offense.

	Gender	
Type of Crime	Male	Female
Violent	117	66
Property	150	160
Drug	109	168
Public-Order	124	106

a. Is this a test of homogeneity or a test of independence?
b. Test the relevant hypotheses using a significance level of .05.

12.45 ● Drivers born under the astrological sign of Capricorn are the worst drivers in Australia, according to an article that appeared in the Australian newspaper *The Mercury* (October 26, 1998). This statement was based on a study of insurance claims that resulted in the following data for male policyholders of a large insurance company.

Astrological Sign	Number of Policyholders
Aquarius	35,666
Aries	37,926
Cancer	38,126
Capricorn	54,906
Gemini	37,179
Leo	37,354
Libra	37,910
Pisces	36,677
Sagittarius	34,175
Scorpio	35,352
Taurus	37,179
Virgo	37,718

a. Assuming that it is reasonable to treat the male policyholders of this particular insurance company as a random sample of male insured drivers in Australia, are the observed data consistent with the hypothesis that the proportion of male insured drivers is the same for each of the 12 astrological signs?
b. Why do you think that the proportion of Capricorn policyholders is so much higher than would be expected if the proportions are the same for all astrological signs?

c. Suppose that a random sample of 1000 accident claims submitted to this insurance company is selected and each claim classified according to the astrological sign of the driver. (The accompanying table is consistent with accident rates given in the article.)

Astrological Sign	Observed Number in Sample
Aquarius	85
Aries	83
Cancer	82
Capricorn	88
Gemini	83
Leo	83
Libra	83
Pisces	82
Sagittarius	81
Scorpio	85
Taurus	84
Virgo	81

Test the null hypothesis that the proportion of accident claims submitted by drivers of each astrological sign is consistent with the proportion of policyholders of each sign. Use the given information on the distribution of policyholders to compute expected frequencies and then carry out an appropriate test.

Continued

Graphing Calculator Explorations

EXPLORATION 12.1 The Goodness-of-Fit Test

Some calculators have a built-in application for performing the goodness-of-fit procedure. Before reading Exploration 12.1, you may wish to check this out! The goodness-of-fit applications that we have seen are very similar to what we will present below, but if you have the goodness-of-fit application, you may be best served by using our discussion and that application together.

For our discussion of using the calculator for a chi-square goodness-of-fit test, we will use Example 12.3, the hybrid car data. The goodness-of-fit procedure, as it develops, will have two parts. First we will calculate the value of X^2; then we will evaluate its statistical significance. We begin by entering the observed counts for the categories in List1. For your reference, observed counts follow.

State	Observed Count
California	250
Virginia	56
Washington	34
Florida	33
Maryland	33

Now we need to compute the expected counts. It might seem natural to calculate the expected counts as was done in the text, and then enter them in List2. However, a different approach actually turns out to be easier. Since expected counts usually follow from the hypothesized category proportions, you can enter the hypothesized category proportions in List2 and use them to calculate the expected values for each

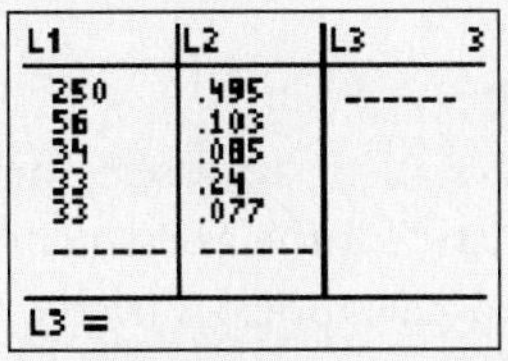

FIGURE 12.3
Calculator screen with observed counts and hypothesized proportions.

cell. After entering the proportions in List2, you should see something like Figure 12.3. (Note: As you work through a problem, this would be a VERY good place to check to make sure your proportions add up to 1.0!)

The expected values are calculated by multiplying the proportions in List2 by the total number of observations. You can find the total number of observations by using the statistics capabilities of the calculator to find the sum of the numbers in List1. You can get lots of statistics, such as the mean, sum, and standard deviation, by pressing the "Stat" button. On some calculators it is possible to get the sum alone by keying in something like "Sum(List1)." If your calculator has a "Sum" list function, you may be able to key in something like:

Sum(List1)

If not, you can find the sum (406 in this example) and then key in

406 * List2 → List3.

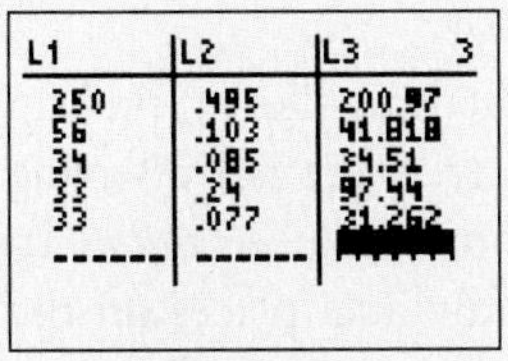

FIGURE 12.4
Expected counts added in List3.

You should now see three lists, similar to the ones shown in Figure 12.4, on your calculator screen.

Now we are in a position to actually calculate X^2. The formula for X^2 is a sum of quantities of the form

$$\frac{(\text{observed cell count} - \text{expected cell count})^2}{(\text{expected cell count})}$$

On your calculator, these quantities can be calculated all at once and then stored in List4:

(List1 − List3)^2/List3 → List4.

The value of the X^2 statistic is then found by finding the sum of the numbers in List4. The calculator we are using has a list function called Sum, so we enter "Sum(List4)" and the calculator returns: 59.4916.

Now that you have calculated the value of the X^2 statistic, you can proceed to assess its significance. Since the goodness-of-fit test is a one-tailed test, we must find the area to the right of $X^2 = 59.4916$ under the chi-square curve with 4 degrees of freedom.

To find the *P*-value on your calculator, you must navigate your menu system to a function that returns cumulative probabilities for X^2 values—most likely called a "Chisqcdf" or "χ^2 cdf." The two parameters necessary to find the *P*-value are the X^2 statistic value and the number of degrees of freedom. Some calculators, as we saw with the normal distribution calculator exploration, use the abbreviation "cdf" loosely, actually finding the probability of a statistic being *between* two values. In the case of the chi-square distribution, this is not too much of a problem since the X^2 statistic cannot be less than zero. If your calculator is one of those that uses the abbreviation "cdf" loosely, you should be able to find the cumulative area by keying in (using the current problem numbers) something like

χ^2 cdf(0, 59.4916, 4)

The calculator should return a number suspiciously close to 1. (Our calculator returns 1.000000000.) The actual *P*-value, remember, will be the area to the right of X^2, 1 − .1.000000000 = .00000000, which agrees with the computer output of Example 12.3.

In the case of the chi-square calculations, your calculator may differ in its syntax from what we have written here. Your calculator manual will once again come to the rescue if there are syntax differences.

EXPLORATION 12.2 Homogeneity, Independence, and the Chi-Square Statistic

In Exploration 12.1, we discussed the use of the chi-square statistic to assess the "goodness of fit" of data to a model. Using the chi-square statistic for the assessment of homogeneity of proportions and the independence of two categorical variables requires a bit more discussion. The calculator procedures for homogeneity and independence are more complicated than the goodness-of-fit procedure because there is more than one row of data to consider. However, once the data are entered into the calculator, the calculation of the expected values is an automatic feature built into the calculator—a great time saver!

There are three steps in performing a chi-square test for independence or homogeneity:

1. Prepare to enter the data.
2. Enter the data.
3. Perform the chi-square calculations.

```
Matrix
Mat A : 2x3
Mat B : 2x2
Mat C : None
```

```
Names Math Edit
1: [A] 2x3
2: [B] 2x2
3: [C]
4: [D]
5: [E]
6: [F]
7: [G]
```

FIGURE 12.5
Common calculator displays for matrix operations.

Preparing to enter the data sounds fairly easy, possibly something like (a) pull up a chair, (b) sharpen your pencil, (c) adjust the lighting. Actually, we're not referring to the preparation of your work environment, but preparation of the *calculator*. In past Explorations you have entered data at the cursor into individual places on the screen, and sets of data into lists. The chi-square data entry will be a little different, because you will enter data into a "matrix." Be very careful here: your calculator may have another possibility for data entry, "tables." Look in your manual under *matrix*. Matrices (plural of matrix) are different from both lists and tables.

The calculator details for working with matrices will differ from calculator to calculator, but generally you must (a) create or redefine a matrix so that it has the same number of rows and columns as the table you are analyzing, and (b) enter numbers into that matrix. Your calculator may already have some predefined matrices, usually labeled "A," "B," etc. Some calculators may have a "matrix" or "matr" key, or you may have to navigate your menu system to get to a menu item with these terms. If you are following along with your calculator, your goal is to navigate to a matrix screen and set up the matrices for data entry. Two common methods for indicating what matrices are already defined are shown in Figure 12.5.

```
MATRIX[A] █ ×3
[ .20000   .25000   .30000 ]
[ 1.0000   1.0000   1.0000 ]
[ 2.0000   0.0000   ⁻1.000 ]
```

FIGURE 12.6
Previous numbers in Matrix A.

The screens in Figure 12.5 show that two matrices are defined. The first one, Matrix "A," has two rows and three columns; the second, Matrix "B," has two rows and two columns. To change, or edit, a matrix you must move your cursor to that matrix and press Enter. Editing matrices is another place where calculators will differ, and we refer you to your manual for edification. On the calculator we are using, we move the cursor over to "Edit" and press Enter. The calculator then shows the screen illustrated in Figure 12.6.

We will use Example 12.5, the data on concussions. Those data, you may notice, use a 3 × 3 table. Our plan is to use Matrix A for the observed values, and happily our existing Matrix A is a 3 × 3. (If it were not, we would consult our calculator manual and change the dimensions!) The matrix after data entry appears as shown in Figure 12.7.

```
MATRIX[A] █ ×3
[ 45.000   25.000   21.000 ]
[ 68.000   15.000   13.000 ]
[ 45.000   5.0000   3.0000 ]
```

FIGURE 12.7
Numbers from Example 12.5.

We also need a matrix for the expected values for the chi-square procedure. (Some calculators may have a "dedicated" matrix for this purpose. If so, it will be named "Expected" or "MatAns" or something similar.) The calculator we are using requires us to specify a matrix to hold the soon-to-be calculated expected values, and we will use Matrix B. (Your calculator will probably automatically resize the matrix of expected values during the chi-square calculation—if so, you don't need to manually resize Matrix B.) After resizing the necessary matrices and entering the data from Example 12.5, you are now ready to proceed with the actual chi-square calculations. The chi-square test is a statistical hypothesis test, so your navigation through your calculator's menus should be a familiar one. When you get to the menu item, "χ^2-test," press Enter or Execute as appropriate. You will be asked to indicate which matrix contains the observed values, Matrix A in our case. If your calculator does not have a dedicated matrix for the expected values, you must specify that matrix also, in our case Matrix B. Then move your cursor to "Calculate" or "Execute" as appropriate.

Your calculator should return a screen that looks something like Figure 12.8. The value of the chi-square statistic, the *P*-value, and the number of degrees of freedom are all reported. (Be really careful here—the calculator has switched to scientific notation. That *P*-value is 0.0003794!) Once again, be sure to compare your numbers with the "correct" answer. If your results differ significantly, enough that round-off error seems unlikely, review your methods and see where you might have made an error. Especially remember to check the original data—incorrect data entry is a common source of errors when working with calculators.

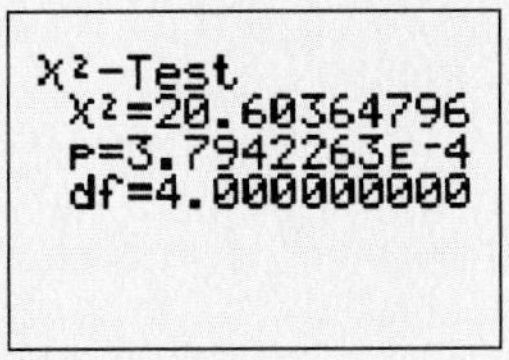

FIGURE 12.8
Calculator display after calculation.

AP* Review Questions for Chapter 12

1. Each person in a random sample of 60 students living in the dorms at a large university was asked whether he or she preferred to study in the dorm room, in the dorm's study lounge, or at the university library. The resulting data is summarized in the table below.

Dorm Room	Study Lounge	Library
18	12	30

In a hypothesis test to determine if there is evidence that the three locations are not equally preferred by students at the university, what is the expected count for the library category?

(A) 10
(B) 12
(C) 20
(D) 30
(E) 40

2. Each person in a random sample of 100 students at a large university was asked whether he or she preferred to attend classes in the morning, the afternoon, or in the evening. The resulting data is summarized in the table below.

Morning	Afternoon	Evening
28	48	24

A hypothesis test will be carried out to determine if there is evidence that the three time periods are not equally preferred by students at the university. The assumptions for the chi-square test were judged to be reasonable. When the null hypothesis is true, the test statistic will have a chi-square distribution with how many degrees of freedom (df)?

(A) 2
(B) 3
(C) 99
(D) 100
(E) Can't tell from the information given.

3. Each person in a random sample of university students was asked which of five flavors of ice cream he or she preferred. The resulting data was used to test the null hypothesis H_0: $p_1 = .2\ p_2 = .2 \ldots p_5 = .2$. The *P*-value associated with this test was .067. If a significance level of .05 is used for the test, which of the following is an appropriate conclusion?

(A) Fail to reject H_0, there is convincing evidence that there is no preference for one flavor of ice cream over another.
(B) Fail to reject H_0, there is not convincing evidence that there is a preference for one flavor of ice cream over another.
(C) Reject H_0, there is convincing evidence that there is no preference for one flavor of ice cream over another.
(D) Reject H_0, there is convincing evidence that there is a preference for one flavor of ice cream over another.
(E) Based on the information given, it is not possible to determine whether H_0 should be rejected or not.

4. Each person in a random sample of 300 female students and each person in a random sample of 300 male students at a university was asked whether or not they always wear a seat belt when driving. Which of the following would be an appropriate null hypothesis for a chi-square test based on these data?

(A) The mean seat belt use for males is equal to the mean seat belt use for females.
(B) The proportion of students who always wear a seat belt and the proportion who do not always wear a seat belt is the same for males and form females.
(C) The proportion of students who always wear a seat belt and the proportion who do not always wear a seat belt is not the same.
(D) There is no association between gender and seat belt use.
(E) There is an association between gender and seat belt use.

*AP and the Advanced Placement Program are registered trademarks of the College Entrance Examination Board, which was not involved in the production of, and does not endorse, this product.

5. One hundred students at a large public university were selected at random. Each student in the sample was asked to indicate how often he or she used on-campus recreational facilities by choosing between the following categories: never, occasionally, and regularly. Whether the student lived on campus or off campus was also noted. Which of the following would be an appropriate null hypothesis for a chi-square test based on these data?

(A) The proportion of students who live on campus is the same for all three recreational use categories.
(B) The proportion of students in each of the three recreational facility use categories is the same for students who live on-campus and those who live off-campus.
(C) The proportion of students in each of the three recreational facility use categories is not the same for students who live on-campus and those who live off-campus.
(D) There is no association between where a student lives and use of recreational facilities.
(E) There is an association between where a student lives and use of recreational facilities.

6. Fifty female students at a large university were selected at random and 50 male students were also selected at random. Each student in the two samples was asked to indicate how often they watched reality TV shows by choosing between the following viewing categories: never, once or twice per week, more than twice a week. Which of the following would be an appropriate null hypothesis for a chi-square test based on these data?

(A) The mean time spent watching TV is the same for males and females.
(B) The proportion of male students is equal to the proportion of female students.
(C) The proportion of students in each of the three viewing categories is the same for males and females.
(D) There is no association between gender and viewing category.
(E) There is an association between gender and viewing category.

7. Fifty female students at a large university were selected at random and 50 male students were also selected at random. Each student in the two samples was asked to indicate how often they watched reality TV shows by choosing between the following viewing categories: never, once or twice per week, more than twice a week. If the assumptions for the chi-square test are satisfied, the test statistic will have a chi-square distribution with how many degrees of freedom (df)?

(A) 2
(B) 3
(C) 5
(D) 6
(E) 98

8. Each person in a sample of 200 males and in a sample of 100 females was asked to indicate political affiliation by choosing between the following categories: Democrat, Republican, Libertarian, Green Party, Independent, Other. Are the sample sizes large enough to support using a chi-square test to determine if the proportion falling into each of the political affiliation categories is different for males and females?

(A) Yes, both samples are large enough.
(B) No, the sample size for the sample of males is large enough, but the sample size for the sample of females is not large enough.
(C) No, the sample size for the sample of females is large enough, but the sample size for the sample of males is not large enough.
(D) No, both samples are too small.
(E) There is not enough information given to determine if the sample sizes are large enough.

9. One hundred compact car owners and 100 full-size car owners were selected at random. Each person in the two samples was asked to indicate whether he or she was not concerned, somewhat concerned, or very concerned about recent increases in the price of gas. It was determined that the assumptions required for the chi-square test of homogeneity of proportions were reasonable. A chi-square test resulted in a *P*-value of .31. If a .05 significance level is used, which of the following is a reasonable conclusion?

(A) Fail to reject H_0, there is not convincing evidence that the proportions in each of the concern categories are different for compact car owners and full-size car owners.
(B) Fail to reject H_0, there is convincing evidence that the proportions in each of the concern categories are the same for compact car owners and full-size car owners.
(C) Reject H_0, there is convincing evidence that the proportion in each of the concern categories is the same for compact car owners and full-size car owners.
(D) Reject H_0, there is convincing evidence that the proportions in each of the concern categories are not the same for compact car owners and full-size car owners.
(E) Cannot determine if H_0 should be rejected based on the given information.

10. A researcher classified each individual in a large random sample of 100 community college students into one of four categories according to his or her ultimate degree goal (Associate, Bachelors, Masters, or Ph.D./Professional) and also by gender. If the assumptions for the chi-square test are satisfied, the test statistic will have a chi-square distribution with how many degrees of freedom (df)?

(A) 2
(B) 3
(C) 4
(D) 8
(E) 99

11. A local newspaper asked each person in a random sample of 40 subscribers which section of the paper he or she read first. The resulting data are shown in the accompanying table.

Section	Frequency
National News	12
Local News	8
Sports	16
Business	4

Which of the following test procedures would be appropriate for determining if the data provides evidence that the proportion choosing each of the sections is not the same?

(A) One-sample *t*-test
(B) Two-sample *t*-test
(C) Chi-square goodness-of-fit test
(D) Chi-square test of association
(E) Chi-square test of homogeneity

12. Which of the following condition(s) must be met in order for the chi-square goodness of fit test to be appropriate?

I. Population distribution is approximately normal
II. $n \geq 30$
III. Sample size is large enough so that all expected counts are at least 5

(A) I only
(B) II only
(C) III only
(D) I and II only
(E) I and III only

13. Which of the following is the number of degrees of freedom (df) for testing independence using bivariate categorical data that has been summarized in a 4×5 two-way table?

(A) 9
(B) 12
(C) 18
(D) 19
(E) 20

14. In a study of the foraging behavior of red-cockaded woodpeckers, males and females were observed landing on trees. Below is a partial table of the data.

Landing Location	Males	Females	Total
Branches	13	*	14
Lower trunk	6	*	40
Upper trunk	120	*	*
Total	139	*	246

If the landing location of these foraging woodpeckers is independent of gender, then the expected number of *males* landing on the *upper trunks* of trees is in which of the following ranges?

(A) 1 to < 10
(B) 10 to < 50
(C) 50 to < 100
(D) 100 to < 125
(E) 125 to < 150

15. The *P*-value for a chi-squared goodness-of-fit test is

(A) the area to the left of the calculated value of X^2 under the appropriate chi-squared curve.
(B) the area to the right of the calculated value of X^2 under the appropriate chi-squared curve.
(C) twice the area to the left of the calculated value of X^2 under the appropriate chi-squared curve.
(D) twice the area to the right of the calculated value of X^2 under the appropriate chi-squared curve.
(E) Cannot be determined in general.

CHAPTER 13

Arne Hodalic/Encyclopedia/Corbis

Simple Linear Regression and Correlation: Inferential Methods

Regression and correlation were introduced in Chapter 5 as techniques for describing and summarizing bivariate numerical data consisting of (x, y) pairs. For example, consider a scatterplot of data on y = percentage of courses taught by teachers with inappropriate or no license and x = spending per pupil for a sample of Missouri public school districts ("Is Teacher Pay Adequate?" *Research Working Papers Series,* Kennedy School of Government, Harvard University, October 2005). A scatterplot of the data shows a surprising linear pattern. The sample correlation coefficient is $r = .27$, and the equation of the least-squares line has a positive slope, indicating that school districts with higher expenditures per student also tended to have a higher percentage of courses taught by teachers with an inappropriate license or no license. Could the pattern observed in the scatterplot be plausibly explained by chance, or does the sample provide convincing evidence of a linear relationship between these two variables for school districts in Missouri? If there is evidence of a meaningful relationship between these two variables, the regression line could be used as the basis for predicting the percentage of teachers with inappropriate or no license for a school district with a specified expenditure per student or for estimating the average percentage of teachers with inappropriate or no license for all school districts with a specified expenditure per student. In this chapter, we develop inferential methods for bivariate numerical data, including a confidence interval (interval estimate) for a mean y value, a prediction interval for a single y value, and a test of hypotheses regarding the extent of correlation in the entire population of (x, y) pairs.

13.1 Simple Linear Regression Model

A *deterministic relationship* is one in which the value of y is completely determined by the value of an independent variable x. Such a relationship can be described using traditional mathematical notation, such as $y = f(x)$ where $f(x)$ is a specified function of x. For example, we might have

$$y = f(x) = 10 + 2x$$

or

$$y = f(x) = 4 - (10)^{2x}$$

However, in many situations, the variables of interest are not deterministically related. For example, the value of y = first-year college grade point average is certainly not determined solely by x = high school grade point average, and y = crop yield is determined partly by factors other than x = amount of fertilizer used.

A description of the relationship between two variables x and y that are not deterministically related can be given by specifying a **probabilistic model.** The general form of an **additive probabilistic model** allows y to be larger or smaller than $f(x)$ by a random amount e. The **model equation** is of the form

$$y = \text{deterministic function of } x + \text{random deviation} = f(x) + e$$

Thinking geometrically, if $e > 0$, the corresponding point will lie above the graph of $y = f(x)$. If $e < 0$ the corresponding point will fall below the graph. If $f(x)$ is a function used in a probabilistic model relating y to x and if observations on y are made for various values of x, the resulting (x, y) points will be distributed about the graph of $f(x)$, some falling above it and some falling below it.

For example, consider the probabilistic model

$$y = \underbrace{50 - 10x + x^2}_{f(x)} + e$$

The graph of the function $y = 50 - 10x + x^2$ is shown as the orange curve in Figure 13.1. The observed point (4, 30) is also shown in the figure. Because

$$f(4) = 50 - 10(4) + 4^2 = 50 - 40 + 16 = 26$$

for the point (4, 30), we can write $y = f(x) + e$, where $e = 4$. The point (4, 30) falls 4 above the graph of the function $y = 50 - 10x + x^2$.

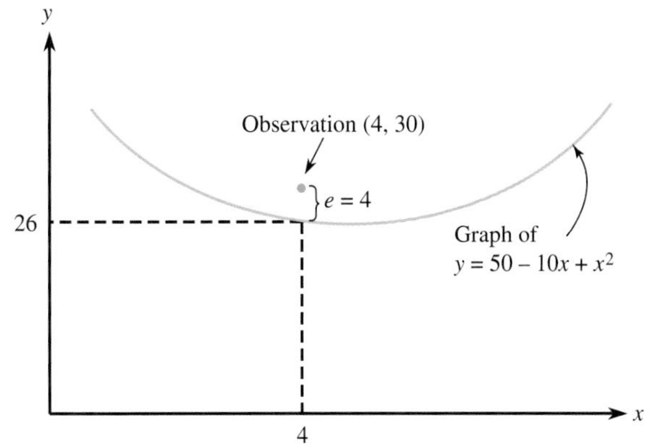

FIGURE 13.1
A deviation from the deterministic part of a probabilistic model.

Simple Linear Regression

The simple linear regression model is a special case of the general probabilistic model in which the deterministic function $f(x)$ is linear (so its graph is a straight line).

DEFINITION

The **simple linear regression model** assumes that there is a line with vertical or y intercept α and slope β, called the **population regression line**. When a value of the independent variable x is fixed and an observation on the dependent variable y is made,

$$y = \alpha + \beta x + e$$

Without the random deviation e, all observed (x, y) points would fall exactly on the population regression line. The inclusion of e in the model equation recognizes that points will deviate from the line by a random amount.

Figure 13.2 shows two observations in relation to the population regression line.

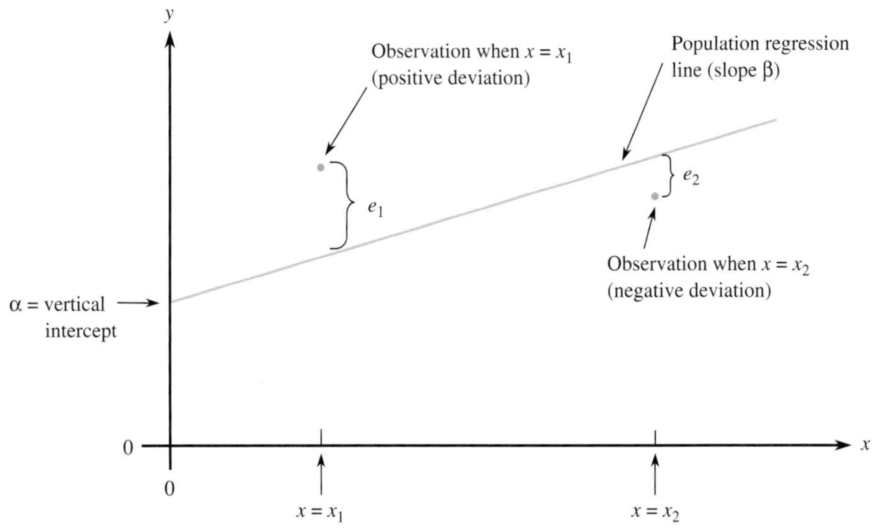

FIGURE 13.2
Two observations and deviations from the population regression line.

Before we make an observation on y for any particular value of x, we are uncertain about the value of e. It could be negative, positive, or even 0. Also, it might be quite large in magnitude (a point far from the population regression line) or quite small (a point very close to the line). In this chapter, we make some assumptions about the distribution of e in repeated sampling at any particular x value.

Basic Assumptions of the Simple Linear Regression Model

1. The distribution of e at any particular x value has mean value 0. That is, $\mu_e = 0$.
2. The standard deviation of e (which describes the spread of its distribution) is the same for any particular value of x. This standard deviation is denoted by σ.
3. The distribution of e at any particular x value is normal.
4. The random deviations $e_1, e_2, \ldots, e_n$ associated with different observations are independent of one another.

These assumptions about the e term in the simple linear regression model also imply that there is variability in the y values observed at any particular value of x. Consider y when x has some fixed value x^*, so that

$$y = \alpha + \beta x^* + e$$

Because α and β are fixed numbers, $\alpha + \beta x^*$ is also a fixed number. The sum of a fixed number and a normally distributed variable (e) is also a normally distributed variable (the bell-shaped curve is simply relocated), so y itself has a normal distribution. Furthermore, $\mu_e = 0$ implies that the mean value of y is $\alpha + \beta x^*$, the height of the population regression line above the value x^*. Finally, because there is no variability in the fixed number $\alpha + \beta x^*$, the standard deviation of y is the same as the standard deviation of e. These properties are summarized in the following box.

At any fixed x value, y has a normal distribution, with

$$\begin{pmatrix}\text{mean } y \text{ value} \\ \text{for fixed } x\end{pmatrix} = \begin{pmatrix}\text{height of the population} \\ \text{regression line above } x\end{pmatrix} = \alpha + \beta x$$

and

$$(\text{standard deviation of } y \text{ for a fixed } x) = \sigma$$

The slope β of the population regression line is the *average* change in y associated with a 1-unit increase in x. The y intercept α is the height of the population line when $x = 0$. The value of σ determines the extent to which (x, y) observations deviate from the population line. When σ is small, most observations will be quite close to the line, but when σ is large, there are likely to be some large deviations.

The key features of the model are illustrated in Figures 13.3 and 13.4. Notice that the three normal curves in Figure 13.3 have identical spreads. This is a consequence of $\sigma_e = \sigma$, which implies that the variability in the y values at a particular x does not depend on the value of x.

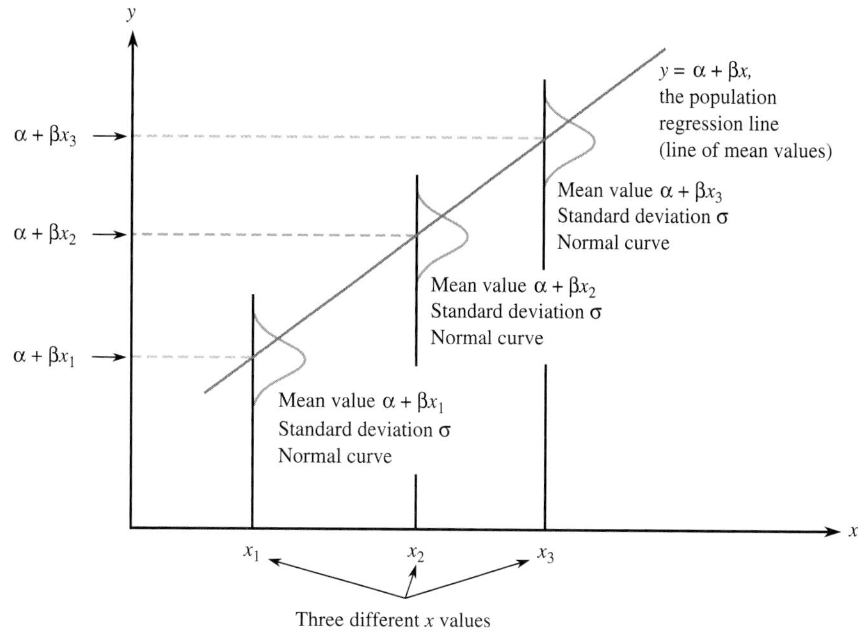

FIGURE 13.3
Illustration of the simple linear regression model.

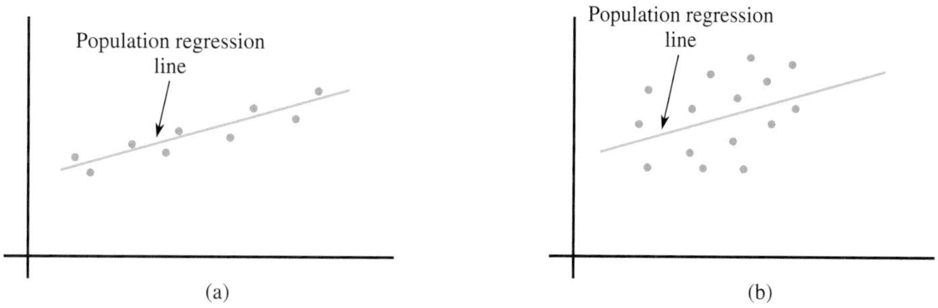

FIGURE 13.4
Data from the simple linear regression model: (a) small σ; (b) large σ.

EXAMPLE 13.1 Stand on Your Head to Lose Weight?

© ImageState Royalty-Free/Alamy

The authors of the article "On Weight Loss by Wrestlers Who Have Been Standing on Their Heads" (paper presented at the Sixth International Conference on Statistics, Combinatorics, and Related Areas, Forum for Interdisciplinary Mathematics, 1999, with the data also appearing in *A Quick Course in Statistical Process Control*, Mick Norton, Pearson Prentice Hall, 2005) stated that "amateur wrestlers who are overweight near the end of the weight certification period, but just barely so, have been known to stand on their heads for a minute or two, get on their feet, step back on the scale, and establish that they are in the desired weight class. Using a headstand as the method of last resort has become a fairly common practice in amateur wrestling."

Does this really work? Data were collected in an experiment in which weight loss was recorded for each wrestler after exercising for 15 minutes and then doing a headstand for 1 minute 45 seconds. Based on these data, the authors of the article concluded that there was in fact a demonstrable weight loss that was greater than that for a control group that exercised for 15 minutes but did not do the headstand. (The authors give a plausible explanation for why this might be the case based on the way blood and other body fluids collect in the head during the headstand and the effect of weighing while these fluids are draining immediately after standing.) The authors also concluded that a simple linear regression model was a reasonable way to describe the relationship between the variables

y = weight loss (in pounds)

and

x = body weight prior to exercise and headstand (in pounds)

Suppose that the actual model equation has $\alpha = 0$, $\beta = 0.001$, and $\sigma = 0.09$ (these values are consistent with the findings in the article). The population regression line is shown in Figure 13.5.

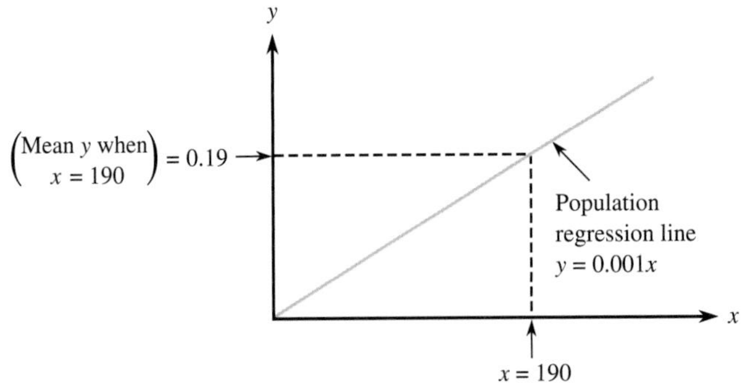

FIGURE 13.5
The population regression line for Example 13.1.

If the distribution of the random errors at any fixed weight (x value) is normal, then the variable y = weight loss is normally distributed with

$$\mu_y = \alpha + \beta x = 0 + 0.001x$$
$$\sigma_y = \sigma = .09$$

For example, when $x = 190$ (corresponding to a 190-pound wrestler), weight loss has mean value

$$\mu_y = 0 + 0.001(190) = .19$$

Because the standard deviation of y is $\sigma = 0.09$, the interval $0.19 \pm 2(0.09) = (0.01, 0.37)$ includes y values that are within 2 standard deviations of the mean value for y when $x = 190$. Roughly 95% of the weight loss observations made for 190 pound wrestlers will be in this range.

The slope $\beta = 0.001$ is the change in average weight loss associated with each additional pound of body weight.

More insight into model properties can be gained by thinking of the population of all (x, y) pairs as consisting of many smaller populations. Each one of these smaller populations contains pairs for which x has a fixed value. For example, suppose that in a large population of college students the variables

x = grade point average in major courses

and

y = starting salary after graduation

are related according to the simple linear regression model. Then there is the population of all pairs with $x = 3.20$ (corresponding to all students with a grade point average of 3.20 in major courses), the population of all pairs having $x = 2.75$, and so on. The model assumes that for each such population, y is normally distributed with the same standard deviation, and the *mean y value* (rather than y itself) is linearly related to x.

In practice, the judgment of whether the simple linear regression model is appropriate must be based on how the data were collected and on a scatterplot of the data. The sample observations should be independent of one another. In addition, the scatterplot should show a linear rather than a curved pattern, and the vertical spread of points should be relatively homogeneous throughout the range of x values. Figure 13.6 shows plots with three different patterns; only the first is consistent with the model assumptions.

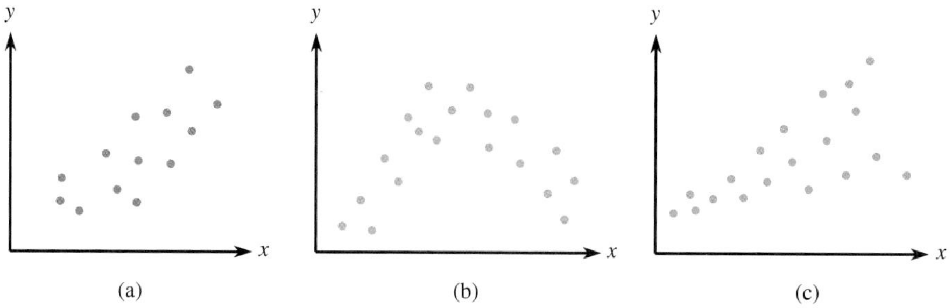

FIGURE 13.6
Some commonly encountered patterns in scatterplots: (a) consistent with the simple linear regression model; (b) suggests a nonlinear probabilistic model; (c) suggests that variability in y changes with x.

Estimating the Population Regression Line

For the remainder of this chapter, we will proceed with the view that the basic assumptions of the simple linear regression model are reasonable. The values of α and β (y intercept and slope of the population regression line) will almost never be known to an investigator. Instead, these values must first be estimated from the sample data $(x_1, y_1), \ldots, (x_n, y_n)$.

Let a and b denote point estimates of α and β, respectively. These estimates are based on the method of least squares introduced in Chapter 5. The sum of squared vertical deviations of points in the scatterplot from the least-squares line is smaller than for any other line.

The point estimates of β, **the slope, and** α, the y intercept of the population regression line, are the slope and y intercept, respectively, of the least-squares line. That is,

$$b = \text{point estimate of } \beta = \frac{S_{xy}}{S_{xx}}$$

$$a = \text{point estimate of } \alpha = \bar{y} - b\bar{x}$$

where

$$S_{xy} = \sum xy - \frac{(\sum x)(\sum y)}{n} \quad \text{and} \quad S_{xx} = \sum x^2 - \frac{(\sum x)^2}{n}$$

The estimated regression line is the familiar least-squares line

$$\hat{y} = a + bx$$

Let x^* denote a specified value of the predictor variable x. Then $a + bx^*$ has two different interpretations:

1. It is a point estimate of the mean y value when $x = x^*$.
2. It is a point prediction of an individual y value to be observed when $x = x^*$.

EXAMPLE 13.2 Mother's Age and Baby's Birth Weight

● Medical researchers have noted that adolescent females are much more likely to deliver low-birth-weight babies than are adult females. Because low-birth-weight babies have higher mortality rates, a number of studies have examined the relationship between birth weight and mother's age for babies born to young mothers.

One such study is described in the article "Body Size and Intelligence in 6-Year-Olds: Are Offspring of Teenage Mothers at Risk?" (Maternal and Child Health Journal [2009]: 847–856). The following data on

x = maternal age (in years)

and

y = birth weight of baby (in grams)

are consistent with summary values given in the referenced article and also with data published by the National Center for Health Statistics.

	OBSERVATION									
	1	2	3	4	5	6	7	8	9	10
x	15	17	18	15	16	19	17	16	18	19
y	2289	3393	3271	2648	2897	3327	2970	2535	3138	3573

A scatterplot of the data is given in Figure 13.7. The scatterplot shows a linear pattern and the spread in the y values appears to be similar across the range of x values. This supports the appropriateness of the simple linear regression model.

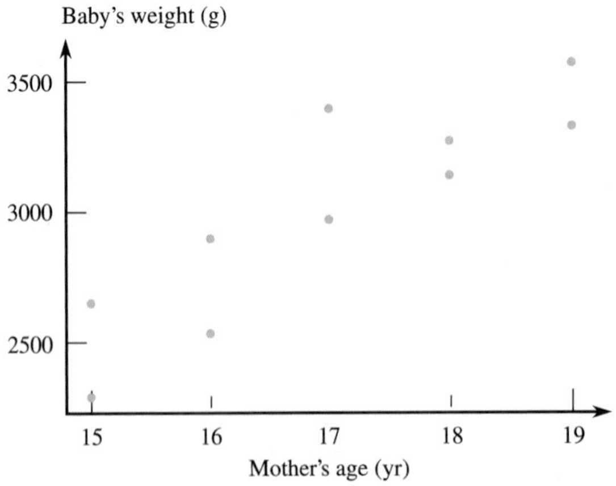

FIGURE 13.7
Scatterplot of the data from Example 13.2.

The summary statistics (computed from the given sample data) are

$$n = 10 \quad \sum x = 170 \quad \sum y = 30{,}041$$
$$\sum x^2 = 2910 \quad \sum xy = 515{,}600 \quad \sum y^2 = 91{,}785{,}351$$

!! Step-by-Step technology instructions available online

● Data set available online

from which

$$S_{xy} = \sum xy - \frac{(\sum x)(\sum y)}{n} = 515{,}600 - \frac{(170)(30{,}041)}{10} = 4903.0$$

$$S_{xx} = \sum x^2 - \frac{(\sum x)^2}{n} = 2910 - \frac{(170)^2}{10} = 20.0$$

$$\bar{x} = \frac{170}{10} = 17.0 \quad \bar{y} = \frac{30041}{10} = 3004.1$$

This gives

$$b = \frac{S_{xy}}{S_{xx}} = \frac{4903.0}{20.0} = 245.15$$

$$a = \bar{y} - b\bar{x} = 3004.1 - (245.1)(17.0) = -1163.45$$

The equation of the estimated regression line is then

$$\hat{y} = a + bx = -1163.45 + 245.15x$$

A point estimate of the mean birth weight of babies born to 18-year-old mothers results from substituting $x = 18$ into the estimated equation:

$$\begin{aligned}(\text{estimated mean } y \text{ when } x = 18) &= a + bx \\ &= -1163.45 + 245.15(18) \\ &= 3249.25 \text{ grams}\end{aligned}$$

Similarly, we would predict the birth weight of a baby to be born to a particular 18-year-old mother to be

$$(\text{predicted } y \text{ value when } x = 18) = a + b(18) = 3249.25 \text{ grams}$$

The point estimate and the point prediction are identical, because the same x value was used in each calculation. However, the interpretation of each is different. One represents our prediction of the weight of a single baby whose mother is 18, whereas the other represents our estimate of the mean weight of *all* babies born to 18-year-old mothers. This distinction will become important in Section 13.4, when we consider interval estimates and predictions.

The least-squares line could have also been fit using a graphing calculator or a statistical software package. Minitab output for the data of this example is shown here. Note that Minitab has rounded the values of the estimated coefficients in the equation of the regression line, which would result in small differences in predictions based on the line.

Regression Analysis: Birth Weight versus Maternal Age

The regression equation is
Birth Weight = –1163 + 245 Maternal Age

Predictor	Coef	SE Coef	T	P
Constant	–1163.4	783.1	–1.49	0.176
Maternal Age	245.15	45.91	5.34	0.001

S = 205.308 R-Sq = 78.1% R-Sq(adj) = 75.4%

In Example 13.2, the x values in the sample ranged from 15 to 19. An estimate or prediction should not be attempted for any x value much outside this range. Without sample data for such values, there is no evidence that the estimated linear relationship can be extrapolated very far. Statisticians refer to this potential pitfall as the **danger of extrapolation.**

Estimating σ^2 and σ

The value of σ determines the extent to which observed points (x, y) tend to fall close to or far away from the population regression line. A point estimate of σ is based on

$$\text{SSResid} = \sum (y - \hat{y})^2$$

where $\hat{y}_1 = a + bx_1, \ldots, \hat{y}_n = a + bx_n$ are the fitted or predicted y values and the residuals are $y_1 - \hat{y}_1, \ldots, y_n - \hat{y}_n$. SSResid is a measure of the extent to which the sample data spread out about the estimated regression line.

DEFINITION

The statistic for estimating the variance σ^2 is

$$s_e^2 = \frac{\text{SSResid}}{n - 2}$$

where

$$\text{SSResid} = \sum (y - \hat{y})^2 = \sum y^2 - a\sum y - b\sum xy$$

The subscript e in s_e^2 reminds us that we are estimating the variance of the "errors" or residuals.

The estimate of σ is the **estimated standard deviation**

$$s_e = \sqrt{s_e^2}$$

The number of degrees of freedom associated with estimating σ^2 or σ in simple linear regression is $n - 2$.

The estimates and number of degrees of freedom here have analogs in our previous work involving a single sample $x_1, x_2, \ldots, x_n$. The sample variance s^2 had a numerator of $\sum (x - \bar{x})^2$, a sum of squared deviations (residuals), and denominator $n - 1$, the number of degrees of freedom associated with s^2 and s. The use of $\bar{x}$ as an estimate of μ in the formula for s^2 reduces the number of degrees of freedom by 1, from n to $n - 1$. In simple linear regression, estimation of α and β results in a loss of 2 degrees of freedom, leaving $n - 2$ as the number of degrees of freedom for SSResid, s_e^2, and s_e.

The coefficient of determination was defined previously (see Chapter 5) as

$$r^2 = 1 - \frac{\text{SSResid}}{\text{SSTo}}$$

where

$$\text{SSTo} = \sum (y - \bar{y})^2 = \sum y^2 - \frac{(\sum y)^2}{n} = S_{yy}$$

The value of r^2 can now be interpreted as the proportion of observed y variation that can be explained by (or attributed to) the model relationship. The estimate s_e also gives another assessment of model performance. Roughly speaking, the value of σ represents the magnitude of a typical deviation of a point (x, y) in the population from the population regression line. Similarly, in a rough sense, s_e is the magnitude of a typical sample deviation (residual) from the least-squares line. The smaller the value of s_e, the closer the points in the sample fall to the line and the better the line does in predicting y from x.

EXAMPLE 13.3 Predicting Election Outcomes

● The authors of the paper "Inferences of Competence from Faces Predict Election Outcomes" (*Science* [2005]: 1623–1626) found that they could successfully predict the outcome of a U.S. congressional election substantially more than half the time based on the facial appearance of the candidates. In the study described in the paper, participants were shown photos of two candidates for a U.S. Senate or House of Representatives election. Each participant was asked to look at the photos and then indicate which candidate he or she thought was more competent. The two candidates were labeled A and B. If a participant recognized either candidate, data from that participant were not used in the analysis. The proportion of participants who chose candidate A as the more competent was computed. After the election, the difference in votes (candidate A − candidate B) expressed as a proportion of the total votes cast in the election was also computed. This difference falls between +1 and −1. It is 0 for an election where both candidates receive the same number of votes, positive for an election where candidate A received more votes than candidate B (with +1 indicating that candidate A received all of the votes), and negative for an election where candidate A received fewer votes than candidate B.

This process was carried out for a large number of congressional races. A subset of the resulting data (approximate values read from a graph that appears in the paper) is given in the accompanying table, which also includes the predicted values and residuals for the least-squares line fit to these data.

Competent Proportion	Difference in Vote Proportion	Predicted y Value	Residual
0.20	−0.70	−0.389	−0.311
0.23	−0.40	−0.347	−0.053
0.40	−0.35	−0.109	−0.241
0.35	0.18	−0.179	0.359
0.40	0.38	−0.109	0.489
0.45	−0.10	−0.040	−0.060
0.50	0.20	0.030	0.170
0.55	−0.30	0.100	−0.400
0.60	0.30	0.170	0.130
0.68	0.18	0.281	−0.101
0.70	0.50	0.309	0.191
0.76	0.22	0.393	−0.173

The scatterplot (Figure 13.8) suggests a positive linear relationship between

x = proportion of participants who judged candidate A as the more competent

and

y = difference in vote proportion.

● Data set available online

The summary statistics are

$$n = 12 \qquad \sum x = 5.82 \qquad \sum y = 0.11$$
$$\sum x^2 = 3.1804 \quad \sum xy = 0.5526 \quad \sum y^2 = 1.5101$$

from which we calculate

$$b = 1.3957 \qquad a = -0.6678$$
$$\text{SSResid} = .81228 \quad \text{SSTo} = 1.50909$$

Thus,

$$r^2 = 1 - \frac{\text{SSResid}}{\text{SSTo}} = 1 - \frac{0.81228}{1.50909} = 1 - .538 = .462$$

$$s_e^2 = \frac{\text{SSResid}}{n-2} = \frac{0.81228}{10} = .081$$

and

$$s_e = \sqrt{.081} = .285$$

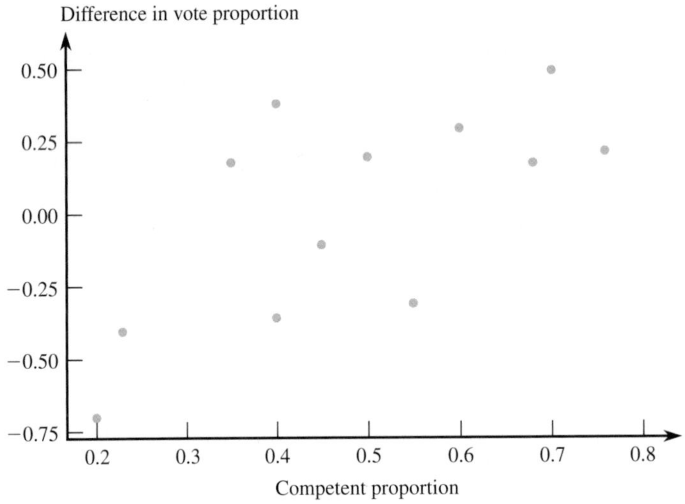

FIGURE 13.8
Minitab scatterplot for Example 13.3.

Approximately 46.2% of the observed variation in the difference in vote proportion y can be attributed to the probabilistic linear relationship with proportion of participants who judged the candidate to be more competent based on facial appearance alone. The magnitude of a typical sample deviation from the least-squares line is about .285, which is reasonably small in comparison to the y values themselves. The model appears to be useful for estimation and prediction; in Section 13.2, we show how a model utility test can be used to judge whether this is indeed the case.

A key assumption of the simple linear regression model is that the random deviation e in the model equation is normally distributed. In Section 13.3, we will indicate how the residuals can be used to determine whether this is plausible.

EXERCISES 13.1 - 13.11

13.1 Let x be the size of a house (in square feet) and y be the amount of natural gas used (therms) during a specified period. Suppose that for a particular community, x and y are related according to the simple linear regression model with

β = slope of population regression line = .017
α = y intercept of population regression line = −5.0

Houses in this community range in size from 1000 to 3000 square feet.

a. What is the equation of the population regression line?
b. Graph the population regression line by first finding the point on the line corresponding to $x = 1000$ and then the point corresponding to $x = 2000$, and drawing a line through these points.
c. What is the mean value of gas usage for houses with 2100 sq. ft. of space?
d. What is the average change in usage associated with a 1 sq. ft. increase in size?
e. What is the average change in usage associated with a 100 sq. ft. increase in size?
f. Would you use the model to predict mean usage for a 500 sq. ft. house? Why or why not?

13.2 The flow rate in a device used for air quality measurement depends on the pressure drop x (inches of water) across the device's filter. Suppose that for x values between 5 and 20, these two variables are related according to the simple linear regression model with population regression line $y = -0.12 + 0.095x$.

a. What is the mean flow rate for a pressure drop of 10 inches? A drop of 15 inches?
b. What is the average change in flow rate associated with a 1 inch increase in pressure drop? Explain.

13.3 The paper "Predicting Yolk Height, Yolk Width, Albumen Length, Eggshell Weight, Egg Shape Index, Eggshell Thickness, Egg Surface Area of Japanese Quails Using Various Egg Traits as Regressors" (*International Journal of Poultry Science* [2008]: 85–88) suggests that the simple linear regression model is reasonable for describing the relationship between y = eggshell thickness (in micrometers) and x = egg length (mm) for quail eggs. Suppose that the population regression line is $y = 0.135 + 0.003x$ and that $\sigma = 0.005$. Then, for a fixed x value, y has a normal distribution with mean $0.135 + 0.003x$ and standard deviation 0.005.

a. What is the mean eggshell thickness for quail eggs that are 15 mm in length? For quail eggs that are 17 mm in length?
b. What is the probability that a quail egg with a length of 15 mm will have a shell thickness that is greater than 0.18 μm?
c. Approximately what proportion of quail eggs of length 14 mm has a shell thickness of greater than .175? Less than .178?

13.4 A sample of small cars was selected, and the values of x = horsepower and y = fuel efficiency (mpg) were determined for each car. Fitting the simple linear regression model gave the estimated regression equation $\hat{y} = 44.0 - .150x$.

a. How would you interpret $b = -.150$?
b. Substituting $x = 100$ gives $\hat{y} = 29.0$. Give two different interpretations of this number.
c. What happens if you predict efficiency for a car with a 300-horsepower engine? Why do you think this has occurred?
d. Interpret $r^2 = 0.680$ in the context of this problem.
e. Interpret $s_e = 3.0$ in the context of this problem.

13.5 Suppose that a simple linear regression model is appropriate for describing the relationship between y = house price (in dollars) and x = house size (in square feet) for houses in a large city. The population regression line is $y = 23{,}000 + 47x$ and $\sigma = 5000$.

a. What is the average change in price associated with one extra square foot of space? With an additional 100 sq. ft. of space?
b. What proportion of 1800 sq. ft. homes would be priced over $110,000? Under $100,000?

13.6 a. Explain the difference between the line $y = \alpha + \beta x$ and the line $\hat{y} = a + bx$.
b. Explain the difference between β and b.
c. Let x^* denote a particular value of the independent variable. Explain the difference between $\alpha + \beta x^*$ and $a + bx^*$.
d. Explain the difference between σ and s_e.

13.7 ● The authors of the paper "Weight-Bearing Activity during Youth Is a More Important Factor for Peak Bone Mass than Calcium Intake" (*Journal of Bone and Mineral Research* [1994], 1089–1096) studied a number of variables they thought might be related to bone mineral density (BMD). The accompanying data on x = weight at age 13 and y = bone mineral density at age 27 are consistent with summary quantities for women given in the paper.

Weight (kg)	BMD (g/cm^2)
54.4	1.15
59.3	1.26
74.6	1.42
62.0	1.06
73.7	1.44
70.8	1.02
66.8	1.26
66.7	1.35
64.7	1.02
71.8	0.91
69.7	1.28
64.7	1.17
62.1	1.12
68.5	1.24
58.3	1.00

A simple linear regression model was used to describe the relationship between weight at age 13 and BMD at age 27. For this data:

$a = 0.558$ $\quad b = 0.009$ $\quad n = 15$

SSTo = 0.356 $\quad$ SSResid = 0.313

a. What percentage of observed variation in BMD at age 27 can be explained by the simple linear regression model?
b. Give a point estimate of σ and interpret this estimate.
c. Give an estimate of the average change in BMD associated with a 1 kg increase in weight at age 13.
d. Compute a point estimate of the mean BMD at age 27 for women whose age 13 weight was 60 kg.

13.8 ● Hormone replacement therapy (HRT) is thought to increase the risk of breast cancer. The accompanying data on x = percent of women using HRT and y = breast cancer incidence (cases per 100,000 women) for a region in Germany for 5 years appeared in the paper "Decline in Breast Cancer Incidence after Decrease in Utilisation of Hormone Replacement Therapy" (*Epidemiology* [2008]: 427–430). The authors of the paper used a simple linear regression model to describe the relationship between HRT use and breast cancer incidence.

HRT Use	Breast Cancer Incidence
46.30	103.30
40.60	105.00
39.50	100.00
36.60	93.80
30.00	83.50

a. What is the equation of the estimated regression line?
b. What is the estimated average change in breast cancer incidence associated with a 1 percentage point increase in HRT use?
c. What would you predict the breast cancer incidence to be in a year when HRT use was 40%?
d. Should you use this regression model to predict breast cancer incidence for a year when HRT use was 20%? Explain.
e. Calculate and interpret the value of r^2.
f. Calculate and interpret the value of s_e.

13.9 The accompanying summary quantities resulted from a study in which x was the number of photocopy machines serviced during a routine service call and y was the total service time (minutes):

$$n = 16 \qquad \sum (y - \bar{y})^2 = 22{,}398.05$$
$$\sum (y - \hat{y})^2 = 2620.57$$

a. What proportion of observed variation in total service time can be explained by a linear relationship between total service time and the number of machines serviced?
b. Calculate the value of the estimated standard deviation s_e. What is the number of degrees of freedom associated with this estimate?

13.10 A simple linear regression model was used to describe the relationship between y = hardness of molded plastic and x = amount of time elapsed since the end of the molding process. Summary quantities included $n = 15$, SSResid = 1235.470, and SSTo = 25,321.368.

a. Calculate a point estimate of σ. On how many degrees of freedom is the estimate based?
b. What percentage of observed variation in hardness can be explained by the simple linear regression model relationship between hardness and elapsed time?

13.11 ● Consider the accompanying data on x = advertising share and y = market share for a particular brand of soft drink during 10 randomly selected years.

x	.103	.072	.071	.077	.086	.047	.060	.050	.070	.052
y	.135	.125	.120	.086	.079	.076	.065	.059	.051	.039

a. Construct a scatterplot for these data. Do you think the simple linear regression model would be appropriate for describing the relationship between x and y?

b. Calculate the equation of the estimated regression line and use it to obtain the predicted market share when the advertising share is .09.

c. Compute r^2. How would you interpret this value?

d. Calculate a point estimate of σ. On how many degrees of freedom is your estimate based?

13.2 Inferences About the Slope of the Population Regression Line

The slope coefficient β in the simple linear regression model represents the average or expected change in the dependent variable y that is associated with a 1-unit increase in the value of the independent variable x. For example, consider x = the size of a house (in square feet) and y = selling price of the house. If we assume that the simple linear regression model is appropriate for the population of houses in a particular city, β would be the average increase in selling price associated with a 1 square foot increase in size. As another example, if x = number of hours per week a computer system is used and y = the annual maintenance expense, then β would be the expected change in expense associated with using the computer system one additional hour per week.

Because the value of β is almost always unknown, it must be estimated from the n independently selected observations $(x_1, y_1), \ldots, (x_n, y_n)$. The slope b of the least-squares line gives a point estimate. As with any point estimate, though, it is desirable to have some indication of how accurately b estimates β. In some situations, the value of the statistic b may vary greatly from sample to sample, so b computed from a single sample may be quite different from the true slope β. In other situations, almost all possible samples yield b values that are close to β, so the error of estimation is almost sure to be small. To proceed further, we need to know about the sampling distribution of b: information about the shape of the sampling distribution curve, where the curve is centered relative to β, and how much the curve spreads out about its center.

AP* EXAM TIP

Inferences about the slope of the regression line are based on the sampling distribution of b. The properties given here depend on the four basic assumptions of the simple linear regression model being met. Later in this chapter, you will see how to check these assumptions.

Properties of the Sampling Distribution of b

When the four basic assumptions of the simple linear regression model are satisfied, the following statements are true:

1. The mean value of b is β. That is, $\mu_b = \beta$, so the sampling distribution of b is always centered at the value of β. This means that b is an unbiased statistic for estimating β.
2. The standard deviation of the statistic b is

$$\sigma_b = \frac{\sigma}{\sqrt{S_{xx}}}$$

3. The statistic b has a normal distribution (a consequence of the model assumption that the random deviation e is normally distributed).

The fact that b is unbiased means only that the sampling distribution is centered at the right place; it gives no information about variability. If σ_b is large, then the sampling distribution of b will be quite spread out around β and an estimate far from β could result. For s_b to be small, the numerator σ should be small (little variability about the population line) and/or the denominator $\sqrt{S_{xx}}$ or, equivalently, $S_{xx} = \sum(x - \bar{x})^2$ itself should be large. Because $\sum(x - \bar{x})^2$ is a measure of how much the observed x values spread out, β tends to be more precisely estimated when the x values in the sample are spread out rather than when they are close together.

The normality of the sampling distribution of b implies that the standardized variable

$$z = \frac{b - \beta}{\sigma_b}$$

has a standard normal distribution. However, inferential methods cannot be based on this variable, because the value of σ_b is not known (since the unknown σ appears in the numerator of σ_b). One way to proceed is to estimate σ with s_e, yielding an estimated standard deviation.

The **estimated standard deviation of the statistic b** is

$$s_b = \frac{s_e}{\sqrt{S_{xx}}}$$

When the four basic assumptions of the simple linear regression model are satisfied, the probability distribution of the standardized variable

$$t = \frac{b - \beta}{s_b}$$

is the t distribution with df $= (n - 2)$.

In the same way that $t = \dfrac{\bar{x} - \mu}{\frac{s}{\sqrt{n}}}$ was used in Chapter 9 to develop a confidence interval for μ, the t variable in the preceding box can be used to obtain a confidence interval (interval estimate) for β.

Confidence Interval for β

When the four basic assumptions of the simple linear regression model are satisfied, a **confidence interval for β**, the slope of the population regression line, has the form

$$b \pm (t \text{ critical value}) \cdot s_b$$

where the t critical value is based on df $= n - 2$. Appendix Table 3 gives critical values corresponding to the most frequently used confidence levels.

The interval estimate of β is centered at b and extends out from the center by an amount that depends on the sampling variability of b. When s_b is small, the interval is narrow, implying that the investigator has relatively precise knowledge of β.

EXAMPLE 13.4 Athletic Performance and Cardiovascular Fitness

John Foxx/Stockbyte/Getty Images

● Is cardiovascular fitness (as measured by time to exhaustion from running on a treadmill) related to an athlete's performance in a 20-km ski race? The following data on

x = treadmill time to exhaustion (in minutes)

and

y = 20-km ski time (in minutes)

were taken from the article "Physiological Characteristics and Performance of Top U.S. Biathletes" (*Medicine and Science in Sports and Exercise* [1995]: 1302–1310):

x	7.7	8.4	8.7	9.0	9.6	9.6	10.0	10.2	10.4	11.0	11.7
y	71.0	71.4	65.0	68.7	64.4	69.4	63.0	64.6	66.9	62.6	61.7

A scatterplot of the data appears in the following figure:

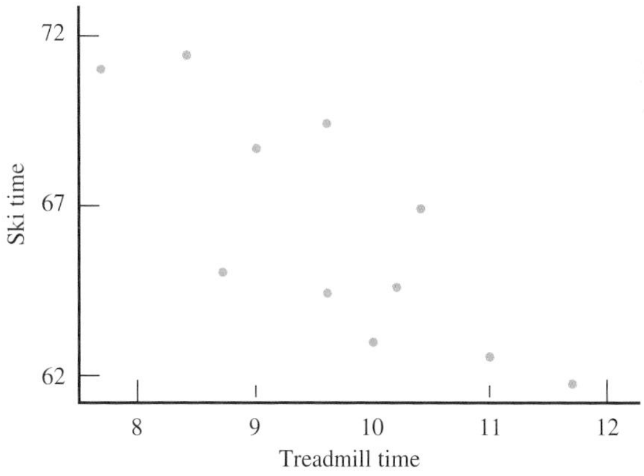

The plot shows a linear pattern, and the vertical spread of points does not appear to be changing over the range of x values in the sample. If we assume that the distribution of errors at any given x value is approximately normal, then the simple linear regression model seems appropriate.

The slope β in this context is the average change in ski time associated with a 1-minute increase in treadmill time. The scatterplot shows a negative linear relationship, so the point estimate of β will be negative.

Straightforward calculation gives

$$n = 11 \qquad \sum x = 106.3 \qquad \sum y = 728.70$$
$$\sum x^2 = 1040.95 \quad \sum xy = 7009.91 \quad \sum y^2 = 48{,}390.79$$

from which

$$b = -2.3335 \qquad a = 88.796$$
$$\text{SSResid} = 43.097 \qquad \text{SSTo} = 117.727$$
$$r^2 = .634$$ (63.4% of the observed variation in ski time can be explained by the simple linear regression model)
$$s_e^2 = 4.789 \qquad s_e = 2.188$$
$$s_b = \frac{s_e}{\sqrt{S_{xx}}} = \frac{2.188}{3.702} = .591$$

!! Step-by-Step technology instructions available online

● Data set available online

Calculation of the 95% confidence interval for β requires a t critical value based on df $= n - 2 = 11 - 2 = 9$, which (from Appendix Table 3) is 2.26. The resulting interval is then

$$\begin{aligned} b \pm (t \text{ critical value}) \cdot s_b &= -2.3335 \pm (2.26)(.591) \\ &= -2.3335 \pm 1.336 \\ &= (-3.671, -.999) \end{aligned}$$

We interpret this interval as follows: Based on the sample data, we are 95% confident that the true average decrease in ski time associated with a 1-minute increase in treadmill time is between 1 and 3.7 minutes.

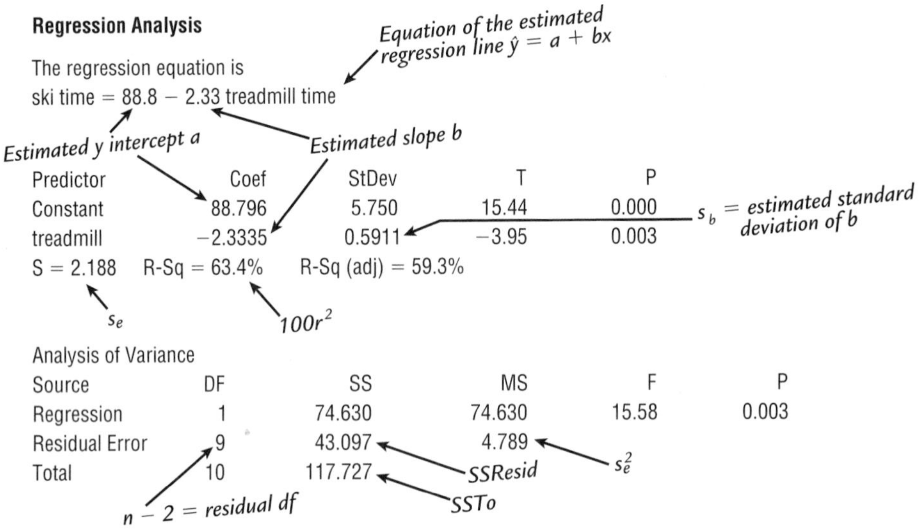

FIGURE 13.9 Partial Minitab output for the data of Example 13.4.

Output from any of the standard statistical computer packages routinely includes the computed values of a, b, SSResid, SSTo, and s_b. Figure 13.9 displays partial Minitab output for the data of Example 13.4. The format from other packages is similar. Rounding occasionally leads to small discrepancies between hand-calculated and computer-calculated values, but there are no such discrepancies in this example.

Hypothesis Tests Concerning β

Hypotheses about β can be tested using a t test similar to the t tests discussed in Chapters 10 and 11. The null hypothesis states that β has a specified hypothesized value. The t statistic results from standardizing b, the point estimate of β, under the assumption that H_0 is true. When H_0 is true, the sampling distribution of this statistic is the t distribution with df $= n - 2$.

AP* EXAM TIP

For simple linear regression, remember that df $= n - 2$.

Summary of Hypothesis Tests Concerning β

Null hypothesis: H_0: $\beta =$ hypothesized value

Test statistic: $t = \dfrac{b - \text{hypothesized value}}{s_b}$

The test is based on df $= n - 2$.

(continued)

Alternative hypothesis:	***P*-value:**
H_a: $\beta >$ hypothesized value	Area to the right of the computed t under the appropriate t curve
H_a: $\beta <$ hypothesized value	Area to the left of the computed t under the appropriate t curve
H_a: $\beta \neq$ hypothesized value	(1) 2(area to the right of t) if t is positive or (2) 2(area to the left of the t) if t is negative

Assumptions: For this test to be appropriate, the four basic assumptions of the simple linear regression model must be met:

1. The distribution of e at any particular x value has mean value 0 (that is $\mu_e = 0$).
2. The standard deviation of e is σ, which does not depend on x.
3. The distribution of e at any particular x value is normal.
4. The random deviations $e_1, e_2, \ldots, e_n$ associated with different observations are independent of one another.

Frequently, the null hypothesis of interest is $\beta = 0$. When this is the case, the population regression line is a horizontal line, and the value of y in the simple linear regression model does not depend on x. That is,

$$y = \alpha + 0 \cdot x + e$$

or equivalently,

$$y = \alpha + e$$

In this situation, knowledge of x is of no use in predicting y. On the other hand, if $\beta \neq 0$, there is a useful linear relationship between x and y, and knowledge of x is useful for predicting y. This is illustrated by the scatterplots in Figure 13.10.

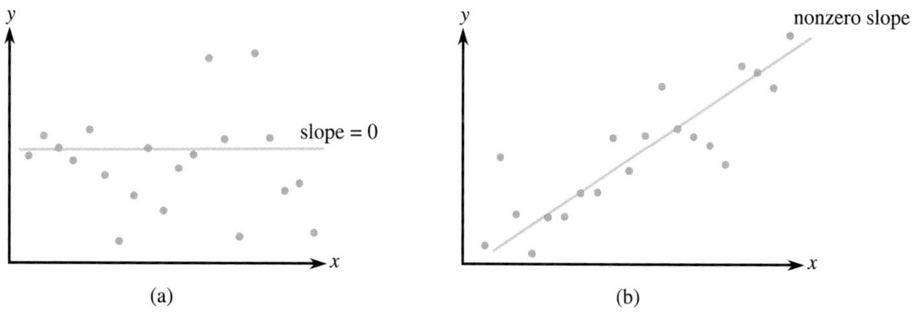

FIGURE 13.10
(a) $\beta = 0$; (b) $\beta \neq 0$.

The test of H_0: $\beta = 0$ versus H_a: $\beta \neq 0$ is called the *model utility test for simple linear regression.*

The Model Utility Test for Simple Linear Regression

The **model utility test for simple linear regression** is the test of

H_0: $\beta = 0$

versus

H_a: $\beta \neq 0$

(continued)

The null hypothesis specifies that there is *no* useful linear relationship between x and y, whereas the alternative hypothesis specifies that there *is* a useful linear relationship between x and y. If H_0 is rejected, we conclude that the simple linear regression model is useful for predicting y. The test procedure in the previous box (with hypothesized value = 0) is used to carry out the model utility test; in particular, the test statistic is $t = b/s_b$.

If a scatterplot and the r^2 value do not provide convincing evidence for a useful linear relationship, we recommend that the model utility test be carried out before using the regression line to make inferences.

EXAMPLE 13.5 University Graduation Rates

● The accompanying data on 6-year graduation rate (%), student-related expenditure per full-time student, and median SAT score for a random sample of the primarily undergraduate public universities and colleges in the United States with enrollments between 10,000 and 20,000 were taken from College Results Online, The Education Trust.

Median SAT	Expenditure	Graduation Rate
1065	7970	49
950	6401	33
1045	6285	37
990	6792	49
950	4541	22
970	7186	38
980	7736	39
1080	6382	52
1035	7323	53
1010	6531	41
1010	6216	38
930	7375	37
1005	7874	45
1090	6355	57
1085	6261	48

Let's first investigate the relationship between graduation rate and median SAT score. With y = graduation rate and x = median SAT score, the summary statistics necessary for a simple linear regression analysis are as follows:

$$n = 15 \qquad \sum x = 15{,}195 \qquad \sum y = 638$$
$$\sum x^2 = 15{,}430{,}725 \qquad \sum xy = 651{,}340 \qquad \sum y^2 = 28{,}294$$

from which

$$b = 0.132 \qquad a = -91.31 \qquad \text{SSResid} = 491.01$$
$$s_e = 6.146 \qquad r^2 = .576 \qquad S_{xx} = 38190$$

Because $r^2 = .576$, about 57.6% of observed variation in graduation rates can be explained by the simple linear regression model. It appears from this that there is a

● Data set available online

useful linear relation between the two variables, but a confirmation requires a formal model utility test. We will use a significance level of .05 to carry out this test.

1. β = the average change in graduation rate associated with an increase of 1 in median SAT score
2. H_0: $\beta = 0$
3. H_a: $\beta \neq 0$
4. $\alpha = .05$
5. Test statistic: $t = \dfrac{b - \text{hypothesized value}}{s_b} = \dfrac{b - 0}{s_b} = \dfrac{b}{s_b}$
6. Assumptions: The data are from a random sample, so the observations are independent. The accompanying scatterplot of the data shows a linear pattern and the variability of points does not appear to be changing with x:

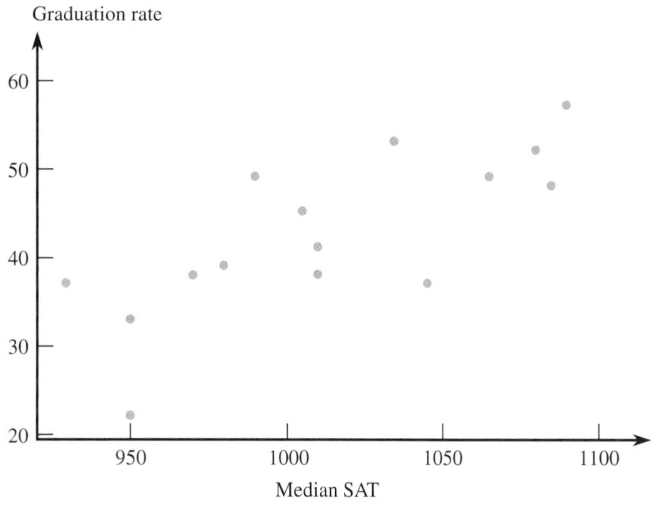

   Assuming that the distribution of errors at any given x value is approximately normal, the assumptions of the simple linear regression model are appropriate.
7. Calculation: The calculation of t requires

$$s_b = \frac{s_e}{\sqrt{S_{xx}}} = \frac{6.146}{195.423} = .031$$

   yielding

$$t = \frac{0.132 - 0}{.031} = 4.26$$

8. P-value: Appendix Table 4 shows that for a t test based on 13 df, $P(t > 4.26) < .001$. The inequality in H_a requires a two-tailed test, so

   $P\text{-value} < 2(.001) = .002.$

9. Conclusion: Since P-value $< .002$ is smaller than the significance level .05, H_0 is rejected. We conclude that there is a useful linear relationship between graduation rate and median SAT score.

Figure 13.11 shows partial Minitab output from a simple linear regression analysis. The Coef column gives $b = 0.13213$; $s_b = 0.03145$ is in the SE Coef column; the T column (for t ratio) contains the value of the test statistic for testing H_0: $\beta = 0$; and the P-value for the model utility test is given in the last column as 0.001 (slightly different from the ones given in Step 8 because of rounding and because the use of the table that produces only approximate *P*-values). Other commonly used statistical packages also include this information in their output.

Regression Analysis: Graduation Rate versus Median SAT

The regression equation is
Graduation Rate = -91.3 + 0.132 Median SAT

Predictor	Coef	SE Coef	T	P
Constant	-91.31	31.90	-2.86	0.013
Median SAT	0.13213	0.03145	4.20	0.001

S = 6.14574 R-Sq = 57.6% R-Sq(adj) = 54.3%

Analysis of Variance

Source	DF	SS	MS	F	P
Regression	1	666.72	666.72	17.65	0.001
Residual Error	13	491.01	37.77		
Total	14	1157.73			

FIGURE 13.11
Minitab output for the data of Example 13.5.

Let's next consider the relationship between graduation rate and expenditure per full-time student. Figure 13.12 shows partial Minitab output from a simple linear regression with expenditure as the predictor variable.

The regression equation is
Graduation Rate = 10.9 + 0.00468 Expenditure

Predictor	Coef	SE Coef	T	P
Constant	10.95	17.51	0.63	0.543
Expenditure	0.004680	0.002574	1.82	0.092

S = 8.42608 R-Sq = 20.3% R-Sq(adj) = 14.1%

FIGURE 13.12
Minitab output using expenditure as the predictor.

The value of the test statistic for the model utility test in this case is $t = 1.82$ and the associated *P*-value is .092. For a .05 level of significance, we would not reject the null hypothesis of H_0: $\beta = 0$. There is not convincing evidence of a linear relationship between graduation rate and expenditure per full-time student.

When H_0: $\beta = 0$ cannot be rejected by the model utility test at a reasonably small significance level, the search for a useful model must continue. One possibility is to relate y to x using a nonlinear model—an appropriate strategy if the scatterplot shows curvature. Alternatively, a multiple regression model using more than one predictor variable can be employed. We introduce such models in Chapter 14.

EXERCISES 13.12 - 13.26

13.12 What is the difference between σ and σ_b? What is the difference between σ_b and s_b?

13.13 Suppose that a single y observation is made at each of the x values 5, 10, 15, 20, and 25.

a. If $\sigma = 4$, what is the standard deviation of the statistic b?

b. Now suppose that a second observation is made at every x value listed in Part (a) (for a total of 10 observations). Is the resulting value of σ_b half of what it was in Part (a)?

c. How many observations at each x value in Part (a) are required to yield a σ_b value that is half the value calculated in Part (a)? Verify your conjecture.

13.14 Refer back to Example 13.3 in which the simple linear regression model was fit to data on x = proportion who judged candidate A as more competent and y = vote difference proportion. For the purpose of estimating β as accurately as possible, would it have been preferable to have observations with x values .05, .1, .2, .3, .4, .5, .6, .7, .8, .9, .95 and .98? Explain your reasoning.

13.15 Exercise 13.10 presented y = hardness of molded plastic and x = time elapsed since the molding was completed.

Summary quantities included

$$n = 15 \quad b = 2.50 \quad \text{SSResid} = 1235.470$$
$$\sum (x - \bar{x})^2 = 4024.20$$

a. Calculate the estimated standard deviation of the statistic b.
b. Obtain a 95% confidence interval for β, the slope of the population regression line.
c. Does the interval in Part (b) suggest that β has been precisely estimated? Explain.

13.16 A simple linear regression model was used to describe the relationship between sales revenue y (in thousands of dollars) and advertising expenditure x (also in thousands of dollars) for fast-food outlets during a 3-month period. A sample of 15 outlets yielded the accompanying summary quantities.

$$\sum x = 14.10 \quad \sum y = 1438.50 \quad \sum x^2 = 13.92$$
$$\sum y^2 = 140{,}354 \quad \sum xy = 1387.20$$
$$\sum (y - \bar{y})^2 = 2401.85 \quad \sum (y - \hat{y})^2 = 561.46$$

a. What proportion of observed variation in sales revenue can be attributed to the linear relationship between revenue and advertising expenditure?
b. Calculate s_e and s_b.
c. Obtain a 90% confidence interval for β, the average change in revenue associated with a \$1000 (that is, 1-unit) increase in advertising expenditure.

13.17 ✦ An experiment to study the relationship between x = time spent exercising (minutes) and y = amount of oxygen consumed during the exercise period resulted in the following summary statistics.

$$n = 20 \quad \sum x = 50 \quad \sum y = 16{,}705 \quad \sum x^2 = 150$$
$$\sum y^2 = 14{,}194{,}231 \quad \sum xy = 44{,}194$$

a. Estimate the slope and y intercept of the population regression line.
b. One sample observation on oxygen usage was 757 for a 2-minute exercise period. What amount of oxygen consumption would you predict for this exercise period, and what is the corresponding residual?
c. Compute a 99% confidence interval for the average change in oxygen consumption associated with a 1-minute increase in exercise time.

13.18 The paper "The Effects of Split Keyboard Geometry on Upper Body Postures" (*Ergonomics* [2009]: 104–111) describes a study to determine the effects of several keyboard characteristics on typing speed. One of the variables considered was the front-to-back surface angle of the keyboard. Minitab output resulting from fitting the simple linear regression model with x = surface angle (degrees) and y = typing speed (words per minute) is given below.

Regression Analysis: Typing Speed versus Surface Angle

The regression equation is
Typing Speed = 60.0 + 0.0036 Surface Angle

Predictor	Coef	SE Coef	T	P
Constant	60.0286	0.2466	243.45	0.000
Surface Angle	0.00357	0.03823	0.09	0.931

S = 0.511766 R-Sq = 0.3% R-Sq(adj) = 0.0%

Analysis of Variance

Source	DF	SS	MS	F	P
Regression	1	0.0023	0.0023	0.01	0.931
Residual Error	3	0.7857	0.2619		
Total	4	0.7880			

a. Assuming that the basic assumptions of the simple linear regression model are reasonably met, carry out a hypothesis test to decide if there is a useful linear relationship between x and y.
b. Are the values of s_e and r^2 consistent with the conclusion from Part (a)? Explain.

13.19 The authors of the paper "Decreased Brain Volume in Adults with Childhood Lead Exposure" (*Public Library of Science Medicine* [May 27, 2008]: e112) studied the relationship between childhood environmental lead exposure and a measure of brain volume change in a particular region of the brain. Data were given for x = mean childhood blood lead level (μg/dL) and y = brain volume change (BVC, in percent). A subset of data read from a graph that appeared in the paper was used to produce the accompanying Minitab output.

```
Regression Analysis: BVC versus Mean Blood Lead Level

The regression equation is
BVC = −0.00179 − 0.00210 Mean Blood Lead Level

Predictor                    Coef      SE Coef      T      P
Constant                -0.001790     0.008303  -0.22  0.830
Mean Blood Lead Level  -0.0021007    0.0005743  -3.66  0.000
```

Carry out a hypothesis test to decide if there is convincing evidence of a useful linear relationship between x and y. Assume that the basic assumptions of the simple linear regression model are reasonably met.

13.20 Do taller adults make more money? The authors of the paper "Stature and Status: Height, Ability, and Labor Market Outcomes" (*Journal of Political Economics* [2008]: 499–532) investigated the association between height and earnings. They used the simple linear regression model to describe the relationship between x = height (in inches) and y = log(weekly gross earnings in dollars) in a very large sample of men. The logarithm of weekly gross earnings was used because this transformation resulted in a relationship that was approximately linear. The paper reported that the slope of the estimated regression line was $b = 0.023$ and the standard deviation of b was $s_b = 0.004$. Carry out a hypothesis test to decide if there is convincing evidence of a useful linear relationship between height and the logarithm of weekly earnings. Assume that the basic assumptions of the simple linear regression model are reasonably met.

13.21 ● Researchers studying pleasant touch sensations measured the firing frequency (impulses per second) of nerves that were stimulated by a light brushing stroke on the forearm and also recorded the subject's numerical rating of how pleasant the sensation was. The accompanying data was read from a graph in the paper "Coding of Pleasant Touch by Unmyelinated Afferents in Humans" (*Nature Neuroscience*, April 12, 2009).

Firing Frequency	Pleasantness Rating
23	0.2
24	1.0
22	1.2
25	1.2
27	1.0
28	2.0
34	2.3
33	2.2
36	2.4
34	2.8

a. Estimate the mean change in pleasantness rating associated with an increase of 1 impulse per second in firing frequency using a 95% confidence interval. Interpret the resulting interval.

b. Carry out a hypothesis test to decide if there is convincing evidence of a useful linear relationship between firing frequency and pleasantness rating.

13.22 ● The accompanying data were read from a plot (and are a subset of the complete data set) given in the article "Cognitive Slowing in Closed-Head Injury" (*Brain and Cognition* [1996]: 429–440). The data represent the mean response times for a group of individuals with closed-head injury (CHI) and a matched control group without head injury on 10 different tasks. Each observation was based on a different study, and used different subjects, so it is reasonable to assume that the observations are independent.

	Mean Response Time	
Study	Control	CHI
1	250	303
2	360	491
3	475	659
4	525	683
5	610	922
6	740	1044
7	880	1421
8	920	1329
9	1010	1481
10	1200	1815

a. Fit a linear regression model that would allow you to predict the mean response time for those suffering a closed-head injury from the mean response time on the same task for individuals with no head injury.

b. Do the sample data support the hypothesis that there is a useful linear relationship between the mean response time for individuals with no head injury and the mean response time for individuals with CHI? Test the appropriate hypotheses using $\alpha = .05$.

c. It is also possible to test hypotheses about the y intercept in a linear regression model. For these data, the null hypothesis H_0: $\alpha = 0$ cannot be rejected at the .05 significance level, suggesting that a model with a y intercept of 0 might be an appropriate model. Fitting such a model results in an estimated regression equation of

CHI = 1.48(Control)

Interpret the estimated slope of 1.48.

13.23 Exercise 13.16 described a regression analysis in which y = sales revenue and x = advertising expenditure. Summary quantities given there yield

$$n = 15 \qquad b = 52.27 \qquad s_b = 8.05$$

a. Test the hypothesis H_0: $\beta = 0$ versus H_a: $\beta \neq 0$ using a significance level of .05. What does your conclusion say about the nature of the relationship between x and y?

b. Consider the hypothesis H_0: $\beta = 40$ versus H_a: $\beta > 40$. The null hypothesis states that the average change in sales revenue associated with a 1-unit increase in advertising expenditure is (at most) \$40,000. Carry out a test using significance level .01.

13.24 ● Consider the accompanying data on x = research and development expenditure (thousands of dollars) and y = growth rate (% per year) for eight different industries.

x	2024	5038	905	3572	1157	327	378	191
y	1.90	3.96	2.44	0.88	0.37	−0.90	0.49	1.01

a. Would a simple linear regression model provide useful information for predicting growth rate from research and development expenditure? Use a .05 level of significance.

b. Use a 90% confidence interval to estimate the average change in growth rate associated with a \$1000 increase in expenditure. Interpret the resulting interval.

13.25 ●✦ The article "Effect of Temperature on the pH of Skim Milk" (*Journal of Dairy Research* [1988]: 277–280) reported on a study involving x = temperature (°C) under specified experimental conditions and y = milk pH. The accompanying data (read from a graph) are a representative subset of that which appeared in the article:

x	4	4	24	24	25	38	38	40
y	6.85	6.79	6.63	6.65	6.72	6.62	6.57	6.52
x	45	50	55	56	60	67	70	78
y	6.50	6.48	6.42	6.41	6.38	6.34	6.32	6.34

$$\sum x = 678 \quad \sum y = 104.54 \quad \sum x^2 = 36{,}056$$
$$\sum y^2 = 683.4470 \quad \sum xy = 4376.36$$

Do these data strongly suggest that there is a negative linear relationship between temperature and pH? State and test the relevant hypotheses using a significance level of .01.

13.26 ● In anthropological studies, an important characteristic of fossils is cranial capacity. Frequently skulls are at least partially decomposed, so it is necessary to use other characteristics to obtain information about capacity. One such measure that has been used is the length of the lambda-opisthion chord. The article "Vertesszollos and the Presapiens Theory" (*American Journal of Physical Anthropology* [1971]) reported the accompanying data for $n = 7$ *Homo erectus* fossils.

x (chord length in mm)	78	75	78	81	84	86	87
y (capacity in cm^3)	850	775	750	975	915	1015	1030

Suppose that from previous evidence, anthropologists had believed that for each 1-mm increase in chord length, cranial capacity would be expected to increase by 20 cm^3. Do these new experimental data strongly contradict prior belief?

13.3 Checking Model Adequacy

The simple linear regression model equation is

$$y = \alpha + \beta x + e$$

where e represents the random deviation of an observed y value from the population regression line $\alpha + \beta x$. The inferential methods presented in Section 13.2 required some assumptions about e. These assumptions include:

1. At any particular x value, the distribution of e is a normal distribution.
2. At any particular x value, the standard deviation of e is σ, which is the same for all values of x (that is σ does not depend on x).

Inferences based on the simple linear regression model continue to be reliable when model assumptions are slightly violated (for example, mild nonnormality of the random deviation distribution). However, using an estimated model in the face of grossly violated assumptions can result in misleading conclusions. In this section, we consider methods for identifying such serious violations and for suggesting how a satisfactory model can be obtained.

Residual Analysis

If the deviations $e_1, e_2, \ldots, e_n$ from the population line were available, they could be examined for any inconsistencies with model assumptions. For example, a normal probability plot would suggest whether or not normality was reasonable. But, because

$$\begin{aligned} e_1 &= y_1 - (\alpha + \beta x_1) \\ &\vdots \\ e_n &= y_n - (\alpha + \beta x_n) \end{aligned}$$

these deviations can be calculated only if the equation of the population line is known. In practice, this will never be the case. Instead, diagnostic checks must be based on the residuals

$$\begin{aligned} y_1 - \hat{y}_1 &= y_1 - (a + bx_1) \\ &\vdots \\ y_n - \hat{y}_n &= y_n - (a + bx_n) \end{aligned}$$

which are the deviations from the *estimated* line.

When all model assumptions are met, the mean value of the residuals at any particular x value is 0. Any observation that gives a large positive or negative residual should be examined carefully for any anomalous circumstances, such as a recording error or exceptional experimental conditions. Identifying residuals with unusually large magnitudes is made easier by inspecting **standardized residuals.**

Recall that a quantity is standardized by subtracting its mean value (0 in this case) and dividing by its estimated standard deviation. So, to obtain standardized residuals, we compute

$$\text{standardized residual} = \frac{\text{residual}}{\text{estimated standard deviation of residual}}$$

The value of a standardized residual tells how many standard deviations the corresponding residual is from its expected value, 0.

Because residuals at different x values have different standard deviations* (depending on the value of x for that observation), computing the standardized residuals can be tedious. Fortunately, many computer regression programs provide standardized residuals as part of the output.

In Chapter 7, the normal probability plot was introduced as a technique for deciding whether the n observations in a random sample could plausibly have come from a normal population distribution. To assess whether the assumption that $e_1, e_2, \ldots e_n$ all come from the same normal distribution is reasonable, we construct a normal probability plot of the standardized residuals. This is illustrated in the following example.

*The estimated standard deviation of the ith residual, $y_i - \hat{y}_i$ is $s_e\sqrt{1 - \frac{1}{n} - \frac{(x_i - \bar{x})^2}{S_{xx}}}$

EXAMPLE 13.6 Political Faces

Example 13.3 introduced data on

x = proportion who judged candidate A as the more competent of two candidates based on facial appearance

and

y = vote difference (candidate A − candidate B) expressed as a proportion of the total number of votes cast

for a sample of 12 congressional elections. (See Example 13.3 for a more detailed description of the study.)

The scatterplot in Figure 13.13 is consistent with the assumptions of the simple linear regression model.

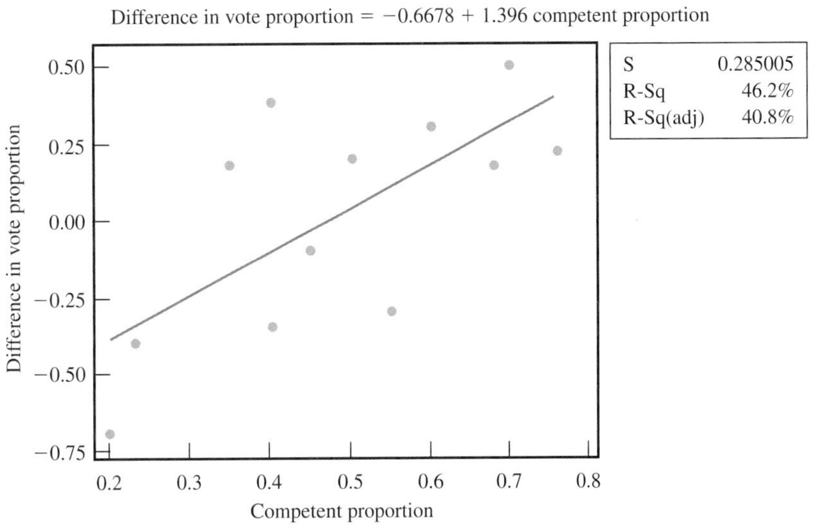

FIGURE 13.13 Minitab output for the data of Example 13.6.

Step-by-Step technology instructions available online

The residuals, their standard deviations, and the standardized residuals (computed using Minitab) are given in Table 13.1. For the residual with the largest mag-

TABLE 13.1 Data, Residuals, and Standardized Residuals for Example 13.6

Observation	Competent Proportion x	Difference in Vote Proportion y	$\hat{y}$	Residual	Estimated Standard Deviation of Residual	Standardized Residual
1	0.20	−0.70	−0.39	−0.31	0.24	−1.32
2	0.23	−0.40	−0.35	−0.05	0.24	−0.22
3	0.40	−0.35	−0.11	−0.24	0.27	−0.89
4	0.35	0.18	−0.18	0.36	0.27	1.35
5	0.40	0.38	−0.11	0.49	0.27	1.81
6	0.45	−0.10	−0.04	−0.06	0.27	−0.22
7	0.50	0.20	0.03	0.17	0.27	0.62
8	0.55	−0.30	0.10	−0.40	0.27	−1.48
9	0.60	0.30	0.17	0.13	0.27	0.49
10	0.68	0.18	0.28	−0.10	0.26	−0.39
11	0.70	0.50	0.31	0.19	0.25	0.75
12	0.76	0.22	0.39	−0.17	0.24	−0.72

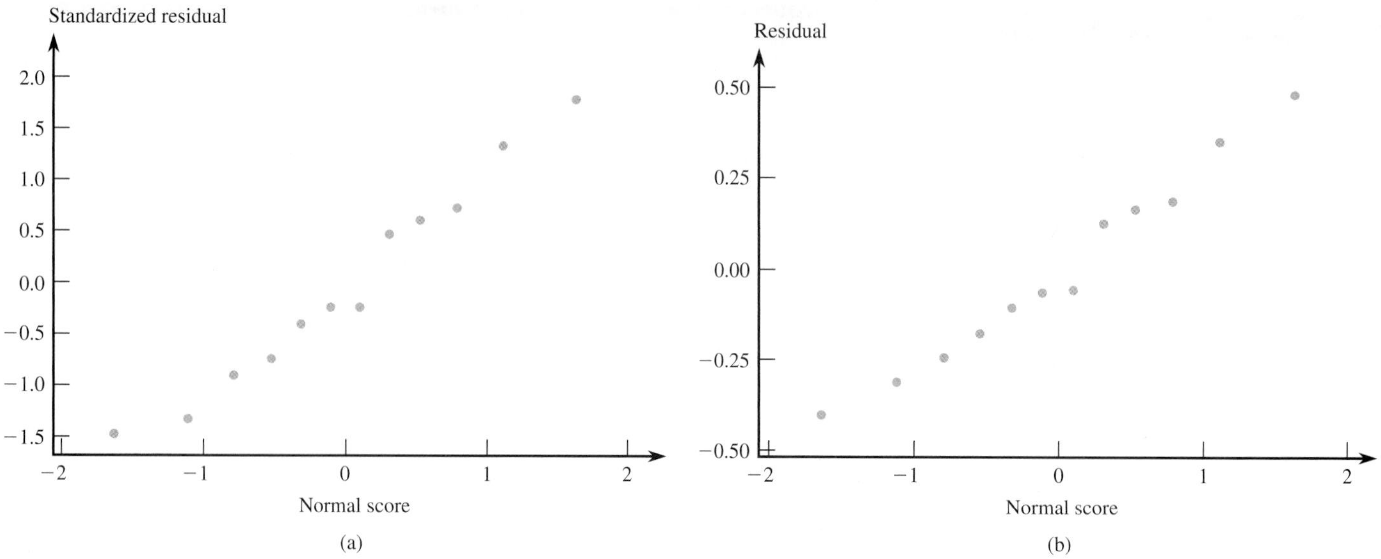

FIGURE 13.14
Normal probability plots for Example 13.6 (from Minitab): (a) standardized residuals; (b) residuals.

nitude, 0.49, the standardized residual is 1.81. That is, this residual is approximately 1.8 standard deviations above its expected value of 0, which is not particularly unusual in a sample of this size. On the standardized scale, no residual here is surprisingly large.

Figure 13.14 displays a normal probability plot of the standardized residuals and also one of the residuals. Notice that in this case the plots are nearly identical; it is usually the case that the two plots are similar. Although it is preferable to work with the standardized residuals, if you do not have access to a computer package or calculator that will produce standardized residuals, a plot of the unstandardized residuals should suffice. Both of the normal probability plots in Figure 13.14 are approximately linear. The plots would not cause us to question the assumption of normality.

Plotting the Residuals

AP* EXAM TIP

When considering linear regression, your first step should be to study the scatterplot and the residual plot. They provide important information about whether a linear model is appropriate.

A plot of the (x, residual) pairs is called a **residual plot,** and a plot of the (x, standardized residual) pairs is a **standardized residual plot.** Residual and standardized residual plots typically exhibit the same general shapes. If you are using a computer package or graphing calculator that calculates standardized residuals, we recommend using the standardized residual plot. If not, it is acceptable to use the residual plot instead.

A standardized residual plot or a residual plot is often helpful in identifying unusual or highly influential observations and in checking for violations of model assumptions. A desirable plot is one that exhibits no particular pattern (such as curvature or a much greater spread in one part of the plot than in another) or one that has no point that is far removed from all the others. A point falling far above or far below the horizontal line at height 0 corresponds to a large standardized residual, which can indicate some kind of unusual behavior, such as a recording error, a nonstandard experimental condition, or an atypical experimental subject. A point that has an x value that differs greatly from others in the data set could have exerted excessive influence in determining the fitted line.

A standardized residual plot, such as the one pictured in Figure 13.15(a) is desirable, because no point lies much outside the horizontal band between −2 and 2 (so there is no unusually large residual corresponding to an outlying observation); there is no point far to the left or right of the others (which could indicate an observation that might greatly influence the fit), and there is no pattern to indicate that the model should somehow be modified. When the plot has the appearance of Figure 13.15(b), the fitted model should be changed to incorporate curvature (a nonlinear model).

The increasing spread from left to right in Figure 13.15(c) suggests that the variance of y is not the same at each x value but rather increases with x. A straight-line model may still be appropriate, but the best-fit line should be obtained by using *weighted least* squares rather than ordinary least squares. This involves giving more weight to observations in the region exhibiting low variability and less weight to observations in the region exhibiting high variability. A specialized regression analysis textbook or a statistician should be consulted for more information on using weighted least squares.

The standardized residual plots of Figures 13.15(d) and 13.15(e) show an outlier (a point with a large standardized residual) and a potentially influential observation, respectively. Consider deleting the observation corresponding to such a point from the data set and refitting the same model. Substantial changes in estimates and various other quantities warn of instability in the data. The investigator should certainly carry out a more careful analysis and perhaps collect more data before drawing any firm conclusions.

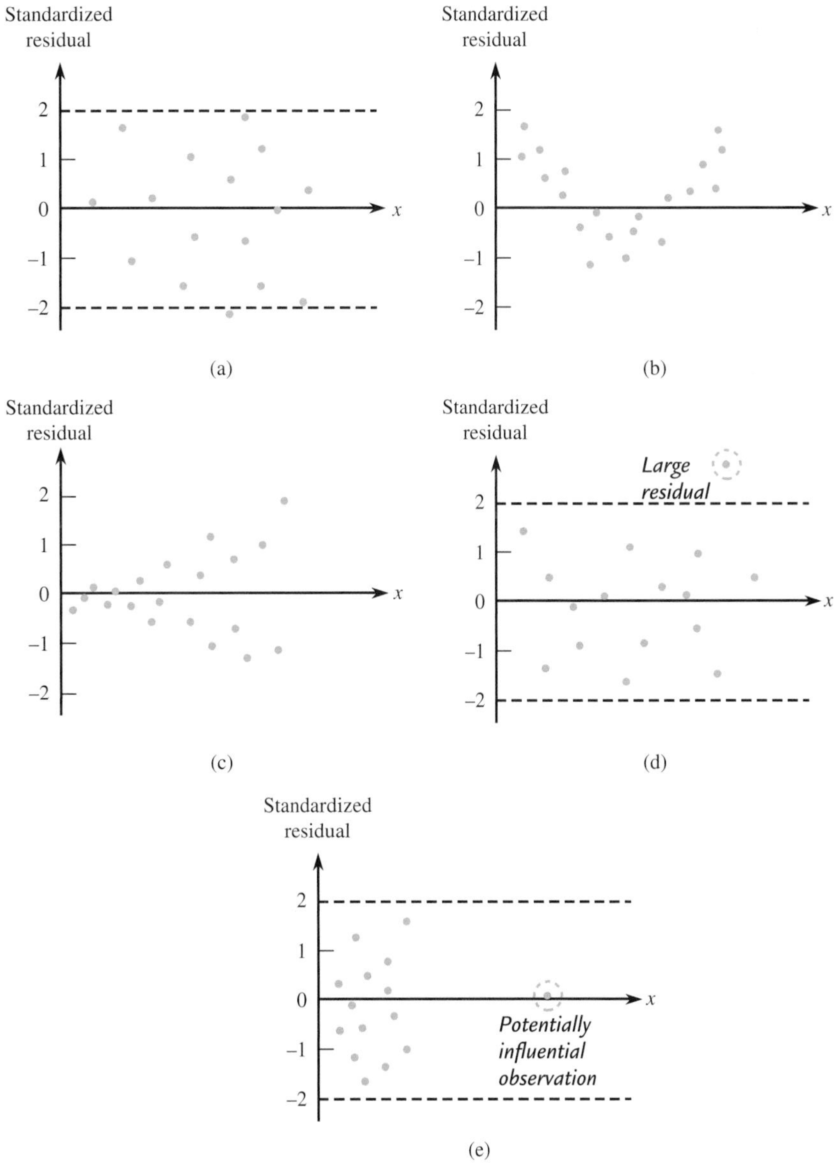

FIGURE 13.15
Examples of residual plots: (a) satisfactory plot; (b) plot suggesting that a curvilinear regression model is needed; (c) plot indicating nonconstant variance; (d) plot showing a large residual; (e) plot showing a potentially influential observation.

EXAMPLE 13.7 Political Faces Revisited

Figure 13.16 displays a standardized residual plot and a residual plot for the data of Example 13.6 on perceived competence based on facial appearance and election outcome. The first observation was at $x_1 = 0.20$, and the corresponding standardized residual was -1.32, so the first plotted point in the standardized residual plot is $(0.20, -1.32)$. Other points are similarly obtained and plotted. The standardized residual plot shows no unusual behavior that might call for model modifications or further analysis. Note that the general pattern in the residual plot is similar to that of the standardized residual plot.

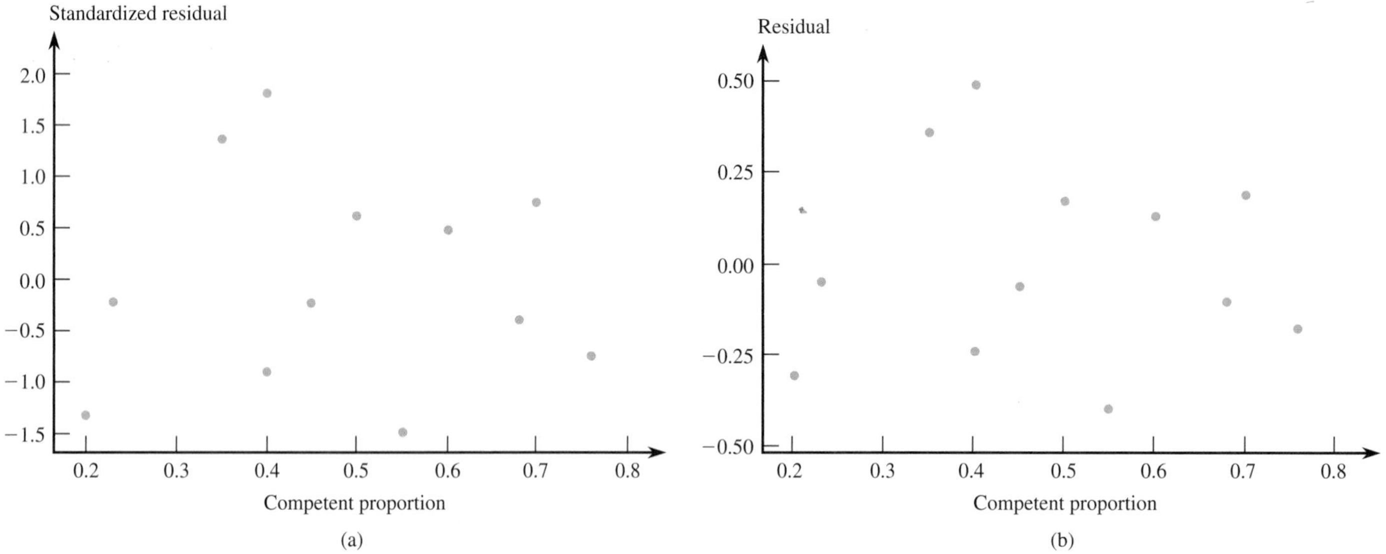

FIGURE 13.16
Plots for the data of Example 13.6 (from Minitab): (a) standardized residual plot; (b) residual plot.

EXAMPLE 13.8 Snow Cover and Temperature

● The article "Snow Cover and Temperature Relationships in North America and Eurasia" (*Journal of Climate and Applied Meteorology* [1983]: 460–469) explored the relationship between October–November continental snow cover (x, in millions of square kilometers) and December–February temperature (y, in °C). The following data are for Eurasia during the $n = 13$ time periods (1969–1970, 1970–1971, . . . , 1981–1982):

x	y	Standardized Residual	x	y	Standardized Residual
13.00	−13.5	−0.11	22.40	−18.9	−1.54
12.75	−15.7	−2.19	16.20	−14.8	0.04
16.70	−15.5	−0.36	16.70	−13.6	1.25
18.85	−14.7	1.23	13.65	−14.0	−0.28
16.60	−16.1	−0.91	13.90	−12.0	−1.54
15.35	−14.6	−0.12	14.75	−13.5	0.58
13.90	−13.4	0.34			

● Data set available online

A simple linear regression analysis done by the authors yielded $r^2 = .52$ and $r = .72$, suggesting a significant linear relationship. This is confirmed by a model utility test. The scatterplot and standardized residual plot are displayed in Figure 13.17. There are no unusual patterns, although one standardized residual, -2.19, is a bit on the large side. The most interesting feature is the observation (22.40, -18.9), corresponding to a point far to the right of the others in these plots. This observation may have had a substantial influence on all aspects of the fit. The estimated slope when all 13 observations are included is $b = -0.459$, and $s_b = 0.133$. When the potentially influential observation is deleted, the estimate of β based on the remaining 12 observations is $b = -0.228$. Then

$$\begin{aligned} \text{change in slope} &= \text{original } b - \text{new } b \\ &= -.459 - (-.288) \\ &= -.231 \end{aligned}$$

The change expressed in standard deviations is $-.231/.133 = -1.74$. Because b has changed by more than 1.5 standard deviations, the observation under consideration appears to be highly influential.

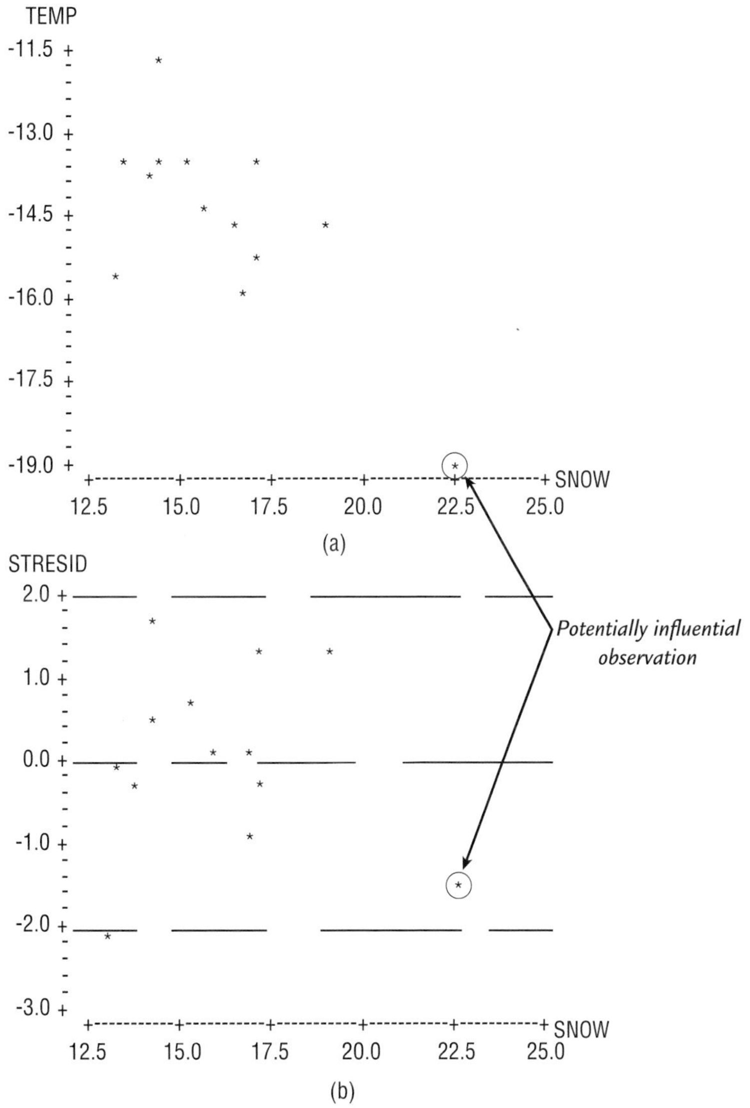

FIGURE 13.17
Plots for the data of Example 13.8 (from Minitab): (a) scatterplot; (b) standardized residual plot.

In addition, r^2 based just on the 12 observations is only .13, and the t ratio for testing $\beta = 0$ is not significant. Evidence for a linear relationship is much less conclusive in light of this analysis.

EXAMPLE 13.9 Treadmill Time and Ski Time Revisited

Example 13.4 presented data on x = treadmill time to exhaustion and y = ski time. A simple linear regression model was fit to the data, and a confidence interval for β, the average change in ski time associated with a 1-minute increase in treadmill time, was constructed. The validity of the confidence interval depends on the assumptions that the distribution of the residuals from the population regression line at any fixed x is approximately normal and that the variance of this distribution does not depend on x. Constructing a normal probability plot of the standardized residuals and a standardized residual plot will provide insight into whether these assumptions are in fact reasonable.

Minitab was used to fit the simple linear regression model and compute the standardized residuals, resulting in the values shown in Table 13.2.

TABLE 13.2 Data, Residuals, and Standardized Residuals for Example 13.9

Observation	Treadmill	Ski Time	Residual	Standardized Residual
1	7.7	71.0	0.172	0.10
2	8.4	71.4	2.206	1.13
3	8.7	65.0	3.494	1.74
4	9.0	68.7	0.906	0.44
5	9.6	64.4	1.994	0.96
6	9.6	69.4	3.006	1.44
7	10.0	63.0	2.461	1.18
8	10.2	64.6	0.394	0.19
9	10.4	66.9	2.373	1.16
10	11.0	62.6	0.527	0.27
11	11.7	61.7	0.206	0.12

Figure 13.18 shows a normal probability plot of the standardized residuals and a standardized residual plot. The normal probability plot is quite straight, and the standardized residual plot does not show evidence of any patterns or of increasing spread. These observations support the use of the confidence interval in Example 13.4.

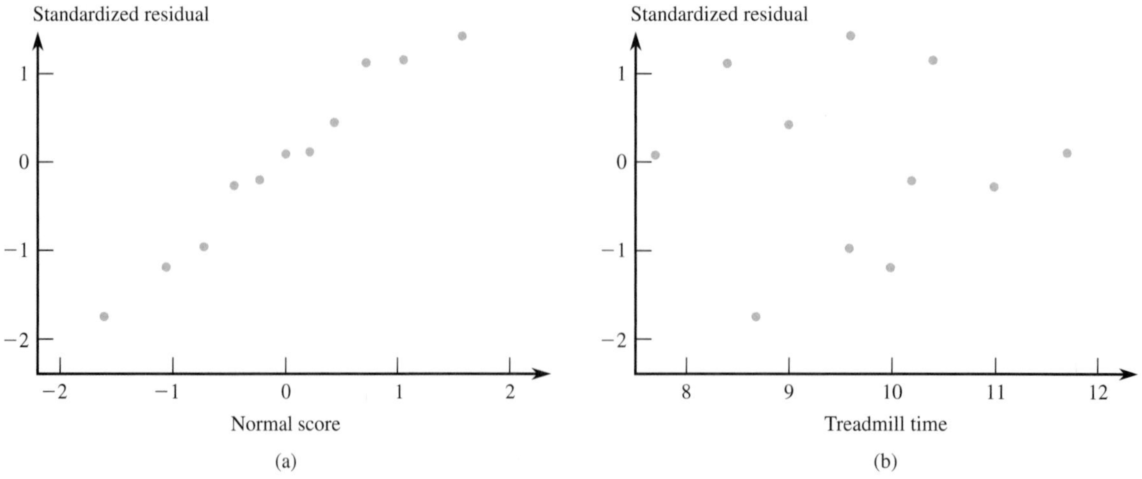

FIGURE 13.18
Plots for Example 13.9: (a) normal probability plot of standardized residuals; (b) standardized residual plot.

EXAMPLE 13.10 More on University Graduation Rates

Use of the model utility test in Example 13.5 led to the conclusion that there was a useful linear relationship between y = graduation rate and x = median SAT score for public undergraduate universities. The validity of this test requires that the distribution of random errors be normal and that the variability of the error distribution not change with x. Let's construct a normal probability plot of the standardized residuals and a standardized residual plot to see whether these assumptions are reasonable. Table 13.3 gives the residuals and standardized residuals that are needed to construct the plots shown in Figure 13.19 (see the following page).

TABLE 13.3 Data, Residuals, and Standardized Residuals for Example 13.10

Observation	Treadmill	Ski Time	Residual	Standardized Residual
1	1065	49	−0.404	−0.071
2	950	33	−1.209	−0.216
3	1045	37	−9.762	−1.668
4	990	49	9.506	1.613
5	950	22	−12.209	−2.181
6	970	38	1.148	0.199
7	980	39	0.827	0.141
8	1080	52	0.614	0.111
9	1035	53	7.560	1.282
10	1010	41	−1.137	−0.192
11	1010	38	−4.137	−0.697
12	930	37	5.433	1.019
13	1005	45	3.524	0.594
14	1090	57	4.293	0.792
15	1085	48	−4.047	−0.737

The normal probability plot is quite straight, and the standardized residual plot does not show evidence of any pattern or increasing spread. This supports the use of the model utility test in Example 13.5.

Occasionally, you will see a residual plot or a standardized residual plot with $\hat{y}$ plotted on the horizontal axis rather than x. Because $\hat{y}$ is just a linear function of x, using $\hat{y}$ rather than x changes the scale of the horizontal axis but does not change the pattern of the points in the plot. As a consequence, residual plots that use $\hat{y}$ on the horizontal axis can be interpreted in the same manner as residual plots that use x.

When the distribution of the random deviation e has heavier tails than does the normal distribution, observations with large standardized residuals are not that unusual. Such observations can have great effects on the estimated regression line when the least-squares approach is used. Recently, statisticians have proposed a number of alternative methods—called **robust,** or **resistant,** methods—for fitting a line. Such methods give less weight to outlying observations than does the least-squares method without deleting the outliers from the data set. The most widely used robust procedures require a substantial amount of computation, so a good computer program is necessary.

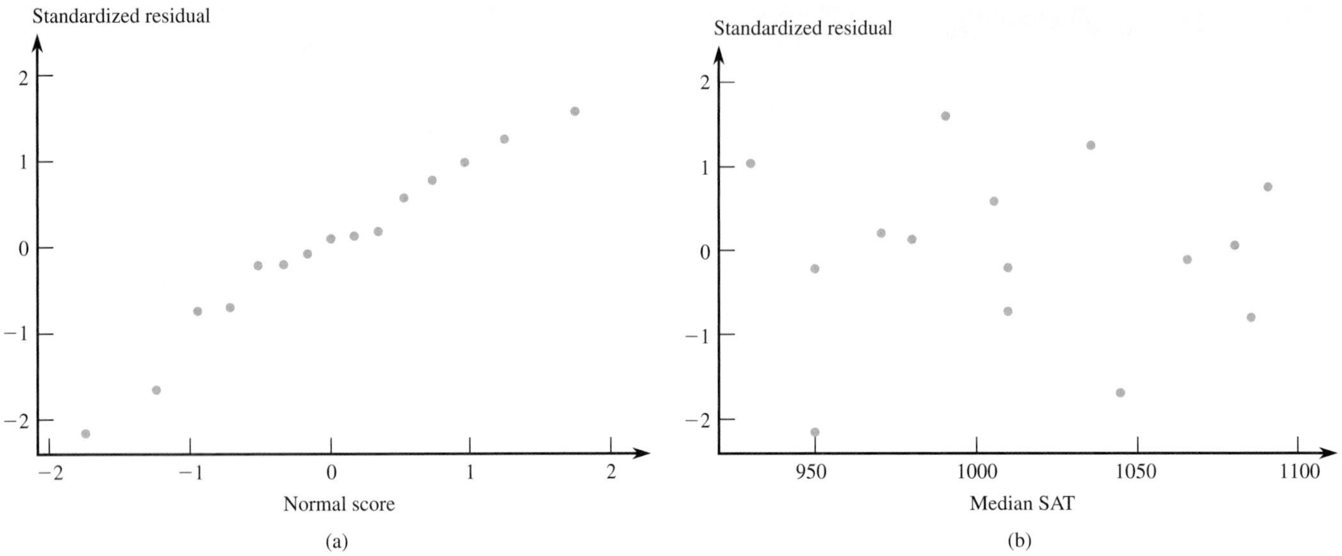

FIGURE 13.19
Plots for Example 13.10:
(a) normal probability plot of standardized residuals;
(b) standardized residual plot.

EXERCISES 13.27 - 13.32

13.27 ● Exercise 13.21 gave data on x = nerve firing frequency and y = pleasantness rating when nerves were stimulated by a light brushing stoke on the forearm. The x values and the corresponding residuals from a simple linear regression are as follows:

Firing Frequency, x	Standardized Residual
23	−1.83
24	0.04
22	1.45
25	0.20
27	−1.07
28	1.19
34	−0.24
33	−0.13
36	−0.81
34	1.17

a. Construct a standardized residual plot. Does the plot exhibit any unusual features?

b. A normal probability plot of the standardized residuals follows. Based on this plot, do you think it is reasonable to assume that the error distribution is approximately normal? Explain.

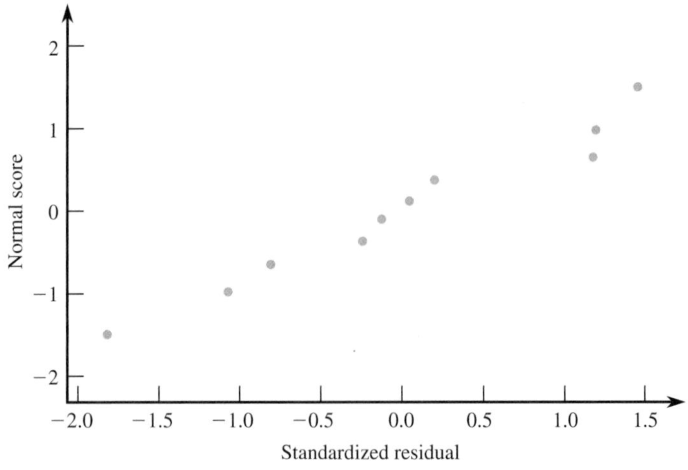

13.28 ● Sea bream are one type of fish that are often raised in large fish farming enterprises. These fish are usually fed a diet consisting primarily of fish meal. The authors of the paper "Growth and Economic Profit of Gilthead Sea Bream (*Sparus aurata*, L.) Fed Sunflower Meal" (*Aquaculture* [2007]: 528–534) describe a study to investigate whether it would be more profitable to substitute plant protein in the form of sunflower meal for some of the fish meal in the sea bream's diet. The accompanying data are consistent with summary quantities given in the paper for x = percentage of sunflower meal in the diet and y = average weight of fish after 248 days (in grams).

Sunflower Meal (%)	Average Fish Weight
0	432
6	450
12	455
18	445
24	427
30	422
36	421

The estimated regression line for these data is $\hat{y} = 448.536 - 0.696x$ and the standardized residuals are as given.

Sunflower Meal (%), x	Standardized Residual
0	−1.96
6	0.58
12	1.42
18	0.84
24	−0.46
30	−0.58
36	−0.29

Construct a standardized residual plot. What does the plot suggest about the adequacy of the simple linear regression model?

13.29 ● The article "Vital Dimensions in Volume Perception: Can the Eye Fool the Stomach?" (*Journal of Marketing Research* [1999]: 313–326) gave the accompanying data on the dimensions of 27 representative food products (Gerber baby food, Cheez Whiz, Skippy Peanut Butter, and Ahmed's tandoori paste, to name a few).

Product	Maximum Width (cm)	Minimum Width (cm)
1	2.50	1.80
2	2.90	2.70
3	2.15	2.00
4	2.90	2.60
5	3.20	3.15
6	2.00	1.80
7	1.60	1.50
8	4.80	3.80
9	5.90	5.00
10	5.80	4.75
11	2.90	2.80
12	2.45	2.10
13	2.60	2.20
14	2.60	2.60
15	2.70	2.60
16	3.10	2.90
17	5.10	5.10
18	10.20	10.20
19	3.50	3.50
20	2.70	1.20
21	3.00	1.70
22	2.70	1.75
23	2.50	1.70
24	2.40	1.20
25	4.40	1.20
26	7.50	7.50
27	4.25	4.25

(continued)

a. Fit the simple linear regression model that would allow prediction of the maximum width of a food container based on its minimum width.

b. Calculate the standardized residuals (or just the residuals if you don't have access to a computer program that gives standardized residuals) and make a residual plot to determine whether there are any outliers.

c. The data point with the largest residual is for a 1-liter Coke bottle. Delete this data point and refit the regression. Did deletion of this point result in a large change in the equation of the estimated regression line?

d. For the regression line of Part (c), interpret the estimated slope and, if appropriate, the intercept.

e. For the data set with the Coke bottle deleted, do you think that the assumptions of the simple linear regression model are reasonable? Give statistical evidence for your answer.

13.30 ● ✦ The authors of the article "Age, Spacing and Growth Rate of Tamarix as an Indication of Lake Boundary Fluctuations at Sebkhet Kelbia, Tunisia" (*Journal of Arid Environments* [1982]: 43–51) used a simple linear regression model to describe the relationship between y = vigor (average width in centimeters of the last two annual rings) and x = stem density (stems/m^2). The estimated model was based on the following data. Also given are the standardized residuals.

x	4	5	6	9	14
y	0.75	1.20	0.55	0.60	0.65
St. resid.	−0.28	1.92	−0.90	−0.28	0.54
x	15	15	19	21	22
y	0.55	0.00	0.35	0.45	0.40
St. resid.	0.24	−2.05	−0.12	0.60	0.52

a. What assumptions are required for the simple linear regression model to be appropriate?
b. Construct a normal probability plot of the standardized residuals. Does the assumption that the random deviation distribution is normal appear to be reasonable? Explain.
c. Construct a standardized residual plot. Are there any unusually large residuals?
d. Is there anything about the standardized residual plot that would cause you to question the use of the simple linear regression model to describe the relationship between x and y?

13.31 ● ✦ Carbon aerosols have been identified as a contributing factor in a number of air quality problems. In a chemical analysis of diesel engine exhaust, x = mass (μg/cm^2) and y = elemental carbon (μg/cm^2) were recorded ("Comparison of Solvent Extraction and Thermal Optical Carbon Analysis Methods: Application to Diesel Vehicle Exhaust Aerosol" *Environmental Science Technology* [1984]: 231–234). The estimated regression line for this data set is $\hat{y} = 31 + .737x$. The accompanying table gives the observed x and y values and the corresponding standardized residuals.

x	164.2	156.9	109.8	111.4	87.0
y	181	156	115	132	96
St. resid.	2.52	0.82	0.27	1.64	0.08
x	161.8	230.9	106.5	97.6	79.7
y	170	193	110	94	77
St. resid.	1.72	−0.73	0.05	−0.77	−1.11
x	118.7	248.8	102.4	64.2	89.4
y	106	204	98	76	89
St. resid.	−1.07	−0.95	−0.73	−0.20	−0.68
x	108.1	89.4	76.4	131.7	100.8
y	102	91	97	128	88
St. resid.	−0.75	−0.51	0.85	0.00	−1.49
x	78.9	387.8	135.0	82.9	117.9
y	86	310	141	90	130
St. resid.	−0.27	−0.89	0.91	−0.18	1.05

a. Construct a standardized residual plot. Are there any unusually large residuals? Do you think that there are any influential observations?
b. Is there any pattern in the standardized residual plot that would indicate that the simple linear regression model is not appropriate?
c. Based on your plot in Part (a), do you think that it is reasonable to assume that the variance of y is the same at each x value? Explain.

13.32 ● An investigation of the relationship between x = traffic flow (thousands of cars per 24 hours) and y = lead content of bark on trees near the highway (mg/g dry weight) yielded the accompanying data. A simple linear regression model was fit, and the resulting estimated regression line was $\hat{y} = 28.7 + 33.3x$. Both residuals and standardized residuals are also given.

x	8.3	8.3	12.1	12.1	17.0
y	227	312	362	521	640
Residual	−78.1	6.9	−69.6	89.4	45.3
St. resid.	−0.99	0.09	−0.81	1.04	0.51
x	17.0	17.0	24.3	24.3	24.3
y	539	728	945	738	759
Residual	−55.7	133.3	107.2	−99.8	−78.8
St. resid.	−0.63	1.51	1.35	−1.25	−0.99

a. Plot the (x, residual) pairs. Does the resulting plot suggest that a simple linear regression model is an appropriate choice? Explain your reasoning.
b. Construct a standardized residual plot. Does the plot differ significantly in general appearance from the plot in Part (a)?

13.4 Inferences Based on the Estimated Regression Line (Optional)

The number obtained by substituting a particular x value, x^*, into the equation of the estimated regression line has two different interpretations: It is a point estimate of the mean y value when $x = x^*$, and it is also a point prediction of a single y value to be observed when $x = x^*$. How precise is this estimate or prediction? That is, how close is $a + bx^*$ to the actual mean value $\alpha + \beta x^*$ or to a particular y observation? Because both a and b vary in value from sample to sample (each one is a statistic), the statistic $a + bx^*$ also has different values for different samples. The way in which this statistic varies in value with different samples is summarized by its sampling distribution. Properties of the sampling distribution are used to obtain both a confidence interval formula for $\alpha + \beta x^*$ and a prediction interval formula for a particular y observation. The width of the corresponding interval conveys information about the precision of the estimate or prediction.

Properties of the Sampling Distribution of $a + bx$ for a Fixed x Value

Let x^* denote a particular value of the independent variable x. When the four basic assumptions of the simple linear regression model are satisfied, the sampling distribution of the statistic $a + bx^*$ has the following properties:

1. The mean value of $a + bx^*$ is $\alpha + \beta x^*$, so $a + bx^*$ is an unbiased statistic for estimating the mean y value when $x = x^*$.
2. The standard deviation of the statistic $a + bx^*$, denoted by σ_{a+bx^*}, is given by

$$\sigma_{a+bx^*} = \sigma\sqrt{\frac{1}{n} + \frac{(x^* - \bar{x})^2}{S_{xx}}}$$

3. The distribution of $a + bx^*$ is normal.

As you can see from the formula for σ_{a+bx^*} the standard deviation of $a + bx^*$ is larger when $(x^* - \bar{x})^2$ is large than when $(x^* - \bar{x})^2$ is small; that is, $a + bx^*$ tends to be a more precise estimate of $\alpha + \beta x^*$ when x^* is close to the center of the x values at which observations were made than when x^* is far from the center.

The standard deviation σ_{a+bx^*} cannot be calculated from the sample data, because the value of σ is unknown. However, σ_{a+bx^*} can be estimated by using s_e in place of σ. Using the mean and estimated standard deviation to standardize $a + bx^*$ gives a variable with a t distribution.

The **estimated standard deviation of the statistic $a + bx^*$**, denoted by s_{a+bx^*}, is given by

$$s_{a+bx^*} = s_e\sqrt{\frac{1}{n} + \frac{(x^* - \bar{x})^2}{S_{xx}}}$$

When the four basic assumptions of the simple linear regression model are satisfied, the probability distribution of the standardized variable

$$t = \frac{a + bx^* - (\alpha + \beta x^*)}{s_{a+bx^*}}$$

is the t distribution with df $= n - 2$.

Inferences About the Mean y Value $\alpha + \beta x^*$

In previous chapters, standardized variables were manipulated algebraically to give confidence intervals of the form

(point estimate) $\pm$ (critical value)(estimated standard deviation)

A parallel argument leads to the following interval.

Confidence Interval for a Mean y Value

When the basic assumptions of the simple linear regression model are met, a **confidence interval for $\alpha + \beta x^*$,** the mean y value when x has value x^*, is

$$a + bx^* \pm (t \text{ critical value})\cdot s_{a+bx^*}$$

where the t critical value is based on df $= n - 2$. Appendix Table 3 gives critical values corresponding to the most frequently used confidence levels.

Because s_{a+bx^*} is larger the farther x^* is from $\bar{x}$, the confidence interval becomes wider as x^* moves away from the center of the data.

EXAMPLE 13.11 Shark Length and Jaw Width

● Physical characteristics of sharks are of interest to surfers and scuba divers as well as to marine researchers. The following data on x = length (in feet) and y = jaw width (in inches) for 44 sharks were found in various articles appearing in the magazines *Skin Diver* and *Scuba News*:

x	18.7	12.3	18.6	16.4	15.7	18.3	14.6	15.8	14.9	17.6	12.1
y	17.5	12.3	21.8	17.2	16.2	19.9	13.9	14.7	15.1	18.5	12.0
x	16.4	16.7	17.8	16.2	12.6	17.8	13.8	12.2	15.2	14.7	12.4
y	13.8	15.2	18.2	16.7	11.6	17.4	14.2	14.8	15.9	15.3	11.9
x	13.2	15.8	14.3	16.6	9.4	18.2	13.2	13.6	15.3	16.1	13.5
y	11.6	14.3	13.3	15.8	10.2	19.0	16.8	14.2	16.9	16.0	15.9
x	19.1	16.2	22.8	16.8	13.6	13.2	15.7	19.7	18.7	13.2	16.8
y	17.9	15.7	21.2	16.3	13.0	13.3	14.3	21.3	20.8	12.2	16.9

Malcolm Schuyl/Alamy

Because it is difficult to measure jaw width in living sharks, researchers would like to determine whether it is possible to estimate jaw width from body length, which is more easily measured. A scatterplot of the data (Figure 13.20) shows a linear pattern and is consistent with use of the simple linear regression model.

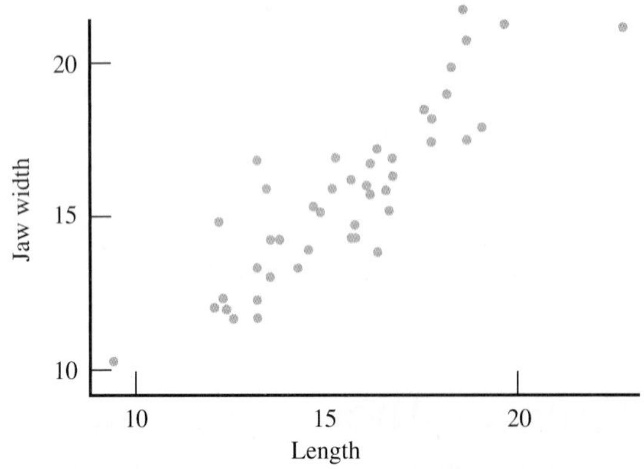

FIGURE 13.20
A scatterplot for the data of Example 13.11.

From the accompanying Minitab output, it is easily verified that

$$a = .688 \qquad b = .96345 \qquad \text{SSResid} = 79.49$$
$$\text{SSTo} = 339.02 \qquad s_e = 1.376 \qquad r^2 = .766$$

Step-by-Step technology instructions available online

● Data set available online

Regression Analysis

The regression equation is

Jaw Width = 0.69 + 0.963 Length

Predictor	Coef	StDev	T	P
Constant	0.688	1.299	0.53	0.599
Length	0.96345	0.08228	11.71	0.000
S = 1.376	R-Sq = 76.6%	R-Sq(adj) = 76.0%		

Analysis of Variance

Source	DF	SS	MS	F	P
Regression	1	259.53	259.53	137.12	0.000
Residual Error	42	79.49	1.89		
Total	43	339.02			

From the data, we can also compute $S_{xx} = 279.8718$. Because $r^2 = .766$, the simple linear regression model explains 76.6% of the variability in jaw width. The model utility test also confirms the usefulness of this model (*P*-value = .000).

Let's use the data to compute a 90% confidence interval for the mean jaw width for 15-foot-long sharks. The mean jaw width when length is 15 feet is $\alpha + \beta(15)$. The point estimate is

$$a + b(15) = .688 + .96345(15) = 15.140 \text{ in.}$$

Since

$$\bar{x} = \frac{\sum x}{n} = \frac{685.80}{44} = 15.586$$

the estimated standard deviation of $a + b(15)$ is

$$\begin{aligned} s_{a+b(15)} &= s_e\sqrt{\frac{1}{n} + \frac{(15 - \bar{x})^2}{S_{xx}}} \\ &= (1.376)\sqrt{\frac{1}{44} + \frac{(15 - 15.586)^2}{279.8718}} \\ &= .213 \end{aligned}$$

The t critical value for df = 42 is 1.68 (using the tabulated value for df = 40 from Appendix Table 3). We now have all the relevant quantities needed to compute a 90% confidence interval:

$$\begin{aligned} a + b(15) \pm (t \text{ critical value})\cdot s_{a+bx^*} &= 15.140 \pm (1.68)(.213) \\ &= 15.140 \pm .358 \\ &= (14.782, 15.498) \end{aligned}$$

Based on these sample data, we can be 90% confident that the mean jaw width for sharks of length 15 feet is between 14.782 and 15.498 inches. As with all confidence intervals, the 90% confidence level means that we have used a *method* that has a 10% error rate to construct this interval estimate.

We have just considered estimation of the mean y value at a fixed $x = x^*$. When the basic assumptions of the simple linear regression model are met, the value of this mean is $\alpha + \beta x^*$. The reason that our point estimate $\alpha + bx^*$ is not exactly equal to $\alpha + \beta x^*$ is that the values of α and β are not known, so they have been estimated from sample data. As a result, the estimate $a + bx^*$ is subject to sampling variability and the extent to which the estimated line might differ from the population line is reflected in the width of the confidence interval.

Prediction Interval for a Single *y*

We now turn our attention to the problem of predicting a single y value at a particular $x = x^*$ (rather than estimating the mean y value when $x = x^*$). This problem is equivalent to trying to predict the y value of an individual point in a scatterplot of the population. If we use the estimated regression line to obtain a point prediction $a + bx^*$, this prediction will probably not be exactly equal to the true y value for two reasons. First, as was the case when estimating a mean y value, the estimated line is not going to be exactly equal to the population regression line. But, in the case of predicting a single y value, there is an additional source of error: e, the deviation from the line. Even if we knew the population line, individual points would not fall exactly on the population line. This implies that there is more uncertainty associated with predicting a single y value at a particular x^* than with estimating the mean y value at x^*. This extra uncertainty is reflected in the width of the corresponding intervals.

An interval for a single y value, y^*, is called a **prediction interval** (to distinguish it from the confidence interval for a mean y value). The interpretation of a prediction interval is similar to the interpretation of a confidence interval. A 95% prediction interval for y^* is constructed using a method for which 95% of all possible samples would yield interval limits capturing y^*; only 5% of all samples would give an interval that did not include y^*.

Manipulation of a standardized variable similar to the one from which a confidence interval was obtained gives the following prediction interval.

Prediction Interval for a Single *y* Value

When the four basic assumptions of the simple linear regression model are met, a **prediction interval for y^***, a single y observation made when $x = x^*$, has the form

$$a + bx^* \pm (t \text{ critical value}) \cdot \sqrt{s_e^2 + s_{a+bx^*}^2}$$

The prediction interval and the confidence interval are centered at exactly the same place, $a + bx^*$. The addition of s_e^2 under the square-root symbol makes the prediction interval wider—often substantially so—than the confidence interval.

EXAMPLE 13.12 Jaws II

In Example 13.11, we computed a 90% confidence interval for the mean jaw width of sharks of length 15 feet. Suppose that we are interested in predicting the jaw width of a single shark of length 15 feet. The required calculations for a 90% prediction interval for y^* are

$$a + b(15) = .688 + .96245(15) = 15.140$$
$$s_e^2 = (1.376)^2 = 1.8934$$
$$s_{a+b(15)}^2 = (.213)^2 = .0454$$

The t critical value for df = 42 and a 90% prediction level is 1.68 (using the tabled value for df = 40). Substitution into the prediction interval formula then gives

$$\begin{aligned} a + b(15) \pm (t \text{ critical value})\sqrt{s_e^2 + s_{a+b(15)}^2} &= 15.140 \pm (1.68)\sqrt{1.9388} \\ &= 15.140 \pm 2.339 \\ &= (12.801, 17.479) \end{aligned}$$

We can be 90% confident that an individual shark of length 15 feet will have a jaw width between 12.801 and 17.479 inches. Notice that, as expected, this 90% prediction interval is much wider than the 90% confidence interval when $x^* = 15$ from Example 13.11.

Figure 13.21 gives Minitab output that includes a 95% confidence interval and a 95% prediction interval when $x^* = 15$ and when $x^* = 20$. The intervals for $x^* = 20$ are wider than the corresponding intervals for $x^* = 15$ because 20 is farther from $\bar{x}$ (the center of the sample x values) than is 15. Each prediction interval is wider than the corresponding confidence interval. Figure 13.22 is a Minitab plot that shows the estimated regression line as well as 90% confidence limits and prediction limits.

FIGURE 13.21
Minitab output for the data of Example 13.12.

Regression Analysis

The regression equation is
Jaw Width = 0.69 + 0.963 Length

Predictor	Coef	StDev	T	P
Constant	0.688	1.299	0.53	0.599
Length	0.96345	0.08228	11.71	0.000

S = 1.376   R-Sq = 76.6%   R-Sq(adj) = 76.0%

Analysis of Variance

Source	DF	SS	MS	F	P
Regression	1	259.53	259.53	137.12	0.000
Residual Error	42	79.49	1.89		
Total	43	399.02			

Predicted Values

	Fit	StDev Fit	95.0% CI	95.0% PI
$x^* = 15$ →	15.140	0.213	(14.710, 15.569)	(12.330, 17.949)
$x^* = 20$ →	19.957	0.418	(19.113, 20.801)	(17.055, 22.859)

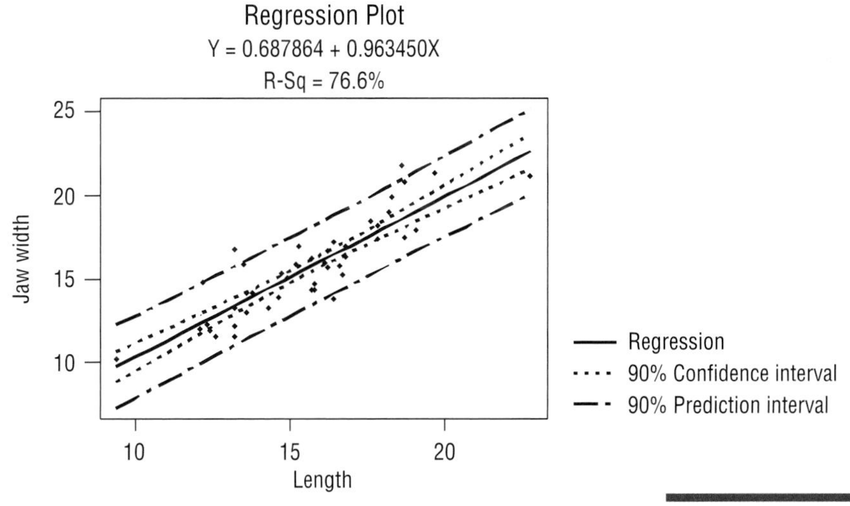

FIGURE 13.22
Minitab plot showing estimated regression line and 90% confidence and prediction limits for the data of Example 13.12.

EXERCISES 13.33 - 13.46

13.33 Explain the difference between a confidence interval and a prediction interval. How can a prediction level of 95% be interpreted?

13.34 Suppose that a regression data set is given and you are asked to obtain a confidence interval. How would you tell from the phrasing of the request whether the interval is for β or for $\alpha + \beta^*$?

13.35 In Exercise 13.17, we considered a regression of y = oxygen consumption on x = time spent exercising. Summary quantities given there yield

$n = 20$ $\bar{x} = 2.50$ $S_{xx} = 25$
$b = 97.26$ $a = 592.10$ $s_e = 16.486$

a. Calculate $s_{a+b(2.0)}$, the estimated standard deviation of the statistic $a + b(2.0)$.
b. Without any further calculation, what is $s_{a+b(3.0)}$ and what reasoning did you use to obtain it?
c. Calculate the estimated standard deviation of the statistic $a + b(2.8)$.
d. For what value x^* is the estimated standard deviation of $a + bx^*$ smallest, and why?

13.36 Example 13.3 gave data on x = proportion who judged candidate A as more competent and y = vote difference proportion. Calculate a 95% confidence interval for the mean vote-difference proportion for congressional races where 60% judge candidate A as more competent.

13.37 The data of Exercise 13.25, in which x = milk temperature and y = milk pH, yield

$n = 16$ $\bar{x} = 42.375$ $S_{xx} = 7325.75$
$b = -.00730608$ $a = 6.843345$ $s_e = .0356$

a. Obtain a 95% confidence interval for $\alpha + \beta(40)$, the mean milk pH when the milk temperature is 40°C.
b. Calculate a 99% confidence interval for the mean milk pH when the milk temperature is 35°C.
c. Would you recommend using the data to calculate a 95% confidence interval for the mean pH when the temperature is 90°C? Why or why not?

13.38 Return to the regression of y = milk pH on x = milk temperature described in the previous exercise.
a. Obtain a 95% prediction interval for a single pH observation to be made when milk temperature = 40°C.
b. Calculate a 99% prediction interval for a single pH observation when milk temperature = 35°C.
c. When the milk temperature is 60°C, would a 99% prediction interval be wider than the intervals of Parts (a) and (b)? You should be able to answer without calculating the interval.

13.39 A subset of data read from a graph that appeared in the paper "Decreased Brain Volume in Adults with Childhood Lead Exposure" (*Public Library of Science Medicine* [May 27, 2008]: e112) was used to produce the following Minitab output, where x = mean childhood blood lead level (μg/dL) and y = brain volume change (percentage). (See Exercise 13.19 for a more complete description of the study described in this paper)

Regression Analysis: Response versus Mean Blood Lead Level

The regression equation is
Response = −0.00179 − 0.00210 Mean Blood Lead Level

Predictor	Coef	SE Coef	T	P
Constant	−0.001790	0.008303	−0.22	0.830
Mean Blood Lead Level	−0.0021007	0.0005743	−3.66	0.000

a. What is the equation of the estimated regression line?
b. For this dataset, $n = 100$, $\bar{x} = 11.5$, $s_e = 0.032$, and $S_{xx} = 1764$. Estimate the mean brain volume change for people with a childhood blood lead level of 20 μg/dL, using a 90% confidence interval.
c. Construct a 90% prediction interval for brain volume change for a person with a childhood blood lead level of 20 μg/dL.
d. Explain the difference in interpretation of the intervals computed in Parts (b) and (c).

13.40 An experiment was carried out by geologists to see how the time necessary to drill a distance of 5 feet in rock (y, in minutes) depended on the depth at which the drilling began (x, in feet, between 0 and 400). We show part of the Minitab output obtained from fitting the simple linear regression model ("Mining Information," *American Statistician* [1991]: 4–9).

The regression equation is
Time = 4.79 + 0.0144depth

Predictor	Coef	Stdev	t-ratio	p
Constant	4.7896	0.6663	7.19	0.000
depth	0.014388	0.002847	5.05	0.000

s = 1.432 R-sq = 63.0% R-sq(adj) = 60.5%

Analysis of Variance

Source	DF	SS	MS	F	p
Regression	1	52.378	52.378	25.54	0.000
Error	15	30.768	2.051		
Total	16	83.146			

a. What proportion of observed variation in time can be explained by the simple linear regression model?
b. Does the simple linear regression model appear to be useful?
c. Minitab reported that $s_{a+b(200)} = .347$. Calculate a 95% confidence interval for the mean time when depth = 200 feet.
d. A single observation on time is to be made when drilling starts at a depth of 200 feet. Use a 95% prediction interval to predict the resulting value of time.

e. Minitab gave (8.147, 10.065) as a 95% confidence interval for mean time when depth = 300. Calculate a 99% confidence interval for this mean.

13.41 ● According to "Reproductive Biology of the Aquatic Salamander Amphiuma tridactylum in Louisiana" (*Journal of Herpetology* [1999]: 100–105), the size of a female salamander's snout is correlated with the number of eggs in her clutch. The following data are consistent with summary quantities reported in the article. Partial Minitab output is also included.

Snout-Vent Length	32	53	53	53	54
Clutch Size	45	215	160	170	190
Snout-Vent Length	57	57	58	58	59
Clutch Size	200	270	175	245	215
Snout-Vent Length	63	63	64	67	
Clutch Size	170	240	245	280	

```
The regression equation is
Y = -133 + 5.92x
Predictor     Coef     StDev       T        P
Constant   -133.02     64.30    2.07    0.061
x            5.919     1.127    5.25    0.000
s = 33.90    R-Sq = 69.7%    R-Sq(adj) = 67.2%
```

Additional summary statistics are

$$n = 14 \qquad \bar{x} = 56.5 \qquad \bar{y} = 201.4$$
$$\sum x^2 = 45{,}958 \quad \sum y^2 = 613{,}550 \quad \sum xy = 164{,}969$$

a. What is the equation of the regression line for predicting clutch size based on snout-vent length?
b. What is the value of the estimated standard deviation of b?
c. Is there sufficient evidence to conclude that the slope of the population line is positive?
d. Predict the clutch size for a salamander with a snout-vent length of 65 using a 95% interval.
e. Predict the clutch size for a salamander with a snout-vent length of 105 using a 90% interval.

13.42 The article first introduced in Exercise 13.29 of Section 13.3 gave data on the dimensions of 27 representative food products.

a. Use the data set given there to test the hypothesis that there is a positive linear relationship between x = minimum width and y = maximum width of an object.
b. Calculate and interpret s_e.
c. Calculate a 95% confidence interval for the mean maximum width of products with a minimum width of 6 cm.
d. Calculate a 95% prediction interval for the maximum width of a food package with a minimum width of 6 cm.

13.43 ● The shelf life of packaged food depends on many factors. Dry cereal is considered to be a moisture-sensitive product (no one likes soggy cereal!) with the shelf life determined primarily by moisture content. In a study of the shelf life of one particular brand of cereal, x = time on shelf (days stored at 73°F and 50% relative humidity) and y = moisture content (%) were recorded. The resulting data are from "Computer Simulation Speeds Shelf Life Assessments" (*Package Engineering* [1983]: 72–73).

x	0	3	6	8	10	13	16
y	2.8	3.0	3.1	3.2	3.4	3.4	3.5
x	20	24	27	30	34	37	41
y	3.1	3.8	4.0	4.1	4.3	4.4	4.9

a. Summary quantities are

$$\sum x = 269 \quad \sum y = 51 \quad \sum xy = 1081.5$$
$$\sum y^2 = 190.78 \quad \sum x^2 = 7745$$

Find the equation of the estimated regression line for predicting moisture content from time on the shelf.
b. Does the simple linear regression model provide useful information for predicting moisture content from knowledge of shelf time?
c. Find a 95% interval for the moisture content of an individual box of cereal that has been on the shelf 30 days.
d. According to the article, taste tests indicate that this brand of cereal is unacceptably soggy when the moisture content exceeds 4.1. Based on your interval in Part (c), do you think that a box of cereal that has been on the shelf 30 days will be acceptable? Explain.

13.44 For the cereal data of the previous exercise, the mean x value is 19.21. Would a 95% confidence interval with $x^* = 20$ or $x^* = 17$ be wider? Explain. Answer the same question for a prediction interval.

13.45 A regression of x = tannin concentration (mg/L) and y = perceived astringency score was considered in Examples 5.2 and 5.6. The perceived astringency was computed from expert tasters rating a wine on a scale from 0 to 10 and then standardizing the rating by computing a z-score. Data for 32 red wines (given in Example 5.2) was used to compute the following summary statistics and estimated regression line:

$$n = 32 \quad \bar{x} = .6069 \quad \sum (x - \bar{x})^2 = 1.479$$
$$\text{SSResid} = 1.936 \quad \hat{y} = -1.59 + 2.59x$$

a. Calculate a 95% confidence interval for the mean astringency rating for red wines with a tannin concentration of .5 mg/L.

b. When two 95% confidence intervals are computed, it can be shown that the simultaneous confidence level is at least $[100 - 2(5)]\% = 90\%$. That is, if both intervals are computed for a first sample, for a second sample, for a third sample, and so on, in the long run at least 90% of the samples will result in intervals which both capture the values of the corresponding population characteristics. Calculate confidence intervals for the mean astringency rating when the tannin concentration is .5 mg/L and when the tannin concentration is .7 mg/L in such a way that the simultaneous confidence level is at least 90%.

c. If two 99% confidence intervals were computed, what do you think could be said about the simultaneous confidence level?

d. If a 95% confidence interval were computed for the mean astringency rating when $x = .5$, another confidence interval was computed for $x = .6$, and yet another one for $x = .7$, what do you think would be the simultaneous confidence level for the three resulting intervals?

13.46 ● The article "Performance Test Conducted for a Gas Air-Conditioning System" (*American Society of Heating, Refrigerating, and Air Conditioning Engineering* [1969]: 54) reported the following data on maximum outdoor temperature (x) and hours of chiller operation per day (y) for a 3-ton residential gas air-conditioning system:

x	72	78	80	86	88	92
y	4.8	7.2	9.5	14.5	15.7	17.9

Suppose that the system is actually a prototype model, and the manufacturer does not wish to produce this model unless the data strongly indicate that when maximum outdoor temperature is 82°F, the true average number of hours of chiller operation is less than 12. The appropriate hypotheses are then

$$H_0\colon \alpha + \beta(82) = 12 \quad \text{versus} \quad H_a\colon \alpha + \beta(82) < 12$$

Use the statistic

$$t = \frac{a + b(82) - 12}{s_{a+b(82)}}$$

which has a t distribution based on $(n - 2)$ df when H_0 is true, to test the hypotheses at significance level .01.

13.5 Inferences About the Population Correlation Coefficient (Optional)

The sample correlation coefficient r, defined in Chapter 5, measures how strongly the x and y values in a *sample* of pairs are linearly related to one another. There is an analogous measure of how strongly x and y are linearly related in the entire *population* of pairs from which the sample $(x_1, y_1), \ldots, (x_n, y_n)$ was obtained. It is called the **population correlation coefficient** and is denoted by ρ. As with r, ρ must be between -1 and 1, and it assesses the extent of any linear relationship in the population. To have $\rho = 1$ or $\rho = -1$, all (x, y) pairs in the population must lie exactly on a straight line. The value of ρ is a population characteristic and is generally unknown. The sample correlation coefficient r can be used as the basis for making inferences about ρ.

Test for Independence ($\rho = 0$)

Investigators are often interested in detecting not just linear association but also association of *any* kind. When there is no association of any type between the x and y values, statisticians say that the two variables are *independent*. In general, $\rho = 0$ is not equivalent to the independence of x and y. However, there is one special—yet frequently occurring—situation in which the two conditions ($\rho = 0$ and independence) are identical. This is when the pairs in the population have what is called a **bivariate normal distribution.** The essential feature of such a distribution is that for *any* fixed x value, the distribution of associated y values is normal, and for *any* fixed y value, the distribution of x values is normal.

As an example, suppose that height x and weight y have a bivariate normal distribution in the American adult male population. (There is good empirical evidence for this.) Then, when $x = 68$ inches, weight y has a normal distribution; when $x = 72$ inches, weight is normally distributed; when $y = 160$ pounds, height x has a normal distribution; when $y = 175$ pounds, height has a normal distribution; and so on. In this example, of course, x and y are not independent, because large height values tend to be paired with large weight values and small height values tend to be paired with small weight values.

There is no easy way to check the assumption of bivariate normality, especially when the sample size n is small. A partial check can be based on the following property: If (x, y) has a bivariate normal distribution, then x alone has a normal distribution and so does y. This suggests constructing a normal probability plot of $x_1, x_2, \ldots x_n$, and a separate normal probability plot of $y_1, y_2, \ldots, y_n$. If either plot shows a substantial departure from a straight line, then bivariate normality is a questionable assumption. If both plots are reasonably straight, then bivariate normality is plausible, although no guarantee can be given.

For a bivariate normal population, the test of independence (correlation = 0) is a t test. The formula for the test statistic involves standardizing the estimate r under the assumption that the null hypothesis H_0: $\rho = 0$ is true.

A Test for Independence in a Bivariate Normal Population

Null hypothesis: H_0: $\rho = 0$

Test statistic: $$t = \frac{r}{\sqrt{\frac{1 - r^2}{n - 2}}}$$

The test is based on df $= n - 2$.

Alternative hypothesis:	***P*-Value:**
H_a: $\rho > 0$ (positive dependence)	Area under the appropriate t curve to the right of the computed t
H_a: $\rho < 0$ (negative dependence)	Area under the appropriate t curve to the left of the computed t
H_a: $\rho \neq 0$ (dependence)	(1) 2(area to the right of t) if t is positive or (2) 2(area to the left of t) if t is negative

Assumptions: r is the correlation coefficient for a *random sample* from a *bivariate normal population.*

EXAMPLE 13.13 Sleepless Nights

The relationship between sleep duration and the level of the hormone leptin (a hormone related to energy intake and energy expenditure) in the blood was investigated in the paper "Short Sleep Duration is Associated with Reduced Leptin, Elevated Ghrelin, and Increased Body Mass Index" (*Public Library of Science Medicine*, [December 2004]: 210–217). Average nightly sleep (x, in hours) and blood leptin level (y) were recorded for each person in a sample of 716 participants in the Wisconsin Sleep Cohort Study. The sample correlation coefficient was

$r = 0.11$. Does this support the claim in the title of the paper that short sleep duration is associated with reduced leptin? Let's carry out a test using a significance level of .01.

1. ρ = the correlation between average nightly sleep and blood leptin level for the population of adult Americans.
2. H_0: $\rho = 0$
3. H_a: $\rho > 0$ (small values of y = average nightly sleep tend to be associated with small values of x = blood leptin level—that is, short sleep duration tends to be paired with lower leptin levels)
4. $\alpha = .01$
5. Test statistic: $t = \dfrac{r}{\sqrt{\dfrac{1 - r^2}{n - 2}}}$
6. Assumptions: Without the actual data, it is not possible to assess whether the assumption of bivariate normality is reasonable. For purposes of this example, we will assume that it is reasonable and proceed with the test. Had the data been available, we would have looked at normal probability plots of the x values and of the y values. We will also assume (as did the authors of the paper) that it is reasonable to regard the sample of participants in the study as representative of the larger population of adult Americans.
7. Calculation: $t = \dfrac{.11}{\sqrt{\dfrac{1 - (.11)^2}{714}}} = \dfrac{.11}{\sqrt{.00138}} = 2.96$
8. *P*-value: The t curve with 714 df is essentially indistinguishable from the z curve, and Appendix Table 4 shows that the area under this curve and to the right of 2.96 is .0015. That is, *P*-value = .0015.
9. Conclusion: *P*-value $\leq .01$. We reject H_0, as did the authors of the article, and confirm the conclusion that there is a positive association between sleep duration and blood leptin level. Notice, though, that according to the guidelines described in Chapter 5, $r = .11$ suggests only a weak linear relationship. Since $r^2 = .0121$, fitting the simple linear regression model to the data would result in only about 1% of observed variation in average nightly sleep being explained.

In the context of regression analysis, the hypothesis of no linear relationship (H_0: $\beta = 0$) was tested using the t ratio $t = \dfrac{b}{s_b}$. Some algebraic manipulation shows that

$$\frac{r}{\sqrt{\dfrac{1 - r^2}{n - 2}}} = \frac{b}{s_b}$$

Therefore the model utility test can also be used to test for independence in a bivariate normal population. The reason for using the formula for t that involves r is that when we are interested only in correlation, the extra effort involved in computing the regression quantities b, a, SSResid, s_e, and s_b need not be expended.

Other inferential procedures for drawing conclusions about ρ—a confidence interval or a test of hypothesis with nonzero hypothesized value—are somewhat complicated. The reference by Neter, Wasserman, and Kutner in the back of the book can be consulted for details.

EXERCISES 13.47 - 13.54

13.47 Explain the difference between r and ρ.

13.48 If the sample correlation coefficient is equal to 1, is it necessarily true that $\rho = 1$? If $\rho = 1$, is it necessarily true that $r = 1$?

13.49 A sample of $n = 353$ college faculty members was obtained, and the values of x = teaching evaluation index and y = annual raise were determined ("Determination of Faculty Pay: An Agency Theory Perspective," *Academy of Management Journal* [1992]: 921–955). The resulting value of r was .11. Does there appear to be a linear association between these variables in the population from which the sample was selected? Carry out a test of hypothesis using a significance level of .05. Does the conclusion surprise you? Explain.

13.50 It seems plausible that higher rent for retail space could be justified only by a higher level of sales. A random sample of $n = 53$ specialty stores in a chain was selected, and the values of x = annual dollar rent per square foot and y = annual dollar sales per square foot were determined, resulting in $r = .37$ ("Association of Shopping Center Anchors with Performance of a Nonanchor Specialty Chain Store," *Journal of Retailing* [1985]: 61–74). Carry out a test at significance level .05 to see whether there is in fact a positive linear association between x and y in the population of all such stores.

13.51 Television is regarded by many as a prime culprit for the difficulty many students have in performing well in school. The article "The Impact of Athletics, Part-Time Employment, and Other Activities on Academic Achievement" (*Journal of College Student Development* [1992]: 447–453) reported that for a random sample of $n = 528$ college students, the sample correlation coefficient between time spent watching television (x) and grade point average (y) was $r = -.26$.

a. Does this suggest that there is a negative correlation between these two variables in the population from which the 528 students were selected? Use a test with significance level .01.

b. Would the simple linear regression model explain a substantial percentage of the observed variation in grade point average? Explain your reasoning.

13.52 The accompanying summary quantities for x = particulate pollution ($\mu g/m^3$) and y = luminance (.01 cd/m^2) were calculated from a representative sample of data that appeared in the article "Luminance and Polarization of the Sky Light at Seville (Spain) Measured in White Light" (*Atmospheric Environment* [1988]: 595–599).

$$n = 15 \quad \sum x = 860 \quad \sum y = 348$$
$$\sum x^2 = 56{,}700 \quad \sum y^2 = 8954 \quad \sum xy = 22{,}265$$

a. Test to see whether there is a positive correlation between particulate pollution and luminance in the population from which the data were selected.

b. What proportion of observed variation in luminance can be attributed to the approximate linear relationship between luminance and particulate pollution?

13.53 ● In a study of bacterial concentration in surface and subsurface water ("Pb and Bacteria in a Surface Microlayer" *Journal of Marine Research* [1982]: 1200–1206), the accompanying data were obtained.

Concentration ($\times 10^6$ /mL)

Surface	48.6	24.3	15.9	8.29	5.75
Subsurface	5.46	6.89	3.38	3.72	3.12
Surface	10.8	4.71	8.26	9.41	
Subsurface	3.39	4.17	4.06	5.16	

Summary quantities are

$$\sum x = 136.02 \quad \sum y = 39.35$$
$$\sum x^2 = 3602.65 \quad \sum y^2 = 184.27 \quad \sum xy = 673.65$$

Using a significance level of .05, determine whether the data support the hypothesis of a linear relationship between surface and subsurface concentration.

13.54 A sample of $n = 10{,}000$ (x, y) pairs resulted in $r = .022$. Test H_0: $\rho = 0$ versus H_a: $\rho \neq 0$ at significance level .05. Is the result statistically significant? Comment on the practical significance of your analysis.

13.6 Interpreting and Communicating the Results of Statistical Analyses

Although regression analysis can be used as a tool for summarizing bivariate data, it is also widely used to enable researchers to make inferences about the way in which two variables are related.

What to Look For in Published Data

Here are some things to consider when you evaluate research that involves fitting a simple linear regression model:

- Which variable is the dependent variable? Is it a numerical (rather than a qualitative) variable?
- If sample data have been used to estimate the coefficients in a simple linear regression model, is it reasonable to think that the basic assumptions required for inference are met?
- Does the model appear to be useful? Are the results of a model utility test reported? What is the *P*-value associated with the test?
- Has the model been used in an appropriate way? Has the regression equation been used to predict y for values of the independent variable that are outside the range of the data?
- If a correlation coefficient is reported, is it accompanied by a test of significance? Are the results of the test interpreted properly?

Both correlation and linear regression methods were used by the authors of the paper "Obesity, Cigarette Smoking, and Telomere Length in Women" (*Lancet* [2005]: 6632–664) in the analysis of factors related to aging. The telomere is a region at the end of a chromosome, and because telomeres can erode each time a chromosome replicates, telomere length is thought to decrease with age. The paper states:

> Telomere length decreased steadily with age at a mean rate of 27 bp per year and a highly significant negative correlation was detected. The proportion of the variance in telomere length accounted for by age was 20.6%. Squared and cubed terms were also added to the model and had no significant effect on telomere length ($p = 0.92$ and $p = 0.98$, respectively) suggesting a linear relation between [telomere length] and age.

A correlation coefficient of -0.455 and an associated *P*-value of .0001 were reported to support the statement that there was a significant negative correlation. This also implies that a model utility test would have also indicated a useful linear relationship between y = telomere length and x = age. A scatterplot of telomere length versus age was given in the paper, and it was consistent with the basic assumptions required for the validity of the model utility test. From the quoted passage, $r^2 = .206$ (from 20.6% of variability in telomere length explained by age). Although the authors did not report the equation of the least-squares regression line, we can tell from the quoted passage that the slope of the line is -27 (the mean change in telomere length for a change of 1 in age).

In another study, the effects of caffeine were examined in the article "Withdrawal Syndrome After the Double-Blind Cessation of Caffeine Consumption" (*New England Journal of Medicine* [1992]: 1109–1113). The authors found that the dose of caffeine was significantly correlated with a measure of insomnia and also with latency on a test of reaction time. They reported $r = .26$ (*P*-value = .042) for insomnia and $r = .31$ (P-value $= .014$) for latency. Because both P-values are small, the authors concluded that the population correlation coefficients differ from 0. We should also note, however, that the reported correlation coefficients are not particularly large and do not indicate a strong linear relationship.

A Word to the Wise: Cautions and Limitations

In addition to the cautions and limitations described in Chapter 5 (which also apply here), here are a few additional things to keep in mind:

1. It doesn't make sense to use a regression line as the basis for making inferences about a population if there is no convincing evidence of a useful linear relationship between the two variables under study. It is particularly important to remember this when you are working with small samples. If the sample size is small, it is not uncommon for a weak linear pattern in the scatterplot to be due to chance rather than to a meaningful relationship in the population of interest.
2. As with all inferential procedures, it makes sense to carry out a model utility test or to construct confidence or prediction intervals only if the linear regression is based on a random sample from some larger population. It is not unusual to see a least-squares line used as a descriptive tool in situations where the data used to construct the line cannot reasonably be viewed as a sample. In this case, the inferential methods of this chapter are not appropriate.
3. Don't forget to check assumptions. If you are used to checking assumptions before doing much in the way of computation, it is sometimes easy to forget to check them in this setting because the equation of the least-squares line and then the residuals must be computed before a residual plot or a normal probability plot of the standardized residuals can be constructed. Be sure to step back and think about whether the linear regression model is appropriate and reasonable before using the model to draw inferences about a population.

EXERCISE 13.55

13.55 The paper "Stature and Status: Height, Ability, and Labor Market Outcomes" (*Journal of Political Economy* [2008]: 499–532) describes a study of the association between height and cognitive ability. The paper states: "We first regress individual test scores on growth between ages 11 and 16 and then on growth between ages 16 and 33. We estimate separate models for boys and girls." Cognitive ability at age 11 was measured by three different tests—verbal language, nonverbal language, and math. Six different simple linear regression models were used to describe the relationships between height gain from age 11 to 16 and each of the three test scores and between height gain from age 16 to 33 and each of the three test scores. The following table gives the slopes for each of the six regression models for boys.

x	y	Slope of estimated regression line
Height gain from age 11–16	Verbal language score	2.0
Height gain from age 11–16	Nonverbal language score	2.3
Height gain from age 11–16	Math Score	3.0
Height gain from age 16–33	Verbal language score	−3.1
Height gain from age 16–33	Nonverbal language score	−3.8
Height gain from age 16–33	Math Score	−3.8

a. In this study, height gain (the x variable) was measured in inches and the test scores were reported as percentage correct. The paper states that boys who grew more from age 11 to 16 had, on average, higher cognitive test scores at age 11, with each extra inch of height gain being associated with an increase in test scores of between 2 and 3 percentage points. Explain how the reported slopes are consistent with this statement.

b. The paper also states that boys who had a late growth spurt (after age 16) had lower test scores at age 11, with each extra inch of height gain being associated with a decrease in test scores of between 3.1 and 3.8 percentage points. Explain how the reported slopes are consistent with this statement.

c. The authors of the paper conclude that boys who grow early (age 11 to 16) have higher cognitive scores at age 11 than boys who grow late (age 16 to 33). Consider two boys who were the same height at age 11 and who both had total height gains of 5 inches. If one boy had his 5-inch height gain before age 16 and the other boy had his 5-inch height gain after age 16, what would you estimate the difference in their age 11 math scores to have been? Is this consistent with the authors' conclusion?

ACTIVITY 13.1 Are Tall Women from "Big" Families?

In this activity, you should work with a partner (or in a small group).

Consider the following data on height (in inches) and number of siblings for a random sample of 10 female students at a large university.

1. Construct a scatterplot of the given data. Does there appear to be a linear relationship between y = height and x = number of siblings?

Height (y)	Number of Siblings (x)	Height (y)	Number of Siblings (x)
64.2	2	65.5	1
65.4	0	67.2	2
64.6	2	66.4	2
66.1	6	63.3	0
65.1	3	61.7	1

2. Compute the value of the correlation coefficient. Is the value of the correlation coefficient consistent with your answer from Step 1? Explain.
3. What is the equation of the least-squares line for these data?
4. Is the slope of the least-squares regression line from Step 3 equal to 0? Does this necessarily mean that there is a meaningful relationship between height and number of siblings in the population of female students at this university? Discuss this with your partner, and then write a few sentences of explanation.
5. For the population of all female students at the university, do you think it is reasonable to assume that the distribution of heights at each particular x value is approximately normal and that the standard deviation of the height distribution at each particular x value is the same? That is, do you think it is reasonable to assume that the distribution of heights for female students with zero siblings is approximately normal and that the distribution of heights for female students with one sibling is approximately normal with the same standard deviation as for female students with no siblings, and so on? Discuss this with your partner, and then write a few sentences of explanation.
6. Carry out the model utility test (H_0: $\beta = 0$). Explain why the conclusion from this test is consistent with your explanation in Step 4.
7. Would you recommend using the least-squares regression line as a way of predicting heights for women at this university? Explain.
8. After consulting with your partner, write a paragraph explaining why it is a good idea to include a model utility test (H_0: $\beta = 0$) as part of a regression analysis.

Summary of Key Concepts and Formulas

TERM OR FORMULA	COMMENT
Simple linear regression model, $y = \alpha + \beta x + e$	This model assumes that there is a line with slope β and y intercept α, called the population regression line, such that an observation deviates from the line by a random amount e. The random deviation is assumed to have a normal distribution with mean zero and standard deviation σ, and random deviations for different observations are assumed to be independent of one another.
Estimated regression line, $\hat{y} = a + bx$	The least-squares line introduced in Chapter 5.
$s_e = \sqrt{\frac{\text{SSResid}}{n - 2}}$	The point estimate of the standard deviation σ, with associated degrees of freedom $n - 2$.
$s_b = \frac{s_e}{\sqrt{S_{xx}}}$	The estimated standard deviation of the statistic b.
$b \pm (t \text{ critical value}) s_b$	A confidence interval for the slope β of the population regression line, where the t critical value is based on $n - 2$ degrees of freedom.
$t = \frac{b - \text{hypothesized value}}{s_b}$	The test statistic for testing hypotheses about β. The test is based on $n - 2$ degrees of freedom.
Model utility test, with test statistic $t = \frac{b}{s_b}$	A test of H_0: $\beta = 0$, which asserts that there is no useful linear relationship between x and y, versus H_a: $\beta \neq 0$, the claim that there is a useful linear relationship.
Residual analysis	Methods based on the residuals or standardized residuals for checking the assumptions of a regression model.
Standardized residual	A residual divided by its standard deviation.
Standardized residual plot	A plot of the (x, standardized residual) pairs. A pattern in this plot suggests that the simple linear regression model may not be appropriate.
$s_{a+bx^*} = s_e\sqrt{\frac{1}{n} + \frac{(x^* - \bar{x})^2}{S_{xx}}}$	The estimated standard deviation of the statistic $a + bx^*$, where x^* denotes a particular value of x.
$a + bx^* \pm (t \text{ critical value}) s_{a+bx^*}$	A confidence interval for $\alpha + \beta x^*$, the mean value of y when $x = x^*$.
$a + bx^* \pm (t \text{ critical value})\sqrt{s_e^2 + s_{a+bx^*}^2}$	A prediction interval for a single y value to be observed when $x = x^*$.
Population correlation coefficient ρ	A measure of the extent to which the x and y values in an entire population are linearly related.
$t = \frac{r}{\sqrt{\frac{1 - r^2}{n - 2}}}$	The test statistic for testing H_0: $\rho = 0$, according to which (assuming a bivariate normal population distribution) x and y are independent of one another.

Chapter Review Exercises 13.56 - 13.70

13.56 The effects of grazing animals on grasslands have been the focus of numerous investigations by ecologists. One such study, reported in "The Ecology of Plants, Large Mammalian Herbivores, and Drought in Yellowstone National Park" (*Ecology* [1992]: 2043–2058), proposed using the simple linear regression model to relate y = green biomass concentration (g/cm^3) to x = elapsed time since snowmelt (days).

a. The estimated regression equation was given as $\hat{y} = 106.3 - .640x$. What is the estimate of average change in biomass concentration associated with a 1-day increase in elapsed time?

b. What value of biomass concentration would you predict when elapsed time is 40 days?

c. The sample size was $n = 58$, and the reported value of the coefficient of determination was .470. Does this suggest that there is a useful linear relationship between the two variables? Carry out an appropriate test.

13.57 A random sample of $n = 347$ students was selected, and each one was asked to complete several questionnaires, from which a Coping Humor Scale value x and a Depression Scale value y were determined ("Depression and Sense of Humor," (*Psychological Reports* [1994]: 1473–1474). The resulting value of the sample correlation coefficient was $-.18$.

a. The investigators reported that P-value $< .05$. Do you agree?

b. Is the sign of r consistent with your intuition? Explain. (Higher scale values correspond to more developed sense of humor and greater extent of depression.)

c. Would the simple linear regression model give accurate predictions? Why or why not?

13.58 Example 13.4 gave data on x = treadmill run time to exhaustion and y = 20-km ski time for a sample of 11 biathletes. Use the accompanying Minitab output to answer the following questions.

The regression equation is
ski = 88.8 – 2.33tread

Predictor	Coef	Stdev	t-ratio	p
Constant	88.796	5.750	15.44	0.000
tread	–2.3335	0.5911	–3.95	0.003

s = 2.188 R-sq = 63.4% R-sq(adj) = 59.3%

Analysis of Variance

Source	DF	SS	MS	F
Regression	1	74.630	74.630	15.58
Error	9	43.097	4.789	
Total	10	117.727		

a. Carry out a test at significance level .01 to decide whether the simple linear regression model is useful.

b. Estimate the average change in ski time associated with a 1-minute increase in treadmill time, and do so in a way that conveys information about the precision of estimation.

c. Minitab reported that $s_{a+b(10)} = .689$. Predict ski time for a single biathlete whose treadmill time is 10 minutes, and do so in a way that conveys information about the precision of prediction.

d. Minitab also reported that $s_{a+b(11)} = 1.029$. Why is this larger than $s_{a+b(10)}$?

13.59 A sample of $n = 61$ penguin burrows was selected, and values of both y = trail length (m) and x = soil hardness (force required to penetrate the substrate to a depth of 12 cm with a certain gauge, in kg) were determined for each one ("Effects of Substrate on the Distribution of Magellanic Penguin Burrows," *The Auk* [1991]: 923–933). The equation of the least-squares line was $\hat{y} = 11.607 - 1.4187x$, and $r^2 = .386$.

a. Does the relationship between soil hardness and trail length appear to be linear, with shorter trails associated with harder soil (as the article asserted)? Carry out an appropriate test of hypotheses.

b. Using $s_e = 2.35$, $\bar{x} = 4.5$, and $\sum(x - \bar{x})^2 = 250$, predict trail length when soil hardness is 6.0 in a way that conveys information about the reliability and precision of the prediction.

c. Would you use the simple linear regression model to predict trail length when hardness is 10.0? Explain your reasoning.

13.60 ● The article "Photocharge Effects in Dye Sensitized Ag[Br,I] Emulsions at Millisecond Range Exposures" (*Photographic Science and Engineering* [1981]: 138–144) gave the accompanying data on x = % light absorption and y = peak photovoltage.

x	4.0	8.7	12.7	19.1	21.4	24.6	28.9	29.8	30.5
y	0.12	0.28	0.55	0.68	0.85	1.02	1.15	1.34	1.29

$$\sum x = 179.7 \quad \sum x^2 = 4334.41$$
$$\sum y = 7.28 \quad \sum y^2 = 7.4028 \quad \sum xy = 178.683$$

a. Construct a scatterplot of the data. What does it suggest?
b. Assuming that the simple linear regression model is appropriate, obtain the equation of the estimated regression line.
c. How much of the observed variation in peak photovoltage can be explained by the model relationship?
d. Predict peak photovoltage when percent absorption is 19.1, and compute the value of the corresponding residual.
e. The authors claimed that there is a useful linear relationship between the two variables. Do you agree? Carry out a formal test.
f. Give an estimate of the average change in peak photovoltage associated with a 1 percentage point increase in light absorption. Your estimate should convey information about the precision of estimation.
g. Give an estimate of mean peak photovoltage when percentage of light absorption is 20, and do so in a way that conveys information about precision.

13.61 ● Reduced visual performance with increasing age has been a much-studied phenomenon in recent years. This decline is due partly to changes in optical properties of the eye itself and partly to neural degeneration throughout the visual system. As one aspect of this problem, the article "Morphometry of Nerve Fiber Bundle Pores in the Optic Nerve Head of the Human" (*Experimental Eye Research* [1988]: 559–568) presented the accompanying data on x = age and y = percentage of the cribriform area of the lamina scleralis occupied by pores.

x	22	25	27	39	42	43	44	46	46
y	75	62	50	49	54	49	59	47	54

x	48	50	57	58	63	63	74	74
y	52	58	49	52	49	31	42	41

a. Suppose that prior to this study the researchers had believed that the average decrease in percentage area associated with a 1-year age increase was .5%. Do the data contradict this prior belief? State and test the appropriate hypotheses using a .10 significance level.
b. Estimate true average percentage area covered by pores for all 50-year-olds in the population in a way that conveys information about the precision of estimation.

13.62 ● Occasionally an investigator may wish to compute a confidence interval for α, the y intercept of the true regression line, or test hypotheses about α. The estimated y intercept is simply the height of the estimated line when $x = 0$, since $a + b(0) = a$. This implies that s_a the estimated standard deviation of the statistic a, results from substituting $x^* = 0$ in the formula for s_{a+bx^*}. The desired confidence interval is then

$$a \pm (t \text{ critical value})s_a$$

and a test statistic is

$$t = \frac{a - \text{hypothesized value}}{s_a}$$

a. The article "Comparison of Winter-Nocturnal Geostationary Satellite Infrared-Surface Temperature with Shelter-Height Temperature in Florida" (*Remote Sensing of the Environment* [1983]: 313–327) used the simple linear regression model to relate surface temperature as measured by a satellite (y) to actual air temperature (x) as determined from a thermocouple placed on a traversing vehicle. Selected data are given (read from a scatterplot in the article).

x	−2	−1	0	1	2	3	4
y	−3.9	−2.1	−2.0	−1.2	0.0	1.9	0.6

x	5	6	7
y	2.1	1.2	3.0

Estimate the population regression line.
b. Compute the estimated standard deviation s_a. Carry out a test at level of significance .05 to see whether the y intercept of the population regression line differs from zero.
c. Compute a 95% confidence interval for α. Does the result indicate that $\alpha = 0$ is plausible? Explain.

13.63 ● In some studies, an investigator has n (x, y) pairs sampled from one population and m (x, y) pairs from a second population. Let β and β' denote the slopes of the first and second population lines, respectively, and let b and b' denote the estimated slopes calculated from the first and second samples, respectively. The investigator may then wish to test the null hypothesis H_0: $\beta - \beta' = 0$ (that is, $\beta = \beta'$) against an appropriate alternative hypothesis. Suppose that σ^2, the variance about the population line, is the same for both populations. Then this common variance can be estimated by

$$s^2 = \frac{\text{SSResid} + \text{SSResid}'}{(n-2) + (m-2)}$$

where SSResid and SSResid′ are the residual sums of squares for the first and second samples, respectively. With S_{xx} and S'_{xx} denoting the quantity $\sum(x - \bar{x})^2$ for the first and second samples, respectively, the test statistic is

$$t = \frac{b - b'}{\sqrt{\frac{s^2}{S_{xx}} + \frac{s^2}{S'_{xx}}}}$$

When H_0 is true, this statistic has a t distribution based on $(n + m - 4)$ df.

The data below are a subset of the data in the article "Diet and Foraging Model of Bufa marinus and Leptodactylus ocellatus" (*Journal of Herpetology* [1984]: 138–146). The independent variable x is body length (cm) and the dependent variable y is mouth width (cm), with $n = 9$ observations for one type of nocturnal frog and $m = 8$ observations for a second type. Carry out a test to determine if the slopes of the true regression lines for the two different frog populations are equal. Use a sigificance level of .05. (Summary statistics are also given in the accompanying table.)

Leptodactylus ocellatus

x	3.8	4.0	4.9	7.1	8.1	8.5	8.9	9.1	9.8
y	1.0	1.2	1.7	2.0	2.7	2.5	2.4	2.9	3.2

Bufa marinus

x	3.8	4.3	6.2	6.3	7.8	8.5	9.0	10.0
y	1.6	1.7	2.3	2.5	3.2	3.0	3.5	3.8

	Leptodactylus	*Bufa*
Sample size:	9	8
$\sum x$	64.2	55.9
$\sum x^2$	500.78	425.15
$\sum y$	19.6	21.6
$\sum y^2$	47.28	62.92
$\sum xy$	153.36	163.36

13.64 ● Consider the following four (x, y) data sets: the first three have the same x values, so these values are listed only once (from "Graphs in Statistical Analysis," *American Statistician* [1973]: 17–21).

Data Set Variable	1–3 x	1 y	2 y	3 y	4 x	4 y
	10.0	8.04	9.14	7.46	8.0	6.58
	8.0	6.95	8.14	6.77	8.0	5.76
	13.0	7.58	8.74	12.74	8.0	7.71
	9.0	8.81	8.77	7.11	8.0	8.84
	11.0	8.33	9.26	7.81	8.0	8.47
	14.0	9.96	8.10	8.84	8.0	7.04
	6.0	7.24	6.13	6.08	8.0	5.25
	4.0	4.26	3.10	5.39	19.0	12.50
	12.0	10.84	9.13	8.15	8.0	5.56
	7.0	4.82	7.26	6.42	8.0	7.91
	5.0	5.68	4.74	5.73	8.0	6.89

(continued)

For each of these data sets, the values of the summary quantities $\bar{x}$, $\bar{y}$, $\sum(x - \bar{x})^2$, and $\sum(x - \bar{x})(y - \bar{y})$ are identical, so all quantities computed from these will be identical for the four sets: the estimated regression line, SSResid, s_e, r^2, and so on. The summary quantities provide no way of distinguishing among the four data sets.

Based on a scatterplot for each set, comment on the appropriateness or inappropriateness of fitting the simple linear regression model in each case.

13.65 The accompanying scatterplot, based on 34 sediment samples with x = sediment depth (cm) and y = oil and grease content (mg/kg), appeared in the article "Mined Land Reclamation Using Polluted Urban Navigable Waterway Sediments" (*Journal of Environmental Quality* [1984]: 415–422). Discuss the effect that the observation (20, 33,000) will have on the estimated regression line. If this point were omitted, what can you say about the slope of the estimated regression line? What do you think will happen to the slope if this observation is included in the computations?

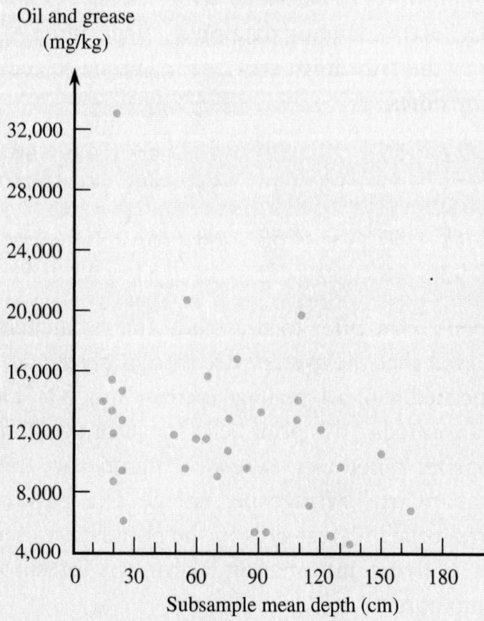

13.66 ● The article "Improving Fermentation Productivity with Reverse Osmosis" (*Food Technology* [1984]: 92–96) gave the following data (read from a scatterplot) on y = glucose concentration (g/L) and x = fermentation time (days) for a blend of malt liquor.

x	1	2	3	4	5	6	7	8
y	74	54	52	51	52	53	58	71

a. Use the data to calculate the estimated regression line.
b. Do the data indicate a linear relationship between y and x? Test using a .10 significance level.
c. Using the estimated regression line of Part (a), compute the residuals and construct a plot of the residuals versus x (that is, of the (x, residual) pairs).
d. Based on the plot in Part (c), do you think that the simple linear regression model is appropriate for describing the relationship between y and x? Explain.

13.67 The employee relations manager of a large company was concerned that raises given to employees during a recent period might not have been based strictly on objective performance criteria. A sample of $n = 20$ employees was selected, and the values of x, a quantitative measure of productivity, and y, the percentage salary increase, were determined for each one. A computer package was used to fit the simple linear regression model, and the resulting output gave the P-value = .0076 for the model utility test. Does the percentage raise appear to be linearly related to productivity? Explain.

13.68 The figure at the top of the page is based on data from the article "Root and Shoot Competition Intensity Along a Soil Depth Gradient" (*Ecology* [1995]: 673–682). It shows the relationship between aboveground biomass and soil depth within the experimental plots. The relationship is described by the estimated regression equation: biomass = −9.85 + 25.29(soil depth) and $r^2 = .65$; $P < 0.001$; $n = 55$. Do you think the simple linear regression model is appropriate here? Explain. What would you expect to see in a plot of the standardized residuals versus x?

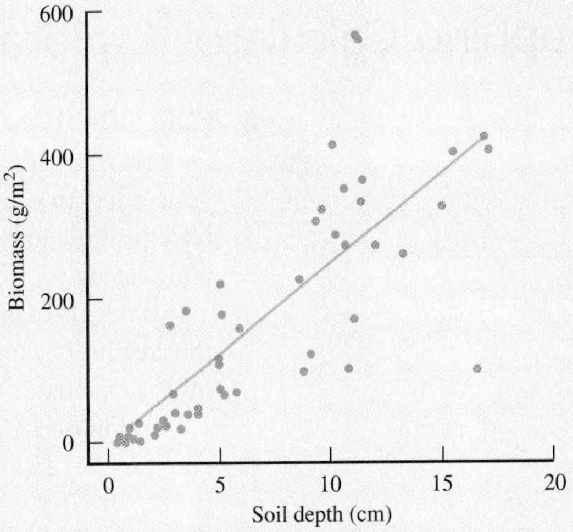

13.69 Give a brief answer, comment, or explanation for each of the following.

a. What is the difference between $e_1, e_2, \ldots, e_n$ and the n residuals?
b. The simple linear regression model states that $y = \alpha + \beta x$.
c. Does it make sense to test hypotheses about b?
d. SSResid is always positive.
e. A student reported that a data set consisting of $n = 6$ observations yielded residuals 2, 0, 5, 3, 0, and 1 from the least-squares line.
f. A research report included the following summary quantities obtained from a simple linear regression analysis:

$$\sum(y - \bar{y})^2 = 615 \quad \sum(y - \hat{y})^2 = 731$$

Graphing Calculator Exploration

EXPLORATION 13.1 Inference for the Regression Slope

By this time you are an old hand at performing hypothesis tests. You can navigate your calculator menu with aplomb and punch keys with the best of them! With this background, inferences concerning the slope of a population regression line using your calculator will hold few surprises.

Enter the data from Example 13.4, the treadmill data, into your calculator. Enter the treadmill run time in List1 and the ski time in List2. Navigating the menu system on the calculator should lead you to a screen similar to the one in Figure 13.23.

LinRegTTest
Xlist: L1
Ylist: L2
Freq: 1
β & ρ: ≠0 <0 >0:
RegEq:
Calculate

FIGURE 13.23
Setup window.

In Figure 13.23, L1 and L2 are the default values chosen by the calculator; if you entered the data in a different list, you will have to change these lists. The line β & ρ: $\neq 0 < 0 > 0$ is where the alternative hypothesisis is selected. For this example, we have selected the alternative hypothesis $\beta \neq 0$.

Placing the calculator's cursor on Calculate and pressing Enter produces the screen shown in Figure 13.24, another larger-than-life presentation. Comparing the screen in Figure 13.24 with the quantities calculated in the text, you will find all the information needed to complete the hypothesis test. The notation is standard, except for the equation $s = 2.1883$. This s, after checking with the quantities in the discussion of Example 13.4, turns out to be s_e, the estimated standard deviation of the random deviations. It is *not* the estimated standard deviation of the sample slope, s_b. This is unfortunate, since to construct a confidence interval for b we need to calculate $b \pm (t \text{ critical value}) \cdot s_b$.

LinRegTTest
Y = a+bx
$\beta \neq 0$ and $\rho \neq 0$
t = −3.9478
p = .0034
df = 9.0000
a = 88.7956
b = −2.3335
s = 2.1883
r^2 = .6339
r = .7962

FIGURE 13.24
Output screen

Worry not! You can construct the confidence interval for b with the aid of algebra and the statistics capabilities of your calculator. The standard error for b can be calculated using the given information and the sample variance of the treadmill times:

$$s_b = \frac{s_e}{\sqrt{S_{xx}}} = \frac{s_e}{\sqrt{(x - \bar{x})^2}} = \frac{s_e}{\sqrt{(n-1)s_x^2}} = \frac{s_e}{s_x\sqrt{(n-1)}}$$

There are 11 data points; $s_x = 1.1707030$ (from the statistics menu for List1). Substituting gives

$$s_b = \frac{s_e}{s_x\sqrt{(n-1)}} = \frac{2.188286324}{1.1707030\sqrt{10}} = .5910952$$

With the information now available, you can calculate the 95% confidence interval for the population slope:

$$b \pm (t \text{ critical value}) \cdot s_b$$
$$-2.3335 \pm (2.26) \cdot (.5910952)$$
$$(-3.6694, -.9976)$$

Cumulative Review Exercises CR13.1-CR13.18

CR13.1 The article "You Will Be Tested on This" (*The Chronicle of Higher Education*, June 8, 2007) describes an experiment to investigate the effect of quizzes on student learning. The goal of the experiment was to determine if students who take daily quizzes have better end-of-semester retention than students who attend the same lectures and complete the same homework assignments but who do not take the daily quizzes. Describe how you would design such an experiment using the 400 students enrolled in an introductory psychology course as subjects.

CR13.2 The paper "Pistachio Nut Consumption and Serum Lipid Levels" (*Journal of the American College of Nutrition* [2007]: 141–148) describes a study to determine if eating pistachio nuts can have an effect on blood cholesterol levels in people with high cholesterol. Fifteen subjects followed their regular diet for 4 weeks and then followed a diet in which 15% of the daily caloric intake was from pistachio nuts for 4 weeks. Total blood cholesterol was measured for each subject at the end of each of the 2 four-week periods, resulting in two samples (one for the regular diet and one for the pistachio diet).

a. Are the two samples independent or paired? Explain.
b. The mean difference in total cholesterol (regular diet—pistachio diet) was 11 mg/dL. The standard deviation of the differences was 24 mg/dL. Assume that it is reasonable to regard the 15 study participants as representative of adults with high cholesterol and that total cholesterol differences are approximately normally distributed. Do the data support the claim that eating the pistachio diet for 4 weeks is effective in reducing total cholesterol level? Test the relevant hypotheses using $\alpha = .01$.

CR13.3 ● The article "Fines Show Airline Problems" (*USA Today*, February 2, 2010) gave the accompanying data on the number of fines for violating FAA maintenance regulations assessed against each of the 25 U.S. airlines from 2004 to 2009.

1	12	3	7	23	36	6	14	1	3
4	10	6	2	2	2	2	2	3	1
2	2	1	0	0					

a. Construct a boxplot of these data. Are any of the observations in the data set outliers? If so, which ones?
b. Explain why it may not be reasonable to assume that the two airlines with the highest number of fines assessed are the worst airlines in terms of maintenance violations.

CR13.4 The article "Odds Are, It's Wrong" (*Science News*, March 27, 2010) poses the following scenario:

> Suppose that a test for steroid use among baseball players is 95% accurate—that is, it correctly identifies actual steroid users 95% of the time, and misidentifies non-users as users 5 percent of the time. . . . Now suppose, based on previous testing, that experts have established that about 5 percent of professional baseball players use steroids.

Answer the following questions for this scenario.

a. If 400 professional baseball players are selected at random, how many would you expect to be steroid users and how many would you expect to be non-users?
b. How many of the steroid users would you expect to test positive for steroid use?
c. How many of the players who do not use steroids would you expect to test positive for steroid use (a false positive)?
d. Use your answers to Parts (b) and (c) to estimate the proportion of those who test positive for steroid use who actually do use steroids.
e. Write a few sentences explaining why, in this scenario, the proportion of those who test positive for steroid use who actually use steroids is not .95.

CR13.5 The press release "Luxury or Necessity? The Public Makes a U-Turn" (Pew Research Center, April 23, 2009) summarizes results from a survey of a nationally representative sample of $n = 1003$ adult Americans.

a. One question in the survey asked participants if they think of a landline phone as a necessity or as a luxury that they could do without. Sixty-eight percent said they thought a landline phone was a necessity. Estimate the proportion of adult Americans who view a landline phone as a necessity using a 95% confidence interval.
b. In the same survey, 52% said they viewed a television set as a necessity. Is there convincing evidence that a majority of adult Americans view a television set as a necessity? Test the relevant hypotheses using $\alpha = .05$.

c. The press release also described a survey conducted in 2003. When asked about a microwave oven, 68% of the 2003 sample regarded a microwave oven as a necessity, whereas only 47% of the 2009 sample said they thought a microwave oven was a necessity. Assume that the sample size for the 2003 survey was also 1003. Is there convincing evidence that the proportion of adult Americans who regard a microwave oven as a necessity decreased between 2003 and 2009? Test the appropriate hypotheses using $\alpha = .01$.

CR13.6 The accompanying graphical display appeared in *USA Today* (February 19, 2010). It is meant to be a pie chart, but an oval rather than a circle is used to represent the whole pie. Do you think this graph does a good job of conveying the proportion falling into each of the three response categories? Explain why or why not.

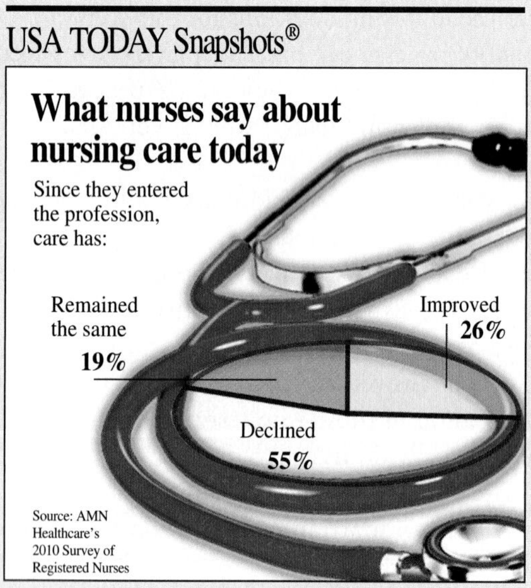

By Anne R. Carey and Suzy Parker, USA TODAY

CR13.7 The following quote describing 18- to 29-year-olds is from the article "Study: Millennial Generation More Educated, Less Employed" (*USA Today*, February 23, 2010): "38% have a tattoo (and half of those with tattoos have two to five; 18% have six or more)." These percentages were based on a representative sample of 830 Americans age 18 to 29, but for purposes of this exercise, suppose that they hold for the population of all Americans in this age group. Define the random variable x = number of tattoos for a randomly selected American age 18 to 29. Find the following probabilities:

a. $P(x = 0)$
b. $P(x = 1)$
c. $P(2 \leq x \leq 5)$
d. $P(x > 5)$

CR13.8 To raise revenues, many airlines now charge fees to check luggage. Suppose that the number of checked bags was recorded for each person in a random sample of 100 airline passengers selected before fees were imposed and also for each person in a random sample of 100 airline passengers selected after fees were imposed, resulting in the accompanying data. Do the data provide convincing evidence that the proportions in each of the number of checked bags categories is not the same before and after fees were imposed? Test the appropriate hypotheses using a significance level of .05.

	Number of Checked Bags		
	0	1	2 or more
Before fees	7	70	23
After Fees	22	64	14

CR13.9 ● Consider the following data on y = number of songs stored on an MP3 player and x = number of months the user has owned the MP3 player for a sample of 15 owners of MP3 players.

x	y
23	486
35	747
2	81
28	581
5	117
32	728
23	445
10	128
4	61
26	476
1	35
8	121
13	266
9	126
5	141

a. Construct a scatterplot of the data. Does the relationship between x and y look approximately linear?
b. What is the equation of the estimated regression line?
c. Do you think that the assumptions of the simple linear regression model are reasonable? Justify your answer using appropriate graphs.
d. Is the simple linear regression model useful for describing the relationship between x and y? Test the relevant hypotheses using a significance level of .05.

CR13.10 Many people take ginkgo supplements advertised to improve memory. Are these over-the-counter supplements effective? In a study reported in the paper "Ginkgo for Memory Enhancement" (*Journal of the American Medical Association* [2002]: 835–840), elderly adults were assigned at random to either a treatment group or a control group. The 104 participants who were assigned to the treatment group took 40 mg of ginkgo three times a day for 6 weeks. The 115 participants assigned to the control group took a placebo pill three times a day for 6 weeks. At the end of 6 weeks, the Wechsler Memory Scale (a test of short-term memory) was administered. Higher scores indicate better memory function. Summary values are given in the following table.

	n	$\bar{x}$	s
Ginkgo	104	5.6	.6
Placebo	115	5.5	.6

Based on these results, is there evidence that taking 40 mg of ginkgo three times a day is effective in increasing mean performance on the Wechsler Memory Scale? Test the relevant hypotheses using $\alpha = .05$.

CR13.11 ● The Harvard University Institute of Politics surveys undergraduates across the United States annually. Responses to the question "When it comes to voting, do you consider yourself to be affiliated with the Democratic Party, the Republican Party, or are you Independent or unaffiliated with a major party?" for the survey conducted in 2003, 2004, and 2005 are summarized in the given table. The samples for each year were independently selected and are considered to be representative of the population of undergraduate students in the year the survey was conducted. Is there evidence that the distribution of political affiliation is not the same for all three years for which data are given?

	Year		
Political Affiliation	2005	2004	2003
Democrat	397	409	325
Republican	301	349	373
Independent / unaffiliated	458	397	457
Other	60	48	48

CR13.12 ● The survey described in the previous exercise also asked the following question: "Please tell me whether you trust the President to do the right thing all of the time, most of the time, some of the time, or never. Use the data in the given table and an appropriate hypothesis test to determine if there is evidence that trust in the President was not the same in 2005 as it was in 2002.

	Year	
Response	2005	2002
All of the time	132	180
Most of the time	337	528
Some of the time	554	396
Never	169	96

CR13.13 ● The report "Undergraduate Students and Credit Cards in 2004" (Nellie Mae, May 2005) included information collected from individuals in a random sample of undergraduate students in the United States. Students were classified according to region of residence and whether or not they have one or more credit cards, resulting in the accompanying two-way table. Carry out a test to determine if there is evidence that region of residence and having a credit card are not independent. Use $\alpha = .05$.

	Credit Card?	
Region	At Least One Credit Card	No Credit Cards
Northeast	401	164
Midwest	162	36
South	408	115
West	104	23

CR13.14 ● The report described in the previous exercise also classified students according to region of residence and whether or not they had a credit card with a balance of more than $7000. Do these data support the conclusion that there is an association between region of residence and whether or not the student has a balance exceeding $7000? Test the relevant hypotheses using a .01 significance level.

	Balance Over $7000?	
Region	No	Yes
Northeast	28	537
Midwest	162	182
South	42	481
West	9	118

CR13.15 The discharge of industrial wastewater into rivers affects water quality. To assess the effect of a particular power plant on water quality, 24 water specimens were taken 16 km upstream and 4 km downstream of the plant. Alkalinity (mg/L) was determined for each specimen, resulting in the summary quantities in the accompanying table. Do the data suggest that the true mean alkalinity is higher downstream than upstream by more than 50 mg/L? Use a .05 significance level.

Location	n	Mean	Standard Deviation
Upstream	24	75.9	1.83
Downstream	24	183.6	1.70

CR13.16 ● The report of a European commission on radiation protection titled "Cosmic Radiation Exposure of Aircraft Crew" (2004) measured the exposure to radiation on eight international flights from Madrid using several different methods for measuring radiation. Data for two of the methods are given in the accompanying table. Use these data to test the hypothesis that there is no significant difference in mean radiation measurement for the two methods.

Flight	Method 1	Method 2
1	27.5	34.4
2	41.3	38.6
3	3.5	3.5
4	24.3	21.9
5	27.0	24.4
6	17.7	21.4
7	12.0	11.8
8	20.9	24.1

CR13.17 ● It is hypothesized that when homing pigeons are disoriented in a certain manner, they will exhibit no preference for any direction of flight after takeoff. To test this, 120 pigeons are disoriented and released, and the direction of flight of each is recorded. The resulting data are given in the accompanying table.

Direction	Frequency
0° to < 45°	12
45° to < 90°	16
90° to < 135°	17
135° to < 180°	15
180° to < 225°	13
225° to < 270°	20
270° to < 315°	17
315° to < 360°	10

Use the goodness-of-fit test with significance level .10 to determine whether the data are consistent with this hypothesis.

CR 13.18 The authors of the paper "Inadequate Physician Knowledge of the Effects of Diet on Blood Lipids and Lipoproteins" (*Nutrition Journal* [2003]: 19–26) summarize the responses to a questionnaire on basic knowledge of nutrition that was mailed to 6000 physicians selected at random from a list of physicians licensed in the United States. Sixteen percent of those who received the questionnaire completed and returned it. The authors report that 26 of 120 cardiologists and 222 of 419 internists did not know that carbohydrate was the diet component most likely to raise triglycerides.

a. Estimate the difference between the proportion of cardiologists and the proportion of internists who did not know that carbohydrate was the diet component most likely to raise triglycerides using a 95% confidence interval.
b. What potential source of bias might limit your ability to generalize the estimate from Part (a) to the populations of all cardiologists and all internists?

AP* Review Questions for Chapter 13

Use the following information for questions 1–6.

A study was carried out to investigate the relationship between x = the number of components needing repair and y = the time of the service call (in minutes) for a computer repair company. The number of components and the service time for a random sample of 20 service calls was used to fit a simple linear regression model. Partial computer output is shown below.

```
The regression equation is
Time = 37.2 + 9.97 Number
Predictor     Coef       SE Coef        T        P
Constant      37.213     7.985          4.66     0.000
Number        9.9695     0.7218         13.81    0.000
S = 18.7534     R-Sq = 89.7%     R-Sq(adj) = 89.2%
```

1. Which of the following statements is a correct interpretation of the value 9.97?
   (A) The average number of components needing repair goes up 9.97 for each 1 minute increase in the service time of a call.
   (B) On average, the service call time goes up 9.97 minutes for each additional component needing repair.
   (C) The service call time is 9.97 minutes when there are 0 components to repair.
   (D) Approximately 9.97% of the observed variation in the service call times can be explained by the linear relationship between service time and number of components requiring repair.
   (E) If this regression equation is used to predict service call times, we can expect predictions to be within 9.97 minutes of the actual time.

2. Which of the following statements is a correct interpretation of the value 89.7%?
   (A) On average, the service call time goes up 89.7 minutes for each additional component needing repair.
   (B) The magnitude of a typical difference between an observed service call time and the service call time predicted by the linear model is approximately 89.7 minutes.
   (C) The correlation between service call time and number of components needing repair is 89.7%.
   (D) Approximately 89.7% of the observed variation in service call time can be explained by the linear relationship between service call time and number of components needing repair.
   (E) If this regression equation is used to predict service call times, we can expect predictions to be within 89.7 minutes of the actual time.

3. The value of s_e is 18.75. Which of the following is an appropriate interpretation of this value?
   (A) 18.75% of the variability in service time can be explained by the linear relationship between service call time and number of components needing repair.
   (B) There is a positive correlation between service call time and number of components needing repair.
   (C) For every 1-component increase in the number of components needing repair, the predicted service call time increases by about 18.75 minutes.
   (D) The magnitude of a typical difference between an observed service time and the service call time predicted by the linear model is approximately 18.75 minutes.
   (E) The average service call time is 18.75 minutes.

4. The value of s_e was 18.75. If the assumptions of the simple linear regression model are satisfied, which of the following is correct?

   (A) The width of a 95% confidence interval for the slope of the population regression line is $2(18.75) = 37.50$.
   (B) It would be unlikely that a prediction based on the regression line will be greater than 18.75 minutes.
   (C) It would be unlikely that a prediction based on the regression line will differ from the actual value by more than $2(18.75) = 37.50$ minutes.
   (D) Errors associated with predictions based on the regression line will always be less than 18.75 minutes.
   (E) The value of s_e does not provide any information about the anticipated magnitude of prediction errors.

5. Which of the following is a 95% confidence interval for the change in service time associated with a 1-unit increase in the number of components needing repair?

   (A) $37.21 \pm (1.96)(7.985)$
   (B) $37.21 \pm (2.10)(7.985)$
   (C) $9.97 \pm (1.96)(0.7218)$
   (D) $9.97 \pm (2.10)(0.7218)$
   (E) $9.97 \pm 2(18.7534)$

6. If the basic assumptions of the simple linear regression model are reasonable, what conclusion should be reached regarding model utility if a significance level of .05 is used for the model utility test?

   (A) There is convincing evidence of a negative linear relationship between service call time and number of components needing repair.
   (B) There is convincing evidence that the model is not useful for predicting service call time.
   (C) There is convincing evidence that the model is useful for predicting service call time.
   (D) There is not convincing evidence that the model is useful for predicting service call time.
   (E) A conclusion cannot be reached based on the given information.

7. If there is a positive linear relationship between two variables x and y, which of the following must be true of β, the slope of the population regression line?

   (A) $\beta < 0$
   (B) $\beta > 0$
   (C) $\beta = 0$
   (D) $\beta > 1$
   (E) $-1 < \beta < 1$

8. The plots shown are residual plots resulting from fitting a linear regression. Which of these plots indicates that the relationship between the two variables used to fit the line may not be linear?

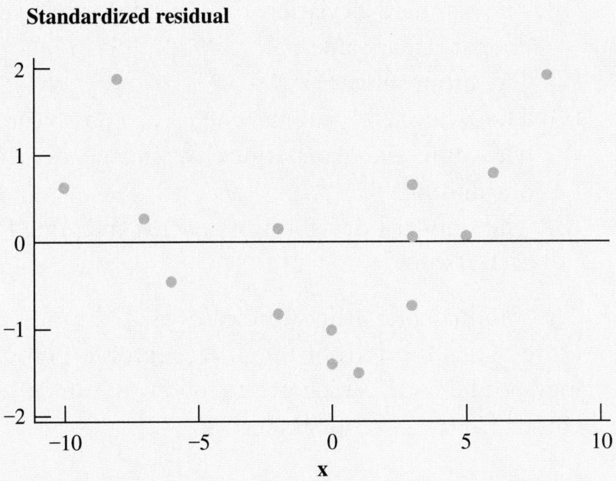

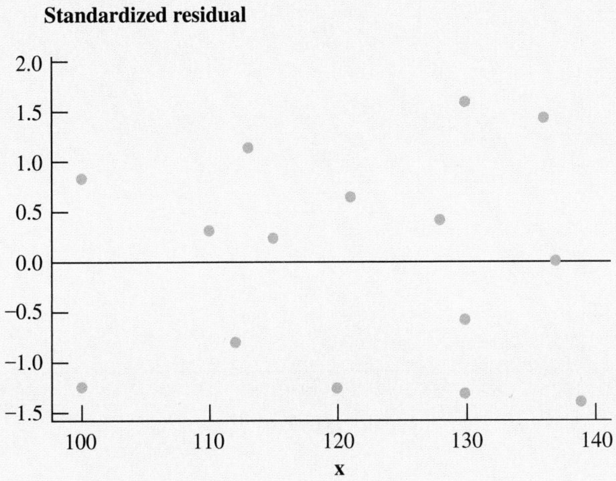

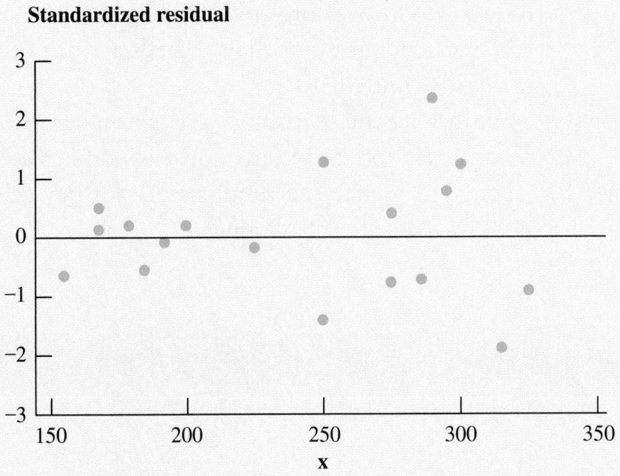

(A) I only
(B) II only
(C) III only
(D) I and III only
(E) II and III only

Use the scatterplot below to answer questions 9 and 10.

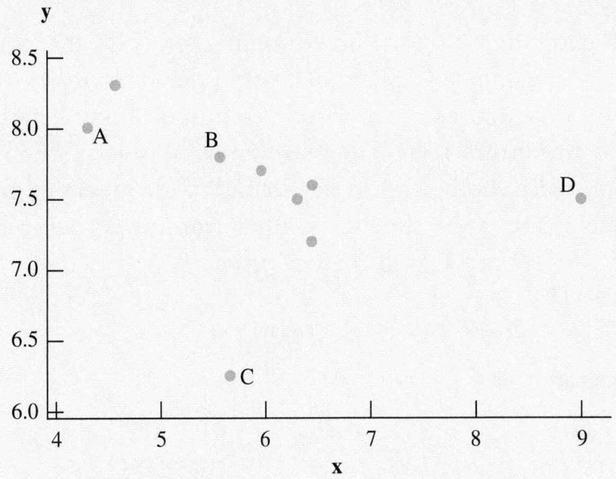

9. Which of the labeled points would have the largest residual when a linear model is fit to the data?

(A) A
(B) B
(C) C
(D) D
(E) Both C and D

10. Which of the labeled points corresponds to a potentially influential observation if a linear model is to be fit to the data?

(A) A
(B) B
(C) C
(D) D
(E) Both C and D

11. If there is evidence of a linear relationship between x and y, what decision will be made in a test of H_0: $\beta = 0$ versus H_0: $\beta \neq 0$?

(A) Reject H_0 and conclude that there is no evidence that the linear model is useful
(B) Reject H_0 and conclude that there is evidence that the linear model is useful
(C) Fail to reject H_0 and conclude that there is no evidence that the linear model is useful
(D) Fail to reject H_0 and conclude that there is evidence that the linear model is useful
(E) Not enough information to say.

Use the following information to answer questions 12 and 13.

As part of a study of the swimming speed of sharks, a random sample of 18 lemon sharks (*Triakis semifasciata*) were observed in a laboratory sea tunnel. Body lengths and maximum sustainable swimming speeds ("MSSS," reported in body lengths per second) were measured for each shark. The computer output from a regression of MSSS on body length is given below.

Linear Fit

MSSS = 1.8928955 - 0.0104278*Length

Summary of Fit

RSquare	0.526395
RSquare Adj	0.496794
S	0.272031
Mean of Response	1.24
N Observations	18

Analysis of Variance

Source	DF	Sum of Squares	Mean Square	F Ratio
Model	1	1.3159870	1.31599	17.7834
Error	16	1.1840130	0.07400	**Prob > F**
Total	17	2.5000000		0.0007*

Parameter Estimates

Term	Estimate	Std Error	t Ratio	Prob>|t|
Intercept	1.8928955	0.167575	11.30	<.0001*
Length(cm)	-0.010428	0.002473	-4.22	0.0007*

12. For this data set, the model utility test is based on how many degrees of freedom?

(A) 15
(B) 16
(C) 17
(D) 18
(E) 19

13. What is the *P*-value associated with the model utility test?

(A) 0.0001
(B) 0.0007
(C) 0.07400
(D) 0.167575
(E) 0.526395

14. Which of the following is *not* an assumption that is made about the random deviation of e in a simple linear regression model?

(A) The distribution of e is normal.
(B) The standard deviation of e, σ_e, depends upon the particular value of x.
(C) The mean value of e is 0.
(D) The random deviations, $e_1, e_2, \ldots, e_n$, associated with different observations are independent of one another.
(E) The standard deviation of e, σ_e, is the same for each x value.

15. The residual plot below indicates that the one or more of assumptions of the linear regression model may not be met. Which of the following can be included from this residual plot?

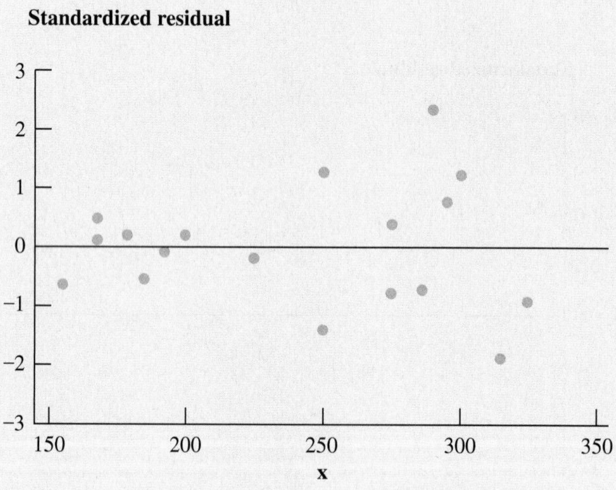

(A) The residual plot clearly indicates a non-linear model would be more appropriate.
(B) There is evidence that the residuals are not normally distributed.
(C) The slope of the regression line is non-zero.
(D) The correlation between x and y is non-zero.
(E) There is evidence the residuals do not have the same variance for all x values.

CHAPTER 14

© David Zimmerman/Getty Images

Multiple Regression Analysis

The general objective of regression analysis is to model the relationship between a dependent variable y and one or more independent (i.e., predictor or explanatory) variables. The simple linear regression model $y = \alpha + \beta x + e$, discussed in Chapter 13, has been used successfully by many investigators in a wide variety of disciplines to relate y to a single predictor variable x. In many situations, the relationship between y and any single predictor variable is not strong, but knowing the values of several independent variables may considerably reduce uncertainty about the associated y value. For example, some variation in house prices in a large city can certainly be attributed to house size, but knowledge of size by itself would not usually enable a bank appraiser to accurately predict a home's value. Price is also determined to some extent by other variables, such as age, lot size, number of bedrooms and bathrooms, and distance from schools.

In this chapter, we extend the regression methodology developed in the previous chapter to *multiple regression models*, which include at least two predictor variables.

Make the most of your study time by accessing everything you need to succeed online with CourseMate.
Visit http://www.cengagebrain.com where you will find:

- An interactive eBook, which allows you to take notes, highlight, bookmark, search the text, and use in-context glossary definitions
- Step-by-step instructions for Minitab, Excel, TI-83/84, SPSS, and JMP
- Video solutions to selected exercises
- Data sets available for selected examples and exercises
- Online quizzes
- Flashcards
- Videos

Fortunately, many of the concepts developed in the context of simple linear regression carry over to multiple regression with little or no modification. The calculations required to fit a multiple regression model and make further inferences are *much* more tedious than those for simple linear regression, so a computer is an indispensable tool. Computer use has led to the development of new methods for analyzing large data sets with many predictor variables. These include techniques for fitting numerous alternative models and choosing between them, tools for identifying influential observations, and both algebraic and graphical diagnostics designed to reveal potential violations of model assumptions. A single chapter can do little more than scratch the surface of this important subject area.

14.1 Multiple Regression Models

The relationship between a dependent or response variable y and two or more independent or predictor variables is deterministic if the value of y is completely determined, with no uncertainty, once values of the independent variables have been specified. Consider, for example, a school district in which teachers with no prior teaching experience and no college credits beyond a bachelor's degree start at an annual salary of \$38,000. Suppose that for each year of teaching experience up to 20 years, a teacher receives an additional \$800 per year and that each unit of postcollege coursework up to 75 units results in an extra \$60 per year. Consider the following three variables:

y = salary of a teacher who has at most 20 years of teaching experience and at most 75 postcollege units
x_1 = number of years of teaching experience
x_2 = number of postcollege units

Previously, x_1 and x_2 denoted the first two observations on the single variable x. In the usual notation for multiple regression, however, x_1 and x_2 represent two different variables.

For these variables, the value of y is entirely determined by values of x_1 and x_2 through the equation

$$y = 38{,}000 + 800x_1 + 60x_2$$

If $x_1 = 10$ and $x_2 = 30$ then

$$\begin{aligned} y &= 38{,}000 + 800(10) + 60(30) \\ &= 38{,}000 + 8000 + 1800 \\ &= 47{,}800 \end{aligned}$$

If two different teachers both have the same x_1 values and the same x_2 values, they will also have identical y values.

Only rarely is y deterministically related to predictors $x_1, \ldots, x_k$; a probabilistic model is more realistic in most situations. A probabilistic model results from adding a random deviation e to a deterministic function of the x_i's.

DEFINITION

A **general additive multiple regression model**, which relates a dependent variable y to k predictor variables $x_1, x_2, \ldots, x_k$, is given by the model equation

$$y = \alpha + \beta_1 x_1 + \beta_2 x_2 + \cdots + \beta_k x_k + e$$

(continued)

The random deviation e is assumed to be normally distributed with mean value 0 and standard deviation σ for any particular values of $x_1, \ldots x_k$. This implies that for fixed $x_1, x_2, \ldots, x_k$ values, y has a normal distribution with standard deviation σ and

$$\begin{pmatrix} \text{mean } y \text{ value for fixed} \\ x_1, \ldots, x_k \text{ values} \end{pmatrix} = \alpha + \beta_1 x_1 + \beta_2 x_2 + \cdots + \beta_k x_k$$

The β_i's are called **population regression coefficients**. Each β_i can be interpreted as the mean change in y when the predictor x_i increases by 1 unit *and* the values of all the other predictors remain fixed.

$\alpha + \beta_1 x_1 + \beta_2 x_2 + \cdots + \beta_k x_k$ is called the **population regression function.**

As in simple linear regression, if σ (the standard deviation of the random error distribution) is quite close to 0, any particular observed y will tend to be quite near its mean value. When σ is large, y observations may deviate substantially from their mean y values.

EXAMPLE 14.1 Sophomore Success

What factors contribute to the academic success of college sophomores? Data collected in a survey of approximately 1000 second-year college students suggest that GPA at the end of the second year is related to the student's level of interaction with faculty and staff and to the student's commitment to his or her major ("An Exploration of the Factors that Affect the Academic Success of College Sophomores," *College Student Journal* [2005] 367–376). Consider the variables

y = GPA at the end of the sophomore year
x_1 = level of faculty and staff interaction (measured on a scale from 1 to 5)
x_2 = level of commitment to major (measured on a scale from 1 to 5)

One possible population model might be

$$y = 1.4 + .33x_1 + .16x_2 + e$$

with

$$\sigma = 0.15$$

The population regression function is

$$(\text{mean } y \text{ value for fixed } x_1, x_2) = 1.4 + .33x_1 + .16x_2$$

For sophomore students whose level of interaction with faculty and staff is rated at 4.2 and whose level of commitment to their major is rated as 2.1,

$$(\text{mean value of GPA}) = 1.4 + .33(4.2) + .16(2.1) = 3.12$$

With $2\sigma = 2(.15) = .30$, it is likely that an actual y value will be within .30 of the mean value (that is, in the interval from 2.82 to 3.42 when $x_1 = 4.2$ and $x_2 = 2.1$).

A Special Case: Polynomial Regression

Consider again the case of a single independent variable x, and suppose that a scatterplot of the n sample (x, y) pairs has the appearance of Figure 14.1. The simple linear regression model is clearly not appropriate, but it does look as though a parabola (quadratic function) with equation $y = \alpha + \beta_1 x + \beta_2 x^2$ would provide a very good fit to the data for appropriately chosen values of α, β_1, and β_2. Just as the inclusion of the random deviation e in simple linear regression allowed an observation to deviate from the population regression line by a random amount, adding e to this quadratic function yields a probabilistic model in which an observation is allowed to fall above or below the parabola. The quadratic regression model equation is

$$y = \alpha + \beta_1 x + \beta_2 x^2 + e$$

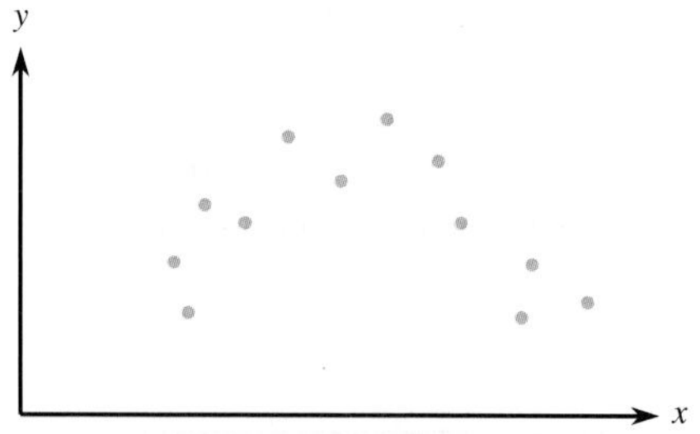

FIGURE 14.1
A scatterplot that suggests the appropriateness of a quadratic probabilistic model.

Let's rewrite the model equation by using x_1 to denote x and x_2 to denote x^2. The model equation then becomes

$$y = \alpha + \beta_1 x_1 + \beta_2 x_2 + e$$

This is a special case of the general multiple regression model with $k = 2$. You may wonder about the legitimacy of allowing one predictor variable to be a mathematical function of another predictor—here, $x_2 = (x_1)^2$. However, there is nothing in the general multiple regression model that prevents this. *In the model* $y = \alpha + \beta_1 x_1 + \beta_2 x_2 + \cdots + \beta_k x_k + e$ *it is permissible to have predictors that are mathematical functions of other predictors.* For example, starting with the two independent variables x_1 and x_2, we could create a model with $k = 4$ predictors in which x_1 and x_2 themselves are the first two predictor variables and $x_3 = (x_1)^2$, $x_4 = x_1 x_2$. (We will soon discuss the consequences of using a predictor such as x_4.) In particular, the general polynomial regression model begins with a single independent variable x and creates predictors $x_1 = x$, $x_2 = x^2$, $x_3 = x^3, \ldots, x_k = x^k$ for some specified value of k.

DEFINITION

The **kth-degree polynomial regression model**

$$y = \alpha + \beta_1 x + \beta_2 x^2 + \cdots + \beta_k x^k + e$$

is a special case of the general multiple regression model with

$$x_1 = x \quad x_2 = x^2 \quad x_3 = x^3 \quad \ldots \quad x_k = x^k$$

The **population regression function** (mean value of y for fixed values of the predictors) is

$$\alpha + \beta_1 x + \beta_2 x^2 + \cdots + \beta_k x^k$$

(continued)

The most important special case other than simple linear regression ($k = 1$) is the **quadratic regression model**

$$y = \alpha + \beta_1 x + \beta_2 x^2 + e$$

This model replaces the line of mean values $\alpha + \beta x$ in simple linear regression with a parabolic curve of mean values $\alpha + \beta_1 x + \beta_2 x^2$. If $\beta_2 > 0$, the curve opens upward, whereas if $\beta_2 < 0$, the curve opens downward. A less frequently encountered special case is that of cubic regression, in which $k = 3$. (See Figure 14.2.)

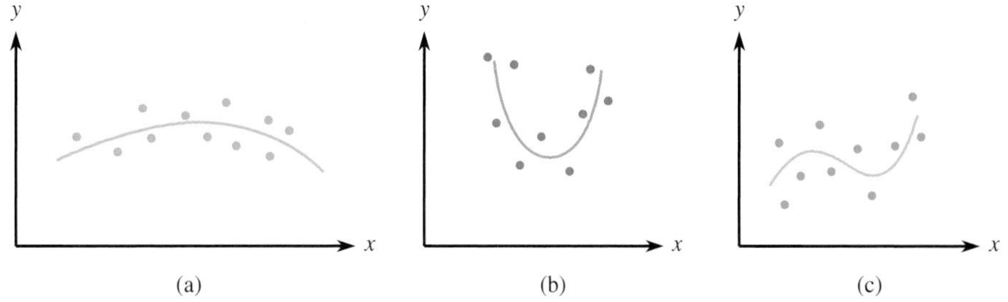

FIGURE 14.2
Polynomial regression: (a) quadratic regression model with $\beta_2 < 0$; (b) quadratic regression model with $\beta_2 > 0$; (c) cubic regression model with $\beta_3 > 0$.

EXAMPLE 14.2 Increased Risk of Heart Attack

Many researchers have examined factors that are believed to contribute to the risk of heart attack. The authors of the paper "Obesity and the Risk of Myocardial Infarction in 27,000 Participants from 53 Countries: A Case-Control Study" (*The Lancet* [2005]: 1640–1649) found that hip-to-waist ratio was a better predictor of heart attacks than body-mass index. A plot that appeared in the paper of a measure of heart-attack risk (y) versus hip-to-waist ratio (x) exhibited a curved relationship. Larger values of y indicate a higher risk of heart attack. A model consistent with summary values given in the paper is

$$y = 1.023 + 0.024x + 0.060x^2 + e$$

Then the population regression function is

$$\begin{pmatrix}\text{mean value of}\\ \text{heart-attack risk measure}\end{pmatrix} = 1.023 + 0.024x + 0.060x^2$$

For example, if $x = 1.3$

$$\begin{pmatrix}\text{mean value of}\\ \text{heart-attack risk measure}\end{pmatrix} = 1.023 + 0.024(1.3) + 0.060(1.3)^2 = 1.16$$

If $\sigma = .25$, then it is quite likely that the heart-attack-risk measure for a person with a hip-to-waist ratio of 1.3 would be between .66 and 1.66.

The interpretation of β_i previously given for the general multiple regression model cannot be applied in polynomial regression. This is because all predictors are functions of the single variable x, so $x_i = x^i$ cannot be increased by 1 unit without changing the values of all the other predictor variables as well. *In general, the interpretation of regression coefficients requires extra care when some predictor variables are mathematical functions of other variables.*

Interaction Between Variables

Suppose that an industrial chemist is interested in the relationship between product yield (y) from a certain chemical reaction and two independent variables, x_1 = reaction temperature and x_2 = pressure at which the reaction is carried out. The chemist initially suggests that for temperature values between 80 and 110 in combination with pressure values ranging from 50 to 70, the relationship can be well described by the probabilistic model

$$y = 1200 + 15x_1 - 35x_2 + e$$

The regression function, which gives the mean y value for any specified values of x_1 and x_2 is then $1200 + 15x_1 - 35x_2$. Consider this mean y value for three different particular temperature values:

$$x_1 = 90: \quad \text{mean } y \text{ value} = 1200 + 15(90) - 35x_2 = 2550 - 35x_2$$
$$x_1 = 95: \quad \text{mean } y \text{ value} = 2625 - 35x_2$$
$$x_1 = 100: \quad \text{mean } y \text{ value} = 2700 - 35x_2$$

Graphs of these three mean value functions (each a function only of pressure x_2, because the temperature value has been specified) are shown in Figure 14.3(a). Each graph is a straight line, and the three lines are parallel, each one having slope -35. Because of this, the average change in yield when pressure x_2 is increased by 1 unit is -35, regardless of the fixed temperature value.

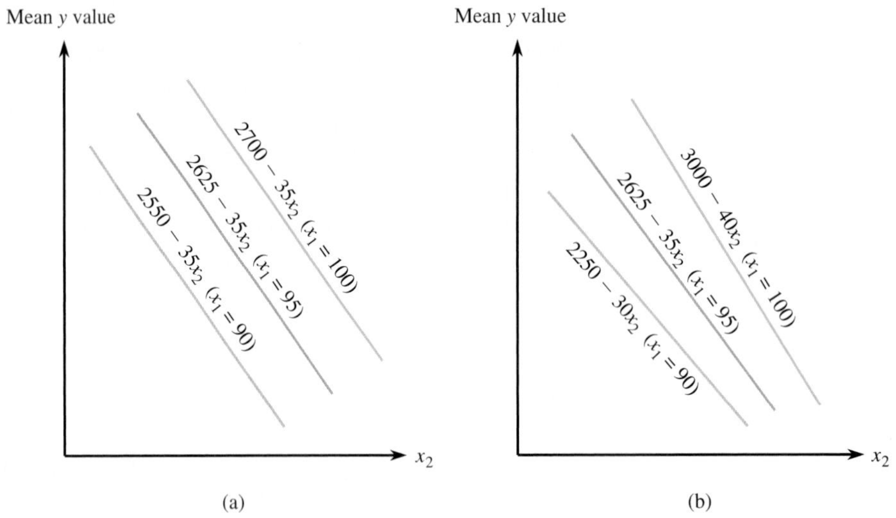

FIGURE 14.3 Graphs of mean y value for two different models: (a) $1200 + 15x_1 - 35x_2$; (b) $-4500 + 75x_1 + 60x_2 - x_1x_2$.

Because chemical theory suggests that the decline in average yield when pressure x_2 increases should be more rapid for a high temperature than for a low temperature, the chemist now has reason to doubt the appropriateness of the proposed model. Rather than the lines being parallel, the line for a temperature of 100 should be steeper than the line for a temperature of 95, and that line in turn should be steeper than the one for $x_1 = 90$. A model that has this property includes, in addition to predictors x_1 and x_2 separately, a third predictor variable $x_3 = x_1x_2$. One such model is

$$y = -4500 + 75x_1 + 60x_2 - x_1x_2 + e$$

which has regression function $-4500 + 75x_1 + 60x_2 - x_1x_2$. Then

$$(\text{mean } y \text{ when } x_1 = 100) = -4500 + 75(100) + 60x_2 - 100x_2$$
$$= 3000 - 40x_2$$

whereas

$$(\text{mean } y \text{ when } x_1 = 95) = 2625 - 35x_2$$
$$(\text{mean } y \text{ when } x_1 = 90) = 2250 - 30x_2$$

These functions are graphed in Figure 14.3(b), where it is clear that the three slopes are different. In fact, each different value of x_1 yields a different slope, so the average change in yield associated with a 1-unit increase in x_2 depends on the value of x_1. When this is the case, the two variables are said to *interact.*

DEFINITION

If the change in the mean y value associated with a 1-unit increase in one independent variable depends on the value of a second independent variable, there is **interaction** between these two variables. When the variables are denoted by x_1 and x_2, such interaction can be modeled by including x_1x_2, the product of the variables that interact, as a predictor variable.

The general equation for a multiple regression model based on two independent variables x_1 and x_2 that also includes an interaction predictor is

$$y = \alpha + \beta_1x_1 + \beta_2x_2 + \beta_3x_1x_2 + e$$

When x_1 and x_2 do interact, this model usually gives a much better fit to the resulting sample data—and thus explains more variation in y—than does the no interaction model. Failure to consider a model with interaction often leads an investigator to conclude incorrectly that there is no strong relationship between y and a set of independent variables.

More than one interaction predictor can be included in the model when more than two independent variables are available. If, for example, there are three independent variables x_1, x_2, and x_3, one possible model is

$$y = \alpha + \beta_1x_1 + \beta_2x_2 + \beta_3x_3 + \beta_4x_4 + \beta_5x_5 + \beta_6x_6 + e$$

where

$$x_4 = x_1x_2 \qquad x_5 = x_1x_3 \qquad x_6 = x_2x_3$$

One could even include a three-way interaction predictor $x_7 = x_1x_2x_3$ (the product of all three independent variables), although in practice this is rarely done.

In applied work, quadratic terms, such as x_1^2 and x_2^2 are often included to model a curved relationship between y and several independent variables. For example, a frequently used model involving just two independent variables x_1 and x_2 but $k = 5$ predictors is the *full quadratic* or **complete second-order model**

$$y = \alpha + \beta_1x_1 + \beta_2x_2 + \beta_3x_1x_2 + \beta_4x_1^2 + \beta_5x_2^2 + e$$

This model replaces the straight lines of Figure 14.3 with parabolas (each one is the graph of the regression function for different values of x_2 when x_1 has a fixed value). With four independent variables, one could examine a model containing four quadratic predictors and six two-way interaction predictor variables. Clearly, with just a few independent variables, one could examine a great many different multiple regression models. In Section 14.5 (online), we briefly discuss methods for selecting one model from a number of competing models.

When developing a multiple regression model, scatterplots of y with each potential predictor can be informative. This is illustrated in Example 14.3, which describes a model that includes a term that is a function of one of the predictor variables and also an interaction term.

EXAMPLE 14.3 Wind Chill Factor

● The wind chill index, often included in winter weather reports, combines information on air temperature and wind speed to describe how cold it really feels. In 2001, the National Weather Service announced that it would begin using a new wind chill formula beginning in the fall of that year (*USA Today*, August 13, 2001). The following table gives the wind chill index for various combinations of air temperature and wind speed.

	TEMPERATURE (°F)														
Wind (mph)	35	30	25	20	15	10	5	0	−5	−10	−15	−20	−25	−30	−35
5	31	25	19	13	7	1	−5	−11	−16	−22	−28	−34	−40	−46	−52
10	27	21	15	9	3	−4	−10	−16	−22	−28	−35	−41	−47	−53	−59
15	25	19	13	6	0	−7	−13	−19	−26	−32	−39	−45	−51	−58	−64
20	24	17	11	4	−2	−9	−15	−22	−29	−35	−42	−48	−55	−61	−68
25	23	16	9	3	−4	−11	−17	−24	−31	−37	−44	−51	−58	−64	−71
30	22	15	8	1	−5	−12	−19	−26	−33	−39	−46	−53	−60	−67	−73
35	21	14	7	0	−7	−14	−21	−27	−34	−41	−48	−55	−62	−69	−76
40	20	13	6	−1	−8	−15	−22	−29	−36	−43	−50	−57	−64	−71	−78
45	19	12	5	−2	−9	−16	−23	−30	−37	−44	−51	−58	−65	−72	−79

Figure 14.4(a) shows a scatterplot of wind chill index versus air temperature with different wind speeds denoted by different colors in the plot. It appears that the wind chill index increases linearly with air temperature at each of the wind speeds, but the linear patterns for the different wind speeds are not quite parallel. This suggests that to model the relationship between y = wind chill index and the two variables x_1 = air temperature and x_2 = wind speed, we should include both x_1 and an interaction term that involves x_2. Figure 14.4(b) shows a scatterplot of wind chill index versus wind speed with different temperatures denoted by different colors. This plot reveals that the relationship between wind chill index and wind speed is nonlinear at each of the different temperatures, and because the pattern is more markedly curved at some temperatures than at others, an interaction is suggested.

These observations are consistent with the new model used by the National Weather Service for relating wind chill index to air temperature and wind speed. The model used is

$$\text{mean } y = 35.74 + 0.621x_1 - 35.75(x_2') + 0.4275x_1x_2'$$

where

$$x_2' = x_2^{0.16}$$

which incorporates a transformed x_2 (to model the nonlinear relationship between wind chill index and wind speed) and an interaction term.

● Data set available online

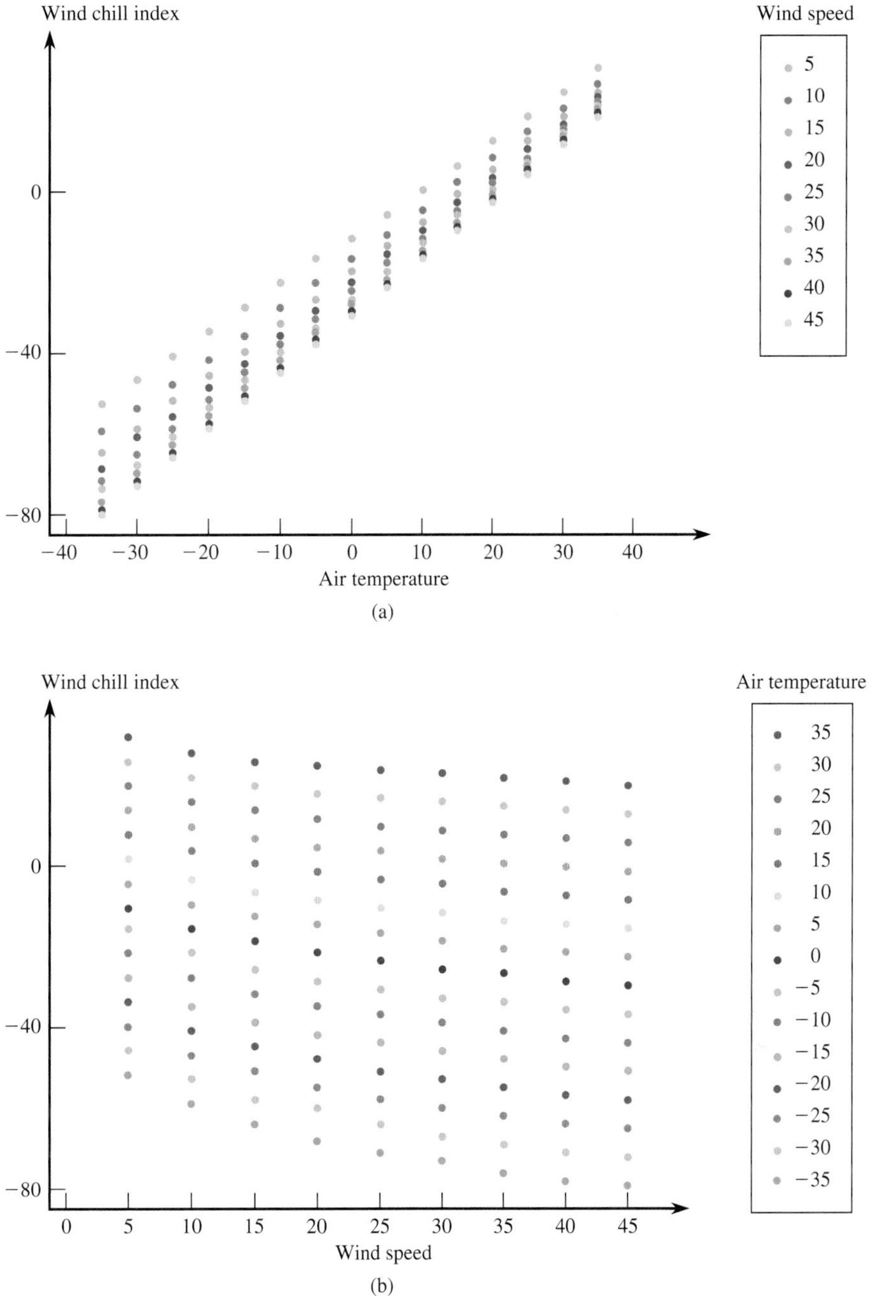

FIGURE 14.4
Scatterplots of wind chill index data of Example 14.3: (a) wind chill index versus air temperature; (b) wind chill index versus wind speed.

Qualitative Predictor Variables

Up to this point, we have explicitly considered the inclusion only of quantitative (numerical) predictor variables in a multiple regression model. Using simple numerical coding, qualitative (categorical) variables can also be incorporated into a model. Let's focus first on a dichotomous variable, one with just two possible categories: male or female, U.S. or foreign manufacture, a house with or without a view, and so on. With any such variable, we associate a numerical variable x whose possible values are

0 and 1, where 0 is identified with one category (for example, married) and 1 is identified with the other possible category (for example, not married). This 0-1 variable is often called **an indicator variable** or **dummy variable**.

EXAMPLE 14.4 Predictors of Writing Competence

The article "Grade Level and Gender Differences in Writing Self-Beliefs of Middle School Students" (*Contemporary Educational Psychology* [1999]: 390–405) considered relating writing competence score to a number of predictor variables, including perceived value of writing and gender. Both writing competence and perceived value of writing were represented by a numerically scaled variable, but gender was a qualitative predictor.

Consider the following variables:

$$y = \text{writing competence score}$$
$$x_1 = \begin{cases} 0 & \text{if male} \\ 1 & \text{if female} \end{cases}$$
$$x_2 = \text{perceived value of writing}$$

One possible multiple regression model is

$$y = \alpha + \beta_1 x_1 + \beta_2 x_2 + e$$

Considering the mean y value first when $x_1 = 0$ and then when $x_1 = 1$ yields

$$\text{average score} = \alpha + \beta_2 x_2 \quad \text{when } x_1 = 0 \text{ (males)}$$
$$\text{average score} = \alpha + \beta_1 + \beta x_2 \quad \text{when } x_1 = 1 \text{ (females)}$$

The coefficient β_1 is the difference in average writing competence score between males and females when perceived value of writing is held fixed.

A second possibility is a model with an interaction term:

$$y = \alpha + \beta_1 x_1 + \beta_2 x_2 + \beta_3 x_1 x_2 + e$$

The regression function for this model is $\alpha + \beta_1 x_1 + \beta_2 x_2 + \beta_3 x_3$ where $x_3 = x_1 x_2$. Now the two cases $x_1 = 0$ and $x_1 = 1$ give

$$\text{average score} = \alpha + \beta_2 x_2 \quad \text{when } x_1 = 0 \text{ (males)}$$
$$\text{average score} = \alpha + \beta_1 + (\beta_2 + \beta_3) \quad \text{when } x_1 = 1 \text{ (females)}$$

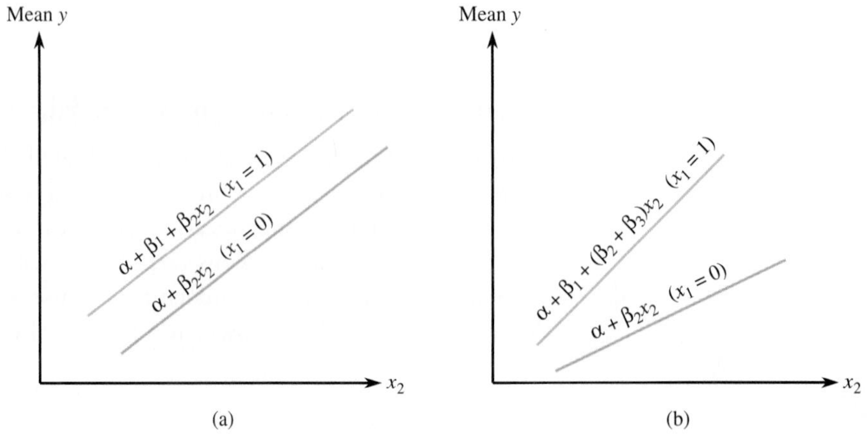

FIGURE 14.5
Regression functions for models with one qualitative variable (x_1) and one quantitative variable (x_2): (a) no interaction; (b) interaction.

For each model, the graph of the average writing competence score, when regarded as a function of perceived value of writing, is a line for either gender (Figure 14.5).

In the no-interaction model, the coefficient of x_2 is β_2 both when $x_1 = 0$ and when $x_1 = 1$, so the two lines are parallel, although their intercepts are different (unless $\beta_1 = 0$). With interaction, the lines not only have different intercepts but also have different slopes (unless $\beta_3 = 0$). For this model, the change in average writing competence score when perceived value of writing increases by 1 unit depends on gender—the two variables *perceived value* and *gender* interact.

You might think that the way to handle a three-category situation is to define a single numerical variable with coded values such as 0, 1, and 2 corresponding to the three categories. This is incorrect because it imposes an ordering on the categories that is not necessarily implied by the problem. The correct approach to modeling a categorical variable with three categories is to define *two* different indicator variables, as illustrated in Example 14.5.

EXAMPLE 14.5 Location, Location, Location

One of the factors that has an effect on the price of a house is location. We might want to incorporate location, as well as numerical predictors such as size and age, into a multiple regression model for predicting house price. Suppose that in a California beach community houses can be classified by location into three categories—ocean-view and beachfront, ocean-view but not beachfront, and no ocean view. Let

$$x_1 = \begin{cases} 1 & \text{if the house is ocean-view and beachfront} \\ 0 & \text{otherwise} \end{cases}$$

$$x_2 = \begin{cases} 1 & \text{if the house has an ocean-view but is not beachfront} \\ 0 & \text{otherwise} \end{cases}$$

$$x_3 = \text{house size}$$

$$x_4 = \text{house age}$$

Thus, $x_1 = 1, x_2 = 0$ indicates a beachfront ocean-view house; $x_1 = 0, x_2 = 1$ indicates a house with an ocean view but not beachfront; and $x_1 = x_2 = 0$ indicates a house that does not have an ocean view. ($x_1 = x_2 = 1$ is not possible.) We could then consider a multiple regression model of the form

$$y = \alpha + \beta_1 x_1 + \beta_2 x_2 + \beta_3 x_3 + \beta_4 x_4 + e$$

This model allows individual adjustments to the predicted price for a house with no ocean view for the other two location categories. For example, β_1 is the amount that would be added to the predicted price for a home with no ocean view to adjust for an oceanfront location (assuming that age and size were the same).

In general, incorporating a categorical variable with c possible categories into a regression model requires the use of $c - 1$ indicator variables. Even one such categorical variable can add many predictors to a model.

EXERCISES 14.1 - 14.15

14.1 Explain the difference between a deterministic and a probabilistic model. Give an example of a dependent variable y and two or more independent variables that might be related to y deterministically. Give an example of a dependent variable y and two or more independent variables that might be related to y in a probabilistic fashion.

14.2 The authors of the paper "Weight-Bearing Activity during Youth Is a More Important Factor for Peak Bone Mass than Calcium Intake" (*Journal of Bone and Mineral Density* [1994]: 1089–1096) used a multiple regression model to describe the relationship between

y = bone mineral density (g/cm^3)
x_1 = body weight (kg)
x_2 = a measure of weight-bearing activity, with higher values indicating greater activity

a. The authors concluded that both body weight and weight-bearing activity were important predictors of bone mineral density and that there was no significant interaction between body weight and weight-bearing activity. What multiple regression function is consistent with this description?
b. The value of the coefficient of body weight in the multiple regression function given in the paper is 0.587. Interpret this value.

14.3 A number of investigations have focused on the problem of assessing loads that can be manually handled in a safe manner. The article "Anthropometric, Muscle Strength, and Spinal Mobility Characteristics as Predictors in the Rating of Acceptable Loads in Parcel Sorting" (*Ergonomics* [1992]: 1033–1044) proposed using a regression model to relate the dependent variable

y = individual's rating of acceptable load (kg)

to $k = 3$ independent (predictor) variables:

x_1 = extent of left lateral bending (cm)
x_2 = dynamic hand grip endurance (seconds)
x_3 = trunk extension ratio (N/kg)

Suppose that the model equation is

$$y = 30 + .90x_1 + .08x_2 - 4.50x_3 + e$$

and that $\sigma = 5$.

a. What is the population regression function?
b. What are the values of the population regression coefficients?
c. Interpret the value of β_1.
d. Interpret the value of β_3.
e. What is the mean rating of acceptable load when extent of left lateral bending is 25 cm, dynamic hand grip endurance is 200 seconds, and trunk extension ratio is 10 N/kg?
f. If repeated observations on rating are made on different individuals, all of whom have the values of x_1, x_2, and x_3 specified in Part (e), in the long run approximately what percentage of ratings will be between 13.5 kg and 33.5 kg?

14.4 The following statement appeared in the article "Dimensions of Adjustment Among College Women" (*Journal of College Student Development* [1998]: 364):

> Regression analyses indicated that academic adjustment and race made independent contributions to academic achievement, as measured by current GPA.

Suppose

y = current GPA
x_1 = academic adjustment score
x_2 = race (with white = 0, other = 1)

What multiple regression model is suggested by the statement? Did you include an interaction term in the model? Why or why not?

14.5 The authors of the paper "Predicting Yolk Height, Yolk Width, Albumen Length, Eggshell Weight, Egg Shape Index, Eggshell Thickness, Egg Surface Area of Japanese Quails Using Various Egg Traits as Regressors" (*International Journal of Poultry Science* [2008]: 85–88) used a multiple regression model with two independent variables where

y = quail egg weight (g)
x_1 = egg width (mm)
x_2 = egg length (mm)

The regression function suggested in the paper is $-21.658 + 0.828x_1 + 0.373x_2$.

a. What is the mean egg weight for quail eggs that have a width of 20 mm and a length of 50 mm?
b. Interpret the values of β_1 and β_2.

14.6 According to "Assessing the Validity of the Post-Materialism Index" (*American Political Science*

Review [1999]: 649–664), one may be able to predict an individual's level of support for ecology based on demographic and ideological characteristics. The multiple regression model proposed by the authors was

$$y = 3.60 - .01x_1 + .01x_2 - .07x_3 + .12x_4 + .02x_5 - .04x_6 - .01x_7 - .04x_8 - .02x_9 + e$$

where the variables are defined as follows:

y = ecology score (higher values indicate a greater concern for ecology)
x_1 = age times 10
x_2 = income (in thousands of dollars)
x_3 = gender (1 = male, 0 = female)
x_4 = race (1 = white, 0 = nonwhite)
x_5 = education (in years)
x_6 = ideology (4 = conservative, 3 = right of center, 2 = middle of the road, 1 = left of center, and 0 = liberal)
x_7 = social class (4 = upper, 3 = upper middle, 2 = middle, 1 = lower middle, and 0 = lower)
x_8 = postmaterialist (1 if postmaterialist, 0 otherwise)
x_9 = materialist (1 if materialist, 0 otherwise)

a. Suppose you knew a person with the following characteristics: a 25-year-old, white female with a college degree (16 years of education), who has a $32,000-per-year job, is from the upper middle class, and considers herself left of center, but who is neither a materialist nor a postmaterialist. Predict her ecology score.
b. If the woman described in Part (a) were Hispanic rather than white, how would the prediction change?
c. Given that the other variables are the same, what is the estimated mean difference in ecology score for men and women?
d. How would you interpret the coefficient of x_2?
e. Comment on the numerical coding of the ideology and social class variables. Can you suggest a better way of incorporating these two variables into the model?

14.7 ✦ The article "The Influence of Temperature and Sunshine on the Alpha-Acid Contents of Hops" (*Agricultural Meteorology* [1974]: 375–382) used a multiple regression model to relate y = yield of hops to x_1 = average temperature (°C) between date of coming into hop and date of picking and x_2 = average percentage of sunshine during the same period. The model equation proposed is

$$y = 415.11 - 6.60x_1 - 4.50x_2 + e$$

a. Suppose that this equation does indeed describe the true relationship. What mean yield corresponds to an average temperature of 20 and an average sunshine percentage of 40?
b. What is the mean yield when the average temperature and average percentage of sunshine are 18.9 and 43, respectively?
c. Interpret the values of the population regression coefficients.

14.8 The article "Readability of Liquid Crystal Displays: A Response Surface" (*Human Factors* [1983]: 185–190) used a multiple regression model with four independent variables, where

y = error percentage for subjects reading a four-digit liquid crystal display
x_1 = level of backlight (from 0 to 122 cd/m)
x_2 = character subtense (from .025° to 1.34°)
x_3 = viewing angle (from 0° to 60°)
x_4 = level of ambient light (from 20 to 1500 lx)

The model equation suggested in the article is

$$y = 1.52 + .02x_1 - 1.40x_2 + .02x_3 - .0006x_4 + e$$

a. Assume that this is the correct equation. What is the mean value of y when $x_1 = 10$, $x_2 = .5$, $x_3 = 50$, and $x_4 = 100$?
b. What mean error percentage is associated with a backlight level of 20, character subtense of .5, viewing angle of 10, and ambient light level of 30?
c. Interpret the values of β_2 and β_3.

14.9 The article "Pulp Brightness Reversion: Influence of Residual Lignin on the Brightness Reversion of Bleached Sulfite and Kraft Pulps" (*TAPPI* [1964]: 653–662) proposed a quadratic regression model to describe the relationship between x = degree of delignification during the processing of wood pulp for paper and y = total chlorine content. Suppose that the population regression model is

$$y = 220 + 75x - 4x^2 + e$$

a. Graph the regression function $220 + 75x - 4x^2$ over x values between 2 and 12. (Substitute x = 2, 4, 6, 8, 10, and 12 to find points on the graph, and connect them with a smooth curve.)
b. Would mean chlorine content be higher for a degree of delignification value of 8 or 10?
c. What is the change in mean chlorine content when the degree of delignification increases from 8 to 9? From 9 to 10?

14.10 The relationship between yield of maize, date of planting, and planting density was investigated in the article "Development of a Model for Use in Maize Replant Decisions" (*Agronomy Journal* [1980]: 459–464). Let

y = percent maize yield
x_1 = planting date (days after April 20)
x_2 = planting density (10,000 plants/ha)

The regression model with both quadratic terms ($y = \alpha + \beta_1 x_1 + \beta_2 x_2 + \beta_3 x_3 + \beta_4 x_4 + e$ where $x_3 = x_1^2$ and $x_4 = x_2^2$) provides a good description of the relationship between y and the independent variables.

a. If $\alpha = 21.09$, $\beta_1 = .653$, $\beta_2 = .0022$, $\beta_3 = 2.0206$, and $\beta_4 = 0.4$, what is the population regression function?
b. Use the regression function in Part (a) to determine the mean yield for a plot planted on May 6 with a density of 41,180 plants/ha.
c. Would the mean yield be higher for a planting date of May 6 or May 22 (for the same density)?
d. Is it legitimate to interpret $\beta_1 = .653$ as the average change in yield when planting date increases by one day and the values of the other three predictors are held fixed? Why or why not?

14.11 Suppose that the variables y, x_1, and x_2 are related by the regression model

$$y = 1.8 + .1x_1 + .8x_2 + e$$

a. Construct a graph (similar to that of Figure 14.5) showing the relationship between mean y and x_2 for fixed values 10, 20, and 30 of x_1.
b. Construct a graph depicting the relationship between mean y and x_1 for fixed values 50, 55, and 60 of x_2.
c. What aspect of the graphs in Parts (a) and (b) can be attributed to the lack of an interaction between x_1 and x_2?
d. Suppose the interaction term $.03x_3$ where $x_3 = x_1x_2$ is added to the regression model equation. Using this new model, construct the graphs described in Parts (a) and (b). How do they differ from those obtained in Parts (a) and (b)?

14.12 A manufacturer of wood stoves collected data on y = particulate matter concentration and x_1 = flue temperature for three different air intake settings (low, medium, and high).

a. Write a model equation that includes indicator variables to incorporate intake setting, and interpret each of the β coefficients.
b. What additional predictors would be needed to incorporate interaction between temperature and intake setting?

14.13 Consider a regression analysis with three independent variables x_1, x_2, and x_3. Give the equation for the following regression models:

a. The model that includes as predictors all independent variables but no quadratic or interaction terms;
b. The model that includes as predictors all independent variables and all quadratic terms;
c. All models that include as predictors all independent variables, no quadratic terms, and exactly one interaction term;
d. The model that includes as predictors all independent variables, all quadratic terms, and all interaction terms (the full quadratic model).

14.14 The article "The Value and the Limitations of High-Speed Turbo-Exhausters for the Removal of Tar-Fog from Carburetted Water-Gas" (*Society of Chemical Industry Journal* [1946]: 166–168) presented data on y = tar content (grains/100 ft^3) of a gas stream as a function of x_1 = rotor speed (rev/minute) and x_2 = gas inlet temperature (°F). A regression model using x_1, x_2, $x_3 = x_2^2$ and $x_4 = x_1x_2$ was suggested:

$$\text{mean } y \text{ value} = 86.8 - .123x_1 + 5.09x_2 - .0709x_3 + .001x_4$$

a. According to this model, what is the mean y value if $x_1 = 3200$ and $x_2 = 57$?
b. For this particular model, does it make sense to interpret the value of a β_2 as the average change in tar content associated with a 1-degree increase in gas inlet temperature when rotor speed is held constant? Explain.

14.15 ✦ Consider the dependent variable y = fuel efficiency of a car (mpg).

a. Suppose that you want to incorporate size class of car, with four categories (subcompact, compact, midsize, and large), into a regression model that also includes x_1 = age of car and x_2 = engine size. Define the necessary indicator variables, and write out the complete model equation.
b. Suppose that you want to incorporate interaction between age and size class. What additional predictors would be needed to accomplish this?

14.2 Fitting a Model and Assessing Its Utility

In Section 14.1, we introduced multiple regression models containing several different types of predictors. Let's now suppose that a particular set of k predictor variables $x_1, x_2, \ldots, x_k$ has been selected for inclusion in the model

$$y = \alpha + \beta_1 x_1 + \beta_2 x_2 + \cdots + \beta_k x_k + e$$

The next steps are to estimate the model coefficients $\alpha, \beta_1, \ldots, \beta_k$ and the regression function $\alpha + \beta_1 x_1 + \cdots + \beta_k x_k$ (the mean y value for specified values of the predictors), assess the model's utility, and if appropriate, use the estimated model to make further inferences. All this, of course, requires sample data. As before, n denotes the number of observations in the sample. With just one predictor variable, the sample consisted of n (x, y) pairs. Now, each observation consists of $k + 1$ numbers: a value of x_1, a value of x_2, ..., a value of x_k, and the associated value of y. The n observations are assumed to have been selected independently of one another.

EXAMPLE 14.6 Graduation Rates at Small Colleges

● One way colleges measure success is by graduation rates. The Education Trust publishes 6-year graduation rates along with other college characteristics on its web site (www.collegeresults.org). We will consider the following variables:

y = 6-year graduation rate
x_1 = median SAT score of students accepted to the college
x_2 = student-related expense per full-time student (in dollars)

$$x_3 = \begin{cases} 1 & \text{if college has only female students or only male students} \\ 0 & \text{if college has both male and female students} \end{cases}$$

The following data represent a random sample of 22 colleges selected from the 1037 colleges in the United States with enrollments under 5000 students. The data consist of 22 observations on each of these four variables.

College	y	x_1	x_2	x_3
Cornerstone University	0.391	1,065	9,482	0
Barry University	0.389	950	13,149	0
Wilkes University	0.532	1,090	9,418	0
Colgate University	0.893	1,350	26,969	0
Lourdes College	0.313	930	8,489	0
Concordia University at Austin	0.315	985	8,329	0
Carleton College	0.896	1,390	29,605	0
Letourneau University	0.545	1,170	13,154	0
Ohio Valley College	0.288	950	10,887	0
Chadron State College	0.469	990	6,046	0
Meredith College	0.679	1,035	14,889	1
Tougaloo College	0.495	845	11,694	0
Hawaii Pacific University	0.410	1,000	9,911	0
University Of Michigan-Dearborn	0.497	1,065	9,371	0
Whittier College	0.553	1,065	14,051	0
Wheaton College	0.845	1,325	18,420	0
Southampton College Of Long Island	0.465	1,035	13,302	0

(continued)

Step-by-Step technology instructions available online

● Data set available online

College	y	x_1	x_2	x_3
Keene State College	0.541	1,005	8,098	0
Mount St Mary's College	0.579	918	12,999	1
Wellesley College	0.912	1,370	35,393	1
Fort Lewis College	0.298	970	5,518	0
Bowdoin College	0.891	1,375	35,669	0

One possible model that could be considered to describe the relationship between y and these three predictor variables is

$$y = \alpha + \beta_1 x_1 + \beta_2 x_2 + \beta_3 x_3 + e$$

We will return to this example after we see how sample data are used to estimate model coefficients.

As in simple linear regression, the principle of least squares is used to estimate the coefficients $\alpha, \beta_1, \dots, \beta_k$. For specified estimates $a, b_1, \dots, b_k$

$$y - (a + b_1 x_1 + b_2 x_2 + \cdots + b_k x_k)$$

is the deviation between the observed y value for a particular observation and the predicted value using the estimated regression function $a + b_1 x_1 + \cdots + b_k x_k$. For example, the first observation in the data set of Example 14.6 is

$$(x_1, x_2, x_3, y) = (1065, 9482, 0, 0.391)$$

The resulting deviation between observed and predicted y values is

$$0.391 - [a + b_1(1065) + b_2(9482) + b_3(0)]$$

Deviations corresponding to other observations are expressed in a similar manner. The principle of least squares then says to use as estimates of α, β_1, β_2, and β_3 the values of a, b_1, b_2, and b_3 that minimize the sum of these squared deviations.

DEFINITION

According to the principle of least squares, the fit of a particular estimated regression function $a + b_1 x_1 + \cdots + b_k x_k$ to the observed data is measured by the sum of squared deviations between the observed y values and the y values predicted by the estimated regression function:

$$\sum [y - (a + b_1 x_1 + \cdots + b_k x_k)]^2$$

The **least-squares estimates** of $\alpha, \beta_1, \dots, \beta_k$ are those values of $a, b_1, \dots, b_k$ that make this sum of squared deviations as small as possible.

The least-squares estimates for a given data set are obtained by solving a system of $k + 1$ equations in the $k + 1$ unknowns $a, b_1, \dots, b_k$ (called the *normal equations*). In the case $k = 1$ (simple linear regression), there are only two equations, and we gave their general solution—the expressions for b and a—in Chapter 5. For $k \geq 2$, it is not as easy to write general expressions for the estimates without using advanced mathematical notation. Fortunately, the computer saves us! Formulas for the estimates have been programmed into all the commonly used statistical software packages.

EXAMPLE 14.7 More on Graduation Rates at Small Colleges

Figure 14.6 displays Minitab output from a regression command requesting that the model $y = \alpha + \beta_1x_1 + \beta_2x_2 + \beta_3x_3 + e$ be fit to the small college data of Example 14.6. Focus on the column labeled Coef (for coefficient) in the table near the top of the figure. The four numbers in this column are the estimated model coefficients:

$$\begin{aligned} a &= -0.3906 \text{ (the estimate of the constant term } \alpha) \\ b_1 &= 0.0007602 \text{ (the estimate of the coefficient } \beta_1) \\ b_2 &= 0.00000697 \text{ (the estimate of the coefficient } \beta_2) \\ b_3 &= 0.12495 \text{ (the estimate of the coefficient } \beta_3) \end{aligned}$$

Regression Analysis: y versus x_1, x_2, x_3

```
The regression equation is
y = -0.391 + 0.000760 x1 + 0.000007 x2 + 0.125 x3

Predictor        Coef       SE Coef      T       P
Constant      -0.3906        0.1976  -1.98   0.064
x1          0.0007602     0.0002300   3.30   0.004
x2         0.00000697    0.00000451   1.55   0.139
x3            0.12495       0.05943   2.10   0.050

S = 0.0844346    R-Sq = 86.1%    R-Sq(adj) = 83.8%
```

a, *b_1*, *b_2*, *b_3*

Coefficient of multiple determination = .861

Analysis of Variance

```
Source          DF       SS        MS       F       P
Regression       3  0.79486   0.26495   37.16   0.000
Residual Error  18  0.12833   0.00713
Total           21  0.92318
```

P-value for model utility test

FIGURE 14.6
Minitab output for the regression analysis of Example 14.7.

Thus, we estimate that the average change in 6-year graduation rate associated with a \$1 increase in expenditure per full-time student while type of institution (same sex or coed) and median SAT score remains fixed is 0.00000697. A similar interpretation applies to b_1. The variable x_3 is an indicator variable that takes on a value of 1 for colleges that have either all female students or all male students. We would interpret the estimated value of $b_3 = 0.125$ as the "correction" that we would make to the predicted 6-year graduation rate of a coed college with the same median SAT and expenditure per full-time student to incorporate the difference associated with having only female or only male students. The estimated regression function is

$$\begin{pmatrix} \text{estimated mean value of } y \\ \text{for specified } x_1, x_2, \text{ and } x_3 \text{ values} \end{pmatrix} = -0.3906 + 0.0007602x_1 + 0.00000697x_2 + 0.12495x_3$$

Substituting $x_1 = 1000$, $x_2 = 11{,}000$, and $x_3 = 0$ gives

$$-0.3906 + 0.0007602(1000) + 0.00000697(11{,}000) + 0.12495(0) = .4462$$

which can be interpreted either as a point estimate for the mean 6-year graduation rate of coed colleges with a median SAT of 1000 and an expenditure per full-time student of \$11,000 or as a point prediction for a single college with these same characteristics.

Is the Model Useful?

The utility of an estimated model can be assessed by examining the extent to which predicted y values based on the estimated regression function are close to the y values actually observed.

DEFINITION

The first predicted value $\hat{y}_1$ is obtained by taking the values of the predictor variables $x_1, x_2, \ldots, x_k$ for the first sample observation and substituting these values into the estimated regression function. Doing this successively for the remaining observations yields the **predicted values** $\hat{y}_2, \ldots, \hat{y}_n$. The **residuals** are then the differences $y_1 - \hat{y}_1, y_2 - \hat{y}_2, \ldots, y_n - \hat{y}_n$ between the observed and predicted y values.

The predicted values and residuals are defined here exactly as they were in simple linear regression, but computation of the values is more tedious because there is more than one predictor. Fortunately, the $\hat{y}$'s and $(y - \hat{y})$'s are automatically computed and displayed in the output of all good statistical software packages. Consider again the college data discussed in Examples 14.6 and 14.7. Because the first y observation, $y_1 = 0.391$, was made with $x_1 = 1065$, $x_2 = 9482$, and $x_3 = 0$, the first predicted value is

$$\hat{y} = -0.3906 + 0.0007602(1065) + 0.00000697(9482) + 0.12495(0) = 0.485$$

The first residual is then

$$y_1 - \hat{y}_1 = 0.391 - 0.485 = -0.094$$

The other predicted values and residuals are computed in a similar fashion. The sum of residuals from a least-squares fit should, except for rounding effects, be 0.

As in simple linear regression, the sum of squared residuals is the basis for several important summary quantities that tell us about a model's utility.

DEFINITION

The **residual (or error) sum of squares, SSResid**, and **total sum of squares, SSTo**, are given by

$$\text{SSResid} = \sum (y - \hat{y})^2 \quad \text{SSTo} = \sum (y - \bar{y})^2$$

where $\bar{y}$ is the mean of the y observations in the sample.

The number of degrees of freedom associated with SSResid is $n - (k + 1)$, because $k + 1$ df are lost in estimating the $k + 1$ coefficients $\alpha, \beta_1, \ldots, \beta_k$.

An estimate of the random deviation variance σ^2 is given by

$$s_e^2 = \frac{\text{SSResid}}{n - (k + 1)}$$

and $s_e = \sqrt{s_e^2}$ is an estimate of σ.

The **coefficient of multiple determination**, R^2, interpreted as the proportion of variation in observed y values that is explained by the fitted model, is

$$R^2 = 1 - \frac{\text{SSResid}}{\text{SSTo}}$$

EXAMPLE 14.8 Small Colleges Revisited

Looking again at Figure 14.6, which contains Minitab output for the college data fit by a three-predictor model, residual sum of squares is found in the Residual Error row and SS column of the table headed Analysis of Variance: SSResid = 0.12833. The associated number of degrees of freedom is $n - (k + 1) = 22 - (3 + 1) = 18$, which appears in the DF column just to the left of SSResid. The sample mean y value is $\bar{y} = .5544$, and SSTo = $\sum(y - .5544)^2 = 0.92318$ appears in the Total row and SS column of the Analysis of Variance table just under the value of SSResid. The values of s_e, s_e^2, and R^2 are then

$$s_e^2 = \frac{\text{SSResid}}{n - (k + 1)} = \frac{0.12833}{18} = 0.007$$

(also found in the MS column of the Minitab output)

$$s_e = \sqrt{s_e^2} = \sqrt{.007} = 0.084$$

(which appears in the Minitab output just above the Analysis of Variance table)

$$R^2 = 1 - \frac{\text{SSResid}}{\text{SSTo}} = 1 - \frac{0.12833}{0.92318} = 1 - .139 = .861$$

Thus, the percentage of variation explained is $100R^2 = 86.1\%$, which appears on the Minitab output as R-Sq = 86.1%. Because the value of R^2 is large and the value of s_e is not too large, the values of R^2 and s_e suggest that the chosen model has been very successful in relating y to the predictors.

In general, a useful model is one that results in both a large R^2 value and a small s_e value. However, there is a catch. These two conditions can be achieved by fitting a model that contains a large number of predictors. Such a model might be successful in explaining y variation in the data in our sample, but it almost always specifies a relationship that cannot be generalized to the population and that may be unrealistic and difficult to interpret. What we really want is a simple model—that is, a model that has relatively few predictors whose roles are easily interpreted and that also explains much of the variation in y.

All statistical software packages include R^2 and s_e in their output, and most also give SSResid. In addition, some packages compute the quantity called the ***adjusted*** $\boldsymbol{R^2}$:

$$\text{adjusted } R^2 = 1 - \left[\frac{n - 1}{n - (k + 1)}\right]\left(\frac{\text{SSResid}}{\text{SSTo}}\right)$$

Because the quantity in square brackets exceeds 1, the number subtracted from 1 is larger than SSResid/SSTo, so the adjusted R^2 is smaller than R^2. The value of R^2 must be between 0 and 1, but the adjusted R^2 can, on rare occasions, be negative. If a large R^2 has been achieved by using just a few model predictors, the adjusted R^2 and R^2 values will not differ greatly. However, the adjustment can be substantial when a great many predictors (relative to the number of observations) have been used or when R^2 itself is small to moderate (which could happen even when there is no relationship between y and the predictors). In Example 14.7, the adjusted $R^2 = .838$, which is not much less than R^2 because the model included only two predictor variables and the sample size was 22.

F Distributions

The model utility test in simple linear regression was based on a test statistic that when H_0: $\beta = 0$ is true, has a t distribution. The model utility test for multiple regression is based on a test statistic that has a probability distribution called an *F distribution.* We digress briefly to describe some general properties of F distributions. An F distribution always arises in connection with a ratio in which the numerator involves one sum of squares and the denominator involves a second sum of squares. Each sum of squares has associated with it a specified number of degrees of freedom, so a particular F distribution is determined by specifying values of df_1 = numerator degrees of freedom and df_2 = denominator degrees of freedom. There is a different F distribution for each different df_1 and df_2 combination. For example, there is an F distribution based on 4 numerator degrees of freedom and 12 denominator degrees of freedom, another F distribution based on 3 numerator degrees of freedom and 20 denominator degrees of freedom, and so on. A typical F curve for specified numerator and denominator degrees of freedom appears in Figure 14.7. All F tests presented in this book are upper-tailed. The P-value for an upper-tailed F test is the area under the associated F curve to the right of the calculated F. Figure 14.7 illustrates this for a test based on $df_1 = 4$ and $df_2 = 6$.

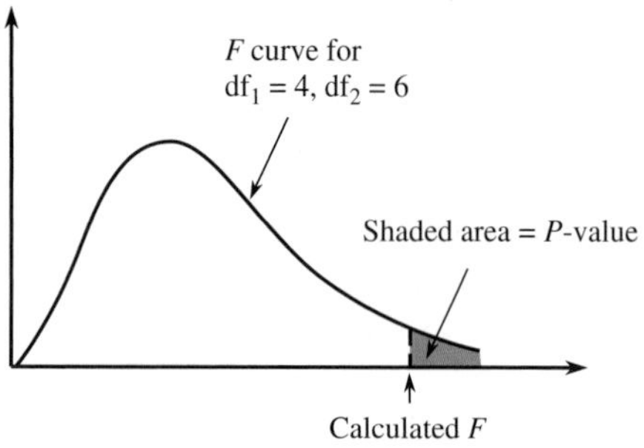

FIGURE 14.7
A P-value for an upper-tailed F test.

Unfortunately, tabulation of these upper-tail areas is much more cumbersome than for t distributions, because here 2 df are involved. For each of a number of different F distributions, our F table (Appendix Table 6) tabulates only four numbers: the values that capture tail areas .10, .05, .01, and .001. Different columns correspond to different values of df_1, and each different group of rows is for a different value of df_2. Figure 14.8 shows how this table is used to obtain P-value information.

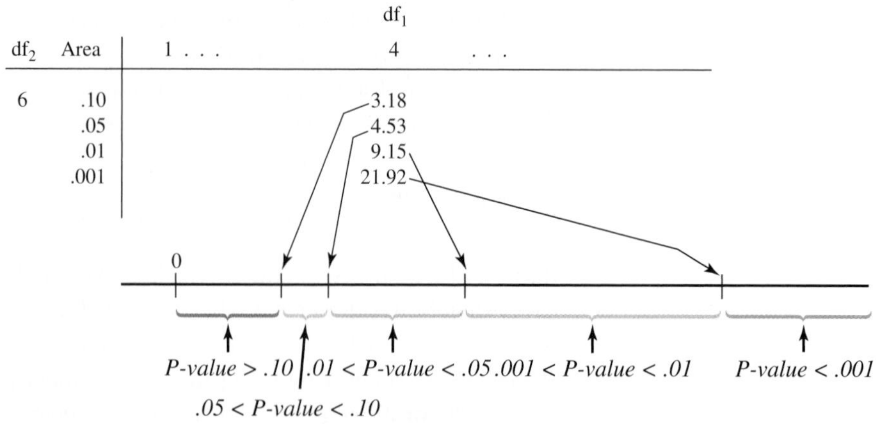

FIGURE 14.8
Obtaining P-value information from the F table.

For example, for a test with $df_1 = 4$ and $df_2 = 6$,

calculated $F = 5.70 \rightarrow .01 < P\text{-value} < .05$
calculated $F = 2.16 \rightarrow P\text{-value} > .10$
calculated $F = 25.03 \rightarrow P\text{-value} < .001$

Only if calculated F equals a tabulated value do we obtain an exact P-value (for example, if calculated $F = 4.53$, then P-value $= .05$). If $.01 < P\text{-value} < .05$, we should reject the null hypothesis at a significance level of .05 but not at a level of .01. When P-value $< .001$, H_0 would be rejected at any reasonable significance level. Statistical computer packages, such as Minitab, and some graphing calculators can also be used to fnd P-values for F distributions.

The *F* Test for Model Utility

In the simple linear model with regression function $\alpha + \beta x$, if $\beta = 0$, there is no useful linear relationship between y and the single predictor variable x. Similarly, if all k coefficients $\beta_1, \beta_2, \ldots, \beta_k$ are 0 in the general k-predictor multiple regression model, there is no useful linear relationship between y and *any* of the predictor variables $x_1, x_2, \ldots, x_k$ included in the model. Before using an estimated multiple regression model to make further inferences (for example, predictions or estimates of mean values), you should confirm the model's utility through a formal test procedure.

Recall that SSTo is a measure of total variation in the observed y values and that SSResid measures the amount of total variation that has not been explained by the fitted model. The difference between total and error sums of squares is itself a sum of squares, called the **regression sum of squares**, which is denoted by SSRegr:

$$\text{SSRegr} = \text{SSTo} - \text{SSResid}$$

SSRegr is interpreted as the amount of total variation that *has* been explained by the model. Intuitively, the model should be judged useful if SSRegr is large relative to SSResid and the model uses a small number of predictors relative to the sample size. The number of degrees of freedom associated with SSRegr is k, the number of model predictors, and the number of degrees of freedom for SSResid is $n - (k + 1)$. The model utility F test is based on the following result.

When all k β_i's are 0 in the model $y = \alpha + \beta_1 x_1 + \beta_2 x_2 + \cdots + \beta_k x_k + e$ and when the distribution of e is normal with mean 0 and variance σ^2 for any particular values of $x_1, x_2, \ldots, x_k$, the statistic

$$F = \frac{\text{SSRegr}/k}{\text{SSResid}/(n - (k + 1))}$$

has an F probability distribution based on numerator df $= k$ and denominator df $= n - (k + 1)$.

The value of F tends to be larger when at least one β_i is not 0 than when all the β_i's are 0, because more variation is typically explained by the model in the former case than in the latter case. An F statistic value far out in the upper tail of the associated F distribution can be more plausibly attributed to at least one nonzero β_i than to something extremely unusual having occurred when all the β_i's are 0. This is why the F test for model utility is upper-tailed.

The Model Utility F Test for Multiple Regression

Null hypothesis: H_0: $\beta_1 = \beta_2 = \cdots = \beta_k = 0$
(There is no useful linear relationship between y and *any* of the predictors.)

Alternative hypothesis: H_a: At least one among $\beta_1, \ldots, \beta_k$ is not zero.
(There is a useful linear relationship between y and *at least one* of the predictors.)

Test statistic: $$F = \frac{\text{SSRegr}/k}{\text{SSResid}/(n - (k + 1))}$$

where SSRegr = SSTo − SSResid.

An equivalent formula is

$$F = \frac{R^2/k}{(1 - R^2)/(n - (k + 1))}$$

The test is upper-tailed, and the information in Appendix Table 6 is used to obtain a bound or bounds on the P-value using numerator $\text{df}_1 = k$ and denominator $\text{df}_2 = n - (k + 1)$.

Assumptions: For any particular combination of predictor variable values, the distribution of e, the random deviation, is *normal* with mean 0 and *constant variance,* σ^2.

For the model utility test, the null hypothesis is the claim that the model is not useful. Unless H_0 can be rejected at a small level of significance, the model has not demonstrated its utility, in which case the investigator must search further for a model that can be judged useful. The alternative formula for F allows the test to be carried out when only R^2, k, and n are available, as is frequently the case in published articles.

EXAMPLE 14.9 Small Colleges One Last Time

The model fit to the college data introduced in Example 14.6 involved $k = 3$ predictors. The Minitab output in Figure 14.6 contains the relevant information for carrying out the model utility test.

1. The model is $y = \alpha + \beta_1x_1 + \beta_2x_2 + \beta_3x_3 + e$ where y = 6-year graduation rate, x_1 = median SAT score, x_2 = expenditure per full-time student, and x_3 is an indicator variable that is equal to 1 for a college that has only female or only male students and is equal to 0 if the college is coed.
2. H_0: $\beta_1 = \beta_2 = \beta_3 = 0$
3. H_a: At least one of the three β_i's is not zero.
4. Significance level: $\alpha = .05$
5. Test statistic: $F = \dfrac{\text{SSRegr}/k}{\text{SSResid}/[n - (k + 1)]}$
6. Assumptions: The accompanying table gives the residuals and standardized residuals (from Minitab) for the model under consideration.

Obs.	y	x1	x2	x3	Residual	Standardized Residual
1	0.391	1065	9482	0	−0.094	−1.166
2	0.389	950	13149	0	−0.034	−0.442
3	0.532	1090	9418	0	0.028	0.358
4	0.893	1350	26969	0	0.069	0.908
5	0.313	930	8489	0	−0.062	−0.779
6	0.315	985	8329	0	−0.101	−1.244
7	0.896	1390	29605	0	0.024	0.319
8	0.545	1170	13154	0	−0.045	−0.575
9	0.288	950	10887	0	−0.119	−1.497
10	0.469	990	6046	0	0.065	0.812
11	0.679	1035	14889	1	0.054	0.806
12	0.495	845	11694	0	0.162	2.388
13	0.410	1000	9911	0	−0.029	−0.350
14	0.497	1065	9371	0	0.013	0.158
15	0.553	1065	14051	0	0.036	0.441
16	0.845	1325	18420	0	0.100	1.381
17	0.465	1035	13302	0	−0.024	−0.292
18	0.541	1005	8098	0	0.111	1.371
19	0.579	918	12999	1	0.056	0.857
20	0.912	1370	35393	1	−0.110	−1.793
21	0.298	970	5518	0	−0.087	−1.091
22	0.891	1375	35669	0	−0.012	−0.189

A normal probability plot of the standardized residuals is shown here; the plot is quite straight, indicating that the assumption of normality of the random deviation distribution is reasonable:

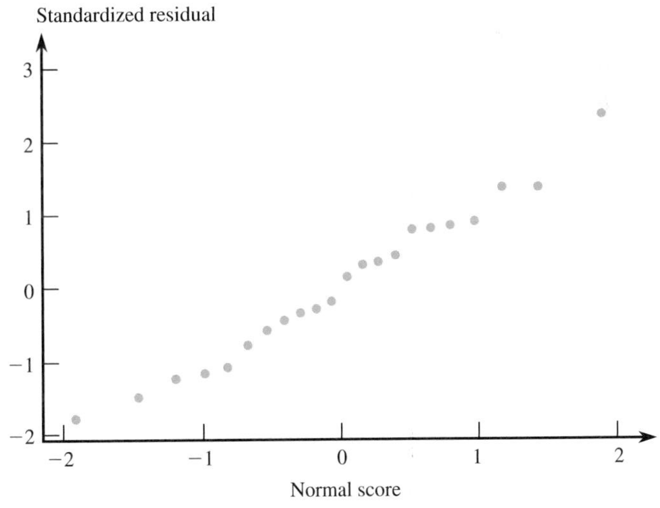

7. Directly from the Analysis of Variance table in Figure 14.6, the SS column gives SSRegr = 0.79486 and SSResid = 0.12833. Thus,

$$F = \frac{0.79486/3}{0.12833/18} = \frac{0.26495}{0.00713} = 37.16 \quad \left(\begin{array}{l}\text{also found in the column labeled F}\\ \text{in Figure 14.6}\end{array}\right)$$

8. Appendix Table 6 shows that for a test based on $df_1 = k = 3$ and $df_2 = n - (k + 1) = 22 - (3 + 1) = 18$, the value 8.49 captures upper-tail F curve area .001. Since calculated $F = 37.16 > 8.49$, it follows that P-value $< .001$. In fact, Figure 14.6 shows that to three decimal places, P-value $= 0$.

9. Because P-value $< .001$, which is less than the significance level of .05, H_0 should be rejected. The conclusion would be the same using $\alpha = .01$ or $\alpha = .001$. The usefulness of the multiple regression model is confirmed. The P-value for the model utility test can also be found in the Minitab output to the right of the value of the F test statistic in the column labeled P.

EXAMPLE 14.10 School Board Politics

A multiple regression analysis presented in the article "The Politics of Bureaucratic Discretion: Educational Access as an Urban Service" (*American Journal of Political Science* [1991]: 155–177) considered a model in which the dependent variable was

y = percentage of school board members in a school district who are black

and the predictors were

x_1 = black-to-white income ratio in the district
x_2 = percentage of whites in the district below the poverty line
x_3 = indicator variable for whether district was in the South
x_4 = percentage of blacks in the district with a high-school education
x_5 = black population percentage in the district

Summary quantities included $n = 140$ and $R^2 = .749$. Does this model specify a useful relationship between y and the five predictors? To answer this question, we carry out a model utility test.

1. The fitted model was $y = \alpha + \beta_1 x_1 + \beta_2 x_2 + \cdots + \beta_5 x_5 + e$
2. H_0: $\beta_1 = \beta_2 = \beta_3 = \beta_4 = \beta_5 = 0$
3. H_a: at least one of the β_i's is not zero
4. Significance level: $\alpha = .01$
5. Test statistic: $F = \dfrac{R^2/k}{(1 - R^2)/(n - (k + 1))}$
6. Assumptions: The raw data were not given in this article, so we are unable to compute standardized residuals or construct a normal probability plot. For this test to be valid, we must be willing to assume that the random deviation distribution is normal.
7. $F = \dfrac{.749/5}{.251/(140 - (5 + 1))} = \dfrac{.1498}{.001873} = 80.0$
8. The test is based on $\text{df}_1 = k = 5$ and $\text{df}_2 = n - (k + 1) = 134$. This latter df is not included in the F table. However, the .001 cutoff value for $\text{df}_2 = 120$ is 4.42, and for $\text{df}_2 = 240$ it is 4.25; so for $\text{df}_2 = 134$, the cutoff value is roughly 4.4. Clearly, 80.0 greatly exceeds this value, implying that P-value $< .001$.
9. Since P-value $< .001$ which is less than the significance level of .01, H_0 is rejected at significance level .01. There appears to be a useful linear relationship between y and at least one of the five predictors.

In Section 14.3 (online), we presume that a model has been judged useful after performing an F test and then show how the estimated coefficients and regression function can be used to draw further conclusions. However, you should realize that in many applications, more than one model's utility could be confirmed by the F test. Also, just because the model utility test indicates that the multiple regression model is useful does not necessarily mean that all the predictors included in the model contribute to the usefulness of the model. This is illustrated in Example 14.11, and strategies for selecting a model are considered later in Section 14.4 (online).

EXAMPLE 14.11 The Cost of Energy Bars

● What factors contribute to the price of energy bars promoted to provide endurance and increase muscle power? The article "Energy Bars, Unwrapped" (*Consumer Reports* [June 2003] 19–21) included the following data on price, calorie content, protein content (in grams), and fat content (in grams) for a sample of 19 energy bars.

Price	Calories	Protein	Fat
1.40	180	12	3.0
1.28	200	14	6.0
1.31	210	16	7.0
1.10	220	13	6.0
2.29	220	17	11.0
1.15	230	14	4.5
2.24	240	24	10.0
1.99	270	24	5.0
2.57	320	31	9.0
0.94	110	5	30.0
1.40	180	10	4.5
0.53	200	7	6.0
1.02	220	8	5.0
1.13	230	9	6.0
1.29	230	10	2.0
1.28	240	10	4.0
1.44	260	6	5.0
1.27	260	7	5.0
1.47	290	13	6.0

Figure 14.9 displays Minitab output from a regression for the model

$$y = \alpha + \beta_1 x_1 + \beta_2 x_2 + \beta_3 x_3 + e$$

where

y = price x_1 = calorie content x_2 = protein content x_3 = fat content

The regression equation is
Price = 0.252 + 0.00125 Calories + 0.0485 Protein + 0.0444 Fat

Predictor	Coef	SE Coef	T	P
Constant	0.2511	0.3524	0.71	0.487
Calories	0.001254	0.001724	0.73	0.478
Protein	0.04849	0.01353	3.58	0.003
Fat	0.04445	0.03648	1.22	0.242

S = 0.2789 R-Sq = 74.7% R-Sq(adj) = 69.6%

Analysis of Variance

Source	DF	SS	MS	F	P
Regression	3	3.4453	1.1484	14.76	0.000
Residual Error	15	1.1670	0.0778		
Total	18	4.6122			

FIGURE 14.9
Minitab output for the energy bar data of Example 14.11.

● Data set available online

From the Minitab output, $F = 14.76$, with an associated P-value of 0.000, indicating that the null hypothesis in the model utility test, H_0: $\beta_1 = \beta_2 = \beta_3 = 0$, should be rejected. We would conclude that there is a useful linear relationship between y and at least one of x_1, x_2, and x_3. However, consider the Minitab output shown in Figure 14.10, which resulted from fitting a model that uses only x_2 = protein content as a predictor. Notice that the F test would also confirm the usefulness of this model and also that the R^2 and adjusted R^2 values of 71.1% and 69.4% are quite similar to those of the model that included all three predictors (74.7% and 69.6% from the Minitab output of Figure 14.9). This suggests that protein content alone explains about the same amount of the variability in price as all three variables together, and so the simpler model with just one predictor may be preferred over the more complicated model with three predictor variables.

```
The regression equation is
Price = 0.607 + 0.0623 Protein

Predictor         Coef      SE Coef       T       P
Constant        0.6072       0.1419    4.28   0.001
Protein       0.062256     0.009618    6.47   0.000
S = 0.279843  R-Sq = 71.1%    R-Sq(adj) = 69.4%

Analysis of Variance
Source             DF         SS        MS       F       P
Regression          1     3.2809    3.2809   41.90   0.000
Residual Error     17     1.3313    0.0763
Total              18     4.6122
```

FIGURE 14.10 Minitab output for the energy bar data of Example 14.11 when only x_2 = protein content is included as a predictor.

EXERCISES 14.16 - 14.35

14.16 ✦ When coastal power stations take in large quantities of cooling water, it is inevitable that a number of fish are drawn in with the water. Various methods have been designed to screen out the fish. The article "Multiple Regression Analysis for Forecasting Critical Fish Influxes at Power Station Intakes" (*Journal of Applied Ecology* [1983]: 33–42) examined intake fish catch at an English power plant and several other variables thought to affect fish intake:

y = fish intake (number of fish)
x_1 = water temperature (°C)
x_2 = number of pumps running
x_3 = sea state (values 0, 1, 2, or 3)
x_4 = speed (knots)

Part of the data given in the article were used to obtain the estimated regression equation

$$\hat{y} = 92 - 2.18x_1 - 19.20x_2 - 9.38x_3 + 2.32x_4$$

(based on $n = 26$). SSRegr = 1486.9 and SSResid = 2230.2 were also calculated.

a. Interpret the values of b_1 and b_4.
b. What proportion of observed variation in fish intake can be explained by the model relationship?
c. Estimate the value of σ.
d. Calculate adjusted R^2. How does it compare to R^2 itself?

14.17 Obtain as much information as you can about the P-value for an upper-tailed F test in each of the following situations:

a. $\text{df}_1 = 3$, $\text{df}_2 = 15$, calculated $F = 4.23$
b. $\text{df}_1 = 4$, $\text{df}_2 = 18$, calculated $F = 1.95$
c. $\text{df}_1 = 5$, $\text{df}_2 = 20$, calculated $F = 4.10$
d. $\text{df}_1 = 4$, $\text{df}_2 = 35$, calculated $F = 4.58$

14.18 Obtain as much information as you can about the P-value for the F test for model utility in each of the following situations:

a. $k = 2$, $n = 21$, calculated $F = 2.47$
b. $k = 8$, $n = 25$, calculated $F = 5.98$
c. $k = 5$, $n = 26$, calculated $F = 3.00$

d. The full quadratic model based on x_1 and x_2 is fit, $n = 20$, and calculated $F = 8.25$.
e. $k = 5$, $n = 100$, calculated $F = 2.33$

14.19 Data from a sample of $n = 150$ quail eggs were used to fit a multiple regression model relating

y = eggshell surface area (mm^2)
x_1 = egg weight (g)
x_2 = egg width (mm)
x_3 = egg length (mm)

("Predicting Yolk Height, Yolk Width, Albumen Length, Eggshell Weight, Egg Shape Index, Eggshell Thickness, Egg Surface Area of Japanese Quails Using Various Egg Traits as Regressors," *International Journal of Poultry Science* [2008]: 85–88).

The resulting estimated regression function was

$$10.561 + 1.535x_1 - 0.178x_2 - 0.045x_3$$

and $R^2 = .996$.

a. Carry out a model utility test to determine if this multiple regression model is useful.
b. A simple linear regression model was also used to describe the relationship between y and x_1, resulting in the estimated regression function $6.254 + 1.387x_1$. The P-value for the associated model utility test was reported to be less than .01, and $r^2 = .994$. Is the linear model useful? Explain.
c. Based on your answers to Parts (a) and (b), which of the two models would you recommend for predicting eggshell surface area? Explain the rationale for your choice.

14.20 ● *This exercise requires the use of a computer package.* The paper "Habitat Selection by Black Bears in an Intensively Logged Boreal Forrest" (*Canadian Journal of Zoology* [2008]: 1307–1316) gave the accompanying data on $n = 11$ female black bears.

Age (years)	Weight (kg)	Home-Range Size (km^2)
10.5	54	43.1
6.5	40	46.6
28.5	62	57.4
6.5	55	35.6
7.5	56	62.1
6.5	62	33.9
5.5	42	39.6
7.5	40	32.2
11.5	59	57.2
9.5	51	24.4
5.5	50	68.7

a. Fit a multiple regression model to describe the relationship between y = home-range size and the predictors x_1 = age and x_2 = weight.
b. Construct a normal probability plot of the 11 standardized residuals. Based on the plot, does it seem reasonable to regard the random deviation distribution as approximately normal? Explain.
c. If appropriate, carry out a model utility test with a significance level of .05 to determine if the predictors *age* and *weight* are useful for predicting home-range size.

14.21 The ability of ecologists to identify regions of greatest species richness could have an impact on the preservation of genetic diversity, a major objective of the World Conservation Strategy. The article "Prediction of Rarities from Habitat Variables: Coastal Plain Plants on Nova Scotian Lakeshores" (*Ecology* [1992]: 1852–1859) used a sample of $n = 37$ lakes to obtain the estimated regression equation

$$\hat{y} = 3.89 + .033x_1 + .024x_2 + .023x_3 + .008x_4 - .13x_5 - .72x_6$$

where y = species richness, x_1 = watershed area, x_2 = shore width, x_3 = drainage (%), x_4 = water color (total color units), x_5 = sand (%), and x_6 = alkalinity. The coefficient of multiple determination was reported as $R^2 = .83$. Use a test with significance level .01 to decide whether the chosen model is useful.

14.22 The article "Impacts of On-Campus and Off-Campus Work on First-Year Cognitive Outcomes" (*Journal of College Student Development* [1994]: 364–370) reported on a study in which y = spring math comprehension score was regressed against x_1 = previous fall test score, x_2 = previous fall academic motivation, x_3 = age, x_4 = number of credit hours, x_5 = residence (1 if on campus, 0 otherwise), x_6 = hours worked on campus, and x_7 = hours worked off campus. The sample size was $n = 210$, and $R^2 = .543$. Test to see whether there is a useful linear relationship between y and at least one of the predictors.

14.23 Is the model fit in Exercise 14.16 useful? Carry out a test using a significance level of .10.

14.24 The accompanying Minitab output results from fitting the model described in Exercise 14.14 to data.

Predictor	Coef	Stdev	t-ratio
Constant	86.85	85.39	1.02
X1	-0.12297	0.03276	-3.75
X2	5.090	1.969	2.58
X3	-0.07092	0.01799	-3.94
X4	0.0015380	0.0005560	2.77
S = 4.784	R-sq = 90.8%	R-sq(adj) = 89.4%	

Analysis of Variance

	DF	SS	MS
Regression	4	5896.6	1474.2
Error	26	595.1	22.9
Total	30	6491.7	

a. What is the estimated regression equation?
b. Using a .01 significance level, perform the model utility test.
c. Interpret the values of R^2 and s_e given in the output.

14.25 For the multiple regression model in Exercise 14.6, the value of R^2 was .06 and the adjusted R^2 was .06. The model was based on a data set with 1136 observations. Perform a model utility test for this regression.

14.26 ● *This exercise requires the use of a computer package.* The article "Movement and Habitat Use by Lake Whitefish During Spawning in a Boreal Lake: Integrating Acoustic Telemetry and Geographic Information Systems" (*Transactions of the American Fisheries Society* [1999]: 939–952) included the accompanying data on 17 fish caught in 2 consecutive years.

Year	Fish Number	Weight (g)	Length (mm)	Age (years)
Year 1	1	776	410	9
	2	580	368	11
	3	539	357	15
	4	648	373	12
	5	538	361	9
	6	891	385	9
	7	673	380	10
	8	783	400	12
Year 2	9	571	407	12
	10	627	410	13
	11	727	421	12
	12	867	446	19
	13	1042	478	19
	14	804	441	18
	15	832	454	12
	16	764	440	12
	17	727	427	12

a. Fit a multiple regression model to describe the relationship between weight and the predictors *length* and *age*. $\hat{y} = -511 + 3.06\text{ length} - 1.11\text{ age}$
b. Carry out the model utility test to determine whether at least one of the predictors *length* and *age* are useful for predicting weight.

14.27 ● *This exercise requires the use of a computer package.* The authors of the article "Absolute Versus per Unit Body Length Speed of Prey as an Estimator of Vulnerability to Predation" (*Animal Behaviour* [1999]: 347–352) found that the speed of a prey (twips/s) and the length of a prey (twips × 100) are good predictors of the time (s) required to catch the prey. (A twip is a measure of distance used by programmers.) Data were collected in an experiment in which subjects were asked to "catch" an animal of prey moving across his or her computer screen by clicking on it with the mouse. The investigators varied the length of the prey and the speed with which the prey moved across the screen. The following data are consistent with summary values and a graph given in the article. Each value represents the average catch time over all subjects. The order of the various speed-length combinations was randomized for each subject.

Prey Length	Prey Speed	Catch Time
7	20	1.10
6	20	1.20
5	20	1.23
4	20	1.40
3	20	1.50
3	40	1.40
4	40	1.36
6	40	1.30
7	40	1.28
7	80	1.40
6	60	1.38
5	80	1.40
7	100	1.43
6	100	1.43
7	120	1.70
5	80	1.50
3	80	1.40
6	100	1.50
3	120	1.90

a. Fit a multiple regression model for predicting catch time using prey length and speed as predictors.
b. Predict the catch time for an animal of prey whose length is 6 and whose speed is 50.

c. Is the multiple regression model useful for predicting catch time? Test the relevant hypotheses using $\alpha = .05$.

d. The authors of the article suggest that a simple linear regression model with the single predictor

$$x = \frac{\text{length}}{\text{speed}}$$

might be a better model for predicting catch time. Calculate the x values and use them to fit this linear regression model.

e. Which of the two models considered (the multiple regression model from Part (a) or the simple linear regression model from Part (d)) would you recommend for predicting catch time? Justify your choice.

14.28 ● *This exercise requires the use of a computer package.* The article "Vital Dimensions in Volume Perception: Can the Eye Fool the Stomach?" (*Journal of Marketing Research* [1999]: 313–326) gave the data below on dimensions of 27 representative food products.

a. Fit a multiple regression model for predicting the volume (in ml) of a package based on its minimum width, maximum width, and elongation score.

b. Why should we consider adjusted R^2 instead of R^2 when attempting to determine the quality of fit of the data to our model?

c. Perform a model utility test.

14.29 ● ✦ The article "The Undrained Strength of Some Thawed Permafrost Soils" (*Canadian Geotechnical Journal* [1979]: 420–427) contained the accompanying data (see page 830) on y = shear strength of sandy soil (kPa), x_1 = depth (m), and x_2 = water content (%). The predicted values and residuals were computed using the estimated regression equation

$$\hat{y} = -151.36 - 16.22x_1 + 13.48x_2 + .094x_3 - .253x_4 + .492x_5$$

where $x_3 = x_1^2$, $x_4 = x_2^2$, and $x_5 = x_1x_2$.

Data for Exercise 14.28

Product	Material	Height	Maximum Width	Minimum Width	Elongation	Volume
1	glass	7.7	2.50	1.80	1.50	125
2	glass	6.2	2.90	2.70	1.07	135
3	glass	8.5	2.15	2.00	1.98	175
4	glass	10.4	2.90	2.60	1.79	285
5	plastic	8.0	3.20	3.15	1.25	330
6	glass	8.7	2.00	1.80	2.17	90
7	glass	10.2	1.60	1.50	3.19	120
8	plastic	10.5	4.80	3.80	1.09	520
9	plastic	3.4	5.90	5.00	0.29	330
10	plastic	6.9	5.80	4.75	0.59	570
11	tin	10.9	2.90	2.80	1.88	340
12	plastic	9.7	2.45	2.10	1.98	175
13	glass	10.1	2.60	2.20	1.94	240
14	glass	13.0	2.60	2.60	2.50	240
15	glass	13.0	2.70	2.60	2.41	360
16	glass	11.0	3.10	2.90	1.77	310
17	cardboard	8.7	5.10	5.10	0.85	635
18	cardboard	17.1	10.20	10.20	0.84	1250
19	glass	16.5	3.50	3.50	2.36	650
20	glass	16.5	2.70	1.20	3.06	305
21	glass	9.7	3.00	1.70	1.62	315
22	glass	17.8	2.70	1.75	3.30	305
23	glass	14.0	2.50	1.70	2.80	245
24	glass	13.6	2.40	1.20	2.83	200
25	plastic	27.9	4.40	1.20	3.17	1205
26	tin	19.5	7.50	7.50	1.30	2330
27	tin	13.8	4.25	4.25	1.62	730

Data for Exercise 14.29

y	x_1	x_2	Predicted y	Residual
14.7	8.9	31.5	23.35	−8.65
48.0	36.6	27.0	46.38	1.62
25.6	36.8	25.9	27.13	−1.53
10.0	6.1	39.1	10.99	−0.99
16.0	6.9	39.2	14.10	1.90
16.8	6.9	38.3	16.54	0.26
20.7	7.3	33.9	23.34	−2.64
38.8	8.4	33.8	25.43	13.37
16.9	6.5	27.9	15.63	1.27
27.0	8.0	33.1	24.29	2.71
16.0	4.5	26.3	15.36	0.64
24.9	9.9	37.8	29.61	−4.71
7.3	2.9	34.6	15.38	−8.08
12.8	2.0	36.4	7.96	4.84

a. Use the given information to compute SSResid, SSTo, and SSRegr.

b. Calculate R^2 for this regression model. How would you interpret this value?

c. Use the value of R^2 from Part (b) and a .05 level of significance to conduct the appropriate model utility test.

14.30 The article "Readability of Liquid Crystal Displays: A Response Surface" (*Human Factors* [1983]: 185–190) used an estimated regression equation to describe the relationship between y = error percentage for subjects reading a four-digit liquid crystal display and the independent variables x_1 = level of backlight, x_2 = character subtense, x_3 = viewing angle, and x_4 = level of ambient light. From a table given in the article, SSRegr = 19.2, SSResid = 20.0, and $n = 30$.

a. Does the estimated regression equation specify a useful relationship between y and the independent variables? Use the model utility test with a .05 significance level.

b. Calculate R^2 and s_e for this model. Interpret these values.

c. Do you think that the estimated regression equation would provide reasonably accurate predictions of error percentage? Explain.

14.31 The article "Effect of Manual Defoliation on Pole Bean Yield" (*Journal of Economic Entomology* [1984]: 1019–1023) used a quadratic regression model to describe the relationship between y = yield (kg/plot) and x = defoliation level (a proportion between 0 and 1). The estimated regression equation based on $n = 24$ was $\hat{y} = 12.39 + 6.67x_1 - 15.25x_2$ where $x_1 = x$ and $x_2 = x^2$. The article also reported that R^2 for this model was .902. Does the quadratic model specify a useful relationship between y and x? Carry out the appropriate test using a .01 level of significance.

14.32 Suppose that a multiple regression data set consists of $n = 15$ observations. For what values of k, the number of model predictors, would the corresponding model with $R^2 = .90$ be judged useful at significance level .05? Does such a large R^2 value necessarily imply a useful model? Explain.

14.33 *This exercise requires the use of a computer package.* Use the data given in Exercise 14.29 to verify that the true regression function

$$\text{mean } y \text{ value} = \alpha + \beta_1x_1 + \beta_2x_2 + \beta_3x_3 + \beta_4x_4 + \beta_5x_5$$

is estimated by

$$\hat{y} = -151.36 - 16.22x_1 + 13.48x_2 + .094x_3 - .253x_4 + .492x_5$$

14.34 ● *This exercise requires the use of a computer package.* The accompanying data resulted from a study of the relationship between y = brightness of finished paper and the independent variables x_1 = hydrogen peroxide (% by weight), x_2 = sodium hydroxide (% by weight), x_3 = silicate (% by weight), and x_4 = process temperature ("Advantages of CE-HDP Bleaching for High Brightness Kraft Pulp Production," *TAPPI* [1964]: 107A–173A).

x_1	x_2	x_3	x_4	y
.2	.2	1.5	145	83.9
.4	.2	1.5	145	84.9
.2	.4	1.5	145	83.4
.4	.4	1.5	145	84.2
.2	.2	3.5	145	83.8
.4	.2	3.5	145	84.7
.2	.4	3.5	145	84.0
.4	.4	3.5	145	84.8
.2	.2	1.5	175	84.5
.4	.2	1.5	175	86.0
.2	.4	1.5	175	82.6
.4	.4	1.5	175	85.1
.2	.2	3.5	175	84.5
.4	.2	3.5	175	86.0
.2	.4	3.5	175	84.0
.4	.4	3.5	175	85.4
.1	.3	2.5	160	82.9
.5	.3	2.5	160	85.5
.3	.1	2.5	160	85.2
.3	.5	2.5	160	84.5
.3	.3	0.5	160	84.7
.3	.3	4.5	160	85.0

(continued)

x_1	x_2	x_3	x_4	y
.3	.3	2.5	130	84.9
.3	.3	2.5	190	84.0
.3	.3	2.5	160	84.5
.3	.3	2.5	160	84.7
.3	.3	2.5	160	84.6
.3	.3	2.5	160	84.9
.3	.3	2.5	160	84.9
.3	.3	2.5	160	84.5
.3	.3	2.5	160	84.6

a. Find the estimated regression equation for the model that includes all independent variables, all quadratic terms, and all interaction terms.

b. Using a .05 significance level, perform the model utility test.

c. Interpret the values of the following quantities: SSResid, R^2, and s_e.

14.35 ● *This exercise requires the use of a computer package.* The cotton aphid poses a threat to cotton crops in Iraq. The accompanying data on

y = infestation rate (aphids/100 leaves)
x_1 = mean temperature (°C)
x_2 = mean relative humidity

appeared in the article "Estimation of the Economic Threshold of Infestation for Cotton Aphid" (*Mesopotamia Journal of Agriculture* [1982]: 71–75). Use the data to find the estimated regression equation and assess the utility of the multiple regression model

$$y = \alpha + \beta_1 x_1 + \beta_2 x_2 + e$$

y	x_1	x_2	y	x_1	x_2
61	21.0	57.0	77	24.8	48.0
87	28.3	41.5	93	26.0	56.0
98	27.5	58.0	100	27.1	31.0
104	26.8	36.5	118	29.0	41.0
102	28.3	40.0	74	34.0	25.0
63	30.5	34.0	43	28.3	13.0
27	30.8	37.0	19	31.0	19.0
14	33.6	20.0	23	31.8	17.0
30	31.3	21.0	25	33.5	18.5
67	33.0	24.5	40	34.5	16.0
6	34.3	6.0	21	34.3	26.0
18	33.0	21.0	23	26.5	26.0
42	32.0	28.0	56	27.3	24.5
60	27.8	39.0	59	25.8	29.0
82	25.0	41.0	89	18.5	53.5
77	26.0	51.0	102	19.0	48.0
108	18.0	70.0	97	16.3	79.5

ACTIVITY 14.1 Exploring the Relationship Between Number of Predictors and Sample Size

This activity requires the use of a statistical computer package capable of fitting multiple regression models.

Background: The given data on y, x_1, x_2, x_3, and x_4 were generated using a computer package capable of producing random observations from any specified normal distribution. Because the data were generated at random, there is no reason to believe that y is related to any of the proposed predictor variables x_1, x_2, x_3, and x_4.

y	x_1	x_2	x_3	x_4
20.5	18.6	22.0	17.1	18.5
20.1	23.9	19.1	21.1	21.3
20.0	20.9	20.7	19.4	20.6
21.7	18.7	18.1	20.9	18.1
20.7	21.1	21.7	23.7	17.0

1. Construct four scatterplots—one of y versus each of x_1, x_2, x_3, and x_4. Do the scatterplots look the way you expected based on the way the data were generated? Explain.
2. Fit each of the following regression models:
   i. y with x_1
   ii. y with x_1 and x_2
   iii. y with x_1 and x_2 and x_3
   iv. y with x_1 and x_2 and x_3 and x_4
3. Make a table that gives the R^2, the adjusted R^2, and s_e values for each of the models fit in Step 2. Write a few sentences describing what happens to each of these three quantities as additional variables are added to the multiple regression model.
4. Given the manner in which these data were generated, what is the implication of what you observed in Step 3? What does this suggest about the relationship between number of predictors and sample size?

Summary of Key Concepts and Formulas

TERM OR FORMULA	COMMENT
Additive multiple regression model, $y = \alpha + \beta_1x_1 + \beta_2x_2 + \cdots + \beta_kx_k + e$	This equation specifies a general probabilistic relationship between y and k predictor variables $x_1, x_2, \ldots, x_k$, where $\alpha, \beta_1, \ldots, \beta_k$ are population regression coefficients and $\alpha + \beta_1x_1 + \beta_2x_2 + \cdots + \beta_kx_k$ is the population regression function (the mean value of y for fixed values of $x_1, x_2, \ldots, x_k$).
Estimated regression function, $\hat{y} = a + b_1x_1 + b_2x_2 + \cdots + b_kx_k$	The estimates $a, b_1, \ldots, b_k$ of $\alpha, \beta_1, \ldots, \beta_k$ result from applying the principle of least squares.
Coefficient of multiple determination, $R^2 = 1 - \dfrac{\text{SSResid}}{\text{SSTo}}$	The proportion of observed y variation that can be explained by the model relationship, where SSResid is defined as it is in simple linear regression but is now based on $n - (k + 1)$ degrees of freedom.
Adjusted R^2	A downward adjustment of R^2 that depends on the number of predictors k and the sample size n.
F distribution	A probability distribution used in the multiple regression model utility test. An F distribution is specified by a numerator df and a denominator df.
$F = \dfrac{\text{SSRegr}/k}{\text{SSResid}/(n - (k + 1))}$ or $F = \dfrac{R^2/k}{(1 - R^2)/(n - (k + 1))}$	The test statistic for testing $H_0: \beta_1 = \beta_2 = \cdots = \beta_k = 0$, which states that there is no useful linear relationship between y and any of the model predictors. The F test is upper-tailed and is based on numerator df $= k$ and denominator df $= n - (k + 1)$.

Royalty Free/Getty Images

Analysis of Variance

In Chapter 11 we discussed methods for testing H_0: $\mu_1 - \mu_2 = 0$ (that is, $\mu_1 = \mu_2$), where μ_1 and μ_2 are the means of two different populations or the mean responses when two different treatments are applied. Many investigations involve a comparison of more than two population or treatment means. For example, an investigation was carried out to study possible consequences of the high incidence of head injuries among soccer players ("No Evidence of Impaired Neurocognitive Performance in Collegiate Soccer Players," *The American Journal of Sports Medicine* [2002]: 157–162). Three groups of college students (soccer athletes, nonsoccer athletes, and a control group consisting of students who did not participate in intercollegiate sports) were considered in the study, and the following information on scores from the Hopkins Verbal Learning Test (which measures immediate memory recall) was given in the paper.

Group	Soccer Athletes	Nonsoccer Athletes	Control
Sample Size	86	95	53
Sample Mean Score	29.90	30.94	29.32
Sample Standard Deviation	3.73	5.14	3.78

Let μ_1, μ_2, and μ_3 denote the population mean scores on the Hopkins test for soccer athletes, nonsoccer athletes, and students who do not participate in collegiate athletics, respectively. Do the data support the claim that $\mu_1 = \mu_2 = \mu_3$, or does it appear that at least two of the μ's are different from one another? This is an example of a **single-factor analysis of variance (ANOVA)** problem, in which the objective is to decide whether the means for more than two populations or treatments are equal. The first two sections of this chapter discuss various aspects of single-factor ANOVA. In Sections 15.3 and 15.4 (which can be found online), we consider more complex ANOVA situations and methods.

15.1 Single-Factor ANOVA and the *F* Test

When two or more populations or treatments are being compared, the characteristic that distinguishes the populations or treatments from one another is called the **factor** under investigation. For example, an experiment might be carried out to compare three different methods for teaching reading (three different treatments), in which case the factor of interest would be *teaching method*, a qualitative factor. If the growth of fish raised in waters having different salinity levels—0%, 10%, 20%, and 30%—is of interest, the factor *salinity level* is quantitative.

A **single-factor analysis of variance (ANOVA)** problem involves a comparison of k population or treatment means $\mu_1, \mu_2, \ldots, \mu_k$. The objective is to test

$$H_0: \mu_1 = \mu_2 = \cdots = \mu_k$$

against

$$H_a: \text{At least two of the } \mu\text{'s are different}$$

When comparing populations, the analysis is based on independently selected random samples, one from each population. When comparing treatment means, the data typically result from an experiment and the analysis assumes random assignment of the experimental units (subjects or objects) to treatments. If, in addition, the experimental units are chosen at random from a population of interest, it is also possible to generalize the results of the analysis to this population. (See Chapter 2 for a more detailed discussion of conclusions that can reasonably be drawn based on data from an experiment.)

Whether the null hypothesis of a single-factor ANOVA should be rejected depends on how substantially the samples from the different populations or treatments differ from one another. Figure 15.1 displays observations that might result when random samples are selected from each of three populations. Each dotplot displays five observations from the first population, four observations from the second population, and six observations from the third population. For both displays, the three sample means are located by arrows. The means of the two samples from Population 1 are identical, and a similar statement holds for the two samples from Population 2 and those from Population 3.

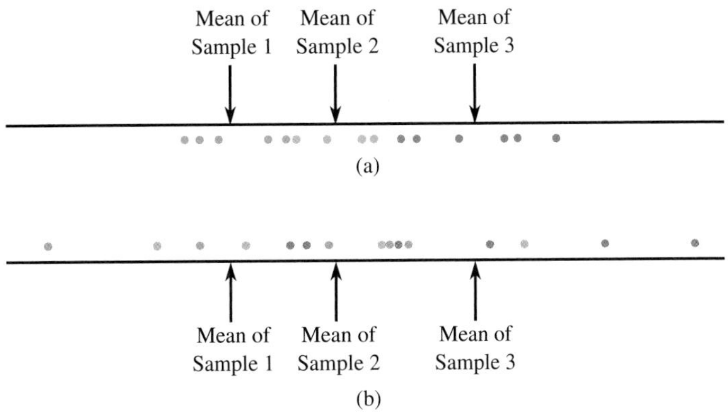

FIGURE 15.1
Two possible ANOVA data sets when three populations are under investigation: green circle = observation from Population 1; orange circle = observation from Population 2; blue circle = observation from Population 3.

After looking at the data in Figure 15.1(a), almost anyone would readily agree that the claim $\mu_1 = \mu_2 = \mu_3$ appears to be false. Not only are the three sample means different, but also the three samples are clearly separated. In other words, differences between the three sample means are quite large relative to the variability within each sample. (If all data sets gave such obvious messages, statisticians would not be in such great demand!)

The situation pictured in Figure 15.1(b) is much less clear-cut. The sample means are as different as they were in the first data set, but now there is considerable overlap among the three samples. The separation between sample means here can plausibly be attributed to substantial variability in the populations (and therefore the samples) rather than to differences between μ_1, μ_2, and μ_3. The phrase *analysis of variance* comes from the idea of analyzing variability in the data to see how much can be attributed to differences in the μ's and how much is due to variability in the individual populations. In Figure 15.1(a), the within-sample variability is small relative to the between-sample variability, whereas in Figure 15.1(b), a great deal more of the total variability is due to variation within each sample. If differences between the sample means can be explained by within-sample variability, there is no compelling reason to reject H_0.

Notations and Assumptions

Notation in single-factor ANOVA is a natural extension of the notation used in Chapter 11 for comparing two population or treatment means.

ANOVA Notation

k = number of populations or treatments being compared

Population or treatment	1	2	...	k
Population or treatment mean	μ_1	μ_2	...	μ_k
Population or treatment variance	σ_1^2	σ_2^2	...	σ_k^2
Sample size	n_1	n_2	...	n_k
Sample mean	$\bar{x}_1$	$\bar{x}_2$	...	$\bar{x}_k$
Sample variance	s_1^2	s_2^2	...	s_k^2

$N = n_1 + n_2 + \cdots + n_k$ (the total number of observations in the data set)

T = grand total = sum of all N observations in the data set $= n_1\bar{x}_1 + n_2\bar{x}_2 + \cdots + n_k\bar{x}_k$

$\bar{\bar{x}}$ = grand mean $= \dfrac{T}{N}$

A decision between H_0 and H_a is based on examining the $\bar{x}$ values to see whether observed discrepancies are small enough to be attributable simply to sampling variability or whether an alternative explanation for the differences is more plausible.

EXAMPLE 15.1 An Indicator of Heart Attack Risk

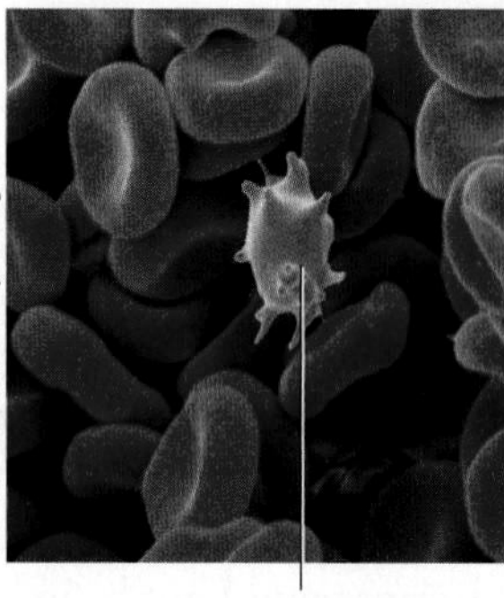

The article "Could Mean Platelet Volume Be a Predictive Marker for Acute Myocardial Infarction?" (*Medical Science Monitor* [2005]: 387–392) described an experiment in which four groups of patients seeking treatment for chest pain were compared with respect to mean platelet volume (MPV, measured in fL). The four groups considered were based on the clinical diagnosis and were (1) noncardiac chest pain, (2) stable angina pectoris, (3) unstable angina pectoris, and (4) myocardial infarction (heart attack). The purpose of the study was to determine if the mean MPV differed for the four groups, and in particular if the mean MPV was different for the heart attack group, because then MPV could be used as an indicator of heart attack risk and an antiplatelet treatment could be administered in a timely fashion, potentially reducing the risk of heart attack.

To carry out this study, patients seen for chest pain were divided into groups according to diagnosis. The researchers then selected a random sample of 35 from each of the resulting $k = 4$ groups. The researchers believed that this sampling process would result in samples that were representative of the four populations of interest and that could be regarded as if they were random samples from these four populations. Table 15.1 presents summary values given in the paper.

TABLE 15.1 Summary Values for MPV Data of Example 15.1

Group Number	Group Description	Sample Size	Sample Mean	Sample Standard Deviation
1	Noncardiac chest pain	35	10.89	0.69
2	Stable angina pectoris	35	11.25	0.74
3	Unstable angina pectoris	35	11.37	0.91
4	Myocardial infarction (heart attack)	35	11.75	1.07

With μ_i denoting the true mean MPV for group i ($i = 1, 2, 3, 4$), let's consider the null hypothesis H_0: $\mu_1 = \mu_2 = \mu_3 = \mu_4$. Figure 15.2 shows a comparative boxplot for the four samples (based on data consistent with summary values given in the paper). The mean MPV for the heart attack sample is larger than for the other three samples and the boxplot for the heart attack sample appears to be shifted a bit higher

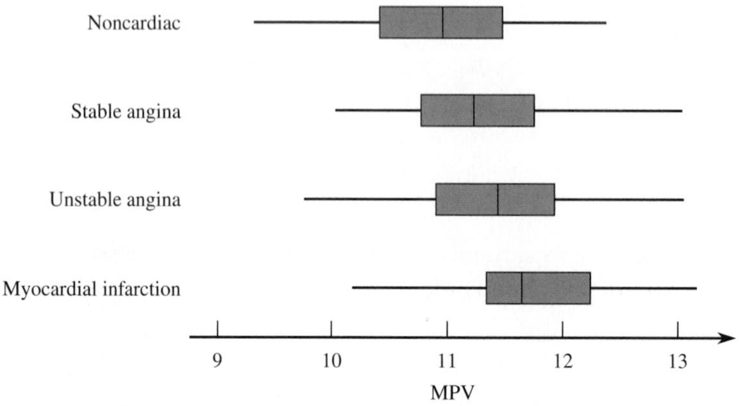

FIGURE 15.2
Boxplots for Example 15.1.

than the boxplots for the other three samples. However, because the four boxplots show substantial overlap, it is not obvious whether H_0 is true or false. In situations such as this, we need a formal test procedure.

As with the inferential methods of previous chapters, the validity of the ANOVA test for H_0: $\mu_1 = \mu_2 = \cdots = \mu_k$ requires some assumptions.

Assumptions for ANOVA

1. Each of the k population or treatment response distributions is normal.
2. $\sigma_1 = \sigma_2 = \cdots = \sigma_k$ (The k normal distributions have identical standard deviations.)
3. The observations in the sample from any particular one of the k populations or treatments are independent of one another.
4. When comparing population means, the k random samples are selected independently of one another. When comparing treatment means, treatments are assigned at random to subjects or objects (or subjects are assigned at random to treatments).

In practice, the test based on these assumptions works well as long as the assumptions are not too badly violated. If the sample sizes are reasonably large, normal probability plots or boxplots of the data in each sample are helpful in checking the assumption of normality. Often, however, sample sizes are so small that a separate normal probability plot or boxplot for each sample is of little value in checking normality. In this case, a single combined plot can be constructed by first subtracting $\bar{x}_1$ from each observation in the first sample, $\bar{x}_2$ from each value in the second sample, and so on and then constructing a normal probability or boxplot of all N deviations from their respective means. The plot should be reasonably straight. Figure 15.3 shows such a normal probability plot for the data of Example 15.1.

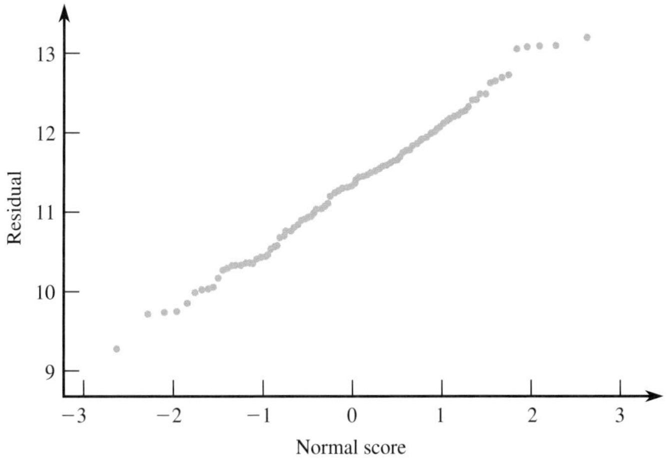

FIGURE 15.3
A normal probability plot using the combined data of Example 15.1.

There is a formal procedure for testing the equality of population standard deviations. Unfortunately, it is quite sensitive to even a small departure from the normality assumption, so we do not recommend its use. Instead, we suggest that the ANOVA F test (to be described later in this section) can safely be used if the largest of the sample standard deviations is at most twice the smallest one. The largest standard deviation in Example 15.1 is $s_4 = 1.07$, which is only about 1.5 times the smallest standard deviation ($s_1 = 0.69$). The book *Beyond ANOVA: The Basics of Applied Statistics* by Rupert (see the references in the back of the book) is a good source for alternative methods of analysis if there appears to be a violation of assumptions.

The analysis of variance test procedure is based on the following measures of variation in the data.

DEFINITION

A measure of differences among the sample means is the **treatment sum of squares,** denoted by **SSTr** and given by

$$\text{SSTr} = n_1(\bar{x}_1 - \bar{\bar{x}})^2 + n_2(\bar{x}_2 - \bar{\bar{x}})^2 + \cdots + n_k(\bar{x}_k - \bar{\bar{x}})^2$$

A measure of variation within the k samples, called **error sum of squares** and denoted by **SSE,** is

$$\text{SSE} = (n_1 - 1)s_1^2 + (n_2 - 1)s_2^2 + \cdots + (n_k - 1)s_k^2$$

Each sum of squares has an associated df:

$$\text{treatment df} = k - 1 \qquad \text{error df} = N - k$$

A **mean square** is a sum of squares divided by its df. In particular,

$$\textbf{mean square for treatments} = \textbf{MSTr} = \frac{\text{SSTr}}{k-1}$$

$$\textbf{mean square for error} = \textbf{MSE} = \frac{SSE}{N-k}$$

The number of error degrees of freedom comes from adding the number of degrees of freedom associated with each of the sample variances:

$$(n_1 - 1) + (n_2 - 1) + \cdots + (n_k - 1) = n_1 + n_2 + \cdots + n_k - 1 - 1 - \cdots - 1$$
$$= N - k$$

EXAMPLE 15.2 Heart Attack Calculations

Let's return to the mean platelet volume (MPV) data of Example 15.1. The grand mean $\bar{\bar{x}}$ was computed to be 11.315. Notice that because the sample sizes are all equal, the grand mean is just the average of the four sample means (this will not usually be the case when the sample sizes are unequal). With $\bar{x}_1 = 10.89$, $\bar{x}_2 = 11.25$, $\bar{x}_3 = 11.37$, $\bar{x}_4 = 11.75$, and $n_1 = n_2 = n_3 = n_4 = 35$,

$$\begin{aligned}\text{SSTr} &= n_1(\bar{x}_1 - \bar{\bar{x}})^2 + n_2(\bar{x}_2 - \bar{\bar{x}})^2 + \cdots + n_k(\bar{x}_k - \bar{\bar{x}})^2 \\ &= 35(10.89 - 11.315)^2 + 35(11.25 - 11.315)^2 + 35(11.37 - 11.315)^2 \\ &\quad + 35(11.75 - 11.315)^2 \\ &= 6.322 + 0.148 + 0.106 + 6.623 \\ &= 13.199\end{aligned}$$

Because $s_1 = 0.69$, $s_2 = 0.74$, $s_3 = 0.91$, and $s_4 = 1.07$

$$\begin{aligned}\text{SSE} &= (n_1 - 1)s_1^2 + (n_2 - 1)s_2^2 + \cdots + (n_k - 1)s_k^2 \\ &= (35 - 1)(0.69)^2 + (35 - 1)(0.74)^2 + (35 - 1)(0.91)^2 + (35 - 1)(1.07)^2 \\ &= 101.888\end{aligned}$$

The numbers of degrees of freedom are

treatment df $= k - 1 = 3$ error df $= N - k = 35 + 35 + 35 + 35 - 4 = 136$

from which

$$\text{MSTr} = \frac{\text{SSTr}}{k-1} = \frac{13.199}{3} = 4.400$$

$$\text{MSE} = \frac{\text{SSE}}{N-k} = \frac{101.888}{136} = 0.749$$

Both MSTr and MSE are quantities whose values can be calculated once sample data are available; that is, they are statistics. Each of these statistics varies in value from data set to data set. Both statistics MSTr and MSE have sampling distributions, and these sampling distributions have mean values. The following box describes the key relationship between MSTr and MSE and the mean values of these two statistics.

When H_0 is true $(\mu_1 = \mu_2 = \cdots = \mu_k)$,

$$\mu_{\text{MSTr}} = \mu_{\text{MSE}}$$

However, when H_0 is false,

$$\mu_{\text{MSTr}} > \mu_{\text{MSE}}$$

and the greater the differences among the μ's, the larger μ_{MSTr} will be relative to μ_{MSE}.

According to this result, when H_0 is true, we expect the two mean squares to be close to one another, whereas we expect MSTr to substantially exceed MSE when some μ's differ greatly from others. Thus, a calculated MSTr that is much larger than MSE casts doubt on H_0. In Example 15.2, MSTr $= 4.400$ and MSE $= 0.749$, so MSTr is about 6 times as large as MSE. Can this difference be attributed solely to sampling variability, or is the ratio MSTr/MSE large enough to suggest that H_0 is false? Before we can describe a formal test procedure, it is necessary to revisit F distributions, first introduced in multiple regression analysis (Chapter 14).

Many ANOVA test procedures are based on a family of probability distributions called F distributions. An F distribution always arises in connection with a ratio. A particular F distribution is obtained by specifying both numerator degrees of freedom (df_1) and denominator degrees of freedom (df_2). Figure 15.4 shows an F curve for a particular choice of df_1 and df_2. All F tests in this book are upper-tailed, so P-values are areas under the F curve to the right of the calculated values of F.

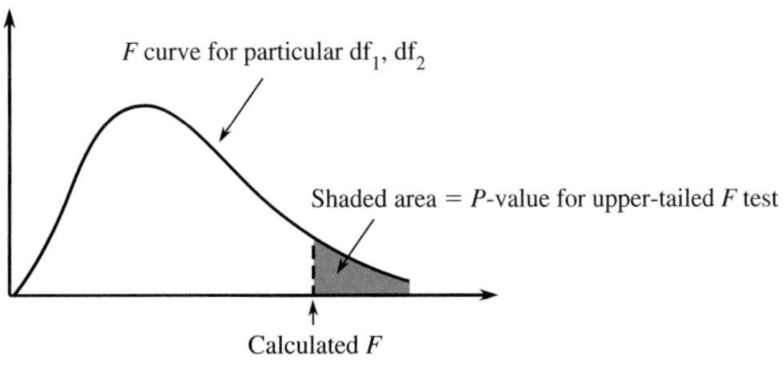

FIGURE 15.4
An F curve and P-value for an upper-tailed test.

Tabulation of these upper-tail areas is cumbersome, because there are two degrees of freedom rather than just one (as in the case of t distributions). For selected (df_1, df_2) pairs, the F table (Appendix Table 6) gives only the four numbers that capture tail areas .10, .05, .01, and .001, respectively. Here are the four numbers for $df_1 = 4$, $df_2 = 10$ along with the statements that can be made about the P-value:

Tail area		.10		.05		.01		.001	
Value		2.61		3.48		5.99		11.28	
	↑		↑		↑		↑		↑
	a		b		c		d		e

a. $F < 2.61 \rightarrow$ tail area $=$ P-value $> .10$
b. $2.61 < F < 3.48 \rightarrow .05 <$ P-value $< .10$
c. $3.48 < F < 5.99 \rightarrow .01 <$ P-value $< .05$
d. $5.99 < F < 11.28 \rightarrow .001 <$ P-value $< .01$
e. $F > 11.28 \rightarrow$ P-value $< .001$

If $F = 7.12$, then $.001 <$ P-value $< .01$. If a test with $\alpha < .05$ is used, H_0 should be rejected, because P-value $\leq \alpha$. The most frequently used statistical computer packages can provide exact P-values for F tests.

The Single-Factor ANOVA *F* Test

Null hypothesis: H_0: $\mu_1 = \mu_2 = \cdots = \mu_k$

Test statistic: $F = \dfrac{\text{MSTr}}{\text{MSE}}$

When H_0 is true and the ANOVA assumptions are reasonable, F has an F distribution with $df_1 = k - 1$ and $df_2 = N - k$.

Values of F more inconsistent with H_0 than what was observed in the data are values even farther out in the upper tail, so the P-value is the area captured in the upper tail of the corresponding F curve. Appendix Table 6, a statistical software package, or a graphing calculator can be used to determine P-values for F tests.

EXAMPLE 15.3 Heart Attacks Revisited

The two mean squares for the MPV data given in Example 15.1 were calculated in Example 15.2 as

$$\text{MSTr} = 4.400 \qquad \text{MSE} = 0.749$$

The value of the F statistic is then

$$F = \frac{\text{MSTr}}{\text{MSE}} = \frac{4.400}{0.749} = 5.87$$

with $df_1 = k - 1 = 3$ and $df_2 = N - k = 140 - 4 = 136$. Using $df_1 = 3$ and $df_2 = 120$ (the closest value to 136 that appears in the table), Appendix Table 6 shows that 5.78 captures tail area .001. Since $5.87 > 5.78$, it follows that P-value $=$ captured tail area $< .001$. The P-value is smaller than any reasonable α, so there is compelling evidence for rejecting H_0: $\mu_1 = \mu_2 = \cdots = \mu_4$. We can conclude that the mean MPV is not the same for all four patient populations. Techniques for determining which means differ are introduced in Section 15.2.

EXAMPLE 15.4 Hormones and Body Fat

● The article "Growth Hormone and Sex Steroid Administration in Healthy Aged Women and Men" (*Journal of the American Medical Association* [2002]: 2282–2292) described an experiment to investigate the effect of four treatments on various body characteristics. In this double-blind experiment, each of 57 female subjects age 65 or older was assigned at random to one of the following four treatments: (1) placebo "growth hormone" and placebo "steroid" (denoted by P + P); (2) placebo "growth hormone" and the steroid estradiol (denoted by P + S); (3) growth hormone and placebo "steroid" (denoted by G + P); and (4) growth hormone and the steroid estradiol (denoted by G + S).

The following table lists data on change in body fat mass over the 26-week period following the treatments that are consistent with summary quantities given in the article.

	CHANGE IN BODY FAT MASS (KG)			
Treatment	P + P	P + S	G + P	G + S
	0.1	−0.1	−1.6	−3.1
	0.6	0.2	−0.4	−3.2
	2.2	0.0	0.4	−2.0
	0.7	−0.4	−2.0	−2.0
	−2.0	−0.9	−3.4	−3.3
	0.7	−1.1	−2.8	−0.5
	0.0	1.2	−2.2	−4.5
	−2.6	0.1	−1.8	−0.7
	−1.4	0.7	−3.3	−1.8
	1.5	−2.0	−2.1	−2.3
	2.8	−0.9	−3.6	−1.3
	0.3	−3.0	−0.4	−1.0
	−1.0	1.0	−3.1	−5.6
	−1.0	1.2		−2.9
				−1.6
				−0.2
n	14	14	13	16
$\bar{x}$	0.064	−0.286	−2.023	−2.250
s	1.545	1.218	1.264	1.468
s^2	2.387	1.484	1.598	2.155

Also, $N = 57$, grand total $= -65.4$, and $\bar{\bar{x}} = \dfrac{-65.4}{57} = -1.15$.

Let's carry out an F test to see whether actual mean change in body fat mass differs for the four treatments.

1. Let μ_1, μ_2, μ_3, and μ_4 denote the true mean change in body fat for treatments P + P, P + S, G + P, and G + S, respectively.

Step-by-Step technology instructions available online

● Data set available online

2. H_0: $\mu_1 = \mu_2 = \mu_3 = \mu_4$
3. H_a: At least two among μ_1, μ_2, μ_3, and μ_4 are different.
4. Significance level: $\alpha = .01$
5. Test statistic: $F = \dfrac{\text{MSTr}}{\text{MSE}}$
6. Assumptions: Figure 15.5 shows boxplots of the data from each of the four samples. The boxplots are roughly symmetric, and there are no outliers. The largest standard deviation ($s_1 = 1.545$) is not more than twice as big as the smallest ($s_2 = 1.264$). The subjects were randomly assigned to treatments. The assumptions of ANOVA are reasonable.

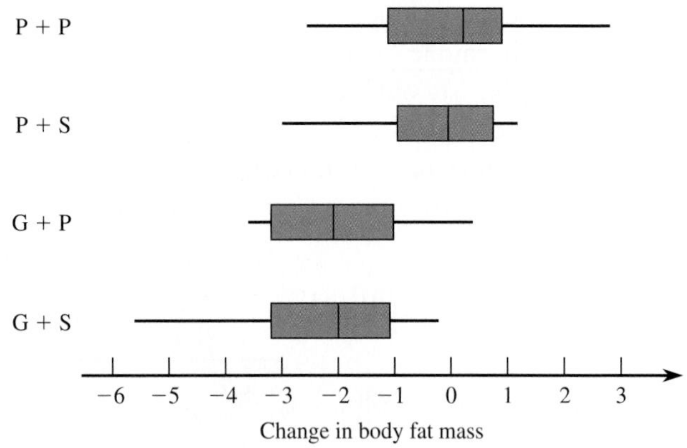

FIGURE 15.5
Boxplots for the data of Example 15.4.

7. Computation:

$$\begin{aligned}\text{SSTr} &= n_1(\bar{x}_1 - \bar{\bar{x}})^2 + n_2(\bar{x}_2 - \bar{\bar{x}})^2 + \cdots + n_k(\bar{x}_k - \bar{\bar{x}})^2\\ &= 14(0.064 - (-1.15))^2 + 14(-0.286 - (-1.15))^2\\ &\quad + 13(-2.023 - (-1.15))^2 + 16(-2.250 - (-1.15))^2\\ &= 60.37\end{aligned}$$

treatment df $= k - 1 = 3$

$$\begin{aligned}\text{SSE} &= (n_1 - 1)s_1^2 + (n_2 - 1)s_2^2 + \cdots + (n_k - 1)s_k^2\\ &= 13(2.387) + 13(1.484) + 12(1.598) + 15(2.155)\\ &= 101.81\end{aligned}$$

error df $= N - k = 57 - 4 = 53$

Thus,

$$F = \frac{\text{MSTr}}{\text{MSE}} = \frac{\text{SSTr/treatment df}}{\text{SSE/error df}} = \frac{60.37/3}{101.81/53} = \frac{20.12}{1.92} = 10.48$$

8. P-value: Appendix Table 6 shows that for $\text{df}_1 = 3$ and $\text{df}_2 = 60$ (the closest tabled df to df = 53), the value 6.17 captures upper-tail area .001. Because $F = 10.48 > 6.17$, it follows $P\text{-value} < .001$.
9. Conclusion: Since $P\text{-value} \le \alpha$, we reject H_0. The mean change in body fat mass is not the same for all four treatments.

Summarizing an ANOVA

ANOVA calculations are often summarized in a tabular format called an ANOVA table. To understand such a table, we must define one more sum of squares.

Total sum of squares, denoted by **SSTo,** is given by

$$\text{SSTo} = \sum_{\text{all } N \text{ obs.}} (x - \bar{\bar{x}})^2$$

with associated df $= N - 1$.

The relationship between the three sums of squares SSTo, SSTr, and SSE is

$$\text{SSTo} = \text{SSTr} + \text{SSE}$$

which is called the *fundamental identity for single-factor ANOVA.*

The quantity SSTo, the sum of squared deviations about the grand mean, is a measure of total variability in the data set consisting of all k samples. The quantity SSE results from measuring variability separately within each sample and then combining as indicated in the formula for SSE. Such within-sample variability is present regardless of whether or not H_0 is true. The magnitude of SSTr, on the other hand, has much to do with whether the null hypothesis is true or false. The more the μ's differ from one another, the larger SSTr will tend to be. Thus, SSTr represents variation that can (at least to some extent) be explained by any differences between means. An informal paraphrase of the fundamental identity for single-factor ANOVA is

total variation = explained variation + unexplained variation

Once any two of the sums of squares have been calculated, the remaining one is easily obtained from the fundamental identity. Often SSTo and SSTr are calculated first (using computational formulas given in the online appendix to this chapter), and then SSE is obtained by subtraction: SSE = SSTo − SSTr. All the degrees of freedom, sums of squares, and mean squares are entered in an ANOVA table, as displayed in Table 15.2. The P-value usually appears to the right of F when the analysis is done by a statistical software package.

TABLE 15.2 General Format for a Single-Factor ANOVA Table

Source of Variation	df	Sum of Squares	Mean Square	F
Treatments	$k - 1$	SSTr	$\text{MSTr} = \dfrac{\text{SSTr}}{k - 1}$	$F = \dfrac{\text{MSTr}}{\text{MSE}}$
Error	$N - k$	SSE	$\text{MSE} = \dfrac{\text{SSE}}{N - k}$	
Total	$N - 1$	SSTo		

An ANOVA table from Minitab for the change in body fat mass data of Example 15.4 is shown in Table 15.3. The reported P-value is .000, consistent with our previous conclusion that P-value $< .001$.

TABLE 15.3 An ANOVA Table from Minitab for the Data of Example 15.4

One-way ANOVA

Source	DF	SS	MS	F	P
Factor	3	60.37	20.12	10.48	0.000
Error	53	101.81	1.92		
Total	56	162.18			

EXERCISES 15.1 - 15.13

15.1 Give as much information as you can about the *P*-value for an upper-tailed *F* test in each of the following situations.

a. $df_1 = 4$, $df_2 = 15$, $F = 5.37$
b. $df_1 = 4$, $df_2 = 15$, $F = 1.90$
c. $df_1 = 4$, $df_2 = 15$, $F = 4.89$
d. $df_1 = 3$, $df_2 = 20$, $F = 14.48$
e. $df_1 = 3$, $df_2 = 20$, $F = 2.69$
f. $df_1 = 4$, $df_2 = 50$, $F = 3.24$

15.2 Give as much information as you can about the *P*-value of the single-factor ANOVA *F* test in each of the following situations.

a. $k = 5$, $n_1 = n_2 = n_3 = n_4 = n_5 = 4$, $F = 5.37$
b. $k = 5$, $n_1 = n_2 = n_3 = 5$, $n_4 = n_5 = 4$, $F = 2.83$
c. $k = 3$, $n_1 = 4$, $n_2 = 5$, $n_3 = 6$, $F = 5.02$
d. $k = 3$, $n_1 = n_2 = 4$, $n_3 = 6$, $F = 15.90$
e. $k = 4$, $n_1 = n_2 = 15$, $n_3 = 12$, $n_4 = 10$, $F = 1.75$

15.3 Employees of a certain state university system can choose from among four different health plans. Each plan differs somewhat from the others in terms of hospitalization coverage. Four samples of recently hospitalized individuals were selected, each sample consisting of people covered by a different health plan. The length of the hospital stay (number of days) was determined for each individual selected.

a. What hypotheses would you test to decide whether mean length of stay was related to health plan? (*Note*: Carefully define the population characteristics of interest.)
b. If each sample consisted of eight individuals and the value of the ANOVA *F* statistic was $F = 4.37$, what conclusion would be appropriate for a test with $\alpha = .01$?
c. Answer the question posed in Part (b) if the *F* value given there resulted from sample sizes $n_1 = 9$, $n_2 = 8$, $n_3 = 7$, and $n_4 = 8$.

15.4 The accompanying summary statistics for a measure of social marginality for samples of youths, young adults, adults, and seniors appeared in the paper "Perceived Causes of Loneliness in Adulthood" (*Journal of Social Behavior and Personality* [2000]: 67–84). The social marginality score measured actual and perceived social rejection, with higher scores indicating greater social rejection. For purposes of this exercise, assume that it is reasonable to regard the four samples as representative of the U.S. population in the corresponding age groups and that the distributions of social marginality scores for these four groups are approximately normal with the same standard deviation. Is there evidence that the mean social marginality score is not the same for all four age groups? Test the relevant hypotheses using $\alpha = .01$.

Age Group	Youths	Young Adults	Adults	Seniors
Sample Size	106	255	314	36
$\bar{x}$	2.00	3.40	3.07	2.84
s	1.56	1.68	1.66	1.89

15.5 ● The authors of the paper "Age and Violent Content Labels Make Video Games Forbidden Fruits for Youth" (*Pediatrics* [2009]: 870–876) carried out an experiment to determine if restrictive labels on video games actually increased the attractiveness of the game for young game players. Participants read a description of a new video game and were asked how much they wanted to play the game. The description also included an age rating. Some participants read the description with an age restrictive label of 7+, indicating that the game was not appropriate for children under the age of 7. Others read the same description, but with an age restrictive label of 12+, 16+, or 18+. The data below for 12- to 13-year-old boys are fictitious, but are consistent with summary statistics given in the paper. (The sample sizes in the actual experiment were larger.) For purposes of this exercise, you can assume that the boys were assigned at random to one of the four age label treatments (7+, 12+, 16+, and 18+). Data shown are the boys' ratings of how much they wanted to play the game on a scale of 1 to 10. Do the data provide convincing evidence that the mean rating associated with the game description by 12- to 13-year-old boys is not the same for all four restrictive rating labels? Test the appropriate hypotheses using a significance level of .05.

7+ label	12+ label	16+ label	18+ label
6	8	7	10
6	7	9	9
6	8	8	6
5	5	6	8
4	7	7	7
8	9	4	6
6	5	8	8
1	8	9	9
2	4	6	10
4	7	7	8

15.6 ● The paper referenced in the previous exercise also gave data for 12- to 13-year-old girls. Data consistent with summary values in the paper are shown below. Do the data provide convincing evidence that the mean rating associated with the game description for 12- to 13-year-old girls is not the same for all four age restrictive rating labels? Test the appropriate hypotheses using $\alpha = .05$.

7+ label	12+ label	16+ label	18+ label
4	4	6	8
7	5	4	6
6	4	8	6
5	6	6	5
3	3	10	7
6	5	8	4
4	3	6	10
5	8	6	6
10	5	8	8
5	9	5	7

15.7 ● The paper "Women's and Men's Eating Behavior Following Exposure to Ideal-Body Images and Text" (*Communication Research* [2006]: 507–529) describes an experiment in which 74 men were assigned at random to one of four treatments:

1. Viewed slides of fit, muscular men
2. Viewed slides of fit, muscular men accompanied by diet and fitness-related text
3. Viewed slides of fit, muscular men accompanied by text not related to diet and fitness
4. Did not view any slides

The participants then went to a room to complete a questionnaire. In this room, bowls of pretzels were set out on the tables. A research assistant noted how many pretzels were consumed by each participant while completing the questionnaire. Data consistent with summary quantities given in the paper are given in the accompanying table. Do these data provide convincing evidence that the mean number of pretzels consumed is not the same for all four treatments? Test the relevant hypotheses using a significance level of .05.

Treatment 1	Treatment 2	Treatment 3	Treatment 4
8	6	1	5
7	8	5	2
4	0	2	5
13	4	0	7
2	9	3	5

(continued)

Treatment 1	Treatment 2	Treatment 3	Treatment 4
1	8	0	2
5	6	3	0
8	2	4	0
11	7	4	3
5	8	5	4
1	8	5	2
0	5	7	4
6	14	8	1
4	9	4	1
10	0	0	
7	6	6	
0	3	3	
12	12		
	5		
	6		
	10		
	8		
	6		
	2		
	10		

15.8 Can use of an online plagiarism-detection system reduce plagiarism in student research papers? The paper "Plagiarism and Technology: A Tool for Coping with Plagiarism" (*Journal of Education for Business* [2005]: 149–152) describes a study in which randomly selected research papers submitted by students during five semesters were analyzed for plagiarism. For each paper, the percentage of plagiarized words in the paper was determined by an online analysis. In each of the five semesters, students were told during the first two class meetings that they would have to submit an electronic version of their research papers and that the papers would be reviewed for plagiarism. Suppose that the number of papers sampled in each of the five semesters and the means and standard deviations for percentage of plagiarized words are as given in the accompanying table. For purposes of this exercise, assume that the conditions necessary for the ANOVA F test are reasonable. Do these data provide evidence to support the claim that mean percentage of plagiarized words is not the same for all five semesters? Test the appropriate hypotheses using $\alpha = .05$.

Semester	n	Mean	Standard deviation
1	39	6.31	3.75
2	42	3.31	3.06
3	32	1.79	3.25
4	32	1.83	3.13
5	34	1.50	2.37

15.9 ● The experiment described in Example 15.4 also gave data on change in body fat mass for men ("Growth Hormone and Sex Steroid Administration in Healthy Aged Women and Men," *Journal of the American Medical Association* [2002]: 2282–2292). Each of 74 male subjects who were over age 65 was assigned at random to one of the following four treatments: (1) placebo "growth hormone" and placebo "steroid" (denoted by P + P); (2) placebo "growth hormone" and the steroid testosterone (denoted by P + S); (3) growth hormone and placebo "steroid" (denoted by G + P); and (4) growth hormone and the steroid testosterone (denoted by G + S). The accompanying table lists data on change in body fat mass over the 26-week period following the treatment that are consistent with summary quantities given in the article.

	Change in Body Fat Mass (kg)			
Treatment	P + P	P + S	G + P	G + S
	0.3	−3.7	−3.8	−5.0
	0.4	−1.0	−3.2	−5.0
	−1.7	0.2	−4.9	−3.0
	−0.5	−2.3	−5.2	−2.6
	−2.1	1.5	−2.2	−6.2
	1.3	−1.4	−3.5	−7.0
	0.8	1.2	−4.4	−4.5
	1.5	−2.5	−0.8	−4.2
	−1.2	−3.3	−1.8	−5.2
	−0.2	0.2	−4.0	−6.2
	1.7	0.6	−1.9	−4.0
	1.2	−0.7	−3.0	−3.9
	0.6	−0.1	−1.8	−3.3
	0.4	−3.1	−2.9	−5.7
	−1.3	0.3	−2.9	−4.5
	−0.2	−0.5	−2.9	−4.3
	0.7	−0.8	−3.7	−4.0
		−0.7		−4.2
		−0.9		−4.7
		−2.0		
		−0.6		
n	17	21	17	19
$\bar{x}$	0.100	−0.933	−3.112	−4.605
s	1.139	1.443	1.178	1.122
s^2	1.297	2.082	1.388	1.259

Also, $N = 74$, grand total $= -158.3$, and $\bar{\bar{x}} = \frac{-158.3}{74} = -2.139$. Carry out an F test to see whether mean change in body fat mass differs for the four treatments.

15.10 ● The article "Compression of Single-Wall Corrugated Shipping Containers Using Fixed and Floating Text Platens" (*Journal of Testing and Evaluation* [1992]: 318–320) described an experiment in which several different types of boxes were compared with respect to compression strength (in pounds). The data at the top of page 847 resulted from a single-factor experiment involving $k = 4$ types of boxes (the sample means and standard deviations are in close agreement with values given in the paper). Do these data provide evidence to support the claim that the mean compression strength is not the same for all four box types? Test the relevant hypothesis using a significance level of .01.

15.11 In the introduction to this chapter, we considered a study comparing three groups of college students (soccer athletes, nonsoccer athletes, and a control group consisting of students who did not participate in intercollegiate sports). The following information on scores from the Hopkins Verbal Learning Test (which measures immediate memory recall) was

Group	Soccer Athletes	Nonsoccer Athletes	Control
Sample size	86	95	53
Sample mean score	29.90	30.94	29.32
Sample standard deviation	3.73	5.14	3.78

In addition, $\bar{\bar{x}} = 30.19$. Suppose that it is reasonable to regard these three samples as random samples from the three student populations of interest. Is there sufficient evidence to conclude that the mean Hopkins score is not the same for the three student populations? Use $\alpha = .05$.

15.12 ● The accompanying data on calcium content of wheat are consistent with summary quantities that appeared in the article "Mineral Contents of Cereal Grains as Affected by Storage and Insect Infestation" (*Journal of Stored Products Research* [1992]: 147–151). Four different storage times were considered. Partial output from the SAS computer package is also shown.

Storage Period	Observations					
0 months	58.75	57.94	58.91	56.85	55.21	57.30
1 month	58.87	56.43	56.51	57.67	59.75	58.48
2 months	59.13	60.38	58.01	59.95	59.51	60.34
4 months	62.32	58.76	60.03	59.36	59.61	61.95

Table for Exercise 15.10

Type of Box	Compression Strength (lb)						Sample Mean	Sample SD
1	655.5	788.3	734.3	721.4	679.1	699.4	713.00	46.55
2	789.2	772.5	786.9	686.1	732.1	774.8	756.93	40.34
3	737.1	639.0	696.3	671.7	717.2	727.1	698.07	37.20
4	535.1	628.7	542.4	559.0	586.9	520.0	562.02	39.87
							$\bar{\bar{x}} = 682.50$	

Dependent Variable: CALCIUM

Source	DF	Sum of Squares	Mean Square	F Value	Pr>F
Model	3	32.13815000	10.71271667	6.51	0.0030
Error	20	32.90103333	1.64505167		
Corrected Total	23	65.03918333			

R-Square	C.V.	Root MSE	CALCIUM Mean
0.494135	2.180018	1.282596	58.8341667

a. Verify that the sums of squares and df's are as given in the ANOVA table.

b. Is there sufficient evidence to conclude that the mean calcium content is not the same for the four different storage times? Use the value of F from the ANOVA table to test the appropriate hypotheses at significance level .05.

15.13 In an experiment to investigate the performance of four different brands of spark plugs intended for use on a 125-cc motorcycle, five plugs of each brand were tested, and the number of miles (at a constant speed) until failure was observed. A partially completed ANOVA table is given. Fill in the missing entries, and test the relevant hypotheses using a .05 level of significance.

Source of Variation	df	Sum of Squares	Mean Square	F
Treatments				
Error		235,419.04		
Total		310,500.76		

15.2 Multiple Comparisons

When H_0: $\mu_1 = \mu_2 = \cdots = \mu_k$ is rejected by the F test, we believe that there are differences among the k population or treatment means. A natural question to ask at this point is, Which means differ? For example, with $k = 4$, it might be the case that $\mu_1 = \mu_2 = \mu_4$, with μ_3 different from the other three means. Another possibility is that $\mu_1 = \mu_4$ and $\mu_2 = \mu_3$. Still another possibility is that all four means are different from one another. A **multiple comparisons procedure** is a method for identifying differences among the μ's once the hypothesis of overall equality has been rejected. We present one such method, the **Tukey-Kramer** (T-K) multiple comparisons procedure.

The T-K procedure is based on computing confidence intervals for the difference between each possible pair of μ's. For example, for $k = 3$, there are three differences to consider:

$$\mu_1 - \mu_2 \qquad \mu_1 - \mu_3 \qquad \mu_2 - \mu_3$$

(The difference $\mu_2 - \mu_1$ is not considered, because the interval for $\mu_1 - \mu_2$ provides the same information. Similarly, intervals for $\mu_3 - \mu_1$ and $\mu_3 - \mu_2$ are not necessary.) Once all confidence intervals have been computed, each is examined to determine whether the interval includes 0. If a particular interval does not include 0, the two means are declared "significantly different" from one another. An interval that does include 0 supports the conclusion that there is no significant difference between the means involved.

Suppose, for example, that $k = 3$ and that the three confidence intervals are

Difference	T-K Confidence Interval
$\mu_1 - \mu_2$	$(-.9, 3.5)$
$\mu_1 - \mu_3$	$(2.6, 7.0)$
$\mu_2 - \mu_3$	$(1.2, 5.7)$

Because the interval for $\mu_1 - \mu_2$ includes 0, we judge that μ_1 and μ_2 do not differ significantly. The other two intervals do not include 0, so we conclude that $\mu_1 \neq \mu_3$ and $\mu_2 \neq \mu_3$.

The T-K intervals are based on critical values for a probability distribution called the *Studentized range distribution*. These critical values appear in Appendix Table 7. To find a critical value, enter the table at the column corresponding to the number of populations or treatments being compared, move down to the rows corresponding to the number of error degrees of freedom, and select either the value for a 95% confidence level or the one for a 99% level.

The Tukey–Kramer Multiple Comparison Procedure

When there are k populations or treatments being compared, $\frac{k(k-1)}{2}$ confidence intervals must be computed. Denoting the relevant Studentized range critical value (from Appendix Table 7) by q, the intervals are as follows:

$$\text{For } \mu_i - \mu_j: \quad (\bar{x}_i - \bar{x}_j) \pm q\sqrt{\frac{\text{MSE}}{2}\left(\frac{1}{n_i} + \frac{1}{n_j}\right)}$$

Two means are judged to differ significantly if the corresponding interval does not include zero.

If the sample sizes are all the same, we can use n to denote the common value of $n_1, \ldots, n_k$. In this case, the $\pm$ factor for each interval is the same quantity

$$q\sqrt{\frac{\text{MSE}}{n}}$$

EXAMPLE 15.5 Hormones and Body Fat Revisited

● Example 15.4 introduced the accompanying data on change in body fat mass resulting from a double-blind experiment designed to compare the following four treatments: (1) placebo "growth hormone" and placebo "steroid" (denoted by P + P); (2) placebo "growth hormone" and the steroid estradiol (denoted by P + S); (3) growth hormone and placebo "steroid" (denoted by G + P); and (4) growth hormone and the steroid estradiol (denoted by G + S). From Example 15.4, MSTr = 20.12, MSE = 1.92, and $F = 10.48$ with an associated P-value $< .001$. We concluded that the mean change in body fat mass is not the same for all four treatments.

● Data set available online

	CHANGE IN BODY FAT MASS (KG)			
Treatment	P + P	P + S	G + P	G + S
	0.1	−0.1	−1.6	−3.1
	0.6	0.2	−0.4	−3.2
	2.2	0.0	0.4	−2.0
	0.7	−0.4	−2.0	−2.0
	−2.0	−0.9	−3.4	−3.3
	0.7	−1.1	−2.8	−0.5
	0.0	1.2	−2.2	−4.5
	−2.6	0.1	−1.8	−0.7
	−1.4	0.7	−3.3	−1.8
	1.5	−2.0	−2.1	−2.3
	2.8	−0.9	−3.6	−1.3
	0.3	−3.0	−0.4	−1.0
	−1.0	1.0	−3.1	−5.6
	−1.0	1.2		−2.9
				−1.6
				−0.2
n	14	14	13	16
$\bar{x}$	0.064	−0.286	−2.023	−2.250
s	1.545	1.218	1.264	1.468
s^2	2.387	1.484	1.598	2.155

Appendix Table 7 gives the 95% Studentized range critical value $q = 3.74$ (using $k = 4$ and error df $= 60$, the closest tabled value to df $= N - k = 53$). The first two T-K intervals are

$$\mu_1 - \mu_2\text{: } (0.064 - (-0.286)) \pm 3.74\sqrt{\left(\frac{1.92}{2}\right)\left(\frac{1}{14} + \frac{1}{14}\right)}$$

$$= 0.35 \pm 1.39$$
$$= (-1.04, 1.74) \leftarrow \text{Includes 0}$$

$$\mu_1 - \mu_3\text{: } (0.064 - (-2.023)) \pm 3.74\sqrt{\left(\frac{1.92}{2}\right)\left(\frac{1}{14} + \frac{1}{13}\right)}$$

$$= 2.09 \pm 1.41$$
$$= (0.68, 3.50) \leftarrow \text{Does not include 0}$$

The remaining intervals are

$\mu_1 - \mu_4$	(0.97, 3.66)	← *Does not include 0*
$\mu_2 - \mu_3$	(0.32, 3.15)	← *Does not include 0*
$\mu_2 - \mu_4$	(0.62, 3.31)	← *Does not include 0*
$\mu_3 - \mu_4$	(−1.145, 1.60)	← *Includes 0*

We would conclude that μ_1 is not significantly different from μ_2 and that μ_3 is not significantly different from μ_4. We would also conclude that μ_1 and μ_2 are significantly different from both μ_3 and μ_4. Note that Treatments 1 and 2 were treatments that administered a placebo in place of the growth hormone and Treatments 3 and 4 were treatments that included the growth hormone. This analysis was the basis of the researchers' conclusion that growth hormone, with or without sex steroids, decreased body fat mass.

Minitab can be used to construct T-K intervals if raw data are available. Typical output (based on Example 15.5) is shown in Figure 15.6. From the output, we see that the confidence interval for μ_1 (P + P) $-$ μ_2 (P + S) is $(-1.039, 1.739)$, that for μ_2 (P + S) $-$ μ_4 (G + S) is (0.619, 3.309), and so on.

```
Tukey 95% Simultaneous Confidence Intervals
All Pairwise Comparisons

Individual confidence level = 98.95%


G + S subtracted from:

        Lower   Center   Upper   --------+---------+---------+---------+-
G + P  -1.145    0.227   1.599                (------*------)
P + S   0.619    1.964   3.309                          (------*------)
P + P   0.969    2.314   3.659                            (------*-----)
                                 --------+---------+---------+---------+-
                                      -2.0       0.0       2.0       4.0

G + P subtracted from:

       Lower   Center   Upper   --------+---------+---------+---------+-
P + S  0.322    1.737   3.153                          (------*------)
P + P  0.672    2.087   3.503                            (------*-------)
                                --------+---------+---------+---------+-
                                     -2.0       0.0       2.0       4.0

P + S subtracted from:

        Lower   Center   Upper   --------+---------+---------+---------+-
P + P  -1.039    0.350   1.739                 (------*------)
                                 --------+---------+---------+---------+-
                                      -2.0       0.0       2.0       4.0
```

FIGURE 15.6
The T-K intervals for Example 15.5 (from Minitab).

Why calculate the T-K intervals rather than use the t confidence interval for a difference between μ's from Chapter 11? The answer is that the T-K intervals control the **simultaneous confidence level** at approximately 95% (or 99%). That is, if the procedure is used repeatedly on many different data sets, in the long run only about 5% (or 1%) of the time would at least one of the intervals not include the value of what the interval is estimating. Consider using separate 95% t intervals, each one having a 5% error rate. In those instances, the chance that at least one interval would make an incorrect statement about a difference in μ's increases dramatically with the number of intervals calculated. The Minitab output in Figure 15.6 shows that to achieve a simultaneous confidence level of about 95% (experimentwise or "family" error rate of 5%) when $k = 4$ and error df $= 76$, the individual confidence level must be 98.95% (individual error rate 1.05%).

An effective display for summarizing the results of any multiple comparisons procedure involves listing the $\bar{x}$'s and underscoring pairs judged to be not significantly different. The process for constructing such a display is described in the box at the top of page 851.

To illustrate this summary procedure, suppose that four samples with $\bar{x}_1 = 19$, $\bar{x}_2 = 27$, $\bar{x}_3 = 24$, and $\bar{x}_4 = 10$ are used to test $H_0\colon \mu_1 = \mu_2 = \mu_3 = \mu_4$ and that this hypothesis is rejected. Suppose the T-K confidence intervals indicate that μ_2 is significantly different from both μ_1 and μ_4, and that there are no other significant differences. The resulting summary display would then be

Population	4	1	3	2
Sample mean	10	19	24	27

Summarizing the Results of the Tukey–Kramer Procedure

1. List the sample means in increasing order, identifying the corresponding population just above the value of each $\bar{x}$.
2. Use the T-K intervals to determine the group of means that do not differ significantly from the first in the list. Draw a horizontal line extending from the smallest mean to the last mean in the group identified. For example, if there are five means, arranged in order,

Population	3	2	1	4	5
Sample mean	$\bar{x}_3$	$\bar{x}_2$	$\bar{x}_1$	$\bar{x}_4$	$\bar{x}_5$

and μ_3 is judged to be not significantly different from μ_2 or μ_1, but is judged to be significantly different from μ_4 and μ_5, draw the following line:

Population	3	2	1	4	5
Sample mean	$\bar{x}_3$	$\bar{x}_2$	$\bar{x}_1$	$\bar{x}_4$	$\bar{x}_5$

3. Use the T–K intervals to determine the group of means that are not significantly different from the second smallest. (You need consider only means that appear to the right of the mean under consideration.) If there is already a line connecting the second smallest mean with all means in the new group identified, no new line need be drawn. If this entire group of means is not underscored with a single line, draw a line extending from the second smallest to the last mean in the new group. Continuing with our example, if μ_2 is not significantly different from μ_1 but is significantly different from μ_4 and μ_5, no new line need be drawn. However, if μ_2 is not significantly different from either μ_1 or μ_4 but is judged to be different from μ_5, a second line is drawn as shown:

Population	3	2	1	4	5
Sample mean	$\bar{x}_3$	$\bar{x}_2$	$\bar{x}_1$	$\bar{x}_4$	$\bar{x}_5$

4. Continue considering the means in the order listed, adding new lines as needed.

EXAMPLE 15.6 Sleep Time

● A biologist wished to study the effects of ethanol on sleep time. A sample of 20 rats, matched for age and other characteristics, was selected, and each rat was given an oral injection having a particular concentration of ethanol per body weight. The rapid eye movement (REM) sleep time for each rat was then recorded for a 24-hour period, with the results shown in the following table:

Treatment	Observations					$\bar{x}$
1. 0 (control)	88.6	73.2	91.4	68.0	75.2	79.28
2. 1 g/kg	63.0	53.9	69.2	50.1	71.5	61.54
3. 2 g/kg	44.9	59.5	40.2	56.3	38.7	47.92
4. 4 g/kg	31.0	39.6	45.3	25.2	22.7	32.76

Table 15.4 (an ANOVA table from SAS) leads to the conclusion that actual mean REM sleep time is not the same for all four treatments; the *P*-value for the *F* test is .0001.

!! Step-by-Step technology instructions available online

● Data set available online

TABLE 15.4 SAS ANOVA Table for Example 15.6

Analysis of Variance Procedure
Dependent Variable: TIME

Source	DF	Sum of Squares	Mean Square	F Value	Pr > F
Model	3	5882.35750	1960.78583	21.09	0.0001
Error	16	1487.40000	92.96250		
Total	**19**	**7369.75750**			

The T-K intervals are

Difference	Interval	Includes 0?
$\mu_1 - \mu_2$	17.74 ± 17.446	no
$\mu_1 - \mu_3$	31.36 ± 17.446	no
$\mu_1 - \mu_4$	46.24 ± 17.446	no
$\mu_2 - \mu_3$	13.08 ± 17.446	yes
$\mu_2 - \mu_4$	28.78 ± 17.446	no
$\mu_3 - \mu_4$	15.16 ± 17.446	yes

The only T-K intervals that include zero are those for $\mu_2 - \mu_3$ and $\mu_3 - \mu_4$. The corresponding underscoring pattern is

$\bar{x}_4$	$\bar{x}_3$	$\bar{x}_2$	$\bar{x}_1$
32.76	47.92	61.54	79.28

Figure 15.7 displays the SAS output that agrees with our underscoring; letters are used to indicate groupings in place of the underscoring.

```
Alpha = 0.05 df = 16 MSE = 92.9625
Critical Value of Studentized Range = 4.046
Minimum Significant Difference = 17.446
Means with the same letter are not significantly different.
Tukey Grouping     Mean     N     Treatment
      A          79.280     5     0 (control)
      B          61.540     5        1 g/kg
  C   B          47.920     5        2 g/kg
  C              32.760     5        4 g/kg
```

FIGURE 15.7
SAS output for Example 15.6.

EXAMPLE 15.7 Roommate Satisfaction

How satisfied are college students with dormitory roommates? The article "Roommate Satisfaction and Ethnic Identity in Mixed-Race and White University Roommate Dyads" (*Journal of College Student Development* [1998]: 194–199) investigated differences among randomly assigned African American/white, Asian/white, Hispanic/white, and white/white roommate pairs. The researchers used a one-way ANOVA to analyze scores on the Roommate Relationship Inventory to see whether a difference in mean score existed for the four types of roommate pairs. They reported "significant differences among the means ($P < .01$). Follow-up Tukey [intervals] . . .

indicated differences between White dyads (M = 77.49) and African American/White dyads (M = 71.27). ... No other significant differences were found."

Although the mean satisfaction score for the Asian/white and Hispanic/white groups were not given, they must have been between 77.49 (the mean for the white/white pairs) and 71.27 (the mean for the African American/white pairs). (If they had been larger than 77.49, they would have been significantly different from the African American/white pairs mean, and if they had been smaller than 71.27, they would have been significantly different from the white/white pairs mean.) An underscoring consistent with the reported information is

White/White	Hispanic/ White and Asian/White	African-American/ White
________________	________________	
	________________	________________

EXERCISES 15.14 - 15.22

15.14 Leaf surface area is an important variable in plant gas-exchange rates. Dry matter per unit surface area (mg/cm^3) was measured for trees raised under three different growing conditions. Let μ_1, μ_2, and μ_3 represent the mean dry matter per unit surface area for the growing conditions 1, 2, and 3, respectively. The given 95% simultaneous confidence intervals are:

Difference	$\mu_1 - \mu_2$	$\mu_1 - \mu_3$	$\mu_2 - \mu_3$
Interval	$(-3.11, -1.11)$	$(-4.06, -2.06)$	$(-1.95, .05)$

Which of the following four statements do you think describes the relationship between μ_1, μ_2, and μ_3? Explain your choice.

a. $\mu_1 = \mu_2$, and μ_3 differs from μ_1 and μ_2.
b. $\mu_1 = \mu_3$, and μ_2 differs from μ_1 and μ_3.
c. $\mu_2 = \mu_3$, and μ_1 differs from μ_2 and μ_3.
d. All three μ's are different from one another.

15.15 The paper "Trends in Blood Lead Levels and Blood Lead Testing among U.S. Children Aged 1 to 5 Years" (*Pediatrics* [2009]: e376–e385) gave data on blood lead levels (in $\mu g/dL$) for samples of children living in homes that had been classified either at low, medium, or high risk of lead exposure based on when the home was constructed. After using a multiple comparison procedure, the authors reported the following:

1. The difference in mean blood lead level between low-risk housing and medium-risk housing was significant.
2. The difference in mean blood lead level between low-risk housing and high-risk housing was significant.
3. The difference in mean blood lead level between medium-risk housing and high-risk housing was significant.

Which of the following sets of T-K intervals (Set 1, 2, or 3) is consistent with the authors' conclusions? Explain your choice.

μ_L = mean blood lead level for children living in low-risk housing
μ_M = mean blood lead level for children living in medium-risk housing
μ_H = mean blood lead level for children living in high-risk housing

Difference	Set 1	Set 2	Set 3
$\mu_L - \mu_M$	$(-0.6, 0.1)$	$(-0.6, -0.1)$	$(-0.6, -0.1)$
$\mu_L - \mu_H$	$(-1.5, -0.6)$	$(-1.5, -0.6)$	$(-1.5, -0.6)$
$\mu_M - \mu_H$	$(-0.9, -0.3)$	$(-0.9, 0.3)$	$(-0.9, -0.3)$

15.16 The accompanying underscoring pattern appears in the article "Women's and Men's Eating Behavior Following Exposure to Ideal-Body Images and Text" (*Communications Research* [2006]: 507–529). Women either viewed slides depicting images of thin female models with no text (treatment 1); viewed the same slides accompanied by diet and exercise-related text (treatment 2); or viewed the same slides accompanied by text that was unrelated to diet and exercise (treatment 3). A fourth group of women did not view any slides (treatment 4). Participants were assigned at random to the four treatments. Participants were then asked to complete a questionnaire in a room where pretzels were set out on the tables. An observer recorded how many pretzels participants ate while completing the questionnaire. Write a few sentences interpreting this underscoring pattern.

Treatment:	2	1	4	3
Mean number of pretzels consumed:	0.97	1.03	2.20	2.65

15.17 The paper referenced in the previous exercise also gave the following underscoring pattern for men.

Treatment:	2	1	3	4
Mean number of pretzels consumed:	6.61	5.96	3.38	2.70

a. Write a few sentences interpreting this underscoring pattern.
b. Using your answers from Part (a) and from the previous exercise, write a few sentences describing the differences between how men and women respond to the treatments.

15.18 ● The paper referenced in Exercise 15.5 described an experiment to determine if restrictive age labeling on video games increased the attractiveness of the game for boys age 12 to 13. In that exercise, the null hypothesis of H_0: $\mu_1 = \mu_2 = \mu_3 = \mu_4$, where μ_1 is the population mean attractiveness rating for the game with the 7+ age label, and μ_2, μ_3, and μ_4 are the population mean attractiveness scores for the 12+, 16+, and 18+ age labels, respectively. The sample data is given in the accompanying table.

7+ label	12+ label	16+ label	18+ label
6	8	7	10
6	7	9	9
6	8	8	6
5	5	6	8
4	7	7	7
8	9	4	6
6	5	8	8
1	8	9	9
2	4	6	10
4	7	7	8

a. Compute the 95% T-K intervals and then use the underscoring procedure described in this section to identify significant differences among the age labels.

b. Based on your answer to Part (a), write a few sentences commenting on the theory that the more restrictive the age label on a video game, the more attractive the game is to 12- to 13-year-old boys.

15.19 The authors of the paper "Beyond the Shooter Game: Examining Presence and Hostile Outcomes among Male Game Players" (*Communication Research* [2006]: 448–466) studied how video-game content might influence attitudes and behavior. Male students at a large Midwestern university were assigned at random to play one of three action-oriented video games. Two of the games involved some violence—one was a shooting game and one was a fighting game. The third game was a nonviolent race car driving game. After playing a game for 20 minutes, participants answered a set of questions. The responses were used to determine values of three measures of aggression: (1) a measure of aggressive behavior; (2) a measure of aggressive thoughts; and (3) a measure of aggressive feelings. The authors hypothesized that the means for the three measures of aggression would be greatest for the fighting game and lowest for the driving game.

a. For the measure of aggressive behavior, the paper reports that the mean score for the fighting game was significantly higher than the mean scores for the shooting and driving game, but that the mean scores for the shooting and driving games were not significantly different. The three sample means were:

	Driving	Shooting	Fighting
Sample mean	3.42	4.00	5.30

Use the underscoring procedure of this section to construct a display that shows any significant differences in mean aggressive behavior score among the three games.

b. For the measure of aggressive thoughts, the three sample means were:

	Driving	Shooting	Fighting
Sample mean	2.81	3.44	4.01

The paper states that the mean score for the fighting game only significantly differed from the mean score for the driving game and that the mean score for the shooting game did not significantly differ from either the fighting or driving games. Use the underscoring procedure of this section to construct a display that shows any significant differences in mean aggressive thoughts score among the three games.

15.20 ● The accompanying data resulted from a flammability study in which specimens of five different fabrics were tested to determine burn times.

	1	17.8	16.2	15.9	15.5	
	2	13.2	10.4	11.3		
Fabric	**3**	11.8	11.0	9.2	10.0	
	4	16.5	15.3	14.1	15.0	13.9
	5	13.9	10.8	12.8	11.7	

MSTr = 23.67
MSE = 1.39
F = 17.08
P-value = .000

The accompanying output gives the T-K intervals as calculated by Minitab. Identify significant differences and give the underscoring pattern.

```
Individual error rate = 0.00750
Critical value = 4.37
Intervals for (column level mean) - (row level mean)

          1        2        3        4
      1.938
2     7.495
      3.278   -1.645
3     8.422    3.912
     -1.050   -5.983   -6.900
4     3.830   -0.670   -2.020
      1.478   -3.445   -4.372    0.220
5     6.622    2.112    0.772    5.100
```

15.21 Do lizards play a role in spreading plant seeds? Some research carried out in South Africa would suggest so ("Dispersal of Namaqua Fig [*Ficus cordata cordata*] Seeds by the Augrabies Flat Lizard [*Platysaurus broadleyi*]," Journal of Herpetology [1999]: 328–330). The researchers collected 400 seeds of this particular type of fig, 100 of which were from each treatment: lizard dung, bird dung, rock hyrax dung, and uneaten figs. They planted these seeds in batches of 5, and for each group of 5 they recorded how many of the seeds germinated. This resulted in 20 observations for each treatment. The treatment means and standard deviations are given in the accompanying table.

Treatment	n	$\bar{x}$	s
Uneaten figs	20	2.40	.30
Lizard dung	20	2.35	.33
Bird dung	20	1.70	.34
Hyrax dung	20	1.45	.28

a. Construct the appropriate ANOVA table, and test the hypothesis that there is no difference between mean number of seeds germinating for the four treatments.

b. Is there evidence that seeds eaten and then excreted by lizards germinate at a higher rate than those eaten and then excreted by birds? Give statistical evidence to support your answer.

15.22 ● Samples of six different brands of diet or imitation margarine were analyzed to determine the level of physiologically active polyunsaturated fatty acids (PAPUFA, in percent), resulting in the data shown in the accompanying table. (The data are fictitious, but the sample means agree with data reported in *Consumer Reports*.)

Imperial	14.1	13.6	14.4	14.3	
Parkay	12.8	12.5	13.4	13.0	12.3
Blue Bonnet	13.5	13.4	14.1	14.3	
Chiffon	13.2	12.7	12.6	13.9	
Mazola	16.8	17.2	16.4	17.3	18.0
Fleischmann's	18.1	17.2	18.7	18.4	

a. Test for differences among the true average PAPUFA percentages for the different brands. Use $\alpha = .05$.

b. Use the T-K procedure to compute 95% simultaneous confidence intervals for all differences between means and give the corresponding underscoring pattern.

ACTIVITY 15.1 Exploring Single-Factor ANOVA

Working with a partner, consider the following:

1. Each of the four accompanying graphs shows a dotplot of data from three separate random samples. For each of the four graphs, indicate whether you think that the basic assumptions for single-factor ANOVA are plausible. Write a sentence or two justifying your answer.

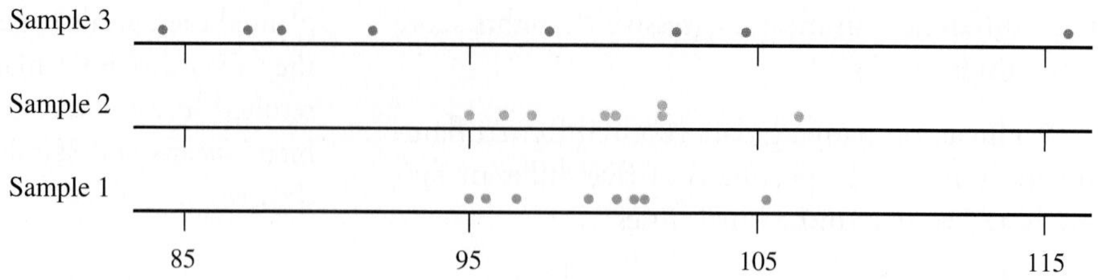

Graph 1

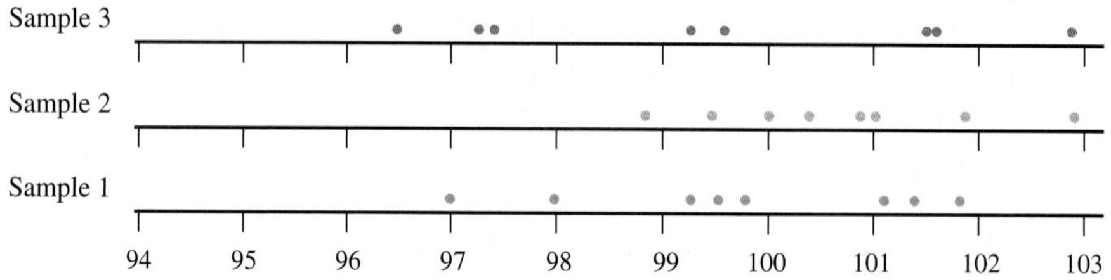

Graph 2

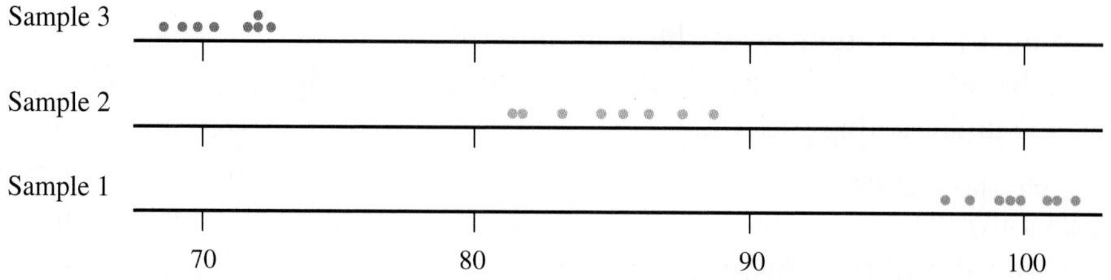

Graph 3

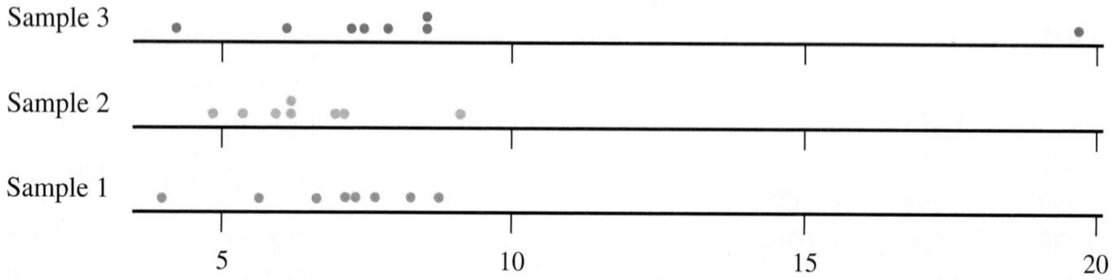

Graph 4

2. Each of the three accompanying graphs shows a dotplot of data from three separate random samples. For each of the three graphs, indicate whether you think that the three population means are probably not all the same, you think that the three population means might be the same, or you are unsure whether the population means could be the same. Write a sentence or two explaining your reasoning.

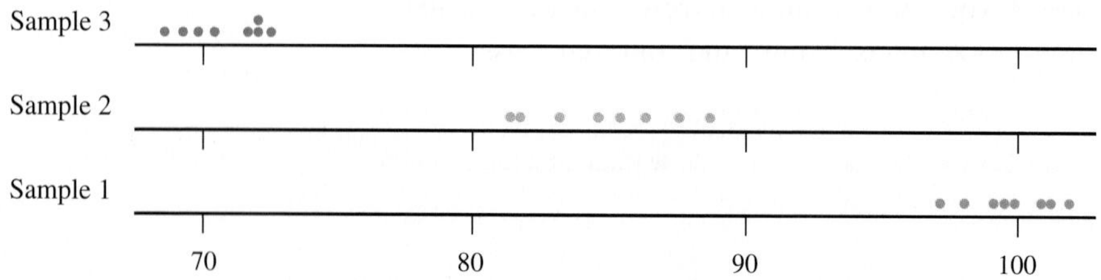

Graph A

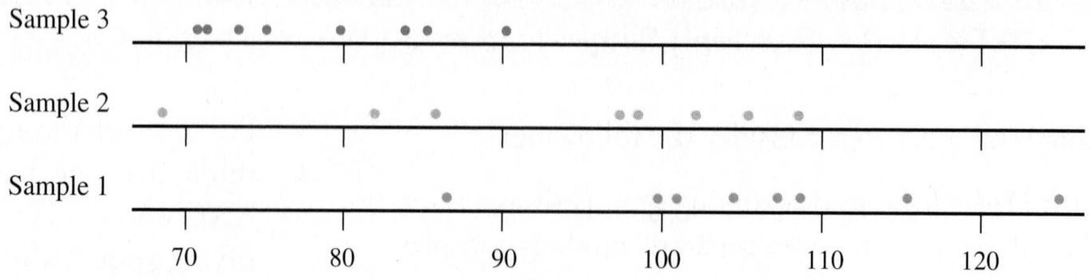

Graph B

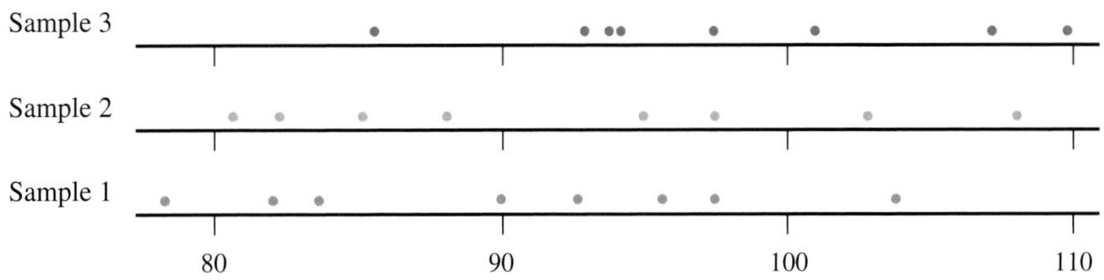

Graph C

3. Sample data for each of the three graphs in Step 2 are shown in the accompanying table. For each of the three graphs, carry out a single-factor ANOVA. Are the results of the F tests consistent with your answers in Step 2? Explain.

GRAPH A			GRAPH B			GRAPH C		
Sample 1	Sample 2	Sample 3	Sample 1	Sample 2	Sample 3	Sample 1	Sample 2	Sample 3
99.7	91.3	69.3	104.2	81.9	71.7	82.3	82.4	94.2
98.0	82.0	72.1	107.0	105.4	79.7	97.4	87.5	109.8
101.4	83.6	71.7	88.6	98.4	70.9	83.7	97.3	94.9
99.2	84.8	69.9	99.6	108.4	76.6	103.6	102.6	85.8
101.0	86.5	68.8	124.3	102.1	85.3	78.6	94.8	97.4
101.8	91.5	70.7	100.7	68.9	90.3	90.1	81.3	101.0
99.5	81.8	72.7	108.3	85.8	84.2	92.8	85.2	93.0
97.0	85.5	72.2	116.5	97.5	74.6	95.5	107.8	107.1

Summary of Key Concepts and Formulas

TERM OR FORMULA	COMMENT
Single-factor analysis of variance (ANOVA)	A test procedure for determining whether there are significant differences among k population or treatment means. The hypotheses tested are H_0: $\mu_1 = \mu_2 = \cdots = \mu_k$ versus H_a: at least two μ's differ.
Treatment sum of squares: $SSTr = n_1(\bar{x}_1 - \bar{\bar{x}})^2 + \cdots + n_k(\bar{x}_k - \bar{\bar{x}})^2$	A measure of how different the k sample means $\bar{x}_1, \bar{x}_2, \ldots, \bar{x}_k$ are from one another; associated df $= k - 1$.
Error sum of squares: $SSE = (n_1 - 1)s_1^2 + \cdots + (n_k - 1)s_k^2$	A measure of the amount of variability within the individual samples; associated df $= N - k$, where $N = n_1 + \cdots + n_k$.
Mean square	A sum of squares divided by its df. For single-factor ANOVA, $MSTr = SSTr/(k - 1)$ and $MSE = SSE/(N - k)$.
$F = \dfrac{MSTr}{MSE}$	The test statistic for testing H_0: $\mu_1 = \mu_2 = \cdots = \mu_k$ in a single-factor ANOVA. When H_0 is true, F has an F distribution with numerator df $= k - 1$ and denominator df $= N - k$.
$SSTo = SSTr + SSE$	The fundamental identity in single-factor ANOVA, where $SSTo$ = total sum of squares $= \sum(x - \bar{\bar{x}})^2$.
Tukey-Kramer multiple comparison procedure	A procedure for identifying significant differences among the μ's once the hypothesis H_0: $\mu_1 = \mu_2 = \cdots = \mu_k$ has been rejected by the ANOVA F test.

Graphing Calculator Exploration

EXPLORATION 15.1 Single Factor ANOVA

Single-factor ANOVA is at the limit of the capability of a graphing calculator unless you have a programmable calculator and *reliable* programs. Nevertheless, for small ANOVA problems, the calculator can be used effectively when access to a computer is limited.

Begin by entering the data, one treatment per List. To illustrate, we will use the data from Exercise 15.10 on box compression strength. Put the data from box type 1 into List1, data from box type 2 into List2, etc. Boxplots or normal probability plots can be used to assess the plausibility of the ANOVA assumptions.

After entering the data, navigate the menus to the ANOVA screen. Screens will differ from one calculator to another; two common versions are shown in Figure 15.8.

ANOVA
How Many: 4
List1 : List 1
List2 : List 2
List3 : List 3
List4 : List 4
Execute

ANOVA
(List1, List2, List3, List4)

FIGURE 15.8
Two common ANOVA screens.

Press either Execute or the Enter key to initiate the ANOVA computations on the calculator. The results should look like one of the two "larger-than-life" displays shown in Figure 15.9.

ANOVA
F = 25.0943
p = 5.5254499E-7
$xp\sigma n - 1$ = 41.1333
Fdf = 3
SS = 127374.755
MS = 1691.94875
Edf = 20
SS = 33838.9750
MS = 1691.94875

One-way ANOVA
F = 25.0942894
p = 5.5254499E-7
Factor
df = 3.0000000
SS = 127374.755
MS = 42458.2515
Error
df = 20.0000000
SS = 33838.9750
MS = 1691.94875
Sxp = 41.1333046

FIGURE 15.9
Results of ANOVA computations.

From the information provided by the calculator, you can reproduce the single-factor ANOVA table.

Source of Variation	df	Sum of Squares	Mean Square	F
Treatments	3	127374.755	42458.2515	25.094
Error	20	33838.9750	1691.94875	
Total	**23**	???		

Check to make sure you understand the correspondence between the calculator output and the ANOVA table. Notice specifically that the total sum of squares does not appear on the calculator screen. It must be calculated by summing the treatment and error sums of squares. The quantity labeled Sxp is $\sqrt{\text{MSE}}$, an estimate of the assumed common population standard deviation σ.

The Tukey-Kramer multiple comparison procedure could be performed by combining the information from statistics calculated from the individual lists and the calculator output, but these procedures are not usually built-in on the calculator. If you anticipate performing many single-factor ANOVAs on your calculator, you might consider downloading a calculator program from the web. Freeware varies in quality, so be sure to check such a program against a known correct solution!

Appendix A

APPENDIX A Statistical Tables 860

Table 1 Random Numbers 860
Table 2 Standard Normal Probabilities (Cumulative z Curve Areas) 862
Table 3 *t* Critical Values 864
Table 4 Tail Areas for *t* Curves 865
Table 5 Curves of $\beta = P(\text{Type II Error})$ for *t* Tests 868
Table 6 Values That Capture Specified Upper-Tail *F* Curve Areas 869
Table 7 Critical Values of *q* for the Studentized Range Distribution 873
Table 8 Upper-Tail Areas for Chi-Square Distributions 874
Table 9 Binomial Probabilities 876

Appendix A: Statistical Tables

TABLE 1 Random Numbers

Row																				
1	4	5	1	8	5	0	3	3	7	1	2	8	4	5	1	1	0	9	5	7
2	4	2	5	5	8	0	4	5	7	0	7	0	3	6	6	1	3	1	3	1
3	8	9	9	3	4	3	5	0	6	3	9	1	1	8	2	6	9	2	0	9
4	8	9	0	7	2	9	9	0	4	7	6	7	4	7	1	3	4	3	5	3
5	5	7	3	1	0	3	7	4	7	8	5	2	0	1	3	7	7	6	3	6
6	0	9	3	8	7	6	7	9	9	5	6	2	5	6	5	8	4	2	6	4
7	4	1	0	1	0	2	2	0	4	7	5	1	1	9	4	7	9	7	5	1
8	6	4	7	3	6	3	4	5	1	2	3	1	1	8	0	0	4	8	2	0
9	8	0	2	8	7	9	3	8	4	0	4	2	0	8	9	1	2	3	3	2
10	9	4	6	0	6	9	7	8	8	2	5	2	9	6	0	1	4	6	0	5
11	6	6	9	5	7	4	4	6	3	2	0	6	0	8	9	1	3	6	1	8
12	0	7	1	7	7	7	2	9	7	8	7	5	8	8	6	9	8	4	1	0
13	6	1	3	0	9	7	3	3	6	6	0	4	1	8	3	2	6	7	6	8
14	2	2	3	6	2	1	3	0	2	2	6	6	9	7	0	2	1	2	5	8
15	0	7	1	7	4	2	0	0	0	1	3	1	2	0	4	7	8	4	1	0
16	6	6	5	1	6	1	8	1	5	5	2	6	2	0	1	1	5	2	3	6
17	9	9	6	2	5	3	5	9	8	3	7	5	0	1	3	9	3	8	0	8
18	9	9	9	6	1	2	9	3	4	6	5	6	4	6	5	8	2	7	4	0
19	2	5	6	3	1	9	8	1	1	0	3	5	6	7	9	1	4	5	2	0
20	5	1	1	9	8	1	2	1	1	6	9	8	1	8	1	9	9	1	2	0
21	1	9	8	0	7	4	6	8	4	0	3	0	8	1	1	0	6	2	3	2
22	9	7	0	9	6	3	8	9	9	7	0	6	5	4	3	6	5	0	3	2
23	1	7	6	4	8	2	0	3	9	6	3	6	2	1	0	7	7	3	1	7
24	6	2	5	8	2	0	7	8	6	4	6	6	8	9	2	0	6	9	0	4
25	1	5	7	1	1	1	9	5	1	4	5	2	8	3	4	3	0	7	3	5
26	1	4	6	6	5	6	0	1	9	4	0	5	2	7	6	4	3	6	8	8
27	1	8	5	0	2	1	6	8	0	7	7	2	6	2	6	7	5	4	8	7
28	7	8	7	4	6	5	4	3	7	9	3	9	2	7	9	5	4	2	3	1
29	1	6	3	2	8	3	7	3	0	7	2	4	8	0	9	9	9	4	7	0
30	2	8	9	0	8	1	6	8	1	7	3	1	3	0	9	7	2	5	7	9
31	0	7	8	8	6	5	7	5	5	4	0	0	3	4	1	2	7	3	7	9
32	8	4	0	1	4	5	1	9	1	1	2	1	5	3	2	8	5	5	7	5
33	7	3	5	9	7	0	4	9	1	2	1	3	2	5	1	9	3	3	8	3
34	4	7	2	6	7	6	9	9	2	7	8	7	5	5	5	2	4	4	3	4
35	9	3	3	7	0	7	0	5	7	5	6	9	5	4	3	1	4	6	6	8
36	0	2	4	9	7	8	1	6	3	8	7	8	0	5	6	7	2	7	5	0
37	7	1	0	1	8	4	7	1	2	9	3	8	0	0	8	7	9	2	8	6
38	9	7	9	4	4	5	3	1	9	3	4	5	0	6	3	5	9	6	9	8
39	0	4	2	5	0	0	9	9	6	4	0	6	9	0	3	8	3	5	7	2
40	0	7	1	2	3	6	1	7	9	3	9	5	4	6	8	4	8	8	0	6
41	3	5	6	6	2	4	4	5	6	3	7	8	7	6	5	2	0	4	3	2
42	6	6	8	5	5	2	9	7	9	3	3	1	6	9	5	9	7	1	1	2
43	9	5	0	4	3	1	1	7	3	9	2	7	7	4	7	0	3	1	2	8
44	5	1	7	8	9	4	7	2	9	2	8	9	9	8	0	6	3	7	2	1
45	1	6	3	9	4	1	3	2	1	1	8	5	6	3	4	1	9	3	1	7
46	4	4	8	6	4	0	3	8	3	8	3	5	9	5	9	4	8	3	9	4
47	7	7	6	6	4	5	4	4	8	4	4	0	3	9	8	5	2	0	2	3
48	2	5	6	6	3	7	0	6	5	6	9	0	1	9	5	2	6	9	1	2

TABLE 1 Random Numbers (*Continued*)

Row																				
49	9	4	0	4	7	5	3	2	8	7	2	7	4	9	3	9	6	5	5	6
50	7	3	1	5	6	6	5	0	3	5	3	7	2	8	6	2	4	1	8	7
51	7	5	8	2	8	8	8	7	6	4	1	1	0	2	3	1	9	3	6	0
52	3	3	6	0	9	1	1	0	3	2	7	8	2	0	5	3	4	8	9	8
53	0	2	9	6	9	8	9	3	8	1	5	3	9	9	7	0	7	7	1	6
54	8	5	9	6	2	9	6	8	2	1	2	4	7	0	6	8	3	4	6	1
55	5	4	7	6	1	0	0	1	0	4	6	1	4	1	5	0	9	6	5	5
56	5	0	3	6	4	1	9	8	4	4	1	2	0	2	5	1	8	1	2	1
57	0	2	6	3	7	5	1	1	6	6	0	5	8	1	2	3	3	6	1	3
58	3	8	1	6	3	8	1	4	5	2	9	4	2	5	7	3	2	3	1	8
59	9	1	5	6	0	6	5	6	6	3	6	2	3	0	0	0	1	8	5	9
60	5	3	5	6	3	9	5	4	7	3	6	6	7	5	0	1	5	6	7	3
61	9	6	6	4	5	7	7	6	1	5	4	4	8	0	6	5	7	6	3	0
62	6	3	0	6	7	9	5	5	4	6	2	2	8	4	4	0	0	9	9	8
63	8	5	8	3	5	2	0	6	6	0	0	6	0	6	3	0	1	7	0	5
64	3	8	2	4	9	0	9	2	6	2	9	5	1	9	1	9	0	8	3	3
65	1	4	4	1	1	7	4	6	3	6	5	6	5	5	7	7	0	3	5	8
66	5	9	9	5	3	7	2	5	1	7	1	1	0	7	1	0	9	2	8	8
67	8	7	1	7	5	2	5	6	8	7	9	9	1	3	9	6	4	9	3	0
68	6	7	2	3	1	4	9	2	1	7	0	8	6	7	8	9	9	4	7	4
69	2	3	2	8	7	0	9	7	1	1	1	2	8	2	9	1	0	6	7	7
70	2	9	5	7	8	4	7	9	0	3	6	9	2	0	6	0	6	2	6	8
71	4	8	9	8	3	2	7	6	9	1	9	8	6	9	5	2	4	9	9	9
72	1	5	6	5	7	7	5	4	3	4	3	8	1	8	9	9	4	4	1	1
73	1	8	1	1	7	2	8	5	5	8	9	9	9	6	2	0	1	6	6	7
74	5	7	7	0	9	5	5	6	8	6	8	2	2	6	0	5	5	1	8	7
75	1	8	6	0	5	4	8	3	4	5	3	5	8	7	7	7	8	5	7	0
76	2	6	6	7	9	4	2	2	8	7	4	3	4	9	6	1	9	4	3	9
77	3	6	6	4	5	7	8	3	0	2	8	4	6	7	2	1	4	5	2	3
78	0	7	8	0	1	2	1	1	3	4	2	1	6	9	3	3	5	4	0	4
79	8	3	6	0	5	7	7	9	1	5	8	8	4	9	5	7	2	2	7	6
80	5	3	6	9	0	6	3	8	7	5	9	5	9	7	4	2	5	6	2	9
81	0	9	3	7	7	2	8	6	4	3	2	9	4	8	2	9	9	6	9	9
82	9	4	7	4	0	0	0	3	5	4	6	6	2	6	2	3	6	1	1	4
83	5	5	4	1	7	8	6	4	2	3	2	9	8	4	6	3	8	3	0	5
84	5	3	0	0	5	4	8	0	7	4	7	6	2	1	1	2	1	2	6	9
85	3	3	0	9	3	2	9	4	0	5	5	4	8	7	5	7	5	3	8	8
86	3	0	5	7	1	9	5	8	0	0	4	5	3	0	3	0	2	7	6	7
87	5	0	8	6	0	8	1	6	2	0	8	6	5	4	0	7	2	9	1	0
88	3	6	4	7	8	2	3	5	7	9	8	5	2	7	6	9	0	2	4	9
89	9	0	4	4	9	1	6	8	5	2	8	9	0	7	5	7	2	5	1	8
90	9	5	2	6	9	3	9	6	5	1	8	8	7	8	2	0	4	4	7	9
91	9	4	5	7	0	3	4	6	4	2	5	4	8	6	1	1	9	1	8	8
92	8	1	1	8	0	5	4	2	8	5	3	3	3	0	1	1	4	4	8	3
93	6	9	4	7	8	3	3	9	1	2	5	0	1	2	3	0	1	1	2	5
94	0	0	6	8	8	7	2	4	4	7	6	6	0	3	4	7	5	6	8	2
95	5	3	3	9	3	8	4	9	1	9	1	7	8	4	5	2	2	5	4	4
96	2	5	6	2	7	6	0	3	8	1	4	4	2	6	8	3	6	3	2	8
97	7	4	3	7	9	6	8	6	2	8	3	8	4	2	2	0	7	0	5	3
98	1	9	0	8	8	0	1	2	2	2	7	5	6	5	5	7	8	7	2	6
99	2	4	8	0	2	5	2	7	0	5	9	6	6	1	5	8	7	9	7	5
100	4	1	7	8	6	7	1	1	5	8	9	4	8	9	8	3	0	9	0	7

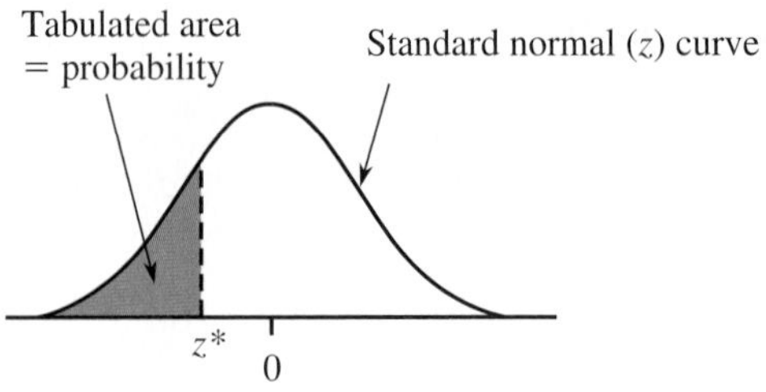

TABLE 2 Standard Normal Probabilities (Cumulative z Curve Areas)

z*	.00	.01	.02	.03	.04	.05	.06	.07	.08	.09
−3.8	.0001	.0001	.0001	.0001	.0001	.0001	.0001	.0001	.0001	.0000
−3.7	.0001	.0001	.0001	.0001	.0001	.0001	.0001	.0001	.0001	.0001
−3.6	.0002	.0002	.0001	.0001	.0001	.0001	.0001	.0001	.0001	.0001
−3.5	.0002	.0002	.0002	.0002	.0002	.0002	.0002	.0002	.0002	.0002
−3.4	.0003	.0003	.0003	.0003	.0003	.0003	.0003	.0003	.0003	.0002
−3.3	.0005	.0005	.0005	.0004	.0004	.0004	.0004	.0004	.0004	.0003
−3.2	.0007	.0007	.0006	.0006	.0006	.0006	.0006	.0005	.0005	.0005
−3.1	.0010	.0009	.0009	.0009	.0008	.0008	.0008	.0008	.0007	.0007
−3.0	.0013	.0013	.0013	.0012	.0012	.0011	.0011	.0011	.0010	.0010
−2.9	.0019	.0018	.0018	.0017	.0016	.0016	.0015	.0015	.0014	.0014
−2.8	.0026	.0025	.0024	.0023	.0023	.0022	.0021	.0021	.0020	.0019
−2.7	.0035	.0034	.0033	.0032	.0031	.0030	.0029	.0028	.0027	.0026
−2.6	.0047	.0045	.0044	.0043	.0041	.0040	.0039	.0038	.0037	.0036
−2.5	.0062	.0060	.0059	.0057	.0055	.0054	.0052	.0051	.0049	.0048
−2.4	.0082	.0080	.0078	.0075	.0073	.0071	.0069	.0068	.0066	.0064
−2.3	.0107	.0104	.0102	.0099	.0096	.0094	.0091	.0089	.0087	.0084
−2.2	.0139	.0136	.0132	.0129	.0125	.0122	.0119	.0116	.0113	.0110
−2.1	.0179	.0174	.0170	.0166	.0162	.0158	.0154	.0150	.0146	.0143
−2.0	.0228	.0222	.0217	.0212	.0207	.0202	.0197	.0192	.0188	.0183
−1.9	.0287	.0281	.0274	.0268	.0262	.0256	.0250	.0244	.0239	.0233
−1.8	.0359	.0351	.0344	.0336	.0329	.0322	.0314	.0307	.0301	.0294
−1.7	.0446	.0436	.0427	.0418	.0409	.0401	.0392	.0384	.0375	.0367
−1.6	.0548	.0537	.0526	.0516	.0505	.0495	.0485	.0475	.0465	.0455
−1.5	.0668	.0655	.0643	.0630	.0618	.0606	.0594	.0582	.0571	.0559
−1.4	.0808	.0793	.0778	.0764	.0749	.0735	.0721	.0708	.0694	.0681
−1.3	.0968	.0951	.0934	.0918	.0901	.0885	.0869	.0853	.0838	.0823
−1.2	.1151	.1131	.1112	.1093	.1075	.1056	.1038	.1020	.1003	.0985
−1.1	.1357	.1335	.1314	.1292	.1271	.1251	.1230	.1210	.1190	.1170
−1.0	.1587	.1562	.1539	.1515	.1492	.1469	.1446	.1423	.1401	.1379
−0.9	.1841	.1814	.1788	.1762	.1736	.1711	.1685	.1660	.1635	.1611
−0.8	.2119	.2090	.2061	.2033	.2005	.1977	.1949	.1922	.1894	.1867
−0.7	.2420	.2389	.2358	.2327	.2296	.2266	.2236	.2206	.2177	.2148
−0.6	.2743	.2709	.2676	.2643	.2611	.2578	.2546	.2514	.2483	.2451
−0.5	.3085	.3050	.3015	.2981	.2946	.2912	.2877	.2843	.2810	.2776
−0.4	.3446	.3409	.3372	.3336	.3300	.3264	.3228	.3192	.3156	.3121
−0.3	.3821	.3783	.3745	.3707	.3669	.3632	.3594	.3557	.3520	.3483
−0.2	.4207	.4168	.4129	.4090	.4052	.4013	.3974	.3936	.3897	.3859
−0.1	.4602	.4562	.4522	.4483	.4443	.4404	.4364	.4325	.4286	.4247
−0.0	.5000	.4960	.4920	.4880	.4840	.4801	.4761	.4721	.4681	.4641

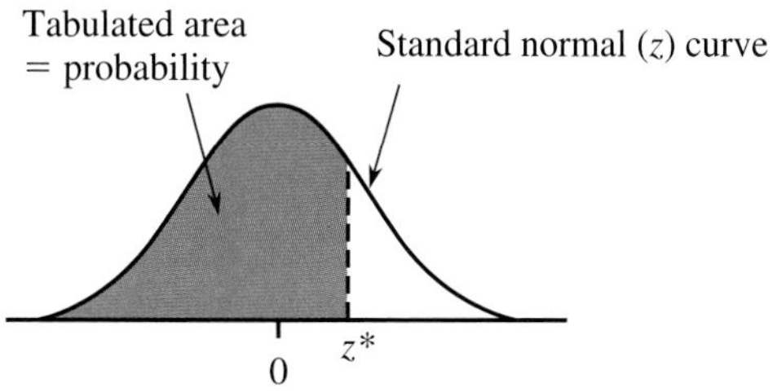

TABLE 2 Standard Normal Probabilities (Cumulative z Curve Areas) (*Continued*)

z*	.00	.01	.02	.03	.04	.05	.06	.07	.08	.09
0.0	.5000	.5040	.5080	.5120	.5160	.5199	.5239	.5279	.5319	.5359
0.1	.5398	.5438	.5478	.5517	.5557	.5596	.5636	.5675	.5714	.5753
0.2	.5793	.5832	.5871	.5910	.5948	.5987	.6026	.6064	.6103	.6141
0.3	.6179	.6217	.6255	.6293	.6331	.6368	.6406	.6443	.6480	.6517
0.4	.6554	.6591	.6628	.6664	.6700	.6736	.6772	.6808	.6844	.6879
0.5	.6915	.6950	.6985	.7019	.7054	.7088	.7123	.7157	.7190	.7224
0.6	.7257	.7291	.7324	.7357	.7389	.7422	.7454	.7486	.7517	.7549
0.7	.7580	.7611	.7642	.7673	.7704	.7734	.7764	.7794	.7823	.7852
0.8	.7881	.7910	.7939	.7967	.7995	.8023	.8051	.8078	.8106	.8133
0.9	.8159	.8186	.8212	.8238	.8264	.8289	.8315	.8340	.8365	.8389
1.0	.8413	.8438	.8461	.8485	.8508	.8531	.8554	.8577	.8599	.8621
1.1	.8643	.8665	.8686	.8708	.8729	.8749	.8770	.8790	.8810	.8830
1.2	.8849	.8869	.8888	.8907	.8925	.8944	.8962	.8980	.8997	.9015
1.3	.9032	.9049	.9066	.9082	.9099	.9115	.9131	.9147	.9162	.9177
1.4	.9192	.9207	.9222	.9236	.9251	.9265	.9279	.9292	.9306	.9319
1.5	.9332	.9345	.9357	.9370	.9382	.9394	.9406	.9418	.9429	.9441
1.6	.9452	.9463	.9474	.9484	.9495	.9505	.9515	.9525	.9535	.9545
1.7	.9554	.9564	.9573	.9582	.9591	.9599	.9608	.9616	.9625	.9633
1.8	.9641	.9649	.9656	.9664	.9671	.9678	.9686	.9693	.9699	.9706
1.9	.9713	.9719	.9726	.9732	.9738	.9744	.9750	.9756	.9761	.9767
2.0	.9772	.9778	.9783	.9788	.9793	.9798	.9803	.9808	.9812	.9817
2.1	.9821	.9826	.9830	.9834	.9838	.9842	.9846	.9850	.9854	.9857
2.2	.9861	.9864	.9868	.9871	.9875	.9878	.9881	.9884	.9887	.9890
2.3	.9893	.9896	.9898	.9901	.9904	.9906	.9909	.9911	.9913	.9916
2.4	.9918	.9920	.9922	.9925	.9927	.9929	.9931	.9932	.9934	.9936
2.5	.9938	.9940	.9941	.9943	.9945	.9946	.9948	.9949	.9951	.9952
2.6	.9953	.9955	.9956	.9957	.9959	.9960	.9961	.9962	.9963	.9964
2.7	.9965	.9966	.9967	.9968	.9969	.9970	.9971	.9972	.9973	.9974
2.8	.9974	.9975	.9976	.9977	.9977	.9978	.9979	.9979	.9980	.9981
2.9	.9981	.9982	.9982	.9983	.9984	.9984	.9985	.9985	.9986	.9986
3.0	.9987	.9987	.9987	.9988	.9988	.9989	.9989	.9989	.9990	.9990
3.1	.9990	.9991	.9991	.9991	.9992	.9992	.9992	.9992	.9993	.9993
3.2	.9993	.9993	.9994	.9994	.9994	.9994	.9994	.9995	.9995	.9995
3.3	.9995	.9995	.9995	.9996	.9996	.9996	.9996	.9996	.9996	.9997
3.4	.9997	.9997	.9997	.9997	.9997	.9997	.9997	.9997	.9997	.9998
3.5	.9998	.9998	.9998	.9998	.9998	.9998	.9998	.9998	.9998	.9998
3.6	.9998	.9998	.9999	.9999	.9999	.9999	.9999	.9999	.9999	.9999
3.7	.9999	.9999	.9999	.9999	.9999	.9999	.9999	.9999	.9999	.9999
3.8	.9999	.9999	.9999	.9999	.9999	.9999	.9999	.9999	.9999	1.0000

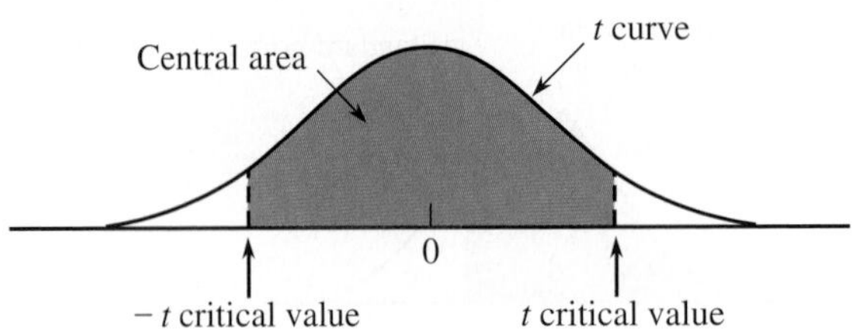

TABLE 3 *t* Critical Values

Central area captured: / Confidence level:		.80 / 80%	.90 / 90%	.95 / 95%	.98 / 98%	.99 / 99%	.998 / 99.8%	.999 / 99.9%
	1	3.08	6.31	12.71	31.82	63.66	318.31	636.62
	2	1.89	2.92	4.30	6.97	9.93	23.33	31.60
	3	1.64	2.35	3.18	4.54	5.84	10.21	12.92
	4	1.53	2.13	2.78	3.75	4.60	7.17	8.61
	5	1.48	2.02	2.57	3.37	4.03	5.89	6.86
	6	1.44	1.94	2.45	3.14	3.71	5.21	5.96
	7	1.42	1.90	2.37	3.00	3.50	4.79	5.41
	8	1.40	1.86	2.31	2.90	3.36	4.50	5.04
	9	1.38	1.83	2.26	2.82	3.25	4.30	4.78
	10	1.37	1.81	2.23	2.76	3.17	4.14	4.59
	11	1.36	1.80	2.20	2.72	3.11	4.03	4.44
	12	1.36	1.78	2.18	2.68	3.06	3.93	4.32
	13	1.35	1.77	2.16	2.65	3.01	3.85	4.22
	14	1.35	1.76	2.15	2.62	2.98	3.79	4.14
	15	1.34	1.75	2.13	2.60	2.95	3.73	4.07
	16	1.34	1.75	2.12	2.58	2.92	3.69	4.02
Degrees of freedom	**17**	1.33	1.74	2.11	2.57	2.90	3.65	3.97
	18	1.33	1.73	2.10	2.55	2.88	3.61	3.92
	19	1.33	1.73	2.09	2.54	2.86	3.58	3.88
	20	1.33	1.73	2.09	2.53	2.85	3.55	3.85
	21	1.32	1.72	2.08	2.52	2.83	3.53	3.82
	22	1.32	1.72	2.07	2.51	2.82	3.51	3.79
	23	1.32	1.71	2.07	2.50	2.81	3.49	3.77
	24	1.32	1.71	2.06	2.49	2.80	3.47	3.75
	25	1.32	1.71	2.06	2.49	2.79	3.45	3.73
	26	1.32	1.71	2.06	2.48	2.78	3.44	3.71
	27	1.31	1.70	2.05	2.47	2.77	3.42	3.69
	28	1.31	1.70	2.05	2.47	2.76	3.41	3.67
	29	1.31	1.70	2.05	2.46	2.76	3.40	3.66
	30	1.31	1.70	2.04	2.46	2.75	3.39	3.65
	40	1.30	1.68	2.02	2.42	2.70	3.31	3.55
	60	1.30	1.67	2.00	2.39	2.66	3.23	3.46
	120	1.29	1.66	1.98	2.36	2.62	3.16	3.37
***z* critical values**	**∞**	1.28	1.645	1.96	2.33	2.58	3.09	3.29

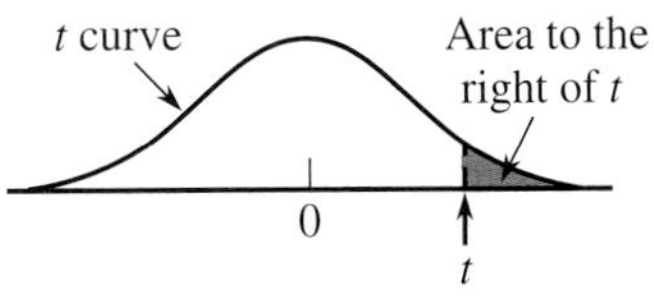

TABLE 4 Tail Areas for *t* Curves

t \ df	1	2	3	4	5	6	7	8	9	10	11	12
0.0	.500	.500	.500	.500	.500	.500	.500	.500	.500	.500	.500	.500
0.1	.468	.465	.463	.463	.462	.462	.462	.461	.461	.461	.461	.461
0.2	.437	.430	.427	.426	.425	.424	.424	.423	.423	.423	.423	.422
0.3	.407	.396	.392	.390	.388	.387	.386	.386	.386	.385	.385	.385
0.4	.379	.364	.358	.355	.353	.352	.351	.350	.349	.349	.348	.348
0.5	.352	.333	.326	.322	.319	.317	.316	.315	.315	.314	.313	.313
0.6	.328	.305	.295	.290	.287	.285	.284	.283	.282	.281	.280	.280
0.7	.306	.278	.267	.261	.258	.255	.253	.252	.251	.250	.249	.249
0.8	.285	.254	.241	.234	.230	.227	.225	.223	.222	.221	.220	.220
0.9	.267	.232	.217	.210	.205	.201	.199	.197	.196	.195	.194	.193
1.0	.250	.211	.196	.187	.182	.178	.175	.173	.172	.170	.169	.169
1.1	.235	.193	.176	.167	.162	.157	.154	.152	.150	.149	.147	.146
1.2	.221	.177	.158	.148	.142	.138	.135	.132	.130	.129	.128	.127
1.3	.209	.162	.142	.132	.125	.121	.117	.115	.113	.111	.110	.109
1.4	.197	.148	.128	.117	.110	.106	.102	.100	.098	.096	.095	.093
1.5	.187	.136	.115	.104	.097	.092	.089	.086	.084	.082	.081	.080
1.6	.178	.125	.104	.092	.085	.080	.077	.074	.072	.070	.069	.068
1.7	.169	.116	.094	.082	.075	.070	.066	.064	.062	.060	.059	.057
1.8	.161	.107	.085	.073	.066	.061	.057	.055	.053	.051	.050	.049
1.9	.154	.099	.077	.065	.058	.053	.050	.047	.045	.043	.042	.041
2.0	.148	.092	.070	.058	.051	.046	.043	.040	.038	.037	.035	.034
2.1	.141	.085	.063	.052	.045	.040	.037	.034	.033	.031	.030	.029
2.2	.136	.079	.058	.046	.040	.035	.032	.029	.028	.026	.025	.024
2.3	.131	.074	.052	.041	.035	.031	.027	.025	.023	.022	.021	.020
2.4	.126	.069	.048	.037	.031	.027	.024	.022	.020	.019	.018	.017
2.5	.121	.065	.044	.033	.027	.023	.020	.018	.017	.016	.015	.014
2.6	.117	.061	.040	.030	.024	.020	.018	.016	.014	.013	.012	.012
2.7	.113	.057	.037	.027	.021	.018	.015	.014	.012	.011	.010	.010
2.8	.109	.054	.034	.024	.019	.016	.013	.012	.010	.009	.009	.008
2.9	.106	.051	.031	.022	.017	.014	.011	.010	.009	.008	.007	.007
3.0	.102	.048	.029	.020	.015	.012	.010	.009	.007	.007	.006	.006
3.1	.099	.045	.027	.018	.013	.011	.009	.007	.006	.006	.005	.005
3.2	.096	.043	.025	.016	.012	.009	.008	.006	.005	.005	.004	.004
3.3	.094	.040	.023	.015	.011	.008	.007	.005	.005	.004	.004	.003
3.4	.091	.038	.021	.014	.010	.007	.006	.005	.004	.003	.003	.003
3.5	.089	.036	.020	.012	.009	.006	.005	.004	.003	.003	.002	.002
3.6	.086	.035	.018	.011	.008	.006	.004	.004	.003	.002	.002	.002
3.7	.084	.033	.017	.010	.007	.005	.004	.003	.002	.002	.002	.002
3.8	.082	.031	.016	.010	.006	.004	.003	.003	.002	.002	.001	.001
3.9	.080	.030	.015	.009	.006	.004	.003	.002	.002	.001	.001	.001
4.0	.078	.029	.014	.008	.005	.004	.003	.002	.002	.001	.001	.001

(continued)

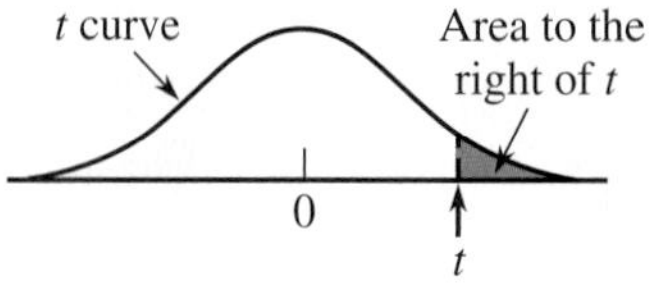

TABLE 4 Tail Areas for t Curves (*Continued*)

t \ df	13	14	15	16	17	18	19	20	21	22	23	24
0.0	.500	.500	.500	.500	.500	.500	.500	.500	.500	.500	.500	.500
0.1	.461	.461	.461	.461	.461	.461	.461	.461	.461	.461	.461	.461
0.2	.422	.422	.422	.422	.422	.422	.422	.422	.422	.422	.422	.422
0.3	.384	.384	.384	.384	.384	.384	.384	.384	.384	.383	.383	.383
0.4	.348	.347	.347	.347	.347	.347	.347	.347	.347	.347	.346	.346
0.5	.313	.312	.312	.312	.312	.312	.311	.311	.311	.311	.311	.311
0.6	.279	.279	.279	.278	.278	.278	.278	.278	.278	.277	.277	.277
0.7	.248	.247	.247	.247	.247	.246	.246	.246	.246	.246	.245	.245
0.8	.219	.218	.218	.218	.217	.217	.217	.217	.216	.216	.216	.216
0.9	.192	.191	.191	.191	.190	.190	.190	.189	.189	.189	.189	.189
1.0	.168	.167	.167	.166	.166	.165	.165	.165	.164	.164	.164	.164
1.1	.146	.144	.144	.144	.143	.143	.143	.142	.142	.142	.141	.141
1.2	.126	.124	.124	.124	.123	.123	.122	.122	.122	.121	.121	.121
1.3	.108	.107	.107	.106	.105	.105	.105	.104	.104	.104	.103	.103
1.4	.092	.091	.091	.090	.090	.089	.089	.089	.088	.088	.087	.087
1.5	.079	.077	.077	.077	.076	.075	.075	.075	.074	.074	.074	.073
1.6	.067	.065	.065	.065	.064	.064	.063	.063	.062	.062	.062	.061
1.7	.056	.055	.055	.054	.054	.053	.053	.052	.052	.052	.051	.051
1.8	.048	.046	.046	.045	.045	.044	.044	.043	.043	.043	.042	.042
1.9	.040	.038	.038	.038	.037	.037	.036	.036	.036	.035	.035	.035
2.0	.033	.032	.032	.031	.031	.030	.030	.030	.029	.029	.029	.028
2.1	.028	.027	.027	.026	.025	.025	.025	.024	.024	.024	.023	.023
2.2	.023	.022	.022	.021	.021	.021	.020	.020	.020	.019	.019	.019
2.3	.019	.018	.018	.018	.017	.017	.016	.016	.016	.016	.015	.015
2.4	.016	.015	.015	.014	.014	.014	.013	.013	.013	.013	.012	.012
2.5	.013	.012	.012	.012	.011	.011	.011	.011	.010	.010	.010	.010
2.6	.011	.010	.010	.010	.009	.009	.009	.009	.008	.008	.008	.008
2.7	.009	.008	.008	.008	.008	.007	.007	.007	.007	.007	.006	.006
2.8	.008	.007	.007	.006	.006	.006	.006	.006	.005	.005	.005	.005
2.9	.006	.005	.005	.005	.005	.005	.005	.004	.004	.004	.004	.004
3.0	.005	.004	.004	.004	.004	.004	.004	.004	.003	.003	.003	.003
3.1	.004	.004	.004	.003	.003	.003	.003	.003	.003	.003	.003	.002
3.2	.003	.003	.003	.003	.003	.002	.002	.002	.002	.002	.002	.002
3.3	.003	.002	.002	.002	.002	.002	.002	.002	.002	.002	.002	.001
3.4	.002	.002	.002	.002	.002	.002	.002	.001	.001	.001	.001	.001
3.5	.002	.002	.002	.001	.001	.001	.001	.001	.001	.001	.001	.001
3.6	.002	.001	.001	.001	.001	.001	.001	.001	.001	.001	.001	.001
3.7	.001	.001	.001	.001	.001	.001	.001	.001	.001	.001	.001	.001
3.8	.001	.001	.001	.001	.001	.001	.001	.001	.001	.000	.000	.000
3.9	.001	.001	.001	.001	.001	.001	.000	.000	.000	.000	.000	.000
4.0	.001	.001	.001	.001	.000	.000	.000	.000	.000	.000	.000	.000

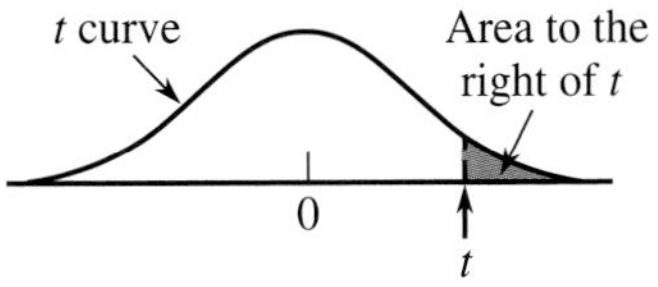

TABLE 4 Tail Areas for t Curves (*Continued*)

t \ df	25	26	27	28	29	30	35	40	60	120	∞(=z)
0.0	.500	.500	.500	.500	.500	.500	.500	.500	.500	.500	.500
0.1	.461	.461	.461	.461	.461	.461	.460	.460	.460	.460	.460
0.2	.422	.422	.421	.421	.421	.421	.421	.421	.421	.421	.421
0.3	.383	.383	.383	.383	.383	.383	.383	.383	.383	.382	.382
0.4	.346	.346	.346	.346	.346	.346	.346	.346	.345	.345	.345
0.5	.311	.311	.311	.310	.310	.310	.310	.310	.309	.309	.309
0.6	.277	.277	.277	.277	.277	.277	.276	.276	.275	.275	.274
0.7	.245	.245	.245	.245	.245	.245	.244	.244	.243	.243	.242
0.8	.216	.215	.215	.215	.215	.215	.215	.214	.213	.213	.212
0.9	.188	.188	.188	.188	.188	.188	.187	.187	.186	.185	.184
1.0	.163	.163	.163	.163	.163	.163	.162	.162	.161	.160	.159
1.1	.141	.141	.141	.140	.140	.140	.139	.139	.138	.137	.136
1.2	.121	.120	.120	.120	.120	.120	.119	.119	.117	.116	.115
1.3	.103	.103	.102	.102	.102	.102	.101	.101	.099	.098	.097
1.4	.087	.087	.086	.086	.086	.086	.085	.085	.083	.082	.081
1.5	.073	.073	.073	.072	.072	.072	.071	.071	.069	.068	.067
1.6	.061	.061	.061	.060	.060	.060	.059	.059	.057	.056	.055
1.7	.051	.051	.050	.050	.050	.050	.049	.048	.047	.046	.045
1.8	.042	.042	.042	.041	.041	.041	.040	.040	.038	.037	.036
1.9	.035	.034	.034	.034	.034	.034	.033	.032	.031	.030	.029
2.0	.028	.028	.028	.028	.027	.027	.027	.026	.025	.024	.023
2.1	.023	.023	.023	.022	.022	.022	.022	.021	.020	.019	.018
2.2	.019	.018	.018	.018	.018	.018	.017	.017	.016	.015	.014
2.3	.015	.015	.015	.015	.014	.014	.014	.013	.012	.012	.011
2.4	.012	.012	.012	.012	.012	.011	.011	.011	.010	.009	.008
2.5	.010	.010	.009	.009	.009	.009	.009	.008	.008	.007	.006
2.6	.008	.008	.007	.007	.007	.007	.007	.007	.006	.005	.005
2.7	.006	.006	.006	.006	.006	.006	.005	.005	.004	.004	.003
2.8	.005	.005	.005	.005	.005	.004	.004	.004	.003	.003	.003
2.9	.004	.004	.004	.004	.004	.003	.003	.003	.003	.002	.002
3.0	.003	.003	.003	.003	.003	.003	.002	.002	.002	.002	.001
3.1	.002	.002	.002	.002	.002	.002	.002	.002	.001	.001	.001
3.2	.002	.002	.002	.002	.002	.002	.001	.001	.001	.001	.001
3.3	.001	.001	.001	.001	.001	.001	.001	.001	.001	.001	.000
3.4	.001	.001	.001	.001	.001	.001	.001	.001	.001	.000	.000
3.5	.001	.001	.001	.001	.001	.001	.001	.001	.000	.000	.000
3.6	.001	.001	.001	.001	.001	.001	.000	.000	.000	.000	.000
3.7	.001	.001	.000	.000	.000	.000	.000	.000	.000	.000	.000
3.8	.000	.000	.000	.000	.000	.000	.000	.000	.000	.000	.000
3.9	.000	.000	.000	.000	.000	.000	.000	.000	.000	.000	.000
4.0	.000	.000	.000	.000	.000	.000	.000	.000	.000	.000	.000

TABLE 5 Curves of $\beta = P$(Type II Error) for t Tests

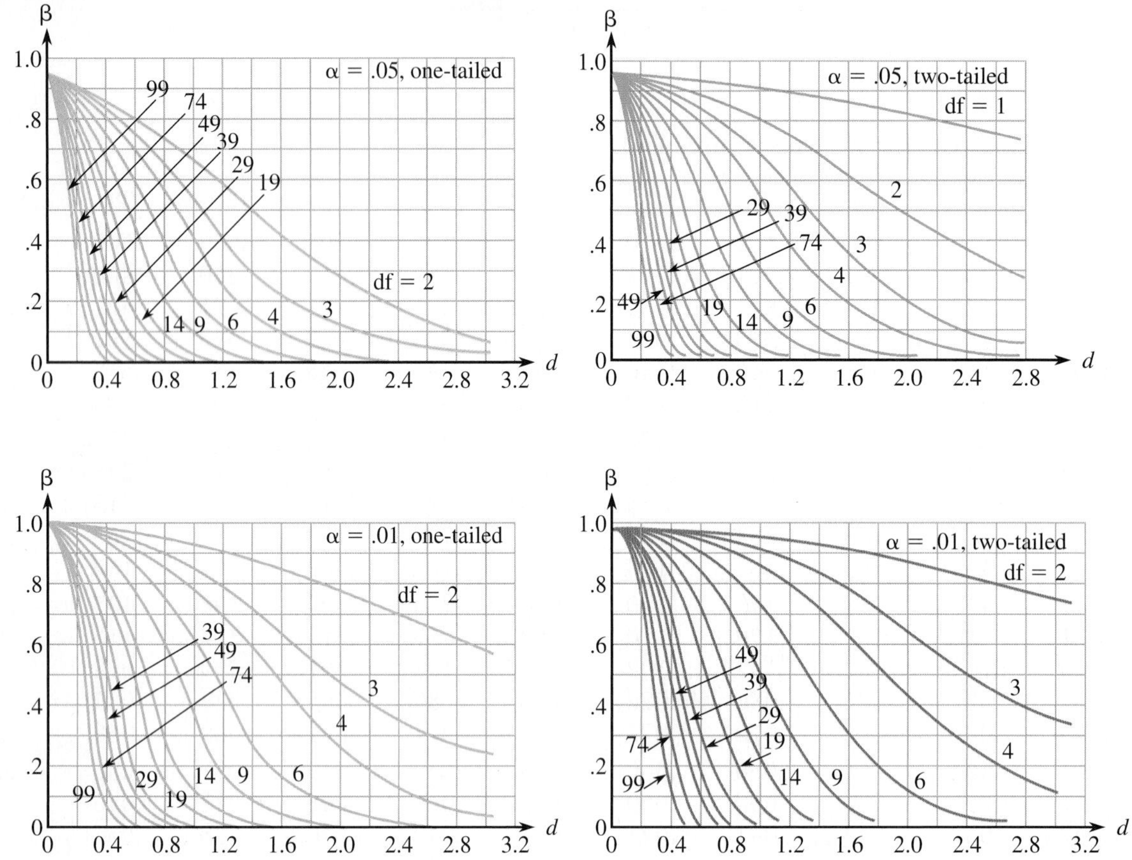

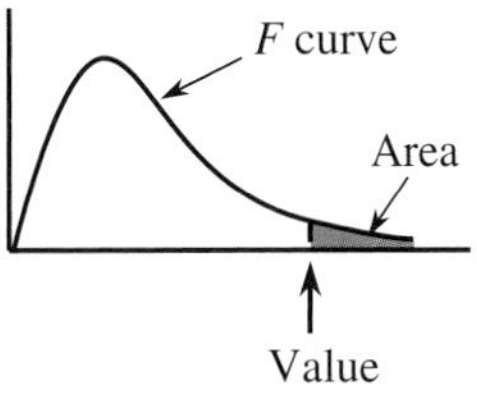

TABLE 6 Values That Capture Specified Upper-Tail F Curve Areas

		df_1									
df_2	Area	1	2	3	4	5	6	7	8	9	10
1	**.10**	39.86	49.50	53.59	55.83	57.24	58.20	58.91	59.44	59.86	60.19
	.05	161.40	199.50	215.70	224.60	230.20	234.00	236.80	238.90	240.50	241.90
	.01	4052.00	5000.00	5403.00	5625.00	5764.00	5859.00	5928.00	5981.00	6022.00	6056.00
2	**.10**	8.53	9.00	9.16	9.24	9.29	9.33	9.35	9.37	9.38	9.39
	.05	18.51	19.00	19.16	19.25	19.30	19.33	19.35	19.37	19.38	19.40
	.01	98.50	99.00	99.17	99.25	99.30	99.33	99.36	99.37	99.39	99.40
	.001	998.50	999.00	999.20	999.20	999.30	999.30	999.40	999.40	999.40	999.40
3	**.10**	5.54	5.46	5.39	5.34	5.31	5.28	5.27	5.25	5.24	5.23
	.05	10.13	9.55	9.28	9.12	9.01	8.94	8.89	8.85	8.81	8.79
	.01	34.12	30.82	29.46	28.71	28.24	27.91	27.67	27.49	27.35	27.23
	.001	167.00	148.50	141.10	137.10	134.60	132.80	131.60	130.60	129.90	129.20
4	**.10**	4.54	4.32	4.19	4.11	4.05	4.01	3.98	3.95	3.94	3.92
	.05	7.71	6.94	6.59	6.39	6.26	6.16	6.09	6.04	6.00	5.96
	.01	21.20	18.00	16.69	15.98	15.52	15.21	14.98	14.80	14.66	14.55
	.001	74.14	61.25	56.18	53.44	51.71	50.53	49.66	49.00	48.47	48.05
5	**.10**	4.06	3.78	3.62	3.52	3.45	3.40	3.37	3.34	3.32	3.30
	.05	6.61	5.79	5.41	5.19	5.05	4.95	4.88	4.82	4.77	4.74
	.01	16.26	13.27	12.06	11.39	10.97	10.67	10.46	10.29	10.16	10.05
	.001	47.18	37.12	33.20	31.09	29.75	28.83	28.16	27.65	27.24	26.92
6	**.10**	3.78	3.46	3.29	3.18	3.11	3.05	3.01	2.98	2.96	2.94
	.05	5.99	5.14	4.76	4.53	4.39	4.28	4.21	4.15	4.10	4.06
	.01	13.75	10.92	9.78	9.15	8.75	8.47	8.26	8.10	7.98	7.87
	.001	35.51	27.00	23.70	21.92	20.80	20.03	19.46	19.03	18.69	18.41
7	**.10**	3.59	3.26	3.07	2.96	2.88	2.83	2.78	2.75	2.72	2.70
	.05	5.59	4.74	4.35	4.12	3.97	3.87	3.79	3.73	3.68	3.64
	.01	12.25	9.55	8.45	7.85	7.46	7.19	6.99	6.84	6.72	6.62
	.001	29.25	21.69	18.77	17.20	16.21	15.52	15.02	14.63	14.33	14.08
8	**.10**	3.46	3.11	2.92	2.81	2.73	2.67	2.62	2.59	2.56	2.54
	.05	5.32	4.46	4.07	3.84	3.69	3.58	3.50	3.44	3.39	3.35
	.01	11.26	8.65	7.59	7.01	6.63	6.37	6.18	6.03	5.91	5.81
	.001	25.41	18.49	15.83	14.39	13.48	12.86	12.40	12.05	11.77	11.54
9	**.10**	3.36	3.01	2.81	2.69	2.61	2.55	2.51	2.47	2.44	2.42
	.05	5.12	4.26	3.86	3.63	3.48	3.37	3.29	3.23	3.18	3.14
	.01	10.56	8.02	6.99	6.42	6.06	5.80	5.61	5.47	5.35	5.26
	.001	22.86	16.39	13.90	12.56	11.71	11.13	10.70	10.37	10.11	9.89

(continued)

TABLE 6 Values That Capture Specified Upper-Tail *F* Curve Areas (*Continued*)

		df_1									
df_2	Area	1	2	3	4	5	6	7	8	9	10
10	**.10**	3.29	2.92	2.73	2.61	2.52	2.46	2.41	2.38	2.35	2.32
	.05	4.96	4.10	3.71	3.48	3.33	3.22	3.14	3.07	3.02	2.98
	.01	10.04	7.56	6.55	5.99	5.64	5.39	5.20	5.06	4.94	4.85
	.001	21.04	14.91	12.55	11.28	10.48	9.93	9.52	9.20	8.96	8.75
11	**.10**	3.23	2.86	2.66	2.54	2.45	2.39	2.34	2.30	2.27	2.25
	.05	4.84	3.98	3.59	3.36	3.20	3.09	3.01	2.95	2.90	2.85
	.01	9.65	7.21	6.22	5.67	5.32	5.07	4.89	4.74	4.63	4.54
	.001	19.69	13.81	11.56	10.35	9.58	9.05	8.66	8.35	8.12	7.92
12	**.10**	3.18	2.81	2.61	2.48	2.39	2.33	2.28	2.24	2.21	2.19
	.05	4.75	3.89	3.49	3.26	3.11	3.00	2.91	2.85	2.80	2.75
	.01	9.33	6.93	5.95	5.41	5.06	4.82	4.64	4.50	4.39	4.30
	.001	18.64	12.97	10.80	9.63	8.89	8.38	8.00	7.71	7.48	7.29
13	**.10**	3.14	2.76	2.56	2.43	2.35	2.28	2.23	2.20	2.16	2.14
	.05	4.67	3.81	3.41	3.18	3.03	2.92	2.83	2.77	2.71	2.67
	.01	9.07	6.70	5.74	5.21	4.86	4.62	4.44	4.30	4.19	4.10
	.001	17.82	12.31	10.21	9.07	8.35	7.86	7.49	7.21	6.98	6.80
14	**.10**	3.10	2.73	2.52	2.39	2.31	2.24	2.19	2.15	2.12	2.10
	.05	4.60	3.74	3.34	3.11	2.96	2.85	2.76	2.70	2.65	2.60
	.01	8.86	6.51	5.56	5.04	4.69	4.46	4.28	4.14	4.03	3.94
	.001	17.14	11.78	9.73	8.62	7.92	7.44	7.08	6.80	6.58	6.40
15	**.10**	3.07	2.70	2.49	2.36	2.27	2.21	2.16	2.12	2.09	2.06
	.05	4.54	3.68	3.29	3.06	2.90	2.79	2.71	2.64	2.59	2.54
	.01	8.68	6.36	5.42	4.89	4.56	4.32	4.14	4.00	3.89	3.80
	.001	16.59	11.34	9.34	8.25	7.57	7.09	6.74	6.47	6.26	6.08
16	**.10**	3.05	2.67	2.46	2.33	2.24	2.18	2.13	2.09	2.06	2.03
	.05	4.49	3.63	3.24	3.01	2.85	2.74	2.66	2.59	2.54	2.49
	.01	8.53	6.23	5.29	4.77	4.44	4.20	4.03	3.89	3.78	3.69
	.001	16.12	10.97	9.01	7.94	7.27	6.80	6.46	6.19	5.98	5.81
17	**.10**	3.03	2.64	2.44	2.31	2.22	2.15	2.10	2.06	2.03	2.00
	.05	4.45	3.59	3.20	2.96	2.81	2.70	2.61	2.55	2.49	2.45
	.01	8.40	6.11	5.18	4.67	4.34	4.10	3.93	3.79	3.68	3.59
	.001	15.72	10.66	8.73	7.68	7.02	6.56	6.22	5.96	5.75	5.58
18	**.10**	3.01	2.62	2.42	2.29	2.20	2.13	2.08	2.04	2.00	1.98
	.05	4.41	3.55	3.16	2.93	2.77	2.66	2.58	2.51	2.46	2.41
	.01	8.29	6.01	5.09	4.58	4.25	4.01	3.84	3.71	3.60	3.51
	.001	15.38	10.39	8.49	7.46	6.81	6.35	6.02	5.76	5.56	5.39
19	**.10**	2.99	2.61	2.40	2.27	2.18	2.11	2.06	2.02	1.98	1.96
	.05	4.38	3.52	3.13	2.90	2.74	2.63	2.54	2.48	2.42	2.38
	.01	8.18	5.93	5.01	4.50	4.17	3.94	3.77	3.63	3.52	3.43
	.001	15.08	10.16	8.28	7.27	6.62	6.18	5.85	5.59	5.39	5.22

TABLE 6 Values That Capture Specified Upper-Tail F Curve Areas (*Continued*)

		df$_1$									
df$_2$	Area	1	2	3	4	5	6	7	8	9	10
20	**.10**	2.97	2.59	2.38	2.25	2.16	2.09	2.04	2.00	1.96	1.94
	.05	4.35	3.49	3.10	2.87	2.71	2.60	2.51	2.45	2.39	2.35
	.01	8.10	5.85	4.94	4.43	4.10	3.87	3.70	3.56	3.46	3.37
	.001	14.82	9.95	8.10	7.10	6.46	6.02	5.69	5.44	5.24	5.08
21	**.10**	2.96	2.57	2.36	2.23	2.14	2.08	2.02	1.98	1.95	1.92
	.05	4.32	3.47	3.07	2.84	2.68	2.57	2.49	2.42	2.37	2.32
	.01	8.02	5.78	4.87	4.37	4.04	3.81	3.64	3.51	3.40	3.31
	.001	14.59	9.77	7.94	6.95	6.32	5.88	5.56	5.31	5.11	4.95
22	**.10**	2.95	2.56	2.35	2.22	2.13	2.06	2.01	1.97	1.93	1.90
	.05	4.30	3.44	3.05	2.82	2.66	2.55	2.46	2.40	2.34	2.30
	.01	7.95	5.72	4.82	4.31	3.99	3.76	3.59	3.45	3.35	3.26
	.001	14.38	9.61	7.80	6.81	6.19	5.76	5.44	5.19	4.99	4.83
23	**.10**	2.94	2.55	2.34	2.21	2.11	2.05	1.99	1.95	1.92	1.89
	.05	4.28	3.42	3.03	2.80	2.64	2.53	2.44	2.37	2.32	2.27
	.01	7.88	5.66	4.76	4.26	3.94	3.71	3.54	3.41	3.30	3.21
	.001	14.20	9.47	7.67	6.70	6.08	5.65	5.33	5.09	4.89	4.73
24	**.10**	2.93	2.54	2.33	2.19	2.10	2.04	1.98	1.94	1.91	1.88
	.05	4.26	3.40	3.01	2.78	2.62	2.51	2.42	2.36	2.30	2.25
	.01	7.82	5.61	4.72	4.22	3.90	3.67	3.50	3.36	3.26	3.17
	.001	14.03	9.34	7.55	6.59	5.98	5.55	5.23	4.99	4.80	4.64
25	**.10**	2.92	2.53	2.32	2.18	2.09	2.02	1.97	1.93	1.89	1.87
	.05	4.24	3.39	2.99	2.76	2.60	2.49	2.40	2.34	2.28	2.24
	.01	7.77	5.57	4.68	4.18	3.85	3.63	3.46	3.32	3.22	3.13
	.001	13.88	9.22	7.45	6.49	5.89	5.46	5.15	4.91	4.71	4.56
26	**.10**	2.91	2.52	2.31	2.17	2.08	2.01	1.96	1.92	1.88	1.86
	.05	4.23	3.37	2.98	2.74	2.59	2.47	2.39	2.32	2.27	2.22
	.01	7.72	5.53	4.64	4.14	3.82	3.59	3.42	3.29	3.18	3.09
	.001	13.74	9.12	7.36	6.41	5.80	5.38	5.07	4.83	4.64	4.48
27	**.10**	2.90	2.51	2.30	2.17	2.07	2.00	1.95	1.91	1.87	1.85
	.05	4.21	3.35	2.96	2.73	2.57	2.46	2.37	2.31	2.25	2.20
	.01	7.68	5.49	4.60	4.11	3.78	3.56	3.39	3.26	3.15	3.06
	.001	13.61	9.02	7.27	6.33	5.73	5.31	5.00	4.76	4.57	4.41
28	**.10**	2.89	2.50	2.29	2.16	2.06	2.00	1.94	1.90	1.87	1.84
	.05	4.20	3.34	2.95	2.71	2.56	2.45	2.36	2.29	2.24	2.19
	.01	7.64	5.45	4.57	4.07	3.75	3.53	3.36	3.23	3.12	3.03
	.001	13.50	8.93	7.19	6.25	5.66	5.24	4.93	4.69	4.50	4.35
29	**.10**	2.89	2.50	2.28	2.15	2.06	1.99	1.93	1.89	1.86	1.83
	.05	4.18	3.33	2.93	2.70	2.55	2.43	2.35	2.28	2.22	2.18
	.01	7.60	5.42	4.54	4.04	3.73	3.50	3.33	3.20	3.09	3.00
	.001	13.39	8.85	7.12	6.19	5.59	5.18	4.87	4.64	4.45	4.29

(continued)

TABLE 6 Values That Capture Specified Upper-Tail F Curve Areas (*Continued*)

		df_1									
df_2	Area	1	2	3	4	5	6	7	8	9	10
30	**.10**	2.88	2.49	2.28	2.14	2.05	1.98	1.93	1.88	1.85	1.82
	.05	4.17	3.32	2.92	2.69	2.53	2.42	2.33	2.27	2.21	2.16
	.01	7.56	5.39	4.51	4.02	3.70	3.47	3.30	3.17	3.07	2.98
	.001	13.29	8.77	7.05	6.12	5.53	5.12	4.82	4.58	4.39	4.24
40	**.10**	2.84	2.44	2.23	2.09	2.00	1.93	1.87	1.83	1.79	1.76
	.05	4.08	3.23	2.84	2.61	2.45	2.34	2.25	2.18	2.12	2.08
	.01	7.31	5.18	4.31	3.83	3.51	3.29	3.12	2.99	2.89	2.80
	.001	12.61	8.25	6.59	5.70	5.13	4.73	4.44	4.21	4.02	3.87
60	**.10**	2.79	2.39	2.18	2.04	1.95	1.87	1.82	1.77	1.74	1.71
	.05	4.00	3.15	2.76	2.53	2.37	2.25	2.17	2.10	2.04	1.99
	.01	7.08	4.98	4.13	3.65	3.34	3.12	2.95	2.82	2.72	2.63
	.001	11.97	7.77	6.17	5.31	4.76	4.37	4.09	3.86	3.69	3.54
90	**.10**	2.76	2.36	2.15	2.01	1.91	1.84	1.78	1.74	1.70	1.67
	.05	3.95	3.10	2.71	2.47	2.32	2.20	2.11	2.04	1.99	1.94
	.01	6.93	4.85	4.01	3.53	3.23	3.01	2.84	2.72	2.61	2.52
	.001	11.57	7.47	5.91	5.06	4.53	4.15	3.87	3.65	3.48	3.34
120	**.10**	2.75	2.35	2.13	1.99	1.90	1.82	1.77	1.72	1.68	1.65
	.05	3.92	3.07	2.68	2.45	2.29	2.18	2.09	2.02	1.96	1.91
	.01	6.85	4.79	3.95	3.48	3.17	2.96	2.79	2.66	2.56	2.47
	.001	11.38	7.32	5.78	4.95	4.42	4.04	3.77	3.55	3.38	3.24
240	**.10**	2.73	2.32	2.10	1.97	1.87	1.80	1.74	1.70	1.65	1.63
	.05	3.88	3.03	2.64	2.41	2.25	2.14	2.04	1.98	1.92	1.87
	.01	6.74	4.69	3.86	3.40	3.09	2.88	2.71	2.59	2.48	2.40
	.001	11.10	7.11	5.60	4.78	4.25	3.89	3.62	3.41	3.24	3.09
∞	**.10**	2.71	2.30	2.08	1.94	1.85	1.77	1.72	1.67	1.63	1.60
	.05	3.84	3.00	2.60	2.37	2.21	2.10	2.01	1.94	1.88	1.83
	.01	6.63	4.61	3.78	3.32	3.02	2.80	2.64	2.51	2.41	2.32
	.001	10.83	6.91	5.42	4.62	4.10	3.74	3.47	3.27	3.10	2.96

TABLE 7 Critical Values of q for the Studentized Range Distribution

Error df	Confidence level	Number of populations, treatments, or levels being compared							
		3	4	5	6	7	8	9	10
5	**95%**	4.60	5.22	5.67	6.03	6.33	6.58	6.80	6.99
	99%	6.98	7.80	8.42	8.91	9.32	9.67	9.97	10.24
6	**95%**	4.34	4.90	5.30	5.63	5.90	6.12	6.32	6.49
	99%	6.33	7.03	7.56	7.97	8.32	8.61	8.87	9.10
7	**95%**	4.16	4.68	5.06	5.36	5.61	5.82	6.00	6.16
	99%	5.92	6.54	7.01	7.37	7.68	7.94	8.17	8.37
8	**95%**	4.04	4.53	4.89	5.17	5.40	5.60	5.77	5.92
	99%	5.64	6.20	6.62	6.96	7.24	7.47	7.68	7.86
9	**95%**	3.95	4.41	4.76	5.02	5.24	5.43	5.59	5.74
	99%	5.43	5.96	6.35	6.66	6.91	7.13	7.33	7.49
10	**95%**	3.88	4.33	4.65	4.91	5.12	5.30	5.46	5.60
	99%	5.27	5.77	6.14	6.43	6.67	6.87	7.05	7.21
11	**95%**	3.82	4.26	4.57	4.82	5.03	5.20	5.35	5.49
	99%	5.15	5.62	5.97	6.25	6.48	6.67	6.84	6.99
12	**95%**	3.77	4.20	4.51	4.75	4.95	5.12	5.27	5.39
	99%	5.05	5.50	5.84	6.10	6.32	6.51	6.67	6.81
13	**95%**	3.73	4.15	4.45	4.69	4.88	5.05	5.19	5.32
	99%	4.96	5.40	5.73	5.98	6.19	6.37	6.53	6.67
14	**95%**	3.70	4.11	4.41	4.64	4.83	4.99	5.13	5.25
	99%	4.89	5.32	5.63	5.88	6.08	6.26	6.41	6.54
15	**95%**	3.67	4.08	4.37	4.59	4.78	4.94	5.08	5.20
	99%	4.84	5.25	5.56	5.80	5.99	6.16	6.31	6.44
16	**95%**	3.65	4.05	4.33	4.56	4.74	4.90	5.03	5.15
	99%	4.79	5.19	5.49	5.72	5.92	6.08	6.22	6.35
17	**95%**	3.63	4.02	4.30	4.52	4.70	4.86	4.99	5.11
	99%	4.74	5.14	5.43	5.66	5.85	6.01	6.15	6.27
18	**95%**	3.61	4.00	4.28	4.49	4.67	4.82	4.96	5.07
	99%	4.70	5.09	5.38	5.60	5.79	5.94	6.08	6.20
19	**95%**	3.59	3.98	4.25	4.47	4.65	4.79	4.92	5.04
	99%	4.67	5.05	5.33	5.55	5.73	5.89	6.02	6.14
20	**95%**	3.58	3.96	4.23	4.45	4.62	4.77	4.90	5.01
	99%	4.64	5.02	5.29	5.51	5.69	5.84	5.97	6.09
24	**95%**	3.53	3.90	4.17	4.37	4.54	4.68	4.81	4.92
	99%	4.55	4.91	5.17	5.37	5.54	5.69	5.81	5.92
30	**95%**	3.49	3.85	4.10	4.30	4.46	4.60	4.72	4.82
	99%	4.45	4.80	5.05	5.24	5.40	5.54	5.65	5.76
40	**95%**	3.44	3.79	4.04	4.23	4.39	4.52	4.63	4.73
	99%	4.37	4.70	4.93	5.11	5.26	5.39	5.50	5.60
60	**95%**	3.40	3.74	3.98	4.16	4.31	4.44	4.55	4.65
	99%	4.28	4.59	4.82	4.99	5.13	5.25	5.36	5.45
120	**95%**	3.36	3.68	3.92	4.10	4.24	4.36	4.47	4.56
	99%	4.20	4.50	4.71	4.87	5.01	5.12	5.21	5.30
∞	**95%**	3.31	3.63	3.86	4.03	4.17	4.29	4.39	4.47
	99%	4.12	4.40	4.60	4.76	4.88	4.99	5.08	5.16

TABLE 8 Upper-Tail Areas for Chi-Square Distributions

Right-tail area	df = 1	df = 2	df = 3	df = 4	df = 5
>0.100	< 2.70	< 4.60	< 6.25	< 7.77	< 9.23
0.100	2.70	4.60	6.25	7.77	9.23
0.095	2.78	4.70	6.36	7.90	9.37
0.090	2.87	4.81	6.49	8.04	9.52
0.085	2.96	4.93	6.62	8.18	9.67
0.080	3.06	5.05	6.75	8.33	9.83
0.075	3.17	5.18	6.90	8.49	10.00
0.070	3.28	5.31	7.06	8.66	10.19
0.065	3.40	5.46	7.22	8.84	10.38
0.060	3.53	5.62	7.40	9.04	10.59
0.055	3.68	5.80	7.60	9.25	10.82
0.050	3.84	5.99	7.81	9.48	11.07
0.045	4.01	6.20	8.04	9.74	11.34
0.040	4.21	6.43	8.31	10.02	11.64
0.035	4.44	6.70	8.60	10.34	11.98
0.030	4.70	7.01	8.94	10.71	12.37
0.025	5.02	7.37	9.34	11.14	12.83
0.020	5.41	7.82	9.83	11.66	13.38
0.015	5.91	8.39	10.46	12.33	14.09
0.010	6.63	9.21	11.34	13.27	15.08
0.005	7.87	10.59	12.83	14.86	16.74
0.001	10.82	13.81	16.26	18.46	20.51
<0.001	>10.82	>13.81	>16.26	>18.46	>20.51

Right-tail area	df = 6	df = 7	df =8	df = 9	df = 10
>0.100	<10.64	<12.01	<13.36	<14.68	<15.98
0.100	10.64	12.01	13.36	14.68	15.98
0.095	10.79	12.17	13.52	14.85	16.16
0.090	10.94	12.33	13.69	15.03	16.35
0.085	11.11	12.50	13.87	15.22	16.54
0.080	11.28	12.69	14.06	15.42	16.75
0.075	11.46	12.88	14.26	15.63	16.97
0.070	11.65	13.08	14.48	15.85	17.20
0.065	11.86	13.30	14.71	16.09	17.44
0.060	12.08	13.53	14.95	16.34	17.71
0.055	12.33	13.79	15.22	16.62	17.99
0.050	12.59	14.06	15.50	16.91	18.30
0.045	12.87	14.36	15.82	17.24	18.64
0.040	13.19	14.70	16.17	17.60	19.02
0.035	13.55	15.07	16.56	18.01	19.44
0.030	13.96	15.50	17.01	18.47	19.92
0.025	14.44	16.01	17.53	19.02	20.48
0.020	15.03	16.62	18.16	19.67	21.16
0.015	15.77	17.39	18.97	20.51	22.02
0.010	16.81	18.47	20.09	21.66	23.20
0.005	18.54	20.27	21.95	23.58	25.18
0.001	22.45	24.32	26.12	27.87	29.58
<0.001	>22.45	>24.32	>26.12	>27.87	>29.58

TABLE 8 Upper-Tail Areas for Chi-Square Distributions (*Continued*)

Right-tail area	df = 11	df = 12	df = 13	df = 14	df = 15
>0.100	<17.27	<18.54	<19.81	<21.06	<22.30
0.100	17.27	18.54	19.81	21.06	22.30
0.095	17.45	18.74	20.00	21.26	22.51
0.090	17.65	18.93	20.21	21.47	22.73
0.085	17.85	19.14	20.42	21.69	22.95
0.080	18.06	19.36	20.65	21.93	23.19
0.075	18.29	19.60	20.89	22.17	23.45
0.070	18.53	19.84	21.15	22.44	23.72
0.065	18.78	20.11	21.42	22.71	24.00
0.060	19.06	20.39	21.71	23.01	24.31
0.055	19.35	20.69	22.02	23.33	24.63
0.050	19.67	21.02	22.36	23.68	24.99
0.045	20.02	21.38	22.73	24.06	25.38
0.040	20.41	21.78	23.14	24.48	25.81
0.035	20.84	22.23	23.60	24.95	26.29
0.030	21.34	22.74	24.12	25.49	26.84
0.025	21.92	23.33	24.73	26.11	27.48
0.020	22.61	24.05	25.47	26.87	28.25
0.015	23.50	24.96	26.40	27.82	29.23
0.010	24.72	26.21	27.68	29.14	30.57
0.005	26.75	28.29	29.81	31.31	32.80
0.001	31.26	32.90	34.52	36.12	37.69
<0.001	>31.26	>32.90	>34.52	>36.12	>37.69

Right-tail area	df = 16	df = 17	df = 18	df = 19	df = 20
>0.100	<23.54	<24.77	<25.98	<27.20	<28.41
0.100	23.54	24.76	25.98	27.20	28.41
0.095	23.75	24.98	26.21	27.43	28.64
0.090	23.97	25.21	26.44	27.66	28.88
0.085	24.21	25.45	26.68	27.91	29.14
0.080	24.45	25.70	26.94	28.18	29.40
0.075	24.71	25.97	27.21	28.45	29.69
0.070	24.99	26.25	27.50	28.75	29.99
0.065	25.28	26.55	27.81	29.06	30.30
0.060	25.59	26.87	28.13	29.39	30.64
0.055	25.93	27.21	28.48	29.75	31.01
0.050	26.29	27.58	28.86	30.14	31.41
0.045	26.69	27.99	29.28	30.56	31.84
0.040	27.13	28.44	29.74	31.03	32.32
0.035	27.62	28.94	30.25	31.56	32.85
0.030	28.19	29.52	30.84	32.15	33.46
0.025	28.84	30.19	31.52	32.85	34.16
0.020	29.63	30.99	32.34	33.68	35.01
0.015	30.62	32.01	33.38	34.74	36.09
0.010	32.00	33.40	34.80	36.19	37.56
0.005	34.26	35.71	37.15	38.58	39.99
0.001	39.25	40.78	42.31	43.81	45.31
<0.001	>39.25	>40.78	>42.31	>43.81	>45.31

TABLE 9 Binomial Probabilities

n = 5

	p												
x	0.05	0.1	0.2	0.25	0.3	0.4	0.5	0.6	0.7	0.75	0.8	0.9	0.95
0	.774	.590	.328	.237	.168	.078	.031	.010	.002	.001	.000	.000	.000
1	.204	.328	.410	.396	.360	.259	.156	.077	.028	.015	.006	.000	.000
2	.021	.073	.205	.264	.309	.346	.313	.230	.132	.088	.051	.008	.001
3	.001	.008	.051	.088	.132	.230	.313	.346	.309	.264	.205	.073	.021
4	.000	.000	.006	.015	.028	.077	.156	.259	.360	.396	.410	.328	.204
5	.000	.000	.000	.001	.002	.010	.031	.078	.168	.237	.328	.590	.774

n = 10

	p												
x	0.05	0.1	0.2	0.25	0.3	0.4	0.5	0.6	0.7	0.75	0.8	0.9	0.95
0	.599	.349	.107	.056	.028	.006	.001	.000	.000	.000	.000	.000	.000
1	.315	.387	.268	.188	.121	.040	.010	.002	.000	.000	.000	.000	.000
2	.075	.194	.302	.282	.233	.121	.044	.011	.001	.000	.000	.000	.000
3	.010	.057	.201	.250	.267	.215	.117	.042	.009	.003	.001	.000	.000
4	.001	.011	.088	.146	.200	.251	.205	.111	.037	.016	.006	.000	.000
5	.000	.001	.026	.058	.103	.201	.246	.201	.103	.058	.026	.001	.000
6	.000	.000	.006	.016	.037	.111	.205	.251	.200	.146	.088	.011	.001
7	.000	.000	.001	.003	.009	.042	.117	.215	.267	.250	.201	.057	.010
8	.000	.000	.000	.000	.001	.011	.044	.121	.233	.282	.302	.194	.075
9	.000	.000	.000	.000	.000	.002	.010	.040	.121	.188	.268	.387	.315
10	.000	.000	.000	.000	.000	.000	.001	.006	.028	.056	.107	.349	.599

TABLE 9 Binomial Probabilities (*Continued*)

$n = 15$

	p												
x	0.05	0.1	0.2	0.25	0.3	0.4	0.5	0.6	0.7	0.75	0.8	0.9	0.95
0	.463	.206	.035	.013	.005	.000	.000	.000	.000	.000	.000	.000	.000
1	.366	.343	.132	.067	.031	.005	.000	.000	.000	.000	.000	.000	.000
2	.135	.267	.231	.156	.092	.022	.003	.000	.000	.000	.000	.000	.000
3	.031	.129	.250	.225	.170	.063	.014	.002	.000	.000	.000	.000	.000
4	.005	.043	.188	.225	.219	.127	.042	.007	.001	.000	.000	.000	.000
5	.001	.010	.103	.165	.206	.186	.092	.024	.003	.001	.000	.000	.000
6	.000	.002	.043	.092	.147	.207	.153	.061	.012	.003	.001	.000	.000
7	.000	.000	.014	.039	.081	.177	.196	.118	.035	.013	.003	.000	.000
8	.000	.000	.003	.013	.035	.118	.196	.177	.081	.039	.014	.000	.000
9	.000	.000	.001	.003	.012	.061	.153	.207	.147	.092	.043	.002	.000
10	.000	.000	.000	.001	.003	.024	.092	.186	.206	.165	.103	.010	.001
11	.000	.000	.000	.000	.001	.007	.042	.127	.219	.225	.188	.043	.005
12	.000	.000	.000	.000	.000	.002	.014	.063	.170	.225	.250	.129	.031
13	.000	.000	.000	.000	.000	.000	.003	.022	.092	.156	.231	.267	.135
14	.000	.000	.000	.000	.000	.000	.000	.005	.031	.067	.132	.343	.366
15	.000	.000	.000	.000	.000	.000	.000	.000	.005	.013	.035	.206	.463

$n = 20$

	p												
x	0.05	0.1	0.2	0.25	0.3	0.4	0.5	0.6	0.7	0.75	0.8	0.9	0.95
0	.358	.122	.012	.003	.001	.000	.000	.000	.000	.000	.000	.000	.000
1	.377	.270	.058	.021	.007	.000	.000	.000	.000	.000	.000	.000	.000
2	.189	.285	.137	.067	.028	.003	.000	.000	.000	.000	.000	.000	.000
3	.060	.190	.205	.134	.072	.012	.001	.000	.000	.000	.000	.000	.000
4	.013	.090	.218	.190	.130	.035	.005	.000	.000	.000	.000	.000	.000
5	.002	.032	.175	.202	.179	.075	.015	.001	.000	.000	.000	.000	.000
6	.000	.009	.109	.169	.192	.124	.037	.005	.000	.000	.000	.000	.000
7	.000	.002	.055	.112	.164	.166	.074	.015	.001	.000	.000	.000	.000
8	.000	.000	.022	.061	.114	.180	.120	.035	.004	.001	.000	.000	.000
9	.000	.000	.007	.027	.065	.160	.160	.071	.012	.003	.000	.000	.000
10	.000	.000	.002	.010	.031	.117	.176	.117	.031	.010	.002	.000	.000
11	.000	.000	.000	.003	.012	.071	.160	.160	.065	.027	.007	.000	.000
12	.000	.000	.000	.001	.004	.035	.120	.180	.114	.061	.022	.000	.000
13	.000	.000	.000	.000	.001	.015	.074	.166	.164	.112	.055	.002	.000
14	.000	.000	.000	.000	.000	.005	.037	.124	.192	.169	.109	.009	.000
15	.000	.000	.000	.000	.000	.001	.015	.075	.179	.202	.175	.032	.002
16	.000	.000	.000	.000	.000	.000	.005	.035	.130	.190	.218	.090	.013
17	.000	.000	.000	.000	.000	.000	.001	.012	.072	.134	.205	.190	.060
18	.000	.000	.000	.000	.000	.000	.000	.003	.028	.067	.137	.285	.189
19	.000	.000	.000	.000	.000	.000	.000	.000	.007	.021	.058	.270	.377
20	.000	.000	.000	.000	.000	.000	.000	.000	.001	.003	.012	.122	.358

(*continued*)

TABLE 9 Binomial Probabilities (*Continued*)

$n = 25$

	p												
x	0.05	0.1	0.2	0.25	0.3	0.4	0.5	0.6	0.7	0.75	0.8	0.9	0.95
0	.277	.072	.004	.001	.000	.000	.000	.000	.000	.000	.000	.000	.000
1	.365	.199	.024	.006	.001	.000	.000	.000	.000	.000	.000	.000	.000
2	.231	.266	.071	.025	.007	.000	.000	.000	.000	.000	.000	.000	.000
3	.093	.226	.136	.064	.024	.002	.000	.000	.000	.000	.000	.000	.000
4	.027	.138	.187	.118	.057	.007	.000	.000	.000	.000	.000	.000	.000
5	.006	.065	.196	.165	.103	.020	.002	.000	.000	.000	.000	.000	.000
6	.001	.024	.163	.183	.147	.044	.005	.000	.000	.000	.000	.000	.000
7	.000	.007	.111	.165	.171	.080	.014	.001	.000	.000	.000	.000	.000
8	.000	.002	.062	.124	.165	.120	.032	.003	.000	.000	.000	.000	.000
9	.000	.000	.029	.078	.134	.151	.061	.009	.000	.000	.000	.000	.000
10	.000	.000	.012	.042	.092	.161	.097	.021	.001	.000	.000	.000	.000
11	.000	.000	.004	.019	.054	.147	.133	.043	.004	.001	.000	.000	.000
12	.000	.000	.001	.007	.027	.114	.155	.076	.011	.002	.000	.000	.000
13	.000	.000	.000	.002	.011	.076	.155	.114	.027	.007	.001	.000	.000
14	.000	.000	.000	.001	.004	.043	.133	.147	.054	.019	.004	.000	.000
15	.000	.000	.000	.000	.001	.021	.097	.161	.092	.042	.012	.000	.000
16	.000	.000	.000	.000	.000	.009	.061	.151	.134	.078	.029	.000	.000
17	.000	.000	.000	.000	.000	.003	.032	.120	.165	.124	.062	.002	.000
18	.000	.000	.000	.000	.000	.001	.014	.080	.171	.165	.111	.007	.000
19	.000	.000	.000	.000	.000	.000	.005	.044	.147	.183	.163	.024	.001
20	.000	.000	.000	.000	.000	.000	.002	.020	.103	.165	.196	.065	.006
21	.000	.000	.000	.000	.000	.000	.000	.007	.057	.118	.187	.138	.027
22	.000	.000	.000	.000	.000	.000	.000	.002	.024	.064	.136	.226	.093
23	.000	.000	.000	.000	.000	.000	.000	.000	.007	.025	.071	.266	.231
24	.000	.000	.000	.000	.000	.000	.000	.000	.002	.006	.024	.199	.365
25	.000	.000	.000	.000	.000	.000	.000	.000	.000	.001	.004	.072	.277

Appendix B - References

Chapter 1

Hock, Roger R. *Forty Studies That Changed Psychology: Exploration into the History of Psychological Research.* New York: Prentice-Hall, 1995.

Moore, David, and William Notz. *Statistics: Concepts and Controversies*, 7th ed. New York: W. H. Freeman, 2009. (A nice, informal survey of statistical concepts and reasoning.)

Peck, Roxy, ed. *Statistics: A Guide to the Unknown*, 4th ed. Belmont, CA: Duxbury Cengage Learning, 2006. (Short, nontechnical articles by a number of well-known statisticians and users of statistics on the application of statistics in various disciplines and subject areas.)

Utts, Jessica. *Seeing Through Statistics*, 3rd ed. Belmont, CA: Duxbury Cengage Learning, 2005. (A nice introduction to the fundamental ideas of statistical reasoning.)

Chapter 2

Cobb, George. *Introduction to the Design and Analysis of Experiments.* New York: Wiley, 1998. (An interesting and thorough introduction to the design of experiments.)

Freedman, David, Robert Pisani, and Roger Purves. *Statistics*, 4th ed. New York: W. W. Norton, 2007. (The first two chapters contain some interesting examples of both well-designed and poorly designed experimental studies.)

Lohr, Sharon. *Sampling Design and Analysis,* 2nd edition. Belmont, CA: Duxbury Cengage Learning, 2010. (A nice discussion of sampling and sources of bias at an accessible level.)

Moore, David, and William Notz. *Statistics: Concepts and Controversies*, 7th ed. New York: W. H. Freeman, 2009. (Contains an excellent chapter on the advantages and pitfalls of experimentation and another chapter in a similar vein on sample surveys and polls.)

Scheaffer, Richard L., William Mendenhall, and Lyman Ott. *Elementary Survey Sampling*, 6th ed. Belmont, CA: Duxbury Cengage Learning, 2006. (An accessible yet thorough treatment of the subject.)

Sudman, Seymour, and Norman Bradburn. *Asking Questions: A Practical Guide to Questionnaire Design.* San Francisco: Jossey-Bass, 1982. (A good discussion of the art of questionnaire design.)

Chapter 3

Chambers, John, William Cleveland, Beat Kleiner, and Paul Tukey. *Graphical Methods for Data Analysis.* Belmont, CA: Wadsworth, 1983. (This is an excellent survey of methods, illustrated with numerous interesting examples.)

Cleveland, William. *The Elements of Graphing Data*, 2nd ed. Summit, NJ: Hobart Press, 1994. (An informal and informative introduction to various aspects of graphical analysis.)

Freedman, David, Robert Pisani, and Roger Purves. *Statistics*, 4th ed. New York: W. W. Norton, 2007. (An excellent, informal introduction to concepts, with some insightful cautionary examples concerning misuses of statistical methods.)

Moore, David, and William Notz. *Statistics: Concepts and Controversies*, 7th ed. New York: W. H. Freeman, 2009. (A nonmathematical yet highly entertaining introduction to our discipline. Two thumbs up!)

Chapter 4

Chambers, John, William Cleveland, Beat Kleiner, and Paul Tukey. *Graphical Methods for Data Analysis.* Belmont, CA: Wadsworth, 1983. (This is an excellent survey of methods, illustrated with numerous interesting examples.)

Cleveland, William. *The Elements of Graphing Data*, 2nd ed. Summit, NJ: Hobart Press, 1994. (An informal and informative introduction to various aspects of graphical analysis.)

Freedman, David, Robert Pisani, and Roger Purves. *Statistics*, 4th ed. New York: W. W. Norton, 2007. (An excellent, informal introduction to concepts, with some insightful cautionary examples concerning misuses of statistical methods.)

Moore, David, and William Notz. *Statistics: Concepts and Controversies*, 7th ed. New York: W. H. Freeman, 2009. (A nonmathematical yet highly entertaining introduction to our discipline. Two thumbs up!)

Chapter 5

Neter, John, William Wasserman, and Michael Kutner. *Applied Linear Statistical Models*, 5th ed. New York: McGraw-Hill, 2005. (The first half of this book gives a comprehensive treatment of regression analysis without overindulging in mathematical development; a highly recommended reference.)

Chapter 6

Devore, Jay L. *Probability and Statistics for Engineering and the Sciences*, 7th ed. Belmont, CA: Brooks/Cole Cengage Learning, 2008. (The treatment of probability in this source is more comprehensive and at a somewhat higher mathematical level than ours is in this textbook.)

Mosteller, Frederick, Robert Rourke, and George Thomas. *Probability with Statistical Applications*. Reading, MA: Addison-Wesley, 1970. (A good introduction to probability at a modest mathematical level.)

Chapter 8

Freedman, David, Robert Pisani, Roger Purves. *Statistics*, 4th ed. New York: W. W. Norton, 2007. (This book gives an excellent informal discussion of sampling distributions.)

Chapter 9

Devore, Jay L. *Probability and Statistics for Engineering and the Sciences*, 7th ed. Belmont, CA: Brooks/Cole Cengage Learning, 2008. (This book gives a somewhat general introduction to confidence intervals.)

Freedman, David, Robert Pisani, and Roger Purves, *Statistics*, 4th ed. New York: W. W. Norton, 2007. (This book contains an informal discussion of confidence intervals.)

Chapter 10

The books by Freedman et al. and Moore listed in previous chapter references are excellent sources. Their orientation is primarily conceptual, with a minimum of mathematical development, and both sources offer many valuable insights.

Chapter 11

Devore, Jay. *Probability and Statistics for Engineering and the Sciences*, 7th ed. Belmont, CA: Duxbury Cengage Learning, 2008. (Contains a somewhat more comprehensive treatment of the inferential material presented in this and the two previous chapters, although the notation is a bit more mathematical than that of the present textbook.)

Chapter 12

Agresti, Alan, and B. Finlay. *Statistical Methods for the Social Sciences*, 4th ed. Englewood Cliffs, NJ: Prentice-Hall, 2009. (This book includes a good discussion of measures of association for two-way frequency tables.)

Everitt, B. S. *The Analysis of Contingency Tables*. New York: Halsted Press, 1977. (A compact but informative survey of methods for analyzing categorical data.)

Mosteller, Frederick, and Robert Rourke. *Sturdy Statistics*. Reading, Mass.: Addison-Wesley, 1973. (Contains several readable chapters on the varied uses of the chi-square statistic.)

Chapter 13

Neter, John, William Wasserman, and Michael Kutner. *Applied Linear Statistical Models*, 5th ed. New York: McGraw-Hill, 2005. (The first half of this book gives a comprehensive treatment of regression analysis without overindulging in mathematical development; a highly recommended reference.)

Chapter 14

Kerlinger, Fred N., and Elazar J. Pedhazur, *Multiple Regression in Behavioral Research*, 3rd ed. Austin, Texas: Holt, Rinehart & Winston, 1997. (A readable introduction to multiple regression.)

Neter, John, William Wasserman, and Michael Kutner. *Applied Linear Statistical Models,* 4th ed. New York: McGraw-Hill, 1996. (The first half of this book gives a comprehensive treatment of regression analysis without overindulging in mathematical development; a highly recommended reference.)

Chapter 15

Miller, Rupert. *Beyond ANOVA: The Basics of Applied Statistics.* New York: Wiley, 1986. (This book contains a wealth of information concerning violations of basic assumptions and alternative methods of analysis.)

Winer, G. J., D. R. Brown, and K. M. Michels, *Statistical Principles in Experimental Design*, 3rd edition. Boston: McGraw-Hill, 1991. (This book contains extended discussion of ANOVA with many examples worked out in great detail.)

Chapter 16

Conover, W. J. *Practical Nonparametric Statistics*, 3rd ed. New York: Wiley, 1999. (An accessible presentation of distribution-free methods.)

Daniel, Wayne. *Applied Nonparametric Statistics*, 2nd ed. Boston: PWS-Kent, 1990. (An elementary presentation of distribution-free methods, including the rank-sum test discussed in Section 16.1.)

Mosteller, Frederick, and Richard Rourke. *Sturdy Statistics*. Reading, Mass.: Addison-Wesley, 1973. (A readable, intuitive development of distribution-free methods, including those based on ranks.)

AP* Free-Response Questions

CHAPTER 2

1. A pharmaceutical company is testing a new drug designed to help balding men grow more hair. The company has data on about 1000 current customers who use other products that the company produces but who have not previously used any type of treatment for baldness. The data contains information about hair color (light or dark), age, and percentage of baldness. A partial list is shown below. For this experiment, the pharmaceutical company would like to select a sample that is representative of their customers.

Cust #	Hair color	Age (yrs)	Percentage of Baldness
1	Light	67	83
2	Dark	62	73
3	Light	41	25
4	Dark	52	50
5	Dark	43	14
6	Light	69	96
7	Dark	56	57
...	...	...	...
1000	Light	32	40

(a) Briefly describe a process to select a simple random sample of size $n = 20$ from this list of customers, using a random number table.

(b) Describe how a stratified random sample with strata defined by hair color could be selected. Do you think that stratifying by hair color is a good idea? Explain.

2. A common method of sampling to estimate bird populations is to walk along defined paths and count the number of birds seen. During hunting season biologists wear brightly colored clothes as a protective measure. Unfortunately, birds may react to these brightly colored clothes. As an example, a robin may be more afraid of a biologist wearing a brown color than one wearing an orange protective vest. A robin more afraid of the biologist may be more difficult to see and therefore "count" because the robin flees before being seen. If that happens the process of sampling would give an estimate of the robin population that is too small. To test this theory a biologist wore either a bright orange vest or a brown vest. She first trained herself to accurately estimate distances. Then a robin was placed in an enclosed space and the biologist would approach the robin and record how close she could get to the robin before it flew away from her. This process was repeated with 40 robins, for a total of 40 trials. The biologist randomly selects 20 of the 40 trials when she will wear the brown vest. She will wear the orange vest on the other 20 trials.

(a) What is the explanatory variable (factor) for this experiment?

(b) What is the response variable for this experiment?

(c) Suppose that the 40 trials will be carried out over two days and that the biologist worries that weather conditions, such as wind speed and temperature, might be different on the two days. She thinks that weather conditions might affect the way the birds respond. What changes would you make to the design of this experiment to address this concern?

CHAPTER 3

3. Iowa is an agricultural state with a large number of rivers. The use of chemical pesticides and increasing size of livestock herds has potentially degraded the water quality in the state. A researcher recently analyzed concentrations of certain chemicals at 100 different locations in Iowa's Cedar River. A cumulative relative frequency plot of nitrogen concentration appears below.

(a) Approximately what percent of the Nitrogen concentration measurements are less than 10 mg/L?

(b) Approximately what percent of the Nitrogen concentration measurements are 12 mg/L or more?

(c) 50% of the Nitrogen concentration measurements lie below what approximate value?

(d) Which of the two histograms shown here (Histogram 1 or Histogram 2) could not be the histogram corresponding to this data set? Explain how you made your decision.

HISTOGRAM 1

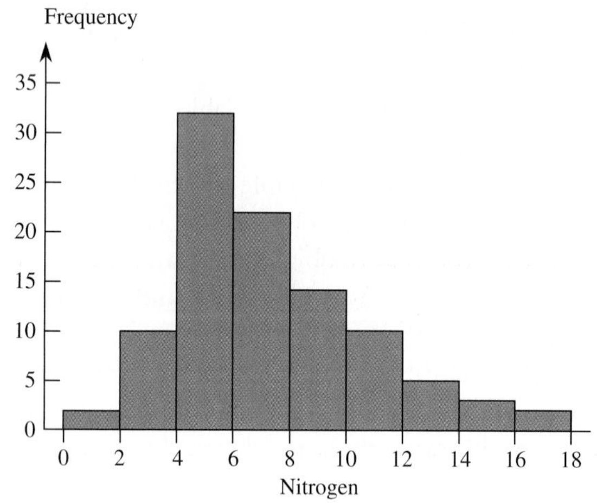

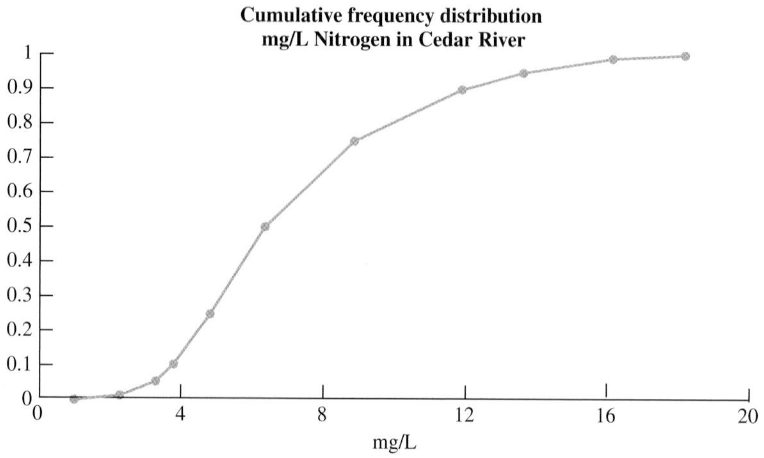

FIGURE EXR 3

HISTOGRAM 2

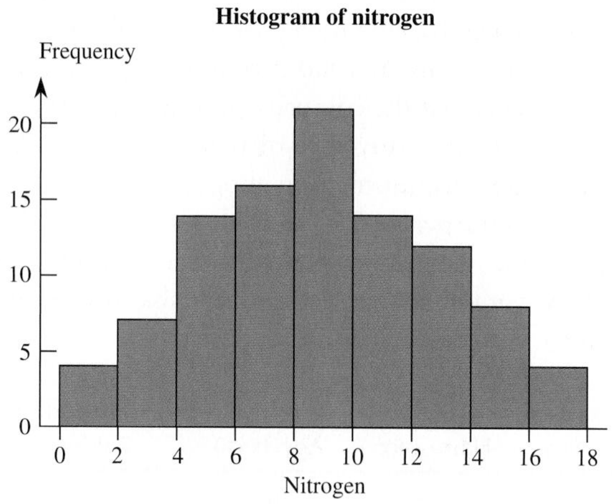

4. A survey designed by investigators at the University of Iowa Injury Prevention Research Center assessed compliance with Iowa's seatbelt law. The table below shows the results for 5 Iowa cities.

City	Percent Age 2–5 Properly Restrained	Percent Age 6–10 Properly Restrained
Belle Plaine	84	93
Cedar Rapids	79	94
Gutenberg	58	68
Iowa City	92	99
Manchester	59	82

(a) Display these data in a comparative bar chart so that the different ages can be compared for the different cities.

(b) Write a brief description of the differences and similarities in the patterns you observe in your bar chart for Part (a).

CHAPTER 4

5. The *New York Times* reported the average number of square feet per standing passenger in 2 successive years for 19 subway stops. The NYC Transit Authority managers had attempted to improve the space problem on subway cars (more space is better—trust us!) by adding cars to trains during the rush hours. These data were used to compute the *change* (Year 2 – Year 1) in the amount of space available to standing passengers for each of the 19 subway stops. The changes as well as summary information for the changes is presented below.

(a) Using the raw data and summary information for the change data presented in the tables, construct boxplots on the scales provided to compare the changes in available space the morning and afternoon.

(b) The Transit System wishes to know if their efforts to improve the standing space were successful. (Remember, more space is better!) Does the data support a claim of improvement? What specific aspects of the plots in Part (a) support your answer?

Changes in the Space per Standing Passenger

Change A.M.	Change P.M.
−0.4	−5.1
−1.1	−1.5
0	0.3
4.6	8.1
−0.7	3.3
0	0.5
3	−1.2
−1.8	−1.2
1	−3.2
0.8	−0.4
−3	5.3
−3	16.9
−0.9	−0.1
−0.3	−0.5
−0.5	0.6
0.2	−0.2
−0.3	−0.4
−0.3	−1.1
0.4	0.6

Partial Summary of Change Data

	Quartiles		
Time	Lower Quartile	Medan	Upper Quartile
A.M.	−0.9	−0.3	0.4
P.M.	−1.2	−0.2	0.6

Means and Standard Deviations for Change Data

Time	Mean	St. Dev.
A.M.	−0.121	1.766
P.M.	1.089	4.784

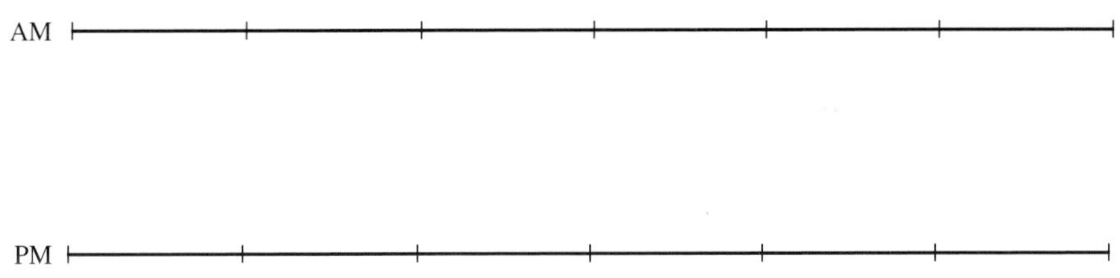

FIGURE EXR 5

6. The forces that determine the size of groups ("swarms") of social insects and the rates at which they grow are not well understood. Biologists have observed large variability in the size of colonies across species. In a study of the social wasp, *Polybia occidentalis*, investigators dismantled a nest of these insects and marked a few for future identification in new swarms. Twenty-five days after dismantling the original swarm they had located new swarms of wasps from the original colony. The data below present the numbers of drones in the new colonies. (The study was replicated in two different years.) "Drones" are fertile males that mate with the queen.

Number of Drones in First and Second Surveys

First Year Swarm Colony #	Drones	Second Year Swarm Colony #	Drones
1	598	1	355
2	24	2	691
3	567	3	278
4	371	4	719
5	279	5	152
6	44	6	156
7	42	7	41
8	126		
9	108		
10	79		

(a) Construct a comparative (back to back) stem-and-leaf plot of the numbers of drones in the swarms in the first and second years.

(b) Using your plot in Part (a), compare the distributions of the numbers of drones in the two swarms, noting any interesting features of the distributions.

(c) The table below presents some summary statistics from the distribution of drones. Construct comparative boxplots of the numbers of adults in the swarms in the first and second years.

Partial Summary of Data

	Numbers of Drones		
Swarm	Lower Quartile	Median	Upper Quartile
First year	43.5	117	420
Second year	152	278	691

CHAPTER 5

7. When estimating the size of animal populations from aerial surveys, game managers have found that animals may bunch together, making it difficult to distinguish and count them accurately. For example, a horse standing alone is easy to spot from a plane; if seven horses huddled close together some may be missed, resulting in an undercount. The relative frequency of undercounts is typically reported as a percent. For example, if there are 10 horses in a group, a person in the plane may count fewer than 10 horses 20% of the time. In a recent study, the percent of sightings that resulted in an undercount (P) was related to the group size (GS) of horses and donkeys. The following data were gathered:

Percent Undercount (P) vs. Group Size (GS) for Horses and Donkeys

Group Size	Percent Occurrence Undercount	Group Size	Percent Occurrence Undercount
2	5	9	6
3	5	10	7
4	6	11	5
5	10	12	5
6	5	14	14
7	7	16	13
8	5	18	23

After fitting a straight line model, $\hat{P} = a + b(GS)$, significant curvature was detected in the residual plot, and two nonlinear models were chosen for further analysis. The computer output for these models is given below, and the residual plots are on the next page.

$\log P = a + b(GS)$ (Exponential)

Bivariate Fit of Log%U By GS

Linear Fit

Log%U=0.586+0.031 GS

Summary of Fit

RSquare	0.499
RSquare Adj	0.458
St. Dev. Of Residuals	0.156

$\log P = a + b \log(GS)$ (Power)

Bivariate Fit of Log%U By LogGS

Linear Fit

Log%U=0.476+0.440 LogGS

Summary of Fit

RSquare	0.337
RSquare Adj	0.282
St. Dev. Of Residuals	0.180

Residual Plots

$\log P = a + b(GS)$

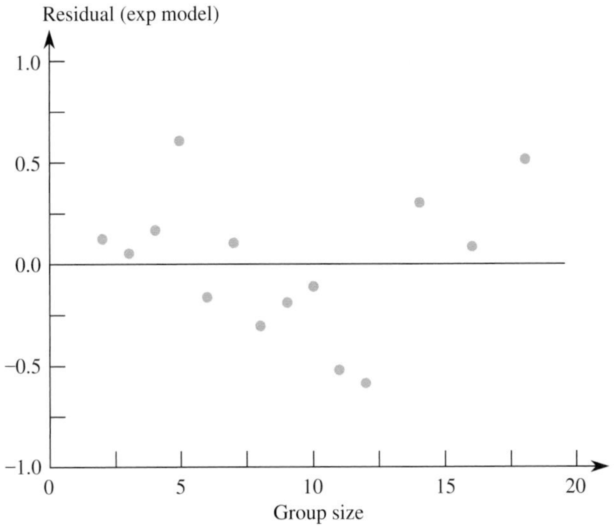

$\log P = a + b \log(GS)$

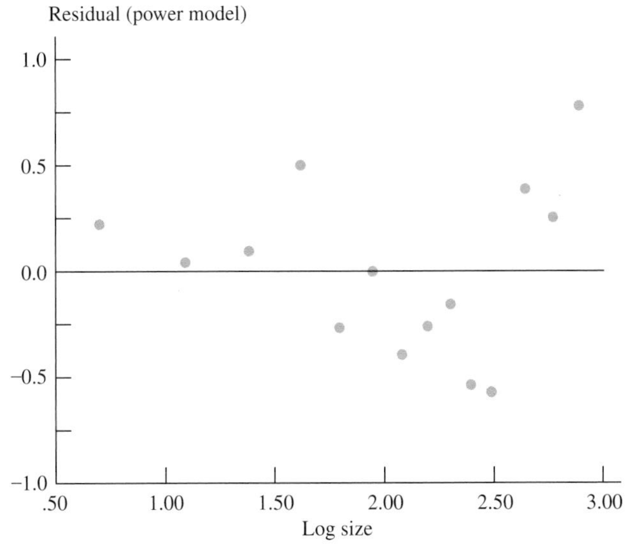

(a) For the exponential model, calculate the predicted *log (%undercount)* for a group size = 10.
(b) Use your calculations from Part (a) to predict the *%undercount* for a group size = 10
(c) Generally speaking, which of the two models, power or exponential, is better at predicting the log (% Undercount)? Provide statistical justification for your choice.

8. The data below were gathered on a random sample of five basking sharks, swimming through the water and filter-feeding (passively letting the water bring food into their mouths).

Body Length (meters)	Mean Speed (meters/second)
4.0	0.89
4.5	0.83
4.0	0.76
6.5	0.94
5.5	0.94

(a) What is the value of the correlation coefficient for these data?
(b) What is the equation of the least-squares line describing the relationship between x = body length and y = mean speed.
(c) If these sharks are representative of the population of basking sharks, what would you predict is the mean speed for a filter-feeding basking shark that is 5.0 meters in length?
(d) The largest basking shark in the sample is measured as 6.5 meters long, but it is known that basking sharks can grow as long as 12.5 meters. Would it be reasonable to use the equation from Part (b) above to predict the mean filter-feeding speed for a 12-meter-long basking shark? Why or why not?

CHAPTER 6

9. One method for increasing sales of boxes of cereal is to suggest to children that they collect a complete "set" of small toys. Suppose that one of five different toys is put in every box. One strategy the company could use to distribute the toys is to put each toy in 20% of the boxes. Your task is to design a simulation that will be used to assess this strategy in terms of the number of boxes of cereal a person would need to buy in order to get a complete set of toys.

(a) Assign digits to represent each of the five toys in a way that is consistent with the manufacturer placing each toy in 20% of the cereal boxes.

Toy 1 Digits: Toy 2 Digits:
Toy 3 Digits: Toy 4 Digits:
Toy 5 Digits:

(b) Describe how you would use a random digit table to conduct one run of a simulation of the process of buying boxes of cereal, noting the toy received, and then continuing to buy one box of cereal at a time until all of the five different toys have been obtained.

(c) Use the list of random digits below (start at the beginning of the first line) to carry out one run of the simulation using the process you described in Part (b). (You may mark on the digits to help explain your procedure.) How many boxes of cereal had to be purchased in order to get all 5 toys?

61790	55300	05756	72765	96409
12531	35013	82853	73676	57890
99400	37754	42648	82425	36290
45467	71709	77558	00095	32863
29485	82226			

(d) Suppose that the cereal company decides instead to put the toys in the boxes in a way that makes some of the toys harder to find. Toy 1 will be put in 30% of the boxes, Toys 2 and 3 will be put in 20% of the boxes, and Toys 4 and 5 will be put in 15% of the boxes. Assign digits to the toys that are consistent with these percentages.

Toy 1 Digits: Toy 2 Digits:
Toy 3 Digits: Toy 4 Digits:
Toy 5 Digits:

(e) Use the list of random digits at the top of the next column (start at the beginning of the first line) to carry out five runs, noting the number of boxes purchased for each run. Use your results to estimate the probability that it would take more than 10 boxes to complete the set of 5 toys. (You may mark on the digits to help explain your procedure.)

19223	95734	05756	28713	96409
12531	42544	82853	73676	47150
99400	37754	42648	82425	36290
45467	71709	77558	00095	32863
29485	82226	68417	35013	15529
72765	85089	57067	50211	47487
82739	57890	20807	81676	55300
94383	14893	60940	72024	17868
24943	61790	90656	87964	47140
29385	67067	15803	12589	52167
18568	23243	55770	90846	86664

(f) The probability estimate in Part (e) may not be a very good estimate of the actual probability that more than 10 boxes must be purchased. What would you recommend doing to increase the accuracy of this estimated probability?

10. Investigators recently reported the results a study designed to assess whether the herb St. John's Wort is effective in treating moderately severe cases of depression. The study involved 338 subjects, randomly assigned to receive one of three treatments: St. John's Wort, Zoloft, or a placebo. After treatment, the response to the treatment (full response, partial response, or no response) was noted for each subject. The resulting data are summarized in the table below.

	St. John's Wort	Placebo	Zoloft	Total
Full Response	27	37	27	**91**
Partial Response	16	13	26	**55**
No Response	70	66	56	**192**
Total	**113**	**116**	**109**	**338**

(a) What is the probability that a randomly selected subject had no response?

(b) What is the probability that a randomly selected subject was treated with Zoloft and had a full response?

(c) What is the probability that a randomly selected subject had a full or partial response given that they were treated with St. John's Wort?

(d) What is the probability that a randomly selected subject who didn't have a full response was treated with Placebo?

CHAPTER 7

11. In the old Roman Coliseum, two horses would be placed in tandem (side by side) and hitched to a chariot. Since the fast chariots needed to be able to pass the slow chariots, it was of some importance that the horses have room to run, but also that they should not be too large. For chariot-hitching purposes, the widest measure across a horse occurs in the rump area. Suppose that the mean rump width of horses is 27 inches and that the standard deviation of rump width is 2 inches. Let random variable w = width in inches across the rump of a randomly selected horse.

(a) The usual length measure as it applies to horses is the "hand," which is by definition equal to 4 inches. Define random variable h = width in hands across the rump of a randomly selected horse. What are the mean and standard deviation of h?

(b) Suppose horses are randomly chosen for a particular Roman chariot. Define random variable $b = w_1 + w_2$ to be the total rump width (in inches) of two randomly selected horses. What are the mean and standard deviation of b?

(c) In the original chariot design a 16-inch separation of the horses is specified so that the horses have room to avoid each other. Define the random variable "chariot width" as: $c = 16 + w_1 + w_2$. How do the mean and standard deviation of b in Part (b) differ from the mean and standard deviation of the random variable, c? You should be able to answer without recalculating the mean and standard deviation.

12. The owners of the Burger Emporium are looking for new supplier of onions. The owners have determined that for use in their burgers the onion slice should be roughly the same diameter as the hamburger patty. After careful analysis, they determine that only onions with diameters between 9 and 10 cm will be used for burgers. (Onions that are not suitable for burgers are diced for tacos.) Company A's onions have a diameter distribution that is approximately normal with mean 10.5 cm and standard deviation of 1.1 cm. Company B's onions have a diameter distribution that is approximately normal with mean 10.3 cm and standard deviation of 0.8 cm. Which company provides the higher proportion of burger-usable onions? Justify your choice with an appropriate statistical argument.

CHAPTER 8

13. One method for estimating the availability of office space in large cities is to select a random sample of offices and calculate the proportion of offices currently being used. Suppose that a real-estate agent believes that the proportion of offices currently being used is $p = 0.70$ and decides to take a sample to assess his belief. He is considering a sample size of $n = 40$.

(a) If the real-estate agent's belief is correct, is the sample size is large enough for the sampling distribution of $\hat{p}$ to be approximately normal? Justify your answer.

(b) If the real-estate agent's belief is correct, what is the mean of the sampling distribution of $\hat{p}$?

(c) If the real-estate agent's belief is correct, what is the standard deviation of the sampling distribution of $\hat{p}$?

(d) If the real-estate agent's belief is correct, what is the probability that a sample proportion, $\hat{p}$, would differ from $p = 0.70$ by as much as 0.05?

14. Consider sampling from a *skewed* population. As the sample size, n, increases, some characteristics of the sampling distribution of $\bar{x}$ will change. Does an increasing sample size result in changes in the characteristics of the sampling distribution listed in (a) through (c) below? If so, explain how the characteristic of the sampling distribution changes.

(a) The mean of the sampling distribution of $\bar{x}$

(b) The standard deviation of the sampling distribution of $\bar{x}$

(c) The shape of the sampling distribution of $\bar{x}$

CHAPTER 9

15. Conventional home smoke alarms have too often failed to awaken sleeping children. Researchers are studying the possibility that a personalized "voice" smoke alarm would be more effective than mere sound. The idea is that a recording of the mother's voice calling the child's name may be an improvement over existing systems.

(a) The researchers would like to estimate p, the proportion of sleeping children who would be awakened by their mother's voice, to within 0.05 with 95% confidence. Past experience has shown that conventional alarms are effective about 0.58 of the time. If the proportion for conventional alarms is accepted as a reasonable initial estimate of p, what is the smallest sample size that should be used for this study?

(b) Suppose the researchers felt that the proportion who wake up could be quite different for the mother's voice alarm than for the conventional alarm. Explain how your procedure for choosing a samples size would differ from the solution in Part (a) (You do not need to calculate a new estimate of the necessary sample size!)

16. Reading comprehension is arguably the single most important skill a student can possess. To assess the levels of reading comprehension in 3rd grade, 35 students were randomly selected from school district class lists and given a reading comprehension test. The mean and standard deviation of the resulting reading comprehension scores were 180 and 20.12, respectively.

(a) Estimate μ, the mean reading comprehension score for 3rd-graders in this school district using a 90% confidence interval.

(b) Explain what the confidence level of 90% associated with the interval estimate in Part (a) means.

(c) Would it be reasonable to generalize this estimate to the population of all 3rd-grade children? Explain why or why not.

CHAPTER 10

17. Children develop "representational insight," a connection between an object and a symbol for that object. A random sample of 2-year-olds was shown a video of someone putting a toy under one of four boxes that had been placed in a room familiar to the child. Then they were taken to the room, and asked to "find the toy." The investigators reasoned that a child without representational insight would only pick the correct box on the first try about 25% of the time. Thirty out of 57 children found the toy by turning over the correct box on the first try. Is there convincing evidence that the proportion of 2-year olds children who choose the correct box on the first try is greater than 0.25? Use a significance level of $\alpha = .05$ to test the appropriate hypothesis.

18. People tend make classifications based on their "typicality." For example, a dog is more readily classified as a mammal than is a whale because dogs are "more typical" of mammals than are whales. Previous studies have established that when young children are shown a picture of a songbird and asked if it is a bird they respond "yes" in an average of 750 milliseconds. Do children regard chickens as representative of birds? Let μ represent the mean time it takes children to respond to a question about whether a chicken is a bird. The investigators wish to determine whether the mean classification time for chickens differs from the known mean time to classify songbirds.

(a) What is the appropriate null hypothesis in this study?

(b) What is the appropriate alternative hypothesis in this study?

(c) In the context of this study, write a few sentences distinguishing between a Type I and a Type II error.

(d) Suppose that data from a random sample of 40 children was used to carry out the hypothesis test, resulting in a P-value of 0.024. What conclusion should be reached if a .05 significance level is used for the test?

CHAPTER 11

19. In many social mammalian species the adult male assumes a sentry role, warning adult females and juveniles of approaching predators. Some students of animal behavior believe that this tendency is active in humans also. An investigator in Seattle observed people crossing the street—alone and in mixed gender pairs—at an intersection with no traffic control and noted the scanning behavior ("looking both ways") of adult females. The investigator reasoned that if the adult female assumed a protected role, the proportion of females who scan when alone would be greater than when accompanied by an adult male. Data from this study is given below

Female Percent Scanning ("Looking Both Ways")

Situation	Scanned	Did Not Scan	Totals
Alone	60	20	80
With adult male	37	39	76

Do these data support the investigator's hypothesis that the female scanning proportion is less when accompanied by a male than when alone? Provide *statistical* justification for your answer.

20. In a study of captive nectar-feeding bats (*Leptonycteris sanborni*), nectar intake over a 5-minute flight period was recorded. The bats were weighed before and after feeding, and the resulting data are given in the table below. (Notice that each bat has a unique identification number in the left-hand column.)

Bat #	Sex	Original Weight	Post-feeding Weight	Difference (Post − Original)
1	F	18.6	19.8	1.2
2	F	18.5	20.8	2.3
3	F	18.6	20.0	1.4
4	F	20.4	21.9	1.5
5	F	21.5	23.0	1.5
6	F	20.3	22.0	1.7
7	F	17.0	18.5	1.5
8	F	17.0	19.0	2.0
9	F	17.5	19.2	1.7
10	F	19.7	21.0	1.3
11	M	18.2	20.2	2.0
12	M	20.2	22.3	2.1
13	M	19.0	20.5	1.5
14	M	17.3	18.5	1.2
15	M	17.8	19.0	1.2
16	M	19.5	21.6	2.1
17	M	21.0	22.8	1.8
18	M	17.0	18.4	1.4
19	M	18.3	19.3	1.0

For the following questions, **make no graphs, and do no calculations**! You are only to indicate *which procedure* you would use and indicate *which bat numbers* you would use to address the questions asked. Refer to the bats by bat number and the variables by column names. You can assume that the bats used in this study are representative of nectar-feeding bats.

(a) Suppose that a bat-ologist wanted to know if it is reasonable to conclude that mean weight gain is different for males and females. How would you check the normality assumption(s) necessary for the appropriate inference procedure?

(b) Suppose that a bat-ologist wanted to estimate the mean weight gain for female bats after a 5-minute feeding period. How would he or she do this?

(c) Suppose that a bat-ologist wanted to find out if it is reasonable to conclude that the mean weight gain after a 5-minute feeding period for the population of nectar-feeding bats is *more than* 1.5 g. How would he or she do this?

(d) Suppose a bat-ologist wanted to know if it is reasonable to conclude that irrespective of gender and prefeeding weight, male and female bats consume different amounts of nectar on average after a 5-minute feeding period. How would he or she do this?

CHAPTER 12

21. Black bears (*Ursus americanus*) in National Parks can be a problem for humans. Bears' travels are governed by the need for food and some humans accidentally or purposefully feed the bears—encouraging bears to harass humans for food. When a bear becomes troublesome, park rangers may try to relocate the bear by taking it to a distant location so that the bear probably will not be able to find its way back. In a 10-year study of this relocation strategy, researchers followed bears in a simple random sample of troublesome bears. One question of interest was whether relocation works equally well for male and female bears. Data on relocation outcome and gender for the sample of bears are summarized in the table below.

Relocation Outcome	Male	Female	Totals
Successful	32	17	**49**
Returned to capture area	34	45	**79**
Nuisance in another area	14	4	**18**
Totals	**80**	**66**	**146**

(a) For this study, would the question of interest be answered by carrying out a test of independence or a test of homogeneity of proportions? Explain why.

(b) Carry out the test specified in Part (a) using a significance level of 0.01.

22. Wildlife biologists are interested in the hunting strategies of predators. Do predators take the first prey that comes along, or are they selective? In a study of winter prey selection in a national park, radio-tagged cougars were observed to have killed prey according to the table below. At the most recent census in the National Park there were about 3500 white-tailed deer, 1000 elk, and 500 moose.

Prey Selection by Cougars

White-tailed deer	118
Elk	8
Moose	2
Total	**128**

Do these data provide sufficient evidence at the .05 level that the cougars are not selecting their prey at random? That is, is there evidence that the proportions of deer, elk, and moose killed by cougars differ from the park population? Justify your response with an appropriate statistical analysis.

CHAPTER 13

23. In a random sample of large cities around the world, the ozone level (in parts per million) and the population (in millions) were measured. Fitting the simple linear regression model gave the estimated regression equation $ozone = 8.89 + 16.6pop$

(a) How would you interpret the value of $b = 16.6$?

(b) Substituting $x = 3$ into the estimated regression equation gives $\hat{y} = 58.69$. Give two different interpretations of this number.

(c) Do you think this equation should be used for predicting ozone in small towns in Iowa? Explain your response in a few sentences.

(d) The value of r^2 is not given here, but explain how you would interpret the value r^2 in the context of this problem.

24. The computer output shows a regression of Body Mass (g) vs. Wing Length (mm) for a sample of moths.

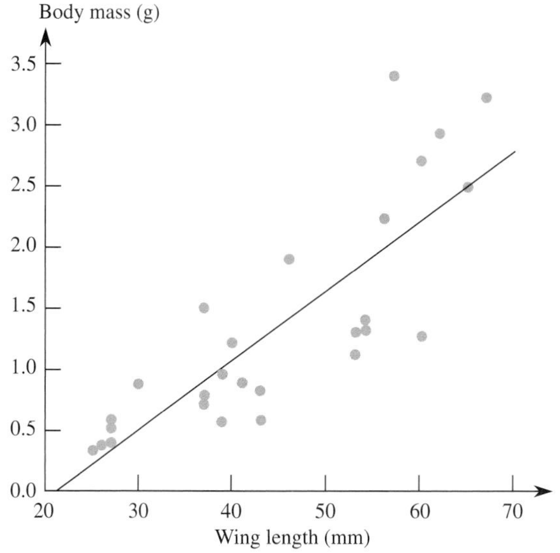

Regression Analysis

Body Mass = −1.211 + 0.057 Wing Length

Summary of Fit

RSquare	0.694
RSquare Adj	0.682
S	0.513

Analysis of Variance

Source	DF	SS	MS	F	P-value
Model	1	15.54	15.541	59.03	<.0001
Error	26	6.84	0.263		
Total	27	22.39			

Parameter Estimates

Term	Estimate	Std Error	t Ratio	Prob>|t|
Intercept	−1.2116	0.3424	−3.539	0.0015
Wing Length	0.0573	0.0072	7.9588	<.0001

(a) What is the equation of the estimated regression line?

(b) Using the computer output, carry out a model utility test using a 0.05 level of significance.

(c) Calculate and interpret a 95% confidence interval for the value of the slope of the population regression line.

(d) What is the value of s_e?

(e) Interpret the value of s_e in the context of this problem.

Answers to Selected Odd-Numbered Exercises

Chapter 1

1.1 *Descriptive statistics* is the branch of statistics that involves the organization and summary of the values in a data set. *Inferential statistics* is the branch of statistics concerned with reaching conclusions about a population based on the information provided by a sample.
1.3 The percentages would have been computed from a sample.
1.5 The population of interest is the set of all 15,000 students at the university. The sample is the 200 students who are interviewed.
1.7 The population is the set of all 7000 property owners. The sample is the group of 500 owners included in the survey.
1.9 The population is the set of 5000 used bricks. The sample is the set of 100 bricks she checks.
1.11 **a.** The researchers wanted to compare the effectiveness of the new flu vaccine with the effectiveness of the conventional vaccine. They wanted to learn whether the new vaccine significantly reduced the incidence of influenza and whether the incidence of ear infections would be reduced in children who *did* get the flu.
b. We would want to know if the subjects in the experiment were randomly assigned to the treatments. To compare the effectiveness of the new and old vaccines, it might have been useful to include a group of subjects who are given the conventional vaccine. A larger number of subjects could have been included in the group of subjects who were given the new vaccine. With just 1% of the 1070 subjects contracting influenza (approximately 11 subjects), it will be difficult to accurately estimate the proportion who get the flu and who then get an ear infection.
1.13 **a.** Categorical **b.** Categorical **c.** Numerical (discrete) **d.** Numerical (continuous) **e.** Categorical **f.** Numerical (continuous)
1.15 **a.** Continuous **b.** Continuous **c.** Continuous **d.** Discrete
1.17 **a.** Gender of purchaser, brand of motorcycle, telephone area code **b.** Number of previous motorcycles **c.** Bar chart **d.** Dotplot
1.19 **b.** Meat and poultry items appear to be relatively low cost sources of protein.
1.21 The most common reason was financial, accounting for 30.2% of students who left for non-academic reasons. The next two most common reasons were health and other personal reasons, accounting for 19.0% and 15.9% respectively, of the students who left for non-academic reasons.
1.23 **a.** There were two sites that received far greater numbers of visits than the remaining 23 sites. Also, the distribution of the number of visits has the greatest density of points for the smaller numbers of visits, with the density decreasing as the number of visits increases. **b.** There were two sites that were used by far greater numbers of individuals (unique visitors) than the remaining 23 sites. However, these two sites are less far above the others in terms of the number of unique visitors than they are in terms of the total number of visits. **c.** The statistic "visits per unique visitor" tells us how heavily the individuals are using the sites.
1.25 **b.** Eastern states have, on average, lower wireless percents than states in the other two regions. The West and Middle states regions have, on average, roughly equal wireless percents.
1.27 **a.** *Rate per 10,000 flights*
1.29 **b.** The categories "Easy access to junk food," "Eating unhealthy food," and "Overeating" could be combined.
1.31

Type of Household	Relative Frequency
Nonfamily	0.29
Married with children	0.27
Married without children	0.29
Single parent	0.15

1.33 **a.** Categorical **b.** No
1.35 The most frequently occurring violation categories were security (43%) and maintenance (39%). The least frequently occurring violation categories were flight operations (6%) and hazardous materials (3%).

Chapter 2

2.1 **a.** This is an observational study. **b.** No, cause-and-effect conclusions cannot be made on the basis of an observational study.
2.3 **a.** This is an observational study. **b.** Yes **c.** No **d.** No
2.5 On the whole, it is quite possible that well-qualified students who go to "most selective" colleges are naturally better motivated than well-qualified students who go to "least selective" colleges.
2.7 We are told that moderate drinkers, as a group, tended to be better educated, wealthier, and more active than nondrinkers. It is possible the observed reduction in the risk of heart disease among moderate drinkers is caused by one of these attributes and not by the moderate drinking.
2.9 No, cause-and-effect conclusions cannot be made on the basis of an observational study.
2.11 **a.** The data would need to be collected from a simple random sample of affluent Americans. **b.** No
2.13 *Method 1:* Use a random number generator to select 20 from a numbered list of graduates. *Method 2:* Write the numbers from 1 to 140 on slips of paper. Mix them well and then draw out 20 to determine which students should be selected from a numbered list of graduates. Other methods are also possible.
2.15 Using a list of the cases, number the cases 1–870. Use a random number generator to randomly select a whole number between 1 and 870. The number selected represents the first case to be included in the sample. Repeat the number selection, ignoring repeated numbers, until 50 cases have been selected.

2.17 The method used by researcher B is preferable.
2.19 **a.** Using the list, first number the part-time students 1–3000. Use a random number generator on a calculator or computer to randomly select a whole number between 1 and 3000. The number selected represents the first part-time student to be included in the sample. Repeat the number selection, ignoring repeated numbers, until 10 part-time students have been selected. Then number the full-time students 1–3500 and select 10 full-time students using the same procedure. **b.** No
2.21 **a.** The pages of the book have already been numbered between 1 and the highest page number in the book. Use a random number generator on a calculator or computer to randomly select a whole number between 1 and the highest page number in the book. The number selected will be the first page to be included in the sample. Repeat the number selection, ignoring repeated numbers, until the required number of pages has been selected. **b.** Pages that include exercises tend to contain more words than pages that do not include exercises. Therefore, it would be sensible to stratify according to this criterion. Assuming that 20 nonexercise pages and 20 exercise pages will be included in the sample, the sample should be selected as follows: Use a random number generator to randomly select a whole number between 1 and the highest page number in the book; the number selected will be the first page to be included in the sample; repeat the number selection, ignoring repeated numbers and keeping track of the number of pages of each type selected, until 20 pages of one type have been selected; then continue in the same way, but ignore numbers corresponding to pages of that type; when 20 pages of the other type have been selected, stop the process. **c.** Randomly select one page from the first 20 pages in the book. Include in your sample that page and every 20th page from that page onward. **d.** Roughly speaking, in terms of the numbers of words per page, each chapter is representative of the book as a whole. It is therefore sensible for the chapters to be used as clusters. Using a random number generator, randomly choose three chapters. Then count the number of words on each page in those three chapters. **e.** Answers will vary. **f.** Answers will vary.
2.23 The researchers should be concerned about nonresponse bias.
2.25 It is not reasonable to consider the participants to be representative of all students with regard to their truthfulness in the various forms of communication. Also, the students knew they were surveying themselves as to the truthfulness of their interactions. This could easily have changed their behavior in particular social contexts and, therefore, could have distorted the results of the study.
2.27 It is quite possible that people who read that newspaper or access this web site differ from the population in some relevant way, particularly considering that they are both New York City-based publications.
2.29 Scheme 2
2.31 Different subsets of the population might have responded by different methods. For example, it is quite possible that younger people (who might generally be in favor of continuing the parade) chose to respond via the Internet while older people (who on the whole might be against the parade) chose to use the telephone to make their responses.
2.33 **a.** Binding strength **b.** Type of glue **c.** The extraneous variables mentioned are the number of pages in the book and whether the book is bound as a hardback or a paperback. Further extraneous variables that might be considered include the weight of the material used for the cover and the type of paper used.
2.35 Random assignment should have been used to determine which drink would be consumed during which break for each cyclist.
2.37 We rely on random assignment to produce comparable experimental groups. If the researchers had hand-picked the treatment groups, they might unconsciously have favored one group over the other in terms of some variable that affects the subjects' ability to deal with multiple inputs.
2.39 **a.** If the participants had been able to choose their own avatars, then it is quite possible, for example, that people with a lot of self-confidence would tend to choose the attractive avatar while those with less self-confidence would tend to choose the unattractive avatar.
2.41 We rely on random assignment to produce comparable experimental groups.
2.45 **a.** The improvement in group 3 compared to group 1 cannot be attributed to the use of Sweet Talk since group 3 differs from group 1 in two respects: the incorporation of Sweet Talk and the use of the new intensive insulin therapy in place of the conventional insulin therapy. **b.** The experiment needs to be modified by the addition of a group (group 4) that receives the intensive insulin therapy without Sweet Talk support.
2.47 **a.** Red wine, yellow onions, black tea **b.** Absorption of flavonol into the blood **c.** Gender, amount of flavonols consumed apart from experimental treatment, tolerance of alcohol in wine
2.49 "Blinding" is ensuring that the experimental subjects do not know which treatment they were given and/or ensuring that the people who measure the response variable do not know who was given which treatment.
2.51 **a.** In order to know that the results of this experiment are valid, it is necessary to know that the assignment of the women to the groups was done randomly. If the women were allowed to choose which groups they went into, it would be impossible to tell whether the stated results were caused by the discussions of art or by the greater social nature of the women in the art discussion group. **b.** Suppose that all the women took part in weekly discussions of art, and that, generally, an improvement in the medical conditions mentioned was observed among the subjects. Then it would be impossible to tell whether these health improvements had been caused by the discussions of art or by some factor that was affecting all the subjects, such as an improvement in the weather over the 4 months. By including a control group, and by observing that the improvements did not take place (generally speaking) for those in the control group, factors such as this can be discounted, and the discussions of art are established as the cause of the improvements.
2.55 Suppose that the dog handlers and/or the experimental observers had known which patients did and did not have cancer. It would then be possible for some sort of (conscious or unconscious) communication to take place between these people and the dogs so that the dogs would pick up the conditions of the patients from these people rather than through their perception of the patients' breath. By making sure that the dog handlers and the experimental observers do not know who has the disease and who does not, it is ensured that the dogs are getting the information from the patients.
2.57 **a.** If the judges had known which chowder came from which restaurant, then it is unlikely that Denny's chowder would have won the contest, since the judges would probably be conditioned by this knowledge to choose chowders from more expensive restaurants. **b.** In experiments, if the people measuring the response are not blinded, they will often be conditioned to see different responses to some treatments over other treatments, in the same way as the judges would have been conditioned to favor the expensive restaurant chowders. Therefore, it is necessary that the people measuring the response should not know which subject received which

treatment, so that the treatments can be compared on their own merits.
2.59 a. A placebo group would be necessary if the mere thought of having amalgam fillings could produce kidney disorders. However, since the experimental subjects were sheep, the researchers do not need to be concerned that this would happen. **b.** A resin filling treatment group would be necessary in order to provide evidence that it is the material in the amalgam fillings, rather than the process of filling the teeth, or just the presence of foreign bodies in the teeth, that is the cause of the kidney disorders. If the amalgam filling group developed the kidney disorders and the resin filling group did not, then this would provide evidence that it is some ingredient in the amalgam fillings that is causing the kidney problems. **c.** Since there is concern about the effect of amalgam fillings, it would be considered unethical to use humans in the experiment.
2.61 Answers will vary.
2.63 Answers will vary.
2.65 Answers will vary.
2.67 a. This is an observational study. **b.** In order to evaluate the study, we need to know whether the sample was a random sample.
c. No. Since the sample used in the Healthy Steps study was known to be nationally representative, and since the paper states that, compared with the HS trial, parents in the study sample were disproportionately older, white, more educated, and married, it is clear that it is not reasonable to regard the sample as representative of parents of all children at age 5.5 years. **d.** The potential confounding variable mentioned is what the children watched.
e. The quotation from Kamila Mistry makes a statement about cause and effect and therefore is inconsistent with the statement that the study cannot show that TV was the cause of later problems.
2.69 Answers will vary.
2.71 The first criticism describes measurement bias. The second criticism describes selection bias.
2.73 We rely on random assignment to produce comparable experimental groups. If the researchers had hand-picked the treatment groups, they might unconsciously have favored one group over the other in terms of some variable that affects the ability of the people at the centers to respond to the materials provided.
2.75 a. Observational study **b.** It is quite possible that the children who watched large amounts of TV in their early years were also those, generally speaking, who received less attention from their parents, and it was the lack of attention from their parents that caused the later attention problems, not the TV-watching.
2.77 For example, it is possible that people who are not married are more likely to go out alone (except for the widowed who are older and therefore tend to stay home). It could then be possible that going out alone is causing the risk of being a victim of violent crime, not the marital status.
2.79 All the participants were women, from Texas, and volunteers. All three of these facts tell us that it is likely to be unreasonable to generalize the results of the study to all college students.
2.81 a. The extraneous variables identified are gender, age, weight, lean body mass, and capacity to lift weights. They were dealt with by direct control: all the volunteers were male, about the same age, and similar in weight, lean body mass, and capacity to lift weights.
b. Yes, it is important that the men were not told which treatment they were receiving; otherwise the effect of giving a placebo would have been removed. If the participants *were* told which treatment they were receiving, then those taking the creatine would have the additional effect of the mere taking of a supplement thought to be helpful (the placebo effect) and those getting the fake preparation would not get this effect. It would then be impossible to distinguish the influence of the placebo effect from the effect of the creatine itself. **c.** Yes, it would have been useful if those measuring the increase in muscle mass had not known who received which treatment. With this knowledge, it is possible that the people would have been unconsciously influenced into exaggerating the increase in muscle mass for those who took the creatine.

Chapter 3

3.3 a. The second and third categories ("Permitted for business purposes only" and "Permitted for limited personal use" were combined into one category ("No, but some limits apply"). **c.** Pie chart, regular bar graph
3.5 Since the number of categories is relatively high, a bar graph is suitable.
3.7 b. Were the surveys carried out on random samples of married women from those countries? How were the questions worded?
c. In one country, Japan, the percentage of women who say they never get help from their husbands is far higher than the percentages in any of the other four countries included. The percentages in the other four countries are similar, with Canada showing the lowest percentage of women who say they do not get help from their husbands.
3.11 b. The comparative bar graph shows that a much higher proportion of adolescents is unfit compared to adults. It also shows that while the proportion unfit among adolescents is roughly the same for females and males, the proprotion is higher among adults for females than it is for males.
3.13 a. No. A pie chart is unsuitable when there is such a large number of categories. **b.** Yes, it is easier to see the differences between the relative frequencies for the different hazards, particularly for those with small relative frequencies.
3.15

10	578
11	79
12	1114
13	001122478899
14	0011112235669
15	11122445599
16	1227
17	1
18	
19	
20	8

Stem: Ones
Leaf: Tenths

A typical number of births per thousand of the population is around 14, with most birth rates concentrated in the 13.0 to 15.9 range. The distribution has just one peak (at the 14–15 class). There is an extreme value, 20.8, at the high end of the data set, and this is the only birth rate above 17.1. The distribution is not symmetrical, since it has a greater spread to the right of its center than to the left.
3.17 a.

0H	55567889999
1L	0000111113334
1H	556666666667789
2L	00001122233
2H	5

Stem: Tens
Leaf: Ones

A typical percentage of households with only a wireless phone is around 15.

b.

West		East
998	0H	555789
110	1L	00011134
8766	1H	666
21	2L	00
5	2H	

Stem: Tens
Leaf: Ones

A typical percentage of households with only a wireless phone for the West is around 16, which is greater than that for the East (around 11). There is a slightly greater spread of values in the West than in the East, with values in the West ranging from 8 to 25 (a range of 17) and values in the East ranging from 5 to 20 (a range of 15). The distribution for the West is roughly symmetrical, while the distribution in the East shows a slightly greater spread to the right of its center than to the left. Neither distribution has any outliers.

3.19 a.

-1	100
-0	9999888877655555554444332222211110
0	000011244577
1	179
2	2

Stem: Tens
Leaf: Ones

b. Split each stem into two, one taking the lower leaves (0–4) and the other taking the higher leaves (5–9). So, for example, the stem "0" would be split into "0L" and "0H", with 0L taking the leaves "000011244" and 0H taking the leaves "44577". **c.** The three states with the greatest percentage increase in the number of 25- to 44-year-olds are Nevada, Utah, and Arizona, all desert states.

3.21

0t	333
0f	44444455555
0s	66666666667777777777
0*	88888888999
1.	0000

Stem: Tens
Leaf: Ones

The stem-and-leaf display shows that the distribution of high school dropout rates is roughly symmetrical. A typical dropout rate is 7%. The great majority of rates are between 4% and 9%, inclusive.

3.23 The distribution of maximum wind speeds is positively skewed and is bimodal, with peaks at the 35-40 and 60-65 intervals.

3.25 b. The typical percentage of workers belonging to a union is around 11, with values ranging from 3.5 to 24.9. There are three states with percentages that stand out as being higher than those of the rest of the states. The distribution is positively skewed. **c.** The dotplot is more informative as it shows where the data points actually lie. For example, in the histogram we can tell that there are three observations in the 20 to 25 interval, but we don't see the actual values and miss the fact that these values are actually considerably higher than the other values in the data set. **d.** The histogram in Part (a) could be taken to imply that there are states with a percent of workers belonging to a union near zero. It is clear from this second histogram that this is not the case. Also, the second histogram shows that there is a gap at the high end and that the three largest values are noticeably higher than those of the other states. This fact is not clear from the histogram in Part (a).

3.27 c. The histograms are very similar, except that the Credit Bureau results show 7% of students having a debt of $7000 or more, whereas in the survey no student admitted to having a debt this size. **d.** Yes. It is quite possible that the students who did not respond included those with a debt of over $7000, particularly as students with such a large debt would probably not want to admit it.

3.29 a. First, the class intervals do not all have the same width, and so use of relative frequency on the *y*-axis would not be appropriate. Second, we are not given an upper boundary for the last class interval, so we don't have enough information to draw the histogram. **c.** By far, the highest density of educational debts occurs in the $0–5000 range, with 43% of the students having debts in this relatively narrow interval. Among the remaining 57% of students, there seems to be a roughly symmetrical distribution of debts, with the greatest density of debts occurring in the $50,000–100,000 range.

3.33 Answers will vary.

3.35 a.

Years Survived	Relative Frequency
0 to < 2	.10
2 to < 4	.42
4 to < 6	.02
6 to < 8	.10
8 to < 10	.04
10 to < 12	.02
12 to < 14	.02
14 to < 16	.28

c. The histogram shows a bimodal distribution, with peaks at the 2–4 year and 14–16 year intervals. All the other survival times were considerably less common than these two. **d.** We would need to know that the set of patients used in the study formed a random sample of all patients younger than 50 years old who had been diagnosed with the disease and had received the high dose chemotherapy.

3.37 Answers will vary. One possibility for each part is shown below.

a.

Class Interval	100 to <120	120 to <140	140 to <160	160 to <180	180 to <200
Frequency	5	10	40	10	5

b.

Class Interval	100 to <120	120 to <140	140 to <160	160 to <180	180 to <200
Frequency	20	10	4	25	11

c.

Class Interval	100 to <120	120 to <140	140 to <160	160 to <180	180 to <200
Frequency	33	15	10	7	5

d.

Class Interval	100 to <120	120 to <140	140 to <160	160 to <180	180 to <200
Frequency	5	7	10	15	33

3.39 The graph shows an upward trend in the percentage of homes with only a wireless phone service from June 2005 to December 2008. The increase has been at a roughly steady rate, with only the periods June to December 2005 and December 2006 to June 2007 showing a slightly lower rate of growth.

3.41 a. There is a weak relationship between cost and quality rating, with higher costs being loosely associated with lower ratings.

b. The range of costs for men's athletic shoes is slightly greater than for women's (with just one type of men's shoe providing a cheaper option). For any given cost, there is generally speaking a greater spread of ratings for men's shoes than for women's, with the women's shoes tending to show slightly higher ratings than the men's. For women's shoes, the relationship between cost and quality rating is very weak. For men's shoes, the relationship is stronger for that of the women's (and stronger than that for the combined data set).

3.43 The plot shows that the amount of waste collected for recycling had grown substantially (not slowly, as is stated in the article) in the years 1990 to 2005. The amount increased from under 30 million tons to nearly 60 million tons in that period, which means that the amount had almost doubled.

3.45 According to the 2001 and 2002 data, there are seasonal peaks at weeks 4, 9, and 14, and seasonal lows at weeks 2, 6, 10–12, and 18.

3.47 b. The graphical display created in Part (a) is more informative, since it gives an accurate representation of the proportions of the ethnic groups. **c.** The people who designed the original display possibly felt that the four ethnic groups shown in the segmented bar section might seem to be underrepresented at the college if they used a single pie chart.

3.49 The first graphical display is not drawn appropriately. The Z's have been drawn so that their heights are in proportion to the percentages shown. However, the widths and the perceived depths are also in proportion to the percentages, and so neither the areas nor the perceived volumes of the Z's are proportional to the percentages. The graph is therefore misleading to the reader. In the second graphical display, however, *only* the heights of the cars are in proportion to the percentages shown. The widths of the cars are all equal. Therefore the areas of the cars are in proportion to the percentages, and this is an appropriately drawn graphical display.

3.51 The piles of cocaine have been drawn so that their heights are in proportion to the percentages shown. However, the widths are also in proportion to the percentages, and therefore neither the areas (nor the perceived volumes) are in proportion to the percentages. The graph is therefore misleading to the reader.

3.55

1	9	
2	23788999	
3	0011112233459	Stem: Tens
4	0123	Leaf: Ones

A typical calorie content for these light beers is 31 calories per 100 ml, with the great majority lying in the 22–39 range. The distribution is negatively skewed, with one peak (in the 30–39 range). There are no gaps in the data.

3.57 a.

0	0033344555568888888999999	
1	0001223344567	
2	001123689	
3	0	
4	0	
5		Stem: Tens
6	6	Leaf: Ones

b. A typical percentage population increase is around 10, with the great majority of states in the 0–29 range. The distribution is positively skewed, with one peak (in the 0–9 range). There are two states showing significantly greater increases than the other 48 states: one at 40 (Arizona) and one at 66 (Nevada).

c.

West		East	
9988880	0	033344555568889999	
432	1	0001234567	
982100	2	136	
0	3		
0	4		
	5		Stem: Tens
6	6		Leaf: Ones

On average, the percentage population increases in the West were greater than those for the East, with a typical value for the West of about 14 and a typical value for the East of about 9. There is a far greater spread in the values in the West, with values ranging from 0 to 66, than in the East where values ranged from 0 to 26. Both distributions are positively skewed, with a single peak for the East data, and two peaks for the West. In the West, there are two states showing significantly greater increases than the remaining states, with values at 40 and 60. There are no such extreme values in the East.

3.59 a. High graft weight ratios are clearly associated with low body weights (and vice versa), and the relationship is not linear. (In fact, roughly speaking, there seems to be, an inverse proportionality between the two variables, apart from a small increase in the graft weight ratios for increasing body weights among those recipients with the greater body weights. This is interesting in that an inverse proportionality between the variables would imply that the actual weights of transplanted livers are chosen independently of the recipients' body weights.) **b.** A likely reason for the negative relationship is that the livers to be transplanted are probably chosen according to whatever happens to be available at the time. Therefore, lighter patients are likely to receive livers that are too large and heavier patients are likely to receive livers that are too small.

3.61 b. Continuing the growth trend, we estimate that the average home size in 2010 will be approximately 2500 square feet.

3.63

Disney		Other	
975332100	0	0001259	
765	1	156	
920	2	0	
	3		
	4		Stem: Hundreds
4	5		Leaf: Tens

On average, the total tobacco exposure times for the Disney movies are higher than the others, with a typical value for Disney of about 90 seconds and a typical value for the other companies of about 50 seconds. Both distributions have one peak and are positively skewed. There is one extreme value (548) in the Disney data and no extreme value in the data for the other companies. There is a greater spread in the Disney data, with values ranging from 6 seconds to 540 seconds, than for the other companies, with values ranging from 1 second to 205 seconds.

3.65 c. The segmented bar graph is slightly preferable in that it is a little easier in it than in the pie chart to see that the proportion of children responding "Most of the time" was slightly higher than the proportion responding "Some of the time."

3.67 The peaks were probably caused by the incidence of major hurricanes in those years.

3.69 b. In every year the number of related donors was much greater than the number of unrelated donors. In both categories the number of transplants increased every year, but the increases in unrelated donors were greater proportionately than the increases in related donors.

3.71 a.

Skeletal Retention	Frequency
0.15 to <0.20	4
0.20 to <0.25	2
0.25 to <0.30	5
0.30 to <0.35	21
0.35 to <0.40	9
0.40 to <0.45	9
0.45 to <0.50	4
0.50 to <0.55	0
0.55 to <0.60	1

b. The histogram is centered at approximately 0.34, with values ranging from 0.15 to 0.5, plus one extreme value in the 0.55–0.6 range. The distribution has a single peak and is slightly positively skewed.

Cumulative Review 3

CR3.1 No. For example, it is quite possible that men who ate a high proportion of cruciferous vegetables generally speaking also had healthier lifestyles than those who did not, and that it was the healthier lifestyles that were causing the lower incidence of prostate cancer, not the eating of cruciferous vegetables.

CR3.3 Very often those who choose to respond generally have a different opinion on the subject of the study from those who do not respond. (In particular, those who respond often have strong feelings against the status quo.) This can lead to results that are not representative of the population that is being studied.

CR3.5 Only a small proportion (around 11%) of the doctors responded, and it is quite possible that those who did respond had different opinions regarding managed care than the majority who did not. Therefore, the results could have been very inaccurate for the population of doctors in California.

CR3.7 For example, suppose the women had been allowed to choose whether or not they participated in the program. Then it is quite possible, generally speaking, that those women with more social awareness would have chosen to participate, and those with less social awareness would have chosen not to. Then it would be impossible to tell whether the stated results came about as a result of the program or of the greater social awareness among the women who participated. By randomly assigning the women to participate or not, comparable groups of women would have been obtained.

CR3.9 **b.** Between 2002 and 2003 and between 2003 and 2004, the pass rates rose for both the high school and the state, with a particularly sharp rise between 2003 and 2004 for the state. However, the pass rate for the county fell between 2002 and 2003 and then rose between 2003 and 2004.

CR3.11

a.

0	123334555599
1	00122234688
2	1112344477
3	0113338
4	37
5	23778

Stem: Thousands
Leaf: Hundreds

The stem-and-leaf display shows a positively skewed distribution with a single peak. There are no extreme values. A typical total length is around 2100 and the great majority of total lengths lie in the 100 to 3800 range.

c. The number of subdivisions that have total lengths less than 2000 is 12 + 11 = 23, and so the proportion of subdivisions that have total lengths less than 2000 is 23/47 = 0.489.

The number of subdivisions that have total lengths between 2000 and 4000 is 10 + 7 = 17, and so the proportion of subdivisions that have total lengths between 2000 and 4000 is 17/47 = 0.361.

CR3.13 The histogram shows a smooth positively skewed distribution with a single peak. A typical time difference between the two phases of the race is 150 seconds, with the majority of time differences lying between 50 and 350 seconds. There are about three values that could be considered extreme, with those values lying in the 650 to 750 range. Estimating the frequencies from the histogram we see that approximately 920 runners were included in the study and that approximately eight of those runners ran the late distance more quickly than the early distance (indicated by a negative time difference). Therefore the proportion of runners who ran the late distance more quickly than the early distance is approximately 8/920 = 0.009.

CR3.15 There is a strong negative linear relationship between racket resonance frequency and sum of peak-to-peak accelerations. There are two rackets with data points separated from the remaining data points. Those two rackets have very high resonance frequencies and their peak-to-peak accelerations are lower than those of all the other rackets.

Chapter 4

4.1 $\bar{x}$ = \$2118.71. Median = \$1688. The median is better since it is not influenced by the two extreme values.

4.3 The mean caffeine concentration for the brands of coffee listed = 125.417 mg/cup. Therefore, the mean caffeine concentration of the coffee brands in mg/ounce is 15.677. This is significantly greater than the previous mean caffeine concentration of the energy drinks.

4.5 It tells us that a small number of individuals who donate a large amount of time are greatly increasing the mean.

4.7 **a.** The mean is greater than the median. **b.** The mean is 683,315.2. The median is 433,246.5. **c.** The median **d.** It is not reasonable to generalize this sample of daily newspapers to the population of the United States since the sample consists only of the top 20 newspapers in the country.

4.9 **a.** The mean is 448.3. **b.** The median is 446.

c. This sample represents the 20 days with the highest number of speeding-related fatalities, and so it is not reasonable to generalize from this sample to the other 345 days of the year.

4.11 Neither statement is correct. Regarding the first statement, we should note that unless the "fairly expensive houses" constitute a majority of the houses selling, these more costly houses will not have an effect on the median. Turning to the second statement, we point out that the small number of very high or very low prices will have no effect on the median, whatever the number of sales. Both statements can be corrected by replacing the median with the mean.

4.13 The two possible solutions are x_5 = 32 and x_5 = 39.5.

4.15 The median is 680 hours. The 20% trimmed mean is 661.667 hours.

4.17 **a.** $\bar{x}$ = 52.111. Variance = 279.111. s = 16.707.

b. The addition of the very expensive cheese would increase both the mean and the standard deviation.
4.19 a. Lower quartile = 4th value = **41**. Upper quartile = 12th value = **62**. Iqr = **21**. **b.** The iqr for cereals rated good (calculated in exercise 4.18) is 24. This is greater than the value calculated in Part (a).
4.21 a. $\bar{x} = 2118.71429$. Variance = 1176027.905. The fairly large value of the standard deviation tells us that there is considerable variation between the repair costs. **b.** For minivans, mean = 1355.833, variance = 93,698.967, and standard deviation = 306.103. The mean repair cost for minivans is less than for the smaller cars, showing a lower typical repair cost for the minivans. The standard deviation for minivans is considerably less than for the smaller cars, showing lower repair cost variability for the minivans.
4.23 a. Lower quartile = **0**. Upper quartile = 195. Interquartile range = 195. **b.** The lower quartile equals the minimum value for this data set because there is a large number of equal values (zero in this case) at the lower end of the distribution. This is unusual, and therefore, generally speaking, the lower quartile is not equal to the minimum value.
4.25 This data set would have a large standard deviation because parents differ greatly in the amount of money they spend.
4.27 a. Standard deviation = 50.058. **b.** The standard deviation for Memorial Day would be smaller than the standard deviation for New Year's Day. **c.** The standard deviations for Memorial Day, Labor Day, and Thanksgiving are 18.224, 17.725, and 15.312, respectively. The standard deviations for the other three holidays are 50.058, 47.139, and 52.370. The standard deviations for the same-day-of-the-week holidays are all smaller than all of the standard deviations for the holidays that can occur on different days. There is less variability for the holidays that always occur on the same day of the week.
4.29 a. The average price for the combined areas would have to take into account the fact that more houses were sold in Los Osos than in Morrow Bay. **b.** The results for Paso Robles are likely to have the higher standard deviation since the range for Paso Robles (1,405,000) is greater than the range for Grover Beach (478,000). **c.** Assuming that the distributions of house prices are roughly symmetrical, we would expect the median price for Grover Beach to be around 481,000 and the median price for Paso Robles to be around 872,500. We expect Paso Robles to have the higher median price.
4.31 a.

	Mean	Standard Deviation	Coefficient of Variation
Sample 1	7.81	0.398	5.102
Sample 2	49.68	1.739	3.500

b. The values of the coefficient of variation are given in the table in Part (a). The fact that the coefficient of variation is smaller for Sample 2 than for Sample 1 is not surprising since, relative to the actual amount placed in the containers, it is easier to be more accurate when larger amounts are being placed in the containers.
4.33 a. Median = 58. Lower quartile = 13th value = 53.5. Upper quartile = 38th value = 64.4. **b.** Lower quartile − 1.5(iqr) = 53.5 −1.5(10.9) = 37.15. Since 28.2 and 35.7 are both less than 37.15, they are both outliers. **c.** The median percentage of population born and still living in the state is 58. There are two outliers at the lower end of the distribution. If they are disregarded the distribution is roughly symmetrical, with values ranging from 40.4 to 75.8.
4.35 No, the boxplot is not roughly symmetric. It is positively skewed.
4.37 a. It would be more appropriate to use the interquartile range than the standard deviation. **b.** Lower quartile = 81.5, upper quartile = 94, iqr = 12.5. (Lower quartile) − 3(iqr) = 81.5 − 3(12.5) = 44. (Lower quartile) − 1.5(iqr) = 81.5 − 1.5(12.5) = 62.75 (Upper quartile) + 1.5(iqr) = 94 + 1.5(12.5) = 112.75. (Upper quartile) + 3(iqr) = 94 + 3(12.5) = 131.5. Since the value for students (152) is greater than 131.5, this is an extreme outlier. Since the value for farmers (43) is less than 44, this is an extreme outlier. There are no mild outliers. **d.** The insurance company might decide only to offer discounts to occupations that are outliers at the lower end of the distribution, in which case only farmers would receive the discount. If the company was willing to offer discounts to the quarter of occupations with the lowest accident rates, then the last 10 occupations on the list should be the ones to receive discounts.
4.39 a. Roughly 68% of speeds would have been between those two values. **b.** Roughly 16% of speeds would exceed 57 mph.
4.41 a. At least 75% of observations must lie between those two values. **b.** The required interval is (2.90, 70.94). **c.** The distribution cannot be approximately normal.
4.43 For the first test, $z = 1.5$; for the second test, $z = 1.875$. Since the student's z score in the second test is higher, the student did better relative to the other test takers in the second test.
4.45 a. 68% **b.** 5% **c.** Approximately 13.5% of observations lie between 2000 and 2500. **d.** Chebyshev's Rule can only tell us that the required proportions are "at least" something or "at most" something. The Empirical Rule estimates the actual proportions required.
4.47 The best conclusion we can reach is that at most 16% of weight readings will be between 49.75 and 50.25.
4.49 The distribution is positively skewed. Using Chebyshev's Rule, we can conclude that at most, 18 students changed at least six answers from correct to incorrect.
4.51 a.

Per Capita Expenditure	Frequency
0 to <2	13
2 to <4	18
4 to <6	10
6 to <8	5
8 to <10	1
10 to <12	2
12 to <14	0
14 to <16	0
16 to <18	2

b. i. 3.4 **ii.** 5.0 **iii.** 0.8 **iv.** 8.0 **v.** 2.8
4.53 a. The minimum value and the lower quartile were both 1. **b.** More than half of the data values were equal to the minimum value. **c.** Between 25% and 50% of patients had unacceptable times to defibrillation.
d. (Upper quartile) + 3(iqr) = 9. Since 7 is less than 9, 7 must be a mild outlier.
4.55 a. $\bar{x} = 287.714$. The seven deviations are: 209.286, −94.714, 40.286, −132.714, 38.286, −42.714, −17.714. **b.** The sum of the rounded deviations is 0.002. **c.** Variance = 12,601.905. Standard deviation = 112.258
4.57 This is the median, and its value is $4286. The other measure of center is the mean, and its value is $3968.67. This is smaller than the median and, therefore, less favorable to the supervisors.

4.59 **a.** This is a correct interpretation of the median. **b.** Here the word "range" is being used to describe the interval from the minimum value to the maximum value. The statement claims that the median is defined as the midpoint of this interval, which is not true. **c.** If there is no home below \$300,000, then certainly the median will be greater than \$300,000 (unless more than half of the homes cost exactly \$300,000).
4.61 The new mean is $\bar{x} = 38.364$. The new values and their deviations from the mean are shown in the table below.

Value	Deviation
52	13.636
13	−25.364
17	−21.364
46	7.636
42	3.636
24	−14.364
32	−6.364
30	−8.364
58	19.636
35	−3.364

The value of s^2 for the new values is the same as for the old values.
4.63 **a.** Lower quartile = 44, upper quartile = 53, iqr = 9. (Lower quartile) − 1.5(iqr) = 44 − 1.5(9) = 30.5. (Upper quartile) + 1.5(iqr) = 53 + 1.5(9) = 66.5. Since there are no data values less than 30.5 and no data values greater than 66.5, there are no outliers. **b.** The median of the distribution is 46. The middle 50% of the data range from 44 to 53 and the whole data set ranges from 33 to 60. There are no outliers. The lower half of the middle 50% of data values shows less spread than the upper half of the middle 50% of data values. The spread of the lowest 25% of data values is slightly greater than the spread of the highest 25% of data values.
4.65 **a.** $\bar{x} = 192.571$. This is a measure of center that incorporates all the sample values. Median = 189. This is a measure of center that is the "middle value" in the sample. **b.** The mean would decrease and the median would remain the same. **c.** Trimmed mean = 191. Trimming percentage = 7.1%. **d.** If 244 is changed to 204 then the largest observation is now 211, and one value of 211 will be eliminated from the calculation. This makes the largest three data values in the calculation 204, 205, 211, as compared to data values 205, 211, 211 in the previous calculation. Therefore the trimmed mean will decrease. If 244 is changed to 284, then there is no change in the trimmed mean.
4.67 The median aluminum contamination is 119. There is one (extreme) outlier—a value of 511. If the outlier is disregarded, the data values range from 30 to 291. The middle 50% of data values range from 87 to 182. Even if the outlier is disregarded, the distribution is positively skewed.
4.69 The medians for the three different types of hotel are roughly the same, with the median for the midrange hotels slightly higher than the other two medians. The midrange hotels have two outliers (one extreme) at the lower end of the distribution and the first-class hotels have one (extreme) outlier at the lower end. There are no outliers for the budget hotels. If the outliers are taken into account, the midrange and first-class groups have a greater range than the budget group. If the outliers are disregarded, the budget group has a much greater spread than the other two groups. If the outliers are taken into account, all three distributions are negatively skewed. If the outliers are disregarded, the distribution for the budget group is negatively skewed whereas the distributions for the other two groups are positively skewed.
4.71 The distribution is positively skewed.
4.73 **a.** The 84th percentile is 120. **b.** The standard deviation is approximately **20**. **c.** $z = -0.5$. **d.** 140 is at approximately the 97.5th percentile. **e.** A score of 40 is 3 standard deviations below the mean, and so the proportion of scores below 40 would be approximately (100 − 99.7)/2 = 0.15%. Therefore, there would be very few scores below 40.

Chapter 5

5.1 **a.** Positive **b.** Negative **c.** Positive **d.** Close to zero **e.** Positive **f.** Positive **g.** Negative **h.** Close to zero
5.5 **a.** $r = 0.204$, weak positive linear relationship **b.** $r = 0.241$, slightly greater than the correlation coefficient for the per-serving data
5.7 The correlation coefficient for college GPA and academic self-worth was 0.48, indicating a weak-to-moderate positive linear relationship. The correlation coefficient of 0.46 between college GPA and high school GPA also indicates a weak-to-moderate positive linear relationship. The correlation coefficient of −0.36 between college GPA and the procrastination measure indicates a weak negative linear relationship.
5.9 **a.** $r = 0.118$ **b.** Yes. The scatterplot does not suggest a strong relationship between the variables.
5.11 $r = 0.935$. There is a strong positive linear relationship.
5.13 The correlation coefficient is most likely to be close to −0.9.
5.15 **a.** There is a moderate positive linear relationship. **b.** $\hat{y} = -0.14282 + 0.016141x$ **c.** $\hat{y} = 0.0993$ **d.** The higher the temperature, the greater the proportion of larvae that were captured moving upstream. **e.** Approximately 8.8°C.
5.17 **a.** The dependent variable is the number of fruit-and-vegetable servings per day; the predictor variable is the number of hours of television viewed per day. **b.** Negative. As the number of hours of television viewed per day increases, the number of fruit-and-vegetable servings per day (on average) decreases.
5.19 **b.** $r = 0.786$ **c.** $\hat{y} = 714.1470 + 42.5196x$ **d.** $\hat{y} = 790.682$ ml **e.** The value $x = 3.0$ is substantially outside the range of the x-values in the data set, and we do not know that the observed linear pattern continues outside this range.
5.21 Since the slope of the least-squares line is −9.30, each extra minute waiting for paramedics to arrive is associated with a decrease in the chance of survival by 9.3 percentage points.
5.23 **a.** 0.700, moderate linear relationship **b.** −0.332, weak negative linear relationship **c.** Size is the better predictor of sale price since the absolute value of the correlation between sale price and size is larger than the absolute value of the correlation between sale price and land-to-building ratio. **d.** $\hat{y} = 1.3281 + 0.0053x$
5.25 We do not know that the same linear relationship applies for x values outside the range of the data.
5.27 $b = r(s_y/s_x)$, where s_y and s_x are the standard deviations of the y values and the x values, respectively. Since standard deviations are always positive, b and r must have the same sign.
5.29 **a.** The scatterplot shows a linear pattern between the representative ages of 10 and 17, but there is a greater increase in the median distance walked between the representative ages of 7 and 10 than there is between any other two consecutive age groups. **b.** $\hat{y} = 492.79773 + 14.76333x$

c. Residuals: −7.551, −12.141, 26.869, 8.997, −16.174. The residual plot reflects the sharp increase in the median distance walked between the representative ages of 7 and 10, with a clear negative residual at $x = 7$ and large positive residual at $x = 10$.
5.31 a. Residuals: −26.47, −42.0262, 36.3811, 15.5188, 12.4064, 4.11. **b.** $r = -0.581$, moderate **c.** There is one point with an x value far greater than that of the other points, suggesting that this point might be influential. **d.** Including the point for the West, the slope of the least-squares line is −4.691 and the intercept is 1082.244. If we remove this point, the resulting slope is −7.107 and the intercept is 1154.371. There is a substantial change in the slope, so the point is influential.
5.33 a. Yes, strong linear relationship. **b.** $\hat{y} = 18.483 + 0.00287x$ **c.** The point (3928, 46.8) is unlikely to be influential as its x value does not differ greatly from the others in the data set. **d.** The two points are not influential. **e.** $s_e = 9.16217$. This is a typical deviation of a percentage-transported value from the value predicted by the regression line. **f.** $r^2 = 0.832$. 83.2% of the variation in the percentage-transported values can be attributed to the approximate linear relationship between total number and percentage transported.
5.35 $r^2 = 0.948$, $s_e = 20.566$
5.37 a. 0.154 **b.** No, since the r^2 value for y = first-year-college GPA and x = SAT II score was 0.16, which is not large. Only 16% of the variation in first-year-college GPA can be attributed to the approximate linear relationship between SAT II score and first-year-college GPA.
5.39 b. $\hat{y} = 85.334 - 0.0000259x$, $r^2 = 0.016$. The line will not give accurate predictions. **c.** Deleting the point (620231, 67), the equation of the least-squares line is now $\hat{y} = 83.402 + 0.0000387x$. Removal of the point does have a large effect on the equation of the line.
5.41 $r^2 = 0.951$; 95.1% of the variation in hardness is attributable to the approximate linear relationship between time elapsed and hardness.
5.43 a. $r = 0$, $\hat{y} = \bar{y}$. **b.** For values of r close to 1 or −1, s_e will be much smaller than s_y. **c.** $s_e \approx 1.5$. **d.** $\hat{y} = 7.92 + 0.544x$, $s_e \approx 1.02$
5.45 a. $\hat{y} = 0.8660 - 0.008452x + 0.000410x^2$ **b.** $\hat{y} = 0.861$
5.47 a. The relationship between sparrow density and field strength appears to be nonlinear. **b.** When $x' = \sqrt{x}$, there is evidence of a curve in the residual plot, but when $x' = \log(x)$, there is no evidence of a curve in the residual plot. Thus, $x' = \log(x)$ is the preferable transformation. **c.** $\hat{y} = 14.80508 - 24.28005 \cdot \log(x)$ **d.** When $x = 0.5$, $\hat{y} = 22.114$. When $x = 2.5$, $\hat{y} = 5.143$.
5.49 A scatterplot of the untransformed data would resemble segment 3 in Figure 5.38.
5.51 a. Initially, as the cloud cover index (x) increases from zero, the values of the sunshine index (y) rise. Then, between $x = 0.2$ and $x = 0.3$, the y values seem to decrease sharply, and then increase again from that point. Neither a linear nor a quadratic model could adequately fit that pattern; however, a cubic regression might be appropriate. **b.** $\hat{y} = 10.8768 + 1.4604x - 7.2590x^2 + 9.2342x^3$ **c.** There seems to be a random pattern in the residual plot, suggesting that the cubic regression was appropriate. **d.** 10.932 **e.** 10.905 **f.** The value 0.75 is well outside the range of the original x values.
5.53 a. From 1990 to 1999, the number of people waiting for organ transplants increased, with the number increasing by greater amounts each year. **b.** One possible transformation is $y' = y^{0.15}$ (with $x' = x$). This produces a linear pattern in the scatterplot and a random pattern in the residual plot. **c.** $\hat{y}^{0.15} = 1.552753 + 0.034856x$. When $x = 11$, $\hat{y}^{0.15} = 1.936164$ and $\hat{y} = 81.837$. The least-squares line predicts that in 2000 the number of patients waiting will be around 81,800. **d.** We must be confident that the pattern observed between 1990 and 1999 will continue until 2000. This is reasonable as long as circumstances remain basically the same. However, to expect the same pattern to continue to 2010 would be unreasonable.
5.55 The relationship between age and canal length is not linear. One transformation that makes the plot roughly linear is $x' = 1/\sqrt{x}$ (with $y' = y$).
5.57 0.702
5.59 a. Yes, the plots have roughly the shape you would expect from "logistic" plots.
b.

Exposure (days) (x)	Cloud Forest Proportion (p)	$y' = \ln(p/(1 - p))$
1	0.75	1.09861
2	0.67	0.70819
3	0.36	−0.57536
4	0.31	−0.80012
5	0.14	−1.81529
6	0.09	−2.31363
7	0.06	−2.75154
8	0.07	−2.58669

The least-squares line relating y' and x (where x is the exposure time in days) is $\hat{y}' = 1.51297 - 0.58721x$. The negative slope reflects the fact that as exposure time increases, the hatch rate decreases. **c.** 0.438; 0.194 **d.** 2.577 days
5.61 b. $\hat{y}' = -1.55892 + 5.76671x$. The positive slope indicates that as concentration increases, the proportion of mosquitoes that die increases. **c.** 0.270 g/cc
5.65 a. $r = 0.943$, strong positive linear relationship. No, we cannot conclude that lead exposure causes increased assault rates. A value of r close to 1 tells us that there is a strong linear association but tells us nothing about causation. **b.** $\hat{y} = -24.08 + 327.41x$. When $x = 0.5$, $\hat{y} = 139.625$ assaults per 100,000 people. **c.** 0.89 **d.** The two time-series plots, generally speaking, move together. Thus, high assault rates are associated with high lead exposures 23 years earlier, and low assault rates are associated with low lead exposures 23 years earlier.
5.67 a. $r = -0.981$, strong linear relationship **b.** The word *linear* is not the most effective description of the relationship. A curve would provide a better fit.
5.69 a. One point, (0, 77), is far separated from the other points in the plot. There is a negative relationship. **b.** There appears to be a negative linear relationship between test anxiety and exam score. **c.** $r = -0.912$. This is consistent with the observations given in Part (b). **d.** No, we cannot conclude that test anxiety caused poor exam performance.
5.71 a. There is a clear, positive relationship between the percentages of students who were proficient at the two times. There is the suggestion of a curve in the plot. **b.** $\hat{y} = -3.13603 + 1.52206x$ **c.** When $x = 14$, $\hat{y} = 18.173$. This is slightly lower than the actual value of 20 for Nevada.
5.73 a. $y - \hat{y} = 20.796$ **b.** $r = -0.755$ **c.** $s_e = 11.638$
5.75 a. $r = -0.717$ **b.** $r = -0.835$; the absolute value of this correlation is greater than the absolute value of the correlation calculated in Part (a). This suggests that the transformation was successful in straightening the plot.

5.77 b. Using log(y) and log(x), 15.007 parts per million
5.79 a. $r = 0$ **b.** For example, adding the point (6, 1) gives $r = 0.510$. (Any y-coordinate greater than 0.973 will work.) **c.** For example, adding the point (6, −1) gives $r = -0.510$. (Any y-coordinate less than −0.973 will work.)

Cumulative Review 5

CR5.3 The peaks in rainfall do seem to be followed by peaks in the number of *E. coli* cases, with rainfall peaks around May 12, May 17, and May 23 followed by peaks in the number of cases on May 17, May 23, and May 28. (The incubation period seems to be more like 5 days than the 3 to 4 days mentioned in the caption.) Thus, the graph does show a close connection between unusually heavy rainfall and the incidence of the infection. The storms may not be *responsible* for the increased illness levels, however, since the graph can only show us association, not causation.
CR5.5 The random pattern in the scatterplot shows there is little relationship between the weight of the mare and the weight of her foal. This is supported by the value of the correlation coefficient.
CR5.7 b. Mean = 3.654%, median = 3.35%. **c.** smaller
CR5.9 b. Approximately equal **c.** Mean = \$9.459, median = \$9.48 **e.** Mean = \$72.85, median = \$68.61
CR5.11 a. $\bar{x} = 2965.2$, $s^2 = 294416.622$, $s = 542.602$, Lower quartile = 2510, Upper quartile = 3112, Interquartile range = 602 **b.** less
CR5.13 a. $\bar{x} = 4.93$, Median = 3.6. The mean is greater than the median. This is explained by the fact that the distribution of blood lead levels is positively skewed. **b.** The median blood lead level for the African Americans (3.6) is slightly higher than for the Whites (3.1). Both distributions are positively skewed. There are two outliers in the data set for the African Americans. The distribution for the African Americans shows a greater range than the distribution for the Whites, even disregarding the two outliers.
CR5.15 a. Yes **b.** Strong positive linear relationship **c.** Perfect correlation would result in the points lying exactly on some straight line, but not necessarily on the line described.
CR5.17 a. 76.64% of the variability in clutch size can be attributed to the approximate linear relationship between snout-vent length and clutch size. **b.** $s_e = 29.250$. This is a typical deviation of an observed clutch size from the clutch size predicted by the least-squares line.
CR5.19 a. Yes, the scatterplot shows a strong positive association. **b.** The plot seems to be straight, particularly if you disregard the point with the greatest x value. **c.** This transformation is successful in straightening the plot. Also, unlike the plot in Part (b), the variability of the quantity measured on the vertical axis does not seem to increase as x increases. **d.** No, this transformation has not been successful in producing a linear relationship. There is a clear curve in the plot.

Chapter 6

6.1 A chance experiment is any activity or situation in which there is uncertainty about which of two or more possible outcomes will result.
6.3 a. {AA, AM, MA, MM} **c. i.** B = {AA, AM, MA} **ii.** C = {AM, MA} **iii.** D = {MM}. D is a simple event. **d.** B *and* C = {AM, MA} B *or* C = {AA, AM, MA}.
6.5 b. $A^C = \{(15, 50), (15, 100), (15, 150), (15, 200)\}$

$$A \cup B = \left\{\begin{matrix}(10, 50), (10, 100), (10, 150), (10, 200), (12, 50) \\ (12, 100), (12, 150), (12, 200), (15, 50), (15, 100)\end{matrix}\right\}$$

$$A \cap B = \{(10, 50), (10, 100), (12, 50), (12, 100)\}$$

c. A and C are not disjoint. B and C are disjoint.
6.7 b. A = {3, 4, 5} **c.** C = {125, 15, 215, 25, 5}
6.9 a. A = {NN, DNN} **b.** B = {DDNN} **c.** The number of outcomes is infinite.
6.13 a. {expedited overnight delivery, expedited second-business-day delivery, standard delivery, delivery to the nearest store for customer pick-up} **b. i.** 0.2 **ii.** 0.4 **iii.** 0.6
6.15 a. {fiction hardcover, fiction paperback, fiction digital, fiction audio, nonfiction hardcover, nonfiction paperback, nonfiction digital, nonfiction audio} **b.** No **c.** 0.72 **d.** 0.28; 0.28 **e.** 0.8
6.17 a. 0.001 **b.** Classical
6.21 a. 35% of all tennis racquets purchased have a grip size of 4½ inches. **b.** 0.65 **c.** 0.55 **d.** 0.7
6.23 a. 0.4 **b.** 0.81 **c.** 0.94
6.25 a. 0.000495, 0.00198 **b.** 0.024 **c.** 0.146
6.27 a. BC, BM, BP, BS, CM, CP, CS, MP, MS, PS **b.** 0.1 **c.** 0.4 **d.** 0.3
6.29 a. $P(O_1) = P(O_3) = P(O_5) = 1/9$ and $P(O_2) = P(O_4) = P(O_6) = 2/9$ **b.** 1/3, 4/9 **c.** 9/21, 2/7
6.31 a. 0.24 **b.** 0.36 **c.** 0.12 **d.** 0.75
6.33 a. 0.72 **b.** The value 0.45 is the conditional probability that the selected individual drinks 2 or more cups a day given that he or she drinks coffee. We know this because the percentages given in the display total 100, and yet we know that only 72% of Americans drink coffee. So, the percentages given in the table must be the proportions *of coffee drinkers* who drink the given amounts.
6.37 $P(A|B)$ is larger. $P(A|B)$ is the probability that a randomly chosen professional basketball player is over 6 feet tall—a reasonably large probability. $P(B|A)$ is the probability that a randomly chosen person over 6 feet tall is a professional basketball player—a very small probability.
6.39 a. 0.337 **b.** 0.762 **c.** 0.625 **d.** 0.788 **e.** 0.869 **f.** Current smokers are the least likely to believe that smoking is very harmful, and those who have never smoked are the most likely to think that smoking is very harmful. This is not surprising since you would expect those who smoke to be the most confident about the health prospects of a smoker, with those who formerly smoked being a little more concerned, and those who have never smoked being the most concerned.
6.41 a. i. 0.167 **ii.** 0.068 **iii.** 0.238 **iv.** 0.833 **v.** 0.41 **vi.** 0.18 **b.** 18- to 24-year-olds are more likely than seniors to regularly wear seat belts.
6.43 a. 85% **b.** 0.15 **c.** 0.7225 **d.** 0.1275 **e.** 0.255 **f.** It is not reasonable.
6.45 $P(L)P(F) = 0.29$, not independent
6.47 Not independent
6.49 a. 0.001. We have to assume that she deals with the three errands independently. **b.** 0.999 **c.** 0.009
6.51 a. 0.81 **b.** P(1–2 subsystem doesn't work) = 0.19, P(3–4 subsystem doesn't work) = 0.19 **c.** P(system won't work) = 0.0361, P(system will work) = 0.9639 **d.** 0.9931, increases **e.** 0.9266, decreases
6.53 a. The expert was assuming that there was a 1 in 12 chance of a valve being in any one of the 12 clock positions and that the positions of the two air valves were independent. **b.** The positions of the two air valves are *not* independent, and 1/144 is smaller than the correct probability.

6.55 **a.** No **b.** 0.992 **c.** $P(E_2|E_1) = 39/4999 = 0.00780$. $P(E_2|notE_1) = 40/4999 = 0.00800$. If the first board is defective, then it is slightly less likely that the second board will be defective than if the first board is not defective. **d.** Yes
6.57 **a.** 0.00391 **b.** 0.00383
6.59 **a.** 0.6, slightly smaller
6.61 **a.** 0.55 **b.** 0.45 **c.** 0.4 **d.** 0.25
6.63 **a.** $P(F) = 0.0303$, $P(S|F) = 0.7776$, $P(D|S \cap F) = 0.01012$ **b.** $P(F \cap S \cap D) = 0.000240$
6.65 **a.** Yes **b.** 0.64
6.67 The statement is unlikely to be correct.
6.69 **a.** **i.** 0.307 **ii.** 0.693 **iii.** 0.399 **iv.** 0.275 **v.** 0.122 **b.** 30.7% of faculty members use Twitter; 69.3% of faculty members do not use Twitter; 39.9% of faculty members who use Twitter also use it to communicate with students; 27.5% of faculty members who use Twitter also use it as a learning tool in the classroom; 12.2% of faculty members use Twitter and use it to communicate with students **c.** 0.122 **d.** 0.084
6.71 There are different numbers of people driving the three different types of vehicle (and also that there are some drivers who are driving vehicles not included in those three types).
6.75 **a.** Yes **b.** 0.08, 0.70 **c.** No
6.77 **b.** 0.00095 **c.** 0.10085 **d.** 0.00942
6.79 **b.** 0.27 **c.** 0.43 **d.** Not independent **e.** 0.526 **f.** 0.140
6.81 **a.** 0.425 **b.** 0.314 **c.** 0.4375 **d.** 0.005 **e.** 0.201 **f.** 0.196 **g.** 0.335 **h.** 0.177 **i.** 0.488 **j.** 0.295 **k.** 0.566
6.83 **b.** This is not a fair way to distribute licenses, since any given company applying for multiple licenses has approximately the same chance of obtaining all of its licenses as an individual applying for a single license has of obtaining his/her license. It might be fairer for companies who require two licenses to submit two separate applications and companies who require three licenses to submit three separate applications (with individuals/companies applying for single licenses submitting applications as before). Then, 10 of the applications would be randomly selected and licenses would be awarded accordingly.
6.85 Results of the simulation will vary. The probability should be approximately 0.8468.
6.87 **b.** 0.025 **c.** 0.069
6.89 **a.** 0.140 **b.** 0.218 **c.** 0.098 **d.** 0.452 **e.** 0.704
6.91 Dependent events
6.93 **a.** 0.018 **b.** $P(A_1|L) = 0.444$, $P(A_2|L) = 0.278$, $P(A_3|L) = 0.278$
6.97 0.6
6.99 **a.** 0.106 **b.** 0.446 **c.** 0.547
6.101 **a.** 4/5 **b.** 19/24 **c.** 18/23 **d.** 0.496
6.103 **a.** 0.512 **b.** 0.608

Chapter 7

7.1 **a.** Discrete **b.** Continuous **c.** Discrete **d.** Discrete **e.** Continuous
7.3 Positive integers
7.5 The possible values are the real numbers between 0 and 100, inclusive; y is continuous.
7.7 **a.** 3, 4, 5, 6, 7 **b.** −3, −2, −1, 0, 1, 2, 3 **c.** 0, 1, 2 **d.** 0, 1
7.9 **a.** 0.01 **b.** Over a large number of cartons, about 20% will contain one broken egg. **c.** 0.95. Over a large number of cartons, 95% will contain at most two broken eggs. **d.** 0.85. It does not include exactly two broken eggs. **e.** 0.1 **f.** 0.95
7.11 **a.** 0.82 **b.** 0.18 **c.** 0.65, 0.27
7.15 **a.**

x	0	1	2	3	4
$p(x)$	0.4096	0.4096	0.1536	0.0256	0.0016

b. 0 and 1 **c.** 0.1808
7.17 **a.** The smallest possible y value is 1, and the corresponding outcome is S. The second smallest y value is 2, and the corresponding outcome is FS. **b.** The set of positive integers. **c.** $p(y) = (0.3)^{y-1}(0.7)$, for $y = 1, 2, 3, \ldots$
7.19

y	0	1	2	3
$p(y)$	0.16	0.33	0.32	0.19

7.21 **a.** 0.5 **b.** 0.2
7.23 **b.** 0.08 **c.** 0.36 **d.** 0.4, 0.4; equal because associated areas are equal
7.25 **a.** 0.5, 0.25 **b.** 0.25 **c.** 18
7.27 **a.** 0.375, 0.21875, 0.34375 **b.** 0.401
7.29 **a.** 0.56 **b.** 65% **c.** The mean is not $(0 + 1 + 2 + 3 + 4)/5$ since, for example, far more cartons have 0 broken eggs than 4 broken eggs, and so 0 needs a much greater weighting than 4 in the calculation of the mean.
7.31 **a.** 0.14 **b.** $\mu - 2\sigma = 4.66 - 2(1.2) = 2.26$. $\mu + 2\sigma = 4.66 + 2(1.2) = 7.06$. The values of x more than 2 standard deviations away from the mean are 1 and 2. The probability that x is more than 2 standard deviations away from its mean is 0.05.
7.33 **a.**

d_1	0	650	2000
$p(d_1)$	1/3	1/3	1/3

b. 883.333 **c.** 833.000 **d.** The probability distributions of d_2 and d_3 are:

d_2	0	650	1350
$p(d_2)$	1/3	1/3	1/3

d_3	0	1350	2000
$p(d_3)$	1/3	1/3	1/3

Neither of these probability distributions is the same as the probability distribution of d_1.
e.

t	650	3350
$p(t)$	2/3	1/3

f. **i.** True **ii.** False
7.35 **a.** 46.5 **b.** $890
7.39 **a.** Whether y is positive or negative tells us whether or not the peg will fit into the hole. **b.** 0.003 **c.** 0.00632 **d.** Yes. Since there is no reason to believe that the pegs are being specially selected to match the holes (or vice versa), it is reasonable to think that x_1 and x_2 are independent. **e.** Since 0 is less than half a standard deviation from the mean in the distribution of y, it is relatively likely that a value of y will be negative, and, therefore, that the peg will be too big to fit the hole.
7.41 **a.** 2.8, 1.288 **b.** 0.7, 0.781 **c.** 8.4, 14.94 **d.** 7, 61 **e.** 3.5, 2.27 **f.** 15.4, 75.94
7.43 **a.** Six outcomes have exactly one success. The outcomes are: SFFFFF, FSFFFF, FFSFFF, FFFSFF, FFFFSF, and FFFFFS. **b.** 184756, 15504, 15504

7.45 a. 0.246. Over a large number of random selections of six passengers, 24.6% will have exactly four people resting or sleeping. **b.** 0.262 **c.** 0.901
7.47 a. 0.264 **b.** 0.633 **c.** 0.367 **d.** 0.736
7.49 a. 0.630 **b.** 0.000 **c.** More likely to be .8.
7.51 a. 0.197 **b.** 0.180 **c.** 75, 7.984 **d.** The value 25 is more than 6 standard deviations below the mean. It is surprising that fewer than 25 are said to have failed the test.
7.53 200, 13.416
7.55 a. Binomial distribution with $n = 100$ and $p = 0.2$ **b.** 20 **c.** 16, 4 **d.** A score of 50 is $(50 - 20)/4 = 7.5$ standard deviations from the mean in the distribution of x. So, a score of over 50 is very unlikely.
7.57 a. 0.017 **b.** 0.811, 0.425 **c.** The error probability when $p = 0.7$ is now 0.902. The error probability when $p = 0.6$ is now 0.586.
7.59 a. There is not a fixed number of trials. **b. i.** 0.062 **ii.** 0.284 **iii.** 0.716 **iv.** 0.779
7.61 a. 0.0975 **b.** 0.043 **c.** 0.815
7.63 a. 0.9599 **b.** 0.2483 **c.** 0.1151 **d.** 0.9976 **e.** 0.6887 **f.** 0.6826 **g.** 1.0000
7.65 a. 0.9909 **b.** 0.9909 **c.** 0.1093 **d.** 0.1267 **e.** 0.0706 **f.** 0.0228 **g.** 0.9996 **h.** approximately 1
7.67 a. -1.96 **b.** -2.33 **c.** -1.645 **d.** $z^* = 2.05$ **e.** $z^* = 2.33$ **f.** $z^* = 1.28$
7.69 a. $z^* = 1.96$ **b.** $z^* = 1.645$ **c.** $z^* = 2.33$ **d.** $z^* = 1.75$
7.71 a. 0.5 **b.** 0.9772 **c.** 0.9772 **d.** 0.8185 **e.** 0.9938 **f.** Approximately 1
7.73 Those with emissions > 2.113 parts per billion
7.75 a. 0.2843 **b.** 0.0918 **c.** 0.4344 **d.** 29.928
7.77 0.4013, 0.1314
7.79 The second machine
7.81 94.4 seconds or less
7.83 a. The clear curve in the normal probability plot tells us that the distribution of fussing times is not normal. **b.** The transformation results in a pattern that is much closer to linear than the pattern in Part (a).
7.85 a. No. The distribution of x is positively skewed. **b.** Yes. The histogram shows a distribution that is slightly closer to being symmetric than the distribution of the untransformed data. **c.** Both transformations produce histograms that are closer to being symmetric than the histogram of the untransformed data, but neither transformation produces a distribution that is truly close to being normal.
7.87 Yes. The curve in the normal probability plot suggests that the distribution is not normal.
7.89 Since the pattern in the normal probability plot is very close to linear, it is plausible that disk diameter is normally distributed.
7.91 a. The histogram is positively skewed. **b.** No. The transformation has resulted in a histogram which is still clearly positively skewed.
7.93 Yes. In each case, the transformation has resulted in a histogram that is much closer to symmetric than the original histogram.
7.95 a. 0.0016 **b.** 0.9946 **c.** 0.7925
7.97 a. 0.1114 **b.** 0.0409 **c.** 0.0968 **d.** 0.9429 **e.** 0.9001
7.99 a. There is a fixed number of trials, in which the probability of an undetected tumor is the same in each trial, and the outcomes of the trials are independent since the sample is random. Thus, it is reasonable to think that the distribution of x is binomial. **b.** Yes, since $np = 15.5 \geq 10$ and $n(1 - p) = 484.5 \geq 10$. **c. i.** 0.0606 **ii.** 0.9345 **iii.** 0.0985
7.101 a. 0.7970 **b.** 0.7016 **c.** 0.0143 **d.** 0.05
7.103 a. No, since $np = 50(0.05) = 2.5 < 10$. **b.** Now $n = 500$ and $p = 0.05$, so $np = 500(0.05) = 25 \geq 10$. So the techniques of this section can be used $P(\text{at least 20 are defective}) \approx 0.8708$.
7.105 a. No. The proportion of the population that is being sampled is $5000/40000 = 0.125$, which is more than 5%. **b.** $\mu = 27.5$ and $\sigma = 4.465$ **c.** No. Since n is being doubled, the standard deviation, which is $\sqrt{np(1 - p)}$, is multiplied by $\sqrt{2}$.
7.107 a. 0.7 **b.** 0.45 **c.** 0.55 **d.** 0.71 **e.** 0.65 **f.** 0.45
7.109 a. 0.64 **b.** 0.256 **c.** 0.02048 **d.** In order for it to take y selections to find two acceptable batteries, the first $y - 1$ batteries must include exactly 1 acceptable battery (and, therefore, $y - 2$ unacceptable batteries), and the yth battery must be acceptable. There are $y - 1$ ways in which the first $y - 1$ batteries can include exactly 1 acceptable battery. So $p(y) = (y - 1)(0.8)^1(0.2)^{y-2} \cdot (0.8) = (y - 1)(0.2)^{y-2}(0.8)^2$.
7.111 a. 0.5934 **b.** $P(x < 25) = 0.0000$. Yes, you are very unlikely to select a car of this model with a fuel efficiency of less than 25 mpg. **c.** $P(x > 32) = 0.0475$. So, if three cars are selected, the probability that they all have fuel efficiencies more than 32 mpg is $(0.0475)^3 = 0.0001$. **d.** 28.026
7.113 $\sigma_x^2 = 2.52$, $\sigma_x = 1.587$
7.115 a. 0.9876 **b.** 0.9888 **c.** 6.608
7.117 a. No, since 5 feet 7 inches is 67 inches, and if x = height of a randomly chosen woman, then $P(x < 67) = 0.6915$, which is not more than 94%. **b.** About 69%
7.119 a.

w	0	1	2	3	4	5
$p(w)$	1/6	5/18	2/9	1/6	1/9	1/18

b. 1.944 hours
7.121 a. 0.1552 **b.** 0.2688
c.

x	4	5	6	7
$p(x)$	0.1552	0.2688	0.29952	0.27648

d. 5.697
7.123 The lowest score to be designated an A is 85.28. Since 89 > 85.28,yes, I received an A.
7.125 658 hours

Cumulative Review 7

CR7.3 No. The percentages given in the graph are said to be, for each year, the "percent increase in the number of communities installing" red-light cameras. This presumably means the percentage increase in the number of communities with red-light cameras *installed*, in which case the positive results for all of the years 2003 to 2009 show that a great many more communities had red-light cameras installed in 2009 than in 2002.
CR7.5 0.1243
CR7.7 $P(\text{Service 1}|\text{Late}) = 0.349$ and $P(\text{Service 2}|\text{Late}) = 0.651$. Service 2 is more likely to have been used.
CR7.9 1. $P(M) = 0.021$ 2. $P(M|B) = 0.043$ 3. $P(M|W) = 0.07$
CR7.13 a. 0.09 **b.** 0.045 **c.** 0.135 **d.** 0.667
CR7.15 a. $\mu_x = 2.3$. **b.** $\sigma_x^2 = 0.81$, $\sigma_x = 0.9$
CR7.17 Let x be the number of correct identifications. Assume that the graphologist was merely guessing—in other words, that the probability of success on each trial was 0.5. Then $P(x \geq 6) = 0.377$. Since this probability is not particularly small, it would not have been unlikely for him/her to get six or more correct

identifications when guessing. No ability to distinguish the handwriting of psychotics is indicated.
CR7.19 **a.** 0.1587 **b.** 51.4 minutes **c.** 41.65 minutes
CR7.21 **b.** Positive **c.** Yes. If a symmetrical distribution were required, then a transformation would be advisable.

Chapter 8

8.1 A population characteristic is a quantity that summarizes the whole population. A statistic is a quantity calculated from the values in a sample.
8.3 **a.** Population characteristic **b.** Statistic **c.** Population characteristic **d.** Statistic **e.** Statistic
8.5 Answers will vary.
8.7 **a.**

$\bar{x}$	1.5	2	2.5	3	3.5
$p(\bar{x})$	1/6	1/6	1/3	1/6	1/6

b.

$\bar{x}$	1	1.5	2	2.5	3	3.5	4
$p(\bar{x})$	1/16	1/8	3/16	1/4	3/16	1/8	1/16

c. Both distributions are symmetrical, and their means are equal (2.5). However, the "with replacement" version has a greater spread than the first distribution, with values ranging from 1 to 4 in the "with replacement" distribution and from 1.5 to 3.5 in the "without replacement" distribution. The stepped pattern of the "with replacement" distribution more closely resembles a normal distribution than does the shape of the "without replacement" distribution.
8.9

$\bar{x}$	$2^2/_3$	3	$3^1/_3$	$3^2/_3$
$p(\bar{x})$	0.1	0.4	0.3	0.2

Sample Median	3	4
p(Sample Median)	0.7	0.3

(Max + Min)/2	2.5	3	3.5
p((Max + Min)/2)	0.1	0.5	0.4

The means of the three statistics are $\mu_{\bar{x}} = 3.2$, $\mu_{\text{median}} = 3.3$, and $\mu_{(\text{Max}+\text{Min})/2} = 3.15$. Since $\mu = 3.2$ and $\mu_{\bar{x}} = 3.2$, $\bar{x}$ is an unbiased estimator of μ, which is not the case for either of the two other statistics. Since the distribution of the sample mean has less variability than either of the other two sampling distributions, the sample mean will tend to produce values that are *closer* to μ than the values produced by either of the other statistics.
8.11 The sampling distribution of $\bar{x}$ will be approximately normal for the sample sizes in Parts (c)–(f), since those sample sizes are all greater than or equal to 30.
8.13 **a.** $\mu_{\bar{x}} = 40$, $\sigma_{\bar{x}} = 0.625$, approximately normal **b.** 0.5762 **c.** 0.2628
8.15 **a.** $\mu_{\bar{x}} = 2$, $\sigma_{\bar{x}} = 0.267$ **b.** In each case $\mu_{\bar{x}} = 2$. When $n = 20$, $\sigma_{\bar{x}} = 0.179$, and when $n = 100$, $\sigma_{\bar{x}} = 0.08$. All three centers are the same, and the larger the sample size, the smaller the standard deviation of $\bar{x}$. Since the distribution of $\bar{x}$ when $n = 100$ is the one with the smallest standard deviation of the three, this sample size is most likely to result in a value of $\bar{x}$ close to μ.
8.17 **a.** 0.8185, 0.0013 **b.** 0.9772, 0.0000
8.19 $P(0.49 < \bar{x} < 0.51) = 0.9974$; the probability that the manufacturing line will be shut down unnecessarily is $1 - 0.9974 = 0.0026$.
8.21 Approximately 0.
8.23 **a.** $\mu_{\hat{p}} = 0.65$, $\sigma_{\hat{p}} = 0.151$. **b.** $\mu_{\hat{p}} = 0.65$, $\sigma_{\hat{p}} = 0.107$. **c.** $\mu_{\hat{p}} = 0.65$, $\sigma_{\hat{p}} = 0.087$. **d.** $\mu_{\hat{p}} = 0.65$, $\sigma_{\hat{p}} = 0.067$. **e.** $\mu_{\hat{p}} = 0.65$, $\sigma_{\hat{p}} = 0.048$. **f.** $\mu_{\hat{p}} = 0.65$, $\sigma_{\hat{p}} = 0.034$.
8.25 **a.** $\mu_{\hat{p}} = 0.65$, $\sigma_{\hat{p}} = 0.026$ **b.** No, since $np = 100(0.07) = 7$, which is not greater than or equal to 10. **c.** The mean is unchanged, but the standard deviation changes to $\sigma_{\hat{p}} = 0.018$ **d.** Yes, since $np = 14$ and $n(1 - p) = 186$, which are both greater than or equal to 10. **e.** 0.0485
8.27 **a.** $\mu_{\hat{p}} = 0.005$, $\sigma_{\hat{p}} = 0.007$
b. No, since $np = 0.5$, which is not greater than or equal to 10.
c. We need both np and $n(1 - p)$ to be greater than or equal to 10; need $n \geq 2000$.
8.29 **a.** If $p = 0.5$, $\mu_{\hat{p}} = 0.5$, $\sigma_{\hat{p}} = 0.0333$, approximately normal. If $p = 0.6$, $\mu_{\hat{p}} = 0.6$, $\sigma_{\hat{p}} = 0.0327$, approximately normal. **b.** If $p = 0.5$, $P(\hat{p} \geq 0.6) = 0.0013$. If $p = 0.6$, $P(\hat{p}|0.6) = 0.5$. **c.** For a larger sample size, the value of $\hat{p}$ is likely to be closer to p. So, for $n = 400$, when $p = 0.5$, $P(\hat{p} \geq 0.6)$ will be smaller. When $p = 0.6$, $P(\hat{p} \geq 0.6)$ will still be 0.5, and it will remain the same.
8.31 **a.** 0.9744 **b.** Approximately 0
8.33 **a.** $\bar{x}$ is approximately normally distributed with mean 50 and standard deviation 0.1. **b.** 0.9876 **c.** 0.5
8.35 **a.** 0.8185 **b.** 0.8357, 0.9992
8.37 0.0793

Chapter 9

9.1 Statistics II and III are preferable to Statistic I since they are unbiased (their means are equal to the value of the population characteristic). However, Statistic II is preferable to Statistic III since its standard deviation is smaller. So Statistic II should be recommended.
9.3 $\hat{p} = 0.277$
9.5 $\hat{p} = 0.7$
9.7 **a.** $\bar{x} = 421.429$ **b.** $s^2 = 10414.286$ **c.** $s = 102.050$. No, s is not an unbiased statistic for estimating σ.
9.9 **a.** $\bar{x} = 120.6$ therms **b.** The value of τ is estimated to be 10000(120.6) = 1,206,000 therms. **c.** $\hat{p} = 0.8$ **d.** sample median = 120 therms
9.11 **a.** 1.96 **b.** 1.645 **c.** 2.58 **d.** 1.28 **e.** 1.44
9.13 **a.** The larger the confidence level, the wider the interval. **b.** The larger the sample size, the narrower the interval. **c.** Values of $\hat{p}$ further from 0.5 give smaller values of $\hat{p}(1 - \hat{p})$. Therefore, the further the value of $\hat{p}$ from 0.5, the narrower the interval.
9.15 (0.877, 0.923). We are 99% confident that the proportion of all drivers who have engaged in careless or aggressive driving in the last six months is between 0.877 and 0.923.
9.17 (0.675, 0.705). We are 98% confident that the proportion of all coastal residents who would evacuate is between 0.675 and 0.705. If we were to take a large number of random samples of size 5046, about 98% of the resulting confidence intervals would contain the true proportion of all coastal residents who would evacuate.
9.19 **a.** (0.642, 0.677). We are 90% confident that the proportion of all Americans age 8 to 18 who own a cell phone is between 0.642 and 0.677. **b.** (0.745, 0.776). We are 90% confident that the proportion of all Americans age 8 to 18 who own an MP3 player is between 0.745 and 0.776. **c.** The interval in Part (b) is narrower than

the interval in Part (a) because the sample proportion in Part (b) is further from 0.5.
9.21 a. (0.660, 0.740). We are 95% confident that the proportion of all potential jurors who regularly watch at least one crime-scene investigation series is between 0.660 and 0.740. **b.** Wider
9.23 a. (0.223, 0.298). We are 95% confident that the proportion of all U.S. businesses that have fired workers for misuse of the Internet is between 0.223 and 0.298. **b.** The estimated standard error is smaller and the confidence level is lower.
9.25 0.024. We are 95% confident that proportion of all adults who believe that the shows are either "totally made up" or "mostly distorted" is within 0.024 of the sample proportion of 0.82.
9.27 We are 95% confident that proportion of all adult drivers who would say that they often or sometimes talk on a cell phone while driving is within $1.96\sqrt{\hat{p}(1-\hat{p})/n} = 0.030$ (that is, 3.0 percentage points) of the sample proportion of 0.36.
9.29 a. (0.119, 0.286). We are 95% confident that the proportion of all patients under 50 years old who experience a failure within the first 2 years after receiving this type of defibrillator is between 0.119 and 0.286. **b.** (0.011, 0.061). We are 99% confident that the proportion of all patients age 50 or older who experience a failure within the first 2 years after receiving this type of defibrillator is between 0.011 and 0.061. **c.** Using the estimate of p from the study, 18/89, the required sample size is $n = 688.685$. A sample of size at least 689 is required.
9.31 A sample size of 2401 is required.
9.33 A sample size of 385 is required.
9.35 a. 2.12 **b.** 1.80 **c.** 2.81 **d.** 1.71 **e.** 1.78 **f.** 2.26
9.37 The second interval is based on the larger sample size; the interval is narrower.
9.39 a. (7.411, 8.069). **b.** (41.439, 44.921).
9.41 a. The fact that the mean is much greater than the median suggests that the distribution of times spent volunteering in the sample was positively skewed. **b.** With the sample mean much greater than the sample median, and with the sample regarded as representative of the population, it seems very likely that the population is strongly positively skewed and, therefore, not normally distributed. **c.** Since $n = 1086 \geq 30$, the sample size is large enough for us to use the t confidence interval, even though the population distribution is not approximately normal. **d.** (5.232, 5.968). We are 98% confident that the mean time spent volunteering for the population of parents of school-age children is between 5.232 and 5.968 hours.
9.43 a. Narrower. **b.** The statement is not correct. The population mean, μ, is a constant, and therefore, we cannot talk about the probability that it falls within a certain interval. **c.** The statement is not correct. We can say that *on average* 95 out of every 100 samples will result in confidence intervals that will contain μ, but we cannot say that in 100 such samples, *exactly* 95 will result in confidence intervals that contain μ.
9.45 a. The samples from 12 to 23 month and 24 to 35 month are the ones with the greater variability. **b.** The less-than-12-month sample is the one with the greater sample size. **c.** The new interval has a 99% confidence level.
9.47 a. (179.02, 186.98). We are 95% confident that the mean summer weight is between 179.02 and 186.98 pounds.
b. (185.423, 194.577). We are 95% confident that the mean winter weight is between 185.423 and 194.577 pounds. **c.** Based on the Frontier Airlines data, neither recommendation is likely to be an accurate estimate of the mean passenger weight, since 190 is not contained in the confidence interval for the mean summer weight and 195 is not contained in the confidence interval for the mean winter weight.
9.49 A boxplot shows that the distribution of the sample values is negatively skewed, and so the population may not be not approximately normally distributed. Therefore, since the sample is small, it is not appropriate to use the t confidence interval method of this section.
9.51 A reasonable estimate of σ is given by (sample range)/4 = 162.5. A sample size of 1015 is needed.
9.53 First, we need to know that the information is based on a random sample of middle-income consumers age 65 and older. Second, it would be useful if some sort of margin of error was given for the estimated mean of $10,235.
9.55 a. The paper states that queens flew for an *average of* 24.2 ± 9.21 minutes on their mating flights, and so this interval is a confidence interval for a population mean. **b.** (3.301, 5.899).
9.57 (0.217, 0.475).
9.59 The standard error for the mean cost for Native Americans is much larger than that for Hispanics since the sample size was much smaller for Native Americans.
9.61 (0.586, 0.714). We are 90% confident that the proportion of all Utah residents who favor fluoridation is between 0.586 and 0.714. Since the whole of this interval is above 0.5, the interval is consistent with the statement that fluoridation is favored by a clear majority of Utah residents.
9.63 (0.144, 0.189).
9.65 A sample size of 97 is required.
9.67 A sample size of 246 is required.
9.69 20.004 days
9.71 (8.571, 9429)
9.73 (17.899, 25.901)

Chapter 10

10.1 $\bar{x}$ is a *sample* statistic.
10.3 H_a: $\mu > 100$ will be used.
10.7 H_0: $p = 0.5$ H_a: $p > 0.5$
10.9 H_0: $p = 0.5$ H_a: $p > 0.5$
10.11 H_0: $\mu = 40$ H_a: $\mu \neq 40$
10.13 a. Type I error, 0.091 **b.** 0.097
10.15 a. A Type I error would be concluding the man is not the father when in fact he is. A Type II error would be concluding the man is the father when in fact he is not the father.
b. $\alpha = 0.001$, $\beta = 0$ **c.** $\beta = 0.008$
10.17 a. A Type I error concluding that there is evidence that more than 1% of a shipment is defective when in fact (at least) 1% of the shipment is defective. A Type II error is not being convinced that more than 1% of a shipment is defective when in fact more than 1% of the shipment is defective. **b.** Type II **c.** Type I
10.19 a. Before filing charges of false advertising against the company, the consumer advocacy group would require convincing evidence that more than 10% of the flares are defective.
10.21 a. The researchers failed to reject H_0. **b.** Type II error **c.** Yes
10.23 a. A P-value of 0.0003 means that it is very unlikely (probability = 0.0003), assuming that H_0 is true, that you would get a sample result at least as inconsistent with H_0 as the one obtained in the study. Thus, H_0 is rejected. **b.** A P-value of 0.350 means that it is not particularly unlikely (probability = 0.350), assuming that H_0 is true, that you would get a sample result at least as inconsistent with H_0 as the one obtained in the study. Thus, there is no reason to reject H_0.

10.25 **a.** H_0 is not rejected. **b.** H_0 is not rejected. **c.** H_0 is not rejected. **d.** H_0 is rejected. **e.** H_0 is not rejected. **f.** H_0 is not rejected.
10.27 **a.** Not appropriate **b.** Is appropriate **c.** Is appropriate **d.** Not appropriate
10.29 **a.** $z = 2.530$, P-value $= 0.0057$, reject H_0 **b.** No. The survey only included women age 22 to 35.
10.31 $z = 6.647$, P-value ≈ 0, reject H_0
10.33 $z = 2.236$, P-value $= 0.0127$, reject H_0
10.35 $z = 15.436$, P-value ≈ 0, reject H_0
10.37 $z = 0.791$, P-value $= 0.2146$, fail to reject H_0
10.39 **a.** $z = -1.897$, P-value $= 0.0289$, reject H_0 **b.** $z = -0.6$, P-value $= 0.274$, fail to reject H_0 **c.** Both results *suggest* that fewer than half of adult Americans believe that movie quality is getting worse. However, getting 470 out of 1000 people responding this way (as opposed to 47 out of 100) provides much *stronger* evidence of this fact.
10.41 The "38%" value given in the article is a proportion of *all* felons; in other words, it is a *population* proportion. Therefore, we know that the population proportion is less than 0.4, and there is no need for a hypothesis test.
10.43 **a.** 0.484 **b.** 0.686 **c.** 0.025 **d.** 0.000 **e.** 0.097
10.45 **a.** H_0 is rejected. **b.** H_0 is not rejected. **c.** H_0 is not rejected.
10.47 **a.** $t = 0.748$, P-value $= 0.468$, fail to reject H_0 **b.** $t = 8.731$, P-value ≈ 0, reject H_0
10.49 $t = 2.417$, P-value $= 0.010$, reject H_0
10.51 $t = 14.266$, P-value ≈ 0, reject H_0
10.53 $t = -5.001$, P-value ≈ 0, reject H_0
10.55 **a.** $t = 1.265$, P-value $= 0.103$, fail to reject H_0 **b.** $t = 3.162$, P-value $= 0.001$, reject H_0
10.57 **a.** Yes. Since the pattern in the normal probability plot is roughly linear, and since the sample was a random sample from the population, the t test is appropriate. **b.** The boxplot shows a median of around 245, and since the distribution is a roughly symmetrical distribution, this tells us that the sample mean is also around 245. This might initially suggest that the population mean differs from 240. But, the sample is relatively small, and the sample values range all the way from 225 to 265; such a sample mean would still be feasible if the population mean were 240. **c.** $t = 1.212$, P-value $= 0.251$, fail to reject H_0
10.59 **a.** Increasing the sample size increases the power. **b.** Increasing the significance level increases the power.
10.61 **a.** 0.1003 **b.** 0.2358 **c.** 0.0001 **d.** Power when $\mu = 9.8$ is $1 - 0.2358 = 0.7642$; power when $\mu = 9.5$ is $1 - 0.0001 = 0.9999$.
10.63 **a.** $t = 0.466$, P-value $= 0.329$, fail to reject H_0 **b.** $\beta \approx 0.75$ **c.** Power $\approx 1 - 0.75 = 0.25$
10.65 **a.** $\beta \approx 0.04$ **b.** $\beta \approx 0.04$ **c.** $\beta \approx 0.24$ **d.** $\beta \approx 0$ **e.** $\beta \approx 0.04$ **f.** $\beta \approx 0.01$
10.67 **a.** $z = 3.370$, P-value $= 0.0004$, reject H_0
10.69 $z = -11.671$, P-value ≈ 0, reject H_0
10.71 $t = -5.051$, P-value ≈ 0, reject H_0
10.73 $z = 1.069$, P-value $= 0.143$, fail to reject H_0
10.75 $z = -1.927$, P-value $= 0.027$, reject H_0
10.77 $t = -0.599$, P-value $= 0.277$, fail to reject H_0
10.79 $z = 4.186$, P-value ≈ 0, reject H_0
10.81 $t = -5.324$, P-value ≈ 0, reject H_0

Cumulative Review 10

CR10.3 **a.** Three airlines stand out from the rest and have large numbers of delayed flights. These airlines are ExpressJet, Delta, and Continental, with 93, 81, and 72 delayed flights, respectively. **b.** A typical number of flights delayed per 100,000 flights is around 1.1, with most rates lying between 0 and 1.6. Four airlines stand out from the rest and have high rates, with two of those four having *particularly* high rates. **c.** The rate per 100,000 flights data should be used, since this measures the likelihood of any given flight being late. An airline could stand out in the number of flights delayed data purely as a result of having a large number of flights.
CR10.5 **a.** 0.134 **b.** 0.041 **c.** $\mu_x = 25$, $\sigma_x = 4.330$ **d.** 0.102
CR10.7 **a.** 0.4 **b.** 0.18 **c.** 0.26 **d.** 0.45 **e.** Since anyone who accepts a job offer must have received at least one job offer, $P(O|A) = 1$. **f.** 0.18
CR10.9 **a.** (0.244, 0.416). We are 95% confident that the proportion of all U.S. medical residents who work moonlighting jobs is between 0.244 and 0.416. **b.** (0.131, 0.252). We are 90% confident that the proportion of all U.S. medical residents who have credit card debt of more than $3000 is between 0.131 and 0.252. **c.** The interval in Part (a) is wider than the interval in Part (b) because the confidence level in Part (a) (95%) is greater than the confidence level in Part (b) (90%) and because the sample proportion in Part (a) (38/115) is closer to 0.5 than the sample proportion in Part (b) (22/115).
CR10.11 A reasonable estimate of σ is given by (sample range)/4 = 0.1. A sample size of 385 is needed.
CR10.13 $z = 7.557$, P-value ≈ 0, reject H_0
CR10.15 **a.** With a sample mean of 14.6, the sample standard deviation of 11.6 places zero just over one standard deviation below the mean. Since no teenager can spend a negative time online, to get a typical deviation from the mean of just over 1, there must be values that are substantially more than one standard deviation above the mean. This suggests that the distribution of online times in the sample is positively skewed. **b.** $t = 9.164$, P-value ≈ 0, reject H_0

Chapter 11

11.1 The distribution of $\bar{x}_1 - \bar{x}_2$ is approximately normal with mean 5 and standard deviation 0.529.
11.3 **a.** We need to assume that the 22 heart attack patients who were dog owners formed a random sample from the set of all heart attack patients who are dog owners and that the 80 heart attack patients who did not own a dog formed an independent random sample from the set of all heart attack patients who do not own a dog. Also, since the sample of size 22 is not large, we need to assume that the distribution of the HRVs of all heart attack patients who are dog owners is approximately normal. **b.** $t = 2.237$, P-value $= 0.032$, reject H_0
11.5 **a.** Since boxplots are roughly symmetrical and since there is no outlier in either sample, the assumption of normality is justified, and it is reasonable to carry out a two-sample t test. **b.** $t = 3.332$, P-value $= 0.001$, reject H_0 **c.** (0.423, 2.910). We are 98% confident that the difference between the mean number of hours per day spent using electronic media in 2009 and 1999 is between 0.423 and 2.910.
11.7 $t = -0.445$, P-value $= 0.660$, fail to reject H_0
11.9 **a.** If the vertebroplasty group had been compared to a group of patients who did not receive any treatment, and if, for example, the people in the vertebroplasty group experienced a greater pain reduction on average than the people in the "no treatment" group, then it

would be impossible to tell whether the observed pain reduction in the vertebroplasty group was caused by the treatment or merely by the subjects' knowledge that some treatment was being applied. By using a placebo group, it is ensured that the subjects in both groups have the knowledge of some "treatment," so that any differences between the pain reduction in the two groups can be attributed to the nature of the vertebroplasty treatment. **b.** $(-0.687, 1.287)$. We are 95% confident that the difference in mean pain intensity 3 days after treatment for the vertebroplasty treatment and the fake treatment is between -0.687 and 1.287. **c.** $(-1.186, 0.786)$. We are 95% confident that the difference in mean pain intensity 14 days after treatment for the vertebroplasty treatment and the fake treatment is between -1.186 and 0.786. $(-1.722, 0.322)$. We are 95% confident that the difference in mean pain intensity 1 month after treatment for the vertebroplasty treatment and the fake treatment is between -1.722 and 0.322. **d.** The fact that all of the intervals contain zero tells us that we do not have convincing evidence of a difference in the mean pain intensity for the vertebroplasty treatment and the fake treatment at any of the three times.

11.11 $t = 1.065$, $P\text{-value} \approx 0.288$, fail to reject H_0

11.13 **a.** μ_1 = mean payment for claims not involving errors; μ_2 = mean payment for claims involving errors; H_0: $\mu_1 - \mu_2 = 0$; H_a: $\mu_1 - \mu_2 < 0$ **b.** Answer: (ii) 2.65. Since the samples are large, we are using a t distribution with a large number of degrees of freedom, which can be approximated with the standard normal distribution. $P(z > 2.65) = 0.004$, which is the P-value given. None of the other possible values of t gives the correct P-value.

11.15 **a.** $(-68.668, -19.299)$ **b.** $t = 2.762$, $P\text{-value} = 0.015$, reject H_0

11.17 **a.** $t = 10.359$, $P\text{-value} \approx 0$, reject H_0 **b.** $t = -16.316$, $P\text{-value} \approx 0$, reject H_0 **c.** $t = 4.690$, $P\text{-value} \approx 0$, reject H_0 **d.** The results do seem to provide convincing evidence of a gender basis in the monkeys' choices of how much time to spend playing with each toy, with the male monkeys spending significantly more time with the "masculine toy" than the female monkeys, and with the female monkeys spending significantly more time with the "feminine toy" than the male monkeys. However, the data also provide convincing evidence of a difference between male and female monkeys in the time they choose to spend playing with a "neutral toy." It is possible that it was some attribute other than masculinity/femininity in the toys that was attracting the different genders of monkey in different ways. **e.** The given mean time playing with the police car and mean time playing with the doll for female monkeys are sample means for the same sample of female monkeys. The two-sample t test can only be performed when there are two independent random samples.

11.19 **a.** Since the samples are small it is necessary to know—or to assume—that the distributions from which the random samples were taken are normal. However, in this case, since both standard deviations are large compared to the means, it seems unlikely that these distributions would have been normal. **b.** Since the samples are large, it is appropriate to carry out the two-sample t test. **c.** $t = -2.207$, $P\text{-value} = 0.030$, fail to reject H_0

11.21 **a.** $t = -9.863$, $P\text{-value} \approx 0$, reject H_0 **b.** For the two-sample t test, $t = -9.979$, $\text{df} = 22.566$, and $P\text{-value} \approx 0$. Thus, the conclusion is the same.

11.23 For each pipe, one side (left/right) could be coated with the first type of coating, and the other side could be coated with the other type of coating, with the sides chosen at random for each pipe. Then, the two coatings are being tested under almost exactly equal conditions in terms of the extraneous variables mentioned.

11.25 $t = -0.515$, $P\text{-value} = 0.612$, fail to reject H_0

11.27 **a.** $t = -3.106$, $P\text{-value} = 0.006$, reject H_0 **b.** $(-2.228, -0.852)$.

11.29 **a.** $t = 4.451$, $P\text{-value} \approx 0$, reject H_0 **b.** $(-0.210, 0.270)$. **c.** $t = 3.094$, $P\text{-value} = 0.001$, reject H_0 **d.** In Part (a), the male profile heights and the male actual heights are paired (according to which individual has the actual height and the height stated in the profile), and with paired samples, we use the paired t test. In Part (c), we were dealing with two independent samples (the sample of males and the sample of females), and therefore, the two-sample t test was appropriate.

11.31 $t = -2.457$, $P\text{-value} = 0.018$, reject H_0

11.33 **a.** $t = 4.321$, $P\text{-value} \approx 0$, reject H_0 **b.** $t = 1.662$, $P\text{-value} = 0.055$, fail to reject H_0 **c.** A smaller standard deviation in the sample of differences means that we have a lower estimate of the standard deviation of the population of differences. Assuming that the mean wrist extensions for the two mouse types are the same (in other words, that the mean of the population of differences is zero), a sample mean difference of as much as 8.82 is much less likely when the standard deviation of the population of differences is around 10 than when the standard deviation of the population of differences is around 26.

11.35 $P\text{-value} = 0.001$, reject H_0

11.37 $z = -1.667$, $P\text{-value} = 0.048$, reject H_0

11.39 **a.** $z = 1.172$, $P\text{-value} = 0.121$, fail to reject H_0 **b.** $(-0.036, 0.096)$. We are 99% confident that the difference between the proportion of Gen Y and the proportion of Gen X who made a donation via text message is between -0.036 and 0.096. In repeated sampling with random samples of size 400, approximately 99% of the resulting confidence intervals would contain the true difference in proportions who donated via text message.

11.41 **a.** $z = -0.298$, $P\text{-value} = 0.766$, fail to reject H_0 **b.** $z = -2.022$, $P\text{-value} = 0.043$, reject H_0 **c.** Assuming that the population proportions are equal, you are much less likely to get a difference in sample proportions as large as the one given when the samples are very large than when the samples are relatively small.

11.43 **a.** $(-0.078, 0.058)$. **b.** Zero is included in the confidence interval. This tells us that there is not convincing evidence of a difference between the proportions.

11.45 No. It is not appropriate to use the two-sample z test because the groups are not large enough. We are not told the sizes of the groups, but we know that each is, at most, 81. The sample proportion for the fish oil group is 0.05, and $81(0.05) = 4.05$, which is less than 10. So, the conditions for the two-sample z test are not satisfied.

11.47 $z = 0.767$, $P\text{-value} = 0.443$, fail to reject H_0

11.49 $(0.018, 0.082)$. Zero is not included in the confidence interval. This means that we have convincing evidence at the 0.05 significance level of a difference between the proportions of people owning MP3 players in 2006 and 2005.

11.51 $z = 6.306$, $P\text{-value} \approx 0$, reject H_0

11.53 $z = 3.800$, $P\text{-value} \approx 0$, reject H_0

11.55 **a.** $z = 9.169$, $P\text{-value} \approx 0$, reject H_0 **b.** No. Since this is an observational study, causation cannot be inferred from the result.

11.57 Since the data given are population characteristics, an inference procedure is not applicable. It is *known* that the rate of Lou Gehrig's disease among soldiers sent to the war is higher than for those not sent to the war.

11.59 **b.** If we want to know whether the e-mail intervention *reduces* (as opposed to *changes*) adolescents' display of risk behavior in their profiles, then we use one-sided alternative hypotheses and the P-values are halved. If that is the case, using a 0.05 significance level, we are convinced that the intervention is effective with regard to reduction of references to sex and that the proportion showing any of the three protective changes is greater for those receiving the e-mail intervention. Each of the other two apparently reduced proportions could have occurred by chance.

11.61 **a.** $t = -6.565$, P-value ≈ 0, reject H_0 **b.** $t = 6.249$, P-value ≈ 0, reject H_0 **c.** $t = 0.079$, P-value $= 0.937$, fail to reject H_0. This does not imply that students and faculty consider it acceptable to talk on a cell phone during class; in fact, the low sample mean ratings for both students and faculty show that both groups, on the whole, feel that the behavior is inappropriate.

11.63 **a.** $t = -17.382$, P-value ≈ 0, reject H_0 **b.** $t = 2.440$, P-value $= 0.030$, reject H_0 **c.** No, the paired t test would not be appropriate since the treatment and control groups were not paired samples.

11.65 $z = 4.245$, P-value ≈ 0, reject H_0

11.67 **a.** $t = -11.952$, P-value ≈ 0, reject H_0 **b.** $t = -68.803$, P-value ≈ 0, reject H_0 **c.** $t = 0.698$, P-value $= 0.494$, fail to reject H_0

11.69 $t = 0.856$, P-value $= 0.210$, fail to reject H_0

11.71 $t = -1.336$, P-value $= 0.193$, fail to reject H_0

11.73 $z = -1.263$, P-value $= 0.103$, fail to reject H_0

11.75 $(-0.274, -0.082)$. We are 90% confident that $p_1 - p_2$ lies between -0.274 and -0.082, where p_1 is the proportion of children in the community with fluoridated water who have decayed teeth and p_2 is the proportion of children in the community without fluoridated water who have decayed teeth. The interval does not contain zero, which means that we have evidence at the 0.1 level of a difference between the proportions of children with decayed teeth in the two communities, and evidence at the 0.05 level that the proportion of children with decayed teeth is smaller in the community with fluoridated water.

11.77 **a.** $(-4.738, 22.738)$. **b.** $t = 0.140$, P-value $= 0.890$, fail to reject H_0 **c.** $t = -0.446$, P-value $= 0.330$, fail to reject H_0

11.79 **a.** $t = 3.948$, P-value ≈ 0, reject H_0 **b.** $t = -1.165$, P-value $= 0.249$, fail to reject H_0

11.81 $z = 5.590$, P-value ≈ 0, reject H_0

Chapter 12

12.1 **a.** P-value $= 0.024$; H_0 is not rejected. **b.** P-value $= 0.043$; H_0 is not rejected. **c.** P-value $= 0.035$; H_0 is not rejected. **d.** P-value $= 0.0002$; H_0 is rejected. **e.** P-value $= 0.172$; H_0 is not rejected.

12.3 **a.** P-value $= 0.0002 < 0.001$, so H_0 is rejected. **b.** The smallest expected count is $40(0.1) = 4$, which is less than 5. The chi-square test would not be appropriate.

12.5 $X^2 = 19.599$, P-value ≈ 0, reject H_0

12.7 $X^2 = 457.464$, P-value ≈ 0, reject H_0

12.9 **a.** $X^2 = 166.958$, P-value ≈ 0, reject H_0 **b.** $X^2 = 5.052$, P-value $= 0.025$, reject H_0

12.11 $X^2 = 25.486$, P-value ≈ 0, reject H_0

12.13 $X^2 = 1.469$, P-value $= 0.690$, fail to reject H_0

12.15 **a.** P-value $= 0.844$, fail to reject H_0 **b.** P-value $= 0.106$, fail to reject H_0

12.17 $X^2 = 29.507$, P-value $= 0.001$, reject H_0

12.19 **a.** $X^2 = 90.853$, P-value ≈ 0, reject H_0 **b.** The particularly high contributions to the chi-square statistic (in order of importance) come from the field of communication, languages, and cultural studies, in which there was a disproportionately high number of smokers; from the field of mathematics, engineering, and sciences, in which there was a disproportionately low number of smokers; and from the field of social science and human services, in which there was a disproportionately high number of smokers.

12.21 **a.** $X^2 = 2.314$, P-value $= 0.128$, fail to reject H_0 **b.** Yes **c.** Yes. Since P-value $= 0.127 > 0.05$, we do not reject H_0. **d.** The two P-values are almost equal; in fact, the difference between them is only due to rounding errors in the Minitab program.

12.23 **a.** $X^2 = 96.506$, P-value ≈ 0, reject H_0 **b.** The result of Part (a) tells us that the level of the gift seems to make a difference. Looking at the data given, 12% of those receiving no gift made a donation, 14% of those receiving a small gift made a donation, and 21% of those receiving a large gift made a donation. (These percentages can be compared to 16% making donations among the expected counts.) So, it seems that the most effective strategy is to include a large gift, with the small gift making very little difference compared to no gift at all.

12.25 $X^2 = 46.515$, P-value ≈ 0, reject H_0

12.27 $X^2 = 3.030$, P-value $= 0.387$, fail to reject H_0

12.29 $X^2 = 49.813$, P-value ≈ 0, reject H_0

12.31 $X^2 = 1.978$, P-value $= 0.372$, fail to reject H_0

12.33 **b.** $X^2 = 8.034$, P-value $= 0.005$, reject H_0

12.35 $X^2 = 1.08$, P-value $= 0.982$, fail to reject H_0

12.37 $X^2 = 881.360$, P-value ≈ 0, reject H_0

12.39 $X^2 = 4.035$, P-value $= 0.258$, fail to reject H_0

12.41 $X^2 = 10.976$, P-value < 0.001, reject H_0

12.43 $X^2 = 22.855$, P-value ≈ 0, reject H_0

12.45 **a.** $X^2 = 8216.476$, P-value ≈ 0, reject H_0 **b.** This could occur if the birthrate is higher for the time of year designated as "Capricorn" than it is for other times of the year. **c.** The total number of policyholders listed in the first table is 460,168. Therefore, for example, the proportion of policyholders born under Aquarius is 35666/460168. The total number of claims listed in the second table is 1000. So, if the numbers of claims were in proportion to the numbers of policyholders, then we would expect the number of claims for policyholders born under Aquarius to be $1000(35666/460168) = 77.506$. This is the expected count for Aquarius, and the other expected counts are calculated in a similar way. $X^2 = 10.748$, P-value $= 0.465$, fail to reject H_0

Chapter 13

13.1 **a.** $y = -5.0 + 0.017x$ **c.** 30.7 **d.** 0.017 **e.** 1.7 **f.** No, the model should not be used to predict outside the range of the data.

13.3 **a.** When $x = 15$, $\mu_y = 0.18$. When $x = 17$, $\mu_y = 0.186$. **b.** When $x = 15$, $P(y > 0.18) = 0.5$. **c.** When $x = 14$, $P(y > 0.175) = 0.655$, $P(y < 0.178) = 0.579$.

13.5 **a.** 47, 4700 **b.** 0.3156, 0.0643

13.7 **a.** 0.121 **b.** $s_e = 0.155$; This is a typical vertical deviation of a bone mineral density value in the sample from the value predicted by the least-squares line. **c.** 0.009 g/cm^2 **d.** 1.098 g/cm^2

13.9 **a.** $r^2 = 0.883$ **b.** $s_e = 13.682$, df $= 14$

13.11 **a.** The plot shows a linear pattern, and the vertical spread of points does not appear to be changing over the range of x values in the sample. If we assume that the distribution of errors at any given x value is approximately normal, then the simple linear regression model seems appropriate. **b.** $\hat{y} = -0.00227 + 1.247x$; when $x = 0.09, \hat{y} = 0.110$. **c.** $r^2 = 0.436$, 43.6% of the variation in market share can be explained by the linear regression model relating market share and advertising share. **d.** $s_e = 0.0263$, df = 8

13.13 a. 0.253 **b.** 0.179; no **c.** 4

13.15 a. 0.1537 **b.** (2.17, 2.83) **c.** Yes, the interval is relatively narrow.

13.17 a. $a = 592.1$, $b = 97.26$ **b.** When $x = 2, \hat{y} = 786.62$, $y - \hat{y} = -29.62$. **c.** (87.76, 106.76)

13.19 $t = -3.66$, P-value ≈ 0, reject H_0

13.21 a. (0.081, 0.199) We are 95% confident that the mean change in pleasantness rating associated with an increase of 1 impulse per second in firing frequency is between 0.081 and 0.199. **b.** $t = 5.451$, P-value = 0.001, reject H_0

13.23 a. $t = 6.493$, P-value ≈ 0, reject H_0 **b.** $t = 1.56$, P-value = 0.079, fail to reject H_0

13.25 $t = -17.57$, P-value ≈ 0, reject H_0

13.27 a. The plot supports the assumption that the simple linear regression model applies. **b.** Yes. Since the normal probability plot shows a roughly linear pattern, it is reasonable to assume that the error distribution is approximately normal.

13.29 a. $\hat{y} = 0.939 + 0.873x$ **b.** The standardized residual plot shows that there is one point that is a clear outlier (the point whose standardized residual is 3.721). This is the point for product 25. **c.** $\hat{y} = 0.703 + 0.918x$, removal of the point resulted in a reasonably substantial change in the equation of the estimated regression line. **d.** For every 1-cm increase in minimum width, the mean maximum width is estimated to increase by 0.918 cm. The intercept would be an estimate of the mean maximum width when the minimum width is zero. It is clearly impossible to have a container whose minimum width is zero. **e.** The pattern in this plot suggests that the variances of the y distributions decrease as x increases, and therefore that the assumption of constant variance is not valid.

13.31 a. There is one unusually large standardized residual, 2.52, for the point (164.2, 181). The point (387.8, 310) would seem to be an influential point. **b.** Apart from the one point that has a large residual, the arrangement of points in the residual plot seems consistent with the simple linear regression model. **c.** If we include the point with the unusually large standardized residual we might begin to suspect that the variances of the y distributions decrease as the x values increase. However, from the relatively small number of points included we do not have particularly strong evidence that the assumption of constant variance does not apply.

13.33 A *confidence* interval is an estimate of the mean value of y when $x = x^*$. A *prediction* interval is a prediction of an individual y value when $x = x^*$. A prediction level of 95% means that the prediction interval has been calculated using a method that has a 5% error rate.

13.35 a. 4.038 **b.** Since 3 is the same distance from 2.5 as is 2, $s_{a+b(3.0)} = s_{a+b(2.0)} = 4.038$. **c.** 3.817 **d.** $x^* = \bar{x} = 2.5$

13.37 a. (6.532, 6.570) We are 95% confident that the mean milk pH when the milk temperature is 40°C is between 6.532 and 6.570. **b.** (6.560, 6.616) **c.** No, 90 is outside the range of x values in the data set.

13.39 a. $\hat{y} = -0.001790 - 0.0021007x$ **b.** (−0.055, −0.032) **c.** (−0.097, 0.009) **d.** The answer to Part (b) gives an interval in which we are 90% confident that the *mean* brain volume change for people with a childhood blood lead level of 20 μg/dL lies. The answer to Part (c) states that if we were to find the brain volume change for *one person* with a childhood blood lead level of 20 μg/dL, we are 90% confident that this value will lie within the interval found.

13.41 a. $\hat{y} = -133.02 + 5.92x$ **b.** 1.127 **c.** Yes. Since the estimated slope is positive and since the P-value is small (given as 0.000 in the output) we have convincing evidence that the slope of the population regression line is positive. **d.** (173.252, 330.178) **e.** It would not be appropriate to use the estimated regression line to predict the clutch size for a salamander with a snout-vent length of 105, since 105 is far outside the range of the x values in the original data set.

13.43 a. $\hat{y} = 2.78551 + 0.04462x$ **b.** $t = 10.848$, P-value ≈ 0, reject H_0 **c.** (3.672, 4.576); we are 95% confident that the moisture content for a box of cereal that has been on the shelf for 30 days will be between 3.672 and 4.576 percent. **d.** Since 4.1 is included in the confidence interval constructed in Part (c), a moisture content exceeding 4.1 percent is quite plausible when the shelf time is 30 days.

13.45 a. (−0.397, −0.193) **b.** When $x = 0.5$: (−0.397, −.0193); when $x = 0.7$: (0.123, 0.323) **c.** The simultaneous confidence level would be $[100 - 2(1)]\% = 98\%$. **d.** The simultaneous confidence level would be $[100 - 3(5)]\% = 85\%$.

13.47 The statistic r is the correlation coefficient for a sample, while ρ denotes the correlation coefficient for the population.

13.49 $t = 2.073$, P-value = 0.039, reject H_0

13.51 a. $t = -6.175$, P-value ≈ 0, reject H_0 **b.** Since $r^2 = (-0.26)^2 = 0.0676$, only 6.76% of the observed variation in grade point average would be explained by the regression line. This is not a substantial percentage.

13.53 $t = 1.855$, P-value = 0.106, fail to reject H_0

13.55 a. The slope of the estimated regression line for y = verbal language score against x = height gain from age 11 to 16 is 2.0. This tells us that for each extra inch of height gain the average verbal language score at age 11 increased by 2.0 percentage points. The equivalent results for nonverbal language scores and math scores were 2.3 and 3.0. Thus the reported slopes are consistent with the statement that each extra inch of height gain was associated with an increase in test scores of between 2 and 3 percentage points. **b.** The slope of the estimated regression line for y = verbal language score against x = height gain from age 16 to 33 is −3.1. This tells us that for each extra inch of height gain the average verbal language score at age 11 decreased by 3.1 percentage points. The equivalent results for nonverbal language scores and math scores were both −3.8. Thus the reported slopes are consistent with the statement that each extra inch of height gain was associated with a decrease in test scores of between 3.1 and 3.8 percentage points. **c.** Between the ages of 11 and 16 the first boy grew 5 inches more than the second boy. So the first boy's age 11 math score is predicted to be $5 \cdot 3 = 15$ percentage points higher than that of the second boy. Between the ages of 16 and 33 the second boy grew 5 inches more than the first boy. According to this information the first boy's age 11 math score is predicted to be $5 \cdot 3.8 = 19$ percentage points higher than that of the second boy. These two results are consistent with the conclusion that on the whole boys who did their growing early had higher cognitive scores at age 11 than those whose growth occurred later.

13.57 a. With $t = -3.399$ and df = 345, P-value = 0.05. **b.** Yes, we expect that those with greater coping humor ratings would have smaller depression ratings. **c.** No. Since $r^2 = (-0.18)^2 = 0.0324$, we know that only 3.2% of the variation in depression scale values is attributable to the approximate linear relationship with the coping humor scale. So the linear regression model will generally not give accurate predictions.

13.59 **a.** $t = -6.090$, P-value ≈ 0, reject H_0 **b.** A 95% prediction interval is (−1.667, 7.856). Other prediction levels are possible. **c.** No. For $x = 10$ the least-squares line predicts $y = -2.58$. Since it is not possible to have a negative trail length, it is clear that the simple linear regression model does not apply at $x = 10$. So the simple linear regression model is not suitable for this prediction.
13.61 **a.** $t = 0.488$, P-value $= 0.633$, fail to reject H_0 **b.** A 95% confidence interval is (47.076, 54.106). Other confidence levels are possible
13.63 H_0: $\beta = \beta'$, H_a: $\beta \neq \beta'$, $t = -1.03457$, P-value $= 0.320$, fail to reject H_0; we do not have convincing evidence that the slopes of the population regression lines for the two different frog populations are not equal.
13.65 If the point (20, 33000) is not included, then the slope of the least-squares line would be relatively small and negative (appearing close to horizontal when drawn to the scales of the scatterplot given in the question). If the point is included then the slope of the least-squares line would still be negative, but much further from zero.
13.67 The small P-value indicates that there is convincing evidence of a useful linear relationship between percentage raise and productivity.
13.69 **a.** The values $e_1, \ldots, e_n$ are the vertical deviations of the y observations from the *population* regression line. The residuals are the vertical deviations from the *sample* regression line. **b.** False. The simple linear regression model states that the *mean* value of y is equal to $\alpha + \beta x$. **c.** No. You only test hypotheses about population characteristics; b is a sample statistic. **d.** Strictly speaking this statement is false, since a set of points lying exactly on a straight line will give a zero result for SSResid. However, it is certainly true to say that, since SSResid is a sum of squares, its value must be *nonnegative*. **e.** This is not possible, since the sum of the residuals is always zero. **f.** This is not possible, since SSResid (here said to be equal to 731) is always less than or equal to SSTo (here said to be 615).

Cumulative Review 13

CR13.1 Randomly assign the 400 students to two groups of equal size, Group A and Group B. Have the 400 students take the same course, attending the same lectures and being given the same homework assignments. The only difference between the two groups should be that the students in Group A should be given daily quizzes and the students in Group B should not. After the final exam the exam scores for the students in Group A should be compared to the exam scores for the students in Group B.
CR13.3 **b.** The two airlines with the highest numbers of fines assessed may not be the worst in terms of maintenance violations since these airlines might have more flights than the other airlines.
CR13.5 **a.** (0.651, 0.709) We are 95% confident that the proportion of all adult Americans who view a landline phone as a necessity is between 0.651 and 0.709. **b.** $z = 1.267$, P-value $= 0.103$, fail to reject H_0 **c.** $z = 9.513$, P-value ≈ 0, reject H_0
CR13.7 **a.** 0.62 **b.** 0.1216 **c.** 0.19 **d.** 0.0684
CR13.9 **b.** $\hat{y} = -12.887 + 21.126x$ **d.** $t = 21.263$, P-value ≈ 0, reject H_0
CR13.11 $X^2 = 26.175$, P-value ≈ 0, reject H_0
CR13.13 $X^2 = 15.106$, P-value $= 0.002$, reject H_0
CR13.15 $t = -113.17$, df $= 45$, P-value ≈ 0, reject H_0
CR13.17 $X^2 = 4.8$, P-value $= 0.684$, fail to reject H_0

Chapter 14

14.1 A deterministic model does not have the random deviation component e, while a probabilistic model does contain such a component.
14.3 **a.** (mean y value for fixed values of $x1$, $x2$, $x3$) $=$ $30 + 0.90x_1 + 0.08x_2 - 4.5x_3$
b. $\beta_0 = 30, \beta_1 = 0.9, \beta_2 = 0.08, \beta_3 = -4.50$ **c.** The average change in acceptable load associated with a 1-cm increase in left lateral bending, when grip endurance and trunk extension ratio are held fixed, is 0.90 kg. **d.** The average change in acceptable load associated with a 1 N/kg increase in trunk extension ratio, when grip endurance and left lateral bending are held fixed, is −4.5 kg. **e.** 23.5 **f.** 95%
14.5 **a.** 13.552 g. **b.** When length is fixed, the mean increase in weight associated with a 1-mm increase in width is 0.828 g. When width is fixed, the mean increase in weight associated with a 1-mm increase in length is 0.373 g.
14.7 **a.** 103.11 **b.** 96.87 **c.** $\beta_1 = -6.6$; 6.6 is the expected decrease in yield associated with a one-unit increase in mean temperature when the mean percentage of sunshine remains fixed. $\beta_2 = -4.5$; 4.5 is the expected decrease in yield associated with a one-unit increase in mean percentage of sunshine when mean temperature remains fixed.
14.9 **b.** Higher for $x = 10$ **c.** When the degree of delignification increases from 8 to 9 the mean chlorine content increases by 7. Mean chlorine content decreases by 1 when degree of delignification increases from 9 to 10.
14.11 **c.** The parallel lines in each graph are attributable to the lack of interaction between the two independent variables.
14.13
a. $y = \alpha + \beta_1x_1 + \beta_2x_2 + \beta_3x_3 + e$
b. $y = \alpha + \beta_1x_1 + \beta_2x_2 + \beta_3x_3 + \beta_4x_1^2 + \beta_5x_2^2 + \beta_6x_3^2 + e$
c. $y = \alpha + \beta_1x_1 + \beta_2x_2 + \beta_3x_3 + \beta_4x_1x_2 + e$;
$y = \alpha + \beta_1x_1 + \beta_2x_2 + \beta_3x_3 + \beta_4x_1x_3 + e$;
$y = \alpha + \beta_1x_1 + \beta_2x_2 + \beta_3x_3 + \beta_4x_2x_3 + e$
d. $y = \alpha + \beta_1x_1 + \beta_2x_2 + \beta_3x_3 + \beta_4x_1^2 + \beta_5x_2^2 + \beta_6x_3^2 + \beta_7x_1x_2 + \beta_8x_1x_3 + \beta_9x_2x_3 + e$
14.15 **a.** Three dummy variables would be needed to incorporate a nonnumerical variable with four categories. For example, you could define $x_3 = 1$ if the car is a subcompact and 0 otherwise, $x_4 = 1$ if the car is a compact and 0 otherwise, and $x_5 = 1$ if the car is a midsize and 0 otherwise. The model equation is then $y = \alpha + \beta_1x_1 + \beta_2x_2 + \beta_3x_3 + \beta_4x_4 + \beta_5x_5 + e$. **b.** For the variables defined in Part (a), $x_6 = x_1x_3$, $x_7 = x_1x_4$, and $x_8 = x_1x_5$ are the additional predictors needed to incorporate interaction between age and size class.
14.17 **a.** $0.01 < P$-value < 0.05 **b.** P-value > 0.10 **c.** P-value $= 0.01$ **d.** $0.001 < P$-value < 0.01
14.19 **a.** $F = 12118$, P-value ≈ 0, reject H_0 **b.** Since the P-value is small and r^2 is close to 1, there is strong evidence that the model is useful. **c.** The model in Part (b) should be recommended, since adding the variables x_1 and x_2 to the model [to obtain the model in Part (a)] only increases the value of R^2 a small amount (from 0.994 to 0.996).
14.21 $F = 24.41$, P-value < 0.001, reject H_0 and conclude that the model is useful.
14.23 $F = 3.5$, $0.01 < P$-value < 0.05, reject H_0 and conclude that the model is useful.
14.25 $F = 7.986$, P-value < 0.001, reject H_0 and conclude that the model is useful.

14.27 a. $\hat{y} = 1.44 - 0.0523 length + 0.00397 speed$ **b.** 1.3245 **c.** $F = 24.02$, P-value ≈ 0, reject H_0 and conclude that the model is useful. **d.** $\hat{y} = 1.59 - 1.40\left(\frac{length}{speed}\right)$ **e.** The model in part (a) has $R^2 = 0.75$ and R^2 adjusted $= 0.719$, whereas the model in part (d) has $R^2 = 0.543$ and R^2 adjusted $= 0.516$.
14.29 a. SSResid = 390.4347, SSTo = 1618.2093, SSRegr = 1227.7746 **b.** $R^2 = 0.759$; this means that 75.9% of the variation in the observed shear strength values has been explained by the fitted model. **c.** $F = 5.039$, $0.01 < P$-value < 0.05, reject H_0, and conclude that the model is useful.
14.31 $F = 96.64$, P-value < 0.001, reject H_0, and conclude that the model is useful.
14.35 $\hat{y} = 35.8 - 0.68x_1 + 1.28x_2$, $F = 18.95$, P-value < 0.001, reject H_0, and conclude that the model is useful.

Chapter 15

15.1 a. $0.001 < P$-value < 0.01 **b.** P-value > 0.10 **c.** P-value $= 0.01$ **d.** P-value < 0.001 **e.** $0.05 < P$-value < 0.10 **f.** $0.01 < P$-value < 0.05 (using $df_1 = 4$ and $df_2 = 60$)
15.3 a. $H_0: \mu_1 = \mu_2 = \mu_3 = \mu_4$, H_a: At least two of the four μ_i's are different. **b.** P-value $= 0.012$, fail to reject H_0 **c.** P-value $= 0.012$, fail to reject H_0
15.5 $F = 6.687$, P-value $= 0.001$, reject H_0
15.7 $F = 5.273$, P-value $= 0.002$, reject H_0
15.9 $F = 53.8$, P-value < 0.001, reject H_0
15.11 $F = 2.62$, $0.05 < P$-value < 0.10, fail to reject H_0
15.13

Source of Variation	df	Sum of Squares	Mean Square	F
Treatments	3	75,081.72	25,027.24	1.70
Error	16	235,419.04	14,713.69	
Total	19	310,500.76		

$F = 1.70$, P-value > 0.10, fail to reject H_0
15.15 Since there is a significant difference in all three of the pairs we need a set of intervals none of which includes zero. Set 3 is therefore the required set.
15.17 a. In *decreasing* order of the resulting mean numbers of pretzels eaten the treatments were: slides with related text, slides with no text, slides with unrelated text, and no slides. There were no significant differences between the results for slides with no text and slides with unrelated text, and for slides with unrelated text and no slides. However there was a significant difference between the results for slides with related text and each one of the other treatments, and between the results for no slides and for slides with no text (and for slides with related text). **b.** The results for the women and men are almost exactly the reverse of one another, with, for example, slides with related text (treatment 2) resulting in the smallest mean number of pretzels eaten for the women and the largest mean number of pretzels eaten for the men. For the men, treatment 2 was significantly different from all the other treatments; however for women treatment 2 was not significantly different from treatment 1. For both women and men there was a significant difference between treatments 1 and 4 and no significant difference between treatments 3 and 4. However, between treatments 1 and 3 there was a significant difference for the women but no significant difference for the men.
15.19 a.

	Driving	Shooting	Fighting
Sample mean	.42	4.00	5.30

(Driving and Shooting underlined together)

b.

	Driving	Shooting	Fighting
Sample mean	2.81	3.44	4.01

(Driving and Shooting underlined together; Shooting and Fighting underlined together)

15.21 a. $F = 45.64$, P-value ≈ 0, reject H_0 **b.** Yes; T-K interval is (0.388, 0.912)

Index

1 in *k* systematic sample, 45

A

A and B, 323
A or B, 323
Addition rule, general, 363–365
Additive multiple regression model, general, 802–803
Additive probabilistic model, 742–743
Adjusted coefficient of multiple determination (R^2), 819
Alternative hypothesis, 578–580
Ambiguity and survey questions, 72
ANOVA. *see* Single-factor analysis of variance (ANOVA)
Apgar score, 418–419, 421
Assumption of independence, 359
Axis, broken, 154

B

Bar chart
  activity, 25
  for categorical data, 14–15
  comparative. *see* Comparative bar chart
  other uses for, 102–104
Bayes, Thomas, 370
Bayes' Rule, 370–372
Bell-shaped curve, 128
Bernoulli, James, 332
Bias in sampling, 38–39
Binomial distribution
  defined, 430–437
  normal approximation to, 474–475
  normal approximation to and graphing calculators, 491–493
Binomial distribution formula, 434
Binomial experiment, 430–431
Binomial probability calculation (graphing calculator), 484–487
Binomial probability distribution
  binomial probabilities table and, 434–435
  defined, 430–432
  discrete random variables and, 434
  example, 432–433, 435–436
  sampling without replacement and, 435
Binomial random variable, 436–437
Bivariate data. *see also* Categorical data
  cautions and limitations, 298–299
  defined, 11
  example, 12
  examples of interpreting results of, 296–298
  reporting results of analysis of, 296
Bivariate data set
  defined, 139
  scatterplot of, 224–225, 226
  unusual points in, 253
Bivariate normal distribution, 784–786
Blocking
  defined, 53
  diagram of, 61
  example, 54
  extraneous variables and, 54
  overview, 50
  random assignment and, 62
Bound on error of estimation
  defined, 544–545
  sample size choice and, 558–559
Boxplot
  activity, 215
  comparative, 198
  graphing calculators and, 220
  modified, 196–198
  skeletal, 194–195
  small sample sizes and, 213

C

Cardano, Girolamo, 328
Categorical data
  activity, 158
  bar chart for, 14–15
  chi-square tests for, 700–708
  comparative bar charts and, 96–97
  defined, 11
  differences in counts and, 703
  frequency distribution for, 13–14
  notation for, 700–701
  numerical summary quantities for, 181
  pie charts and, 97–100
  summarizing results of, 712
Categorical data set, 699
Categorical variable
  with more than two categories, 811
  in multiple regression models, 809–811
  testing for independence, 718–722
Causation
  association and, 648–649
  correlation and, 232
Cause-and-effect, determining, 33–34
Cell count. *see also* Expected cell count; Observed cell count
  displaying, 714
  in a two-way frequency table, 712
Census, 38
Center of data set
  describing, 174
  interpreting, 200–206
Central Limit Theorem
  confidence intervals and, 550
  sampling distribution and, 509–510
Chance experiment, 320, 322
Chebyshev's Rule, 201–203
Chi-square distribution, 704
Chi-square statistic
  formula for, 708
  graphing calculators and, 738–739
  homogeneity test and, 713
Chi-square test
  cautions and limitations, 729–730
  for homogeneity testing, 713
  statistical analysis reporting and, 727–728
  for univariate data, 700–708
CI. *see* Confidence interval (CI)
Class interval
  defined, 122
  density, 125
  example, 122–123
Cluster, 44
Cluster sampling, 44–45
Coefficient of determination, 253–257

Coefficient of multiple determination (R^2), 818
Common population proportion, 673
Comparative bar chart
  activity, 158
  example, 97
  vs. pie chart, 100
  for visual comparisons, 96
Comparative boxplot, 198
Comparative notation
  for population or treatment means, 638
  for population or treatment proportions, 671
Complement of A, 323
Complete second-order model, 807
Completely randomized design, 61
Comprehension and survey respondents, 71
Conclusion, drawing from statistical studies, 34–35
Conditional probability, 343–349
Confidence interval (CI)
  for $\alpha + \beta x$, 778
  activity, 568–569, 570–571
  of β, 756–758
  cautions and limitations, 566–567
  for comparing population or treatment means using independent samples, 649–651
  for comparing population or treatment means using paired samples, 664–666
  for comparing population or treatment proportions, 677–678
  defined, 537
  example, 539–540, 778–779
  general form of, 543–544
  graphing calculators and mean differences and, 696
  graphing calculators and population means and, 575
  graphing calculators and population proportion differences and, 697–698
  graphing calculators and population proportions and, 574–575
  for large populations, 539
  large-sample, for a population proportion, 542
  for a mean y value, 778–779
  for normal distributions, 538
  normal distributions and, 550
  one-sample, 549–550
  prediction interval and, 780–781
  probability and, 540–541
  published data and standard deviation, 564–565
  published data and two-sample, 683
  statistical analysis reporting and, 563
  unknown population standard deviation and, 551, 553–558
Confidence level
  activity, 568–569
  defined, 537
  for a population proportion, 542–543
Confounded variables, 50
Confounding variable, 33
Contingency table, 712
Continuity correction, 474
Continuous data
  defined, 13
  frequency distribution for, 122–123
  histograms for, 123–127
Continuous random variable, 400, 402, 410
Control, of variables, 50
Control group, 57, 66
Convenience sampling, 46
Correlation
  activity, 302
  causation and, 232
  and regression technology, activity, 302
  types of coefficients, 224–232
Correlation coefficient
  checking normality with, 462–463
  defined, 224
  examples, 226–230, 256–257
  reporting the value of, 296
Cumulative area, 413
Cumulative relative frequency, 131–133
Cumulative relative frequency plot, 132–134
Curve, finding using transformations, 276–277

D

Danger of extrapolation
  least-squares lines and, 239, 240
  simple linear regression and, 749–750
Data. *see also* specific types
  defined, 11
  sensible collection, 31
  types, 10–13
Data analysis process, 6
Data collection issues
  activity, 687–688
  for experimental studies, 77
  limitations, 77–78
  for observational studies, 76–77
Data set
  describing the center, 174
  describing variability in, 185–191
  summarizing, 194–198
de Fermat, Pierre, 328
de Mere, Chevalier, 328
Degree of freedom, 189
  ANOVA and, 838–839
  chi-square distributions and, 704
  sample comparison and, 640
  simple linear regression and, 750
  t distributions and, 552–553
  test power and Type II error probabilities, 620–621
  two-sample t test and, 648
Density, class interval, 125
Density curve, 411–412
Density function, 411
Density scale, 125
Dependent variable, 235
Descriptive statistics, 7
Deterministic relationship, 742
Diagram of experimental designs, 58–62
Dichotomous variable, 809–810
Dichotomy, 181
Direct control
  defined, 53
  example, 54, 56
  extraneous variables and, 54
  overview, 50
Discrete data, 13, 112–127
Discrete distribution, approximating, 473–475
Discrete probability distribution
  common types, 430–439
  graphing calculators and, 483–484
Discrete random variable
  defined, 400
  example, 402
  examples, 401–402
  mean value of, 417–418
  normal curves and, 473–474
  probability distribution of, 404–405
  probability distribution table for, 405–406
  standard deviation of, 419–421
  variance of, 420
Disjoint event
  additional rule for, 337–339
  defined, 324
  example, 325
Distribution. *see* specific types

Dotplot, 16–18
Double-blind experiment, 68
Dummy variable, 809–810

E

Empirical Rule
abnormal distribution and, 213
defined, 203
example, 204
standard normal curves and, 445, 448
z score and, 205
Error sum of squares, 838
Estimated regression line, inferences based on, 776–781
Estimation
activity, 26–27, 81
choosing a statistic for computing, 531–534
large-sample, for a population proportion, 536–546
point, 530–534
standard deviation and bias and, 534
Event. *see also* specific types
defined, 322
dependent, defined, 355
disjoint, 324
examples, 323, 324
forming new, 323, 325
independent, defined, 355
multiplication rule for more than two independent, 357
multiplication rule for two independent, 355
mutually exclusive, 324
with no common outcomes, 324
simulating independent with a graphing calculator, 395–396
simulating nonindependent with a graphing calculator, 396–397
Expected cell count
computing, 714
defined, 701
Expected value, 418
Experiment
activity, 80
chance, 320, 322
data collection issues, 77
defined, 33, 49
double-blind, 68
example, 56, 57
pre-questions, 62
single-blind, 67–68
using a control group, 57, 66
using volunteers, 68
well-defined requirements, 50
Experimental condition, 49
Experimental design
activity, 81
evaluating, 56–57
goal of, 65
underlying structure of, 58–62
Experimental unit
defined, 58
replication and, 68
Experimentation and data collection, 32–33
Explanatory variable
defined, 49, 53
in regression analysis, 235
Extraneous variable
dealing with, 54
defined, 50
Extreme outlier, 195
Extreme values, 449–450

F

F distribution
ANOVA and, 839–840
defined, 820–821
F test for model utility, 821–826
Factor
in comparisons, 834
defined, 32, 33
Fitted value. *see* Predicted value
Five-number summary, 195
Fixed number properties, 744
Frequency, 13
Frequency distribution
area and, 152–153
for categorical data, 13–14
compacting, 119
for continuous numerical data, 122–123
example, 14, 118
grouping data, 120–121
uses, 117
Full quadratic model, 807
Fundamental identity for single-factor ANOVA, 843

G

Galileo, 328
General addition rule, 363–365
General additive multiple regression model, 802–803
General multiplication rule, 365–368
Geometric distribution, 437–439
Geometric probability calculation and graphing calculators, 487–488
Geometric probability distribution, 437–439
Geometric random variable, 437–438
Golden ratio for rectangles, 197
Goodness-of-fit statistic, 703
Goodness-of-fit test
chi-square distributions and, 704–708
graphing calculators and, 736–737
for homogeneity, 715
for independence of more than two categorical variables, 722
for independence of two categorical variables, 718–722
Grand total in a two-way frequency table, 712
Graphical display
cautions and limitations, 152–155
interpreting, 149–152
for statistical reporting, 148–149
Graphing calculator explorations
binomial probability calculations and, 484–487
boxplots and, 220
communicating with, 308–309
confidence intervals and population means and, 575
confidence intervals and population proportions and, 574–575
differences in proportions and, 697–698
discrete probability distributions and, 483–484
geometric probability calculations and, 487–488
goodness-of-fit test and, 736–737
histogram scaling, 167
homogeneity, independence, and the chi-square statistic, 738–739
independent event simulations and, 395–396
inference about differences in means, 695–696
linear regression, 307
lists and, 165
mean differences and paired samples and, 696–697
nonindependent event simulations and, 396–397
nonlinear regressions and, 310–312
normal approximation to binomial distribution and, 491–492
normal curves and normal probability distribution and, 489–491
population mean hypothesis test and, 631

Graphing calculator explorations (*continued*)
population proportion hypothesis test and, 630–631
probabilities and, 394–395
quartiles, 219–220
random assignment to treatment, 89–90
random assignment to treatment with blocking, 90–91
random integer generation, 87–88
random real number generation, 91–93
regression slope inference and, 796
residuals and, 309–310
sampling distribution of the mean, 524–525
sampling distribution of the sample proportion, 526–527
scaling histograms on, 167
scatterplots and, 168
simulations and the seq function, 397–398
single-factor ANOVA, 858
statistics window setup, 166–167
study of statistics and, 87
z score and, 221–222

H

Heavy-tailed curve, 128
Histogram
for continuous numerical data and equal class interval widths, 124–125
for continuous numerical data and unequal class interval widths, 125, 126
for discrete numerical data, 119
example, 4, 5, 119–120
grouping data, 121
sample, 129
scaling, on graphing calculators, 167
shapes, 127–129
tails, 128
using density, 127
Homogeneity
graphing calculators and, 738–739
test of in population or treatment comparisons, 713–718
Hypergeometric distribution, 435
Hypothesis. *see also* specific types
defined, 578
testing about treatment differences, 645
Hypothesis test
for β, 758–759
cautions and limitations, 624–625, 685
defined, 578
errors in, 583–584
graphing calculators and, 695
graphing calculators and population mean and, 631
graphing calculators and population proportion differences and, 697–698
graphing calculators and population proportions and, 630–631
interpreting, 623–624
large-sample, for a population proportion, 588–599
for a population mean, 602–610
population proportions and, summary, 596
power of. *see* Hypothesis test power
purpose, 581
sample comparison and, 640–645
significance level of, 584
steps for, 597
summarizing results of, 623
Hypothesis test power
calculating, 616–617
defined, 613–614
effects of factors on, 614–615
for testing hypotheses about proportions, 618
Type II error probabilities and, 615–616

I

Inappropriate actions in data interpretation, 77–78
Independence (event)
example, 356
multiplication rule for more than two, 357
multiplication rule for two, 355
probability and, 353–357
simulating with a graphing calculator, 395–396
without replacement, 359
Independence (variable)
graphing calculators and, 738–739
testing for, 718–722
Independent sample, 639, 658
Independent variable, 235
Indicator variable, 809–810
Inferential statistics
defined, 7
objective of, 529
Influential observation, 251, 253
Information retrieval and survey respondents, 73
Interaction predictor in multiple regression models, 807
Intercept
Interquartile range, 189, 190
Intersection of two events, 323
Interval estimate. *see* Confidence interval (CI)
IQ score, 453–454

J

Jittering, 287
Joint probability table, 354

L

Large-sample confidence interval
for a population proportion, 536–546
for proportion differences, 677–678
Large-sample confidence interval for p, 542
alternative to, 543
alternative to, activity, 570
Large-sample test
for comparison problems, 672–677
computing a *P*-value for, 593–596
Law of large numbers and probability, 332
Law of total probability, 368–370
Leaf, numerical data and, 107
Least-squares estimate and regression function fit, 816–817
Least-squares line. *see also* Sample regression line
defined, 237
deviations from, 247
examples, 238–240, 240–241
population regression line and, 747
predicting value of y with, 242
slope of, 238, 755–762
standard deviation about, 257–260
weighted, 769
Least-squares principle
regression function fit and, 816
straight lines and, 236–238
Line
assessing fit of, 246–260
equation of, 235

fitting straight, 236–238
goodness of fit, 237
graphs of, 236
least-squares principal and, 236–238
Linear combination
addition vs. multiplication, 426–427
of random variables, 423–426
Linear function
addition vs. multiplication, 426–427
mean, standard deviation, and variance of, 422–423
Linear regression
bivariate data and, 235–242
graphing calculators and, 307
simple model for, 742–752
Linear relationship strength, 228
Logarithmic transformation, 464–467
Logistic regression
binary variables and, 286–298
data transformation and, 290–293
equation for, 288–289
Lurking variable, 54

M

Margin of error, 564
Marginal total in a two-way frequency table, 712
Mean. *see also* specific types
of a binomial random variable, 436–437
combining with standard deviation, 200–201
comparison of, 638
continuous variables and, 421–422
defined, 174
denoting, 175
deviations from, 185–187
of a discrete random variable, 417–418
example, 175
graphing calculators and differences in, 695–697
for linear combinations, 424
of linear functions, 422–423
vs. median, 178–179
of a normal distribution, 442
outliers and, 177
population mean and, 418
of the probability distribution of *x*, 417
of a random variable, defined, 415–416
of the random variable *x*, 417
Mean square, 838–839
Mean value of a difference in means, 639
Measurement bias, 38, 39
Measures of relative standing, 204–205
Median
defined, 177
example, 178
vs. mean, 178–179
outliers and, 178
as percentile, 205
Memory and survey respondents, 73
Mild outlier, 195
Minitab
jittering and, 287
numerical descriptive measures from, 188
outliers and, 197
Model utility test
for independence in a bivariate normal population, 786
for simple linear regression, 759–762
Modified boxplot, 196–197
Monte Carlo methods and graphing calculators, 92–93
Multimodal histogram, 127
Multiple comparisons procedure, 847–851
Multiple regression model
activity, 831
defined, 801
example, 803, 808–809
fitting, 815–817
general additive, 802–803
model utility *F* test for, 821
polynomial, 804–806
utility of, 818–826
variable interaction in, 807
Multiplication rule, general, 365–368
Multivariate data
defined, 11
goodness-of-fit testing and, 722
Mutually exclusive events, 324

N

Newton, Isaac, 330
Nonlinear regression and graphing calculators, 310–312
Nonlinear relationships and transformations, 265–286
Nonresponse bias, 38–40
Normal approximation to a binomial distribution, 474–475
Normal curve
defined, 128, 442
discrete variables and, 473–474
equality of standard and nonstandard areas, 450–451
graphing calculators and normal probability distribution and, 489–491
Normal distribution
calculating probabilities for, 451–452
defined, 442–443
discrete distribution approximations and, 473–475
examples, 452–454
extreme values in, 455–456
graphing calculators and normal curves and, 489–491
mean value of, 442
other types, 450–451
random variables and, 443
standard. *see* Standard normal distribution
standard deviation of, 442
vs. *t* distribution (activity), 626–627
Normal probability plot
correlation coefficient and, 462–463
defined, 461
nonnormal distributions in, 461–462
purpose, 460
standardized residuals and, 766–768, 772–774
Normal score, normal probability plots and, 460
Not A, 323
Null hypothesis
categorical data analysis and, 701
defined, 578–581
example, 579, 580–581
population mean comparison and, 640–641, 644
Numerical data
activity, 214
defined, 11
displaying bivariate, 139–145
dotplots for, 16–18
example, 13
frequency distribution for, 122–127
histograms for, 122–127
stem-and-leaf displays and, 107–113
types, 12
Numerical summary measures. *see also* specific types
cautions and limitations, 212–213

Numerical summary measures (*continued*)
interpreting, 211
for statistical reporting, 209–210

O

Observational study
data collection and, 32–33
data collection issues, 76–77
defined, 33, 648
difficulties with, 648
surveys and, 70–74
Observed cell count, 712, 714
Observed significance level. *see* *P*-value
One-sample t confidence interval
for comparison problems, 664–666
for a population mean, 553–558
One-sample *t* test, 605–609
One-sample *z* confidence interval, 549
One-way frequency table, 700
Outlier
boxplots and, 195
defined, 109
example report after removal, 151
numerical summary measures and, 213
observation as, 253
Overcoverage, 76

P

Paired data
benefits of using, 666
defined, 18
Paired sample
defined, 639, 658
example, 659–670
graphing calculators and mean differences and, 696–697
methods of inference for, 660
paired *t* test and, 660–664
Paired *t* confidence interval, 665
Paired *t* statistic, 664
Paired *t* test, 660–664
Parabola, quadratic functions and, 266
Pascal, Blaise, 328
Pearson's sample correlation coefficient. *see also* Correlation coefficient
defined, 225
example, 231
properties of, 228
Percentile, 205, 206
Pie chart
activity, 158
categorical summaries and, 97
categorical variables and, 99–100
vs. comparative bar chart, 100
constructing, 98–99
example, 98
other uses for, 102–103
vs. segmented bar graph, 101
Placebo, 66–67
Placebo effect, 67
Placebo treatment, 84
Point estimation
defined, 530
example, 530–531
sample selection and, 536
simple linear regression and, 747, 749
statistical analysis reporting and, 563
Point prediction
interpreting, 749
simple linear regression and, 747
Polynomial regression
curve descriptions for, 268
as multiple regression model, 804–806
nonlinear relationships and, 265–267
Pooled *t* test, 648
Population
comparing using a categorial variable, 714
defined, 7
test of homogeneity when comparing, 713–718
Population correlation coefficient
defined, 231–232
inferences about, 784–786
Population data and sampling, 129–131
Population interquartile range, 191
Population mean
comparing using independent samples, 631–651
comparing using paired samples, 658–666
confidence interval for, 549–559
defined, 175
example, 176
graphing calculators and confidence intervals and, 575
graphing calculators and hypotheses tests and, 631
hypothesis tests for, 602–610
mean value symbol and, 418
one-sample *t* test for, 605–609
Population proportion
graphing calculators and confidence intervals and, 574–575
graphing calculators and differences in, 697–698
graphing calculators and hypotheses tests and, 630–631
large-sample difference inferences for, 671–678
large-sample hypothesis tests for, 588–599
of S's, denoting, 181
Population regression coefficient, 803
Population regression function
for general additive multiple regressions, 803
for polynomial regressions, 805
Population regression line
defined, 743
estimating, 747–750
Population regression line slope
estimating, 755
least-squares line slope and, 755–762
Population standard deviation, 188
Population variance, 188
Power transformation, 277–281
Power transformation ladder, 278
Practical significance, 609–610
Predicted value
example, 248–249
obtaining, 247
reporting, 296
Prediction interval for a single *y* value, 780–781
Predictor variable, 235
Principle of least squares
fitting a straight line and, 236–238
regression function fit and, 816
Probabilistic model, 742–743
Probability
beginnings of study of, 327–328
calculating for normal distributions, 451–452
classical approach limitations, 329–330
classical approach to for equally likely outcomes, 328–329, 334
conditional, 342–349, 378
defined, 319
determining, 334
disjoint events and, 337–339
equally likely outcomes and, 337
estimating activity, 388
estimating empirically, 377–379
estimating using simulation, 379–385
experimentation activity, 388–389
fundamental properties activity, 389
fundamental properties of, 334–337
general rules for, 363–372
hypothesis testing and, 591–592
independence and, 353–357

as long-run relative frequency (graphing calculators and), 394–395
relative frequency approach to, 330–333, 334
simulations and graphing calculators and, 397–398
subjective approach to, 333–334
Probability distribution
activities, 478–479
for continuous random variables, 410–411
of discrete random variables, 404–405
graphs of, 416
properties of discrete, 406
for random variables, 403
rules of probability and, 406–408
Probability distribution table, 405–406
Probability histogram, 406–407, 410–411
Probability of success, 288
Proportion, example comparison of, 715–716
Published data
bivariate data and, 296
chi-square tests and, 728–729
confidence intervals and, 683–685
interpreting graphical displays, 151–152
interpreting hypotheses tests, 623–624
interpreting numerical summary measures, 211
interval estimates and, 564–565
two-sample hypothesis tests and, 683–685
P-value
calculating, 594–599
computing and alternative hypotheses, 593
defined, 591
determining with a *z* test statistic, 595
finding for a *t* test, 603–604
goodness-of-fit statistic and, 704
indications of size of, 592–593
significance levels and, 593
two-sample *t* test and, 648
two-tailed tests and, 594

Q

Quadratic model, 267–268
Quadratic regression
computing, 266–267
example, 267–270
Quadratic regression model, 805
Qualitative data, 11
Qualitative variable
predictor, 809–811
testing for independence, 718–722
Quantitative data, 11
Quartile
defined, 189
example, 190
graphing calculators and, 219–220
as percentiles, 205

R

r. see Pearson's sample correlation coefficient
rand process, graphing calculators and, 394–395
Random assignment
activity, 82
defined, 53
diagram of, 60
example, 54, 56
extraneous variables and, 54
graphing calculators and, 89–91
overview, 51–52
performing, 54–56
Random integer generation and graphing calculators, 87–88
Random mechanism, 55
Random number
converting to integer, 88
probability simulation and, 380, 383
Random real numbers and graphing calculators, 91–93
Random sample, simple
defined, 40
selecting, 41–42
Random sampling
example, 42
goal, 43
overview, 40–43
stratified, 44
Random variable. *see also* specific types
defined, 400
linear function of, 422–423
mean value of, defined, 415
probability and continuous, 412–413
standard deviation of, defined, 415
Randomized controlled experiment, 649
Range of a data set, 185
Rectangle, golden ratio for, 197
Reexpression. *see* Transformation
Regression, 241–242
Regression analysis. *see also* Linear regression; Multiple regression model
activity, 790
defined, 242
example, 758
objective of, 235, 801
test for independence and, 786
variable interaction in, 806–809
Regression coefficient, 805
Regression slope inference and graphing calculators, 796
Regression sum of squares, 821
Relative frequency
area and, 152–153
combining multiple, 123
cumulative, 131–134
equation, 13
example of use, 97
long-run and probabilities (graphing calculators and), 394–395
probability and, 330–334
Relative frequency distribution
comparative bar charts and, 96–97
defined, 13
Replication
defined, 52, 53
example, 54, 56, 57
purpose, 68
Research study evaluation, 8–9
Residual
defined for a multiple regression model, 818
defined for a regression line, 247
example, 248–249
graphing calculators and, 309–310
plotting, 249–253, 768–774
Residual analysis, 766–768
Residual plot
defined, 249, 768
example, 250, 251–252, 770
standardized, 768–774
Residual sum of squares
defined for a multiple regression model, 818
defined for a regression line, 254
example, 254–255
Response bias, 38, 39
Response reporting and survey respondents, 73–74
Response variable
defined, 49, 53
in regression analysis, 235
Right-tailed curve, 128

S

Sample
defined, 7
independent, 639, 658
paired, 639, 658
Sample mean
defined, 174
deviations from, 185–187
example, 175
sampling distribution of, 504–513
Sample median, 178
Sample proportion of successes
comparison properties of, 672
confidence intervals and, 537
defined, 181
for large populations, 515–518
purpose, 515
Sample regression line, 237, 241. *see also* Least-squares line
Sample size
bound on error of estimation and, 544–545, 558–559
as a reflection of the whole, 43–44
Sample space, 320, 322
Sample standard deviation, 187–188
Sample variance, 187, 188
Sampling. *see also* specific types
activity, 79–80
bias in, 38–39
random, 40–43
with replacement, 42, 358, 359
selection process, 37–38
size of, 359–360
variability, 129–131
without replacement, 42, 358–359, 435
Sampling distribution
of $a + bx$, 777
defined, 503
of the mean, graphing calculators and, 524–525
of a sample mean, 504–513
of a sample proportion, 515–519, 537–538
of $x_1 - x_2$, 639, 640
Sampling distribution of x
activity, 521–522
confidence intervals for population means and, 549
general properties of, 508–510
for nonnormal small populations, 510–511, 513
for normal large populations, 505–506
purpose, 499
for skewed populations, 506–507
for small populations, 511–512
Sampling frame, 41
Sampling variability, 500–502
Scatterplot
axes intersection, 142–143
bivariate data and, 224–225, 226
defined, 139
example, 140–141
on graphing calculators, 168
interpreting patterns in, 155
simple linear regression and, 747
Segmented bar graph, 101–102
Selection bias, 38, 39
seq function (graphing calculator), 397–398
Sequence of trials
defined, 52
diagram of, 59
example, 66
Significance level
defined, 584
P-values and, 593
Simple event, 322, 324
Simple linear regression
activity, 790
example, 746
model utility test for, 759–762
Simple linear regression model
basic assumptions of, 744
cautions and limitations, 789
checking adequacy of, 765–774
confidence interval for β and, 756
confidence intervals and, 778
defined, 743
equation for, 766
estimated standard deviation of statistic *b* and, 756
example, 760–762
key assumption of, 752
key features of, 744–745
population regression line and, 755–762
property insights for, 746–747
published data and, 788–789
residual analysis and, 766–768
scatterplot patterns with, 747
Simple random sample
defined, 40
selecting, 41–42
Simulation, probability estimation and, 379–385
Simultaneous confidence level, 850
Single-blind experiment, 67–68
Single-factor analysis of variance (ANOVA)
activity, 855–857
assumptions for, 837
defined, 834–835
example, 836, 852–853
F test for, 840–842
graphing calculators and, 858
notation in, 835
summarizing, 842–844
Skeletal boxplot, 194–195
Skewed histogram, 128
Slope
defined, 235
of least-squares line, 238
point estimates of for population regression line, 747
Smoothed histogram, 127
Squared deviation
line fit and, 237
variance and, 187–188
Square-root transformation, 463–464
Stacked bar graph. *see* Segmented bar graph
Standard deviation
about the least-squares line, 257–260
of a binomial random variable, 436–437
combining with mean, 200–201
continuous variables and, 421–422
defined, 187, 188
of a discrete random variable, 419–421
estimated, 750–752
estimated, of statistic *b*, 756
estimated, of the statistic $a + bx$, 777
example, 187–188
for linear combinations, 424
of linear functions, 422–423
of a normal distribution, 442
of a random variable, defined, 415–416
as statistical standard error, 544
variance and, 420
Standard error, 544, 564
Standard normal curve
areas of, 446–448
defined, 444
standardizing endpoints of, 451
table of areas, 445–446
Standard normal distribution, 444
Standardization, 205
Standardized residual
defined, 766
example, 767–768
plot examples, 770–774

Standardized score. *see* Z score
Statistic
biased, 532–534
defined, 500
standard error of, 544
unbiased, 532–534
Statistic $a + bx$, 777
Statistic b
estimated standard deviation of, 756
linear regression model slope coefficient and, 755
properties of sampling distribution of, 755
Statistical analysis
chi-square test interpretation and, 727–728
confidence intervals for reporting, 563
graphical displays for reporting, 148–149
interpreting graphical displays, 149–151
interpreting numerical summaries, 210
interpreting population characteristic estimates, 563–564
interpreting results of, 295–299
interpreting two-sample confidence intervals, 683
numerical measures for reporting, 209–210
point estimates for reporting, 563
published data and graphical displays, 151–152
published data and numerical measures, 211
published data and simple linear regression models, 788–789
Statistical significance, 609–610
Statistical study
drawing conclusions from, 34–35
experimentation, 32–33
graphing calculators and, 87
observation, 32–33
purpose, 76
Statistics
defined, 1
process of using, 2, 3
purpose, 1, 2
Stem, numerical data and, 107
Stem-and-leaf display
activity, 158–159
alternative display types, 110
comparative, 112
constructing, 109
defined, 107
example, 108–109
optimal number of items, 110
repeating stems, 111
uses, 109
Strata, 44
Stratified random sampling, 44
Stroop effect, 80
Studentized range distribution, 848
Survey, 71
Survey respondent's tasks, 71–74
Symmetric histogram, 127–128
Systematic sampling, 44

T

t distribution
degrees of freedom and, 552–553
vs. normal distribution (activity), 626–627
properties of, 552
sample comparison and, 640
t test
for bivariate normal populations, 785
finding P-values for, 603–604
one-sample for a population mean, 605–609
paired, 660–664
pooled for population comparison, 648
power of and Type II error probabilities, 619–621
two-sample for population comparison, 641–644
two-sample for treatment comparison, 645–648
Test procedure, hypothesis
defined, 578
power of. *see* Hypothesis test power
process of, 591
purpose, 582, 588–591
for sample comparison, 640–645
Test statistic
defined, 591
P-value determination and z, 595–596
Time-series plot
defined, 144
examples, 144–145
unequal spacing in, 154–155
Total sum of squares
ANOVA and, 843
defined for a multiple regression model, 818
defined for a regression line, 254
example, 254–255
Transformation. *see also* specific types
common types, 273
defined, 270–271
example, 271–272, 273–276
example of power, 279–281
example of reversing, 277
finding curves using, 276–277
graphing calculators and, 310–312
logistic regression and, 290–293
to obtain normality, 463–467
power, 277–278
selecting, 467–468
Treatment
comparing, 645–648
comparing using a categorial variable, 714
defined, 49, 53
proportion, 671–678
test of homogeneity when comparing, 713–718
Treatment mean
comparing using independent samples, 631–651
comparing using paired samples, 658–666
Treatment sum of squares, 838
Tree diagram, 321
Trial, mathematical, 430
Trimmed mean, 179–180
Trimming percentage, 179
Tukey-Kramer (T-K) multiple comparisons procedure
defined, 847–848
example, 848–849, 851–852
results summary of, 851
simultaneous confidence level and, 850
Two-sample t confidence interval
defined, 649–650
example, 650–651
Two-sample t statistic, 664
Two-sample t test
improper use of, 663
for population comparison, 641–644
for treatment comparison, 645–648
Two-sample test
activity, 687
cautions and limitations, 685
Two-sample z test, 675–677
Two-way frequency table
activity, 732
defined, 712
Two-way table, 711–713

Type I error
defined, 583
examples, 583–584
probability of, 584–586
Type II error
defined, 583
examples, 584–586
probability of, 584
probability of, and *t* test power, 619–621
probability of, and test power, 613–621

U

Unconditional probability, 347
compared to conditional probability, 347
Undercoverage
defined, 38
results of, 76
Uniform distribution, 412
Unimodal histogram, 127
Union of two events, 323
Univariate data, 11
chi-square tests for categorical, 700–708
defined, 11
stem-and-leaf displays for, 107
transforming, 463–464

V

Variability
activity, 26, 214
data set range and, 185
deviations from the mean, 185–187
interpreting, 200–206
nature and role, 3–5
sample variance and, 187
Variable. *see also* specific types
binary and logistic regression, 286
confounded, 50
confounding, 33
defined, 11
direct control of, 50
explanatory, 49, 53
extraneous, 50, 54
interaction between multiple, 806–809
lurking, 54
qualitative predictor, 809–811
random. *see* Random variable
in regression analysis, 235
relationship description of two, 742–743
response, 49, 53
test for independence of, 784–786
Variance
defined, 187
of a difference of independent quantities, 639
of a discrete random variable, 420
for linear combinations, 424
of linear functions, 422–423
standard deviation and, 420
Venn diagram, 324, 325
Vertical intercept, 235
Voluntary response sampling, 46
Volunteer subjects, 68

Y

y-intercept
defined, 235
point estimates of for population regression line, 747

Z

Z curve. *see* Standard normal curve
Z score
calculating, 451
converting to *x* value, 456–457
defined, 204, 205
graphing calculators and, 221–222
Pearson's sample correlation coefficient and, 225
uses, 455

Standard normal probabilities (*continued*)

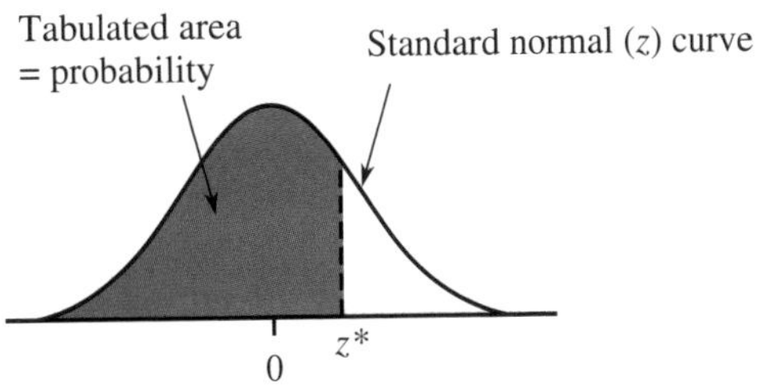

z*	.00	.01	.02	.03	.04	.05	.06	.07	.08	.09
0.0	.5000	.5040	.5080	.5120	.5160	.5199	.5239	.5279	.5319	.5359
0.1	.5398	.5438	.5478	.5517	.5557	.5596	.5636	.5675	.5714	.5753
0.2	.5793	.5832	.5871	.5910	.5948	.5987	.6026	.6064	.6103	.6141
0.3	.6179	.6217	.6255	.6293	.6331	.6368	.6406	.6443	.6480	.6517
0.4	.6554	.6591	.6628	.6664	.6700	.6736	.6772	.6808	.6844	.6879
0.5	.6915	.6950	.6985	.7019	.7054	.7088	.7123	.7157	.7190	.7224
0.6	.7257	.7291	.7324	.7357	.7389	.7422	.7454	.7486	.7517	.7549
0.7	.7580	.7611	.7642	.7673	.7704	.7734	.7764	.7794	.7823	.7852
0.8	.7881	.7910	.7939	.7967	.7995	.8023	.8051	.8078	.8106	.8133
0.9	.8159	.8186	.8212	.8238	.8264	.8289	.8315	.8340	.8365	.8389
1.0	.8413	.8438	.8461	.8485	.8508	.8531	.8554	.8577	.8599	.8621
1.1	.8643	.8665	.8686	.8708	.8729	.8749	.8770	.8790	.8810	.8830
1.2	.8849	.8869	.8888	.8907	.8925	.8944	.8962	.8980	.8997	.9015
1.3	.9032	.9049	.9066	.9082	.9099	.9115	.9131	.9147	.9162	.9177
1.4	.9192	.9207	.9222	.9236	.9251	.9265	.9279	.9292	.9306	.9319
1.5	.9332	.9345	.9357	.9370	.9382	.9394	.9406	.9418	.9429	.9441
1.6	.9452	.9463	.9474	.9484	.9495	.9505	.9515	.9525	.9535	.9545
1.7	.9554	.9564	.9573	.9582	.9591	.9599	.9608	.9616	.9625	.9633
1.8	.9641	.9649	.9656	.9664	.9671	.9678	.9686	.9693	.9699	.9706
1.9	.9713	.9719	.9726	.9732	.9738	.9744	.9750	.9756	.9761	.9767
2.0	.9772	.9778	.9783	.9788	.9793	.9798	.9803	.9808	.9812	.9817
2.1	.9821	.9826	.9830	.9834	.9838	.9842	.9846	.9850	.9854	.9857
2.2	.9861	.9864	.9868	.9871	.9875	.9878	.9881	.9884	.9887	.9890
2.3	.9893	.9896	.9898	.9901	.9904	.9906	.9909	.9911	.9913	.9916
2.4	.9918	.9920	.9922	.9925	.9927	.9929	.9931	.9932	.9934	.9936
2.5	.9938	.9940	.9941	.9943	.9945	.9946	.9948	.9949	.9951	.9952
2.6	.9953	.9955	.9956	.9957	.9959	.9960	.9961	.9962	.9963	.9964
2.7	.9965	.9966	.9967	.9968	.9969	.9970	.9971	.9972	.9973	.9974
2.8	.9974	.9975	.9976	.9977	.9977	.9978	.9979	.9979	.9980	.9981
2.9	.9981	.9982	.9982	.9983	.9984	.9984	.9985	.9985	.9986	.9986
3.0	.9987	.9987	.9987	.9988	.9988	.9989	.9989	.9989	.9990	.9990
3.1	.9990	.9991	.9991	.9991	.9992	.9992	.9992	.9992	.9993	.9993
3.2	.9993	.9993	.9994	.9994	.9994	.9994	.9994	.9995	.9995	.9995
3.3	.9995	.9995	.9995	.9996	.9996	.9996	.9996	.9996	.9996	.9997
3.4	.9997	.9997	.9997	.9997	.9997	.9997	.9997	.9997	.9997	.9998
3.5	.9998	.9998	.9998	.9998	.9998	.9998	.9998	.9998	.9998	.9998
3.6	.9998	.9998	.9999	.9999	.9999	.9999	.9999	.9999	.9999	.9999
3.7	.9999	.9999	.9999	.9999	.9999	.9999	.9999	.9999	.9999	.9999
3.8	.9999	.9999	.9999	.9999	.9999	.9999	.9999	.9999	.9999	1.0000

Standard normal probabilities (cumulative z curve areas)

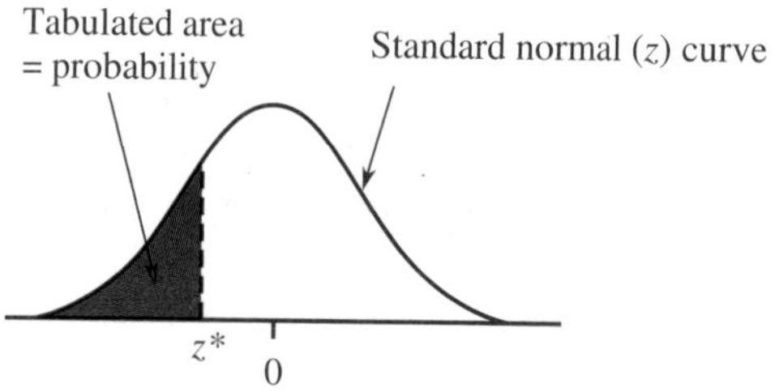

z*	.00	.01	.02	.03	.04	.05	.06	.07	.08	.09
−3.8	.0001	.0001	.0001	.0001	.0001	.0001	.0001	.0001	.0001	.0000
−3.7	.0001	.0001	.0001	.0001	.0001	.0001	.0001	.0001	.0001	.0001
−3.6	.0002	.0002	.0001	.0001	.0001	.0001	.0001	.0001	.0001	.0001
−3.5	.0002	.0002	.0002	.0002	.0002	.0002	.0002	.0002	.0002	.0002
−3.4	.0003	.0003	.0003	.0003	.0003	.0003	.0003	.0003	.0003	.0002
−3.3	.0005	.0005	.0005	.0004	.0004	.0004	.0004	.0004	.0004	.0003
−3.2	.0007	.0007	.0006	.0006	.0006	.0006	.0006	.0005	.0005	.0005
−3.1	.0010	.0009	.0009	.0009	.0008	.0008	.0008	.0008	.0007	.0007
−3.0	.0013	.0013	.0013	.0012	.0012	.0011	.0011	.0011	.0010	.0010
−2.9	.0019	.0018	.0018	.0017	.0016	.0016	.0015	.0015	.0014	.0014
−2.8	.0026	.0025	.0024	.0023	.0023	.0022	.0021	.0021	.0020	.0019
−2.7	.0035	.0034	.0033	.0032	.0031	.0030	.0029	.0028	.0027	.0026
−2.6	.0047	.0045	.0044	.0043	.0041	.0040	.0039	.0038	.0037	.0036
−2.5	.0062	.0060	.0059	.0057	.0055	.0054	.0052	.0051	.0049	.0048
−2.4	.0082	.0080	.0078	.0075	.0073	.0071	.0069	.0068	.0066	.0064
−2.3	.0107	.0104	.0102	.0099	.0096	.0094	.0091	.0089	.0087	.0084
−2.2	.0139	.0136	.0132	.0129	.0125	.0122	.0119	.0116	.0113	.0110
−2.1	.0179	.0174	.0170	.0166	.0162	.0158	.0154	.0150	.0146	.0143
−2.0	.0228	.0222	.0217	.0212	.0207	.0202	.0197	.0192	.0188	.0183
−1.9	.0287	.0281	.0274	.0268	.0262	.0256	.0250	.0244	.0239	.0233
−1.8	.0359	.0351	.0344	.0336	.0329	.0322	.0314	.0307	.0301	.0294
−1.7	.0446	.0436	.0427	.0418	.0409	.0401	.0392	.0384	.0375	.0367
−1.6	.0548	.0537	.0526	.0516	.0505	.0495	.0485	.0475	.0465	.0455
−1.5	.0668	.0655	.0643	.0630	.0618	.0606	.0594	.0582	.0571	.0559
−1.4	.0808	.0793	.0778	.0764	.0749	.0735	.0721	.0708	.0694	.0681
−1.3	.0968	.0951	.0934	.0918	.0901	.0885	.0869	.0853	.0838	.0823
−1.2	.1151	.1131	.1112	.1093	.1075	.1056	.1038	.1020	.1003	.0985
−1.1	.1357	.1335	.1314	.1292	.1271	.1251	.1230	.1210	.1190	.1170
−1.0	.1587	.1562	.1539	.1515	.1492	.1469	.1446	.1423	.1401	.1379
−0.9	.1841	.1814	.1788	.1762	.1736	.1711	.1685	.1660	.1635	.1611
−0.8	.2119	.2090	.2061	.2033	.2005	.1977	.1949	.1922	.1894	.1867
−0.7	.2420	.2389	.2358	.2327	.2296	.2266	.2236	.2206	.2177	.2148
−0.6	.2743	.2709	.2676	.2643	.2611	.2578	.2546	.2514	.2483	.2451
−0.5	.3085	.3050	.3015	.2981	.2946	.2912	.2877	.2843	.2810	.2776
−0.4	.3446	.3409	.3372	.3336	.3300	.3264	.3228	.3192	.3156	.3121
−0.3	.3821	.3783	.3745	.3707	.3669	.3632	.3594	.3557	.3520	.3483
−0.2	.4207	.4168	.4129	.4090	.4052	.4013	.3974	.3936	.3897	.3859
−0.1	.4602	.4562	.4522	.4483	.4443	.4404	.4364	.4325	.4286	.4247
−0.0	.5000	.4960	.4920	.4880	.4840	.4801	.4761	.4721	.4681	.4641